# THE OFFICIAL PRICE GUIDE TO

## BY
## RUTH M. POLLARD

We have compiled the information contained herein through a *patented computerized process* which relies primarily on a nationwide sampling of information provided by noteworthy collectible experts, auction houses and specialized dealers. This sophisticated retrieval system enables us to provide the reader with the most current and accurate information available.

### EDITOR
### THOMAS E. HUDGEONS III

✓ **W9-ASV-075**

### FIFTH EDITION
THE HOUSE OF COLLECTIBLES, INC., ORLANDO, FLORIDA 32809

# TABLE OF CONTENTS

## ACKNOWLEDGEMENTS

I wish to express my deepest thanks to all the wonderful artists and publishers who submitted material and photos in order that we might bring to you a current book full of information. There are so many in the business that space will not allow the listing of individual names, however, I do thank each and every one. Also my thanks go to the wonderful network of dealers who are supporting this project. A very special thanks to Mr. and Mrs. John Rudisill, The Alt Print Haus and Sandy Verdin, Icart Vendor for their valuable assistance in special categories.

## RETRACTION

Ruth M. Pollard, author, and the House of Collectibles, publisher, regrets that the following statements made about artist Guy Coheleach in the previous editions of The Official Price Guide to Collector Prints were incorrect: "He is the only wildlife artist listed in *The Dictionary of International Biography, International Who's Who in Art and Antiques,* and the *International Men of Achievement.* He was the first wildlife artist listed in *Who's Who in American Art."* In the case of the above named publications, wildlife artist Roger Preuss, Minneapolis, Minnesota, was the first artist listed therein. Also, Mr. Preuss was the first wildlife artist listed in *Who's Who in the World.*

## ABOUT THE AUTHOR

Ms. Pollard has been a dealer in limited editions and collectibles for over thirty years. She was owner of Beru's, Inc., a store designed with the collector in mind for eleven years, and recently sold in order to devote more time to writing and traveling. She is the editor of the American Artist Print Price Trends for a national magazine.

She is past charter member of the National Association of Limited Edition Dealers and the American Limited Edition Association; life member of Indiana Audubon Society, member of National Audobon society; President of the Irvington Businessmen's Association in Indianapolis for two terms.

She was awarded Dealer of the Year award by Frame House Gallery for outstanding sales and advertisement in 1973 and the President's Cup in 1977 for her continuing efforts in behalf of both dealer and collector in the limited edition print field.

*The author welcomes any comments, corrections or additions which will either be answered personally or used in any future updating of this price guide. Please write:*
Ruth M. Pollard
P. O. Box 39038
Indianapolis, IN 46239

***Ruth M. Pollard***

## PICTURE COPYRIGHTS

All pictures reproduced in this book are copyrighted. The copyrights are owned by the artist, his estate, or his publisher. Permission has been granted to the author and publisher for their use herein. Their reproduction elsewhere, without written express permission of the owners of the copyrights, is strictly forbidden.

## PHOTOGRAPHIC RECOGNITION

*Color Separations:* World Color, Ormond Beach, FL 32074.

## BECOME AN "OFFICIAL" CONTRIBUTOR TO THE WORLD'S LEADING PRICE GUIDES

Are you an experienced collector with access to information not covered in this guide? Do you possess knowledge, data, or ideas that should be included? If so, The House of Collectibles invites you to **GET INVOLVED.** The House of Collectibles continuously seeks to improve, expand, and update the material in the **OFFICIAL PRICE GUIDE SERIES.** The assistance and cooperation of numerous collectors and dealers has added immeasurably to the success of the books in this series. If you think you qualify as a contributor, our editors would like to offer your expertise to the readers of the **OFFICIAL PRICE GUIDE SERIES.** As the publishers of the most popular and authoritative price guides, The House of Collectibles can provide a far-reaching audience for your collecting accomplishments. Help the hobby grow by letting others benefit from the knowledge that you have discovered while building your collection. If your contribution appears in the next edition, you'll become an **"OFFICIAL"** member of the world's largest hobby-publishing team. Your name will appear on the acknowledgement page, plus you will receive a free complimentary copy. Send a full outline of the type of material you wish to contribute. Please include your phone number. Write to: The House of Collectibles, Inc., Editorial Department, 1900 Premier Row, Orlando, Florida, 32809. *(No phone calls please.)*

### NOTE TO READERS

All advertisements appearing in this book have been accepted in good faith, but the publisher assumes no responsibility in any transactions that occur between readers and advertisers.

## ATTENTION ARTISTS

All artists, including those listed in the guide and those who want to be included, are encouraged to send their current address and their galleries' address to The House of Collectibles. Before the next edition of the OFFICIAL PRICE GUIDE TO COLLECTOR PRINTS is issued, The House of Collectibles will contact each artist for their information.

Artists should send their addresses to The House of Collectibles, Attn: Prints, Orlando Central Park, 1900 Premier Row, Orlando, FL 32809.

# MARKET REVIEW

In 1983, the public showed a renewed interest in the arts by opening new shows, offering large purses in art competitions, financially backing art shows and sales, and strongly investing in the art market.

Auctions are always an excellent determinant of the public's willingness to invest in art. In 1983, New York auction houses reported some of the best sales in recent years. Naturally, Audubon prints are taking top prices. "Trumpeter Swan" sold for $25,000, while other Audubon prints are fetching between $2,500 and $5,000.

The year showed other signs of public interest in the arts. The field is seeing an influx of renewed media exposure. In November 1983, PBS televised a series of twelve half-hour programs on contemporary American artists. Bob Kuhn, John Clymer and Wilson Hurley were artists included in the programs.

New art shows, larger winning purses for artists and corporate support of the arts were strong in 1983. The first Annual Southern Illinois Wildlife Art Show was held during the year. This show along with five others in Tulsa, Kansas City, Minneapolis, Omaha and Wichita will serve to introduce wildlife art to the midwest public. In Ohio, the Cincinnati Zoo held its first international wildlife show during June. Called "Wondrous Wildlife," the show featured 111 works by 70 artists from six nations. In South Carolina, Charleston hosted its first wildlife show. An attendance of 20,000 left no doubt of the public's art interest.

Prestigious art competitions offering high purses and public exposure are on the rise. One notable western art sale held by the National Academy of Western Art offers the winner of their highest award, the Prix de West, a gold medal, all expense paid trip to Europe and western clothing. Past winners of this prestigious event have included John Clymer and Howard Terpning.

It is always a good sign to see national companies backing art shows, tours, and competitions. During 1984, Gulf Oil Corporation is hosting a national tour of the annual Leigh Yawkey Woodson Art Museum's "Birds in Art" exhibition. This tour will include 148 works by international artists.

Not only is the public showing strong interest in art, but the artists themselves are donating their prints to humanitarian causes. This positive effort is a benefit for everyone involved. A good example of this is artist P. Buckley Moss. A special edition of 151 Moss prints brought more than $20,000 to a Virginia public television station in 1983. One of the prints sold for $2,000. Besides this fund raiser, Moss, on a U.S. and European personal appearance gallery tour, held two benefits for the Kidney Foundation.

The art industry is a growing business. With artists donating prints to organizations and with increasing public interest by way of new shows, increasing competition winnings, and corporate involvement only points to a strong future for all of the arts including collector prints.

# PRINTMAKING PROCESSES

Following is a brief description of the three common forms of printmaking. These include original lithograph, offset lithograph and serigraph.

**Original lithographs** are made from hand drawn stones or plates. With the stone method, the artist does not engrave the stone, but rather paints on it like a canvas. The artist must reverse his drawing so when it is transferred to the paper it will be viewed in the proper perspective. For illustrating, the artist can use several items from crayons to brushes.

After the drawing is finished, a solution of gum arabic, water and nitric acid is used to act as a protection against any air or dust particles. Since the stone must be kept wet during printing, the solution also prevents any alterations of the drawing.

The plate process is very similar to the stone method. Using pencils, pens, or brushes, the artist draws on the plate. The images on the plates are transferred to aluminum plates, which are then wetted with a solution to retard drying. Next the plates are rolled with ink. The non-image areas of the plate reject the ink while the image areas accept it. To hold the plates in the correct position, registration pins are used. Pressure created by the roller forces the ink against the paper and an image is made.

Color lithographs are difficult because a stone or plate must be made for each color used. Then, the stones or plates must register perfectly on the paper to have the color fall in the correct place. Therefore, the artist and lithographer must work closely together to obtain the correct color and ultimately the finished print.

An **offset lithograph** is a photomechanical reproduction of the original work. By using filters over a camera lens, particulars colors are separated. The result is a halftone negative. When this method first began, only four basic colors were used to print. Today, it is common to use ten or more halftones to reproduce the artist's work. Through this advancement, it is difficult to tell the original painting from the print.

Each halftone is transferred to a metal plate. The plates are put on a printing press with a rubber-blanketed roller. Each time the paper is fed through the press the registration of each color must be perfect to obtain the finished print. Reproductions vary from 500 to 5,000. The plates are destroyed in a limited edition series.

**Serigraph or silk screening** is a method of printing using a squeegie. The squeegie forces the ink through a screen in which a stencil forms the area where the ink is to go. A different screen or set of stencils is used for each color. With each screen, one can print solid colors but not graduated values.

Prints can be made on all types of surfaces including paper, cardboard, glass or metal.

**Old prints** are works of art made before photomechanical reproduction began. They were produced by hand printing and were hand colored.

Some famous artists of old prints include Nathaniel Currier and James Ives, John James Audubon, and Louis Icart.

Determining values is complicated. Several factors are used to compile prices including authenticity, subject, condition, size, artist's workmanship, printing technique, quality of material, and the artist himself.

This book includes some of the more popular artists among old print collectors.

# Recommended Reading . . .

**The Official Price Guide to Collector Prints** *is designed for the novice as well as the seasoned collector. Information on price trends, industry development, investing, and collecting techniques such as care and repair, storage, or building a collection is written in a way a beginning hobbist will understand yet gives specific details and helpful hints the hard core collector will find useful.*

This guide also offers up-to-date prices for both rare and common collectibles that are available in the current secondary market. This guide will give any collector confidence when determining what articles to purchase at what price. With the knowledge gained from this guide, a collector will move from flea market to auction house with ease knowing which items are "hot" and which articles are definitely overpriced.

As your interest in collecting grows, you may want to start a reference library of your favorite areas. For the collector who needs more extensive coverage of the collectibles market, The House of Collectibles publishes a complete line of comprehensive companion guides which are itemized at the back of this book. They contain full coverage on buying, selling, and caring of valuable articles, plus listings with thousands of prices for rare, unusual, and common antiques and collectibles.

$9.95-2nd Edition, 672 pgs., Order #393-7

The House of Collectibles recommends **The Official Price Guide to Collector Plates,** second edition, as the companion to this guide.

- **Over 18,000 current collector values** — The most complete listing of U.S. and Foreign plate manufacturers and distributors in print!
- **COMPARE CURRENT MARKET VALUES WITH THE ORIGINAL ISSUE PRICE** — Our special price column will enable you to spot the best investment potential in one glance!
- **INVESTMENT REVIEW** — Certain types of plates, artists and manufacturers are more valuable . . . learn which ones are and why!
- **EVERY KNOWN COLLECTOR PLATE, FROM 1895 TO DATE** — Each plate listing includes title and series, original release date, designing artist, production methods used, quantities issued, issue price and current price range.
- **EXPANDED GALLERY OF ARTISTS** — Read about the legendary artists who create collector plates including tributes to the late Ted De Grazia and Frances Hook.
- **FULLY ILLUSTRATED**

*Available from your local dealer or order direct from:*
**THE HOUSE OF COLLECTIBLES, see order blank**

**A COMPLETE COURSE OF LITHOGRAPHY;** by Alois Senefelder
**AMERICAN ART & ANTIQUES;** One Worth Avenue, Marion, Ohio 43302
**AMERICAN ARTIST;** One Astor Plaza, New York, N.Y. 10036
**AMERICAN ART REVIEW;** P. O. Box 65007, Los Angeles, CA 90065
**ANTIQUE JOURNAL;** P. O. Box 1046, Dubuque, IA 52001
**ANTIQUES MAGAZINE;** Stright Enterprises Inc., 551 Fifth Avenue,
    New York, N.Y. 10017
**ANTIQUE TRADER;** P. O. Box 1050, Dubuque, IA 52001
**ART IN AMERICA;** 150 East 58th St., New York, N.Y. 10022
**ART INVESTMENT REPORT;** Wall Street Transcript, 120 Wall St.,
    New York, N.Y. 10005
**AUDUBON MAGAZINE;** 950 Third Avenue, New York, N.Y. 10022
**COLLECTOR'S NEWS;** Box 156, Grundy Center, IA 50638
**COLLECTOR'S EDITIONS;** A Quarterly . . . Acquire Publishing Co., 170 Fifth Ave.,
    New York, N.Y. 10010
**CURRIER & IVES PRINTS;** An Illustrated Checklist; Frederick A.
    Conningham, revised edition updated by Colin Simkin, Copyright Mary Barton
    Conningham 1970, Crown Publishers, One Park Avenue, New York, N.Y. 10016
**DUCK STAMP DATA;** Bureau of Sport Fisheries and Wildlife, U.S. Government
    Printing Office, Washington, D.C. 20402 (Further information available
    under Federal Duck Stamp listing).
**PLATE COLLECTOR;** 100 N. Edward Gray, P. O. Box 1729, San Marcos, TX 78667.
**PRINT COLLECTOR'S NEWSLETTER;** 205 East 78th Street, New York, N.Y. 10021
**PRINT TRADER;** 6762 79th Street, Middle Village, N.Y. 11379
**PRINTS;** P. O. Box 1468, Alton, IL 62002

# CONSERVATORS SPECIALIZING IN PAPER RESTORATION

**American Association of
Conservators and Restorers**
1250 E. Ridgwood Ave.
Ridgewood, N. J. 07450

**Mr. Arthur Beale
The Center For Conservation and
    Technical Studies**
Fogg Art Museum
Harvard University
Cambridge, MA 02138

**Ms. Brigitte Boyadjian**
43 Fern Street
Lexington, MA 02173

**Brooklyn Museum**
Brooklyn, N.Y. 11238

**Art Institute of Chicago**
Chicago, IL 60603

**Conservation Center of the Institute
    of Fine Arts**
New York University
1 East 78th Street
New York, NY 10028

**Ms. Christa M. Gaehde**
55 Falmouth Road
Arlington, MA 02174

**Ms. Mary Todd Glaser**
73 E. Linden Avenue
Englewood, N. J. 07631

**Graphic Conversation Company**
325 W. Huron, Room 408
Chicago, IL 60610

**Mr. Robert A. Hauser
Busyhaus**
P. O. Box 422
North Andover, MA 01845

**Mrs. Florence Hodes**
145 Central Park West
New York, N.Y. 10023

**Mrs. Carolyn Horton**
430 W. 22nd Street
New York, N.Y. 10011

**Murray Lebwohl Studio, Inc.**
1212 I Street
Alexandria, VA 22307

**Ms. Edith MacKennan**
11 Rosalind Road
Poughkeepsie, N.Y. 12601

**Museum of Modern Art**
11 W. 53rd Street
New York, N.Y. 10019

**National Gallery of Art**
Washington, D. C. 20565

**Ms. Wynne H. Phelan**
3721 Ella Lee Lane
Houston, TX 77027

**Pennsylvania Academy of Fine Arts**
Philadelphia, PA 19102

**John Pofelski**
190 South Wood Dale Road
Wood Dale, IL 60191

**Ms. Shirley J. Riddick**
6561 Hil-Mar Drive, #203
Forestville, MD 20028

**Ms. Marilyn Weidner**
612 Spruce Street
Philadelphia, PA 19106

## GLOSSARY OF TECHNICAL TERMS

*ALBUM* A Portfolio or series of prints.
*ANNOTE* Marked, designated, numbered.
*AQUATINT* A process used in etching or engraving to obtain effects similar to a wash.
*ARTIST* A painter, engraver, sculptor, etc. who creates an original artwork. Word "Painter" is often misused for a person who has created a work of art.
*ARTIST PROOF* A term used in print making processes meaning the plate which the artist must approve before the final prints are reproduced.
*AVANT LA LETTRE* Dedications, descriptions, lettering. Frequently added after the print has been finished and proofed. Proofs made before *Avant La Lettre* are quite rare and usually command high prices.
*BLEED* When the picture image extends beyond the margin of the paper or the papers edge so there is no border.
*BRUSH STROKED* A clear plastic material which has the consistency of regular paint and is brushed on a picture and allowed to dry. This creates an illusion of being an original rather than a photomechanically reproduced print.
*BURIN* A needle used in engraving, especially used on copper.
*CATALOG OF PRINTS* The graphic work of an artist, cataloged and numbered with notes for easy identification of the prints. Normally contains title, date, edition and description of various works which exist at that time.
*CANCELLED PLATE* A metal plate which has been defaced or destroyed. In offset lithography, the plates are cancelled to insure a limited edition.
*CHROMOLITH* A highly refined photo-mechanical reproductive process whereby an exact reproduction of a picture is produced. Tone, line and color are reproduced not by the reduction of an original to a pattern of dots, but by taking a negative directly from the original in such a way that a reproductive plate can be made that precisely incorporates all of the continuous tones of the original. (Not to be confused with *Chromolithography*.)
*CHROMOLITHOGRAPHY* Printing lithographs in color from several plates.
*COLLECTION* An accumulation of a number of pieces of art.
*COLLECTORS MARK* It is the custom of some collectors and most museums to place a mark or monogram on the back of a print identifying it as part of a collection.
*COLLOTYPE* A process for making very high quality photo-mechanical reproductions. Normally used for printing on a soft finish or handmade paper. Reproduces with great fidelity the most delicate gradations of tone. Contains no dot process as does offset lithographs.

*COLOR SEPARATION* A term used in photo-mechnical reproduction which refers to the number of different plates used in separating colors from the original painting.

*COMMISSION* An order placed with an artist for an original work of art.

*CONDITION* Referred to as the preservation of a print. Faultless or mint means no marks, no creases, no finger marks or absolutely perfect. Nice means very few or very slight markings with no creases. Poor means print has had careless handling with dominant creases and marks plainly visible.

*CONDITIONS OF SALE* Means terms set out in writing between print owner and gallery.

*COPY* Facsimile of another piece.

*COLOUR* The proper term for a lithograph printed from various plates in colour.

*DECKLE EDGE* An irregular, untrimmed edge of paper.

*DRY MOUNT* Means to glue a picture to a stiff board or cardboard by means of a dry adhesive. Never recommended for a fine print or reproduction. Should be used only as a last resort to salvage a badly damaged print.

*DRY STAMP* Used by publishers to verify the genuineness of prints.

*EDITION* Number produced from a plate. Edition number does not usually include any artist's proofs pulled from the plate. There are regular and special editions.

*ENGRAVING* Design is cut into plate by means of a *"burin"*. A type of intaglio.

*EPREUVE* A proof. There are artist's, trial, state and printer's proofs.

*ETAT* If this appears on a print it means a proof was pulled at some stage prior to completion for the artist to determine if he is attaining the desired effect or to detect any errors and correct them prior to the final printing.

*ETCHING* The process of producing pictures by printing from a metal surface which has been etched. The artist draws the design into the acid resistant wax. The plate is then placed in an acid solution which "burns" the design into the plate where the wax has been removed. The wax is then removed, ink is applied to the plate, and a print is pulled.

*FILLET* A small divider used in the rabbet of a frame to hold a print away from the glass to protect it from damage due to moisture condensation. This term is sometimes used to describe the thin area of a second color mat used by many framers.

*FOXING* A term used to describe damage found on prints. It is characterized by small dark stains, sometimes with a darker center, which resemble iron rust (but which are usually a species of mold) appearing anywhere on the picture.

*GRAPHIC* A nondescript term; used when referring to an original print.

*HORS DE COMMERCE* Means a print outside or apart from. Not for sale.

*ILLUSTRATION* A term used for drawings or original works of art.

*IMAGE SIZE* Means size of the picture area only, not the size of paper.

*IMPRESSIONS* The number of times a picture has been printed from a plate.

*INK* A colored liquid material used for printing.

*INTAGLIO* One of four techniques of original printmaking where the image is sunk below the surface of the print.

*JAPON* A Japanese paper.

*JAUNIE* Means yellowing of the paper, often occurs with age.

*LITHOGRAPH* There are two types of lithographs. An original lithograph is produced by an artist drawing directly on a stone or plate. Offset lithographs are produced by a photo-mechanical method.

*MAT* A cardboard material, used as decorative trim when framing.

*MEZZOTINT* A type of intaglio where a metal plate is entirely and evenly pitted and roughened with tiny holes. The holes are then burnished flat in all areas but where the artist wants the plate to hold ink. It is then inked and printed.

*NUMBERED* A process used to show the limit of an edition. The number is usually placed over the size of the edition for example, 1/100. This indicates it is print number one of an edition of one hundred. In an etching or engraving the earlier numbers pulled are normally much sharper in appearance.

**PAINTER** One who applies a solution of pigment to a surface.

**PEINTRE-GRAVEUR** French term for a painter or sculptor who produces original graphic works.

**PLATE** A piece of stone or metal used in lithography.

**PLATE SIGNED** Means the artist has signed the plate upon which he has placed his design and the signature is printed along with the design. Usually no hand signed signature by the artist appears on a plate signed print.

**PLATE SIZE** Actual size of the printing plate, the size of the image on the printed picture; not the paper size.

**RABBET** The inner portion of the frame material used to secure the print or painting and the glass or mats.

**RAGBOARD** A hundred percent rag content cardboard or mat board. It is completely free of any harmful substances which might damage or alter a picture. Used as backing and protection for fine picture framing and storage.

**RAG PAPER** A paper used in the printing process of lithography. It is a combination of cotton, rag, and wood pulp. It is manufactured in twenty-five, fifty and a hundred percent rag.

**RELIEF PROCESS** The lines or surfaces which are raised in comparison to the surrounding areas.

**REMARQUE** French term for a small sketch often made outside the actual area of the drawing or picture. It is normally done in pencil.

**REPRODUCTION** A picture, replica or copy of an original art work produced by various methods. A facsimile.

**RESTRIKE** A print pulled from a plate after the original edition is issued. Restrikes are not part of an edition but constitute a legitimate print if unsigned and not represented as an original print of the artist. If the plate was not defaced it is very difficult to tell the restrike from the original.

**SECONDARY MARKET VALUE** It is the value of a print as determined by its being bought, sold and traded by collectors and dealers after the edition is exhausted or sold out by the publisher or distributor.

**SERIGRAPH (SILK-SCREEN)** A stencil method of producing an original print.

**SIGNATURE** The writing of an artist's name on the plate itself or on the print.

**STEEL ENGRAVING** A picture made from engraving a design on a steel plate or steel-faced copper plate. Very fine lines and subtle tones are possible in steel engravings and the plate can withstand a large printing.

**STONE** A concentration of mineral matter. In lithography, porous limestone from Solnhofen, Bavaria is used.

**TRIAL PROOF** Impression taken while the artwork is in progress.

**VIGNETTE** Term describing the fading of a background into the blank area surrounding the image.

**WOODCUT** This process begins with the artist drawing on a block of wood. Ink is then applied to the surface. A sheet of paper is placed over the block and passed through a press. When the paper is removed, the design has been imprinted on it.

**WOOD ENGRAVING** A variation of woodcut. Instead of a block the plate is cut from a cross-section of a tree and the work is done on the end grain. Engraving tools may be used. It is printed like engraving.

**ZINCOGRAPHY** A chemical printing process using a zinc plate.

# HOW TO START A COLLECTION

A beginning print collector must become an investigator. First, he must examine the artist's style and subject material to determine if it is enjoyable to him. He must find out how often the artist releases limited edition prints and how many are in the editions. The collector must ask himself are the particular artist prints affordable.

Then, he must do some footwork. Visiting galleries or talking with an artist who is visiting a gallery is recommended. Many artists are happy to answer questions about their background and techniques. Most artists or galleries supply brochures and catalogs to interested collectors.

When a collector has found an affordable artist whose style and subject matter he enjoys, then he has almost started a collection. When he buys his first print, the investigation is over and the collection begins.

## CARE, STORAGE AND DISPLAY

After purchasing a print, care must be taken so it will remain in mint condition. Damage could result through handling, exposure to environmental extremes such as unfavorable temperatures and humidity, and restoration completed by an unqualified individual.

There are several ways to keep a print in good condition. There are binders made specifically for storing prints. Many contain ten acetate sheets with an inside paper cover enabling you to show several prints in one binder. Usually galleries stock this item.

Many galleries also have shrink wrap machines. This machine takes a print and wraps it in clear plastic, which is shrunk with heat to the print size.

Museum mounting is preferred when framing a print. Prints are usually produced on 100% rag paper. Rag paper is susceptible to mat bleed which means the color of the inner mat transfers to the print. Prints issued with a 50% or more rag content need two ply ragboard placed on top and behind the print.

When displaying a print, use a regular picture hook. Usually professional framers will attach one to the back of the picture. When storing a framed print, the picture should not be exposed to extreme temperatures, which results in condensation between the glass and the print.

## INVESTING AND SELLING

Three things should be considered when buying a print. Primarily the print should appeal to the purchaser. The print edition and artist popularity should also be considered. For example, a popular artist's limited edition of 500 prints should sell out within a short period of time. Therefore, any person interested in the sold out print would have to purchase it from a secondary market. What a person is willing to pay or has paid is how secondary market prices are determined.

There are a number of ways for a collector to sell his "sold-out" prints.

Throughout the U.S. there are a number of galleries dealing in the secondary market. There is a ten to twenty-five percent fee for this service. Several periodicals accept ads from collectors who want to sell their prints themselves. There are many auction houses dealing with prints including Bernet, Christies, and Phillips. Usually auction houses charge a ten percent fee to the buyer and seller.

## FUTURE TRENDS

Despite a chaotic economy, art has held its own in the past few years. Although the first two years of this decade were an almost depression state, the 1983-84 market is gaining momentum. With a stronger economy, the consumer will naturally begin buying more aggressively again.

Art is still a good investment but just like the many money markets enticing investors, one must study the area he will be putting his money into.

In the collector print market, the ever popular artists like John James Audubon or Norman Rockwell are consistent best-sellers. But there are many current artists who are becoming steady favorites also. Western artist Jerry Crandall or wildlife artist Ray Harm are notable examples.

Another good investment is celebrity art. Motorcycle stuntman, Evel Knievel, has recently received considerable press about his art. His works are quickly commanding higher prices not only for its quality but because his name is already known to the masses.

When investing two points should be considered: do the artist's prints sell out quickly and has the secondary market value risen considerably over the issue price. If the prints consistently sell out and the secondary market value rises substantially over a three to five year period, then the prints should be considered as a possible investment.

The last two years have been lean art investing ones, but with the upsurge in the economy, art should rise again.

## PUBLISHER'S AND DISTRIBUTOR'S CODE

At the end of each listing in the Contemporary Prints section is the initials for the publisher or distributor of each artist's print. Below is the list of initials with the company name and address following.

*no longer in business

    **A—ARMSTRONG'S**, 150 East Third, Pomona, CA 91766

**A & C—ALLISON & COMPANY,** Limited editions, P.O. Box 32265,
    San Antonio, TX 78216

**AIAC—AMERICAN INDIAN ARTS COLLECTION,** Route 2 Box 311A,
    Shawnee, OK 74801*

    **ALI—ARTS LIMITED INC.,** P.O. Box 6385, San Antonio, TX 78209

    **ALL—AMERICAN LEGACY LTD.,** 2131 N. Edwards, South El Monte,
    CA 91733

**AMF—AMERICAN MASTERS FOUNDATION,** 10688 Haddington, Suite 1200,
    Houston, TX 77043

**AQUA**—**AQUA DECOR,** 1124 N. Greenacre Ave., Los Angeles, CA 90046

**ARI**—**ART RECOLLECTIONS, INC.,** 704 N. Glebe Rd., Suite 212, Arlington, VA 22203

**AG**—**ATLAS GALLERY,** 4168 N. Harlem Ave., Norridge, IL 60634

**BBS**—**BRAD BENNETT STUDIOS,** 405 65th St., Kenosha, WI 53140

**BDP**—**BURTON DYE PRINTS,** 302 W. Vine St., Murfreesboro, TN 37130

**BG**—**BURGER GALLERIES,** 238 Airport Road, Whispering Pines, NC 28389

**BI**—**BERGSMA ILLUSTRATIONS,** 1756 Iowa St., Bellingham, WA 98226

**BJAD**—**B & J ART DESIGNS,** P. O. Box 67, Georgetown, TX 78626

**BM**—**BERNARD MARTIN,** C-70 Lake Lotawana, MO 64063

**CAP**—**COMMODORE ART PUBLISHING,** 10404 Patterson Ave., Suite 206, Richmond, VA 23233

**CBW**—**CHARLES BANKS WILSON,** 100½ North Main, Miami, OK 74354

**CC**—**COLLECTORS COVEY,** 15 Highland Park Village, Dallas, TX 75205

**CDR**—**CHARLES D. ROGERS,** 11051 N. Clermont Dr., Thornton, CO 80233

**CF**—**CHESTER FIELDS,** E. 14210 22nd Ct., Veradale, WA 99037

**CFAC**—**CIRCLE FINE ARTS CORP.,** 232 E. Ohio St., Chicago, IL 60611

**CFRC**—**C. FORD RILEY & COMPANY,** 1843 Woodmere Dr., Jacksonville, FL 32210, 904-388-1441

**CG**—**COURT GALLERIES,** 7876 Montgomery Rd., Cincinnati, OH 45236

**CGAL**—**CONNOISSEUR'S GALLERY OF ART, LTD.,** P. O. Box 94354, Schaumburg, IL 60194

**CHWA**—**COTTAGE HILL WILDLIFE ART,** no current address available.*

**CII**—**CONTEMPLATIVE INVESTMENTS, INC.,** 2067 Range Rd., Clearwater, FL 33575

**CIL**—**COLLECTORS INTERNATIONAL LTD.,** 67 Putnam St., Mount Vernon, NY 10550

**COS**—**CROSSROADS OF SPORT,** 5 East 47th St., New York, NY 10017

**CS**—**COUNTRYSIDE STUDIO,** Box 88, Cottontown, TN 37048

**CSH**—**CARDWELL S. HIGGINS STUDIO,** 1511 Garfield St., Hollywood, FL 33020

**DDS**—**DORLA DEAN SLIDER,** 1387 Kutz Dr., Pottstown, PA 19464

**DLG**—**DAVID LANCE GOINES,** c/o Hang Up Gallery Ltd., 23 W. Court St., Doylestown, PA 18901 or Thackrey & Robertson Gallery, 2266 Union St., San Francisco, CA 94123

**DPC**—**DOLPHIN PUBLISHING CO.,** 2063 Range Rd., Clearwater, FL 33575

**DRN**—**D. R. NUTE FINE ARTS,** 912 Coldbranch Dr., Columbia, SC 29204

**EDTW**—**EDGE OF THE WILD,** 8643 King Memorial Highway, Mentor, OH 44060*

**EE**—**ETCHINGS, ETC.,** P.O. Box 127, Alta Loma, CA 91701*

**EEI**—**ELEANOR ETTINGER, INC.,** 305 East 47th St., New York, NY 10017

**EHC**—**EDNA HIBEL CORP.,** P. O. Box 9967, Riviera Beach, FL 33404

**EJ**—**EDNA B. JOHNSON,** 913 Pinson St., Forney, TX 75126

**EJB**—**EJB EDITIONS,** P. O. Box 31, 8833 Lake Hill Dr., Lorton, VA 22079

**EP—EVERGREEN PUBLISHING, INC.,** 2619 South Broad St., Trenton, NJ 08610*

**EW—ED WARD,** 296 Homecrest Avenue, Trenton, NJ 08638

**EWGI—EDWARD WESTON GRAPHICS, INC.,** 19355 Business Center #3, Northridge, CA 91324

**FFFA—FOXFIRE FINE ARTS INC.,** 2730 N. Graham, Charlotte, NC 28206

**FHG—FRAME HOUSE GALLERY, INC.,** 110 East Market Street, Louisville, KY 40202

**FI—FELICIE, INC.,** 141 East 56th St., New York, NY 10022*

**FOP—FOXMAN'S OIL PAINTINGS, LTD.,** 3350 Church St., Evanston, IL 60203

**FTGS—FRANT T. GEE STUDIO,** P.O. Box 12752, Nashville, TN 37212

**GB—GEORGE BOUTWELL,** 3913 Ave. C., Austin, TX 78751

**GBSL—GRAPHICS BUYING SERVICE, LTD.,** 225 W. Hubbard, Chicago, IL 60610

**GI—GUILDHALL, INC.,** 2535 Weisenberger, Ft. Worth, TX 76107

**GPL—GRANSTAFF PRINTS LTD.,** Route 2, Princeton, KY 42445

**GRG—GEORGE RODRIGUE GALLERY,** 1206 Jefferson St., Lafayette, LA 70501

**GSP—GREY STONE PRESS,** 207 Louise Ave., Nashville, TN 37203

**GU—GIROUARD UNLIMITED,** P. O. Box 391, Ormond Beach, FL 32074

**GW—GREENWICH WORKSHOP (The),** 30 Lindeman Dr., Trumbull, CT 06611

**HC—HERB CHIDLEY,** 240 N. Bothwell, Palatine, IL 60067

**HHS—HAMPTON HOUSE STUDIOS, INC.,** Route 1 Box 169, McDonald, TN 37353

**HP—HAMMER PUBLISHING CO.,** 33 West 57th St., New York, NY 10019

**HG—HANCOCK GALLERY,** 6151 Estero Blvd., Fort Myers, FL 33931

**HUI—HANG UPS INC.,** 1319 West Katella Ave., Orange, CA 92667

**IG—INTERNATIONAL GALLERY,** 224 Orlando Square, Orlando Park, IL 60462

**IS—IRENE SPENCER,** 1202 Star View Dr., Vista, CA 92083

**IV—ICART VENDOR,** 7956 Beverly Blvd., Los Angeles, CA 90048

**JAG—JONS ART GALLERY,** 913 Pinson, Forney, TX 75126

**JARP—JAR PUBLISHERS,** now a division of the Edna Hibel Corp. (see EHC)

**JBFA—JOHN BRINDLE FINE ARTS,** 28944 Marlies Street, Agoura, CA 91301

**JC—JERRY CRANDALL,** P. O. Box 2606, Ledona, AZ 86336

**JGE—JOSEPH GETSINGER ENTERPRISES,** P. O. Box 97, Blackwood Terrace, NJ 08096

**JKI—JOHN F. KOLODY, INC.,** 22 East 49th St., New York, NY 10017

**JTAC—JEROME TIGER ART CO.,** P. O. Box C, Muskogee, OK 74401

**JTJ—J T J IMAGES,** 10240 S. W. Nimbus, Suite L-11, Portland, OR 97223

**KMS—KATHRYN MILLER STUDIOS,** 122 East Oglethorpe Avenue, Savannah, GA 31401

**KNC—KALAMAZOO NATURE CENTER,** 7000 N. Westnedge, Kalamazoo, MI 49007

**LBA—LENORE BERAN ART,** 7332 Camellia Ave., No. Hollywood, CA 91605

**LC—LEGEND'S CORPORATION,** 9960 York Alpha Dr., North Royalton, OH 44133

**M—MOONRISE,** P. O. Box 1971, Auburn, AL 36831

**MEI—McCALLA ENTERPRISES, INC.,** Box 75, Groom Creek Route, Prescott, AZ 86301

**MLC—MEREDITH LONG & COMPANY,** 2323 San Felipe, Houston, TX 77019

**MM—MIDWEST MARKETING,** P. O. Box 137, Sullivan, IL 61951

**MMFC—MASTERPIECE MOULDING & FRAME,** P. O. Box 926, Morganton, NC 28655

**MMGI—ART SPECTRUM,** a Div. of Mitch Morse Gallery Inc., no longer representing artist listing please note GBSL

**MP—MOSS PORTFOLIO (The),** 1055 Thomas Jefferson St., N. W., Washington, D.C. 20007

**MPPI—MILL POND PRESS, INC.,** 208 South Nassau Street, Venice, FL 33595

**MS—MALONE STUDIOS,** 2331 Pikewood Dr., Germantown, TN 38138

**NC—NORTHWOODS CRAFTSMAN,** 4144 Briar Ridge Lane, Colgate, WI 53017

**NHFA—NATURAL HERITAGE FINE ART,** P. O. Box 207, Carey, Idaho 83320

**NHI—NATURE HOUSE, INC.,** Purple Martin Junction, Griggsville, IL 62340

**NWA—NORTHWOODS WILDLIFE ART,** changed name to Wilderness Art (see WA)

**NWAEI—NATIONAL WILDLIFE ART EXCHANGE, INC.,** P. O. Drawer 3385, 1601 20th St., Vero Beach, FL 32960

**NWDH—NI-WO-DI-HI GALLERIES,** P. O. Box 746, Austin, TX 78767

**PGL—PANDION GALLERY LTD.,** Route 3 Box 448, Crystal River, FL 32629

**PHFA—PEPPER HOUSE FINE ARTS LTD.,** 30 Capital Drive, Ottowa K26 OE9 Ontario, Canada*

**PP—PETERSEN PRINTS,** 6725 Sunset Blvd., Los Angeles, CA 90028

**PSGI—PAUL SAWYIER GALLERIES, INC.,** Route 3 U.S. 60E, Frankfort, KY 40601

**RAF—RUSSELL A. FINK,** 9843 Gunston Road, P. O. Box 250, Lorton, VA 22079

**RG—RAINTREE GRAPHICS,** 50 Music Square West, United Artists Tower, Suite 100, Nashville, TN 37203

**RGF—ROBERT G. FRANKOWIAK,** 4972 S. 20th St., Milwaukee, WI 53221

**RHAI—REGENCY HOUSE ART, INC.,** P. O. Box 147, Plainview, NY 11803, name changed to World Wildlife Art Museum, see WWAM

**RI—REMARQUE, INC.** 514-16 N. Wrenn St., High Point, NC 27262

**ROPH—RUDISILL'S OLDE PRINT HAUS,** 3 Lakewood Dr., Medfield, MA 02052

**RS—ROZEMA STUDIO,** 226 Plymouth, N.E., Grand Rapids, MI 49503

**RTG**—*RICHARD THOMPSON GALLERY,* 80 Maiden Lane, San Francisco, CA 94108

**SAG**—*SEVEN ARTS GALLERY PUBLISHING,* P. O. Drawer H, Maryville, TN 37803

**SB**—*SCHMID BROS., INC.,* 55 Pacella Park Dr., Randolph, MA 02368

**SCG**—*SALT CREEK GRAPHICS,* P. O. Box 39, 3333 West Yellowstone, Casper, WY 82601

**SEL**—*SPORTSMAN'S EDGE, LTD.,* 136 East 74th Street, New York, NY 10021

**SGL**—*SWAN GRAPHICS, LTD.,* P. O. Box 15185, Chattanooga, TN 37415

**SIAG**—*SEA ISLAND ART GALLERY,* 52 Sweetbriar Rd., Greenville, SC 29615

**SLA**—*STREAMSIDE LIMITED ART,* 736 Wooster Pike, Terrace Park, OH 45174

**SP**—*SAGE PRESS,* Cody, Wyoming 82414 . . . prints available through M. C. Poulsen, 2019 Kerper Blvd., Cody, WY 82414

**SRS**—*SPRING RIVER STUDIO,* R.R.1 Box 211-D, Miami, OK 74354, 918-542-9262

**SRWA**—*STEEP ROCK WILDLIFE ART,* P. O. Box 107, Bridgewater, CT 06752

**SS**—*STEARNS & ASSOCIATES,* Rd. 2 Box 320, Chestertown, MD 21620

**SSWASI**—*SALT SPRINGS ART STUDIOS, INC.,* RR 2 Box 1078, Ft. McCoy, FL 32637

**TAP**—*TEXAS ART PRESS,* 1400 Main St., Dallas, TX 75202

**TCG**—*THE CLOVER GROUP,* 1706 S. 320th, Federal Way, WA 98003

**THC**—*THE HERITAGE COMPANY,* Box 1027, Lexington, NC 27292

**TRAD**—*TRADITIONS,* 2109 Woodmere Drive, Knoxville, TN 37920

**VFL**—*VANITY FAIR LTD.,* prints now available thru Clive A. Burden, Inc., P. O. Box 2792, Naples, FL 33939

**VA**—*VIRGINIA ARTS,* P. O. Box 6, Lynchburg, VA 24505

**VOS**—*THE VAN ORDER STUDIO,* P. O. Box 402, Boulder Junction, WI 54512

**VSL**—*VAGUE SHADOWS LIMITED,* Box 116, Staten Island, NY 10309

**WA**—*WILDERNESS ART,* P. O. Box 1297, Manistique, MI 49854

**WAEL**—*WORLD ART EDITIONS LTD.,* 67 Putnam St., Mt. Vernon, NY 10550, name changed to Collectors International, Ltd.

**WAG**—*WILDLIFE ART GALLERY II,* P. O. Box 1971, Auburn, AL 36830

**WAS**—*WILDLIFE ART STUDIOS,* Rt. 6, Box 1078, Ft. McCoy, FL 32037

**WB**—*THE WOODEN BIRD,* 8600 Kennedy Memorial Dr., St. Bonifacius, MN 55375

**WEI**—*WINDBERG ENTERPRISES, INC.,* 2032 Centimeter Circle, Austin, TX 78758

**WII**—*WILDLIFE INTERNATIONALE, INC.,* 6290 Old U.S. 68, Georgetown, OH 45121

**WNG**—*WREN'S NEST GALLERY,* P. O. Box 507, Piedmont, AL 36272

**WOA**—*WILDLIFE OF AMERICA,* P. O. Box 556, Minneapolis, MN 55440

**WP**—*WATERMARK PRESS,* P. O. Box 145, Glen Morgan, WV 25847

**WSI**—*WILDERNESS STUDIO, INC.,* 6800 S. Cloverdale Rd., Boise, ID 83709

**WWAM**—*WORLD WILDLIFE ART MUSEUM,* P. O. Box 1000, Monument, CO 80132

**WWI**—*WILD WINGS, INC.,* Lake City, MN 55041

# HOW TO USE THIS BOOK

The artist sections in this book are divided into three parts. These are Old Prints, Contemporary Prints, and Federal and State Duck Stamp Prints.

The Old Prints section is made up of early American artists' prints which are highly collectible. Audubon, Currier And Ives, Louis Icart, Maxfield Parrish, Mark Catesby and Vanity Fair are included in this section.

The Contemporary Prints section is alphabetized by artist name. The information in the listings under each artist follows this format: title, issue date, edition number, if the print is signed and numbered, size, and publisher. Any missing information means it was unavailable. Although most prints are produced photomechanically, when available it is stated whether the print is a lithograph or etching.

Issue price is the price of the print upon its release on the market to dealers. Current Price is the current selling price. Sold Out means the publisher or distributor is sold out, however, there still may be prints available through the dealer network.

Explanation and key to codes in the listings are as follows:

**s/n**—signed and numbered
**s/o**—signed only
**i/n**—initialed and numbered
**i/o**—initialed only
**n/o**—numbered only
**N/A**—information not available
**Cl. Out**—closed out edition
**sw/seal**—signed with seal
**D.U. Print**—Ducks Unlimited Print

**rem.**—remarqued print*
**u/s**—unsigned
**s/s**—with state seal
**litho**—original lithograph
**etch**—original etching
**pub**—publisher
**distr.**—distributor
*remarqued copies are currently worth $85.00 to $100.00 more than the regular print in an edition

Also upon occasion you will find the word "embossed" in a listing which means that the publisher or artist has embossed the paper with a trademark to ensure its authenticity.

# OLD PRINTS

## JOHN JAMES AUDUBON
### (1785-1851)

John James Audubon is a name synonymous with pictures of birds. His "Birds of America" are recognized everywhere.

Audubon was born in Haiti, but grew up in France. He came to America around 1803 and settled in Louisiana. Audubon turned to ornithology and his artistic talents to painting all of the known birds of North America. Between 1826 and 1842 he traveled throughout the United States and Canada, working and gathering material for his art, and at the same time selling subscriptions for the finished project. He roamed through most of the forests and swamps of America to create his original paintings for this tremendous and monumental task.

Because it was a tremendous job, Audubon had a difficult time finding engravers. He turned to Englishman William Lizars who completed the first ten plates but could not finish the project because of labor problems. Audubon took his plates to R. Havell in London. Although Havell died in 1832, his son completed the work.

In all there were 435 plates in the completed work called **"The Birds of America"**. They originally sold for $1,000.00 per set. It is believed that fewer than 200 sets were actually bound into volumes. There are a varying number of loose prints because several of the original subscribers defaulted and then additional persons subscribed during the eleven years it was in the making.

These prints are called the double-elephant-folio-size (approximately 25½ " x 38 "). All birds are life size in the prints. All prints are aquatint engravings, hand printed and hand-colored by the Havells on Whatman watermarked paper. These are considered an excellent investment in the art field.

## JOHN JAMES AUDUBON
## THE ORIGINAL EDITION
## ENGRAVED BY HAVELL AND SON

| PLATE NUMBER | SUBJECT | CURRENT RETAIL PRICE | PLATE NUMBER | SUBJECT | CURRENT RETAIL PRICE |
|---|---|---|---|---|---|
| ☐ 1 | Turkey Cock | $33,000.00 | ☐ 21 | Mockingbird | 11,000.00 |
| ☐ 2 | Yellow-billed Cuckoo | 3,410.00 | ☐ 22 | Purple Martin | 2,650.00 |
| ☐ 3 | Prothonotary Warbler | 1,760.00 | ☐ 23 | Maryland Yellow Throat | 1,550.00 |
| ☐ 4 | Purple Finch | 1,210.00 | ☐ 24 | Roscoe's Yellow Throat | 800.00 |
| ☐ 5 | Bonaparte's Flycatcher | 1,760.00 | ☐ 25 | Song Sparrow | 1,550.00 |
| ☐ 6 | Hen Turkey | 17,500.00 | ☐ 26 | Carolina Parrot | 17,250.00 |
| ☐ 7 | Purple Grackle | 2,750.00 | ☐ 27 | Red-headed Woodpecker | 3,500.00 |
| ☐ 8 | White-throated Sparrow | 1,980.00 | ☐ 28 | Solitary Flycatcher | 1,200.00 |
| ☐ 9 | Salby's Flycatcher | 1,100.00 | ☐ 29 | Towhe Bunting | 2,900.00 |
| ☐ 10 | Brown Lark | 880.00 | ☐ 30 | Vigor's Vireo | 2,000.00 |
| ☐ 11 | Bird of Washington | 4,730.00 | ☐ 31 | White-headed Eagle | 6,750.00 |
| ☐ 12 | Baltimore Oriole | 6,600.00 | ☐ 32 | Black-billed Cuckoo | 4,000.00 |
| ☐ 13 | Snow Bird | 700.00 | ☐ 33 | American Goldfinch | 2,500.00 |
| ☐ 14 | Prairie Warbler | 1,550.00 | ☐ 34 | Worm-eating Warbler | 1,600.00 |
| ☐ 15 | Blue Yellow-backed Warbler | 1,900.00 | ☐ 35 | Children's Warbler | 825.00 |
| | | | ☐ 36 | Stanley Hawk | 4,750.00 |
| ☐ 16 | Great Footed Hawk | 4,500.00 | ☐ 37 | Golden-winged Woodpecker | 6,750.00 |
| ☐ 17 | Carolina Pigeon | 11,000.00 | | | |
| ☐ 18 | Bewick's Wren | 1,500.00 | ☐ 38 | Kentucky Warbler | 1,400.00 |
| ☐ 19 | Louisiana Water Thrush | 1,100.00 | ☐ 39 | Crested Titmouse | 2,250.00 |
| ☐ 20 | Blue-winged Yellow Warbler | 2,300.00 | ☐ 40 | American Redstart | 2,200.00 |
| | | | ☐ 41 | Ruffed Grouse | 8,500.00 |

| PLATE NUMBER | SUBJECT | CURRENT RETAIL PRICE | PLATE NUMBER | SUBJECT | CURRENT RETAIL PRICE |
|---|---|---|---|---|---|
| ☐ 42 | Orchard's Oriole | 3,000.00 | ☐105 | Red-breasted Nuthatch | 1,200.00 |
| ☐ 43 | Cedar Waxwing | 3,500.00 | ☐106 | Black Vulture | 4,000.00 |
| ☐ 44 | Summer Tanager | 4,000.00 | ☐107 | Canada Jay | 6,000.00 |
| ☐ 45 | Traill's Flycatcher | 900.00 | ☐108 | Fox Colored Sparrow | 1,550.00 |
| ☐ 46 | Barred Owl | 5,000.00 | ☐109 | Savannah Finch | 1,500.00 |
| ☐ 47 | Ruoy-throated Hummingbird | 11,000.00 | ☐110 | Hooded Warbler | 880.00 |
| | | | ☐111 | Pileated Woodpecker | 11,750.00 |
| ☐ 48 | Cerulean Warbler | 1,500.00 | ☐112 | Downy Woodpecker | 4,500.00 |
| ☐ 49 | Blue Green Warbler | 900.00 | ☐113 | Blue Bird | 2,750.00 |
| ☐ 50 | Swainson's Warbler | 900.00 | ☐114 | White-crowned Sparrow | 1,350.00 |
| ☐ 51 | Red-tailed Hawk | 3,400.00 | ☐115 | Wood Pewee | 825.00 |
| ☐ 52 | Chuck Will's Widow | 2,800.00 | ☐116 | Ferruginous Thrush | 5,000.00 |
| ☐ 53 | Painted Bunting | 3,500.00 | ☐117 | Mississippi Kite | 2,500.00 |
| ☐ 54 | Rice Bunting | 2,300.00 | ☐118 | Warbling Flycatcher | 2,750.00 |
| ☐ 55 | Cuvier's Wren | 1,650.00 | ☐119 | Yellow Throat | 1,500.00 |
| ☐ 56 | Red-shouldered Hawk | 6,250.00 | ☐120 | Pewit Flycatcher | 850.00 |
| ☐ 57 | Loggerhead Shrike | 1,800.00 | ☐121 | Snowy Owl | 21,000.00 |
| ☐ 58 | Hermit Thrush | 1,000.00 | ☐122 | Blue Grosbeak | 3,500.00 |
| ☐ 59 | Chestnut-sided Warbler | 850.00 | ☐123 | Black and Yellow Warbler | 2,500.00 |
| ☐ 60 | Carbonated Warbler | 1,000.00 | ☐124 | Green Black-capped Flycatcher | 1,100.00 |
| ☐ 61 | Great Horned Owl | 7,100.00 | | | |
| ☐ 62 | Passenger Pigeon | 9,500.00 | ☐125 | Brown-headed Nuthatch | 1,000.00 |
| ☐ 63 | White-eyed Flycatcher | 1,000.00 | ☐126 | White-headed Eagle (young) | 3,700.00 |
| ☐ 64 | Swamp Sparrow | 1,100.00 | | | |
| ☐ 65 | Rathbone Warbler | 1,750.00 | ☐127 | Rose-breasted Grosbeak | 2,900.00 |
| ☐ 66 | Ivory-billed Woodpecker | 14,000.00 | ☐128 | Catbird | 1,900.00 |
| ☐ 67 | Red-winged Starling | 2,500.00 | ☐129 | Great Crested Flycatcher | 1,300.00 |
| ☐ 68 | Cliff Swarrow | 1,000.00 | ☐130 | Yellow-winged Sparrow | 1,650.00 |
| ☐ 69 | Bay-breasted Warbler | 1,000.00 | ☐131 | American Robin | 7,250.00 |
| ☐ 70 | Henslow's Bunting | 900.00 | ☐132 | Three-toed Woodpecker | 2,250.00 |
| ☐ 71 | Winter Hawk | 4,500.00 | ☐133 | Black Poll Warbler | 1,000.00 |
| ☐ 72 | Swallow-tailed Hawk | 3,500.00 | ☐134 | Hemlock Warbler | 1,300.00 |
| ☐ 73 | Wood Thrush | 1,500.00 | ☐135 | Blackburnian Warbler | 1,100.00 |
| ☐ 74 | Indigo Bunting | 2,250.00 | ☐136 | Meadow Lark | 11,550.00 |
| ☐ 75 | Le Petit Caporal | 1,800.00 | ☐137 | Yellow-breasted Chat | 3,500.00 |
| ☐ 76 | Virginia Partridge | 15,500.00 | ☐138 | Connecticut Warbler | 1,200.00 |
| ☐ 77 | Belted Kingfisher | 8,000.00 | ☐139 | Field Sparrow | 1,600.00 |
| ☐ 78 | Great Carolina Wren | 2,900.00 | ☐140 | Pine-creeping Warbler | 1,100.00 |
| ☐ 79 | Tyrant Flycatcher | 1,400.00 | ☐141 | Goshawk | 3,750.00 |
| ☐ 80 | Prairie Titlak | 900.00 | ☐142 | American Sparrow Hawk | 3,850.00 |
| ☐ 81 | Fish Hawk | 17,500.00 | ☐143 | Golden Crowned Thrush | 1,400.00 |
| ☐ 82 | Whip-Poor-Will | 3,400.00 | ☐144 | Small Green Crested Flycatcher | 1,000.00 |
| ☐ 83 | House Wren | 2,750.00 | | | |
| ☐ 84 | Blue Gray Flycatcher | 1,000.00 | ☐145 | Yellow Red Poll Warbler | 1,100.00 |
| ☐ 85 | Yellow-throated Warbler | 880.00 | ☐146 | Fish Crow | 2,800.00 |
| ☐ 86 | Black Warrior | 2,500.00 | ☐147 | Night Hawk | 3,500.00 |
| ☐ 87 | Florida Jay | 4,750.00 | ☐148 | Pine Swamp Warbler | 1,000.00 |
| ☐ 88 | Autumnal Warbler | 800.00 | ☐149 | Sharp-tailed Finch | 2,000.00 |
| ☐ 89 | Nashville Warbler | 2,000.00 | ☐150 | Red-eyed Vireo | 825.00 |
| ☐ 90 | Black and White Creeper | 800.00 | ☐151 | Turkey Buzzard | 2,300.00 |
| ☐ 91 | Broad-winged Hawk | 5,500.00 | ☐152 | White Breasted Nuthatch | 2,200.00 |
| ☐ 92 | Pigeon Hawk | 3,000.00 | ☐153 | Yellow Crown Warbler | 1,000.00 |
| ☐ 93 | Sea Side Finch | 4,000.00 | ☐154 | Tennessee Warbler | 1,200.00 |
| ☐ 94 | Bay-winged Bunting | 1,300.00 | ☐155 | Black-throated Blue Warbler | 1,000.00 |
| ☐ 95 | Blue-eyed Yellow Warbler | 1,100.00 | | | |
| ☐ 96 | Columbia Jay | 5,225.00 | ☐156 | American Crow | 5,200.00 |
| ☐ 97 | Little Screech Owl | 6,750.00 | ☐157 | Rusty Grackle | 1,500.00 |
| ☐ 98 | Marsh Wren | 1,000.00 | ☐158 | American Swift | 825.00 |
| ☐ 99 | Cow Bunting | 900.00 | ☐159 | Cardinal Grosbeak | 7,250.00 |
| ☐100 | White-bellied Sparrow | 800.00 | ☐160 | Black-capped Titmouse | 1,000.00 |
| ☐101 | Raven | 3,500.00 | ☐161 | Caracara Eagle | 4,400.00 |
| ☐102 | Blue Jay | 5,750.00 | ☐162 | Zenaida Dove | 3,750.00 |
| ☐103 | Canada Warbler | 2,000.00 | ☐163 | Palm Warbler | 1,650.00 |
| ☐104 | Chipping Sparrow | 1,450.00 | ☐164 | Tawny Thrush | 1,800.00 |

**PLATE 203 HAVELL EDITION "Fresh Water Marsh Wren (King Rail)"**

| PLATE NUMBER | SUBJECT | CURRENT RETAIL PRICE |
|---|---|---|
| ☐165 | Bachman's Finch | 2,000.00 |
| ☐166 | Rough-legged Falcon | 2,900.00 |
| ☐167 | Key West Dove | 4,500.00 |
| ☐168 | Fork-tailed Flycatcher | 4,500.00 |
| ☐169 | Mangrove Cuckoo | 1,850.00 |
| ☐170 | Gray Tyrant | 1,350.00 |
| ☐171 | Barn Owl | 9,000.00 |
| ☐172 | Blue-headed Pigeon | 2,000.00 |
| ☐173 | Barn Swallow | 2,500.00 |
| ☐174 | Olive Sided Flycatcher | 850.00 |
| ☐175 | Marsh Wren | 1,650.00 |
| ☐176 | Spotted Grouse | 6,000.00 |
| ☐177 | White-crowned Pigeon | 7,150.00 |
| ☐178 | Orange-crowned Warbler | 1,100.00 |
| ☐179 | Wood Wren | 2,650.00 |
| ☐180 | Pine Finch | 1,350.00 |
| ☐181 | Golden Eagle | 4,000.00 |
| ☐182 | Ground Dove | 3,250.00 |
| ☐183 | Golden-crested Wren | 900.00 |
| ☐184 | Mangrove Hummingbird | 2,650.00 |
| ☐185 | Bachman's Warbler | 2,750.00 |
| ☐186 | Pinnated Grouse | 7,250.00 |
| ☐187 | Boat-tailed Grackle | 3,500.00 |
| ☐188 | Tree Sparrow | 1,300.00 |
| ☐189 | Snow Bunting | 1,000.00 |
| ☐190 | Yellow-bellied Woodpecker | 1,600.00 |
| ☐191 | Willow Grouse | 5,500.00 |
| ☐192 | Great American Shrike | 1,500.00 |
| ☐193 | Lincoln Finch | 2,300.00 |
| ☐194 | Canadian Titmouse | 1,200.00 |
| ☐195 | Ruby-crowned Wren | 2,000.00 |
| ☐196 | Labrador Falcon | 3,500.00 |
| ☐197 | American Crossbill | 2,500.00 |
| ☐198 | Worm-eating Warbler | 1,650.00 |
| ☐199 | Little Owl | 1,500.00 |
| ☐200 | Shore Lark | 700.00 |
| ☐201 | Canada Goose | 21,000.00 |
| ☐202 | Red-throated Diver | 4,500.00 |
| ☐203 | Fresh Water Marsh Wren | 2,750.00 |
| ☐204 | Salt Water Marsh Wren | 1,850.00 |
| ☐205 | Virginia Rail | 2,000.00 |
| ☐206 | Summer or Wood Duck | 13,750.00 |
| ☐207 | Booby Gannet | 3,250.00 |
| ☐208 | Esquimaux Curlew | 1,100.00 |
| ☐209 | Wilson's Plover | 900.00 |
| ☐210 | Least Bittern | 2,500.00 |
| ☐211 | Great Blue Heron | 42,000.00 |
| ☐212 | Common Gull | 1,900.00 |
| ☐213 | Puffin | 5,000.00 |
| ☐214 | Razor Bill | 1,100.00 |
| ☐215 | Phalarope | 950.00 |
| ☐216 | Wood Ibis | 20,000.00 |
| ☐217 | Louisiana Heron | 11,500.00 |
| ☐218 | Foolish Guillemar | 1,200.00 |
| ☐219 | Black Guillemar | 1,300.00 |
| ☐220 | Piping Plover | 900.00 |
| ☐221 | Mallard Duck | 25,500.00 |
| ☐222 | White Ibis | 9,250.00 |
| ☐223 | Pied Oyster Catcher | 1,500.00 |
| ☐224 | Kittiwake Gull | 1,350.00 |
| ☐225 | Kildeer Plover | 1,500.00 |
| ☐226 | Whooping Crane | 14,000.00 |
| ☐227 | Pin-tailed Duck | 7,250.00 |
| ☐228 | Green-wing Teal | 5,500.00 |
| ☐229 | Scaup Duck | 3,850.00 |
| ☐230 | Ruddy Plover | 850.00 |
| ☐231 | Long-billed Curlew | 20,000.00 |
| ☐232 | Hooded Merganser | 4,500.00 |
| ☐233 | Sora or Rail | 1,700.00 |
| ☐234 | Tufted Duck | 3,250.00 |

**PLATE 246 HAVELL EDITION "Eider Duck (American Eider)"**

| PLATE NUMBER | SUBJECT | CURRENT RETAIL PRICE | PLATE NUMBER | SUBJECT | CURRENT RETAIL PRICE |
|---|---|---|---|---|---|
| ☐235 | Sooty Tern | 1,350.00 | ☐269 | Greenshank | 2,750.00 |
| ☐236 | Night Heron | 10,500.00 | ☐270 | Stormy Petrel | 825.00 |
| ☐237 | Great Esquimaux Curlew | 2,400.00 | ☐271 | Frigate Pelican | 4,500.00 |
| ☐238 | Great Marbled Codwit | 2,500.00 | ☐272 | Richardson's Jager | 1,200.00 |
| ☐239 | American Coot | 2,400.00 | ☐273 | Cayenne Tern | 2,750.00 |
| ☐240 | Roseate Tern | 3,000.00 | ☐274 | Semipalmated Snipe | 1,500.00 |
| ☐241 | Black Backed Gull | 2,000.00 | ☐275 | Noddy Tern | 1,200.00 |
| ☐242 | Snowy Heron | 25,500.00 | ☐276 | King Duck | 3,400.00 |
| ☐243 | American Snipe | 4,000.00 | ☐277 | Hutchin's Goose | 4,500.00 |
| ☐244 | Common Gallinule | 1,350.00 | ☐278 | Schinz's Sandpiper | 950.00 |
| ☐245 | Large-billed Guillemot | 1,000.00 | ☐279 | Sandwich Tern | 2,400.00 |
| ☐246 | Eider Duck | 12,750.00 | ☐280 | Black Tern | 950.00 |
| ☐247 | Velvet Duck | 2,000.00 | ☐281 | Great White Heron | 27,500.00 |
| ☐248 | American Pied Dobchick | 1,900.00 | ☐282 | White-winged Silvery Gull | 1,320.00 |
| ☐249 | Tufted Auk | 1,600.00 | ☐283 | Wandering Shearwater | 825.00 |
| ☐250 | Arctic Tern | 2,500.00 | ☐284 | Purple Sandpiper | 1,100.00 |
| ☐251 | Brown Pelican | 15,500.00 | ☐285 | Fork-tailed Gull | 1,000.00 |
| ☐252 | Florida Cormorant | 3,500.00 | ☐286 | White-fronted Goose | 6,500.00 |
| ☐253 | Jager | 1,200.00 | ☐287 | Ivory Gull | 1,650.00 |
| ☐254 | Wilson's Phalarope | 1,100.00 | ☐288 | Yellow Shank | 3,800.00 |
| ☐255 | Red Phalarope | 1,000.00 | ☐289 | Solitary Sandpiper | 1,200.00 |
| ☐256 | Purple Heron | 16,500.00 | ☐290 | Red-backed Sandpiper | 1,200.00 |
| ☐257 | Double Crested Cormorant | 2,500.00 | ☐291 | Herring Gull | 4,300.00 |
| ☐258 | Hudsonian Godwit | 1,200.00 | ☐292 | Crested Gerbe | 3,000.00 |
| ☐259 | Horned Grebe | 1,900.00 | ☐293 | Large-billed Puffin | 1,650.00 |
| ☐260 | Fork-tail Petrel | 1,500.00 | ☐294 | Pectoral Sandpiper | 1,100.00 |
| ☐261 | Whooping Crane | 16,500.00 | ☐295 | Manx Shearwater | 900.00 |
| ☐262 | Tropic Bird | 3,500.00 | ☐296 | Barnacle Goose | 2,800.00 |
| ☐263 | Pigmy Curlew | 1,000.00 | ☐297 | Harlequin Duck | 3,000.00 |
| ☐264 | Fulmar Petrel | 1,100.00 | ☐298 | Red-nicked Grebe | 1,500.00 |
| ☐265 | Buff Breasted Sandpiper | 1,000.00 | ☐299 | Dusky Petrel | 825.00 |
| ☐266 | Common Cormorant | 3,000.00 | ☐300 | Golden Plover | 800.00 |
| ☐267 | Arctic Jager | 1,700.00 | ☐301 | Canvasback Duck | 18,750.00 |
| ☐268 | American Woodcock | 5,250.00 | ☐302 | Black Duck | 7,750.00 |

**PLATE 308 HAVELL EDITION "Greater Yellow Legs"**

| PLATE NUMBER | SUBJECT | CURRENT RETAIL PRICE |
|---|---|---|
| ☐303 | Upland Plover | 2,000.00 |
| ☐304 | Turnstone | 1,250.00 |
| ☐305 | Purple Gallinule | 2,500.00 |
| ☐306 | Common Loon | 13,250.00 |
| ☐307 | Little Blue Heron | 15,000.00 |
| ☐308 | Greater Yellow Legs | 2,500.00 |
| ☐309 | Common Tern | 2,250.00 |
| ☐310 | Spotted Sandpiper | 2,650.00 |
| ☐311 | White Pelican | 30,000.00 |
| ☐312 | Old Squaw | 3,200.00 |
| ☐313 | Blue-winged Teal | 5,000.00 |
| ☐314 | Laughing Gull | 1,800.00 |
| ☐315 | Knot | 1,300.00 |
| ☐316 | Black-Bellied Darter | 6,000.00 |
| ☐317 | Surf Scoter | 2,000.00 |
| ☐318 | Avocet | 3,000.00 |
| ☐319 | Lesser Tern | 2,000.00 |
| ☐320 | Little Sandpiper | 1,600.00 |
| ☐321 | Roseate Spoonbill | 28,750.00 |
| ☐322 | Red-head Duck | 6,500.00 |
| ☐323 | Black Skimmer | 3,500.00 |
| ☐324 | Bonaparte's Gull | 2,500.00 |
| ☐325 | Bufflehead | 5,000.00 |
| ☐326 | Gannet | 6,000.00 |
| ☐327 | Shoveller Duck | 8,500.00 |
| ☐328 | Blackneck Stilt | 3,000.00 |
| ☐329 | Yellow Rail | 850.00 |
| ☐330 | Plover | 850.00 |
| ☐331 | American Merganser | 6,500.00 |
| ☐332 | Labrador Duck | 4,300.00 |
| ☐333 | Green Heron | 5,700.00 |
| ☐334 | Black-bellied Plover | 950.00 |
| ☐335 | Red-bellied Sandpiper | 1,100.00 |

| PLATE NUMBER | SUBJECT | CURRENT RETAIL PRICE |
|---|---|---|
| ☐336 | Yellow Crowned Night Heron | 8,000.00 |
| ☐337 | American Bittern | 3,500.00 |
| ☐338 | Bemaculated Duck | 5,000.00 |
| ☐339 | Little Auk | 1,400.00 |
| ☐340 | Stormy Petrel | 700.00 |
| ☐341 | Great Auk | 5,000.00 |
| ☐342 | Golden-eyed Duck | 4,500.00 |
| ☐343 | Ruddy Duck | 4,150.00 |
| ☐344 | Long-legged Sandpiper | 1,000.00 |
| ☐345 | American Widgeon | 4,300.00 |
| ☐346 | Black Throated Diver | 9,750.00 |
| ☐347 | American Bittern | 3,500.00 |
| ☐348 | Gadwall Duck | 5,000.00 |
| ☐349 | Least Water Hen | 1,500.00 |
| ☐350 | Rocky Mountain Plover | 700.00 |
| ☐351 | Great Cinereous Owl | 6,200.00 |
| ☐352 | Black-winged Hawk | 3,050.00 |
| ☐353 | Titmouse, Etc. | 1,700.00 |
| ☐354 | Louisiana Tanager | 3,000.00 |
| ☐355 | MacGillivray's Finch | 1,400.00 |
| ☐356 | Marsh Hawk | 3,750.00 |
| ☐357 | American Magpie | 3,000.00 |
| ☐358 | Pine Grosbeak | 1,000.00 |
| ☐359 | Arkansas Flycatcher | 1,700.00 |
| ☐360 | Winter and Rock Wren | 1,900.00 |
| ☐361 | Long-tailed Grouse | 3,500.00 |
| ☐362 | Yellow-billed Magpie | 2,750.00 |
| ☐363 | Bohemian Chatterer | 1,500.00 |
| ☐364 | White-winged Grossbill | 2,000.00 |
| ☐365 | Lapland Longspur | 990.00 |
| ☐366 | Iceland Falcon | 25,500.00 |
| ☐367 | Band-tailed Pigeon | 4,750.00 |

**PLATE 401 HAVELL EDITION "Red Breasted Merganser"**

| PLATE NUMBER | SUBJECT | CURRENT RETAIL PRICE |
|---|---|---|
| ☐368 | Rock Grouse | 3,300.00 |
| ☐369 | Mountain Mockingbird | 1,400.00 |
| ☐370 | American Water Ouzel | 1,000.00 |
| ☐371 | Cock of the Plains | 6,000.00 |
| ☐372 | Common Buzzard | 3,000.00 |
| ☐373 | Evening Grosbeak | 1,400.00 |
| ☐374 | Sharp Shinned Hawk | 1,350.00 |
| ☐375 | Lesser Red Poll | 850.00 |
| ☐376 | Trumpeter Swan | 9,500.00 |
| ☐377 | Scolopaceys Courlan | 3,000.00 |
| ☐378 | Hawk Owl | 1,900.00 |
| ☐379 | Ruff-necked Hummingbird | 3,000.00 |
| ☐380 | Tengmalm's Owl | 1,400.00 |
| ☐381 | Snow Goose | 6,500.00 |
| ☐382 | Sharp-tailed Grouse | 2,750.00 |
| ☐383 | Long-eared Owl | 2,350.00 |
| ☐384 | Black-throated Bunting | 1,350.00 |
| ☐385 | Bank Swallow | 750.00 |
| ☐386 | Great American Egret | 15,500.00 |
| ☐387 | Glossy Ibis | 5,000.00 |
| ☐388 | Troopial (Orioles) | 1,300.00 |
| ☐389 | Red-cockaded Woodpecker | 1,650.00 |
| ☐390 | Prairie Finch | 1,200.00 |
| ☐391 | Brant Goose | 3,000.00 |
| ☐392 | Louisiana Hawk | 3,300.00 |
| ☐393 | Bluebirds and Warbler | 3,000.00 |
| ☐394 | Buntings and Finches | 1,600.00 |
| ☐395 | Audubon's Warbler | 1,250.00 |
| ☐396 | Burgomaster Gull | 3,500.00 |
| ☐397 | Scarlet Ibis | 7,500.00 |
| ☐398 | Lazuli Finch | 1,500.00 |
| ☐399 | Black-throated Warbler | 975.00 |
| ☐400 | Townsend's Finch | 1,000.00 |
| ☐401 | Red Breasted Merganser | 6,500.00 |
| ☐402 | Auks and Guillemots | 2,300.00 |

| PLATE NUMBER | SUBJECT | CURRENT RETAIL PRICE |
|---|---|---|
| ☐403 | Golden-eyed Duck | 2,650.00 |
| ☐404 | Eared Grebe | 1,800.00 |
| ☐405 | Semipalmated Sandpiper | 1,100.00 |
| ☐406 | Trumpeter Swan | 45,250.00 |
| ☐407 | Dusky Albatross | 1,300.00 |
| ☐408 | American Scoter Duck | 3,250.00 |
| ☐409 | Havell's Tern | 2,250.00 |
| ☐410 | Marsh Tern | 1,350.00 |
| ☐411 | Common American Swan | 19,250.00 |
| ☐412 | Violet Green Cormorant | 2,500.00 |
| ☐413 | California Partridge | 3,500.00 |
| ☐414 | Golden-winged Warbler | 750.00 |
| ☐415 | Brown Creeper | 1,200.00 |
| ☐416 | Hairy Woodpecker | 6,500.00 |
| ☐417 | Maris's Woodpecker | 2,900.00 |
| ☐418 | American Ptarmigan | 2,300.00 |
| ☐419 | Little Tawny Thrush | 1,100.00 |
| ☐420 | Prairie Starling | 950.00 |
| ☐421 | Brown Pelican | 12,750.00 |
| ☐422 | Rough-legged Falcon | 3,000.00 |
| ☐423 | Plumed Partridge | 2,900.00 |
| ☐424 | Lazuli Finch | 900.00 |
| ☐425 | Columbian Hummingbird | 2,000.00 |
| ☐426 | California Vulture | 4,500.00 |
| ☐427 | White-legged Oyster Catcher | 2,000.00 |
| ☐428 | Townsend's Sandpiper | 1,050.00 |
| ☐429 | Western Duck | 2,500.00 |
| ☐430 | Slinder-billed Guillemar | 850.00 |
| ☐431 | American Flamingo | 35,500.00 |
| ☐432 | Burrowing Owl | 2,250.00 |
| ☐433 | Bullock's Oriole | 1,500.00 |
| ☐434 | Little Tyrant Pewee | 850.00 |
| ☐435 | Columbian Water Ouzel | 1,000.00 |

## THE BIEN EDITION

The listing of prints that follows is not complete but represents all that could be located as available at publication.

Chromolithographs, in the original double elephant folio size, were done by Julius Bien in New York. There are 150 birds represented by 106 plates, with the smaller birds being printed two on a page. The Civil War halted the printing which was done in 1859 and 1860 and distribution of this edition of the Audubons. They are considered today to be the rarest of all editions.

| PLATE NUMBER | SUBJECT | CURRENT RETAIL PRICE |
|---|---|---|
| | **Full-size Plates:** | |
| ☐ 3 | Black Vulture | $ 850.00 |
| ☐ 7 | Red-tailed Hawk | 1,500.00 |
| ☐ 14 | White-headed Eagle | 2,250.00 |
| ☐ 16 | Black Winged Hawk | 1,500.00 |
| ☐ 18 | Swallow-tailed Hawk | 1,850.00 |
| ☐ 19 | Iceland Falcon | 2,750.00 |
| ☐ 20 | Great Footed Hawk | 1,750.00 |
| ☐ 21 | Pigeon Hawk | 1,250.00 |
| ☐ 22 | Sparrow Hawk | 2,250.00 |
| ☐ 34 | Barn Owl | 2,250.00 |
| ☐ 43 | Night Hawk | 1,250.00 |
| ☐ 44 | American Swift | 350.00 |
| ☐ 45 | Purple Martin | 1,500.00 |
| ☐ 46 | White-bellied Sparrow | 350.00 |
| ☐ 48 | Republican or Cliff Swallow | 350.00 |
| ☐ 48 | Barn Swallow | 350.00 |
| ☐ 53 | Fork-Tailed Flycatcher | 500.00 |
| ☐ 54 | Flycatcher | 500.00 |
| ☐ 55 | Pipiry Flycatcher | 450.00 |
| ☐ 56 | Olive-sided Flycatcher | 350.00 |
| ☐ 57 | Great Crested Flycatcher | 350.00 |
| ☐ 62 | Small Green-crested Flycatcher | 350.00 |
| ☐ 63 | Wood Pewee | 350.00 |
| ☐ 70 | Blue Gray Flycatcher | 350.00 |
| ☐ 71 | Hooded Warbler and Green | 400.00 |
| ☐ 71 | Wilson's Warbler | 350.00 |
| ☐ 72 | Canada Warbler | 400.00 |
| ☐ 73 | Bonaparte Flycatcher | 400.00 |
| ☐ 74 | Kentucky Warbler | 400.00 |
| ☐ 75 | Black Capped Flycatcher | 400.00 |
| ☐ 79 | Yellow-throated Vireo | 350.00 |
| ☐ 80 | Bay Breasted Warbler | 350.00 |
| ☐ 86 | Cerulean Warbler | 400.00 |
| ☐ 88 | Children's Warbler | 400.00 |
| ☐ 89 | Blue eyed Yellow Warbler | 350.00 |
| ☐ 89 | Rathbone Warbler | 300.00 |
| ☐ 90 | Yellow Redpoll | 400.00 |
| ☐ 95 | Black-throated Blue Warbler | 350.00 |
| ☐ 96 | Black n Yellow Warbler | 400.00 |
| ☐ 104 | Worm Eating Warbler | 350.00 |
| ☐ 108 | Bachmans Warbler | 400.00 |
| ☐ 109 | Carbonated Warbler | 400.00 |
| ☐ 113 | Nashville Warbler | 400.00 |
| ☐ 114 | Black & White Creeper | 400.00 |
| ☐ 116 | Winter Wren | 400.00 |
| ☐ 118 | Bewick's Wren | 350.00 |
| ☐ 119 | Wood Wren | 300.00 |
| ☐ 120 | House Wren | 350.00 |

| PLATE NUMBER | SUBJECT | CURRENT RETAIL PRICE |
|---|---|---|
| ☐ 123 | Marsh Wren | 400.00 |
| ☐ 124 | Nuttall's Lesser Marsh Wren | 300.00 |
| ☐ 127 | Carolina Titmouse | 400.00 |
| ☐ 128 | Hudson's Bay Titmouse | 400.00 |
| ☐ 132 | Amer, Golden-crested Wren | 350.00 |
| ☐ 133 | Ruby-crowned Wren | 350.00 |
| ☐ 138 | Mockingbird | 2,500.00 |
| ☐ 141 | Ferruginous Thrush | 1,850.00 |
| ☐ 144 | Hermit Thrush | 350.00 |
| ☐ 144 | Wood Thrush | 400.00 |
| ☐ 150 | Prairie Titlark | 350.00 |
| ☐ 151 | Brown Titlark | 350.00 |
| ☐ 156 | American Crow | 2,250.00 |
| ☐ 159 | Bay Winged Bunting | 350.00 |
| ☐ 163 | Henslow's Bunting | 350.00 |
| ☐ 164 | Field Sparrow | 350.00 |
| ☐ 165 | Chipping Sparrow | 350.00 |
| ☐ 172 | Seaside Finch | 400.00 |
| ☐ 173 | Mac Gillivray's Finch | 350.00 |
| ☐ 174 | Sharp Tailed Finch | 350.00 |
| ☐ 177 | Lincoln Finch | 350.00 |
| ☐ 183 | Pinnated Grouse | 2,500.00 |
| ☐ 189 | Song Sparrow | 400.00 |
| ☐ 191 | White Throated Sparrow | 400.00 |
| ☐ 192 | White-crowned Sparrow | 350.00 |
| ☐ 195 | Towhee Bunting | 350.00 |
| ☐ 196 | Purple Finch | 400.00 |
| ☐ 199 | Pine Grosbeak | 350.00 |
| ☐ 200 | Common Grosbill | 1,250.00 |
| ☐ 205 | Rose breasted Grosbeak | 1,750.00 |
| ☐ 216 | Red-winged Starling | 1,850.00 |
| ☐ 217 | Baltimore Oriole | 2,750.00 |
| ☐ 219 | Orchard Oriole | 1,250.00 |
| ☐ 220 | Boat-tailed Grackle | 1,750.00 |
| ☐ 221 | Purple Grackel | 1,750.00 |
| ☐ 222 | Rusty Grackle | 1,250.00 |
| ☐ 225 | American Crow | 2,250.00 |
| ☐ 226 | Fish Crow | 1,500.00 |
| ☐ 231 | Blue Jays | 1,700.00 |
| ☐ 239 | Solitary Flycatcher | 350.00 |
| ☐ 240 | White-eyed Flycatcher | 350.00 |
| ☐ 243 | Red-eyed Vireo | 350.00 |
| ☐ 244 | Yellow-breasted Chat | 1,100.00 |
| ☐ 245 | Boehemian Chatterer | 400.00 |
| ☐ 246 | Cedar Bird | 450.00 |
| ☐ 251 | Mangrove Hummingbird | 400.00 |
| ☐ 251 | Columbian Hummingbird | 350.00 |
| ☐ 253 | Ruby-throated Hummingbird | 2,250.00 |

| PLATE NUMBER | SUBJECT | CURRENT RETAIL PRICE | PLATE NUMBER | SUBJECT | CURRENT RETAIL PRICE |
|---|---|---|---|---|---|
| ☐ 255 | Belted Kingfisher | 1,500.00 | ☐ 388 | Gadwall Duck | 900.00 |
| ☐ 257 | Pileated Woodpecker | 1,950.00 | ☐ 389 | Crested Grebe | 1,350.00 |
| ☐ 273 | Gold-winged Woodpecker | 1,500.00 | ☐ 391 | Summer or Wood Duck | 2,950.00 |
| ☐ 275 | Yellow billed Cuckoo | 1,950.00 | ☐ 395 | Canvasback Duck | 2,950.00 |
| ☐ 278 | Carolina Parrot | 3,000.00 | ☐ 396 | Red-headed Duck | 1,500.00 |
| ☐ 280 | White-headed Pigeon | 1,500.00 | ☐ 397 | Scaup Duck | 900.00 |
| ☐ 287 | Turkey Cock | 7,500.00 | ☐ 398 | Tufted Duck | 700.00 |
| ☐ 288 | Fish Hawk or Osprey | 2,500.00 | ☐ 405 | Eider Duck | 1,750.00 |
| ☐ 289 | Virginia Partridge | 2,750.00 | ☐ 414 | Smew or White Num | 1,100.00 |
| ☐ 293 | Ruffed Grouse | 2,500.00 | ☐ 428 | Black Skimmer | 850.00 |
| ☐ 294 | Blue Grosbeak | 1,950.00 | ☐ 423 | Brown Pelican | 2,950.00 |
| ☐ 296 | Pinnated Grouse | 1,750.00 | ☐ 434 | Artic Tern | 500.00 |
| ☐ 308 | Least Water Hen | 350.00 | ☐ 465 | Great Auk | 1,550.00 |
| ☐ 308 | Yellow-breasted Rail | 350.00 | ☐ 466 | Razor-billed Auk | 350.00 |
| ☐ 331 | Buff-breasted Sandpiper | 350.00 | ☐ 454 | Puffin | 400.00 |
| ☐ 331 | Little Sandpiper | 400.00 | | | |
| ☐ 332 | Red-backed Sandpiper | 350.00 | | **Half-Page Biens:** | |
| ☐ 332 | Pectoral Sandpiper | 350.00 | ☐ 2 | Yellow Billed Cuckoo | $300.00 |
| ☐ 333 | Curlew Sandpiper | 325.00 | ☐ 48 | Barn Swallows | 300.00 |
| ☐ 336 | Semi-palmated Sandpiper | 325.00 | ☐ 54 | Flycatchers | 300.00 |
| ☐ 342 | Spotted Sandpiper | 350.00 | ☐ 55 | Pipiry Flycatcher | 300.00 |
| ☐ 343 | Solitary Sandpiper | 350.00 | ☐ 73 | Bonaparte's Flycatcher | 300.00 |
| ☐ 344 | Yellow Shank | 400.00 | ☐ 80 | Bay-breasted Warbler | 300.00 |
| ☐ 346 | Green Shank | 350.00 | ☐ 90 | Redpoll Warbler | 300.00 |
| ☐ 353 | Great Marbled Godwit | 350.00 | ☐ 109 | Carbonated Warbler | 300.00 |
| ☐ 357 | Esquimaux Curlew | 350.00 | ☐ 113 | Nashville Warbler | 300.00 |
| ☐ 358 | Glossy Ibis | 1,950.00 | ☐ 118 | Bewick's Wren | 300.00 |
| ☐ 363 | Night Heron | 1,950.00 | ☐ 133 | Ruby-crowned Wren | 300.00 |
| ☐ 364 | Yellow-crowned Heron | 2,750.00 | ☐ 163 | Henslow's Bunting | 300.00 |
| ☐ 367 | Green Heron | 1,500.00 | ☐ 172 | Seaside Finch | 300.00 |
| ☐ 368 | Great White Heron | 2,750.00 | ☐ 195 | Towhee Bunting | 300.00 |
| ☐ 371 | Redish Egret | 2,500.00 | ☐ 231 | Blue Jays | 300.00 |
| ☐ 372 | Blue Crane | 2,500.00 | ☐ 357 | Esquimaux Curlew | 300.00 |
| ☐ 375 | American Flamingo | 2,750.00 | ☐ 388 | Gadwall Duck | 300.00 |
| ☐ 380 | White-fronted Goose | 2,500.00 | ☐ 396 | Red-headed Duck | 300.00 |
| ☐ 385 | Mallard Duck | 2,950.00 | ☐ 434 | Arctic Tern | 300.00 |
| ☐ 386 | Dusky Duck | 2,250.00 | | | |

## AUDUBON QUADRUPEDS

John James Audubon and Reverend John Bachman complied this masterful work together, with Bachman doing the text. This series is known as the first comprehensive study with drawing of the quadruped of North America.

The prints were lithographed and colored by J. T. Bowen & Son of Philadelphia, the plates were issued in imperial folio size (21½" x 27") and later in the octavo (⅛") size. Although these mammal prints have become quite valuable, they have never achieved the value of the bird prints.

| | | | | | |
|---|---|---|---|---|---|
| ☐ 1 | Common American Wildcat | $1,450.00 | ☐ 10 | Common American Shrew Mole | 500.00 |
| ☐ 2 | Maryland Marmot | 500.00 | ☐ 11 | Northern Hare (Two hares) | 1,100.00 |
| ☐ 3 | Townsend's Rocky Mountain Hare | 500.00 | ☐ 12 | Northern Hare (Hare in winter coat) | 900.00 |
| ☐ 4 | Florida Rat | 500.00 | ☐ 13 | Musk-Rat | 500.00 |
| ☐ 5 | Richardson's Columbian Squirrel | 1,250.00 | ☐ 14 | Hudson's Bay Squirrel | 1,100.00 |
| ☐ 6 | American Cross-Fox | 1,750.00 | ☐ 15 | Oregon Flying Squirrel | 1,100.00 |
| ☐ 7 | Carolina Gray Squirrel | 900.00 | ☐ 16 | Canada Lynx | 2,250.00 |
| ☐ 8 | Chipping Squirrel | 1,450.00 | ☐ 17 | Cat Squirrel | 1,100.00 |
| ☐ 9 | Parry's Marmot Squirrel | 500.00 | ☐ 18 | Marsh Hare | 600.00 |

| PLATE NUMBER | SUBJECT | CURRENT RETAIL PRICE | PLATE NUMBER | SUBJECT | CURRENT RETAIL PRICE |
|---|---|---|---|---|---|
| ☐ 19 | Soft-Haired Squirrel | 850.00 | ☐ 78 | Black-Tailed Deer | 1,100.00 |
| ☐ 20 | Townsend's Ground Squirrel | 1,100.00 | ☐ 79 | Annulated Marmot-Squirrel | 500.00 |
| ☐ 21 | Gray Fox | 2,500.00 | ☐ 80 | Leconte's Pine Mouse | 350.00 |
| ☐ 22 | Gray Rabbit | 900.00 | ☐ 81 | Common American Deer | 3,250.00 |
| ☐ 23 | Black Rat | 900.00 | ☐ 82 | Red Texan Wolf | 1,850.00 |
| ☐ 24 | Four-Striped Ground Squirrel | 1,100.00 | ☐ 83 | Little-Chief Hare | 600.00 |
| ☐ 25 | Downy Squirrel | 1,000.00 | ☐ 84 | Franklin's Marmot-Squirrel | 1,250.00 |
| ☐ 26 | Wolverine | 1,750.00 | ☐ 85 | Jumping Mouse | 350.00 |
| ☐ 27 | Long-Haired Squirrel | 1,100.00 | ☐ 86 | Ocelot | 3,250.00 |
| ☐ 28 | Common Flying Squirrel | 1,000.00 | ☐ 87 | American Red Fox | 1,850.00 |
| ☐ 29 | Rocky Mountain Neotoma | 550.00 | ☐ 88 | Wormwood Hare | 700.00 |
| ☐ 30 | Cotton Rat | 550.00 | ☐ 89 | Say's Squirrel | 900.00 |
| ☐ 31 | Collared Peccary | 1,500.00 | ☐ 90 | Common Mouse | 1,100.00 |
| ☐ 32 | Polar Hare | 900.00 | ☐ 91 | Polar Bear | 2,750.00 |
| ☐ 33 | Mink | 1,750.00 | ☐ 92 | Texan Lynx | 2,750.00 |
| ☐ 34 | Black Squirrel | 1,100.00 | ☐ 93 | Black-Footed Ferret | 1,250.00 |
| ☐ 35 | Migratory Squirrel | 1,100.00 | ☐ 94 | Nuttall's Hare | 700.00 |
| ☐ 36 | Canada Porcupine | 900.00 | ☐ 95 | Orange Coloured Mouse | 350.00 |
| ☐ 37 | Swamp Hare | 750.00 | ☐ 96 | Cougar (Male) | 2,750.00 |
| ☐ 38 | Red-Bellied Squirrel | 1,250.00 | ☐ 97 | Cougar (Female and Half grown cub) | 1,750.00 |
| ☐ 39 | Leopard Spermophile | 700.00 | ☐ 98 | Ring-Tailed Bassaris | 1,100.00 |
| ☐ 40 | White-Footed Mouse | 650.00 | ☐ 99 | Prairie Dog | 550.00 |
| ☐ 41 | Pennant's Marten | 1,650.00 | ☐100 | Missouri Mouse | 500.00 |
| ☐ 42 | Common American Skunk | 1,500.00 | ☐101 | Jaguar | 3,250.00 |
| ☐ 43 | Hare Squirrel | 1,100.00 | ☐102 | Large-Tailed Skunk | 900.00 |
| ☐ 44 | Canada Pouched Rat | 550.00 | ☐103 | Hoary Marmot | 900.00 |
| ☐ 45 | Wilson's Meadow Mouse | 350.00 | ☐104 | Collies' Squirrel | 900.00 |
| ☐ 46 | American Beaver | 1,650.00 | ☐105 | Columbia Pouched Rat | 500.00 |
| ☐ 47 | American Badger | 1,650.00 | ☐106 | Columbian Black-Tailed Deer | 2,250.00 |
| ☐ 48 | Douglass Squirrel | 1,000.00 | ☐107 | Lewis' Marmot | 500.00 |
| ☐ 49 | Douglasses Spermophile | 550.00 | ☐108 | Bachman's Hare | 500.00 |
| ☐ 50 | Richardson's Spermophile | 350.00 | ☐109 | Californian Marmot-Squirrel | 500.00 |
| ☐ 51 | Canada Otter | 1,750.00 | ☐110 | Mole-Shaped Pouch Rat | 500.00 |
| ☐ 52 | Swift Fox | 1,950.00 | ☐111 | Musk Ox | 2,500.00 |
| ☐ 53 | Texas Skunk | 1,100.00 | ☐112 | Californian Hare | 1,000.00 |
| ☐ 54 | Brown, or Norway Rat | 800.00 | ☐113 | Esquimaux Dog | 900.00 |
| ☐ 55 | Red-Tailed Squirrel | 1,100.00 | ☐114 | Say's Marmot Squirrel | 1,100.00 |
| ☐ 56 | American Bison (Solitary Male) | 2,500.00 | ☐115 | Yellow-Cheeked Meadow-Mouse | 350.00 |
| ☐ 57 | American Bison (Male, female and calf) | 2,500.00 | ☐116 | American Black or Silver Fox | 2,250.00 |
| ☐ 58 | Orange-Bellied Squirrel | 1,100.00 | ☐117 | Dusky Squirrel | 1,000.00 |
| ☐ 59 | White Weasel | 1,100.00 | ☐118 | Long-Tailed Deer | 950.00 |
| ☐ 60 | Bridled Weasel | 1,100.00 | ☐119 | Hudson's Bay Lemming | 500.00 |
| ☐ 61 | Raccoon | 1,500.00 | ☐120 | Tawny Lemming-Back's Lemming | 500.00 |
| ☐ 62 | American Elk | 2,750.00 | ☐121 | Arctic Fox | 1,750.00 |
| ☐ 63 | Black-Tailed Hare | 900.00 | ☐122 | Canada Otter | 1,750.00 |
| ☐ 64 | Little American Brown Weasel | 1,100.00 | ☐123 | Sewellel | 850.00 |
| ☐ 65 | Little Harvest Mouse | 850.00 | ☐124 | Mexican Marmot-Squirrel | 500.00 |
| ☐ 66 | Virginia Opossum | 1,100.00 | ☐125 | American Marsh-Shrew | 900.00 |
| ☐ 67 | Black American Wolf | 1,850.00 | ☐126 | Caribou | 2,250.00 |
| ☐ 68 | Fox Squirrel | 1,000.00 | ☐127 | Cinnamon Bear | 2,750.00 |
| ☐ 69 | Common Star-Nose Mole | 350.00 | ☐128 | Rocky Mountain Goat | 2,250.00 |
| ☐ 70 | Say's Least Shrew | 350.00 | ☐129 | Northern Meadow-Mouse | 350.00 |
| ☐ 71 | Prairie Wolf | 1,950.00 | ☐130 | Pouched Jerboa Mouse | 900.00 |
| ☐ 72 | White American Wolf | 1,850.00 | ☐131 | Grizzly Bear | 2,750.00 |
| ☐ 73 | Rocky Mountain Sheep | 2,250.00 | ☐132 | Hare Indian Dog | 1,100.00 |
| ☐ 74 | Brewer's Shrew-Mole | 350.00 | ☐133 | Texan Hare | 900.00 |
| ☐ 75 | Carolina Shrew | 350.00 | ☐134 | Yellow-Bellied Marmot | 850.00 |
| ☐ 76 | Moose Deer | 1,850.00 | | | |
| ☐ 77 | Prong-Horned Antelope | 2,750.00 | | | |

| PLATE NUMBER | SUBJECT | CURRENT RETAIL PRICE | PLATE NUMBER | SUBJECT | CURRENT RETAIL PRICE |
|---|---|---|---|---|---|
| ☐135 | Richardson's Meadow-Mouse | 350.00 | ☐144 | Townsend's Arvicola - Sharp-Nosed Arvicola | 350.00 |
| ☐136 | Common Deer | 3,250.00 | ☐145 | Townsend's Shrew Mole | 700.00 |
| ☐137 | Sea Otter | 2,250.00 | ☐146 | Nine-Banded Armadillo | 1,750.00 |
| ☐138 | Pine Marten | 1,750.00 | ☐147 | American Souslik - Oregon Meadow-Mouse, Texan Meadow-Mouse | 350.00 |
| ☐139 | Large-Tailed Spermophile | 500.00 | | | |
| ☐140 | Little Nimble Weasel | 1,100.00 | | | |
| ☐141 | American Black Bear | 2,250.00 | ☐148 | Tawny Weasel | 800.00 |
| ☐142 | Camas Rat | 350.00 | ☐149 | Fremont's Squirrel | 700.00 |
| ☐143 | Severn River Flying Squirrel - Rocky Mountain Flying Squirrel | 900.00 | ☐150 | Southern Pouched Rat - Dekay's Shrew - Long-Nosed Shrew - Silvery Shrew-Mole | 350.00 |

# THE AMSTERDAM AUDUBON EDITION

Done in Amsterdam, these prints are exact facsimiles of the Havell Edition prints. They are printed on rag paper and are limited to 250 copies of each print. Released in 1971, prints are 26½" x 39½" and are priced from $50.00 to $500.00.

# THE OCTAVO EDITION

These small prints are modified reproductions of the Havell edition. They are one-eighth elephant folio size and bound into seven volumes. They are hand colored lithographs done by J. T. Bowen and Son of Philadelphia, and are considered original Audubon prints, as they were done under Audubon's personal supervision. Circa 1840, print size 7" x 10½" and are priced around $200.00-$300.00 each depending on condition of print.

# AUDUBON PRINTS ON TEXTILE

These very rare bird prints on textile are attributed to John Potts. They appeared around 1830. Potts was an original subscriber to Audubon's "Birds of America". Size of these prints are 21½" x 27½" and are considered extremely rare. Prices range in the area of $2,000.00 each.

# MARK CATESBY

Mark Catesby was an English biologist who came to the colonies as a collector of plant and animal specimens for a group of English patrons. Catesby, known as the *"Father of American Ornithology"*, produced the first important work on American birds. Until the works of Alexander Wilson almost a half century later he remained the only artist to have painted any of them from first hand observation. He printed and hand colored most of the prints himself, which no single artist had done before him. Most of his work was done during the years of 1722 to 1726 in the southeastern coastal regions. His two-volume work "A Natural History of Carolina, Florida and the Bahama Islands" originally sold for less than $50.00. Today, a set in mint condition would command a price of around $60,000.00.

All of Catesby's paintings may be found in these two volumes.

| PLATE NUMBER | SUBJECT | CURRENT RETAIL PRICE | PLATE NUMBER | SUBJECT | CURRENT RETAIL PRICE |
|---|---|---|---|---|---|
| ☐ 1 | White-Headed Eagle ..... | 625.00 | ☐ 51 | Purple Martin ........... | 575.00 |
| ☐ 2 | Fishing Hawk .......... | 525.00 | ☐ 52 | Crested Flycatcher ...... | 525.00 |
| ☐ 3 | Pigeon Hawk ........... | 475.00 | ☐ 53 | Blackcap Flycatcher ..... | 575.00 |
| ☐ 4 | Swallow-Tail Hawk ...... | 575.00 | ☐ 54 | Little Brown Flycatcher ... | 495.00 |
| ☐ 5 | Little Hawk ............ | 475.00 | ☐ 55 | Tyrant ................ | 495.00 |
| ☐ 6 | Turkey Buzzard ........ | 375.00 | ☐ 56 | Summer Red Bird ....... | 625.00 |
| ☐ 7 | Little Owl ............. | 495.00 | ☐ 57 | Crested Titmouse ........ | 595.00 |
| ☐ 8 | Goat Sucker ........... | 475.00 | ☐ 58 | Yellow Rump ........... | 450.00 |
| ☐ 9 | Cuckoo of Carolina ...... | 525.00 | ☐ 59 | Bahama Titmouse ....... | 495.00 |
| ☐ 10 | Parrot of Paradise ....... | 625.00 | ☐ 60 | Hooded Titmouse ....... | 495.00 |
| ☐ 11 | Parrot of Carolina ........ | 725.00 | ☐ 61 | Pine Creeper .......... | 475.00 |
| ☐ 12 | Purple Jackdow ......... | 475.00 | ☐ 62 | Yellow-Throated Creeper .. | 450.00 |
| ☐ 13 | Red-Wing Starling ....... | 525.00 | ☐ 63 | Yellow Titmouse ........ | 475.00 |
| ☐ 14 | Rice Bird ............. | 495.00 | ☐ 64 | Finch Creeper .......... | 450.00 |
| ☐ 15 | Crested Jay ........... | 600.00 | ☐ 65 | Hummingbird .......... | 575.00 |
| ☐ 16 | Large White-Bellied Woodpecker ......... | 725.00 | ☐ 66 | Cat Bird .............. | 525.00 |
| | | | ☐ 67 | Red Start ............. | 495.00 |
| ☐ 18 | Gold-Winged Woodpecker . | 625.00 | ☐ 68 | Little Black Bullfinch ..... | 450.00 |
| ☐ 19 | Red-Bellied Woodpecker .. | 495.00 | ☐ 69 | King Fisher ........... | 595.00 |
| ☐ 20 | Red-Headed Woodpecker . | 625.00 | ☐ 70 | Soree or Rail .......... | 450.00 |
| ☐ 21 | Yellow-Bellied Woodpecker | 475.00 | ☐ 71 | Plover ............... | 450.00 |
| ☐ 22 | Nuthatch ............. | 495.00 | ☐ 72 | Turnstone ............ | 450.00 |
| ☐ 23 | Passenger Pigeon ....... | 725.00 | ☐ 73 | Flamingo ............. | 600.00 |
| ☐ 24 | Carolina Turtle Dove...... | 725.00 | ☐ 74 | Bill of Flamingo ........ | 495.00 |
| ☐ 25 | White Crowned Pigeon .... | 600.00 | ☐ 75 | Whooping Crane ........ | 495.00 |
| ☐ 26 | Ground Dove ........... | 400.00 | ☐ 76 | Blue Heron............ | 725.00 |
| ☐ 27 | Mockingbird ........... | 575.00 | ☐ 77 | Little White Heron ...... | 725.00 |
| ☐ 28 | Fox-Colored Thrush ...... | 600.00 | ☐ 78 | Brown Bittern .......... | 495.00 |
| ☐ 29 | Rubin ................ | 525.00 | ☐ 79 | Crested Bittern......... | 750.00 |
| ☐ 30 | Red-Legged Thrush ...... | 495.00 | ☐ 80 | Small Bittern .......... | 725.00 |
| ☐ 31 | Little Thrush .......... | 525.00 | ☐ 81 | Wood Pelican ......... | 675.00 |
| ☐ 32 | Lark ................. | 495.00 | ☐ 82 | White Curlew ......... | 750.00 |
| ☐ 33 | Large Lark ........... | 625.00 | ☐ 83 | Brown Curlew ......... | 750.00 |
| ☐ 34 | Towhee Bird........... | 525.00 | ☐ 85 | Oyster Catcher ........ | 600.00 |
| ☐ 35 | Little Sparrow ......... | 495.00 | ☐ 86 | Great Booby .......... | 495.00 |
| ☐ 36 | Snow Bird ............ | 400.00 | ☐ 87 | Booby ............... | 575.00 |
| ☐ 37 | Bahama Sparrow ....... | 495.00 | ☐ 88 | Noddy ............... | 465.00 |
| ☐ 38 | Red Bird ............. | 625.00 | ☐ 89 | Laughing Gull ........ | 595.00 |
| ☐ 39 | Blue Grosbeak ........ | 575.00 | ☐ 90 | Cut Water ............ | 595.00 |
| ☐ 40 | Purple Grosbeak ....... | 575.00 | ☐ 91 | Pied Bill Dopchick ....... | 450.00 |
| ☐ 41 | Purple Finch .......... | 475.00 | ☐ 92 | Canada Goose ......... | 600.00 |
| ☐ 42 | Bahama Finch ......... | 495.00 | ☐ 93 | Hathera Duck.......... | 750.00 |
| ☐ 43 | American Goldfinch ...... | 525.00 | ☐ 94 | Round Crested Duck ..... | 650.00 |
| ☐ 44 | Painted Finch .......... | 600.00 | ☐ 95 | Buffle-Head Duck........ | 650.00 |
| ☐ 45 | Blue Linnet ........... | 575.00 | ☐ 96 | Blue-Wing Shoveler ..... | 600.00 |
| ☐ 46 | Chatterer ............. | 625.00 | ☐ 97 | Summer Duck ......... | 825.00 |
| ☐ 47 | Blue Bird ............. | 675.00 | ☐ 98 | Little Brown Duck ...... | 575.00 |
| ☐ 48 | Baltimore Bird .......... | 750.00 | ☐ 99 | Blue-Wing Teal ....... | 575.00 |
| ☐ 49 | Orchard Oriole ......... | 625.00 | ☐100 | White-Face Teal........ | 700.00 |
| ☐ 50 | Yellow-Breasted Chat .... | 575.00 | | | |

# CURRIER & IVES

Nathaniel Currier began his career in lithography in 1828. At that time, he was apprenticed at the age of 15, to Pendleton of Boston, one of the earliest American lithographic firms known. After five years, he left and engaged in various business ventures, one of which was with Stodart in New York. It was at this time in 1834 that the print *"Dartmouth College"* was published by Currier.

The venture with Stodart was short-lived; and, in 1835, Currier started his own firm at 1 Wall Street in New York. James Ives joined the firm in 1852 as a book-keeper, after being recommended to Nathaniel Currier by his brother Charles, who also worked in the business. (Ives was married to Charles' sister-in-law.) The firm was located in New York City during its entire existence but occupied several locations over the years. The following chronology shows the addresses and the dates the business was located at each. This information is helpful to collectors interested in determining the dates of a print's publication which is not otherwise dated.

## CHRONOLOGY

| | | |
|---|---|---|
| **Currier & Stodart** | 1834 | 137 Broadway |
| **N. Currier** | 1835 | 1 Wall Street |
| | 1836-1837 | 148 Nassau Street |
| | 1838-1856 | 152 Nassau Street & 2 Spruce Street |
| **Currier & Ives** | 1857-1865 | 152 Nassau Street & 2 Spruce Street |
| | 1866-1872 | 152 Nassau Street & 33 Spruce Street |
| | 1872-1874 | 125 Nassau Street & 33 Spruce Street |
| | 1874-1877 | 123 Nassau Street & 33 Spruce Street |
| | 1877-1894 | 115 Nassau Street & 33 Spruce Street |
| | 1894-1896 | 108 Fulton Street & 33 Spruce Street |
| | 1896-1907 | 33 Spruce Street |

Currier & Ives was the most prolific lithographic business of the time, and its output is estimated to be greater than all other lithographers combined. The prints have come to be recognized as practically our only source of colored pictures depicting American life during the middle and late 1800's. The credit for recognition of the significance and preservation of these works generally goes to the late Harry Peters. Without his efforts, this unique aspect of American life might well have vanished into obscurity. We are, however, fortunate to have not only this historical insight, but also a wide variety of subject matter fully depicting the life style, moral fiber, prejudices, and sentiments of the day. It is believed there were over 7,200 different titles published by Currier & Ives with subject matter ranging from hunting, fishing, whaling, Mexican and Civil War events and, to clipper ships, yachts, portraits and many others covering a panorama of America.

Disaster propelled Currier and the firm into prominence. On January 13, 1840, the steamboat Lexington caught fire and was destroyed. Most of its 140 passengers and crew died. Three days later, an illustrated newspaper extra, "The Extra Sun", was published. It contained a finely drawn picture of the holocaust by Currier. It was a publishing sensation and made Currier a national institution overnight. Also revealed was the sales potential for newsworthy pictures to an interested public. Currier was keen enough to recognize this fact and thereupon launched a business career which is unique in American history.

The firm was unique in its ability to combine artistic talent, skilled craftsmanship, appropriate technology, and merchandising acumen into a successful business enterprise. Well-known artists of the day including Maurer, Palmer, Tait, and Worth were a few who were employed at various times. Appropriate attention to detail is manifest in the work as examination of a clipper ship print or a country scene will attest. Only the finest materials were used: stones from Bavaria (where lithography was invented), lithographic crayons from France, and colors from Austria. The firm contributed to technology by inventing a lithographic crayon, reputed to be superior to any others available anywhere. It also produced a lithographic ink, which contained beef suet, goose grease, white wax, castile soap, gum mastic, shellac, and gas black. Innovative merchandising techniques were used. Mass distribution and low cost were the keys to success. Cost was important. Uncolored prints sold for as little as six cents each and even large-colored folios sold for no more than three dollars. Anyone could afford a print at these prices. Prints were sold door-to-door by peddlers, in the streets by pushcart vendors, in geographically remote places through distributors, and even overseas through agents. Although an estimated ten million prints were sold, only a small percentage are in existence today.

The prints were published in various sizes but are commonly grouped into folio sizes shown below:

| | |
|---|---|
| Very Small | Up to approximately 7″ x 9″ |
| Small | Approximately 8.8″ x 12.8″ |
| Medium | Approximately 9″ x 14″ to 14″ x 20″ |
| Large | Anything over 14″ x 20″ |

The sizes pertain to the picture only, not to the margin around the picture. Often, print owners trimmed the margins of the pictures. Therefore, an uncut print is more valuable than a pared one.

Most of the prints were made in black and white and then handcolored. Although occasionally sold uncolored, usually a group of workers colored the prints by working from a professional artist's rendition. Because of this method, different colorings of the same print were found. Folio sizes very small, small and medium were completed in this manner. However, the large folios were sometimes partially printed in color and then finished by hand usually by only one artist.

Currier and Ives were successful men who worked well together. Currier retired in 1880 and died in 1888. Ives continued to run the business until his death in 1895. Although the sons of both men ran the business from 1895, it soon dissolved in 1907.

Currier and Ives' prints are not only attractive and historically informative, but they represent a sound investment value. Studies indicate these prints have increased in value by 300 to 500 percent in the past twenty years. For example, the large folio "The Life of a Hunter-A Tight Fix" sold in 1928 for $3,000. Recently it sold at an auction for $7,500.

Currier and Ives prints are found in public and private collections. A large collection exists at the New York City Museum which holds over 2,885 of their prints. However, no known collection contains all of the prints because previously unknown titles are uncovered occasionally.

## CURRIER & IVES: IS IT AN ORIGINAL PRINT?

©*Copyright 1978, Rudisill's Alt Print Haus*

During the years we have been collecting and dealing in Currier & Ives lithographs, the most frequent question we are asked concerning the prints is, *"How do I tell if it's a reproduction?"* The numerous books written about the Currier & Ives prints usually touch on this subject, but no one yet has pulled together in one place the various bits of information which can help a collector tell an original from a reproduction. This article is a summary of points of information we have gathered and which can be used effectively in the process of differentiating an original print from a reproduction. It should thus help the collector assure himself that he is buying an original print and, in some cases, the exact print he is seeking.

AMERICAN HOMESTEAD WINTER.

**AMERICAN HOMESTEAD WINTER** *by Currier and Ives*

One note to make at the beginning is that it is always most desirable to examine a print in an unframed condition. Unfortunately, this is not practical at times for various reasons, such as the cumbersome nature of unframing in a shop, a dealer's understandable reluctance to "dismantle" his merchandise, and perhaps the implication such a request has to the dealer. However, this need not be a deterrent to a thorough examination of a print, as this article will make clear.

## PRINT NOTATIONS
Currier & Ives prints have been reproduced at least since the turn of the century by reputable and unreputable persons using a variety of techniques. During this time, and continuing today, reputable firms have identified reproductions as such with a notation below the plate, such as, *"Reprinted from Lithograph by Currier & Ives"*, or *"Reproduction of Currier & Ives Lithograph"*. Although these notations are obvious and would seem to serve to answer the question about authenticity, they are sometimes either overlooked or misunderstood. We are occasionally asked if such prints are originals and, of course, need only point out the notation and its significance.

## COLORING
For many years color printing techniques — including those used in making reproductions — have involved the use of thousands of tiny dots to obtain quality color prints. However, such techniques were not used by Currier & Ives and the detection of such dots in a print identifies it positively as a reproduction. Dot patterns can be discerned easily with the use of about an 8 to 9 power magnifying glass. Dots can even be detected by the unaided, but trained, eye of an expert.

Generally speaking, it will be found that colors on reproductions made by whatever means are not as vivid as, and lack the *"depth"* of, original prints. The differences are most striking when comparing an original in good condition with any reproduction, but less apparent when the comparison is between a good reproduction and an original which has deteriorated from age or lack of care.

It is well known that most of the small and medium folio prints done by Currier & Ives were printed in black and white and hand colored. The colors used were surprisingly consistent so that one becomes quickly accustomed to typical reds, greens, blues, browns, oranges and so on. Deviations from these *"normal"* colors become easily recognized after a little experience and become reasons for not buying a print.

Less well known is the fact that large folio prints were often colored by only one person, sometimes a struggling young artist trying to make a living until he was *"discovered"*. This practice resulted in less *"standardization"* in colors used and, thus, the color tests applied to small and medium folios are not equally applicable to large folios. In other words, a large folio should not be rejected on color test failure alone. A practiced eye or a reputable dealer are better tests to apply to the coloring of a large folio.

Very often Currier & Ives colorists applied a coating of gum arabic to certain portions of a print. Sometimes the application is referred to as *"sheen"*, because of the shiny appearance it gives the to area covered. The purpose in adding this coating was to give *"depth"* — a partial three-dimensional effect — to the print.

The practice of adding *"sheen"* to prints was not followed by those who reproduced prints. We have never seen *"sheen"* applied to a reproduction, even a good quality reproduction. Thus if one finds a print and notices *"sheen"* in certain areas, one has a good indication of authenticity.

A further word of caution is appropriate regarding color tests, especially on large folios. We were nearly hoodwinked on a couple of occasions because the colors looked *"right"*. However, careful examination revealed the prints failed other tests. These prints, it turned out, had been reproduced using photographic techniques, thus faithfully reproducing the original colors. The best protection against buying these prints is careful attention to the results of other tests or, again, a reputable dealer.

## PAPER

As a rule, Currier & Ives used paper which was reasonably heavy — about midway between today's ordinary tablet paper and the school child's construction paper. We have measured the thickness of numerous prints and found the typical thickness to vary about a nominal thickness of ten-thousandths of an inch.

Many of the reproductions we have seen — both old and new — are printed on lighter weight paper and the thickness is about half that of the originals. The weight and stiffness often corresponds to good bond typing paper. Thus an examination of the paper a print is on, and, ideally, a comparison with any known original will be quite helpful in authenticating a print in question. The weight of two sheets of paper of the same length and width will be about proportional to the thickness of the papers. Based upon our measurements, an original print will be about twice as heavy as a reproduction. Although the absolute weights we are talking about are measured in ounces, it does not take many comparisons for a collector to develop a good sense of relative weight.

The tests of thickness and weight are valid and useful. However, there are exceptions in which the tests may fail and yet the print is, in fact, an original. The exceptions are some prints made in the late 1800's, not too many years before the firm of Currier & Ives closed its doors forever. The paper used in some cases in that era was lighter in weight, less stiff in composition, and had a smoother finish. An example of some of these prints is the small folio *"The Armoured Steel Cruiser New York"* dated 1893. In addition, Negro comic prints, done largely in the late 1870's and through the 1880's, many drawn by Thomas Worth, were often on this type of paper.

Another test which can be applied to paper is examination for water marks. Water marks here refers not to discoloration caused by the print having come in contact with water, but to the impression made in the paper to identify the manufacturer. Even though the use of water marks goes back hundreds of years, neither we nor other experts are aware of Currier & Ives having used such papers. This probably reflects the fact that water marked papers are typically higher quality, more expensive products, and that Currier & Ives were producing cheap prints for sale to a mass market. Cheap prints had to be made on inexpensive paper. Examination for water marks cannot be done without removing a print from its frame. Proper examination requires strong backlighting to make the impression visible.

## DEFINITION

The very techniques often used to make reproductions give clues to the fact that they are reproductions. These techniques result in clearly defined objects and figures and coloring is kept inside the outlines of those objects and figures. A print which looks *"too good"* for those reasons should be scrutinized closely.

A brief description of how Currier & Ives produced their prints will help the collector understand what he is looking for in figure and color definition. The original prints were mass produced using lithography and resulting in impressions in black and white and shades of gray. With the exception of some large folios which were done by young artists, coloring was added by an assembly line of women with a touch-up specialist at the end of the line. The intent was to be able to put attractive prints within the economic reach of almost everyone. Accordingly, costs had to be kept down and there was no time to allow precise applications of the colors within the outlines of the figures in print. On most originals, simple examination will reveal the evidence of hand-applied colors while most reproductions will show a sharper, more professional color definition.

## COMPARISON

We were asked to make an appraisal some time ago, and in the process realized a simple lesson in determining originals and reproductions. The print in question was an old reproduction of a desirable railroad scene. The fact was obvious to us, but we had to convince the owner and a companion. Most of the points above were made and accepted for the most part, but some doubt seemed to linger. Nearing the end of our business conversation, we invited our customers to see our collection. During this *"tour"*, the companion suddenly observed that, even without our points, it was obvious that the appraised print was a reproduction because a side-by-side comparison between it and almost any of our originals showed it to lack the depth, clarity, and general quality of an original. Thus a five minute personal observation did a more convincing job than had a half hour discourse. It taught us a lesson which we continue to use today — and which any collector can use for his edification.

## PLATE SIZE

One test of a print is a check of the size of the plate against known dimensions for that print. Although incomplete, the best reference for this use is Conningham's *Currier & Ives Prints*, which was last updated in 1970. We had been told that the information in this book was accurate, usually to within ± $\frac{1}{16}$ inch. Unfortunately, however, we have not been able to verify this degree of accuracy. Instead, we find that some dimensions stated with a precision of two decimal points are, in fact, incorrect by as much as ± ½ inch. As a result, we conclude that the test of plate size using this reference must be regarded as a rough one rather than a highly reliable one.

It is possible to reproduce any size print in any other size. As a result, with reproductions, one will often find large or medium folio originals reprinted in smaller sizes, but less frequently will small folio originals be found in larger sizes. In these cases, where gross differences are involved, a routine check with a book such as Conningham's is a very valuable and reliable way to detect a reprint. If one finds a print of incorrect size, the print is likely to be either a reproduction or an as yet undiscovered and unlisted subject. Because previously unknown titles are still being uncovered today, the latter occurrence is not impossible, but it is remote.

## SUBJECT MATTER

It has been, and is today, possible to reproduce any print dealing with any subject matter. However, in practice it seems the tendency had been and still is to copy the more desirable Currier & Ives subjects. Thus one is more likely to see, say, a sailing ship, winter scene, or railroad print reproduced than, say, religious, juvenile, or portait prints. This being the case, more careful scrutiny of the more desirable subjects is called for to authenticate their originality than is needed for less desirable subjects. This is not to say when one finds a desirable subject that he has probably found a reproduction. Rather, the message is, *"Be on your toes"*.

To elaborate more specifically on subject matter, we have seen fine reproductions of many of the small folio Civil War battle prints. Some of the Negro comic prints have been reproduced. Reproductions of large folio prints of the American Country Life series (four prints) and railroad and clipper ship subjects are in circulation. Large and small folio prints of horses — especially trotters — have been reproduced.

Subjects which we have never seen unidentified reproductions of include portraits of men and women, juveniles, and religious portraits.

Some very specific information on reproductions is that the firm of Andres' Inc. published, in 1942, excellent large folio reprints of the 20 titles listed below. They advertised the prints with *"unframed plate size: 20 in. x 28 in."* Andres' Inc. was in New York, but had displays in Chicago at W. C. Owen, Inc. in the Merchandise Mart. Each print was offered in *"an antiquated mahogany or plain maple frame, 1½ in. wide"*. They were also available in birdseye maple or mahogany at slightly higher cost.

## ANDRES' INC. LARGE FOLIO REPRODUCTIONS

| | |
|---|---|
| *The Lightning Express Trains* | *The American National Game of Baseball* |
| *Hudson Highlands* | *Seasons of Life: Childhood* |
| *Clipper Ship "Sweepstakes"* | *Seasons of Life: Middle Age* |
| *Clipper Ship "Red Jacket"* | *American Winter Scenes: Morning* |
| *Central Park Winter - Skating Pond* | *American Winter Scenes: Evening* |
| *High Water on the Mississippi* | *New England Winter Scene* |
| *Low Water on the Mississippi* | *May Morning* |
| *Landscape Fruit and Flowers* | *The Old Grist Mill* |
| *Home to Thanksgiving* | *American Express Train* |
| *The Road Winter* | *Across the Continent* |

Although not all of these titles are exactly like the title on the original print, they do provide enough information to point out what prints to be wary of. For example, there is no Currier & Ives print called *May Morning*. However, in the series of four large folio *American Country Life* prints, one has a sub-title of *May Morning*. It was this print that Andres' offered.

## TITLES

Some people — often beginning collectors — want to be sure that a print with a given title is contained in a reliable listing of known Currier & Ives prints. Its absence suggests the print may not be authentic. This, however, is not necessarily the case. Conningham's book is still the single most complete listing of Currier & Ives prints available today. It contains 6,896 titles. However, one collector has compiled a supplemental listing of 356 prints not in Conningham's book. Additionally, we have a listing of 26 prints not contained in either of these lists. In recent years, we have been finding about 10-12 prints a year with titles not contained in current listings.

Title verification is a useful exercise to go through in trying to authenticate a print. However, lack of inclusion of a title in a listing of prints should not, in and of itself, be grounds for rejecting a print. This is especially true if the title varies only slightly from one listed.

## THE BEST 50

In 1932, a number of Currier & Ives collectors got together and selected what they believed to be the Best 50 large folio prints published by Currier & Ives. A year later the process was repeated to determine a Best 50 list for small folio prints. (The latter list, although referred to as small folios, actually contains some medium folio prints.) Since that time these prints have enjoyed more popularity than many others and are prized possessions of serious and less serious collectors alike.

The Best 50 small folio list contains titles which appear on more than one Currier & Ives print. For example, *Noah's Ark* is one of the Best 50. Conningham's book lists five prints titled *Noah's Ark,* but with different subject compositions. Thus some collectors may be buying and paying a premium price for what they believe to be one of the Best 50, but, in fact, are obtaining the wrong print.

To help collectors buy what they want to buy, we have listed below the Best 50 small folios and Best 50 large folios and have identified each with the appropriate Conningham number. Those titles followed by an asterisk are known to appear on more than one composition.

## THE BEST FIFTY (small folio)

| TITLE | | PRICE RANGE | |
|---|---|---|---|
| ☐ 1. | The Express Train - 1790* | 750.00 | 1,000.00 |
| ☐ 2. | American Railroad Scene - Snowbound -187* | 900.00 | 1,200.00 |
| ☐ 3. | Beach Snipe Shooting - 445 | 900.00 | 1,100.00 |
| ☐ 4. | Ice-boat Race on the Hudson - 3021 | 1,000.00 | 1,800.00 |
| ☐ 5. | Central Park in Winter - 953 | 900.00 | 1,200.00 |
| ☐ 6. | The Star of the Road - 5701 | 250.00 | 500.00 |
| ☐ 7. | The High Bridge at Harlem, N. Y. - 2810* | 250.00 | 400.00 |
| ☐ 8. | Maple Sugaring, Early Spring in the Northern Woods - 3975 | 400.00 | 600.00 |
| ☐ 9. | Shakers Near Lebanon - 5475. | 600.00 | 900.00 |
| ☐10. | Winter Sports - Pickerel fishing - 6747 | 750.00 | 900.00 |
| ☐11. | The American Clipper Ship Witch of the Wave - 115 | 600.00 | 800.00 |
| ☐12. | Gold Mining in California - 2412 | 700.00 | 900.00 |
| ☐13. | The Great International Boat Race - 2623 | 800.00 | 1,000.00 |
| ☐14. | Wild Turkey Shooting - 6677 | 400.00 | 600.00 |
| ☐15. | Perry's Victory on Lake Erie - 4754. | 400.00 | 550.00 |
| ☐16. | Washington at Mount Vernon, 1797 - 6515 | 250.00 | 350.00 |
| ☐17. | The Whale Fishery. "Laying On" - 6626 | 900.00 | 1,200.00 |
| ☐18. | Chatham Square, New York - 1020 | 450.00 | 600.00 |
| ☐19. | Water Rail Shooting - 6567* | 500.00 | 650.00 |
| ☐20. | The Sleigh Race - 5554* | 500.00 | 800.00 |
| ☐21. | Franklin's Experiment - 2128* | 300.00 | 500.00 |
| ☐22. | Washington Crossing the Delaware - 6523* | 250.00 | 350.00 |

| TITLE | | PRICE RANGE | |
|---|---|---:|---:|
| ☐23. | American Homestead Winter - 172 | 400.00 | 600.00 |
| ☐24. | Washington Taking Leave of the Officers of His Army - 6547 | 250.00 | 350.00 |
| ☐25. | Steamboat Knickerbocker - 5727 | 250.00 | 350.00 |
| ☐26. | Kiss Me Quick! - 3349* | 200.00 | 250.00 |
| ☐27. | On the Mississippi Loading Cotton - 4607 | 250.00 | 350.00 |
| ☐28. | Bound Down the River - 627 | 350.00 | 500.00 |
| ☐29. | American Whalers Crushed in the Ice - 205 | 800.00 | 1,000.00 |
| ☐30. | Dartmouth College - 1446* | 1,000.00 | 1,300.00 |
| ☐31. | Terrific Combat Between the Monitor, 2 Guns, and the Merrimac, 10 Guns - 5996* | 350.00 | 500.00 |
| ☐32. | General Francis Marion - 2250 | 200.00 | 300.00 |
| ☐33. | Art of Making Money Plenty - 275 | 200.00 | 300.00 |
| ☐34. | Hon. Abraham Lincoln - 2895* | 150.00 | 250.00 |
| ☐35. | Gen. George Washington (with cape) - 2261* | 150.00 | 250.00 |
| ☐36. | Black Bass Spearing - 543 | 1,100.00 | 1,300.00 |
| ☐37. | Early Winter - 1652 | 1,500.00 | 2,000.00 |
| ☐38. | Woodcock Shooting - 6773* | 450.00 | 600.00 |
| ☐39. | "Dutchman" and "Hiram Woodruff" - 1640 | 600.00 | 700.00 |
| ☐40. | Great Conflagration at Pittsburg, Pa. - 2581 | 500.00 | 600.00 |
| ☐41. | Bear Hunting, Close Quarters - 446* | 1,500.00 | 2,000.00 |
| ☐42. | The Destruction of Tea at Boston Harbor - 1571 | 600.00 | 800.00 |
| ☐43. | Cornwallis is Taken - 1258 | 250.00 | 400.00 |
| ☐44. | Landing of the Pilgrims at Plymouth, 11th Dec., 1620-3435* | 200.00 | 300.00 |
| ☐45. | The Great Fight for the Championship - 2613 | 300.00 | 500.00 |
| ☐46. | Benjamin Franklin - 499* | 150.00 | 300.00 |
| ☐47. | Noah's Ark - 4494* | 150.00 | 200.00 |
| ☐48. | Black Eyed Susan - 551* | 125.00 | 150.00 |
| ☐49. | The Bloomer Costume - 574* | 150.00 | 175.00 |
| ☐50. | The Clipper Yacht "America" - 1173* | 700.00 | 1,000.00 |

## THE BEST FIFTY (large folio)

| | | | |
|---|---|---:|---:|
| ☐ 1. | Husking - 3008 | 4,000.00 | 8,500.00 |
| ☐ 2. | American Forest Scene-Maple Sugaring - 157 | 3,000.00 | 4,500.00 |
| ☐ 3. | Central Park Winter-The Skating Pond - 954 | 3,000.00 | 5,000.00 |
| ☐ 4. | Home to Thanksgiving - 2882 | 7,000.00 | 8,000.00 |
| ☐ 5. | Life of a Hunter-A Tight Fix - 3522 | 12,000.00 | 15,000.00 |
| ☐ 6. | Life on the Prairie-The Buffalo Hunt - 3527 | 5,500.00 | 6,000.00 |
| ☐ 7. | The Lightning Express Trains Leaving the Junction - 3535* | 5,000.00 | 6,500.00 |
| ☐ 8. | Peytona and Fashion - 4763 | 7,000.00 | 8,000.00 |
| ☐ 9. | The Rocky Mountains-Emigrants Crossing the Plains - 5196 | 7,500.00 | 10,000.00 |
| ☐10. | Trolling for Blue Fish - 6158 | 3,000.00 | 4,000.00 |
| ☐11. | Whale Fishery-The Sperm Whale in a Flurry - 6628* | 7,000.00 | 8,000.00 |
| ☐12. | Winter in the Country-The Old Grist Mill - 6738 | 5,500.00 | 7,000.00 |
| ☐13. | American Farm Scenes No. 4 (Winter) - 136 | 2,000.00 | 4,000.00 |
| ☐14. | American National Game of Baseball - 180 | 8,000.00 | 10,000.00 |
| ☐15. | American Winter Sports-Trout Fishing on Chateaugay Lake - 210* | 3,000.00 | 4,500.00 |
| ☐16. | Mink Trapping-Prime - 4139 | 7,500.00 | 8,000.00 |
| ☐17. | Preparing for Market - 4870* | 1,500.00 | 3,000.00 |
| ☐18. | Winter in the Country-Getting Ice - 6737 | 5,000.00 | 7,500.00 |
| ☐19. | Across the Continent-Westward the Course of Empire Takes its Way - 33 | 7,500.00 | 8,000.00 |
| ☐20. | Life on the Prairie-The Trappers Defense - 3528 | 5,500.00 | 6,000.00 |
| ☐21. | The Midnight Race on the Mississippi - 4116* | 2,000.00 | 3,500.00 |
| ☐22. | The Road-Winter - 5171 | 6,000.00 | 8,000.00 |
| ☐23. | Summer Scenes in New York Harbor - 5876 | 2,000.00 | 3,000.00 |
| ☐24. | Trotting Cracks at the Forge - 6169 | 2,000.00 | 3,500.00 |
| ☐25. | View of San Francisco - 6409 | 4,000.00 | 6,000.00 |
| ☐26. | Wreck of the Steamship "San Francisco" - 5492 | 3,500.00 | 4,500.00 |
| ☐27. | Taking the Back Track "A Dangerous Neighborhood" - 5961 | 5,000.00 | 5,500.00 |
| ☐28. | American Field Sports-Flush'd - 149 | 1,500.00 | 3,000.00 |
| ☐29. | American Hunting Scenes-A Good Chance - 174 | 1,500.00 | 3,000.00 |
| ☐30. | American Winter Scenes-Morning - 208 | 4,000.00 | 6,000.00 |

| TITLE | | PRICE RANGE | |
|---|---|---|---|
| ☐31. | Autumn in New England-Cider Making - 322 | 2,500.00 | 3,500.00 |
| ☐32. | Catching a Trout-"We Hab You Now, Sar" - 845 | 800.00 | 1,000.00 |
| ☐33. | Clipper Ship "Nightingale" - 1159 | 5,500.00 | 7,000.00 |
| ☐34. | The Life of a Fireman-The Race - 3519 | 2,000.00 | 4,000.00 |
| ☐35. | Mac and Zachary Taylor-Horse Race - 3848 | 1,000.00 | 2,000.00 |
| ☐36. | New England Winter Scene - 4420 | 3,500.00 | 5,000.00 |
| ☐37. | Rail Shooting on the Delaware - 5054 | 3,500.00 | 5,000.00 |
| ☐38. | Snowed Up-Ruffed Gouse-Winter - 5581 | 3,000.00 | 4,000.00 |
| ☐39. | Surrender of General Burgoyne at Saratoga - 5907 | 3,000.00 | 3,500.00 |
| ☐40. | Surrender of Cornwallis at Yorktown - 5906 | 3,000.00 | 3,500.00 |
| ☐41. | Clipper Ship "Red Jacket" - 1165* | 4,000.00 | 5,000.00 |
| ☐42. | American Winter Sports-Deer Shooting on the Shattagee - 209 | 3,000.00 | 5,000.00 |
| ☐43. | The Bark "Theoxana" - 371 | 1,500.00 | 2,500.00 |
| ☐44. | The Cares of a Family - 814* | 2,000.00 | 2,500.00 |
| ☐45. | The Celebrated Horse Lexington - 887* | 1,600.00 | 1,800.00 |
| ☐46. | Grand Drive-Central Park - 2481 | 2,000.00 | 3,000.00 |
| ☐47. | The Great Fire at Chicago - 2615 | 2,000.00 | 3,000.00 |
| ☐48. | Landscape, Fruit and Flowers - 3440 | 1,500.00 | 2,500.00 |
| ☐49. | The Life of a Fireman-The Metropolitan System - 3516 | 2,000.00 | 4,000.00 |
| ☐50. | The Splendid Naval Triumph on the Mississippi - 5659 | 750.00 | 1,000.00 |

## STATES AND RESTRIKES

The terms *"second state" (or "third state")* and *"restrike"* are often used interchangeably when reference is made to prints which were made after the first impressions were taken from the stone plate. However, there is a distinction to be made between the terms.

*"State"* is properly used to refer to impressions taken during the development of a print. Thus an original print may have been made from a stone plate. The stone may then have been altered in some significant way. (e.g. adding people to a scene) to insignificant way (e.g. changing a letter in the title) and a print made from the modified stone. The impression made is referred to as a *"second state"*. If the plate were modified again, the print would be referred to as a *"third state"*, and so on. Obviously a *"second state"*, etc. print will closely resemble an original in quality. Collectors today appear to regard *"second state"*, etc. prints as being worth essentially the same as a *"pure"* original.

Restrikes are neither true originals nor true reproductions. They are considered collectible by some people and sometimes command attractive prices. Currier & Ives are believed to have produced restrikes of their own, but others who had access to some of the stone produced prints in the early 1900's. One such example is Joseph Koehler who bought some stones at auctions after Currier & Ives went out of business in 1907. He later published some Darktown comics and a large folio Lincoln portrait under his own name. Another example was a man named Max Williams who issued six restrikes of large folio clipper ships in 1915. The titles of these restrikes are listed below.

*Clipper Ship Dreadnought off Tudkar Light*   *Clipper Ship Ocean Express*
*Clipper Ship Dreadnought off Sandy Hook*   *Clipper Ship Sweepstakes*
*Clipper Ship Flying Cloud*   *Clipper Ship Three Brothers*

Reputable dealers will represent *"second states"*, etc. and restrikes as such and this is yet another reason for doing business with these people.

## MOUNTING

One sometimes finds prints which have been mounted. Mounting usually refers to placing a print onto a heavier piece of paper stock, often similar to mat board. However, it also is used to describe another practice, probably used as a form of preservation, which was to apply a linen backing to prints. The backing served to stiffen the paper and thus make it less susceptible to tearing or damage which might occur from inadvertent bending or rolling. This practice was especially effective on large folios.

If properly done, mounting or backing does not affect the appearance of the print and, in fact, provides a degree of protection against tearing of the paper. Nevertheless, some purists regard such prints as having been *"tampered with"* and regard them as being worth less than unmolested prints.

Mounted prints are almost impossible to detect except when they are unframed. If the collector is sensitive to this factor in buying prints, he should insist on examining the print out of its frame, especially if the surface looks *"too flat"*. Some undulations in the print surface — detectable even though framed — are proof that mounting has not taken place.

## THE DEALER

A final important point for novices and serious collectors alike is to deal with reputable businessmen. As with any other business transactions, knowing from whom you are buying, and dealing with established and knowledgeable dealers, will practically assure against the purchase of undersirable merchandise. Of course, identifying such dealers may be an initial problem, but discreet inquiry can soon separate the wheat from the chaff. We have found that reputable people will answer questions no matter how trivial, admit to ignorance when it exists, refer you to others if they cannot help, allow complete examination of merchandise, agree to refund money if the purchaser is dissatisfied, and generally be helpful and cooperative. Less reputable dealers will show reluctance in one way or another to accommodate the wishes of the customers. We are reminded of a roadside sign often passed on trips we used to take. Its message sums up the point: "If you don't know furs, know your furrier".

It has not been our intention in this writing to condemn reproductions but to show how to recognize them. To the purist, reproductions are anathema. But they have their place in antique lore. More and more they are showing up in antique shops and have the redeeming features of being less expensive than originals, attractive in their own right, and probably represent an investment because we suspect their value will continue to increase with time as most other antiques are doing. However, one should not lose sight of the fact that today their value is primarily that of a pretty picture.

The information offered here is intended to help a purchaser make a sound buy. The elements of *"how to"* were added where appropriate, because the proper application of knowledge is, of course, what yields the desired results. Effectively used, this information will help a collector to avoid the financial loss and the personal embarrassment that come with owning a reproduction when the intent was to own an original.

# LOUIS ICART

Louis Icart was born in the small southern French city of Toulouse. This city was the home of many famous French artists, the most famous being Henri de Toulouse-Lautrec. In this atmosphere Icart became aware of the fine arts. He began his sketching at the early age of six and by the age of fifteen was sketching designs for costumes. As a fashion artist he was quite successful.

While Icart was working for major design studios women's fashions were undergoing a complete transition. Women were demanding less of the billowing skirts, high necklines, and lace and were desiring more of the clinging dresses. Because of his occupation, his first one-man show was not too successful as his critics associated his paintings with dress designing rather than artistic works.

With the outbreak of World War I, Icart went to the front as a soldier. Not completely abandoning his desire as an artist, he would sketch and etch on any available material. At the end of the war, with encouragement from friends, Icart began to make prints of the etchings he had made during this period. When they were published they became an immediate international success.

Icart's works demonstrate a mastery of dry point, line etching, aquatint, and their variations. Icart produced up to 500 prints each of over one thousand subjects. However, his works are scarce, because many have been lost or destroyed.

## THE PRINTS

Most Icart prints are easily identified. Most bear his hallmark which is usually located near the edge of the print. The following picture is his hallmark in actual size.

His signature is also easily identifiable, although subject to forgery and sometimes found on lithographic reproductions of his prints.

Earlier works will have his signature but may not bear the hallmark. Most will, however, bear the stamp of his gallery, an oval shape with the letters EM for l'estampe moderne. It is possible to have an original Icart with no hallmark at all, but this is rare.

The prints are usually numbered in the traditional manner of a first number representing the number of the print then a slash mark followed by a second number. This second number represents the number of prints in the edition (excluding artist's proofs and hors commerce prints if they exist). For example 75/120 means the print is number seventy-five of an edition of one hundred and twenty prints.

Icart pulled two editions frequently, one for Europe and one for American distribution. Sometimes the number is preceded by the letter "A" for an American edition; as in the example a 75/120. All prints were not numbered.

## LOUIS ICART

The following is a listing of prints with current prices compiled from dealer's price lists across the country. These prices are for mint prints (perfect or near perfect), and of course, prices vary from one area of the country to another.

| | | PRICE RANGE | |
|---|---|---:|---:|
| ☐ | After The Raid | 1,550.00 | 2,000.00 |
| ☐ | Above the Wings | 1,850.00 | 2,250.00 |
| ☐ | Amazonia | 4,500.00 | 5,000.00 |
| ☐ | Angry Buddha | 800.00 | |
| ☐ | Apache Dancer | 750.00 | |
| ☐ | Arabian Nite (1926)(Masked nude rear) | 850.00 | |
| ☐ | Attic Room | 1,100.00 | |
| ☐ | Arrival (Woman entering doorway) | 700.00 | |
| ☐ | Autumn Leaves | 750.00 | |
| ☐ | Backstage | 750.00 | |
| ☐ | Ballerina with roses | 750.00 | |
| ☐ | Bathing beauties | 1,500.00 | 2,000.00 |
| ☐ | Before the Raid | 2,500.00 | 3,000.00 |
| ☐ | Bird of Prey (Woman with eagle) | 1,400.00 | 1,800.00 |
| ☐ | Bird Seller | 750.00 | |
| ☐ | Black Fan | 750.00 | |

**COURSING II** *by Louis Icart*

| | PRICE RANGE | |
|---|---|---|
| ☐ Birth of Venus | 2,000.00 | |
| ☐ Blue Book | 750.00 | |
| ☐ Blue Buddha | 750.00 | |
| ☐ Blue Broken Jug | 750.00 | |
| ☐ Blue Parasol | 750.00 | |
| ☐ Bo Peep | 750.00 | |
| ☐ Bubbles | 1,500.00 | 1,800.00 |
| ☐ Butterfly Falls | 1,200.00 | |
| ☐ Carmen | 750.00 | |
| ☐ Cassanova | 850.00 | |
| ☐ Champs (Girls in buggy) | 750.00 | |
| ☐ Charm of Montmarte | 750.00 | |
| ☐ Chestnut Vendor | 750.00 | |
| ☐ Clipped Wings | 750.00 | |
| ☐ Cinderella | 850.00 | |
| ☐ Coach, The | 750.00 | |
| ☐ Conchita | 1,500.00 | |
| ☐ Courage France | 2,000.00 | 2,500.00 |
| ☐ Coursing II | 850.00 | 1,250.00 |
| ☐ Coursing III | 850.00 | 1,250.00 |
| ☐ Cat with paw in fishbowl | 750.00 | |
| ☐ Dame Rose | 750.00 | |
| ☐ Dancer (Finale) | 750.00 | |
| ☐ D'Artagnan | 850.00 | |
| ☐ Date Tree | 750.00 | |
| ☐ Dear Friends | 1,100.00 | |
| ☐ December | 850.00 | |
| ☐ Defense of the Homeland | 1,950.00 | 2,250.00 |
| ☐ Descending Coach | 700.00 | |
| ☐ Dollar | 500.00 | |
| ☐ Don Juan | 950.00 | |
| ☐ Dream Waltz | 1,200.00 | |
| ☐ Ecstacy | 1,500.00 | 2,000.00 |
| ☐ Embrace | 750.00 | |
| ☐ Eve (Nude) (Large Oval) | 1,400.00 | 1,500.00 |
| ☐ Fair Dancer | 750.00 | |
| ☐ Faust | 900.00 | 1,000.00 |
| ☐ Favorites The | 950.00 | |

| | | PRICE RANGE |
|---|---|---|
| ☐ Fashion Early | 700.00 | |
| ☐ Feeding Time | 750.00 | |
| ☐ Finlandia | 850.00 | 1,000.00 |
| ☐ Flower Vendor | 750.00 | |
| ☐ Follies | 3,000.00 | 4,000.00 |
| ☐ Forbidden Fruit | 750.00 | |
| ☐ Fountain, The | 1,000.00 | 1,500.00 |
| ☐ Four Dears | 950.00 | |
| ☐ From From | 850.00 | |
| ☐ France de Foyer | 1,800.00 | 2,000.00 |
| ☐ French Bus | 1,200.00 | 1,500.00 |
| ☐ French Doll | 750.00 | |
| ☐ Gatsby 1920's | 750.00 | |
| ☐ Gay Senorita | 850.00 | |
| ☐ Gay Trio | 1,850.00 | 2,000.00 |
| ☐ German Eagle | 1,850.00 | 2,000.00 |
| ☐ Girl in Crinoline | 800.00 | |
| ☐ Golden Veil | 1,500.00 | |
| ☐ Goosed | 700.00 | |
| ☐ Grande Eve | 7,000.00 | 7,500.00 |
| ☐ Green Broken Jug | 750.00 | |
| ☐ Guardian | 900.00 | |
| ☐ Gust of Wind | 1,250.00 | |
| ☐ Happy Birthday | 1,200.00 | 1,500.00 |
| ☐ Hoop-La | 900.00 | |
| ☐ Hortensia | 750.00 | |
| ☐ Human Grenade | 1,900.00 | 2,300.00 |
| ☐ Illusion | 5,000.00 | 7,000.00 |
| ☐ Inquest | 900.00 | |
| ☐ Intimacy | 750.00 | |
| ☐ Invitation | 850.00 | |
| ☐ Jardinare (Woman lying at urn) | 450.00 | |
| ☐ Joan of Arc | 1,350.00 | |
| ☐ Joy of Life | 1,800.00 | 2,250.00 |
| ☐ Lady of the Camillas | 850.00 | |
| ☐ Lampshade | 600.00 | |
| ☐ Laughing | 1,000.00 | |
| ☐ Laziness | 1,200.00 | |
| ☐ Leda and the Swan | 1,000.00 | 1,250.00 |
| ☐ Les Amis | 1,250.00 | |
| ☐ Lillies | 1,500.00 | |
| ☐ Lindberg | 900.00 | |
| ☐ Love Birds | 700.00 | |
| ☐ Love Letters | 750.00 | |
| ☐ Lovers | 800.00 | |
| ☐ Loves Awakening | 900.00 | |
| ☐ Loves Blossom | 2,250.00 | 2,500.00 |
| ☐ Madame Bovary | 850.00 | |
| ☐ Mannequin | 600.00 | |
| ☐ Manon | 800.00 | |
| ☐ Mardi Gras | 2,000.00 | 2,500.00 |
| ☐ Martini | 1,850.00 | 2,000.00 |
| ☐ Masked | 1,000.00 | |
| ☐ Mealtime (Woman with puppies) | 800.00 | |
| ☐ Memories | 1,800.00 | 2,200.00 |
| ☐ Melody Hour | 7,000.00 | 9,000.00 |
| ☐ Milkmaid | 700.00 | |
| ☐ Mimi looking out window | 700.00 | |
| ☐ Miss America | 1,000.00 | 1,200.00 |
| ☐ Miss Britain | 1,500.00 | 2,000.00 |
| ☐ Miss California | 1,000.00 | 1,200.00 |
| ☐ Miss France | 1,500.00 | |
| ☐ Miss Liberty | 1,500.00 | 1,800.00 |
| ☐ Mockery (The Red Screen) | 750.00 | |

| | | PRICE RANGE |
|---|---|---|
| ☐ Monkeyshines | 850.00 | |
| ☐ Montmarte | 750.00 | |
| ☐ Morning Cup | 850.00 | |
| ☐ Mother and child with soldier in background | 1,800.00 | 2,000.00 |
| ☐ Musetta | 750.00 | 850.00 |
| ☐ Mutt, The | 700.00 | |
| ☐ Nijinsky | 750.00 | |
| ☐ Nurse The | 750.00 | |
| ☐ One Beauty (Also known as ''Dollar''). | 500.00 | |
| ☐ On the Beach | 750.00 | |
| ☐ On the Green | 750.00 | |
| ☐ Orange Seller | 850.00 | |
| ☐ Orchids | 1,500.00 | 2,000.00 |
| ☐ Parasol, The | 1,000.00 | 1,250.00 |
| ☐ Paris (Two women overlooking Paris). | 700.00 | |
| ☐ Paris Flowers | 750.00 | |
| ☐ Peonies | 750.00 | |
| ☐ Pierrot | 750.00 | |
| ☐ Pink Alcove | 750.00 | |
| ☐ Pink Slip | 1,250.00 | 1,400.00 |
| ☐ Playful Pup | 750.00 | |
| ☐ Poem | 1,800.00 | |
| ☐ Puppies | 750.00 | |
| ☐ Rain | 850.00 | |
| ☐ Rainbow | 1,800.00 | 2,000.00 |
| ☐ Recollections (Woman at desk). | 750.00 | |
| ☐ Red Alcove | 750.00 | |
| ☐ Red Riding Hood | 850.00 | |
| ☐ Reflections Pool | 1,500.00 | 1,800.00 |
| ☐ Repose | 4,000.00 | 4,250.00 |
| ☐ Ritz, The | 1,500.00 | 2,000.00 |
| ☐ Salome | 750.00 | |
| ☐ Sappho | 750.00 | |
| ☐ Scherazade | 800.00 | |
| ☐ Seashell (Nude woman on shell). | 1,500.00 | 2,000.00 |
| ☐ Secrets or Blue Book | 750.00 | |
| ☐ Singing Lesson | 850.00 | |
| ☐ Sleeping Beauty | 950.00 | 1,250.00 |
| ☐ Smoke | 1,350.00 | 1,500.00 |
| ☐ Speed (Woman and greyhound). | 850.00 | 1,250.00 |
| ☐ Sofa | 2,500.00 | |
| ☐ Spanish Dancer | 850.00 | |
| ☐ Spilled Apples | 750.00 | |
| ☐ Sprintime | 1,000.00 | |
| ☐ Summer Music | 600.00 | |
| ☐ Swans | 1,500.00 | 2,000.00 |
| ☐ Sweet Mystery | 950.00 | |
| ☐ Symphony in Blue | 850.00 | |
| ☐ Symphony in White | 1,200.00 | 1,500.00 |
| ☐ Tennis | 900.00 | 1,000.00 |
| ☐ Three of Four Seasons | 800.00 | |
| ☐ The Coach (There are several versions). | 750.00 | |
| ☐ Tosca | 850.00 | 950.00 |
| ☐ Thoroughbreds (Woman with horse, Rare). | 3,500.00 | 4,000.00 |
| ☐ Treasure Chest | 600.00 | |
| ☐ Trenches | 1,850.00 | 2,250.00 |
| ☐ Two Beauties | 5,000.00 | |
| ☐ Unmasked | 900.00 | |
| ☐ Venetian Nights | 900.00 | |
| ☐ Venus (Companion to Eve) | 1,500.00 | |
| ☐ Victory in the Skies | 1,950.00 | 2,250.00 |
| ☐ Victory Wreath (Soldier holding woman holding wreath up in air, WWI). | 1,850.00 | 2,250.00 |
| ☐ View of Montmarte | 750.00 | |
| ☐ Voice of the Cannon - WWI | 1,950.00 | 2,500.00 |

**FUMEE - SMOKE** *by Louis Icart*

|  | | PRICE RANGE |
|---|---|---|
| ☐ Waltz Echoes | 1,000.00 | |
| ☐ Waterfall | 1,500.00 | 1,800.00 |
| ☐ White Lillies | 1,500.00 | 2,000.00 |
| ☐ White Underwear | 1,250.00 | |
| ☐ White Wings | 900.00 | |
| ☐ Winsome | 900.00 | |
| ☐ Wishing Well | 600.00 | |
| ☐ Wisteria | 900.00 | |
| ☐ Woman descending coach and coachmen, arrival. | 600.00 | |
| ☐ Woman holding feeding dish, four cats. | 750.00 | |
| ☐ Woman holding little red cage. | 700.00 | |
| ☐ Woman in snow with statue | 750.00 | |
| ☐ Woman on pillow eating grapes. | 700.00 | |
| ☐ Woman in boudoir with black cat | 600.00 | |
| ☐ Woman stepping into coach and coachmen, departure. | 700.00 | |
| ☐ Wounded Dove | 750.00 | |
| ☐ Young Mother | 750.00 | |
| ☐ Youth | 2,500.00 | |
| ☐ Zest | 1,400.00 | |

# MAXFIELD PARRISH

Born in 1870, Maxfield Parrish became a very successful illustrator and artist. In 1889, he studied at the Pennsylvania Academy of the fine arts. By the early 1900s, Parrish had drawn book and advertising illustrations, murals, and magazine covers. He experienced national acclaim until the early 1940s.

Althoug his popularity dwindled for the next twenty years, it soared again in the 1960s. He died in 1966. A popular collector's items is Parrish's Collier magazine covers.

## ADS

| | |
|---|---|
| ☐ Article (Rape of the Rhine-Gold, 16 pages, 16 illustrations-scarce-1898) . . . . . . . . . . . . . . . | 30.00 |
| ☐ Colgate Ad (Violet Talc Ad back cover magazine). Dutch boy & girl pointing to talc can . . . . . . | 25.00 |
| ☐ Colgate Ad (Violet Talc Ad). Dutch boy running away with talc & 4 Dutch maiden . . . . . . . . . | 30.00 |
| ☐ Colgate Ad. Shaving stick & Dutch boy shaving . . . . . . . . . . . . . . . . . . . . . . . . . . . . . . . . . . | 30.00 |
| ☐ Fisk Tire Ad - King on throne, 8¼" x 12". . . . . . . . . . . . . . . . . . . . . . . . . . . . . . . . . . . . . . . . | 25.00 |
| ☐ Fisk Tire Ad - Knave riding on tire cover, 8½" x 12". . . . . . . . . . . . . . . . . . . . . . . . . . . . . . . | 30.00 |
| ☐ Fisk Tire Ad - Fit For A King (king & 2 comical characters pulling tire apart on either side of king), 12" x 16", rare . . . . . . . . . . . . . . . . . . . . . . . . . . . . . . . . . . . . . . . . . . . . . . . . . . . . . . | 25.00 |
| ☐ Ferry Seed Ad. Peter the Husbander (Woman on pumpkin & Peter in chair) . . . . . . . . . . . . . . | 22.00 |
| ☐ Hires Ad (2 gnomes drinking Hires) 6" x 9½" . . . . . . . . . . . . . . . . . . . . . . . . . . . . . . . . . . . | 20.00 |
| ☐ Jello Ad (Polly Put the Kettle On) 7½" x 10½" . . . . . . . . . . . . . . . . . . . . . . . . . . . . . . . . . . . | 20.00 |

## COLLIER COVERS

| | |
|---|---|
| ☐ April Showers (Youth holding umbrella in the rain) 1909 | 20.00 |
| ☐ Arithmetic (Child and schoolmaster among high letters) 1911 . . . . . . . . . . . . . . . | 20.00 |
| ☐ Artist, The (Artist at painting-large blue sky) 1909 . . . . . . . . . . . . . . . . . | 20.00 |
| ☐ Artist (Sitting in front of canvas) 1909 . . . . . . . . . . . . . . . . . . . . . . . . . . . | 25.00 |
| ☐ Balloon Man, The (Gent in long scarf w/balloons) 1908 . . . . . . . . . . . . . . . . . | 25.00 |
| ☐ Botanist 1908 . . . . . . . . . . . . . . . . . . . . . . . . . . . . . . . . . . . . . . . . . . . . . . | 20.00 |
| ☐ Boars Head, The (Gents having feast) 1905 . . . . . . . . . . . . . . . . . . . . . . . . . | 35.00 |
| ☐ Buccaneer with Sword 1909 . . . . . . . . . . . . . . . . . . . . . . . . . . . . . . . . . . . . . | 20.00 |
| ☐ Chef sitting between two giant lobsters 1910 . . . . . . . . . . . . . . . . . . . . . . . . | 25.00 |
| ☐ Comic Cop (little policeman holding billy club), scarce 1905 . . . . . . . . . . . . . . | 20.00 |
| ☐ Comical sign painter painting Colliers 1909 . . . . . . . . . . . . . . . . . . . . . . . . . | 25.00 |
| ☐ Discussion (two gents having a conversation) 1909 . . . . . . . . . . . . . . . . . . . . | 20.00 |
| ☐ End, The (taking his final bow) . . . from Knave of Hearts 1929 . . . . . . . . . . . . | 35.00 |
| ☐ Fourth of July (Soldier w/large Sword) 1908 . . . . . . . . . . . . . . . . . . . . . . . . . | 27.50 |
| ☐ Gardener, The (Gent standing with hoe and watering can) 1906 . . . . . . . . . . . . | 40.00 |
| ☐ Girl on sled going downhill in snow 1910 . . . . . . . . . . . . . . . . . . . . . . . . . . . | 20.00 |
| ☐ Heralds, The (from the Knave of Hearts) 1929 . . . . . . . . . . . . . . . . . . . . . . . . | 25.00 |
| ☐ Idiot, The (comical gent in checkered gown reading book) 1910 . . . . . . . . . . . . | 40.00 |
| ☐ Independence (children carrying flags) 1905 . . . . . . . . . . . . . . . . . . . . . . . . . | 30.00 |
| ☐ Jack Frost (Gnome painting leaves) 1936. . . . . . . . . . . . . . . . . . . . . . . . . . . . | 25.00 |
| ☐ Lincolns Birthday (youth sitting on a rock looking into pool) 1906 . . . . . . . . . . | 20.00 |
| ☐ Little Girl in bed with hand in Christmas stocking 1906 . . . . . . . . . . . . . . . . . | 35.00 |
| ☐ Lone Fisherman, The (Man fishing in large lake) 1909. . . . . . . . . . . . . . . . . . . | 20.00 |
| ☐ Man in top hat fishing from top of piling 1913 . . . . . . . . . . . . . . . . . . . . . . . | 20.00 |
| ☐ Man with oxen walking through snow in the mountains 1906. . . . . . . . . . . . . . . | 25.00 |
| ☐ Manager, The (comical fellow bowing to viewer, from KOH-1929) . . . . . . . . . . . | 40.00 |
| ☐ Nature Lover, The (character in checker robe) 1911 . . . . . . . . . . . . . . . . . . . . | 17.50 |
| ☐ New Year, 1906 (Youth and Father Time). . . . . . . . . . . . . . . . . . . . . . . . . . . . | 27.50 |
| ☐ New Year, 1907 (Father Time shaking hands with youth) . . . . . . . . . . . . . . . . . | 30.00 |
| ☐ Nine little soldiers in a row. 1912 . . . . . . . . . . . . . . . . . . . . . . . . . . . . . . . . | 20.00 |
| ☐ Nude maiden sitting on a swing in trees, scarce. 1906 . . . . . . . . . . . . . . . . . . | 65.00 |
| ☐ Nude pastel surrounded by flowers, rare. 1911 . . . . . . . . . . . . . . . . . . . . . . . | 50.00 |
| ☐ Oklahoma comes in (Indian and Cowboy holding a star) 1907 . . . . . . . . . . . . . | 25.00 |
| ☐ Old Father Time winding clock, scarce. 1905. . . . . . . . . . . . . . . . . . . . . . . . . | 35.00 |
| ☐ Old King Cole (knaves carrying large platters to king) 1909 . . . . . . . . . . . . . . | 35.00 |
| ☐ Old King Cole (he called for his pipe & bowl) 1909 . . . . . . . . . . . . . . . . . . . . | 35.00 |
| ☐ Old King Cole (king with two sentries) 1913 . . . . . . . . . . . . . . . . . . . . . . . . . | 25.00 |
| ☐ Page, The (from the Knave of Hearts) . . . . . . . . . . . . . . . . . . . . . . . . . . . . . . | 35.00 |
| ☐ Philosopher, The (old man sitting, blue sky) 1912 . . . . . . . . . . . . . . . . . . . . . | 25.00 |
| ☐ Prospector finding gold in desert, 1911 . . . . . . . . . . . . . . . . . . . . . . . . . . . . | 55.00 |
| ☐ School Days (Youth surrounded by high letters) 1908 . . . . . . . . . . . . . . . . . . . | 30.00 |
| ☐ Scottish guard in uniform presenting arms. 1911. . . . . . . . . . . . . . . . . . . . . . | 20.00 |
| ☐ Soldiers repeated all over cover. 1912 . . . . . . . . . . . . . . . . . . . . . . . . . . . . . | 30.00 |
| ☐ Spring (Bare breasted maiden in field) scarce, 1905 . . . . . . . . . . . . . . . . . . . | 65.00 |
| ☐ Thanksgiving (man and children walking in snow) 1906 . . . . . . . . . . . . . . . . . | 30.00 |
| ☐ Thanksgiving (Pioneer carrying musket and turkey) 1906 . . . . . . . . . . . . . . . . | 30.00 |
| ☐ Thanksgiving (Hobo sitting by fire) 1905 . . . . . . . . . . . . . . . . . . . . . . . . . . . | 20.00 |
| ☐ Three Shepherds. 1904 . . . . . . . . . . . . . . . . . . . . . . . . . . . . . . . . . . . . . . . . | 25.00 |
| ☐ Tourists, The (Man standing in long coat) 1909 . . . . . . . . . . . . . . . . . . . . . . . | 25.00 |
| ☐ Two chefs leaning over a pot of pudding. 1956. . . . . . . . . . . . . . . . . . . . . . . . | 30.00 |
| ☐ Two comic chefs holding giant spoons, from kolt-1929 . . . . . . . . . . . . . . . . . . | 25.00 |

| | CURRENT RETAIL PRICE |
|---|---|
| ☐ Two comic guards, smile and frown, at attention. 1913 | 20.00 |
| ☐ Two figures facing each other with landscape in background. 1906 | 20.00 |
| ☐ Vaudeviller (comical fellow in checkered suit) 1908 | 35.00 |
| ☐ Wassail Bowl, The (Gent carrying large bowl), rare. 1909 | 55.00 |
| ☐ Young pirate sitting on lighted bomb, writing letter. 1909 | 25.00 |

## MISCELLANEOUS COVERS

| | |
|---|---|
| ☐ Book news cover (maiden reading book), rare, 1897 | 37.50 |
| ☐ Century cover (nude sitting in forest) a prize cover, 1917 | 50.00 |
| ☐ Harpers Monthly cover (Three Cupids) 1901 | 20.00 |
| ☐ Harpers Weekly (Christmas issue-comical chief, scarce cover, 1908 | 25.00 |
| ☐ Ladies Home Journal cover (air castles, nude sitting) award cover, 1904 | 50.00 |
| ☐ Ladies Home Journal cover (Arizona . . . beautiful Arizona mountains sunlite with oranges) 1930 | 27.50 |
| ☐ Ladies Home Journal (Girl water skier) 1930 | 30.00 |
| ☐ Ladies Home Journal (Maiden with trees in background) 1896 | 25.00 |
| ☐ Ladies Home Journal (Princely character & maiden in garden with large urns) 1901 | 20.00 |
| ☐ Ladies Home Journal (A shower of fragrance) 1912 | 25.00 |
| ☐ Ladies Home Journal (Sweet nothings, maidens in window) 1921 | 25.00 |
| ☐ Life cover (Bookstuff No.) 1922 | 30.00 |
| ☐ Life cover (a dark futurist, self portrait) 1923 | 30.00 |
| ☐ Life cover (her window, knave on wall at night) | 50.00 |
| ☐ Life cover (The masquerader, gent in checked costume) | 50.00 |
| ☐ Life cover (Christmas cover, first for life) 1899 | 50.00 |
| ☐ Life cover (St. Valentine) very rare | 50.00 |
| ☐ Scribners cover (Christmas cover, 3 wise men) 1900 | 30.00 |

## PRINTS

| | |
|---|---|
| ☐ Above the Balcony (knaves and maidens in garden) | 35.00 |
| ☐ Air Castles (nude in bubbles) | 125.00 |
| ☐ Aladdin in Cave of 40 Thieves, 12" x 16¼", on quality paper | 85.00 |
| ☐ Aladdin and the Lamp, 10" x 12" | 85.00 |
| ☐ Ancient Trees (large oak tree by lake) | 95.00 |
| ☐ Argonauts, In Quest of the Golden Fleece, The | 40.00 |
| ☐ Atlas (giant holding up sky) | 35.00 |
| ☐ Arizona (landscape of mountain-rich blues) 11" x 13" | 40.00 |
| ☐ Aucassin Seeks Nicolotte (knight on horse), Bookplate SM | 18.00 |
| ☐ Autumn (Maiden standing on hilltop) | 30.00 |
| ☐ Below the Balcony (Knaves and maidens in garden) | 35.00 |
| ☐ Bookplate (John Cox-His Book) | 20.00 |
| ☐ Brazen, The Boatman 10" x 12" | 40.00 |
| ☐ Brown & Bigelow Landscape (the village church) 24" x 27" | 175.00 |
| ☐ Cadmus Showing the Dragons Teeth, 10" x 12" | 40.00 |
| ☐ Canyon (Maiden in canyon) 14" x 17" | 125.00 |
| ☐ Circles Palace (Maiden standing on porch) | 40.00 |
| ☐ Cleopatra, rare, large | 500.00 |
| ☐ Community Plate, 11" x 13", 1918 | 25.00 |
| ☐ Contentment, large Edison Mazda Calendar, large | 375.00 |
| ☐ Dawn (Maiden sitting on rock) Mazda print | 42.00 |
| ☐ Daybreak (nude and maiden on porch), small size | 65.00 |
| ☐ Daybreak, large size | 195.00-225.00 |
| ☐ Dinkey Bird (nude on swing) 13½" x 18", 1904 | 125.00 |
| ☐ Djer-Kiss Ad (Maiden on swing in forest) 10½" x 14" | 40.00 |
| ☐ Dreaming (nude sitting under oak), medium size | 150.00 |
| ☐ Dreaming, large size | 450.00 |
| ☐ Dream Castle in the Sky, 9" x 12" | 35.00 |
| ☐ Duchess at Prayer, illustration for L'Allegro, 10" x 15", 1901 | 20.00 |
| ☐ Ecstasy (Maiden standing on rock), small size | 125.00 |
| ☐ Ecstasy, Large Edison Mazda Calendar | 500.00 |
| ☐ Enchantment (Maiden standing on stars at night) 9½" x 20½", large | 400.00 |
| ☐ Errant Pan, The (Pan sitting by stream) 6" x 8", small | 25.00 |
| ☐ Evening (Nude sitting on rock in lake) | 100.00 |
| ☐ Evening (Nude sitting in lake), 13" x 17" | 90.00 |
| ☐ Fisherman and the Geni, The; 10" x 12" | 40.00 |
| ☐ Florentine Fete (Maidens in garden) 10" x 16" | 30.00 |

**GARDEN OF ALLAH** by *Maxfield Parrish*

|  | | CURRENT RETAIL PRICE |
|---|---|---|
| ☐ | Garden of Allah (3 maidens sitting in garden), medium size | 95.00 |
| ☐ | Garden of Allah, Large Edison Mazda Calendar | 190.00 |
| ☐ | Garden of Opportunity, The (Prince and princess) | 50.00 |
| ☐ | Garden of Opportunity Triptyk, 10″ x 13″ | 50.00 |
| ☐ | Golden Hours (Maidens in forest) Large Edison Mazda Calendar | 350.00 |
| ☐ | Hilltop (youths sitting on mountain), medium size House of Art | 200.00 |
| ☐ | Hilltop, large size, House of Art | 450.00 |
| ☐ | Hilltop, small size | 75.00 |
| ☐ | His Christmas Dinner (Tramp having dinner) | 50.00 |
| ☐ | Interlude (Maidens sitting in garden playing lutes) | 85.00 |
| ☐ | Isola Bella Scene, 9″ x 10″ | 16.00 |
| ☐ | Jason and His Teacher Chiron The Centeur, 1910 | 35.00 |
| ☐ | King of the Black Isles (King on throne) 10″ x 12″, on quality paper | 85.00 |
| ☐ | Kings Son, The (Arab in garden by fountain) | 40.00 |
| ☐ | Knaves and Maidens (conversing in garden) | 50.00 |
| ☐ | Lamplighters, The (Mazda Calendar) 9″ x 13″, 1924 | 90.00 |
| ☐ | Lampseller of Bagdad, The (Maiden on steps), Mazda Calendar | 350.00 |
| ☐ | Land of Make-Believe, The (Maiden to garden) | 20.00 |
| ☐ | Little Princess, The (Princess sitting by fountain) | 18.00 |
| ☐ | Lute Players, small size, House of Art | 70.00 |
| ☐ | Lute Players, large size, House of Art | 375.00 |
| ☐ | Milkmaid, The (Maiden walking in Mountain) | 20.00 |
| ☐ | Morning (Maiden sitting on rock) 13″ x 16″ | 100.00 |
| ☐ | Night Call (Bare breasted girl in surf) 6″ x 8″ | 25.00 |
| ☐ | October - 1900 (Woman in long gown holding fruit draped in her gown. Large orange moon behind her head) 18″ x 23″ | 25.00 |
| ☐ | Old Romance (Nude sitting in pool) 6″ x 8″ | 25.00 |
| ☐ | Old King Cole | 125.00 |
| ☐ | Pandora's Box (Maiden sitting by large box) | 50.00 |
| ☐ | Pierrot (Clown with lute and gorgeous golds in water, sky glittering) 1912 | 50.00 |
| ☐ | Pool of the Vista D'Este (Nude boy lying down besides luminous pool) 7¼″ x 10¾″ | 18.00 |
| ☐ | Pipe Night (Comical men with pipes and coffee urns sitting facing each other at table) 9″ x 12½″ | 25.00 |
| ☐ | Post standing by river in forest | 25.00 |
| ☐ | Potpourri (Nude in garden picking flowers) | 20.00 |
| ☐ | Primitive Man (Unique salesman's sample) 4¾″ x 7½″ | 45.00 |
| ☐ | Prince Goodad (Pirates on boat) | 60.00 |
| ☐ | Prince, The (from Knave of Hearts) 10″ x 12½″, very rare | 100.00 |
| ☐ | Prosperina (Maiden in the sea) 10″ x 12″ | 45.00 |
| ☐ | Providing it By the Book (2 gents at table) | 18.00 |
| ☐ | Queen Gulnare (Maiden on porch) 10″ x 12″ | 45.00 |

**DAYBREAK** *by Maxfield Parrish*

| | CURRENT RETAIL PRICE |
|---|---|
| ☐ Reveries (two maidens sitting by fountain) | 35.00 |
| ☐ Reveries, Large Edison Mazda Calendar | 350.00 |
| ☐ Sandman, The (Sandman with full moon) 6″ x 7½″ | 30.00 |
| ☐ Scribners One of the Wise Men, 10″ x 11½″ | 18.00 |
| ☐ Search for the Singing Tree | 35.00 |
| ☐ Sea Nymphs, 12″ x 14″, 1914 | 45.00 |
| ☐ Seven Green Polls at Cintra, 6″ x 8″ | 25.00 |
| ☐ Shepherd with Sheep, 8½″ x 13½″ | 18.00 |
| ☐ Ship in Ocean, 11″ x 13½″ | 35.00 |
| ☐ Sinbad and The Cyclops, 10″ x 12″ | 35.00 |
| ☐ Sing a Song of Sixpence, 9″ x 12″ | 30.00 |
| ☐ Singing Tree, The; 10″ x 12″ | 40.00 |
| ☐ Stars, House of Art, medium size (Nude sitting on Rock) | 350.00 |
| ☐ Stars, House of Art, large size (Nude sitting on Rock) | 475.00 |
| ☐ Story from Phoebus, 8″ x 10″, 1901 | 16.00 |
| ☐ Sunlit Valley (Scenic of river and mountains) | 125.00 |
| ☐ Sunrise, Edison Mazda Calendar Top | 125.00 |
| ☐ Sunrise, Edison Mazda Calendar, rare, large | 500.00 |
| ☐ Swifts Ham Ad (Jack Sprat and wife) | 40.00 |
| ☐ Turquoise Cup, The (Gent sitting in Villa) | 18.00 |
| ☐ Twilight Had Fallen (Two figures on beach) | 25.00 |
| ☐ Valley of Diamonds (Arab in Valley) | 35.00 |
| ☐ Venetian Lamplighter, Edison Mazda Calendar, 1924 | 85.00 |
| ☐ Villa D'Este (Nude sitting by pool) | 30.00 |
| ☐ Walls of Jasper (Youth and Castle) 12″ x 14″ | 85.00 |
| ☐ Waterfall, small Edison Mazda Calendar | 125.00 |
| ☐ Waterfall, large Edison Mazda Calendar | 550.00 |
| ☐ White Birch (Farmer under large birch) | 35.00 |
| ☐ Wild Geese (Girl on Rock) 13″ x 16″ | 95.00 |
| ☐ Knave of Hearts book, mint | 600.00 |
| ☐ Dreamlight (Maiden sitting on swing in forest) large Edison Mazda Calendar, 9½″ x 20½″, 1925, large | 475.00 |

# VANITY FAIR

## ORIGINAL LITHOGRAPHS

Vanity Fair was a periodical published in London from 1860 to 1914. In its own parlance it was a weekly show of political, social, literary and financial ware, reaching the well-to-do and cultivated classes worldwide. Each issue featured a bound-in lithograph depicting an influential man or woman. The lithograph (either life-like or satirical in nature) was usually accompanied by adjacent prose which extolled or lamented the virtures or vices of the personage being featured. Two of the most famous Vanity Fair artists were "Spy" (Leslie Ward) and "Ape" (Carlo Pilligrini).

From first publication, this feature of Vanity Fair enjoyed great interest and was widely collected among readers. Additional lithographs of the weekly featured subject were available upon request and payment to Vanity Fair. Most renderings were reproduced by stone lithography, thus severely limiting the quality of each issue.

Interest in Original Vanity Fair lithographs increased substantially after the demise of the publication because no new lithographs could be produced. The prints remaining at Vanity Fair were purchased by Paul B. Victorious, owner of a London rare book and print shop. During the war Victorious moved with his family to Charlottesville, Virginia where he lived quietly as the owner of a book, print and framing shop. Largely untouched and uncatalogued, the collection remained in a warehouse until Victorious' death. The collection was offered for sale by executors. Following the purchase, Vanity Fair Ltd. was founded and the next year was spent cataloging and cross indexing the entire collection. Vanity Fair, Ltd. represents the most comprehensive single collection known.

Original Vanity Fair lithographs are limited because the original plates no longer exist, the lithographs are relatively rare in number, and they appeal to a broad audience.

Original Vanity Fair lithographs were a true mirror of the society in which they were produced. They bring collectors a look at the manner, grace, and wit so treasured in the days of Queen Victoria.

## ACCOUNTANT

| CAPTION | YEAR | ARTIST | PRICE |
|---|---|---|---|
| ☐ An Undersheriff | 1891 | SPY | N/S |

## AMBASSADORS FROM ENGLAND

| CAPTION | YEAR | ARTIST | PRICE |
|---|---|---|---|
| ☐ One of the Most Precious | 1870 | APE | N/S |
| ☐ A Liberal and an Enemy | 1871 | APE | N/S |
| ☐ He Might Have Been A King | 1871 | Unsigned | N/S |
| ☐ The Most Interesting | 1871 | APE | N/S |
| ☐ One of the Lambs | 1871 | APE | N/S |
| ☐ The Spanish Minister | 1871 | Unsigned | N/S |
| ☐ Diplomacy | 1873 | Unsigned | $18.00 |
| ☐ Ill-Used | 1874 | APE | 18.00 |
| ☐ Austria | 1875 | APE | N/S |
| ☐ Russia | 1875 | APE | N/S |
| ☐ Ther German Ambassador | 1876 | SPY | N/S |
| ☐ Ambassador To The Porte | 1877 | SPY | 18.00 |
| ☐ A Manipulation of Phrases | 1877 | SPY | N/S |
| ☐ Odo | 1877 | SPY | 18.00 |
| ☐ The Turkish Constitution | 1877 | SPY | N/S |

**THE DEUTSCH PRICE**
**N. Santos Dumont**

**THE POPE**
**His Holiness Pope Leo XIII**

**HYDROPHOBIA**
**M. Louis Pasteur**

**LETTERS TO YOUNG**
**SHOOTERS**
**Sir R.W. Payne, Galwey,**
**Bart**

**CHARLIE WOOD**

**WOMEN'S SUFFRAGE**
**Miss Cristobel Pankhurst**

**PATRONAGE**
**Maj. Gen. H.D. Hutchin**

**EASY EXECUTION**
**M. Ignace Jan Paderewski**

| CAPTION | YEAR | ARTIST | PRICE |
|---|---|---|---|
| ☐ Diplomacy | 1878 | APE | 20.00 |
| ☐ Promotion by Merit | 1878 | APE | 18.00 |
| ☐ Siam | 1879 | SPY | 18.00 |
| ☐ The Baron | 1884 | APE | 18.00 |
| ☐ Justice! Justice! | 1884 | SPY | 18.00 |
| ☐ The Russian Ambassador | 1885 | APE | N/S |
| ☐ A Safe Ambassador | 1886 | APE | N/S |
| ☐ Italy | 1886 | APE | 18.00 |
| ☐ Count Paul Metternich | 1895 | SPY | N/S |
| ☐ Austro-Hungary | 1898 | SPY | N/S |
| ☐ Brazil | 1898 | SPY | 14.00 |
| ☐ Portugal | 1898 | SPY | 18.00 |
| ☐ French Ambassador | 1899 | GUTH | N/S |
| ☐ Tokio | 1901 | SPY | 18.00 |
| ☐ Berlin | 1902 | SPY | 18.00 |
| ☐ The Italian Ambassador | 1902 | SPY | N/S |
| ☐ Japan | 1902 | SPY | 20.00 |
| ☐ Denmark in England | 1903 | SPY | N/S |
| ☐ Russia in England | 1903 | SPY | N/S |
| ☐ Washington | 1903 | SPY | 20.00 |
| ☐ The Belgian Minister | 1904 | SPY | N/S |
| ☐ Washington Post | 1904 | SPY | 20.00 |
| ☐ Diplomacy | 1907 | SPY | 18.00 |
| ☐ Marquis De Soveral | 1907 | K | 18.00 |
| ☐ His Excellency The French Ambassador | 1912 | K | N/S |

## AMERICANS

| CAPTION | YEAR | ARTIST | PRICE |
|---|---|---|---|
| ☐ An Arbitrator | 1872 | Unsigned | 20.00 |
| ☐ Captain, Tanner, Farmer | 1872 | Unsigned | 26.00 |
| ☐ Consequential Damages | 1872 | Unsigned | N/S |
| ☐ The Massive Grievance | 1872 | Unsigned | 20.00 |
| ☐ The United States | 1875 | APE | 20.00 |
| ☐ Uncle Sam | 1880 | SPY | N/S |
| ☐ Barnum | 1882 | SPY | 20.00 |
| ☐ President of the New York | 1889 | SPY | 20.00 |
| ☐ The United States | 1894 | SPY | 20.00 |
| ☐ USA | 1897 | SPY | 20.00 |
| ☐ A Diplomatic Cousin | 1899 | SPY | 20.00 |
| ☐ An American President | 1899 | FLAGG | 20.00 |
| ☐ United States Embassy | 1899 | SPY | 20.00 |
| ☐ U.S.A. | 1902 | FLAGG | 24.00 |
| ☐ Mr. Alfred Gwynne Vanderbilt | 1907 | SPY | 20.00 |
| ☐ The New President | 1913 | HESTER | 24.00 |

## ARCHITECTS AND ENGINEERS

| CAPTION | YEAR | ARTIST | PRICE |
|---|---|---|---|
| ☐ He Suppressed An Isthmus | 1869 | Unsigned | 20.00 |
| ☐ The Obelisk | 1880 | SPY | 20.00 |
| ☐ An Eminent Builder | 1883 | T | N/S |
| ☐ The Afghan Frontier | 1885 | APE | 24.00 |
| ☐ Architecture Militant | 1885 | APE | 20.00 |
| ☐ Gustave Eiffel | 1889 | GUTH | 20.00 |
| ☐ French Warfare | 1891 | GUTH | 20.00 |
| ☐ Imperialist Afrikander | 1893 | SPY | 20.00 |
| ☐ An Agriculturist | 1896 | FTD | N/S |
| ☐ Afghan Engineering | 1900 | SPY | 20.00 |
| ☐ King Dick | 1902 | UNK | 20.00 |
| ☐ United Ireland | 1907 | SPY | N/S |
| ☐ Submarine Telegraphs | 1908 | SPY | 20.00 |
| ☐ A Great Engineer | 1911 | APE JR. | N/S |
| ☐ Architect Matcham | 1911 | NIBS | N/S |
| ☐ The Road Builder | 1911 | WHO | N/S |
| ☐ He Is The One Designer | 1913 | OWL | 20.00 |

# ARTISTS

| CAPTION | YEAR | ARTIST | PRICE |
|---|---|---|---|
| ☐ Fairford Abbey | 1898 | SPY | 20.00 |
| ☐ Max | 1897 | SIC | 30.00 |
| ☐ The Queen's Sculptor | 1881 | SPY | 20.00 |
| ☐ The Queen's Memorial | 1905 | SPY | 20.00 |
| ☐ King Cole | 1871 | Unsigned | N/S |
| ☐ Sensational Art | 1877 | SPY | 24.00 |
| ☐ He Painted the Doctor | 1892 | SPY | 20.00 |
| ☐ The Derby-Day | 1873 | SPY | 24.00 |
| ☐ The Queen's Nephew | 1884 | GO | 20.00 |
| ☐ An Able Artist | 1871 | APE | 20.00 |
| ☐ An Art Critic | 1871 | Unsigned | N/S |
| ☐ The Glorious East | 1884 | GO | 20.00 |
| ☐ Posters | 1912 | STRICKLAND | 20.00 |
| ☐ Painter, Sculptor, Blacksmith | 1884 | FG | 20.00 |
| ☐ The Pre-Raphaelite | 1879 | SPY | 20.00 |
| ☐ He Paints Various Royalties | 1913 | RITCHIE | 20.00 |
| ☐ Athlete and Sculptor | 1883 | Unsigned | 20.00 |
| ☐ A Sacrifice To the Graces | 1872 | Unsigned | 24.00 |
| ☐ A Sculptor | 1877 | SPY | 20.00 |
| ☐ The Grosvenor Gallery | 1883 | Unsigned | 20.00 |
| ☐ A Connoisseur | 1899 | N | 20.00 |
| ☐ Phil | 1895 | SPY | 24.00 |
| ☐ Great French Painter | 1880 | T | 20.00 |
| ☐ Converted Pre-Raphaelite | 1871 | APE | 24.00 |
| ☐ Artist & R.A. | 1898 | SPY | 20.00 |
| ☐ Paris Exhibition | 1878 | SPY | 20.00 |
| ☐ APE | 1898 | AFM | 24.00 |
| ☐ P.R.A. | 1897 | SPY | 20.00 |
| ☐ Val | 1877 | SPY | 20.00 |
| ☐ He Thinks in Marble | 1904 | IMP | 24.00 |
| ☐ A Great Realist | 1909 | MAX | 20.00 |
| ☐ The Wallace Collection | 1909 | WHO | 20.00 |
| ☐ Mr. Archibald Stuart-Wortley | 1890 | SPY | 20.00 |
| ☐ Fifteen Churches | 1879 | SPY | N/S |
| ☐ Ancient Painting | 1879 | APE | 20.00 |
| ☐ Punch | 1878 | SPY | 20.00 |
| ☐ The Graphics | 1894 | SPY | 20.00 |
| ☐ Bronze Statuary | 1892 | SPY | 20.00 |
| ☐ Historic Art | 1873 | SPY | 20.00 |
| ☐ Spy | 1889 | PAL | 24.00 |
| ☐ He Paints Portraits | 1891 | SPY | 20.00 |
| ☐ A Symphony | 1878 | SPY | 40.00 |
| ☐ Val | 1877 | SPY | 20.00 |

# AUTOMOBILE DEVOTEES

| CAPTION | YEAR | ARTIST | PRICE |
|---|---|---|---|
| ☐ Automobile | 1899 | GUTH | 36.00 |
| ☐ Cabs | 1903 | SPY | 36.00 |
| ☐ Steam | 1907 | SPY | 24.00 |
| ☐ The Colonel | 1909 | ELF | N/S |
| ☐ Frizzy | 1909 | HCO | N/S |
| ☐ A Popular Secretary | 1911 | APE JR. | N/S |
| ☐ Orangeman | 1911 | WHO | N/S |

# AVIATORS

| CAPTION | YEAR | ARTIST | PRICE |
|---|---|---|---|
| ☐ The Deutsch Prize | 1901 | GEO. HUM. | 80.00 |
| ☐ The Air | 1907 | SPY | 60.00 |
| ☐ Hastings and Aviation | 1910 | HLO | N/S |
| ☐ All British | 1911 | RITCHIE | N/S |
| ☐ Claudie | 1911 | TEC | 45.00 |
| ☐ Flight | 1912 | WH | 36.00 |

## BANKERS AND FINANCIERS

| CAPTION | YEAR | ARTIST | PRICE |
|---------|------|--------|-------|
| ☐ Winchester | 1883 | SPY | N/S |
| ☐ Swansea Harbor | 1909 | WHO | 18.00 |
| ☐ Go, Gas & Cold | 1895 | SPY | N/S |
| ☐ South Herfordshire | 1891 | SPY | N/S |
| ☐ Egyptian Finance | 1899 | SPY | N/S |
| ☐ Dan | 1908 | SPY | N/S |
| ☐ Colonial | 1881 | SPY | N/S |
| ☐ A Man of Weight | 1873 | Unsigned | N/S |
| ☐ Egypt | 1902 | SPY | N/S |
| ☐ The Whip | 1872 | Unsigned | N/S |
| ☐ Old Mother Hubbard | 1884 | SPY | N/S |
| ☐ Piety and Banking | 1876 | APE | N/S |
| ☐ St. John of Jerusalem | 1883 | T | N/S |
| ☐ The Bank Holiday | 1878 | SPY | 18.00 |
| ☐ C.M. | 1909 | SPY | N/S |
| ☐ Whitechapel | 1886 | LIB | 18.00 |
| ☐ Samuel Hope Morley | 1905 | SPY | N/S |
| ☐ The Birbeck | 1911 | APE JR. | N/S |
| ☐ The Wicked Baron | 1909 | SPY | 18.00 |
| ☐ Barings | 1888 | LIB | N/S |
| ☐ Barings | 1898 | SPY | 18.00 |
| ☐ The Cape | 1891 | SPY | 18.00 |
| ☐ Natty | 1888 | LIB | N/S |
| ☐ Alfred | 1884 | SPY | N/S |
| ☐ Alphonse | 1894 | GUTH | N/S |
| ☐ Eros | 1900 | SPY | N/S |
| ☐ Ferdy | 1889 | HAY | N/S |
| ☐ Racing and Sporting | 1884 | SPY | 20.00 |
| ☐ Baron Lionel | 1877 | APE | 20.00 |
| ☐ The Winner of the Race | 1871 | APE | N/S |
| ☐ The Aylesbury Division | 1900 | SPY | N/S |
| ☐ The Bank of England | 1895 | SPY | 20.00 |
| ☐ Hythie | 1900 | SPY | N/S |
| ☐ Mr. Reuben Sassoon | 1890 | SPY | 20.00 |
| ☐ Free Trade and Finance | 1906 | SPY | N/S |
| ☐ Lloyd's Bank | 1910 | HCO | 20.00 |
| ☐ Canada in London | 1900 | SPY | 20.00 |
| ☐ Eastern Finance | 1899 | SPY | N/S |
| ☐ Copper | 1899 | SPY | 20.00 |
| ☐ Egyptian Finance | 1878 | APE | N/S |

## BOXERS

| CAPTION | YEAR | ARTIST | PRICE |
|---------|------|--------|-------|
| ☐ A Good Lightweight | 1877 | SPY | 24.00 |
| ☐ Hard Hitter | 1896 | SPY | 60.00 |
| ☐ Peggy | 1911 | WH | 24.00 |
| ☐ A Typical Englishman | 1912 | RITCHIE | 30.00 |

## BUSINESSMEN AND EMPIRE BUILDERS

| CAPTION | YEAR | ARTIST | PRICE |
|---------|------|--------|-------|
| ☐ Burton Beer | 1885 | SPY | N/S |
| ☐ The Ogre | 1908 | SPY | N/S |
| ☐ C.P.R. in Europe | 1910 | ELF | 18.00 |
| ☐ Falmouth | 1910 | HCO | 18.00 |
| ☐ An Irish Landowner | 1910 | SPY | 18.00 |
| ☐ Manchester | 1875 | APE | 18.00 |
| ☐ The Commercial Traveller | 1899 | CLOISTER | N/S |
| ☐ A Retired Financier | 1876 | JTJ | N/S |
| ☐ The Lord Harry | 1890 | FC.G | N/S |
| ☐ Telephones | 1888 | LIB | 18.00 |
| ☐ A Master Craftsman | 1912 | WH | N/S |
| ☐ Oil | 1911 | SPY | N/S |
| ☐ Long John | 1910 | QUIP | 24.00 |
| ☐ Burton | 1908 | SPY | 18.00 |

| CAPTION | YEAR | ARTIST | PRICE |
|---|---|---|---|
| ☐ A Dandy | 1909 | SPY | N/S |
| ☐ Prospectuses | 1912 | WH | N/S |
| ☐ A Temperate Ulster Man | 1887 | APE | N/S |
| ☐ Cardiff | 1910 | WHO | N/S |
| ☐ Bexhill & Dunlop | 1896 | SPY | N/S |
| ☐ Tea | 1890 | SPY | N/S |
| ☐ Philip | 1910 | WHO | 18.00 |
| ☐ Small Freeholds | 1908 | SPY | 20.00 |
| ☐ Carberry Tower | 1911 | APE JR. | 24.00 |
| ☐ Horace | 1898 | SPY | N/S |
| ☐ A Well-Known Face | 1911 | HLO | N/S |
| ☐ Not A Small Fry | 1909 | SPY | N/S |
| ☐ The Furness Line | 1908 | SPY | 18.00 |
| ☐ Housing | 1912 | RAY | 18.00 |
| ☐ A Man of Business | 1882 | T | N/S |
| ☐ Brummagem Varsity | 1911 | HLO | 18.00 |
| ☐ Big Things in Oil | 1912 | WH | N/S |
| ☐ Papworth | 1896 | SPY | 18.00 |
| ☐ Malted Milk | 1909 | SPY | N/S |
| ☐ West Marylebone | 1893 | SPY | 18.00 |
| ☐ Endowed Lectures | 1910 | PRY | 18.00 |
| ☐ Great Western | 1908 | SPY | N/S |
| ☐ J | 1895 | SPY | 18.00 |
| ☐ Collieries | 1906 | SPY | 18.00 |
| ☐ Beggar General To The | 1890 | LIB | 18.00 |
| ☐ King of Campsie | 1910 | HCO | 18.00 |
| ☐ Prosperity | 1876 | JTJ | N/S |
| ☐ Fair Trade | 1882 | SPY | 20.00 |
| ☐ Arthur | 1909 | ELF | 18.00 |
| ☐ McEwan & Co. | 1902 | SPY | 18.00 |
| ☐ A Leading Figure in Cotton | 1912 | RITCHIE | 18.00 |
| ☐ Bradford Goods | 1890 | SPY | 18.00 |
| ☐ Metal | 1892 | SPY | N/S |
| ☐ Tea Cum Rubber | 1910 | ELF | 18.00 |
| ☐ The Heir of the Ages | 1888 | APE | 18.00 |
| ☐ Peace | 1887 | SPY | N/S |
| ☐ Bullion | 1890 | SPY | 18.00 |
| ☐ Crystal Palace | 1913 | HIC | N/S |
| ☐ Sir Horace, J.P. | 1909 | SPY | 18.00 |
| ☐ Electric Traction | 1909 | SPY | N/S |
| ☐ The Indian Rothschild | 1879 | SPY | N/S |
| ☐ Self | 1911 | RITCHIE | 18.00 |
| ☐ Beer & Budget & Brains | 1909 | SPY | N/S |
| ☐ Head of the Greatest | 1904 | SPY | N/S |
| ☐ Paper | 1912 | RAY | N/S |
| ☐ Finance & Fruit | 1909 | SPY | N/S |
| ☐ Glasgow | 1883 | Unsigned | 18.00 |
| ☐ Glen | 1910 | HO | 18.00 |
| ☐ Ludgate Hill | 1894 | SPY | N/S |
| ☐ Herbs | 1910 | HCO | N/S |
| ☐ Brightside D. V. | 1909 | SPY | 18.00 |
| ☐ Sir Andrew Barclay | 1890 | LIB | 18.00 |
| ☐ Philip | 1910 | WHO | N/S |
| ☐ The King of Wales | 1873 | SPY | N/S |
| ☐ A Squatter | 1885 | SPY | 18.00 |
| ☐ He Has Engineered Nothing | 1905 | SPY | N/S |

## CHANCELLORS OF EXCHEQUER

| CAPTION | YEAR | ARTIST | PRICE |
|---|---|---|---|
| ☐ An Enemy to Democracy | 1869 | APE | N/S |
| ☐ A Returned Colonist | 1869 | APE | 14.00 |
| ☐ The Theory of Foreign | 1869 | Unknown | 16.00 |
| ☐ He Does His Duty | 1870 | APE | N/S |
| ☐ The Fat of the Land | 1871 | APE | N/S |
| ☐ A Scagliola Appollo | 1874 | APE | 14.00 |
| ☐ A Younger Son | 1880 | SPY | 24.00 |
| ☐ Sugar Bounties | 1885 | APE | N/S |
| ☐ East Worcershershire | 1899 | SPY | 14.00 |

| CAPTION | YEAR | ARTIST | PRICE |
|---|---|---|---|
| ☐ A Retired Leader | 1890 | CLOISTER | 14.00 |
| ☐ Winston | 1900 | SPY | N/S |
| ☐ In the Winning Crew | 1906 | SPY | 14.00 |
| ☐ Winnie | 1911 | NIBS | N/S |

## CLERGY

| CAPTION | YEAR | ARTIST | PRICE |
|---|---|---|---|
| ☐ The Chief Rabbi | 1904 | SPY | 36.00 |
| ☐ Temple Reader | 1892 | SPY | 10.00 |
| ☐ The Primate | 1887 | SPY | 16.00 |
| ☐ The Head of the Dissenters | 1872 | Unsigned | 16.00 |
| ☐ The Salvation Army | 1882 | SPY | 16.00 |
| ☐ Prayers | 1879 | SPY | 16.00 |
| ☐ Fearless But Intemperate | 1904 | SPY | 16.00 |
| ☐ An Earnest and Liberal | 1869 | COICA | 16.00 |
| ☐ The Apostle To The Genteel | 1872 | Unsigned | 16.00 |
| ☐ St. Paul's | 1886 | LIB | 16.00 |
| ☐ The Pentateuch | 1874 | APE | 16.00 |
| ☐ Lay Episcopacy | 1882 | SPY | N/S |
| ☐ The End of the World | 1872 | Unsigned | 16.00 |
| ☐ Derry | 1895 | SPY | 16.00 |
| ☐ A Wet Quacker | 1882 | SPY | 16.00 |
| ☐ Swansea | 1900 | APE | 16.00 |
| ☐ A Court Parson | 1886 | APE | N/S |
| ☐ A Common Prayer Reformer | 1871 | APE | N/S |
| ☐ He Had Decided | 1905 | SPY | 16.00 |
| ☐ Revision | 1885 | SPY | N/S |
| ☐ A Fashion Canon | 1898 | F.T.D. | 16.00 |
| ☐ Chaplain to the Commons | 1891 | SPY | N/S |
| ☐ Chester Square | 1899 | SPY | 16.00 |
| ☐ Carlisle | 1888 | SPY | 16.00 |
| ☐ Come to Jesus | 1872 | Unsigned | N/S |
| ☐ The Revised Edition | 1885 | SPY | 16.00 |
| ☐ An Apostle to Positivism | 1886 | APE | 16.00 |
| ☐ The Parson, The Play | 1888 | APE | 16.00 |
| ☐ St. Margaret's | 1912 | WH | 16.00 |
| ☐ Domestic Chaplain | 1907 | AO | N/S |
| ☐ Roses | 1895 | F.T.D. | 16.00 |
| ☐ The Genial Dean | 1912 | WH | 16.00 |
| ☐ London | 1901 | SPY | 16.00 |
| ☐ One Who Has Grieved | 1870 | APE | 16.00 |
| ☐ Greek | 1876 | SPY | 16.00 |
| ☐ Kensington | 1903 | SPY | 16.00 |
| ☐ An Angel of Peace | 1912 | STRICKLAND | 16.00 |
| ☐ The Pope | 1878 | T | 16.00 |
| ☐ Lichfield | 1897 | STUFF | 16.00 |
| ☐ Convocation | 1884 | SPY | N/S |
| ☐ High Church | 1876 | SPY | N/S |
| ☐ A Persecuted Bishop | 1890 | SPY | N/S |
| ☐ Ecclesiastical History | 1897 | F.T.D. | 16.00 |
| ☐ Father Ignatius | 1887 | APE | 16.00 |
| ☐ Stonehenge 1911 | 1911 | RITCHIE | 16.00 |
| ☐ He Makes Religion A Tragedy | 1870 | APE | 16.00 |
| ☐ The Next Pope | 1871 | APE | 16.00 |
| ☐ The Noblest of English | 1881 | SPY | 20.00 |
| ☐ Tracts For The Times | 1877 | SPY | 20.00 |
| ☐ Not A Brawler | 1869 | APE | 16.00 |
| ☐ Congressional Union | 1884 | APE | 16.00 |
| ☐ If Eloquence Could Justify | 1869 | APE | 16.00 |
| ☐ The Infallible | 1870 | Unsigned | 16.00 |
| ☐ His Holiness Pius X | 1903 | LIB | N/S |
| ☐ Wellington College | 1902 | SPY | 16.00 |
| ☐ High Church | 1875 | APE | 16.00 |
| ☐ D.V. | 1872 | Unsigned | N/S |
| ☐ A Man Right Reverend | 1906 | SPY | 16.00 |
| ☐ The Soldiers Bishop | 1897 | SPY | N/S |
| ☐ An Erudite Dean | 1905 | SPY | N/S |

| CAPTION | YEAR | ARTIST | PRICE |
|---|---|---|---|
| ☐ The Dean | 1912 | WH | N/S |
| ☐ Liverpool | 1881 | APE | 16.00 |
| ☐ Tolerance | 1906 | SPY | 20.00 |
| ☐ A Great Marrier | 1904 | SPY | 16.00 |
| ☐ The Sub-Dean | 1911 | APE JR. | 16.00 |
| ☐ Southwell | 1901 | SPY | 16.00 |
| ☐ No One Has Succeeded | 1870 | APE | 16.00 |
| ☐ Philosophical Belief | 1872 | nsigned | 16.00 |
| ☐ I Felt Very Uncomfortable | 1869 | APE | N/S |
| ☐ A Bishop | 1906 | | N/S |
| ☐ A Quaker | 1886 | SPY | 16.00 |
| ☐ Rochester | 1904 | SPY | 16.00 |
| ☐ Winton | 1911 | RAY | N/S |
| ☐ Oxford University | 1897 | SPY | 16.00 |
| ☐ He Has Displayed Ability | 1869 | Unsigned | 16.00 |
| ☐ Just | 1902 | SPY | 16.00 |
| ☐ Rochester | 1885 | SPY | N/S |
| ☐ The Christian Martyr | 1877 | SPY | 16.00 |
| ☐ A Most Perfect Preacher | 1907 | SPY | 20.00 |
| ☐ A Modern Savonarola | 1907 | SPY | 16.00 |
| ☐ Nolo Episcopari | 1872 | Unsigned | N/S |
| ☐ St. Paul's Knightsbridge | 1902 | SPY | 20.00 |
| ☐ I Have Much To Be Thankful For | 1871 | Unsigned | 20.00 |
| ☐ Calcutta | 1898 | SPY | N/S |
| ☐ The Old Dean | 1876 | SPY | 16.00 |
| ☐ Westminister | 1893 | SPY | 16.00 |
| ☐ Prayers | 1874 | APE | 16.00 |
| ☐ The Chaplain | 1909 | SPY | 16.00 |
| ☐ Truro | 1885 | SPY | 16.00 |
| ☐ Prelate to the Garter | 1901 | SPY | 16.00 |
| ☐ The Archbishop of Society | 1871 | APE | 18.00 |
| ☐ From the Army | 1891 | SPY | 18.00 |

## CRICKETT

| CAPTION | YEAR | ARTIST | PRICE |
|---|---|---|---|
| ☐ Bobby | 1902 | SPY | 24.00 |
| ☐ I Zingari | 1895 | SPY | 24.00 |
| ☐ Charlie | 1910 | ALS | 30.00 |
| ☐ Australian Cricket | 1884 | APE | N/S |
| ☐ An Artful Bowler | 1904 | SPY | 30.00 |
| ☐ In His Father's Steps | 1904 | SPY | 30.00 |
| ☐ The Champion Country | 1913 | OWL | N/S |
| ☐ Cricketing Christianity | 1906 | SPY | 30.00 |
| ☐ Cricket | 1877 | SPY | N/S |
| ☐ Kent | 1881 | SPY | N/S |
| ☐ Yorkshire Cricket | 1892 | SPY | N/S |
| ☐ Tom | 1906 | SPY | 30.00 |
| ☐ Yorkshire | 1903 | SPY | 24.00 |
| ☐ A Tested Centurion | 1912 | WH | 40.00 |
| ☐ Monkey | 1891 | STUFF | 30.00 |
| ☐ A Century Maker | 1907 | SPY | N/S |
| ☐ A Flannelled Fighter | 1902 | SPY | 36.00 |
| ☐ The Lobster | 1902 | SPY | 24.00 |
| ☐ The Croucher | 1901 | SPY | 30.00 |
| ☐ English Cricket | 1884 | APE | 30.00 |
| ☐ Repton, Oxford & Somerset | 1903 | SPY | 24.00 |
| ☐ Oxford Circuit | 1880 | SPY | 30.00 |
| ☐ Ranji | 1897 | SPY | 30.00 |
| ☐ W.W. | 1888 | LIB | 30.00 |
| ☐ The Demon Bowler | 1878 | SPY | N/S |
| ☐ Reggie | 1906 | SPY | 30.00 |
| ☐ A Big Hitter | 1892 | STUFF | 30.00 |
| ☐ Forty-Six Centuries In | 1906 | SPY | 30.00 |
| ☐ Plum | 1903 | SPY | 30.00 |
| ☐ Father | 1907 | SPY | 30.00 |
| ☐ Sammy | 1892 | STUFF | 30.00 |
| ☐ Hampshire | 1898 | CG | 36.00 |

# CRIMINALS

| CAPTION | YEAR | ARTIST | PRICE |
|---|---|---|---|
| The Turf Frauds | 1877 | SPY | N/S |
| Richard Pigott | 1889 | SPY | 24.00 |

# DOCTORS AND SCIENTISTS

| CAPTION | YEAR | ARTIST | PRICE |
|---|---|---|---|
| Astronomy | 1875 | PE | 20.00 |
| Wholemeal Bread | 1911 | RAY | 20.00 |
| Bones | 1909 | ELF | 20.00 |
| Physician To His Majesty's | 1906 | SPY | 20.00 |
| Orthodoxy | 1902 | SPY | 20.00 |
| Hospitals | 1898 | QUIZ | N/S |
| A Literary Oculist | 1892 | STUFF | 20.00 |
| He Has Devoted His Life | 1888 | SPY | N/S |
| Fashionable Surgery | 1874 | APE | 24.00 |
| Anti-Vivisection | 1910 | ELF | 24.00 |
| Alfred | 1897 | SPY | N/S |
| The Transit of Venus | 1908 | SPY | 20.00 |
| Mr. Frank Crisp | 1890 | SPY | 20.00 |
| The King's Oculist | 1905 | SPY | 20.00 |
| Ubi Crookes Ibi Lux | 1903 | SPY | 20.00 |
| His Lordship of London | 1911 | WH | 24.00 |
| Radium | 1904 | IMP | 30.00 |
| The Ear | 1888 | APE | 24.00 |
| Natural Selection | 1871 | Unsigned | 40.00 |
| West Aberdeenshire | 1895 | SPY | 20.00 |
| There Is No Man Of | 1870 | APE | 20.00 |
| The Ilkeston Division | 1894 | SPY | 20.00 |
| A Master of the Knife | 1907 | SPY | 20.00 |
| Electrical Energy | 1910 | HLO | 20.00 |
| Chemistry & Optics | 1891 | SPY | 20.00 |
| Surgical Diagnosis | 1911 | WH | 24.00 |
| Physiological Physic | 1875 | APE | N/S |
| Hydropathy | 1876 | SPY | 20.00 |
| Steel | 1912 | WH | 20.00 |
| How Much? | 1904 | SPY | N/S |
| Mr. Johnathan Hutchinson | 1890 | SPY | 20.00 |
| Spectroscopic Astronomy | 1903 | SPY | 20.00 |
| The Chingford Pump | 1913 | HESTER | 20.00 |
| A Great Medicine Man | 1871 | APE | N/S |
| Army Medical | 1901 | SPY | 20.00 |
| Dr. Jim | 1896 | SPY | 20.00 |
| Physic | 1873 | SPY | 20.00 |
| Dietetics | 1897 | SPY | N/S |
| The King's Physician | 1903 | SPY | 20.00 |
| His Religion Is The Worship | 1905 | SPY | 20.00 |
| Agricultural Science | 1882 | T | 20.00 |
| Horticulture | 1899 | SPY | 20.00 |
| Agriculture | 1883 | SPY | N/S |
| Astronomy | 1878 | SPY | 20.00 |
| Gunshot Wounds | 1896 | SPY | 20.00 |
| Disease of the Throat | 1887 | APE | 20.00 |
| In The Clouds | 1904 | SPY | 20.00 |
| John Bull | 1808 | SPY | 20.00 |
| A Faithful Friend | 1870 | APE | 20.00 |
| Old Bones | 1873 | Unsigned | 20.00 |
| Surgery | 1876 | SPY | N/S |
| Hydrophobia | 1887 | T | 24.00 |
| The Prophet Of | 1913 | RITCHIE | 20.00 |
| Chemistry | 1875 | APE | 20.00 |
| Chests | 1904 | PY | 20.00 |
| Astronomy | 1883 | SPY | 20.00 |
| Lord Beaconsfield's Physician | 1883 | SPY | N/S |
| Homeopathic Society | 1872 | Unsigned | 20.00 |
| Chemistry | 1908 | SPY | 20.00 |
| Argon | 1899 | FTD | 20.00 |
| Petroleum | 1908 | SPY | 20.00 |

| CAPTION | YEAR | ARTIST | PRICE |
|---|---|---|---|
| ☐ Rhys, K.C. | 1913 | OWL | 20.00 |
| ☐ Brighton | 1889 | SPY | 20.00 |
| ☐ Electricity | 1908 | SPY | 20.00 |
| ☐ Oxford Physiology | 1894 | SPY | 20.00 |
| ☐ Mens Sana | 1912 | RAY | N/S |
| ☐ Laryngology | 1902 | SPY | 24.00 |
| ☐ Science & Invention | 1910 | SPY | 20.00 |
| ☐ Philosophy | 1879 | CG | 20.00 |
| ☐ Rhinology | 1902 | SPY | 20.00 |
| ☐ Medical Jurisprudence | 1899 | WAG | 20.00 |
| ☐ A Great Surgeon | 1910 | ELF | 20.00 |
| ☐ Cremation | 1874 | APE | 20.00 |
| ☐ Freddie | 1900 | SPY | 20.00 |
| ☐ The Scientific Use | 1872 | Unsigned | 20.00 |
| ☐ Cellular Pathology | 1893 | SPY | N/S |
| ☐ A Naturalist | 1882 | T | 20.00 |
| ☐ Philosophical Pathology | 1892 | SPY | 20.00 |
| ☐ Dietetics | 1900 | SPY | 20.00 |

## EXPLORERS AND INVENTORS

| CAPTION | YEAR | ARTIST | PRICE |
|---|---|---|---|
| ☐ The Director | 1874 | APE | 20.00 |
| ☐ He Walked Across Africa | 1876 | SPY | 20.00 |
| ☐ Steel | 1880 | SPY | 30.00 |
| ☐ Little Menlo | 1889 | APE | 20.00 |
| ☐ A Traveller | 1892 | SPY | N/S |
| ☐ Privy Councilor, Professor | 1893 | STUFF | 20.00 |
| ☐ Odger | 1895 | SPY | 20.00 |
| ☐ Westralia | 1895 | SPY | N/S |
| ☐ Franz Josef Land | 1897 | SPY | 30.00 |
| ☐ Natural Philosophy | 1897 | SPY | 30.00 |
| ☐ A City Liberal | 1909 | SPY | N/S |
| ☐ Birmingham University | 1904 | SPY | 20.00 |
| ☐ Wires Without Wires | 1905 | SPY | 36.00 |
| ☐ The South Pole | 1909 | KITE | 36.00 |
| ☐ The Cutter of Continents | 1913 | AST | 20.00 |
| ☐ The South Pole | 1913 | HESTER | 36.00 |

## FOX HUNTERS

| CAPTION | YEAR | ARTIST | PRICE |
|---|---|---|---|
| ☐ The Lord Annaly | 1912 | K | 24.00 |
| ☐ The General | 1881 | SPY | 24.00 |
| ☐ The Master Of | 1906 | SPY | 24.00 |
| ☐ An MFH With a Sense | 1905 | SPY | 24.00 |
| ☐ Long Burns | 1900 | CB | 24.00 |
| ☐ To the Manner Born | 1906 | SPY | 24.00 |
| ☐ The Quorn | 1884 | APE | 24.00 |
| ☐ Alfred | 1909 | SPY | 24.00 |
| ☐ The Huntsman | 1884 | SPY | N/S |
| ☐ Billy | 1906 | SPY | 24.00 |
| ☐ Serlby | 1899 | SPY | 24.00 |
| ☐ Fox-Hunting | 1883 | SPY | N/S |
| ☐ A Very Old Master | 1896 | SPY | 24.00 |
| ☐ Belvoir | 1899 | CB | 24.00 |
| ☐ A Masters' Meet | 1895 | SPY | N/S |
| ☐ Kirby Gate | 1901 | CB | 60.00 |
| ☐ A Fox-Hunting Constellation | 1905 | BEDE | N/S |
| ☐ Blackmore Vale | 1897 | CG | 24.00 |
| ☐ Cottesmore | 1906 | Unknown | 24.00 |
| ☐ Mr. Hargreaves | 1887 | SPY | 24.00 |
| ☐ Cattistock | 1906 | Unknown | 24.00 |
| ☐ A Hard Rider | 1904 | SPY | 24.00 |
| ☐ The Master Of The | 1906 | BEDE | 30.00 |
| ☐ Bay | 1883 | T | 24.00 |
| ☐ Tom | 1885 | PAT | 24.00 |
| ☐ Otho | 1902 | CB | 36.00 |

| CAPTION | YEAR | ARTIST | PRICE |
|---|---|---|---|
| ☐ Downing | 1886 | HAY | N/S |
| ☐ An Old Master | 1898 | SPY | 24.00 |
| ☐ Workshop Manor | 1911 | SPY | 24.00 |
| ☐ Doggie | 1884 | APE | 24.00 |
| ☐ The Sinner | 1907 | SPY | 24.00 |
| ☐ A Leicestershire Man | 1899 | GAF | 24.00 |
| ☐ Berks and Bucks | 1903 | AO | 24.00 |
| ☐ A Father | 1900 | CB | 24.00 |

## FREEMASONS

| CAPTION | YEAR | ARTIST | PRICE |
|---|---|---|---|
| ☐ The Most Wonderful | 1860 | Unsigned | 16.00 |
| ☐ Younger Son | 1877 | SPY | 14.00 |
| ☐ The Foreign Office | 1878 | APE | 14.00 |
| ☐ Suffolk | 1881 | SPY | N/S |
| ☐ The Great Western | 1882 | SPY | N/S |
| ☐ A Freemason | 1885 | APE | 14.00 |
| ☐ The Lord Mayor | 1887 | SPY | N/S |
| ☐ The Wimbledon Division | 1898 | SPY | 16.00 |
| ☐ A New Lord Mayor | 1889 | SPY | N/S |
| ☐ North Lancashire | 1900 | SPY | N/S |
| ☐ The Lord Mayor | 1902 | SPY | 14.00 |
| ☐ The Grand Secretary | 1903 | SPY | N/S |
| ☐ The Pro Grand Master | 1904 | SPY | N/S |
| ☐ Jimmy | 1913 | AST | 16.00 |

## GAME HUNTERS

| CAPTION | YEAR | ARTIST | PRICE |
|---|---|---|---|
| ☐ Pointers | 1885 | SPY | 30.00 |
| ☐ Best Game Shot In | 1890 | SPY | 30.00 |
| ☐ Letters to the Young | 1893 | SPY | 30.00 |
| ☐ The Record Revolver Shot | 1893 | VA | 30.00 |
| ☐ Big Game | 1894 | VA | 30.00 |
| ☐ The New Forest | 1897 | SPY | 30.00 |
| ☐ Drive Grouse | 1905 | SPY | 30.00 |
| ☐ Rufford Abbey | 1908 | SPY | 30.00 |
| ☐ Tracks and Triggers | 1909 | WHO | 30.00 |

## GOLFERS

| CAPTION | YEAR | ARTIST | PRICE |
|---|---|---|---|
| ☐ The Irish Secretary | 1887 | SPY | N/S |
| ☐ Mr. Horace Hutchinson | 1890 | SPY | N/S |
| ☐ Mr. John Ball, Jr. | 1892 | LIB | N/S |
| ☐ Hoylake | 1903 | SPY | N/S |
| ☐ Muir | 1903 | SPY | N/S |
| ☐ A Celebrated Oarsman | 1906 | SPY | N/S |
| ☐ John Henry | 1906 | SPY | N/S |
| ☐ North Berwick | 1906 | SPY | N/S |
| ☐ Jimmy | 1907 | SPY | N/S |
| ☐ The Prince of Princes | 1909 | SPY | N/S |
| ☐ Dialectics | 1910 | XIT | N/S |
| ☐ Easton Hall | 1911 | SPY | N/S |

## HORSE TRAINERS

| CAPTION | YEAR | ARTIST | PRICE |
|---|---|---|---|
| ☐ Petrarch | 1876 | SPY | 16.00 |
| ☐ Robert | 1886 | LIB | 16.00 |
| ☐ Mr. John Porter | 1889 | LIB | 16.00 |
| ☐ Punchestown | 1889 | KAY | 16.00 |
| ☐ Baron Hirsch | 1890 | LIB | N/S |
| ☐ Mr. Christopher W. Wilson | 1891 | SPY | 16.00 |
| ☐ He Owns ''Chancellor'' | 1893 | SPY | 18.00 |

| CAPTION | YEAR | ARTIST | PRICE |
|---|---|---|---|
| ☐ Whiskey & Horses | 1907 | SPY | N/S |
| ☐ An Argentine Sportsman | 1910 | WHO | 16.00 |
| ☐ John Porter | 1910 | XIT | N/S |
| ☐ Lutteur | 1910 | HLO | 16.00 |
| ☐ Sollie | 1910 | HCO | 16.00 |

## HORSES

| CAPTION | YEAR | ARTIST | PRICE |
|---|---|---|---|
| ☐ Newmarket 1885 | 1885 | LIB | N/S |
| ☐ Tattersall's 1887 | 1887 | LIB | 60.00 |
| ☐ Cyllene | 1906 | Percy Earl | N/S |
| ☐ Santry | 1907 | F. Paton | N/S |
| ☐ Bayardo | 1909 | Percy Earl | 36.00 |
| ☐ Dean Swift | 1909 | Percy Earl | N/S |
| ☐ Minoru | 1909 | Percy Earl | N/S |
| ☐ Rock Sand | 1910 | Percy Earl | N/S |
| ☐ Flying Fox | N/A | Percy Earl | N/S |
| ☐ Lutteur III | N/A | Emil Adam | N/S |
| ☐ Persimmon | N/A | Percy Earl | N/S |
| ☐ Pretty Polly | N/A | Percy Earl | N/S |
| ☐ Scepter & Maid of Corinth | N/A | Percy Earl | N/S |
| ☐ St. Simon | N/A | Percy Earl | 36.00 |
| ☐ Torpoint | N/A | Percy Earl | N/S |

## JOCKEYS

| CAPTION | YEAR | ARTIST | PRICE |
|---|---|---|---|
| ☐ The Favorite Jockey | 1881 | SPY | N/S |
| ☐ Mr. Abington | 1888 | LIB | N/S |
| ☐ Fred Barrett | 1889 | LIB | N/S |
| ☐ George Barrett | 1887 | LIB | 45.00 |
| ☐ Morny | 1891 | SPY | 40.00 |
| ☐ Tom Cannon | 1885 | SPY | N/S |
| ☐ Count Strickland | 1893 | HAY | N/S |
| ☐ The Baby | 1884 | SPY | 45.00 |
| ☐ Bernard | 1906 | SPY | 40.00 |
| ☐ The Demon | 1882 | SPY | 45.00 |
| ☐ He Rides for Lord Durham | 1906 | SPY | 40.00 |
| ☐ The Winning Post | 1888 | LIB | 60.00 |
| ☐ Top of the List | 1906 | SPY | 40.00 |
| ☐ Wenty | 1897 | SPY | N/S |
| ☐ A King's Jockey | 1904 | AO | 45.00 |
| ☐ Sam Loates | 1896 | SPY | 40.00 |
| ☐ Tom Loates | 1890 | SPY | 40.00 |
| ☐ Otto Madden | 1900 | GDG | 45.00 |
| ☐ Danny | 1903 | AO | 45.00 |
| ☐ Skeets | 1907 | AO | N/S |
| ☐ Johnny | 1887 | LIB | N/S |
| ☐ Roddy | 1891 | SPY | 40.00 |
| ☐ Johnny | 1900 | SPY | 40.00 |
| ☐ Lester | 1900 | SPY | 40.00 |
| ☐ Rick | 1901 | SPY | 45.00 |
| ☐ An American Jockey | 1899 | GDG | 60.00 |
| ☐ A Rising Star | 1906 | SPY | 45.00 |
| ☐ Mr. George | 1907 | SPY | 45.00 |
| ☐ J. E. Watts | 1903 | AO | 45.00 |
| ☐ Johnny Watts | 1887 | SPY | N/S |
| ☐ Fred Webb | 1889 | LIB | 45.00 |
| ☐ Charlie Wood | 1886 | LIB | 40.00 |
| ☐ James Woodburn | 1890 | SPY | 45.00 |
| ☐ Frank Wooten | 1909 | SPY | 45.00 |

# LADIES

| CAPTION | YEAR | ARTIST | PRICE |
|---|---|---|---|
| ☐ H.R.N. The Princess | 1882 | CHARTRAN | 20.00 |
| ☐ The Baroness Burdett-Coutts | 1883 | T | N/S |
| ☐ The Countess Of Dalhousie | 1883 | T | N/S |
| ☐ Gladys, Countess of Lonsdale | 1883 | CHARTRAN | N/S |
| ☐ Her Grace The Duchess | 1883 | CHARTRAN | N/S |
| ☐ The Marchioness of Waterford | 1883 | CHARTRAN | N/S |
| ☐ H.I.M. The Empress | 1884 | GRIMM | 20.00 |
| ☐ The Lady Florence Dixie | 1884 | T | N/S |
| ☐ The Lady Holland | 1884 | T | 20.00 |
| ☐ The Princess Royal | 1884 | NEMO | 20.00 |
| ☐ Mrs. Weldon | 1884 | SPY | N/S |
| ☐ The Marchioness of Tweeddale | 1884 | T | 20.00 |
| ☐ Victory Mary of Teck | 1893 | WARD | 20.00 |
| ☐ Cycling in Hyde Park | 1896 | HAL HURST | 75.00 |
| ☐ Au Bois De Boulogne | 1897 | GUTH | 75.00 |
| ☐ None | 1906 | WARD | 20.00 |
| ☐ Lady Dorothy Nevill | 1908 | WHO | 20.00 |
| ☐ Women's Suffrage | 1910 | SPY | N/S |
| ☐ Her Majesty Queen Alexandra | 1911 | UNK | 20.00 |
| ☐ The Lady Dorothy Nevill | 1912 | K | 20.00 |
| ☐ Mrs. George Cornwallis West | 1912 | K | N/S |

# LEGAL

| CAPTION | YEAR | ARTIST | PRICE |
|---|---|---|---|
| ☐ Dick | 1900 | SPY | 40.00 |
| ☐ Slim | 1904 | SPY | N/S |
| ☐ A Judicial Judge | 1897 | SPY | N/S |
| ☐ Contempt of Court | 1873 | VW | N/S |
| ☐ A Popular Magistrate | 1905 | SPY | 20.00 |
| ☐ The Court of Appeals | 1875 | APE | 20.00 |
| ☐ The Lord Advocate | 1886 | SPY | 20.00 |
| ☐ He Resisted Temptation | 1870 | Unsigned | 40.00 |
| ☐ Good Form | 1906 | SPY | 40.00 |
| ☐ Admiralty Jurisdiction | 1893 | SPY | 40.00 |
| ☐ Lord Justice Barry | 1889 | LIB | 20.00 |
| ☐ Under Sheriff | 1891 | SPY | 20.00 |
| ☐ As Procureur General | 1893 | GUTH | 40.00 |
| ☐ Billy | 1910 | PIP | N/S |
| ☐ Northeast Bethnal Green | 1897 | SPY | 20.00 |
| ☐ We Shall See | 1898 | SPY | 40.00 |
| ☐ Worship Street | 1907 | SPY | 20.00 |
| ☐ A Lord of Appeal | 1881 | SPY | 20.00 |
| ☐ Bosey, Frederick | 1901 | SPY | 40.00 |
| ☐ The Majesty of the Law | 1870 | APE | 40.00 |
| ☐ Judicial Politeness | 1892 | SPY | 40.00 |
| ☐ The Knight of the Malta | 1879 | SPY | N/S |
| ☐ An Arbitrator | 1892 | SPY | 20.00 |
| ☐ The Exchequer | 1876 | SPY | 40.00 |
| ☐ A Man of Law and Broad Acres | 1906 | SPY | 45.00 |
| ☐ Popular Judgment | 1876 | APE | N/S |
| ☐ Birth, Behavior & Business | 1881 | | 20.00 |
| ☐ Justice to Dreyfus | 1898 | GUTH | 20.00 |
| ☐ He Defended Abari | 1889 | SPY | N/S |
| ☐ Holburn | 1892 | SPY | 20.00 |
| ☐ Slow and Steady | 1900 | SPY | N/S |
| ☐ Company Law | 1900 | SPY | N/S |
| ☐ The Solicitor-General | 1913 | OWL | 40.00 |
| ☐ Tommy | 1900 | SPY | 40.00 |
| ☐ Divorce | 1887 | APE | N/S |
| ☐ Chitty's Leader | 1896 | SPY | 40.00 |
| ☐ City Justice | 1880 | SPY | 40.00 |
| ☐ That Won't Do, You Know | 1893 | PY | 40.00 |
| ☐ So Voluble An Advocate | 1906 | SPY | 40.00 |
| ☐ An Amiable Judge | 1898 | SPY | N/S |
| ☐ The New Judge | 1888 | SPY | 40.00 |

| | CAPTION | YEAR | ARTIST | PRICE |
|---|---|---|---|---|
| ☐ | The Umpire | 1885 | SPY | 40.00 |
| ☐ | Sir Edward | 1903 | SPY | 40.00 |
| ☐ | Formerly of the Carlton | 1876 | SPY | 40.00 |
| ☐ | He Has Leathern Lungs | 1891 | STUFF | 40.00 |
| ☐ | The Lord Chief Justice | 1869 | APE | N/S |
| ☐ | The Silvered Voice | 1909 | SPY | 40.00 |
| ☐ | The Lord Chief Justice | 1887 | APE | 40.00 |
| ☐ | A Risen Barrister | 1870 | ATN | 20.00 |
| ☐ | Sir John Coleridge | 1870 | Unsigned | 40.00 |
| ☐ | Smith's Leading Case | 1893 | QUIZ | 40.00 |
| ☐ | Scotch Law | 1873 | SPY | 20.00 |
| ☐ | Guileless | 1888 | SPY | 40.00 |
| ☐ | North Norfolk | 1893 | SPY | 20.00 |
| ☐ | Fair Is Not Beautiful | 1901 | SPY | N/S |
| ☐ | Vicar General | 1902 | SPY | 40.00 |
| ☐ | South Bucks | 1896 | SPY | N/S |
| ☐ | Danky | 1898 | SPY | 40.00 |
| ☐ | Little Darling | 1897 | SPY | 20.00 |
| ☐ | 2nd Commissioner | 1888 | SPY | N/S |
| ☐ | Bargrave | 1898 | SPY | 40.00 |
| ☐ | The First of the Commoners | 1870 | ATN | 40.00 |
| ☐ | He Was An Ornament | 1892 | STUFF | 40.00 |
| ☐ | Public Prosecutions | 1902 | SPY | 20.00 |
| ☐ | His Father Invented Pickwick | 1897 | SPY | 40.00 |
| ☐ | Plausible | 1902 | SPY | 40.00 |
| ☐ | London Sessions | 1891 | SPY | 40.00 |
| ☐ | Law | 1886 | SPY | 20.00 |
| ☐ | George | 1908 | SPY | 40.00 |
| ☐ | Court Roll | 1887 | SPY | 20.00 |
| ☐ | A Good Judge | 1911 | APE JR. | 40.00 |
| ☐ | Powers | 1900 | FTD | 40.00 |
| ☐ | Stay Please | 1887 | SPY | 40.00 |
| ☐ | Hard Head | 1888 | APE | 40.00 |
| ☐ | North London | 1908 | SPY | 20.00 |
| ☐ | Specific Performance | 1891 | SPY | 40.00 |
| ☐ | Dublin University | 1885 | SPY | 20.00 |
| ☐ | The Solicitor General | 1878 | SPY | 20.00 |
| ☐ | Gill Brass | 1891 | SPY | 40.00 |
| ☐ | Barrister & Baronet | 1872 | Unsigned | 20.00 |
| ☐ | Lord Advocate | 1874 | APE | 20.00 |
| ☐ | Bells | 1889 | SPY | 20.00 |
| ☐ | Bench and Bar | 1891 | STUFF | N/S |
| ☐ | Heads of the Law | 1902 | SPY | 40.00 |
| ☐ | Purse, Pussy, Piety | 1882 | T. | 40.00 |
| ☐ | Galvanic Electricity | 1887 | SPY | 34.00 |
| ☐ | Charley | 1888 | SPY | 20.00 |
| ☐ | From the Old Bailey | 1890 | SPY | 40.00 |
| ☐ | The Great Unmarrier | 1888 | SPY | 40.00 |
| ☐ | He Is A Smart Fellow | 1893 | SPY | 20.00 |
| ☐ | When He Who Has | 1869 | APE | 40.00 |
| ☐ | Lord Hatherton | 1895 | STUFF-G | 20.00 |
| ☐ | The Tichborne Case | 1873 | SPY | 40.00 |
| ☐ | Tim | 1886 | SPY | 20.00 |
| ☐ | Whitehaven | 1896 | SPY | N/S |
| ☐ | The New Recorder | 1909 | SPY | 20.00 |
| ☐ | The Irish Serjeant | 1904 | SPY | 20.00 |
| ☐ | The Solicitor General | 1881 | SPY | 20.00 |
| ☐ | Attorney General | 1878 | SPY | 20.00 |
| ☐ | The Autocrat of the | 1886 | SPY | N/S |
| ☐ | A Future Judge | 1874 | APE | 40.00 |
| ☐ | Tubby | 1910 | QUIP | 20.00 |
| ☐ | Hutchy | 1911 | APE JR. | 40.00 |
| ☐ | Divorce Court | 1896 | SPY | 40.00 |
| ☐ | Rufus | 1904 | SPY | 40.00 |
| ☐ | Nervous | 1874 | APE | 40.00 |
| ☐ | Oxford Circuit | 1896 | SPY | 40.00 |
| ☐ | He Believed in the Police | 1899 | SPY | 20.00 |
| ☐ | Ulsterman K.C. | 1903 | SPY | 40.00 |
| ☐ | The Lord Advocate | 1888 | SPY | 20.00 |
| ☐ | He Succeeded Lord Blackburn | 1895 | SPY | 20.00 |

| CAPTION | YEAR | ARTIST | PRICE |
|---------|------|--------|-------|
| ☐ Mr. Justice Manisty | 1889 | QUIZ | 40.00 |
| ☐ Commercial Court | 1896 | SPY | N/S |
| ☐ He Can Marshall Evidence | 1892 | SPY | 40.00 |
| ☐ Parliamentary Practice | 1871 | APE | 40.00 |
| ☐ Appeals | 1876 | SPY | 40.00 |
| ☐ Judges the Claimant | 1873 | SPY | 40.00 |
| ☐ An Irish Lawyer | 1893 | SPY | 20.00 |
| ☐ Patents | 1900 | SPY | 20.00 |
| ☐ For The Times | 1899 | SPY | 40.00 |
| ☐ Lord Advocate | 1896 | SPY | 20.00 |
| ☐ The Marlborough Street | 1893 | SPY | 20.00 |
| ☐ The Claimant's Friend | 1875 | APE | 40.00 |
| ☐ A Lawyer | 1873 | SPY | 40.00 |
| ☐ The Speaker | 1887 | SPY | 40.00 |
| ☐ A Judge & Peer | 1869 | UNK | 40.00 |
| ☐ A Judicial Churchman | 1898 | SPY | 40.00 |
| ☐ For the Crown | 1886 | SPY | 40.00 |
| ☐ Jumbo | 1885 | SPY | 40.00 |
| ☐ The President and the Law | 1905 | SPY | 20.00 |
| ☐ Eton and Cambridge | 1908 | SPY | 40.00 |
| ☐ Mr. Attorney | 1895 | SPY | 40.00 |
| ☐ The New Judge | 1897 | FTD | 40.00 |
| ☐ A Blunt Lord Justice | 1901 | SPY | 40.00 |
| ☐ Mr. Solicitor | 1893 | STUFF | 20.00 |
| ☐ The Solicitor General | 1906 | SPY | 20.00 |
| ☐ Municipal Corporations | 1886 | SPY | 20.00 |
| ☐ Bob | 1891 | STUFF | 40.00 |
| ☐ Lord Beaconfield's Friend | 1881 | SPY | 20.00 |
| ☐ A Splendid Advocate | 1883 | Unsigned | 40.00 |
| ☐ A Son of His Father | 1907 | SPY | 20.00 |
| ☐ Cross Examination | 1890 | QUIZ | N/S |
| ☐ Workingham | 1889 | SPY | N/S |
| ☐ Copyright | 1911 | APE JR. | 40.00 |
| ☐ A Scot's Lawyer | 1903 | SPY | 20.00 |
| ☐ Simple Simon | 1911 | WH | 40.00 |
| ☐ The Serjeant | 1886 | SPY | 20.00 |
| ☐ Equity | 1897 | SPY | 40.00 |
| ☐ The Criminal Code | 1885 | SPY | 40.00 |
| ☐ The New Judge | 1879 | SPY | 20.00 |
| ☐ He Has Written | 1893 | SPY | 20.00 |
| ☐ A Radical Lawyer | 1902 | SPY | 40.00 |
| ☐ A Lawyer on the Bench | 1902 | SPY | 40.00 |
| ☐ Director's Liability | 1891 | STUFF | 40.00 |
| ☐ A Very Sound Judge | 1907 | SPY | 40.00 |
| ☐ Law and Conscience | 1883 | Unsigned | N/S |
| ☐ The Mandarin | 1890 | QUIZ | 40.00 |
| ☐ A Rustic Judge | 1899 | CGD | 20.00 |
| ☐ Benevolence On The Bench | 1896 | SPY | 40.00 |
| ☐ Pridham | 1910 | ELF | 40.00 |
| ☐ A Sporting Lawyer | 1898 | SPY | 40.00 |
| ☐ He Declined Knighthood | 1891 | STUFF | 40.00 |

## LITERARY

| CAPTION | YEAR | ARTIST | PRICE |
|---------|------|--------|-------|
| ☐ French Fiction | 1880 | T | N/S |
| ☐ Waterloo | 1883 | T | 20.00 |
| ☐ I Say The Critic | 1871 | Unsigned | 24.00 |
| ☐ The Literary Mate | 1894 | SPY | 20.00 |
| ☐ The Laureate | 1896 | SPY | 20.00 |
| ☐ The Businessman of | 1913 | OWL | 24.00 |
| ☐ A Prophet | 1885 | APE | N/S |
| ☐ Trafalgar Square | 1888 | SPY | 20.00 |
| ☐ An Artist In Words | 1908 | GUTH | N/S |
| ☐ Modern Poetry | 1875 | APE | 24.00 |
| ☐ The Arabian Night | 1885 | APE | 20.00 |
| ☐ The Manxman | 1896 | JRP | 20.00 |
| ☐ The Diogenes of the Mod | 1870 | APE | N/S |
| ☐ Free Libraries | 1903 | SPY | 24.00 |

| CAPTION | YEAR | ARTIST | PRICE |
|---|---|---|---|
| ☐ Below the Mark | 1908 | SPY | N/S |
| ☐ The Novelist Who Invented | 1872 | Unsigned | 20.00 |
| ☐ The Stickit Master | 1897 | FR | 20.00 |
| ☐ He Wrote Sappho | 1893 | GUTH | 24.00 |
| ☐ Chesterfield Letters | 1874 | APE | 20.00 |
| ☐ Japan Society | 1902 | SPY | 20.00 |
| ☐ He Discovered New America | 1872 | Unsigned | 20.00 |
| ☐ Notes and Queries | 1873 | SPY | 20.00 |
| ☐ Poetry | 1877 | SPY | 24.00 |
| ☐ Trilby | 1896 | SPY | 24.00 |
| ☐ French Fiction | 1879 | T | 24.00 |
| ☐ Mr. Dooley | 1905 | SPY | 20.00 |
| ☐ The Greatest Living Frenchman | 1909 | GUTH | 20.00 |
| ☐ He Created Henry VIII | 1872 | Unsigned | N/S |
| ☐ He Is Very Affluent | 1906 | RUTH | 20.00 |
| ☐ Printed Books | 1895 | SPY | 24.00 |
| ☐ Anything To Beat Grant | 1872 | Unsigned | 30.00 |
| ☐ She | 1887 | SPY | 24.00 |
| ☐ Tess | 1892 | SPY | 24.00 |
| ☐ Unpath'd Waters | 1913 | OWL | 24.00 |
| ☐ The Heathen Chinee | 1879 | SPY | N/S |
| ☐ Anthony Hope | 1895 | SPY | 20.00 |
| ☐ Anecdotes | 1875 | APE | 20.00 |
| ☐ Silas Hocking | 1906 | SPY | 20.00 |
| ☐ Tom Brown | 1872 | Unsigned | 20.00 |
| ☐ A French Poet | 1879 | T | 20.00 |
| ☐ The Master Builder | 1901 | SAPP | 24.00 |
| ☐ Not an M.P. | 1872 | Unsigned | 20.00 |
| ☐ The Apostle of the Flesh | 1872 | Unsigned | 20.00 |
| ☐ Soldiers Three | 1894 | SPY | N/S |
| ☐ The 18th Century | 1882 | SPY | 20.00 |
| ☐ Spearmint | 1906 | SPY | 20.00 |
| ☐ Pierre Loti | 1895 | GUTH | 20.00 |
| ☐ Hosea Riglow | 1880 | T | 20.00 |
| ☐ The Representative | 1870 | APE | 20.00 |
| ☐ The Belgian Poet | 1908 | MAX | 24.00 |
| ☐ Is Life Worth Living? | 1882 | SPY | 20.00 |
| ☐ The Royal Literary Assistant | 1877 | SPY | 20.00 |
| ☐ Four Feathers | 1908 | MAX | 24.00 |
| ☐ The Novelist of Soc. | 1871 | Unsigned | 20.00 |
| ☐ Our First Novelist | 1896 | MAX | 20.00 |
| ☐ A Feminine Philosopher | 1873 | SPY | 20.00 |
| ☐ Esther Waters | 1897 | SIC | 20.00 |
| ☐ Books | 1874 | APE | 20.00 |
| ☐ A Puritan's Wife | 1897 | SPY | 20.00 |
| ☐ The Earl and the Doctor | 1888 | APE | 50.00 |
| ☐ As In A Looking Glass | 1888 | APE | 20.00 |
| ☐ Lady Bountiful | 1891 | SPY | 20.00 |
| ☐ Though It Is | 1906 | BULBO | 20.00 |
| ☐ Impossible Romance | 1873 | Unsigned | 20.00 |
| ☐ La Vie De Jesus | 1879 | T | 20.00 |
| ☐ The Greatest | 1910 | GUTH | 20.00 |
| ☐ The Realization | 1872 | Unsigned | 24.00 |
| ☐ Thermidor | 1891 | RUTH | 24.00 |
| ☐ G.B.S. | 1911 | RITCHIE | N/S |
| ☐ Magnetic | 1907 | RUTH | 30.00 |
| ☐ A Poet | 1880 | APE | 20.00 |
| ☐ Self-Help | 1882 | SPY | 20.00 |
| ☐ A Noble Writer | 1874 | APE | 20.00 |
| ☐ Before Sunrise | 1874 | APE | 20.00 |
| ☐ The Poet Laureate | 1871 | APE | 24.00 |
| ☐ War and Peace | 1901 | SAPP | 24.00 |
| ☐ The Competition Of | 1873 | SPY | 20.00 |
| ☐ A Novelist | 1872 | SPY | 24.00 |
| ☐ An Artist in Verbal | 1913 | HESTER | N/S |
| ☐ Oscar | 1884 | APE | N/S |
| ☐ A Child of the Ghetto | 1897 | SIC | 20.00 |
| ☐ French Realism | 1880 | T | 24.00 |

# MILITARY AND NAVY

| CAPTION | YEAR | ARTIST | PRICE |
|---|---|---|---|
| Aberdeenshire | 1902 | SPY | N/S |
| Adjutant-General to the Forces | 1873 | SPY | 20.00 |
| Ossie | 1896 | SPY | 20.00 |
| The Mite | 1885 | SPY | 20.00 |
| Boy Scouts | 1911 | APE JR. | 24.00 |
| Mafeking | 1900 | DRAWL | N/S |
| An Old Coldstreamer | 1883 | T | 20.00 |
| He Was Born a Serene Highness | 1905 | SPY | 20.00 |
| Western Australia | 1903 | SPY | 20.00 |
| Steam Reserve | 1895 | SPY | 20.00 |
| Fighting Bull | 1879 | SPY | 20.00 |
| Uncle Louis | 1907 | RYG | 20.00 |
| La Revanche | 1887 | T | 20.00 |
| BWAB | 1886 | APE | 20.00 |
| Natal | 1903 | SPY | N/S |
| He Sits For Colchester | 1890 | SPY | 20.00 |
| Sir Sam | 1887 | APE | N/S |
| Redrag | 1900 | SPY | N/S |
| A Crimean Hero | 1883 | T | 20.00 |
| The Auxiliary Forces | 1875 | APE | 20.00 |
| A Radical General | 1907 | SPY | 20.00 |
| Byngo | 1892 | STUFF | 24.00 |
| Vice-Admiral Caillard | 1905 | GUTH | 20.00 |
| 1st Life Guards | 1906 | SPY | 20.00 |
| At Mafeking | 1899 | SPY | N/S |
| Imperial Yeomanry | 1900 | SPY | 20.00 |
| G.K.C. | 1912 | STRICKLAND | 24.00 |
| 19th Hussars | 1910 | WHO | 20.00 |
| Arms and Sport | 1912 | WH | N/S |
| An Admiral of the Fleet | 1903 | SPY | 20.00 |
| The Rule of the Road | 1887 | APE | 20.00 |
| A Jingo | 1881 | T | 20.00 |
| Adm. Sir John E. Commerell | 1889 | SPY | 20.00 |
| Lord Congleton | 1894 | SPY | N/S |
| Mount | 1881 | SPY | N/S |
| Second in Zululand | 1879 | SPY | N/S |
| Bisley Camp | 1912 | WH | N/S |
| A Military Secretary | 1903 | SPY | 20.00 |
| Irish Guards | 1900 | SPY | 20.00 |
| Henry | 1876 | SPY | 20.00 |
| The Kaid | 1904 | SPY | 20.00 |
| The Premier Baron | 1907 | SPY | 20.00 |
| De Wet | 1902 | EBN | N/S |
| H.A.C. | 1894 | SPY | 20.00 |
| Captain the Hon. Henry | 1912 | WH | N/S |
| 40 H.P. in a Dinghy | 1906 | SPY | 20.00 |
| Madras | 1891 | BINT | 20.00 |
| North American and West Indies | 1902 | SPY | 20.00 |
| Smartness | 1883 | SPY | 20.00 |
| A General | 1878 | SPY | 20.00 |
| An Old War Horse | 1911 | APE JR. | 20.00 |
| Madagascar | 1895 | GUTH | 20.00 |
| A Calvary Reformer | 1902 | SPY | 20.00 |
| Brown | 1891 | SPY | 20.00 |
| Nautical Freshness | 1911 | WHO | N/S |
| The Adjutant General | 1877 | APE | N/S |
| The Admiral | 1878 | SPY | 20.00 |
| Major Esterhazy | 1898 | GUTH | 20.00 |
| Croppy | 1881 | T | 20.00 |
| The Star | 1898 | SPY | 20.00 |
| The Queen's Landlord | 1876 | JTJ | 20.00 |
| The Yellow Admiral | 1891 | SPY | N/S |
| Uncle Bill | 1912 | RAY | N/S |
| Jacky | 1902 | SPY | 20.00 |
| Military Music | 1905 | SPY | N/S |
| Shookey | 1902 | SPY | 20.00 |
| An Equerry in Waiting | 1895 | SPY | 20.00 |
| Swordsmanship | 1896 | SPY | 20.00 |

| | CAPTION | YEAR | ARTIST | PRICE |
|---|---|---|---|---|
| ☐ | Conspicuous & Cool | 1879 | SPY | N/S |
| ☐ | Keith | 1880 | SPY | 20.00 |
| ☐ | On 1 China Station | 1894 | PAT | 20.00 |
| ☐ | The Calvary Division | 1900 | GDG | 20.00 |
| ☐ | L'Admiral | 1902 | GUTH | N/S |
| ☐ | V.C. | 1880 | SPY | N/S |
| ☐ | Glick | 1898 | SPY | 20.00 |
| ☐ | The Constable of the Tower | 1873 | SPY | N/S |
| ☐ | Revolution | 1878 | T | 20.00 |
| ☐ | The Ever Victorious | 1881 | APE | N/S |
| ☐ | Bill | 1880 | APE | 20.00 |
| ☐ | Popular Members | 1874 | APE | 20.00 |
| ☐ | Keeper of the Crown Jewels | 1906 | SPY | N/S |
| ☐ | Charles II | 1886 | SPY | 20.00 |
| ☐ | Master of the Horse | 1908 | SPY | 20.00 |
| ☐ | General Sir Francis Grenfell, K.C.B. | 1889 | SPY | N/S |
| ☐ | A General Group | 1900 | SPY | 60.00 |
| ☐ | Rupert | 1905 | SPY | N/S |
| ☐ | Commander-in-Chief | 1876 | M | N/S |
| ☐ | Julian | 1898 | SPY | 20.00 |
| ☐ | He Will Be the Third Duke | 1899 | HADGE | 20.00 |
| ☐ | Mixed Forces | 1901 | SPY | 20.00 |
| ☐ | English Strategy | 1887 | APE | N/S |
| ☐ | The Soldier Who Couldn't | 1879 | SPY | 20.00 |
| ☐ | The Retired List | 1875 | APE | 20.00 |
| ☐ | An Admiral | 1875 | APE | 20.00 |
| ☐ | Pompo | 1901 | SPY | N/S |
| ☐ | A Good Soldier | 1884 | SPY | N/S |
| ☐ | Naval Reserve | 1883 | SPY | N/S |
| ☐ | Hobart Pasha | 1878 | SPY | N/S |
| ☐ | The Beau Ideal | 1877 | SPY | N/S |
| ☐ | Lloyds | 1883 | Unsigned | 20.00 |
| ☐ | Our Youngest General | 1899 | SPY | 20.00 |
| ☐ | Patronage | 1904 | SPY | 20.00 |
| ☐ | Naval Ordnance | 1906 | SPY | 20.00 |
| ☐ | The Imperial Institute | 1897 | SPY | 20.00 |
| ☐ | The Father of the Rag | 1885 | APE | 20.00 |
| ☐ | Monty | 1913 | HESTER | 20.00 |
| ☐ | 6th Division | 1901 | SPY | 20.00 |
| ☐ | Commodore H.M. Yachts | 1909 | SPY | 20.00 |
| ☐ | Little Harry | 1876 | M | N/S |
| ☐ | '94' | 1903 | AO | 20.00 |
| ☐ | Lord Mark | 1886 | SPY | N/S |
| ☐ | A Sea Lord | 1900 | SPY | N/S |
| ☐ | The Court | 1880 | SPY | N/S |
| ☐ | Khartoum | 1899 | SPY | 20.00 |
| ☐ | I Regret To Report | 1905 | IMP | 20.00 |
| ☐ | H.M.S. Powerful | 1900 | SPY | 20.00 |
| ☐ | Rowdy | 1906 | SPY | N/S |
| ☐ | Cuthbert | 1888 | APE | N/S |
| ☐ | Colchester | 1894 | SPY | N/S |
| ☐ | Army, Court & Volunteers | 1882 | SPY | 20.00 |
| ☐ | The Victoria & Geneva Crosses | 1876 | SPY | 20.00 |
| ☐ | Tirah | 1898 | SPY | N/S |
| ☐ | The Vice-Commander | 1876 | SPY | N/S |
| ☐ | Balaklava | 1881 | APE | N/S |
| ☐ | A Keeper of the Tower | 1907 | SPY | 20.00 |
| ☐ | An Earnest African | 1895 | SPY | 20.00 |
| ☐ | Afghan Frontier B-417 | 1885 | SPY | 20.00 |
| ☐ | Joe | 1910 | HCO | 20.00 |
| ☐ | Dan | 1878 | SPY | N/S |
| ☐ | 4th Division | 1901 | SPY | N/S |
| ☐ | Sir Hugh | 1906 | SPY | N/S |
| ☐ | Jim | 1876 | JTJ | N/S |
| ☐ | Rim | 1880 | SPY | N/S |
| ☐ | C.I.V. | 1901 | SPY | 20.00 |
| ☐ | R.M.C. | 1902 | SPY | N/S |
| ☐ | Handsome Fred | 1878 | APE | N/S |
| ☐ | Fred | 1896 | SPY | N/S |
| ☐ | Navy Control | 1903 | SPY | 20.00 |

| CAPTION | YEAR | ARTIST | PRICE |
|---------|------|--------|-------|
| ☐ The Home District | 1892 | SPY | 20.00 |
| ☐ Admiral of the Fleet | 1882 | T | 20.00 |
| ☐ Roley | 1905 | SPY | 20.00 |
| ☐ Modern Strategy | 1884 | GO | 20.00 |
| ☐ Oliver | 1877 | APE | 20.00 |
| ☐ The Master General | 1905 | SPY | 20.00 |
| ☐ Composite Regiment | 1900 | CLOISTER | N/S |
| ☐ Chelsea Hospital | 1903 | SPY | 20.00 |
| ☐ The Nitrate King | 1889 | SPY | N/S |
| ☐ A Sub-Editor | 1897 | SPY | N/S |
| ☐ Bully | 1896 | SPY | 20.00 |
| ☐ Sam | 1912 | WH | N/S |
| ☐ Soudan | 1908 | SPY | 20.00 |
| ☐ A Soldier | 1877 | SPY | 20.00 |
| ☐ Sailor, Politician | 1875 | APE | 20.00 |
| ☐ The Swell of the Ocean | 1876 | SPY | N/S |
| ☐ Order at Wimbledon | 1880 | APE | N/S |
| ☐ Senior Equerry | 1891 | SPY | N/S |
| ☐ Self-Reliant | 1902 | SPY | N/S |
| ☐ Polly | 1901 | SPY | 20.00 |
| ☐ Fresh from the Channel | 1901 | SPY | 20.00 |
| ☐ Soldier & Correspondent | 1899 | SPY | 20.00 |
| ☐ The Royal Borough | 1877 | SPY | 20.00 |
| ☐ Bobs | 1880 | WGR | 20.00 |
| ☐ Bobs | 1900 | SPY | 20.00 |
| ☐ Military Advice | 1874 | APE | 20.00 |
| ☐ Guards | 1875 | APE | N/S |
| ☐ Gunnery | 1903 | SPY | N/S |
| ☐ China | 1901 | SPY | 20.00 |
| ☐ Fortification | 1877 | APE | 20.00 |
| ☐ Slatin | 1899 | SPY | N/S |
| ☐ National Military Training | 1909 | SPY | N/S |
| ☐ Dorren | 1901 | SPY | 20.00 |
| ☐ War | 1879 | APE | N/S |
| ☐ Aldershot | 1878 | APE | 20.00 |
| ☐ Russian, Persian and Turkish | 1902 | SPY | 20.00 |
| ☐ Dear Old Ben | 1887 | SPY | 20.00 |
| ☐ Ahmed Khel | 1887 | APE | N/S |
| ☐ He Is A Living Paradox | 1870 | APE | 20.00 |
| ☐ He Was Made A Statesman | 1870 | APE | N/S |
| ☐ Eddie | 1899 | SPY | 20.00 |
| ☐ A Younger Son | 1876 | SPY | 20.00 |
| ☐ Aldershot Cavalry | 1897 | SPY | 20.00 |
| ☐ Upty | 1888 | APE | 20.00 |
| ☐ Commanding 2nd Life Guards | 1906 | SPY | 20.00 |
| ☐ The Hope of France | 1870 | Unsigned | N/S |
| ☐ Home District | 1902 | SPY | 20.00 |
| ☐ A Permanent Warrior | 1901 | SPY | N/S |
| ☐ Bechuanaland | 1886 | APE | 20.00 |
| ☐ Ladysmith | 1900 | SPY | N/S |
| ☐ In His Military Capacity | 1879 | SPY | 20.00 |
| ☐ The Prince | 1878 | APE | 20.00 |
| ☐ In the Mahdi's Camp | 1897 | SPY | N/S |
| ☐ The Man Who Won't Stop | 1874 | APE | 20.00 |
| ☐ The Flying Column | 1879 | SPY | N/S |
| ☐ Spanish Ironclads | 1877 | JTJ | N/S |
| ☐ Alleno | 1877 | APE | 20.00 |

## MISCELLANEOUS

| CAPTION | YEAR | ARTIST | PRICE |
|---------|------|--------|-------|
| ☐ The Beggar's Friend | 1870 | Unsigned | 18.00 |
| ☐ He Well Deserves His | 1871 | APE | N/S |
| ☐ The Premier Marquess | 1877 | SPY | 18.00 |
| ☐ The Squire | 1877 | APE | N/S |
| ☐ The Great Man Of | 1879 | SPY | 18.00 |
| ☐ Self-Conquest | 1879 | SPY | 18.00 |
| ☐ Amiability | 1881 | SPY | 18.00 |
| ☐ Our Little Duke | 1881 | SPY | N/S |

| CAPTION | YEAR | ARTIST | PRICE |
|---|---|---|---|
| ☐ Brighton | 1882 | Unsigned | 18.00 |
| ☐ Created in 1646 | 1882 | SPY | 18.00 |
| ☐ Lord Leicester's Nephew | 1883 | SPY | N/S |
| ☐ Near the Rose | 1886 | SPY | N/S |
| ☐ The Woolsack | 1886 | SPY | 20.00 |
| ☐ Universal Knowledge | 1887 | APE | 18.00 |
| ☐ In Vanity Fair | 1890 | VARIOUS | 60.00 |
| ☐ Cobham Hall | 1893 | SPY | 18.00 |
| ☐ Charlie Aylesford | 1907 | AO | 18.00 |
| ☐ Dandy Dick | 1913 | AST | 18.00 |
| ☐ Mr. Eadie | 1913 | HESTER | N/S |

## MUSIC

| CAPTION | YEAR | ARTIST | PRICE |
|---|---|---|---|
| ☐ Il Bacio | 1885 | APE | 24.00 |
| ☐ Albert Hall | 1894 | SPY | 24.00 |
| ☐ Sweet Sounds | 1873 | SPY | 24.00 |
| ☐ Westminister Bridge | 1904 | SPY | 24.00 |
| ☐ Royal English Opera | 1891 | SPY | N/S |
| ☐ Orchestration | 1872 | Unsigned | 24.00 |
| ☐ First Violin | 1874 | APE | 24.00 |
| ☐ Ex Opera | 1900 | STUFF | 24.00 |
| ☐ A Wandering Minstrel | 1883 | Unsigned | 24.00 |
| ☐ Patience | 1881 | SPY | N/S |
| ☐ Dan Godfrey | 1888 | SPY | 24.00 |
| ☐ Emotional Music | 1879 | T | N/S |
| ☐ Corney Grain | 1885 | SPY | 24.00 |
| ☐ G | 1891 | SPY | 24.00 |
| ☐ Impromptu | 1908 | SPY | 24.00 |
| ☐ Opera Deluxe | 1911 | RAY | N/S |
| ☐ A Londoner | 1873 | Unsigned | 24.00 |
| ☐ Grand Opera | 1898 | SPY | 24.00 |
| ☐ A Great Cellist | 1897 | CG | 24.00 |
| ☐ The Last Of A Classic | 1905 | SPY | 24.00 |
| ☐ Kubelik | 1903 | SPY | 24.00 |
| ☐ A Great English Composer | 1908 | Unsigned | 24.00 |
| ☐ The Abbe | 1886 | SPY | 24.00 |
| ☐ English Tenor | 1892 | LIB | 24.00 |
| ☐ Cotillion | 1874 | APE | 24.00 |
| ☐ R.A.M. | 1904 | SPY | 24.00 |
| ☐ Crystal Palace | 1895 | SPY | 24.00 |
| ☐ The Intermezzo | 1912 | WH | 24.00 |
| ☐ Cavalleria Rusticana | 1893 | LIB | 24.00 |
| ☐ A Fine Baritone | 1898 | SPY | 24.00 |
| ☐ Prayer & Praise | 1875 | APE | 24.00 |
| ☐ Wagnerian Opera | 1899 | WAG | 24.00 |
| ☐ Nikisch | 1913 | OWL | 24.00 |
| ☐ Easy Execution | 1899 | SPY | N/S |
| ☐ Patron's Fund | 1909 | ELF | N/S |
| ☐ The English Tenor | 1890 | SPY | 24.00 |
| ☐ Polish Tenor | 1891 | SPY | 24.00 |
| ☐ Guildhall | 1913 | AST | N/S |
| ☐ Opera in English | 1913 | AST | 24.00 |
| ☐ Praise & Prayer | 1875 | APE | 24.00 |
| ☐ Student & Singer | 1902 | SPY | 24.00 |
| ☐ Sarasate | 1889 | APE | 24.00 |
| ☐ The Minstrel Boy | 1904 | SPY | N/S |
| ☐ Oxford Music | 1891 | SPY | 24.00 |
| ☐ He Found Harmondy | 1905 | SPY | 24.00 |
| ☐ Eduard Strass | 1895 | EBN | 24.00 |
| ☐ English Music | 1874 | APE | 36.00 |
| ☐ For Ever and Ever | 1885 | APE | 24.00 |
| ☐ Italian Music | 1879 | T | N/S |
| ☐ The Music of the Future | 1877 | SPY | N/S |
| ☐ Queen's Hall | 1907 | SPY | 24.00 |

# NEWSPAPERMEN

| CAPTION | YEAR | ARTIST | PRICE |
|---|---|---|---|
| ☐ The Globe | 1894 | SPY | N/S |
| ☐ New York Herald | 1884 | NEMO | 20.00 |
| ☐ A Good Listener | 1909 | SPY | 20.00 |
| ☐ The "Times" In Paris | 1889 | GUTH | 20.00 |
| ☐ The Morning Post | 1871 | APE | 20.00 |
| ☐ Algy | 1898 | SPY | N/S |
| ☐ An Encyclopedia | 1905 | SPY | N/S |
| ☐ Tommy | 1889 | SPY | N/S |
| ☐ The Governing Classes | 1873 | Unsigned | 20.00 |
| ☐ Punch | 1881 | APE | 20.00 |
| ☐ An Art Critic | 1893 | SPY | 20.00 |
| ☐ The Times | 1879 | SPY | 20.00 |
| ☐ The Daily Times | 1899 | SPY | 20.00 |
| ☐ The Pink 'Un' | 1889 | LIB | N/S |
| ☐ The Pall Mall Gazette | 1894 | SPY | 20.00 |
| ☐ Active | 1878 | APE | 20.00 |
| ☐ The Echo | 1885 | APE | 20.00 |
| ☐ The Fortnightly Review | 1885 | APE | 20.00 |
| ☐ Thorough | 1878 | APE | N/S |
| ☐ "?_____!" | 1911 | RITCHIE | 20.00 |
| ☐ He Created The Pall Mall | 1880 | APE | 20.00 |
| ☐ Peace & War | 1908 | SPY | 20.00 |
| ☐ The Pall Mall Magazine | 1895 | SPY | 20.00 |
| ☐ The National Observer | 1892 | SPY | N/S |
| ☐ The Birmingham Daily Post | 1890 | SPY | 20.00 |
| ☐ The Standard | 1874 | APD | 20.00 |
| ☐ The Daily Telegraph | 1913 | OWL | N/S |
| ☐ The Sheffield Daily | 1890 | SPY | 20.00 |
| ☐ The Daily Telegraph | 1873 | SPY | 20.00 |
| ☐ Irish History | 1885 | SPY | 20.00 |
| ☐ Financial News | 1889 | AJM | N/S |
| ☐ South Africa | 1906 | SPY | 20.00 |
| ☐ The Nonconformist | 1871 | APE | N/S |
| ☐ The Fortnightly Review | 1878 | APE | 20.00 |
| ☐ East Cambridgeshire | 1894 | SPY | N/S |
| ☐ Tax Pay | 1888 | SPY | 20.00 |
| ☐ The Times | 1885 | APE | 20.00 |
| ☐ Joe's Stage Manager | 1904 | SPY | 20.00 |
| ☐ The Saturday Review | 1892 | SPY | 20.00 |
| ☐ New York Tribune | 1902 | SPY | 20.00 |
| ☐ Telegrams | 1872 | Unsigned | N/S |
| ☐ La Vouyoucratie | 11870 | Unsigned | N/S |
| ☐ Our War Correspondence | 1875 | APE | 20.00 |
| ☐ Journalism | 1875 | APE | 20.00 |
| ☐ Three Editors | 1894 | SPY | 20.00 |
| ☐ Newspapers | 1872 | Unsigned | 20.00 |
| ☐ He Found Livingstone | 1872 | Unsigned | 20.00 |
| ☐ Hoxton Division | 1899 | STUFF | 20.00 |
| ☐ Common-Sense in Politics | 1885 | APE | 20.00 |
| ☐ Punch | 1876 | SPY | 20.00 |
| ☐ The Times | 1881 | SPY | 20.00 |
| ☐ P.W.W. | 1911 | RITCHIE | 20.00 |
| ☐ Diplomaticus | 1911 | RITCHIE | 20.00 |
| ☐ The World | 1878 | SPY | 20.00 |

# ORIENTALS

| CAPTION | YEAR | ARTIST | PRICE |
|---|---|---|---|
| ☐ China | 1877 | SPY | N/S |
| ☐ Chinese Customs | 1894 | IMP | N/S |
| ☐ Li | 1896 | GUTH | 20.00 |
| ☐ Emperor of Corea | 1899 | PRY | N/S |
| ☐ China in London | 1903 | SPY | 20.00 |

# PHOTOGRAPHERS

| CAPTION | YEAR | ARTIST | PRICE |
|---|---|---|---|
| ☐ East Birmingham | 1902 | SPY | 36.00 |
| ☐ A Self-Made African | 1904 | SPY | N/S |
| ☐ Kinemacolor | 1914 | SPY | N/S |

# POLICEMEN

| CAPTION | YEAR | ARTIST | PRICE |
|---|---|---|---|
| ☐ The Police Champion | 1872 | Unsigned | 20.00 |
| ☐ Police | 1875 | APE | 18.00 |
| ☐ Force No. Remedy | 1882 | FURNISS | 24.00 |
| ☐ Criminal Investigation | 1883 | SPY | 18.00 |
| ☐ Parliamentary Police | 1884 | APE | 24.00 |
| ☐ Bow Street | 1886 | SPY | 18.00 |
| ☐ Bow Street | 1890 | SPY | 18.00 |
| ☐ Metropolitan Police | 1890 | SPY | 18.00 |
| ☐ Scotland Yard | 1890 | SPY | N/S |
| ☐ Chief Magistrate | 1891 | SPY | 20.00 |
| ☐ Explosives | 1892 | SPY | 18.00 |
| ☐ Marlborough Street | 1898 | SPY | 18.00 |
| ☐ A Model Magistrate | 1900 | WAG | 18.00 |
| ☐ Maryleborn | 1901 | WAG | 18.00 |
| ☐ Finger Prints | 1905 | SPY | 18.00 |
| ☐ Bow Street | 1905 | SPY | 18.00 |
| ☐ Scotland Yard | 1908 | SPY | 18.00 |
| ☐ City Police | 1911 | RAY | N/S |
| ☐ The Universal Puzzle Is | 1913 | OWL | 18.00 |

# POLITICIANS

| CAPTION | YEAR | ARTIST | PRICE |
|---|---|---|---|
| ☐ Promoted From A Viceroyalty | 1869 | APE | N/S |
| ☐ The Tory Bloodhound | 1875 | APE | 14.00 |
| ☐ The Past | 1874 | APE | 14.00 |
| ☐ Three Dowagers | 1880 | T | N/S |
| ☐ Johnnie | 1910 | WHO | N/S |
| ☐ North Paddington | 1891 | SPY | N/S |
| ☐ The Kent Gang | 1885 | APE | 14.00 |
| ☐ Arnold | 1894 | SPY | N/S |
| ☐ The Gatehead Giant | 1893 | SPY | 18.00 |
| ☐ An Expert in Ceremony | 1907 | SPY | N/S |
| ☐ Hungary in Effigy | 1877 | UNK | 14.00 |
| ☐ St. Andrews District | 1897 | SPY | 14.00 |
| ☐ A Practical Patriot | 1880 | SPY | 14.00 |
| ☐ Dundee | 1882 | SPY | 18.00 |
| ☐ The Heritage of Woe | 1905 | SPY | 14.00 |
| ☐ Palmerston's Secretary | 1883 | SPY | N/S |
| ☐ The Patriotic League | 1882 | SPY | N/S |
| ☐ The Conciliator | 1911 | WH | 14.00 |
| ☐ A Great Orator | 1910 | XIT | 14.00 |
| ☐ Brains | 1904 | SPY | 14.00 |
| ☐ The Seventh Duke | 1879 | SPY | 20.00 |
| ☐ Mind and Morality | 1869 | APE | N/S |
| ☐ Rhodes the Second | 1908 | SPY | 14.00 |
| ☐ Baker Pasha | 1878 | APE | 14.00 |
| ☐ Bal | 1899 | SPY | 14.00 |
| ☐ Dialectics | 1910 | XIT | 30.00 |
| ☐ A Chief Secretary | 1896 | SPY | 14.00 |
| ☐ Burnley | 1892 | SPY | 14.00 |
| ☐ J.B. | 1890 | SPY | 14.00 |
| ☐ The Blocker | 1913 | COCK | 18.00 |
| ☐ Isle of Wight | 1910 | SPY | N/S |
| ☐ The Cape of Good Hope | 1887 | SPY | 14.00 |
| ☐ Raby Castle | 1898 | GAF | N/S |
| ☐ Barneu | 1895 | SPY | N/S |
| ☐ A Young Man | 1875 | APE | 14.00 |
| ☐ The Baroness's Husband | 1881 | SPY | 14.00 |

| CAPTION | YEAR | ARTIST | PRICE |
|---|---|---|---|
| ☐ Mid Armagh | 1898 | SPY | 14.00 |
| ☐ Australia | 1902 | SPY | 14.00 |
| ☐ One Of Those | 1886 | SPY | 14.00 |
| ☐ Beer | 1871 | APE | 14.00 |
| ☐ Reciprocity | 1879 | APE | 14.00 |
| ☐ Landed Estates In | 1882 | SPY | 14.00 |
| ☐ Ancient Lineage | 1874 | APE | 14.00 |
| ☐ Frome | 1896 | SPY | 14.00 |
| ☐ A Relic | 1873 | Unsigned | 20.00 |
| ☐ Montrose | 1885 | SPY | 14.00 |
| ☐ West Hampshire | 1895 | SPY | N/S |
| ☐ New South Wales | 1899 | SPY | 14.00 |
| ☐ Whitby | 1904 | SPY | 14.00 |
| ☐ Rousseau | 1896 | SPY | N/S |
| ☐ Little Ben | 1871 | Unsigned | 14.00 |
| ☐ Big Ben | 1871 | Unsigned | 14.00 |
| ☐ The Little Rascal | 1876 | SPY | 14.00 |
| ☐ Southwark | 1876 | SPY | 14.00 |
| ☐ Batavian Grace | 1870 | APE | 14.00 |
| ☐ Fred | 1888 | SPY | N/S |
| ☐ None | 1913 | UNK | N/S |
| ☐ Irish Obstruction | 1877 | SPY | 14.00 |
| ☐ Her Majesty's Private Secretary | 1900 | SPY | 14.00 |
| ☐ A Midland Imperialist | 1908 | SPY | 14.00 |
| ☐ The Fisherman's Friend | 1885 | APE | 14.00 |
| ☐ The Passive Resister's | 1906 | SPY | 14.00 |
| ☐ South Longford | 1894 | SPY | N/S |
| ☐ B | 1881 | T | N/S |
| ☐ Buonparte B | 1893 | SPY | 14.00 |
| ☐ Bobby | 1877 | SPY | N/S |
| ☐ He Did Not Decline | 1872 | Unsigned | N/S |
| ☐ Boycott | 1881 | SPY | N/S |
| ☐ Iconoclast | 1880 | SPY | N/S |
| ☐ North Cambridgeshire | 1894 | SPY | N/S |
| ☐ Mr. Speaker | 1872 | Unsigned | 20.00 |
| ☐ Ordnance | 1884 | SPY | 14.00 |
| ☐ Lord Monk Bretton | 1894 | SPY | N/S |
| ☐ The Private Secretary | 1909 | SPY | 14.00 |
| ☐ The Apostle to Women | 1877 | SPY | 14.00 |
| ☐ John Bright | 1889 | APE | 14.00 |
| ☐ Will The Sentimental | 1869 | APE | 14.00 |
| ☐ Theodore | 1910 | ELF | 22.00 |
| ☐ War | 1901 | SPY | 14.00 |
| ☐ Macclesfield | 1888 | SPY | 14.00 |
| ☐ East Sussex | 1898 | SPY | 14.00 |
| ☐ He Never Attacks Morality | 1913 | RITCHIE | 14.00 |
| ☐ The Golden Pippin | 1879 | SPY | N/S |
| ☐ The Earl of Brownlow | 1913 | WH | 14.00 |
| ☐ He Has Gained Credit | 1869 | APE | N/S |
| ☐ Portsmouth | 1882 | SPY | 14.00 |
| ☐ Cornwall | 1885 | SPY | N/S |
| ☐ A Safe Duke | 1875 | APE | 14.00 |
| ☐ Hammersmith | 1907 | SPY | 14.00 |
| ☐ A Superannuated | 1870 | APE | N/S |
| ☐ North Northamphire | 1887 | APE | 16.00 |
| ☐ Secretary for Scotland | 1902 | SPY | 14.00 |
| ☐ York City | 1901 | SPY | 14.00 |
| ☐ Home-Rule | 1873 | SPY | 14.00 |
| ☐ When Birth Cannot Lead | 1869 | SPY | 14.00 |
| ☐ Chelsea & The Colonies | 1881 | SPY | N/S |
| ☐ Ottoman Public Debt | 1897 | SPY | 14.00 |
| ☐ Indian Authority | 1878 | SPY | 14.00 |
| ☐ The Rt. Hon. James | 1909 | SPY | 14.00 |
| ☐ And Stratheden | 1873 | SPY | 16.00 |
| ☐ The Earl of Camperdown | 1895 | SPY | N/S |
| ☐ If The State Is Happy | 1869 | APE | 14.00 |
| ☐ Bill | 1893 | SPY | N/S |
| ☐ Mid-Herts | 1909 | ELF | 20.00 |
| ☐ The Whole Life | 1869 | APE | 14.00 |
| ☐ Small Holdings | 1907 | SPY | N/S |

| | CAPTION | YEAR | ARTIST | PRICE |
|---|---|---|---|---|
| ☐ | Dublin University | 1893 | LIB | 14.00 |
| ☐ | Dublin University | 1911 | HESTER | 14.00 |
| ☐ | Oxfordshire | 1884 | SPY | 14.00 |
| ☐ | 'C' | 1879 | SPY | 14.00 |
| ☐ | A Cheery Paymaster | 1906 | SPY | N/S |
| ☐ | Amends | 1874 | APE | 14.00 |
| ☐ | Good Fellow | 1886 | SPY | 14.00 |
| ☐ | Heir Presumptive To | 1895 | SPY | N/S |
| ☐ | Chief of the Clans | 1904 | SPY | 14.00 |
| ☐ | Greenwich | 1900 | SPY | 14.00 |
| ☐ | Our Joe | 1877 | SPY | 20.00 |
| ☐ | The Colonies | 1901 | SPY | 18.00 |
| ☐ | War-Worn | 1908 | WHO | 16.00 |
| ☐ | The Great Imperialist | 1914 | AST | N/S |
| ☐ | The Deceased Wife's Sister | 1884 | SPY | 14.00 |
| ☐ | Isandula | 1881 | SPY | 14.00 |
| ☐ | It Is Hardly To Be | 1870 | Unsigned | 16.00 |
| ☐ | French Free Trade | 1875 | APE | 14.00 |
| ☐ | In A New Character | 1889 | LIB | 24.00 |
| ☐ | Conservative Whip | 1904 | SPY | N/S |
| ☐ | The Lord Chamberlain | 1901 | SPY | 14.00 |
| ☐ | To Say That He Is The Best | 1869 | APE | 18.00 |
| ☐ | Southwark | 1880 | SPY | 14.00 |
| ☐ | The Little Great Premier | 1908 | VANITAS | 14.00 |
| ☐ | Black Rod | 1873 | SPY | 14.00 |
| ☐ | Judicious Amelioration | 1871 | Unsigned | 14.00 |
| ☐ | North Ayrshire | 1911 | SPY | N/S |
| ☐ | Lanarkshire | 1885 | SPY | N/S |
| ☐ | 3 Acres and A Cow | 1888 | SPY | N/S |
| ☐ | Noisy Tom | 1873 | SPY | 14.00 |
| ☐ | A Good Fellow | 1873 | SPY | N/S |
| ☐ | The Constitutional Union | 1892 | SPY | N/S |
| ☐ | Sydney | 1882 | SPY | 14.00 |
| ☐ | The Pattern Private Secretary | 1877 | SPY | 14.00 |
| ☐ | A Liberal Whip | 1883 | SPY | 14.00 |
| ☐ | Customs | 1876 | SPY | 14.00 |
| ☐ | The City | 1885 | SPY | 14.00 |
| ☐ | The French Ambassador | 1895 | GUTH | 30.00 |
| ☐ | Proper Self-Sufficiency | 1880 | T | N/S |
| ☐ | Joe | 1878 | SPY | 14.00 |
| ☐ | Newcastle on Tyne | 1872 | Unsigned | N/S |
| ☐ | Cockie | 1909 | KITE | 20.00 |
| ☐ | The New Man | 1874 | APE | 14.00 |
| ☐ | Lowestoft | 1888 | SPY | N/S |
| ☐ | Persia and India | 1892 | SPY | 14.00 |
| ☐ | Il Marchese | 1874 | APE | 14.00 |
| ☐ | The Most Popular | 1873 | SPY | 14.00 |
| ☐ | Ipswich Senior | 1892 | SPY | 14.00 |
| ☐ | Hippy | 1871 | Unsigned | 14.00 |
| ☐ | Ivo | 1904 | SPY | 14.00 |
| ☐ | The Earl of Dartmouth | 1895 | STUFF | 14.00 |
| ☐ | Clever | 1877 | SPY | 14.00 |
| ☐ | Qualis Ab Inepto | 1869 | APE | N/S |
| ☐ | Intelligent Toryism | 1880 | APE | 14.00 |
| ☐ | Australia | 1908 | SPY | 14.00 |
| ☐ | M. Cecrais | 1893 | GUTH | N/S |
| ☐ | Currency | 1872 | Unsigned | 14.00 |
| ☐ | French Foreign Affairs | 1899 | GUTH | N/S |
| ☐ | A Catholic | 1878 | APE | 14.00 |
| ☐ | Education & Defense | 1902 | SPY | 14.00 |
| ☐ | Position | 1874 | APE | 18.00 |
| ☐ | A Far Advanced Radical | 1871 | Unsigned | 14.00 |
| ☐ | The Semi-Official Ambassador | 1913 | OWL | 14.00 |
| ☐ | The Plan of Campaign | 1887 | APE | 14.00 |
| ☐ | Ways and Means | 1871 | Unsigned | 14.00 |
| ☐ | A Most Discreet Under | 1905 | SPY | 14.00 |
| ☐ | East Roumelia | 1879 | SPY | 14.00 |
| ☐ | A Southern Scot | 1896 | SPY | 14.00 |
| ☐ | An Irish Wit | 1871 | APE | N/S |
| ☐ | At Rennes | 1899 | SPY | 14.00 |

| CAPTION | YEAR | ARTIST | PRICE |
|---|---|---|---|
| ☐ Property | 1870 | APE | 14.00 |
| ☐ Fetteresso | 1883 | Unsigned | 14.00 |
| ☐ An Exceptional Irishman | 1870 | ATN | 14.00 |
| ☐ Finsbury | 1887 | APE | 14.00 |
| ☐ Duncannon | 1904 | SPY | 14.00 |
| ☐ Sol | 1897 | SPY | N/S |
| ☐ A Whipper | 1875 | APE | 14.00 |
| ☐ South Warwickshire | 1885 | SPY | 14.00 |
| ☐ Silk | 1871 | Unsigned | 14.00 |
| ☐ The Devon and Somerset | 1887 | APE | 18.00 |
| ☐ The German Attache | 1898 | SPY | N/S |
| ☐ Canadian Finance | 1909 | WHO | N/S |
| ☐ A Princess's Husband | 1889 | SPY | 14.00 |
| ☐ Fulham | 1900 | SPY | N/S |
| ☐ Knight of Kerry | 1909 | SPY | 20.00 |
| ☐ A Message From the Queen | 1873 | SPY | N/S |
| ☐ Bombay | 1874 | APE | 14.00 |
| ☐ None | 1906 | UNK | N/S |
| ☐ Calne | 1878 | SPY | 14.00 |
| ☐ Barnie | 1882 | SPY | 14.00 |
| ☐ Property and Principle | 1878 | APE | N/S |
| ☐ East Sussex | 1898 | SPY | 14.00 |
| ☐ Vive La Polgne! | 1888 | APE | 14.00 |
| ☐ The Senator | 1882 | T | 14.00 |
| ☐ The Friend of Pelissier | 1883 | SPY | 14.00 |
| ☐ South Wilts | 1880 | APE | N/S |
| ☐ Of Newe | 1880 | APE | N/S |
| ☐ The Ex-Father of the House | 1875 | APE | 14.00 |
| ☐ W.A. | 1897 | IMP | 14.00 |
| ☐ If He Is Not An Advanced | 1869 | APE | N/S |
| ☐ An Amateur Whip | 1874 | APE | 14.00 |
| ☐ He Married Lady | 1869 | APE | N/S |
| ☐ Sanitas | 1881 | T | N/S |
| ☐ Mr. A. B. Forwood | 1890 | LIB | 18.00 |
| ☐ The Fisherman's Friend | 1907 | SPY | N/S |
| ☐ The Squire | 1886 | SPY | 14.00 |
| ☐ The City | 1881 | T | N/S |
| ☐ The Sanitary | 1875 | APE | N/S |
| ☐ The Slave Trade | 1873 | SPY | 14.00 |
| ☐ Army Reorganization | 1873 | Unsigned | 14.00 |
| ☐ He Devoured France | 1872 | Unsigned | 14.00 |
| ☐ Greece | 1888 | SPY | 14.00 |
| ☐ A New Peer | 1878 | SPY | 14.00 |
| ☐ The Russian Foreign Office | 1884 | NEMO | N/S |
| ☐ Capital Punishment | 1873 | Unsigned | 18.00 |
| ☐ St. Pancras | 1887 | APE | N/S |
| ☐ His Father's Son | 1882 | SPY | N/S |
| ☐ The Gladstone Memorial | 1882 | Unsigned | N/S |
| ☐ Babble, Birth & | 1880 | T | N/S |
| ☐ Swansea | 1910 | WHO | 14.00 |
| ☐ Practical | 1872 | Unsigned | 14.00 |
| ☐ A Man of Fashion and Politics | 1870 | APE | 16.00 |
| ☐ Treasurer of the | 1892 | SPY | N/S |
| ☐ Tory Organization | 1880 | SPY | 14.00 |
| ☐ West St. Pancras | 1893 | SPY | N/S |
| ☐ Leicester Square | 1874 | APE | 14.00 |
| ☐ A Philosophic Liberal | 1869 | APE | N/S |
| ☐ The Ablest Professor | 1869 | APE | 14.00 |
| ☐ Walpole | 1898 | SPY | 14.00 |
| ☐ East Sussex | 1880 | SPY | 14.00 |
| ☐ A Private Secretary | 1900 | SPY | 14.00 |
| ☐ A Chartered Administrator | 1898 | SPY | 14.00 |
| ☐ A Privileged Person | 1869 | APE | 14.00 |
| ☐ A Liberal Imperialist | 1903 | SPY | 14.00 |
| ☐ The General Colour of the Sec'ty | 1913 | OWL | 14.00 |
| ☐ Mixed Political Wares | 1892 | SPY | N/S |
| ☐ The Fourth Party | 1880 | SPY | 16.00 |
| ☐ The Cabinet Council, 1883 | 1883 | T | 16.00 |
| ☐ Collapse of The Conference | 1913 | MOUSE | 14.00 |
| ☐ At Rennes (Dreyfus) | 1899 | GUTH | N/S |

| CAPTION | YEAR | ARTIST | PRICE |
|---|---|---|---|
| ☐ Empire Makers & Breakers | 1897 | STUFF | 60.00 |
| ☐ Lobby of the House of Commons | 1886 | LIB | 60.00 |
| ☐ On the Terrace | 1893 | SPY | 60.00 |
| ☐ The Lord Protect Us | 1898 | FURNISS | N/S |
| ☐ Monty | 1880 | SPY | N/S |
| ☐ Mr. Speaker | 1896 | SPY | 14.00 |
| ☐ A Commissioner | 1871 | Unsigned | 14.00 |
| ☐ Government Marked | 1913 | OWL | 14.00 |
| ☐ A Hegelian Politician | 1896 | SPY | 18.00 |
| ☐ A Legislator | 1884 | SPY | 14.00 |
| ☐ Torquay | 1882 | SPY | 14.00 |
| ☐ He Fell Off His Horse Into | 1870 | APE | N/S |
| ☐ Southport Division | 1903 | SPY | 14.00 |
| ☐ The Dowager | 1877 | SPY | 14.00 |
| ☐ Bridegroom | 1878 | SPY | 14.00 |
| ☐ Georgie | 1879 | SPY | N/S |
| ☐ Premier Peer of Scotland | 1873 | Unsigned | N/S |
| ☐ Hamlie | 1881 | SPY | 14.00 |
| ☐ Foreign Policy | 1875 | APE | 14.00 |
| ☐ Newcastle-Upon-Tyne | 1893 | SPY | 20.00 |
| ☐ A Financial Secretary | 1896 | SPY | 14.00 |
| ☐ Gentle and Liberal | 1884 | SPY | N/S |
| ☐ Affaires Etrangeres | 1896 | GUTH | 14.00 |
| ☐ Hansard | 1884 | APE | 14.00 |
| ☐ The Lord Mayor | 1886 | APE | N/S |
| ☐ Lulu | 1895 | SPY | N/S |
| ☐ Queer Hardie | 1906 | SPY | N/S |
| ☐ High Political Office | 1874 | APE | 14.00 |
| ☐ Conservative | 1872 | Unsigned | N/S |
| ☐ He Is Conservative | 1895 | SPY | 14.00 |
| ☐ Leverton | 1909 | SPY | N/S |
| ☐ The Sugar of Toryism | 1885 | APE | N/S |
| ☐ The Last Generation | 1871 | APE | N/S |
| ☐ His Ability and Industry | 1869 | APE | N/S |
| ☐ The Right Hon. Marq. | 1888 | SPY | 14.00 |
| ☐ Hereditary Whip | 1881 | T | 20.00 |
| ☐ An Irish Property | 1877 | SPY | 14.00 |
| ☐ He Has Kept His | 1873 | SPY | 20.00 |
| ☐ A Loyal Irishman | 1880 | APE | 14.00 |
| ☐ International Penny Postage | 1887 | SPY | 14.00 |
| ☐ Council | 1874 | SPY | 14.00 |
| ☐ Natal | 1898 | SPY | 14.00 |
| ☐ Grimsby | 1887 | SPY | 14.00 |
| ☐ Common Sense | 1874 | APE | 14.00 |
| ☐ North Western | 1892 | SPY | 14.00 |
| ☐ L.C.D.R. | 1900 | SPY | 14.00 |
| ☐ The Midland | 1908 | SPY | 14.00 |
| ☐ A South Western Director | 1896 | SPY | 14.00 |
| ☐ L. & N.W.R. | 1894 | SPY | N/S |
| ☐ North Leeds | 1899 | SPY | 14.00 |
| ☐ A Whip | 1878 | SPY | N/S |
| ☐ A Railway Director | 1894 | SPY | 14.00 |
| ☐ J.G. | 1910 | PPY | 30.00 |
| ☐ South Western | 1903 | SPY | 14.00 |
| ☐ Railway Trusts | 1891 | SPY | 16.00 |
| ☐ A Railway Commissioner | 1903 | SPY | 14.00 |
| ☐ Father Time | 1888 | LIB | 14.00 |
| ☐ L. and N.W. | 1912 | WH | 18.00 |
| ☐ London & South Western | 1891 | SPY | N/S |
| ☐ The Canadian Pacific | 1908 | SPY | 14.00 |
| ☐ Caledonian Railway | 1895 | SPY | 14.00 |
| ☐ The Railway Interest | 1875 | APE | 14.00 |
| ☐ G.W.R. | 1902 | SPY | 14.00 |
| ☐ Colonial Government | 1875 | APE | 20.00 |
| ☐ Home Rule | 1879 | SPY | 14.00 |
| ☐ Croydon | 1886 | APE | 14.00 |
| ☐ Of Muckross | 1876 | SPY | 14.00 |
| ☐ Accrington | 1892 | SPY | N/S |
| ☐ A Lord-In-Waiting | 1910 | WHO | N/S |
| ☐ The Lord Chamberlain | 1877 | SPY | 14.00 |

| CAPTION | YEAR | ARTIST | PRICE |
|---|---|---|---|
| ☐ Orangeman | 1886 | SPY | 50.00 |
| ☐ A Reformed Radical | 1883 | SPY | 14.00 |
| ☐ Board of Works | 1873 | SPY | 14.00 |
| ☐ An Equerry | 1899 | SPY | 14.00 |
| ☐ The Colonies | 1887 | APE | 14.00 |
| ☐ Military Changes | 1882 | SPY | 30.00 |
| ☐ The Princess's Private | 1905 | SPY | 14.00 |
| ☐ First Conservative Whip | 1903 | SPY | N/S |
| ☐ The Lord Chamberlain | 1900 | SPY | 16.00 |
| ☐ The Eccentric Liberal | 1872 | Unsigned | 14.00 |
| ☐ The Cool of the Evening | 1870 | APE | N/S |
| ☐ A Young Viceroy | 1892 | SPY | 14.00 |
| ☐ Manchester | 1885 | APE | N/S |
| ☐ The Britisher's Best Friend | 1911 | SPY | 14.00 |
| ☐ Dear Boy | 1892 | SPY | 14.00 |
| ☐ Energetic Toryism | 1881 | SPY | 14.00 |
| ☐ A Lancashire Lad | 1895 | SPY | N/S |
| ☐ Rochester | 1886 | APE | N/S |
| ☐ Fifth Earl | 1882 | SPY | 20.00 |
| ☐ Lt. Col. Robert William | 1913 | WH | 14.00 |
| ☐ Candidate for Chelsea | 1880 | SPY | 14.00 |
| ☐ Why Man He Doth | 1913 | OWL | 14.00 |
| ☐ Guiness Trust | 1891 | SPY | 16.00 |
| ☐ A Great French Orator | 1908 | GUTH | 22.00 |
| ☐ Ginx's Baby | 1878 | SPY | 14.00 |
| ☐ The Colossus of Roads | 1875 | APE | 14.00 |
| ☐ Marmaduke | 1912 | WH | 14.00 |
| ☐ New South Wales | 1890 | SPY | 14.00 |
| ☐ Jonesy | 1912 | WH | 14.00 |
| ☐ Jack | 1873 | Unsigned | 14.00 |
| ☐ Prosy Facts & Figures | 1892 | SPY | N/S |
| ☐ Asia Minor | 1878 | APE | N/S |
| ☐ The Lord Chamberlain | 1881 | SPY | 30.00 |
| ☐ Devonshire | 1886 | SPY | 40.00 |
| ☐ Denbigh Borough's | 1888 | SPY | N/S |
| ☐ He Improves If Possible | 1869 | APE | N/S |
| ☐ Charlie | 1883 | SPY | N/S |
| ☐ The King | 1886 | SPY | N/S |
| ☐ A Promising Apprentice | 1870 | APE | N/S |
| ☐ Has Sat For Three | 1884 | SPY | 36.00 |
| ☐ A Fine Old Tory | 1881 | SPY | 36.00 |
| ☐ Black Rod | 1877 | APE | 14.00 |
| ☐ Sir Francis Knollys | 1891 | SPY | N/S |
| ☐ Knox | 1913 | WH | 16.00 |
| ☐ Modest Assurance | 1874 | APE | 14.00 |
| ☐ The Infant Samuel | 1873 | SPY | 14.00 |
| ☐ Willie | 1813 | COCK | 16.00 |
| ☐ Family | 1874 | APE | 14.00 |
| ☐ Sir Frank Lascellos | 1912 | K | N/S |
| ☐ Canada | 1897 | SPY | 14.00 |
| ☐ The Opposition | 1912 | STRICKLAND | 14.00 |
| ☐ The Prince's Cicerone | 1905 | SPY | 14.00 |
| ☐ One of the Best | 1871 | APE | 20.00 |
| ☐ Cirencester | 1893 | SPY | 14.00 |
| ☐ Permissive Prohibition | 1872 | Unsigned | N/S |
| ☐ He Combines the Love | 1869 | APE | N/S |
| ☐ East St. Pancras | 1907 | SPY | N/S |
| ☐ Our Army Critic | 1907 | SPY | N/S |
| ☐ Sir Henry Austin Lee | 1912 | K | 14.00 |
| ☐ A Yorkshire Solicitor | 1872 | Unsigned | 14.00 |
| ☐ Aberdeen | 1879 | SPY | N/S |
| ☐ My Dear George | 1886 | SPY | 14.00 |
| ☐ The Cape High | 1894 | SPY | 14.00 |
| ☐ The Only Man | 1871 | Unsigned | 14.00 |
| ☐ West Essex | 1894 | SPY | N/S |
| ☐ The London School Board | 1896 | FTD | 14.00 |
| ☐ Local Taxation | 1875 | APE | N/S |
| ☐ Mr. Speaker | 1906 | SPY | 18.00 |
| ☐ Thanet | 1900 | SPY | 14.00 |
| ☐ Westmoreland | 1881 | SPY | N/S |

| | CAPTION | YEAR | ARTIST | PRICE |
|---|---|---|---|---|
| ☐ | Foreign Affairs | 1891 | SPY | 14.00 |
| ☐ | Toby M.P. | 1905 | SPY | 14.00 |
| ☐ | Now I Want to Know | 1871 | Unsigned | N/S |
| ☐ | A Man of Position | 1871 | APE | 30.00 |
| ☐ | Marshal of the Ceremonies | 1875 | APE | 14.00 |
| ☐ | The Vice-Empress | 1876 | SPY | 14.00 |
| ☐ | None | 1906 | UNK | N/S |
| ☐ | He Was Lord Salisbury's | 1894 | SPY | 14.00 |
| ☐ | The Member for | 1896 | SPY | N/S |
| ☐ | The Lord Mayor | 1881 | SPY | N/S |
| ☐ | Sir Anthony MacDonnell | 1905 | SPY | 14.00 |
| ☐ | Mac | 1882 | SPY | 30.00 |
| ☐ | An Elder Son | 1876 | SPY | 14.00 |
| ☐ | The Whitehead Torpedo | 1892 | SPY | N/S |
| ☐ | South Donegla | 1902 | SPY | 14.00 |
| ☐ | A Home Ruler | 1872 | Unsigned | N/S |
| ☐ | West Clare | 1894 | SPY | 18.00 |
| ☐ | Mhagthamma | 1885 | SPY | 14.00 |
| ☐ | North-West Suffolk | 1898 | SPY | 14.00 |
| ☐ | Diplomacy | 1874 | APE | 14.00 |
| ☐ | Kim | 1882 | SPY | 14.00 |
| ☐ | The Colonies | 1878 | SPY | 14.00 |
| ☐ | Mac | 1882 | SPY | 30.00 |
| ☐ | Lord Salisbury's Manners | 1887 | APE | 14.00 |
| ☐ | Let Arts and Commerce | 1869 | APE | 14.00 |
| ☐ | Cheap Fares | 1891 | SPY | 14.00 |
| ☐ | Goodwood | 1896 | SPY | 14.00 |
| ☐ | A Conservative Religionist | 1871 | APE | 14.00 |
| ☐ | Brighton | 1883 | T | 14.00 |
| ☐ | J'y suis, J'y reste | 1879 | T | N/S |
| ☐ | The Home Secretary | 1887 | SPY | 14.00 |
| ☐ | Wigtownshire | 1893 | SPY | N/S |
| ☐ | The Conservative Party | 1901 | SPY | 20.00 |
| ☐ | Steward | 1876 | SPY | 14.00 |
| ☐ | Yorkshire | 1875 | APE | 14.00 |
| ☐ | Philip | 1879 | SPY | N/S |
| ☐ | A Persevering Politician | 1883 | SPY | N/S |
| ☐ | High Commissioner | 1897 | SPY | 16.00 |
| ☐ | York | 1885 | APE | N/S |
| ☐ | The Painstaking Irishman | 1871 | APE | 14.00 |
| ☐ | A Working Conservative | 1870 | APE | N/S |
| ☐ | South Hants | 1881 | T | 20.00 |
| ☐ | Alfred | 1878 | SPY | N/S |
| ☐ | A Fifteenth Earl | 1898 | SPY | 14.00 |
| ☐ | Fred | 1893 | SPY | 14.00 |
| ☐ | Burials | 1879 | SPY | 14.00 |
| ☐ | Dissent | 1872 | Unsigned | 14.00 |
| ☐ | Peterborough | 1893 | SPY | 14.00 |
| ☐ | Ninety-One | 1883 | SPY | 14.00 |
| ☐ | Committee of Selection | 1882 | SPY | N/S |
| ☐ | Education and Arbitration | 1871 | Unsigned | N/S |
| ☐ | Birmingham | 1875 | APE | 14.00 |
| ☐ | The British Expedition | 1878 | SPY | N/S |
| ☐ | A Jesuit in Disguise | 1870 | APE | 14.00 |
| ☐ | Jim | 1909 | SPY | N/S |
| ☐ | An Imperialist | 1908 | SPY | N/S |
| ☐ | A Nice Little Fellow | 1871 | APE | N/S |
| ☐ | A Tory | 1871 | SPY | N/S |
| ☐ | By Birth A Man, By | 1871 | Unsigned | N/S |
| ☐ | The Lordship of Compton | 1904 | SPY | 14.00 |
| ☐ | British Rule in India | 1876 | SPY | 14.00 |
| ☐ | The Australian Commonwealth | 1904 | SPY | 14.00 |
| ☐ | The House of Percy | 1884 | SPY | 14.00 |
| ☐ | Colonial Self-Government | 1892 | SPY | N/S |
| ☐ | Roman Catholic Home Rule | 1880 | T | 14.00 |
| ☐ | The O'Donoghue | 1880 | SPY | N/S |
| ☐ | The Joker for Waterford | 1875 | PE | 14.00 |
| ☐ | An Irish Baronet | 1872 | Unsigned | 14.00 |
| ☐ | The Parliamentary Empire | 1870 | Unsigned | 14.00 |
| ☐ | A Parliamentary Title | 1883 | SPY | N/S |

| CAPTION | YEAR | ARTIST | PRICE |
|---|---|---|---|
| The Smart Critic | 1870 | ATN | N/S |
| Chairman of Committees | 1905 | SPY | N/S |
| He Killed the Cat | 1879 | APE | N/S |
| The Clerk Marshal | 1875 | APE | 14.00 |
| Promotion by Marriage | 1880 | T | 14.00 |
| He Was Chairman | 1870 | Unsigned | N/S |
| Lincoln | 1883 | SPY | 16.00 |
| Roger | 1880 | SPY | 14.00 |
| He Refused Woolsack | 1872 | Unsigned | 14.00 |
| The Member For Great Britain | 1909 | SPY | 14.00 |
| Anti-Rent | 1880 | T | 14.00 |
| The Turkish Alliance | 1885 | SPY | 14.00 |
| Harry | 1895 | SPY | N/S |
| The Foreign Office | 1883 | T | 14.00 |
| A Professor Of Strong | 1870 | ATN | N/S |
| Telegraphs | 1871 | Unsigned | 20.00 |
| Slate | 1882 | SPY | 14.00 |
| Cambridge Borough | 1895 | SPY | N/S |
| Northumberland | 1881 | T | N/S |
| Mansion House | 1897 | SPY | 14.00 |
| Bethnal Green | 1888 | SPY | N/S |
| Barnstaple | 1887 | SPY | 16.00 |
| The Sailor's Champion | 1873 | Unsigned | 14.00 |
| Wit & Wisdom | 1908 | SPY | 14.00 |
| Hereditary Eloquence | 1880 | APE | N/S |
| Good Works | 1906 | SPY | 14.00 |
| The Privy Purse | 1883 | T | 14.00 |
| Port | 1878 | SPY | 14.00 |
| The Dasher | 1894 | SPY | N/S |
| The Demon | 1907 | SPY | 14.00 |
| The Manchester School | 1877 | SPY | 14.00 |
| The Brains of Obstruction | 1886 | SPY | 14.00 |
| Mouldy | 1876 | SPY | 14.00 |
| To Abandon Conservative Ideals | 1905 | SPY | 14.00 |
| Devonport | 1882 | SPY | N/S |
| In Society and Member Of | 1889 | LIB | 14.00 |
| Under-Secretary For 'War' | 1901 | SPY | N/S |
| Order, Order | 1875 | APE | 18.00 |
| Liverpool | 1880 | SPY | N/S |
| Huddersfield | 1884 | SPY | N/S |
| He Has Succeeded In | 1870 | APE | 14.00 |
| M.F.H. of Herefordshire | 1913 | OWL | N/S |
| South-East Essex | 1896 | SPY | N/S |
| Our Eastern Policy | 1873 | SPY | 14.00 |
| A Tenant Farmer | 1875 | APE | 14.00 |
| The Lord Dictator | 1875 | APE | 14.00 |
| The Nobleman of the Garden | 1904 | SPY | 14.00 |
| Elisha | 1892 | SPY | N/S |
| The Irish Petrel | 1904 | SPY | N/S |
| Montgomery District | 1907 | SPY | 14.00 |
| Loreburn | 1913 | OWL | 14.00 |
| Property in Suffolk | 1881 | T | N/S |
| Peace | 1880 | SPY | N/S |
| Highly Respectable | 1870 | ATN | N/S |
| Ex-Official | 1881 | APE | N/S |
| East Cornwall | 1882 | SPY | 14.00 |
| Admiralty | 1907 | SPY | N/S |
| Diplomacy & Poetry | 1897 | SPY | 14.00 |
| In Waiting | 1876 | SPY | 14.00 |
| Tear 'Em | 1874 | APE | 20.00 |
| The Clerk of Parliaments | 1885 | SPY | 18.00 |
| The Kirk of Scotland | 1881 | T | 14.00 |
| Borstal System | 1910 | SPY | 18.00 |
| Westminister | 1878 | APE | N/S |
| This Fell Sergeant | 1873 | Unsigned | 14.00 |
| Loyal and Patriotic | 1888 | SPY | 14.00 |
| He Was Once Offered | 1871 | Unsigned | N/S |
| Foreign Policy | 1879 | SPY | 14.00 |
| Foreign Affairs | 1898 | SPY | 16.00 |
| A Soldier's Son | 1889 | SPY | 14.00 |

| CAPTION | YEAR | ARTIST | PRICE |
|---|---|---|---|
| ☐ Peking | 1903 | SPY | 14.00 |
| ☐ A New Lord Mayor | 1890 | SPY | 18.00 |
| ☐ The Caucus | 1892 | STUFF | N/S |
| ☐ The Safe Man | 1874 | APE | 14.00 |
| ☐ East Sussex | 1882 | SPY | N/S |
| ☐ Sheep | 1883 | SPY | N/S |
| ☐ Pigs | 1878 | SPY | N/S |
| ☐ Extinction, Distinction | 1905 | SPY | N/S |
| ☐ Admiralty | 1901 | SPY | 14.00 |
| ☐ Despatches | 1884 | SPY | 14.00 |
| ☐ Albert's Seymour | 1877 | APE | 14.00 |
| ☐ He Is Not As Other Men | 1869 | APE | N/S |
| ☐ The Yankee From Persia | 1912 | WH | N/S |
| ☐ Shuttleworth | 1904 | SPY | 14.00 |
| ☐ A Conservative Whip | 1871 | APE | 14.00 |
| ☐ Manchester | 1884 | APE | 14.00 |
| ☐ Straits Settlements | 1892 | KYO | 14.00 |
| ☐ A Successful First Speech | 1907 | SPY | 14.00 |
| ☐ No Surrender | 1911 | NIBS | N/S |
| ☐ Sammy | 1904 | SPY | 14.00 |
| ☐ First Lord of the Treasury | 1887 | SPY | N/S |
| ☐ Proud and Sincere | 1869 | Unsigned | N/S |
| ☐ An Old-Fashion Duke | 1893 | SPY | N/S |
| ☐ Unlike Wilkes, Who Is | 1912 | RUTH | 14.00 |
| ☐ Bradlaugh's Baby | 1881 | SPY | N/S |
| ☐ The Messenger of Peace | 1870 | APE | 16.00 |
| ☐ The Cape | 1897 | SPY | 14.00 |
| ☐ White Dial | 1883 | SPY | N/S |
| ☐ The Young Man | 1879 | SPY | N/S |
| ☐ He Speaks With One Party | 1869 | APE | N/S |
| ☐ Westhoughton | 1894 | SPY | 14.00 |
| ☐ Pour Encourager Les Autres | 1869 | APE | N/S |
| ☐ Two-and-Eighty | 1884 | SPY | 14.00 |
| ☐ A Country Gentleman | 1875 | APE | 14.00 |
| ☐ Suffolk | 1875 | APE | N/S |
| ☐ Sheffield | 1886 | SPY | N/S |
| ☐ East Dorsetshire | 1892 | SPY | N/S |
| ☐ East and West | 1912 | RAY | N/S |
| ☐ He Received the Royal | 1869 | Unsigned | N/S |
| ☐ The Gull's Friend | 1874 | APE | 14.00 |
| ☐ Our Mark | 1912 | WH | 18.00 |
| ☐ The Blister | 1888 | SPY | 14.00 |
| ☐ Lately Whipped | 1874 | APE | 14.00 |
| ☐ Burra Dick | 1881 | SPY | 14.00 |
| ☐ Dangerous Trades | 1909 | SPY | N/S |
| ☐ Tom | 1883 | Unsigned | 14.00 |
| ☐ Clapham | 1900 | SPY | 14.00 |
| ☐ Baronet or Butcher | 1871 | APE | 18.00 |
| ☐ Cheshire | 1881 | SPY | 14.00 |
| ☐ Finsbury | 1883 | SPY | 14.00 |
| ☐ A Man of the World | 1876 | SPY | 14.00 |
| ☐ Lofty | 1882 | SPY | 14.00 |
| ☐ The Norwood Division | 1897 | SPY | 14.00 |
| ☐ The Lord Mayor | 1908 | SPY | 14.00 |
| ☐ Sir Charles Tupper | 1913 | OWL | N/S |
| ☐ A Late Whip | 1894 | SPY | 14.00 |
| ☐ Oxford City | 1899 | SPY | N/S |
| ☐ Bucks | 1882 | SPY | 14.00 |
| ☐ He Was Considered An Able | 1870 | ATN | 14.00 |
| ☐ He Advocated Free Trade | 1872 | Unsigned | 14.00 |
| ☐ The Imperial Institute | 1893 | SPY | 14.00 |
| ☐ Hook & Eye | 1876 | SPY | 14.00 |
| ☐ Swansea, Sir H. H., M.P. | 1886 | SPY | 14.00 |
| ☐ Always Pleasant | 1870 | SPY | 14.00 |
| ☐ Earl Waldegrave | 1912 | WH | 14.00 |
| ☐ E.D. | 1909 | QUIP | 14.00 |
| ☐ The Hertford Property | 1873 | SPY | 14.00 |
| ☐ He Defended Hyde Park | 1872 | Unsigned | 14.00 |
| ☐ Whip | 1886 | LIB | 14.00 |
| ☐ South Kensington | 1897 | SPY | 14.00 |

| CAPTION | YEAR | ARTIST | PRICE |
|---|---|---|---|
| ☐ Hear! Hear! Hear! | 1884 | APE | 14.00 |
| ☐ Orkney and Shetland | 1909 | WHO | N/S |
| ☐ France at the Congress | 1878 | T. | 14.00 |
| ☐ The Lord Mayor | 1872 | Unsigned | 14.00 |
| ☐ A Cynical Radical | 1906 | SPY | 22.00 |
| ☐ The Treasury | 1910 | HLO | 14.00 |
| ☐ The Iron Duke's Grandson | 1885 | APE | 14.00 |
| ☐ Strathfieldseye | 1903 | SPY | N/S |
| ☐ The Son of Waterloo | 1872 | Unsigned | 26.00 |
| ☐ Madras | 1893 | BINT | 14.00 |
| ☐ Algy | 1892 | SPY | N/S |
| ☐ Denbigshire | 1892 | SPY | 14.00 |
| ☐ An Eminent Christian | 1869 | APE | 14.00 |
| ☐ The Richest Man in England | 1870 | APE | 14.00 |
| ☐ The Great Believer | 1871 | APE | 30.00 |
| ☐ Conservative Conversion | 1875 | APE | 14.00 |
| ☐ Parliamentary Procedure | 1895 | SPY | 16.00 |
| ☐ Bonnie Westmoreland | 1889 | HAY | N/S |
| ☐ Liverpool | 1880 | SPY | 14.00 |
| ☐ Chelsea | 1901 | SPY | 14.00 |
| ☐ Wiggin | 1892 | TUFF | 14.00 |
| ☐ The Champion of the Ladies | 1909 | HLO | N/S |
| ☐ Montgomeryshire | 1879 | SPY | 14.00 |
| ☐ Moray and Nairn | 1909 | HCO | 14.00 |
| ☐ Birdseye | 1893 | SPY | 14.00 |
| ☐ The Lash | 1874 | APE | 14.00 |
| ☐ A Sticker | 1908 | SPY | 20.00 |
| ☐ Consular Chaplains | 1874 | APE | 14.00 |
| ☐ Our Sir George | 1874 | SPY | 14.00 |
| ☐ Hanley | 1896 | SPY | 14.00 |
| ☐ Tariff Reform | 1908 | SPY | 14.00 |
| ☐ A Staffordshire Peer | 1895 | STUFF | 14.00 |
| ☐ Dover and War | 1900 | SPY | 14.00 |
| ☐ Aesthetics | 1880 | SPY | 14.00 |
| ☐ Chester | 1893 | SPY | 18.00 |
| ☐ Chester | 1910 | WHO | 14.00 |
| ☐ Alick | 1881 | SPY | N/S |
| ☐ Ayr Burghs | 1910 | HCO | 14.00 |
| ☐ A Gentleman | 1886 | SPY | 14.00 |
| ☐ Irish Loyalty | 1887 | APE | N/S |

## POLO

| CAPTION | YEAR | ARTIST | PRICE |
|---|---|---|---|
| ☐ Yeoman-Like Polo | 1891 | LIB | 30.00 |
| ☐ Descended From Edward | 1898 | GAF | 30.00 |
| ☐ I Say | 1898 | GAF | 30.00 |
| ☐ Patiala | 1900 | MR | 30.00 |
| ☐ Buck | 1907 | SPY | N/S |

## PRIME MINISTERS

| CAPTION | YEAR | ARTIST | PRICE |
|---|---|---|---|
| ☐ The Greatest Liberal | 1869 | APE | 20.00 |
| ☐ He Educated The Tories | 1869 | SINGE | N/S |
| ☐ He Is Too Honest | 1869 | APE | 20.00 |
| ☐ It Is His Mission To | 1869 | APE | 20.00 |
| ☐ Were He A Worse Man | 1869 | SINGE | 24.00 |
| ☐ The Junior Ambassador | 1878 | APE | N/S |
| ☐ The People's William | 1879 | SPY | 24.00 |
| ☐ Power and Peace | 1879 | SPY | 24.00 |
| ☐ The Grand Old Man | 1887 | SPY | N/S |
| ☐ The Irish Secretary | 1887 | SPY | 24.00 |
| ☐ East Fife | 1891 | SPY | 20.00 |
| ☐ The Opposition | 1899 | SPY | N/S |
| ☐ The Prime Minister | 1900 | SPY | 20.00 |
| ☐ Little Bo-Peep | 1901 | SPY | 20.00 |
| ☐ A Gentle Shepherd | 1905 | SPY | 20.00 |
| ☐ Nonconformist Genius | 1907 | SPY | N/S |

## RAILWAY OFFICIALS

| | CAPTION | YEAR | ARTIST | PRICE |
|---|---|---|---|---|
| ☐ | Great Northern | 1908 | SPY | 20.00 |
| ☐ | Board of Trade | 1880 | SPY | N/S |
| ☐ | Cricket, Railways & Agriculture | 1904 | SPY | 20.00 |
| ☐ | Great Central | 1907 | SPY | N/S |
| ☐ | A Railroad Knight | 1890 | SPY | 20.00 |
| ☐ | North Western | 1892 | SPY | 20.00 |
| ☐ | L.C.D.R. | 1900 | SPY | N/S |
| ☐ | The Midland | 1908 | SPY | 20.00 |
| ☐ | A South Western Director | 1896 | SPY | 20.00 |
| ☐ | L. & N. W.R. | 1894 | SPY | N/S |
| ☐ | North Leeds | 1899 | SPY | 20.00 |
| ☐ | A Whip | 1878 | SPY | N/S |
| ☐ | A Railway Director | 1894 | SPY | 20.00 |
| ☐ | J.G. | 1910 | PRY | 24.00 |
| ☐ | South Western | 1903 | SPY | 20.00 |
| ☐ | Railway Trusts | 1891 | SPY | 20.00 |
| ☐ | A Railway Commissioner | 1903 | SPY | 20.00 |
| ☐ | Father Time | 1888 | LIB | 20.00 |
| ☐ | L. and N.W. | 1912 | WH | 20.00 |
| ☐ | London & South Western | 1891 | SPY | N/S |
| ☐ | The Canadian Pacific | 1908 | SPY | 20.00 |
| ☐ | Caledonian Railway | 1895 | SPY | 20.00 |
| ☐ | The Railway Interest | 1875 | APE | 20.00 |
| ☐ | G.W.R. | 1902 | SPY | 20.00 |

## RED ROBE JUDGES

| | CAPTION | YEAR | ARTIST | PRICE |
|---|---|---|---|---|
| ☐ | A Souvenir | 1870 | ATN | N/S |
| ☐ | The Lord Chief Baron | 1871 | Unsigned | 60.00 |
| ☐ | Gentle Manners | 1887 | SPY | N/S |
| ☐ | 3rd Commissioner | 1888 | SPY | N/S |
| ☐ | One of the Family | 1890 | QUIZ | N/S |
| ☐ | Mr. Justice Grantham | 1890 | SPY | N/S |
| ☐ | The Recorder | 1903 | SPY | 60.00 |
| ☐ | Judicial Light Weight | 1907 | SPY | N/S |
| ☐ | Lorry | 1907 | SPY | 60.00 |
| ☐ | Lord Chief Justice | 1913 | WH | 60.00 |

## ROWING

| | CAPTION | YEAR | ARTIST | PRICE |
|---|---|---|---|---|
| ☐ | Pembroke | 1888 | HAY | 30.00 |
| ☐ | Professional Champion | 1889 | SPY | 30.00 |
| ☐ | Wingfield Sculls | 1889 | SPY | 30.00 |
| ☐ | One of the Presidents | 1890 | SPY | 45.00 |
| ☐ | O.U.B.C. | 1891 | SPY | 30.00 |
| ☐ | Flea | 1893 | SPY | 30.00 |
| ☐ | Benjie | 1894 | SPY | 40.00 |
| ☐ | Fogg | 1894 | SPY | 30.00 |
| ☐ | O.U.B.C. | 1895 | SPY | 30.00 |
| ☐ | Rudy | 1895 | SPY | 30.00 |
| ☐ | Crumbo | 1896 | SPY | 40.00 |
| ☐ | Ducker | 1897 | SPY | 30.00 |
| ☐ | Tarka | 1899 | SPY | 30.00 |
| ☐ | C.U.B.C. | 1900 | SPY | 30.00 |
| ☐ | C.U.B.C. | 1903 | SPY | 30.00 |
| ☐ | Bush | 1907 | SPY | 40.00 |
| ☐ | Duggie | 1907 | SPY | 45.00 |
| ☐ | Ethel | 1908 | SPY | 40.00 |
| ☐ | Bill | 1910 | ELF | 40.00 |
| ☐ | A Good Stroke | 1911 | APE JR. | 30.00 |
| ☐ | The Light Blue Stroke | 1912 | WH | 45.00 |
| ☐ | Steered Three Winning Crews | 1912 | WH | 45.00 |

## ROYALTY

| CAPTION | YEAR | ARTIST | PRICE |
|---|---|---|---|
| ☐ Ote-Toi-De-La-Que | 1869 | COIDE | N/S |
| ☐ Eddie | 1888 | HAY | N/S |
| ☐ The Prince of Monaco | 1900 | SPY | N/S |
| ☐ La Civilisation Russe | 1869 | COIDE | 20.00 |
| ☐ H.R.H. Prince Alexander of Teck | 1908 | SPY | 20.00 |
| ☐ My August Master | 1884 | NEMO | 20.00 |
| ☐ A Born King | 1893 | Unsigned | 20.00 |
| ☐ S. M. Alfonso XIII | 1906 | GUTH | N/S |
| ☐ He Would Be A King | 1872 | Unsigned | 20.00 |
| ☐ The Duke of Aosta | 1903 | LIB | 20.00 |
| ☐ Ahmed Arabi The Egyptian | 1883 | FV | 20.00 |
| ☐ God Bless the Duke | 1869 | APE | N/S |
| ☐ Cuch Behar | 1901 | Unsigned | 20.00 |
| ☐ The Gaekwar | 1901 | MR | N/S |
| ☐ The Head of the Russels | 1874 | APE | 20.00 |
| ☐ The Ablest Statesman | 1870 | Unsigned | 20.00 |
| ☐ Plon-Plon | 1879 | T | 20.00 |
| ☐ Le Prince Du Chic | 1899 | SPY | 20.00 |
| ☐ Sarawak | 1899 | SPY | N/S |
| ☐ Marlborough | 1882 | SPY | 20.00 |
| ☐ The Bute | 1910 | WHO | N/S |
| ☐ Legitimacy | 1876 | SPY | 20.00 |
| ☐ M. Carnot, Pres. | 1889 | PAL | 20.00 |
| ☐ The French Republic | 1894 | GUTH | N/S |
| ☐ Restored | 1882 | SPY | N/S |
| ☐ A Prince of Denmark | 1902 | SPY | 20.00 |
| ☐ H.R.H. The Crown Prince Of | 1895 | SPY | N/S |
| ☐ The Fourth Duke | 1877 | SPY | 20.00 |
| ☐ A Future Commander | 1876 | SPY | 20.00 |
| ☐ H.R.H. | 1913 | HESTER | N/S |
| ☐ Prince Arthur | 1913 | OWL | 20.00 |
| ☐ Our Soldier Prince | 1890 | SPY | 20.00 |
| ☐ The Orleans Family | 1884 | NEMO | 20.00 |
| ☐ The Duc D'Aumale | 1891 | GUTH | 20.00 |
| ☐ (No Caption) | 1878 | SPY | 20.00 |
| ☐ The Pacificator Of Europe | 1910 | XIT | 20.00 |
| ☐ The Prince | 1878 | SPY | N/S |
| ☐ His Majesty the King | 1902 | SPY | 20.00 |
| ☐ The Eminently Respectable | 1895 | GUTH | 20.00 |
| ☐ Greece | 1876 | SPY | 20.00 |
| ☐ His Majesty the King | 1911 | APE JR. | 20.00 |
| ☐ Prince Henry of Orleans | 1897 | GUTH | 20.00 |
| ☐ Italy | 1878 | T | 20.00 |
| ☐ She Has Throughout Her Life | 1869 | COIDE | N/S |
| ☐ The Ex-Khedive | 1881 | T | N/S |
| ☐ Johore | 1891 | KYO | N/S |
| ☐ The Empire | 1877 | SPY | 20.00 |
| ☐ Austria | 1877 | SUE | N/S |
| ☐ An Indian Statesman | 1876 | SPY | N/S |
| ☐ The Aga Khan | 1904 | SPY | 20.00 |
| ☐ Oom Paul | 1900 | DRAWL | N/S |
| ☐ The Student Prince | 1877 | SPY | 20.00 |
| ☐ Un Roi Consitutionel | 1869 | COIDE | 20.00 |
| ☐ The New French President | 1899 | GUTH | 20.00 |
| ☐ Les Mangeoit Pour | 1871 | COIDE | 20.00 |
| ☐ A Prince Royal | 1895 | SPY | 20.00 |
| ☐ An Abyssinian General | 1903 | SPY | 20.00 |
| ☐ Europe's Youngest | 1909 | NIBS | N/S |
| ☐ Blenheim Palace | 1898 | SPY | 20.00 |
| ☐ A Premier of France | 1898 | GUTH | 20.00 |
| ☐ Abyssinia | 1897 | GLICK | 20.00 |
| ☐ Michael | 1891 | SPY | 20.00 |
| ☐ The Emperor | 1891 | PERY | N/S |
| ☐ Persia | 1903 | SPY | 20.00 |
| ☐ La Regime Parlementaire | 1869 | COIDE | N/S |
| ☐ He Endowed Persia | 1873 | SPY | N/S |
| ☐ A Living Monument To English | 1870 | ATN | N/S |

| CAPTION | YEAR | ARTIST | PRICE |
|---|---|---|---|
| ☐ The Little Father | 1897 | GUTH | 20.00 |
| ☐ I'er Conscrit De France | 1890 | GUTH | 20.00 |
| ☐ Messieurs | 1913 | OWL | 20.00 |
| ☐ Hereditary Grand Falconer | 1873 | Unsigned | N/S |
| ☐ President No. 3 | 1880 | APE | 20.00 |
| ☐ The Premier Earl | 1880 | SPY | N/S |
| ☐ Jodhpore | 1887 | SPY | 20.00 |
| ☐ The Maharajah | 1882 | SPY | N/S |
| ☐ Prince Soltykoff | 1889 | SPY | N/S |
| ☐ Ex-President Steyn | 1900 | WAG | 20.00 |
| ☐ Simple and Unassuming | 1870 | APE | N/S |
| ☐ Frank | 1902 | SPY | N/S |
| ☐ The Duke of Teck | 1902 | SPY | 20.00 |
| ☐ The Most Popular | 1870 | ATN | 20.00 |
| ☐ The Khedive | 1883 | FV | 20.00 |
| ☐ Faute-De-Mieux-Premier | 1872 | Unsigned | N/S |
| ☐ Il Re Galantoumo | 1870 | Unsigned | 20.00 |
| ☐ Italia | 1902 | LIB | 20.00 |
| ☐ Victor | 1899 | GUTH | 20.00 |
| ☐ A Cimiez | 1897 | GUTH | 20.00 |
| ☐ (Black & white reprint of above at death) | 1901 | GUTH | N/S |
| ☐ H.R.H. | 1911 | NIBS | N/S |
| ☐ The Prince | 1873 | Unsigned | 20.00 |
| ☐ Our Sailor Prince | 1890 | SPY | 20.00 |
| ☐ Fritz | 1870 | Unsigned | 20.00 |
| ☐ Oh Child, Mayst Thou | 1905 | GUTH | 20.00 |
| ☐ The Premier Marquess | 1904 | SPY | N/S |

## SCOTSMEN

| CAPTION | YEAR | ARTIST | PRICE |
|---|---|---|---|
| ☐ The Queen's Lord Steward | 1894 | SPY | 14.00 |
| ☐ If Everywhere As | 1870 | APE | 16.00 |
| ☐ Restless Peter | 1908 | SPY | 14.00 |
| ☐ Scottish Horse | 1905 | SPY | 14.00 |

## SHIPPING OFFICIALS

| CAPTION | YEAR | ARTIST | PRICE |
|---|---|---|---|
| ☐ Plymouth | 1888 | SPY | 14.00 |
| ☐ The Knight of the Cruise | 1884 | APE | 14.00 |
| ☐ Union Steamship | 1896 | SPY | 18.00 |
| ☐ Shipping | 1890 | SPY | 14.00 |
| ☐ Cunarder | 1904 | SPY | 14.00 |
| ☐ Jim | 1909 | SPY | N/S |
| ☐ White Star | 1894 | LIB | N/S |
| ☐ Docks and Harbours | 1909 | SPY | N/S |
| ☐ He Built the Alabama | 1873 | SPY | N/S |
| ☐ Shipping | 1884 | APE | 14.00 |
| ☐ Harland & Wolff | 1903 | SPY | 14.00 |
| ☐ Naval Construction | 1875 | APE | 14.00 |
| ☐ Tariff Reform League | 1910 | WHO | N/S |
| ☐ Iron Shipbuilding | 1873 | Unsigned | N/S |
| ☐ Manchester Ship Canal | 1910 | ELF | 14.00 |
| ☐ Pando | 1887 | APE | 14.00 |
| ☐ Destroyers | 1905 | SPY | N/S |
| ☐ Naval Construction | 1910 | SPY | 14.00 |
| ☐ Hull | 1885 | APE | 14.00 |

## SPORTS, MISCELLANEOUS
### BILLIARDS

| CAPTION | YEAR | ARTIST | PRICE |
|---|---|---|---|
| ☐ The French Republic | 1879 | T | 14.00 |
| ☐ The Champion Roberts | 1885 | SPY | 14.00 |
| ☐ He Might Be | 1905 | SPY | 14.00 |

# CARRIAGES

| CAPTION | YEAR | ARTIST | PRICE |
|---|---|---|---|
| ☐ A Military Difficulty | 1870 | ATN | N/S |
| ☐ Charlie | 1874 | APE | 14.00 |
| ☐ A Peninsular Veteran | 1876 | APE | 14.00 |
| ☐ A Whip | 1878 | SPY | 14.00 |
| ☐ A Great Officer | 1881 | SPY | 14.00 |
| ☐ Old Times | 1886 | APE | 14.00 |
| ☐ Coaching | 1887 | APE | 14.00 |
| ☐ Four-In-Hand | 1903 | SPY | 14.00 |

# CHESS

| CAPTION | YEAR | ARTIST | PRICE |
|---|---|---|---|
| ☐ Chess | 1888 | APE | 14.00 |

# CURLING

| CAPTION | YEAR | ARTIST | PRICE |
|---|---|---|---|
| ☐ The King of Clubs | 1909 | ELF | N/S |

# DOG JUDGE

| CAPTION | YEAR | ARTIST | PRICE |
|---|---|---|---|
| ☐ A Judge | 1901 | CB | 14.00 |

# DUELLING

| CAPTION | YEAR | ARTIST | PRICE |
|---|---|---|---|
| ☐ A French Duellist | 1879 | T | 14.00 |

# FENCING

| CAPTION | YEAR | ARTIST | PRICE |
|---|---|---|---|
| ☐ He Insists That His Pen | 1905 | SPY | 14.00 |
| ☐ Cold Steel | 1903 | JEST | 14.00 |
| ☐ Henry | 1880 | APE | 14.00 |

# FISHING

| CAPTION | YEAR | ARTIST | PRICE |
|---|---|---|---|
| ☐ Mr. William Black | 1891 | SPY | 14.00 |
| ☐ The Postmaster General | 1907 | SPY | 14.00 |

# GYMNAST

| CAPTION | YEAR | ARTIST | PRICE |
|---|---|---|---|
| ☐ Fred | 1876 | SPY | N/S |

# ICE-SKATING

| CAPTION | YEAR | ARTIST | PRICE |
|---|---|---|---|
| ☐ Old Wares | 1900 | SPY | N/S |

# MISCELLANEOUS

| CAPTION | YEAR | ARTIST | PRICE |
|---|---|---|---|
| ☐ A Real English Gentleman | 1881 | APE | N/S |
| ☐ Mufti | 1881 | SPY | N/S |
| ☐ Dolly | 1889 | HAY | 14.00 |
| ☐ The Consul Market | 1896 | SPY | 14.00 |

| CAPTION | YEAR | ARTIST | PRICE |
|---|---|---|---|
| ☐ The Warwickshire | 1896 | SPY | 16.00 |
| ☐ Basutoland | 1901 | SPY | 14.00 |
| ☐ Orleans | 1903 | CLOISTER | 18.00 |
| ☐ Lord Barrington | 1909 | SPY | 14.00 |
| ☐ His Grace The Duke | 1912 | WH | 14.00 |

## ROLLER-SKATING

| CAPTION | YEAR | ARTIST | PRICE |
|---|---|---|---|
| ☐ The Philanthropist | 1874 | APE | 40.00 |

## RUGBY

| CAPTION | YEAR | ARTIST | PRICE |
|---|---|---|---|
| ☐ Rugby Union | 1890 | SPY | 14.00 |
| ☐ Rugby Union | 1892 | STUFF | 18.00 |

## SOCCER

| CAPTION | YEAR | ARTIST | PRICE |
|---|---|---|---|
| ☐ Soccer | 1912 | WH | N/S |

## SWIMMING

| CAPTION | YEAR | ARTIST | PRICE |
|---|---|---|---|
| ☐ Swam the Channel | 1875 | APE | 24.00 |

## SPORT RIDERS

| CAPTION | YEAR | ARTIST | PRICE |
|---|---|---|---|
| ☐ The Jockey Club | 1882 | SPY | 20.00 |
| ☐ Bucks | 1885 | SPY | 20.00 |
| ☐ A Hard Rider | 1898 | GAF | 20.00 |
| ☐ Clocks | 1883 | SPY | N/S |
| ☐ Science and Sport | 1913 | WH | 20.00 |
| ☐ Born in the Scarlet | 1883 | SPY | 20.00 |
| ☐ A Cunarder | 1881 | SPY | N/S |
| ☐ A Good Sportsman | 1896 | SPY | N/S |
| ☐ The Lord Mayor | 1882 | SPY | 20.00 |
| ☐ A Liberal Peer | 1882 | SPY | 20.00 |
| ☐ Taplow Court | 1890 | SPY | 20.00 |
| ☐ Haute Ecole | 1877 | SPY | 24.00 |
| ☐ Colonel William | 1912 | WH | N/S |
| ☐ Wiltshire | 1886 | SPY | 20.00 |
| ☐ Jim | 1877 | SPY | N/S |
| ☐ A Coachman | 1881 | SPY | N/S |
| ☐ A Father of the Belvoir | 1900 | CB | 20.00 |

## STOCK EXCHANGE OFFICIALS

| CAPTION | YEAR | ARTIST | PRICE |
|---|---|---|---|
| ☐ The Stock Exchange | 1886 | LIB | N/S |
| ☐ Jack in the Box | 1890 | FC.G. | 20.00 |
| ☐ Mr. F. Carruther Gould | 1890 | LIB | 20.00 |
| ☐ Mr. James Coates | 1890 | SPY | N/S |
| ☐ Pakky | 1895 | SPY | N/S |
| ☐ Tommy Dodd | 1901 | SPY | N/S |
| ☐ North Befordshire | 1902 | SPY | N/S |
| ☐ The Official Assignee | 1908 | WHO | N/S |

# TEACHERS AND HEADMASTERS

| CAPTION | YEAR | ARTIST | PRICE |
|---|---|---|---|
| ☐ M'Tutor | 1901 | SPY | 20.00 |
| ☐ All Souls | 1901 | SPY | 20.00 |
| ☐ M.T.S. | 1901 | WAG | 20.00 |
| ☐ Popular Astronomy | 1905 | SPY | 20.00 |
| ☐ Marlborough College | 1902 | SPY | 20.00 |
| ☐ St. John's Oxford | 1893 | SPY | 20.00 |
| ☐ Fasti Etonenses | 1903 | SPY | 20.00 |
| ☐ The Dean of Westminister | 1888 | SPY | 20.00 |
| ☐ Merton College | 1884 | SPY | 20.00 |
| ☐ O.B. | 1888 | HAY | N/S |
| ☐ Winchester | 1903 | SPY | 20.00 |
| ☐ The Master of Trinity | 1889 | HAY | 20.00 |
| ☐ Trinity | 1903 | SPY | 20.00 |
| ☐ Balliol | 1895 | SPY | 20.00 |
| ☐ Walter D. | 1902 | SPY | 20.00 |
| ☐ Goody | 1876 | SPY | 20.00 |
| ☐ Latin Literature | 1894 | SPY | 20.00 |
| ☐ New Harrow | 1912 | STRICKLAND | 20.00 |
| ☐ Corpus | 1899 | FTD | 20.00 |
| ☐ Badger | 1892 | SPY | 20.00 |
| ☐ Merchant Tailors | 1874 | APE | 20.00 |
| ☐ The Head | 1901 | SPY | 20.00 |
| ☐ Jacky | 1892 | SPY | N/S |
| ☐ Ajax M.P. | 1904 | SPY | 20.00 |
| ☐ Jimmy | 1887 | SPY | 20.00 |
| ☐ A Sturdy Educationist | 1911 | WHO | N/S |
| ☐ The Flea | 1901 | SPY | 20.00 |
| ☐ ChristChurch | 1875 | APE | 20.00 |
| ☐ Young Oxford | 1880 | SPY | 20.00 |
| ☐ Haileybury | 1901 | SPY | 20.00 |
| ☐ The School Master | 1907 | SPY | 20.00 |
| ☐ Technical Education | 1891 | S. TEI | N/S |
| ☐ Mike | 1896 | SPY | 20.00 |
| ☐ Red Morgan | 1889 | HAY | 20.00 |
| ☐ Black Morgan | 1889 | HAY | 20.00 |
| ☐ The Science of Language | 1875 | APE | 20.00 |
| ☐ The House | 1894 | SPY | 20.00 |
| ☐ Oxford Modern History | 1895 | SPY | 20.00 |
| ☐ A Professor | 1884 | SPY | 20.00 |
| ☐ Westminister | 1898 | SPY | 20.00 |
| ☐ The Shirt | 1894 | SPY | 20.00 |
| ☐ Spooner | 1898 | SPY | 20.00 |
| ☐ St. Paul's School | 1901 | SPY | 20.00 |
| ☐ The Head | 1885 | SPY | 20.00 |
| ☐ The Vice-Provost | 1901 | SPY | 20.00 |
| ☐ Magdalen College, Oxford | 1893 | SPY | 20.00 |
| ☐ Harrow | 1899 | GAF | 20.00 |

# TENNIS

| CAPTION | YEAR | ARTIST | PRICE |
|---|---|---|---|
| ☐ Tennis | 1882 | T | N/S |
| ☐ Michael Michailovich | 1894 | WAG | N/S |
| ☐ Thrice Champion | 1904 | SPY | N/S |
| ☐ In His Lighter Moments | 1912 | WH | N/S |
| ☐ Baby | 1913 | COCK | N/S |

# THEATRE

| CAPTION | YEAR | ARTIST | PRICE |
|---|---|---|---|
| ☐ Aubrey Tanqueray | 1894 | SPY | 20.00 |
| ☐ The St. James's | 1909 | MAX | 20.00 |
| ☐ Kismet | 1911 | RITCHIE | 20.00 |
| ☐ Tony | 1908 | SPY | 20.00 |
| ☐ B | 1891 | SPY | 20.00 |
| ☐ The Modern Wiertz | 1891 | SPY | 20.00 |

| CAPTION | YEAR | ARTIST | PRICE |
|---|---|---|---|
| ☐ Madame Sarah Bernhardt | 1912 | K | N/S |
| ☐ Sarah Bernhardt | 1879 | T | N/S |
| ☐ A Fellow Infinite | 1905 | SPY | 20.00 |
| ☐ The Sensation Drama | 1882 | SPY | N/S |
| ☐ A.B. | 1896 | SPY | 20.00 |
| ☐ The Palace | 1910 | HCO | 20.00 |
| ☐ Mr. Arthur Cecil | 1889 | SPY | 20.00 |
| ☐ The Guv'nor | 1910 | HESTER | 20.00 |
| ☐ Coquelin Aine | 1893 | GUTH | 20.00 |
| ☐ Coquelin Aine | 1898 | GUTH | 20.00 |
| ☐ Gerald | 1907 | SPY | 24.00 |
| ☐ Gov'nor | 1911 | NIBS | 20.00 |
| ☐ The Man on the Film | 1913 | AST | 20.00 |
| ☐ Forbie | 1895 | SPY | 20.00 |
| ☐ Mr. Forbes-Robertson | 1913 | RITCHIE | N/S |
| ☐ Magic | 1913 | AST | 20.00 |
| ☐ Amateur Theatricals | 1886 | SPY | 20.00 |
| ☐ Sherlock Holmes | 1907 | SPY | N/S |
| ☐ Goochie | 1882 | SPY | 20.00 |
| ☐ The Pinafore | 1888 | SPY | 20.00 |
| ☐ The Duffer | 1905 | SPY | 20.00 |
| ☐ Mr. John Hare | 1890 | SPY | 20.00 |
| ☐ Drury Lane | 1889 | SPY | 20.00 |
| ☐ From Eton to the Stage | 1892 | SPY | 24.00 |
| ☐ The Bells | 1874 | APE | 24.00 |
| ☐ Mr. Laurence Irving | 1912 | WH | 20.00 |
| ☐ Author-Manager | 1892 | SPY | 20.00 |
| ☐ Hereditary Actor | 1907 | SPY | 20.00 |
| ☐ Mr. W. H. Kendal | 1893 | SPY | 20.00 |
| ☐ The Flying Stage | 1912 | RITCHIE | 20.00 |
| ☐ Our Only Comedian | 1875 | APE | N/S |
| ☐ Squirrel | 1897 | SPY | 20.00 |
| ☐ Amateur Theatricals | 1876 | SPY | 20.00 |
| ☐ Charley's Aunt | 1893 | SPY | N/S |
| ☐ Examiner of Plays | 1890 | PAL | 20.00 |
| ☐ Spencer | 1878 | SPY | N/S |
| ☐ Cinematographs | 1911 | APE JR. | 20.00 |
| ☐ Cyrano | 1901 | GUTH | 20.00 |
| ☐ Othello | 1875 | APE | N/S |
| ☐ Ficelle Dramatique | 1890 | T | 20.00 |
| ☐ The Poet's Son | 1879 | APE | 20.00 |
| ☐ The Coliseum | 1911 | APE JR. | 20.00 |
| ☐ The Coliseum | 1913 | OWL | 20.00 |
| ☐ The King's Jester | 1912 | WH | 24.00 |
| ☐ Dorian Gray | 1913 | OWL | 20.00 |
| ☐ Edward O'Connor Terry | 1905 | SPY | N/S |
| ☐ A Spelling Bee | 1876 | SPY | 20.00 |
| ☐ His Majesty's | 1911 | NIBS | 24.00 |
| ☐ Mr. Herbert Beerbohm Tree | 1890 | SPY | 24.00 |
| ☐ Leo | 1905 | SPY | 20.00 |
| ☐ Romantic Drama | 1904 | IMP | 20.00 |
| ☐ Le Doyen | 1914 | AST | 20.00 |
| ☐ Modern Pantomime | 1913 | HESTER | N/S |
| ☐ Through Every Passion | 1910 | ELF | 20.00 |

## TRACK

| CAPTION | YEAR | ARTIST | PRICE |
|---|---|---|---|
| ☐ The Champion | 1884 | APE | 30.00 |
| ☐ Oxford Athletics | 1894 | SPY | 45.00 |
| ☐ A.A.A. | 1895 | WAG | 30.00 |
| ☐ Fitz | 1896 | SPY | 30.00 |
| ☐ O.U.A.C. | 1897 | SPY | 30.00 |

## TRADE UNION OFFICIALS

| | CAPTION | YEAR | ARTIST | PRICE |
|---|---|---|---|---|
| ☐ | Social Revolution | 1879 | T | 18.00 |
| ☐ | The Working Man-Member | 1884 | SPY | 18.00 |
| ☐ | The Agricultural Labourer | 1886 | SPY | 18.00 |
| ☐ | Battersea | 1892 | SPY | 18.00 |
| ☐ | The Laborer is Worthy | 1905 | SPY | 18.00 |
| ☐ | Labour Men | 1908 | SPY | N/S |

## TURF DEVOTEES

| | CAPTION | YEAR | ARTIST | PRICE |
|---|---|---|---|---|
| ☐ | The Marquis | 1888 | LIB | 20.00 |
| ☐ | Bunny | 1876 | SPY | 20.00 |
| ☐ | Beer | 1889 | LIB | 20.00 |
| ☐ | The Head of the Pagets | 1880 | APE | 20.00 |
| ☐ | Fife | 1882 | SPY | N/S |
| ☐ | The Mate | 1877 | SPY | 24.00 |
| ☐ | Jed | 1899 | GAF | 20.00 |
| ☐ | Billy | 1905 | SPY | 20.00 |
| ☐ | Horses | 1880 | SPY | 20.00 |
| ☐ | Badminton | 1893 | SPY | 20.00 |
| ☐ | The Duke of Sport | 1876 | SPY | 20.00 |
| ☐ | The Jubilee Plunger | 1887 | SPY | N/S |
| ☐ | Starting | 1890 | LIB | 20.00 |
| ☐ | Master of the Horse | 1874 | APE | 20.00 |
| ☐ | Fred | 1885 | SPY | 20.00 |
| ☐ | Horsy | 1884 | SPY | 20.00 |
| ☐ | Shandy | 1888 | SPY | N/S |
| ☐ | A Turf Reformer | 1874 | APE | 20.00 |
| ☐ | Racing | 1885 | SPY | N/S |
| ☐ | Earlie | 1881 | APE | N/S |
| ☐ | Good Looks | 1876 | SPY | 20.00 |
| ☐ | Horses | 1888 | SPY | 20.00 |
| ☐ | Master of her Majesty's | 1872 | Unsigned | 20.00 |
| ☐ | Covey | 1881 | APE | 24.00 |
| ☐ | Fairie | 1910 | SPY | N/S |
| ☐ | Topps | 1912 | WH | 20.00 |
| ☐ | Billy | 1886 | LIB | 20.00 |
| ☐ | The Gaffer | 1908 | SPY | 20.00 |
| ☐ | Vixcount Dangan | 1889 | SPY | 20.00 |
| ☐ | Matt | 1886 | LIB | 20.00 |
| ☐ | Old Warren | 1894 | SPY | N/S |
| ☐ | John | 1885 | SPY | N/S |
| ☐ | The Turf | 1877 | SPY | N/S |
| ☐ | Charlie | 1878 | SPY | N/S |
| ☐ | Coals | 1887 | SPY | 20.00 |
| ☐ | Official Handicapper | 1889 | LIB | 20.00 |
| ☐ | Bridgewater House | 1887 | APE | 20.00 |
| ☐ | Never Bets | 1877 | SPY | 20.00 |
| ☐ | The Lad | 1883 | SPY | 20.00 |
| ☐ | Racing & Politics | 1881 | SPY | 20.00 |
| ☐ | Cart Horses | 1888 | SPY | 20.00 |
| ☐ | Condition | 1908 | SPY | 20.00 |
| ☐ | Young Hopeful | 1882 | SPY | 20.00 |
| ☐ | On the Heath | 1896 | SPY | 60.00 |
| ☐ | The French Tattersall | 1913 | OWL | N/S |
| ☐ | Melton | 1886 | SPY | 20.00 |
| ☐ | Havvy | 1901 | SPY | 20.00 |
| ☐ | The Purist of the Turf | 1870 | ATN | N/S |
| ☐ | Lord Hothfield | 1889 | SPY | 20.00 |
| ☐ | The New Steward | 1890 | SPY | 20.00 |
| ☐ | G.P. | 1908 | SPY | 20.00 |
| ☐ | Charley | 1886 | SPY | 20.00 |
| ☐ | Davie | 1908 | SPY | 20.00 |
| ☐ | Sir Robert Jardine | 1890 | SPY | 20.00 |
| ☐ | Willie | 1909 | ELF | 20.00 |
| ☐ | Freddy | 1878 | SPY | N/S |
| ☐ | Stanley House | 1904 | SPY | 20.00 |

| CAPTION | YEAR | ARTIST | PRICE |
|---|---|---|---|
| ☐ George Fox | 1878 | SPY | N/S |
| ☐ The Horse Has No Better Friend | 1912 | WH | 20.00 |
| ☐ Horses | 1886 | SPY | 20.00 |
| ☐ Billy | 1892 | SPY | 20.00 |
| ☐ Mr. H. L. B. McCalmont | 1889 | SPY | N/S |
| ☐ St. Bernards | 1894 | SPY | 20.00 |
| ☐ Jem | 1887 | SPY | 20.00 |
| ☐ The Universal Benefactor | 1889 | LIB | 20.00 |
| ☐ Sir James Milner | 1890 | LIB | 20.00 |
| ☐ Mr. Marcus Henry Miller | 1890 | LIB | 20.00 |
| ☐ Scotland & Racing | 1882 | SPY | N/S |
| ☐ Options | 1908 | ELF | 20.00 |
| ☐ Kilkenny | 1878 | SPY | 20.00 |
| ☐ Dandy | 1888 | SPY | N/S |
| ☐ G.P. | 1875 | APE | 20.00 |
| ☐ The Young Duke | 1882 | SPY | N/S |
| ☐ Horse Race Management | 1884 | SPY | 20.00 |
| ☐ Kemtoll | 1903 | CLOISTER | 20.00 |
| ☐ Horseflesh | 1876 | SPY | 20.00 |
| ☐ The Portly One | 1907 | SPY | 20.00 |
| ☐ Rock | 1883 | SPY | 20.00 |
| ☐ A Pupil | 1888 | LIB | 20.00 |
| ☐ Newmarket | 1904 | SPY | 20.00 |
| ☐ Horses | 1876 | SPY | 20.00 |
| ☐ As Straight As A Reed | 1870 | ATN | 20.00 |
| ☐ Sammy | 1892 | SPY | 20.00 |
| ☐ The Turf | 1880 | SPY | 20.00 |
| ☐ The Earl of Sefton | 1894 | LIB | 20.00 |
| ☐ Charlie | 1909 | SPY | 20.00 |
| ☐ Ralph | 1898 | STUFF | 20.00 |
| ☐ Podge | 1887 | SPY | N/S |
| ☐ He Invented The Conservative | 1880 | APE | N/S |
| ☐ Charlie | 1879 | APE | N/S |
| ☐ Suffield | 1907 | AO | N/S |
| ☐ Dover | 1887 | LIB | 20.00 |
| ☐ The Hatter | 1904 | SPY | 20.00 |
| ☐ Tattersall's | 1886 | LIB | 20.00 |
| ☐ Chippenham Park | 1894 | SPY | 20.00 |
| ☐ J.O.S. | 1907 | SPY | 20.00 |
| ☐ Versatility | 1910 | WHO | N/S |
| ☐ He Patronises Literature | 1906 | SPY | 20.00 |
| ☐ John | 1909 | SPY | N/S |
| ☐ Peter | 1905 | SPY | 20.00 |
| ☐ A Lucky Owner | 1906 | SPY | 20.00 |
| ☐ The Badminton | 1897 | SPY | 20.00 |
| ☐ The Match-Book | 1901 | SPY | 20.00 |
| ☐ Mr. James Weatherby | 1890 | LIB | 20.00 |
| ☐ The Affable Earl | 1883 | SPY | N/S |
| ☐ Sandown Park | 1891 | SPY | 20.00 |
| ☐ High Prices | 1884 | SPY | 20.00 |
| ☐ Youth | 1880 | SPY | 20.00 |
| ☐ Brokelsby | 1896 | SPY | N/S |
| ☐ Arthur | 1900 | UNK | N/S |

## WAGERERS

| CAPTION | YEAR | ARTIST | PRICE |
|---|---|---|---|
| ☐ The Leviathan | 1877 | SPY | N/S |
| ☐ Gang Forward | 1879 | SPY | N/S |
| ☐ No Limit | 1914 | SPY | N/S |

# YACHTING DEVOTEES

| CAPTION | YEAR | ARTIST | PRICE |
|---|---|---|---|
| ☐ An Unexpected Earl | 1873 | Unsigned | N/S |
| ☐ The Commodore | 1873 | Unsigned | N/S |
| ☐ The Ocean Race | 1874 | APE | N/S |
| ☐ Yachting | 1874 | APE | 24.00 |
| ☐ Round the World | 1877 | APE | N/S |
| ☐ Jour De Ma Vie | 1879 | SPY | N/S |
| ☐ Ralph | 1883 | T | 20.00 |
| ☐ The Regalia | 1891 | SPY | N/S |
| ☐ At Cowes | 1894 | SPY | 60.00 |
| ☐ Cambridge Registry | 1894 | SPY | N/S |
| ☐ Saide, R.Y.S. | 1894 | SPY | 20.00 |
| ☐ Vigilant | 1894 | SPY | 20.00 |
| ☐ Derek | 1895 | SPY | N/S |
| ☐ Ailsa | 1896 | MILLER | 20.00 |
| ☐ Giralda | 1896 | SPY | N/S |
| ☐ Knight of Kerry | 1901 | SPY | N/S |
| ☐ Shamrock | 1901 | SPY | 20.00 |
| ☐ Vice-Commodore | 1906 | SPY | 20.00 |
| ☐ Tiggy | 1907 | SPY | N/S |
| ☐ Fyvie | 1909 | SPY | N/S |
| ☐ Tony | 1910 | ELF | 20.00 |
| ☐ Istria | 1913 | OWL | 20.00 |

# CONTEMPORARY PRINTS
## ROBERT ABBETT

Robert Abbett, noted as one of America's contemporary masters of sporting and wildlife art, was born in Indiana and is a graduate of Purdue University and the University of Missouri. After formal art training at the Chicago Academy of Fine Art, Bob pursued a career in editorial and advertising art until a commission to paint "Luke", his first animal portrait, led him from illustration to a full-time artist.

Abbett is an accomplished outdoorsman. Perhaps this is one reason for his repeated success in evoking an emotional reaction in his art.

He paints only in oils, preferably on a gessoed panel on which he can draw, erase and redraw endlessly. The drawing stage of the work is, for him, vital. He feels it to be a learning process in itself, through which he teaches himself what he needs to know about the subject for that picture.

Abbett is associated with the American Artists Group and the Society of Illustrators, and is a member of the Society of Animal Artists. He has exhibited in numerous group and one-man shows, including the National Academy of Western Art Exhibition, and the Brandywine River Museum Exhibit. He was the recipient of the Salmagundi Club Gold Medal in 1973, and his paintings and prints have been shown in Tokyo and Peking.

**BLACK LAB FAMILY** *by Robert Abbett*

**ROBERT ABBETT**

| | ISSUE PRICE | CURRENT PRICE |
|---|---|---|
| ☐ **LUKE,** rel. 1973. ed. 500, s/n, 19″ x 24″, pub SEL. | 50.00 | 115.00 |
| Remarqued print, ed. 50. | 125.00 | 300.00 |
| ☐ **BOBWHITES AND POINTER,** rel. 1974. ed. 1,000, s/n, 27″ x 18¾″, pub TGW. | 65.00 | 180.00 |
| ☐ **GRAY WATER - BLACK LAB,** rel. 1974. ed. 500, s/n, 17″ x 26″, pub SEL. | 60.00 | 200.00 |
| ☐ **WINDFALL,** rel. 1974. ed. 550, s/n, 18¼″ x 26¼″, pub SEL. | 55.00 | 400.00 |
| ☐ **FIRST SEASON,** rel. 1975. ed. 1,000, s/n, 30″ x 22½″, pub TGW. | 65.00 | 150.00 |
| ☐ **RINGNECK AND SETTER,** rel. 1975. ed. 1,000, s/n, 30″ x 22″, pub TGW. | 65.00 | 150.00 |

|  | ISSUE PRICE | CURRENT PRICE |
|---|---|---|
| ☐ GERMAN SHORTHAIRED POINTER AND RUFFED GROUSE, rel. 1976. ed. 1,000, s/n, 28¾" x 22½", pub TGW. | 65.00 | Sold Out |
| ☐ NEW FIELDS, rel. 1976. ed. 1,000, s/n, 29" x 20½", pub TGW. | 65.00 | 85.00 |
| ☐ PARTNERS, rel. 1976. ed. 500, s/n, 15½" x 28⅝", pub SEL. | 70.00 | 125.00 |
| ☐ RINGNECK PHEASANT, rel. 1976. ed. 1,000, s/n, 30" x 17¼", pub TGW. | 65.00 | Sold Out |
| ☐ SETTER & WOODCOCK, rel. 1976. ed. 500, s/n, 23" x 18", pub SEL. | 60.00 | 125.00 |
| ☐ YANKEE DRUMMER, rel. 1976. ed. 500, s/n, 17¼" x 23", pub SEL. | 70.00 | 85.00 |
| ☐ CLOSE HONOR, rel. 1977. ed. 1,000, s/n, 30" x 21", pub TGW. | 75.00 | 150.00 |
| ☐ IRISH SETTER FAMILY, rel. 1977. ed. 1,000, s/n, 34" x 24", pub TGW. | 75.00 | 250.00 |
| ☐ SETTER & GROUSE, rel. 1977. ed. 500, s/n, 18⅛" x 27¼", pub SEL. | 95.00 | 160.00 |
| ☐ SPLIT RAIL BOBS, rel. 1977. ed. 500, s/n, 18⅛" x 27¼", pub SEL. | 95.00 | 200.00 |
| ☐ SPRINGTIME, rel. 1977. ed. 1,000, s/n, 30" x 21", pub TGW. | 65.00 | 85.00 |
| ☐ ENGLISH SETTER FAMILY, rel. 1978. ed. 750, s/n, 17½" x 27¼", pub SEL. | 125.00 | 200.00 |
| ☐ FISHING ON THE BITTERROOT, rel. 1978. ed. 500, s/n, 18¼" x 24", pub SEL. | 125.00 | — |
| ☐ HOLDING TIGHT, rel. 1978. ed. 500, s/n, 18⅛" x 27¼", pub SEL. | 125.00 | — |
| ☐ HUNTING THE EDGES, rel. 1978. ed. 500, s/n, 18" x 27", pub SEL. | 125.00 | — |
| ☐ LATE DAY WOODCOCKS, rel. 1978. ed. 500, s/n, 18" x 27", pub SEL. | 125.00 | — |
| ☐ HASTY EXIT, rel. 1979. ed. 750, s/n, 18⅛" x 27¼", pub SEL. | 125.00 | 250.00 |
| ☐ RIVERVIEW QUAIL, rel. 1979. ed. 750, s/n, 18⅛" x 27¼", pub SEL. | 150.00 | — |
| ☐ TRAINING AT HAWKEYE, rel. 1979. ed. 750, 2/n, 18⅛" x 27¼, pub SEL. | 125.00 | — |
| ☐ WILD COVEY, rel. 1979. ed. 750, s/n, 18⅛" x 27¼", pub SEL. | 125.00 | — |
| ☐ BLACK LAB HEAD, rel. 1980. ed. 500, s/n, 12" x 15", pub SEL. | 70.00 | 95.00 |
| ☐ THE BUCKING STRAP, rel. 1980. ed. 750, s/n, 19" x 24", pub SEL. | 125.00 | — |
| ☐ ENGLISH SETTER HEAD, rel. 1980. ed. 500, s/n, 12" x 15", pub SEL. | 70.00 | — |
| ☐ GERMAN SHORTHAIR HEAD, rel. 1980. ed. 500, s/n, 12" x 15", pub SEL. | 70.00 | — |
| ☐ GOLDEN RETRIEVER HEAD, rel. 1980. ed. 500, s/n, 12" x 15", pub SEL. | 70.00 | — |
| ☐ LATE SUMMER—BEAVERKILL, rel. 1980. ed. 750, s/n, 14" x 20¾", pub SEL. | 80.00 | — |
| ☐ SECOND SEASON, rel. 1980. ed. 750, s/n, 18⅛" x 27¼", pub SEL. | 150.00 | 250.00 |
| ☐ SPRINGER SPANIEL HEAD, rel. 1980. ed. 500, s/n, 12" x 15", pub SEL. | 70.00 | — |
| ☐ YELLOW LAB HEAD, rel. 1980. ed. 500, s/n, 12" x 15", pub SEL. | 70.00 | — |
| ☐ BLACK LAB FAMILY, rel. 1981. ed. 850, s/n, 18⅛"" x 27¼", pub SEL. | 150.00 | — |
| ☐ GERMAN SHEPHERD HEAD, rel. 1981. ed. 500, s/n, 12" x 15", pub SEL. | 75.00 | — |
| ☐ POINTER HEAD, rel. 1981. ed. 500, s/n, 12" x 15", pub SEL. | 75.00 | — |
| ☐ READY TO GO—Golden Retriever, rel. 1981. ed. 750, s/n, 18½" x 27¼", pub SEL. | 150.00 | — |
| ☐ BO AND DUKE, rel. 1982. ed. 850, s/n, size not available, pub WWI. | 125.00 | — |
| ☐ BRITTANY HEAD, rel. 1982. ed. 750, s/n, size N/A, pub WWI. | 75.00 | — |
| ☐ BROOMWEED COVEY RISE, rel. 1982. ed. 850, s/n, size N/A, pub WWI. | 150.00 | — |
| ☐ CROSSING AT SPLIT ROCK, rel. 1982. ed. 750, s/n, size not available, pub WWI. | 125.00 | — |
| ☐ WAITING AT HAWKEYE, rel. 1982. ed. 750, s/n, N/A, pub WWI. | 125.00 | — |

# HARRY ADAMSON

Harry Adamson was born in Seattle in 1916 and raised in the San Francisco Bay Area of California, a region rich in bird, plant and animal life. As a youth, he spent countless hours studying and sketching wildlife in their natural habitats. He experimented with various mediums and subjects, but most of his paintings are done in oil and are primarily of birds in flight.

After high school, Adamson studied under Paul J. Fair, whose instruction in wildlife anatomy was invaluable. He was a book illustrator at the Museum of Vetebrate Zoology, University of California, where he had the opportunity to study preservation and exhibits of thousands of birds and mammals, while pursuing his interest in art. Four years of service in World War II further strengthened his talents, as he took every advantage to observe the Old World's colorful countryside making quick pen and ink sketches, when the opportunity offered. Upon his return, he became a fulltime professional artist and within a few years his oils were finding wide acceptance throughout the United States. In 1952, one of his paintings of Pintail was purchased by Miguel Aleman Valdes, President of Mexico at that time.

In 1979, Adamson was honored as the Ducks Unlimited Artist of the Year. In 1980, his work was selected for the first major wildlife art exhibit at the National Fine Arts Collection of the Smithsonian Institute in Washington, D.C.

## HARRY ADAMSON

| | ISSUE PRICE | CURRENT PRICE |
|---|---|---|
| ☐ **WINGING IN - PINTAILS,** rel. 1971. ed. 450, s/n, 17" x 25", pub WWI . . . . . . . | 50.00 | 675.00 |
| ☐ **WILD BOUNTY - BLACK DUCKS,** rel. 1972. ed. 450, s/n, 17" x 25", pub WWI. | 50.00 | 600.00 |
| ed. 75 remarque artist proof . . . . . . . . . . . . . . . . . . . . . . . . . . . . . . . . . . . . | 125.00 | 800.00 |
| ☐ **AUTUMNS ECHLON - CANADA GEESE,** rel. 1973. ed. 480, s/n, 16" x 24", pub WWI . . . . . . . . . . . . . . . . . . . . . . . . . . . . . . . . . . . . . . . . . . . . . . . . . . . | 55.00 | 60.00 |
| ed. 75 remarque artist proof . . . . . . . . . . . . . . . . . . . . . . . . . . . . . . . . . . . . | 125.00 | — |
| ☐ **OXBOW SORCERY - MALLARDS,** rel. 1973. ed. 480, s/n, 16" x 24", pub WWI. | 55.00 | 500.00 |
| ed. 75 remarque artist proof . . . . . . . . . . . . . . . . . . . . . . . . . . . . . . . . . . . . | 125.00 | 675.00 |
| ☐ **WHISPERING WINGS - PINTAILS,** rel. 1973. ed. 600, s/n, 12" x 16", pub WWI . . . . . . . . . . . . . . . . . . . . . . . . . . . . . . . . . . . . . . . . . . . . . . . . . . . | 40.00 | 400.00 |
| ed. 70 remarque artist proof . . . . . . . . . . . . . . . . . . . . . . . . . . . . . . . . . . . . | 110.00 | 700.00 |
| ☐ **ARCTIC CITADEL - DALL SHEEP,** rel. 1974. ed. 580, s/n, 17½" x 25", pub WWI . . . . . . . . . . . . . . . . . . . . . . . . . . . . . . . . . . . . . . . . . . . . . . . . . . . | 55.00 | 700.00 |
| ☐ **GREENHEAD EXDOUS - MALLARDS,** rel. 1974. ed. 580, s/n, 15½" x 25", pub WWI . . . . . . . . . . . . . . . . . . . . . . . . . . . . . . . . . . . . . . . . . . . . . . . . . . . | 60.00 | 250.00 |
| ed. 50 remarque artist proof . . . . . . . . . . . . . . . . . . . . . . . . . . . . . . . . . . . . | 145.00 | 350.00 |
| ☐ **WINTER QUARTERS - WIGEON,** rel. 1974. ed. 580, s/n, 16" x 24", pub WWI. . | 55.00 | 75.00 |
| ed. 75 remarque artist proof . . . . . . . . . . . . . . . . . . . . . . . . . . . . . . . . . . . . | 125.00 | — |
| ☐ **THE CONCLAVE - DESERT BIGHORNS,** rel. 1975. ed. 580, s/n, 16½" x 25", pub WWI. . . . . . . . . . . . . . . . . . . . . . . . . . . . . . . . . . . . . . . . . . . . . . . . | 70.00 | 85.00 |
| ☐ **THE LOAFING BAR - MALLARDS,** rel. 1975. ed. 580, s/n, 16½" x 25", pub WWI. . . . . . . . . . . . . . . . . . . . . . . . . . . . . . . . . . . . . . . . . . . . . . . . . . . . | 70.00 | 350.00 |
| ed. 50 remarque artist proof . . . . . . . . . . . . . . . . . . . . . . . . . . . . . . . . . . . | 150.00 | 450.00 |
| ☐ **PINTAILS & THE SUTTER BUTTES,** rel. 1975. ed. 580, s/n, 16" x 25", pub WWI. . . . . . . . . . . . . . . . . . . . . . . . . . . . . . . . . . . . . . . . . . . . . . . . . . . | 70.00 | 300.00 |
| ed. 50 remarque artist proof . . . . . . . . . . . . . . . . . . . . . . . . . . . . . . . . . . . | 150.00 | 475.00 |
| ☐ **EVENING FLOTILLA - CANVASBACKS,** rel. 1976. ed. 600, s/n, 10½" x 16", pub WWI. . . . . . . . . . . . . . . . . . . . . . . . . . . . . . . . . . . . . . . . . . . . . . . . | 52.50 | 60.00 |
| ed. 50 remarque artist proof . . . . . . . . . . . . . . . . . . . . . . . . . . . . . . . . . . . | 150.00 | — |
| ☐ **FLURRY OF BLACKS,** rel. 1976. ed. 580, s/n, 16½" x 25", pub WWI. . . . . . . | 70.00 | — |
| ed. 50 remarque artist proof . . . . . . . . . . . . . . . . . . . . . . . . . . . . . . . . . . | 150.00 | — |
| ☐ **WINDY RIDGE - QUAIL,** rel. 1976. ed. 580, s/n, 16½" x 25", pub WWI. . . . . . | 70.00 | 85.00 |
| ☐ **JUGGLING ACT - GREEN WINGED TEAL,** rel. 1977. ed. 580, s/n, 20" x 17", pub WWI. . . . . . . . . . . . . . . . . . . . . . . . . . . . . . . . . . . . . . . . . . . . . . . . | 75.00 | 85.00 |
| ed. 50 remarque . . . . . . . . . . . . . . . . . . . . . . . . . . . . . . . . . . . . . . . . . . . | 160.00 | — |
| ☐ **PINTAILS TAKING FLIGHT,** rel. 1977. ed. 580, s/n, 17¾" x 22½", pub WWI. . | 75.00 | 85.00 |
| ed. 50 remarqued artist proofs . . . . . . . . . . . . . . . . . . . . . . . . . . . . . . . . | 160.00 | — |
| ☐ **SWAMP MIST - MALLARDS,** rel. 1977. ed. 580, s/n, 17¾" x 22½", pub WWI. . . . . . . . . . . . . . . . . . . . . . . . . . . . . . . . . . . . . . . . . . . . . . . . . . . . | 75.00 | 150.00 |
| ed. Proofs . . . . . . . . . . . . . . . . . . . . . . . . . . . . . . . . . . . . . . . . . . . . . . . | 160.00 | 300.00 |
| ☐ **WINGED ELEGANCE — PINTAILS,** rel. 1977. ed. 580, s/n, 16½" x 25", pub WWI. . . . . . . . . . . . . . . . . . . . . . . . . . . . . . . . . . . . . . . . . . . . . . . . . . . | 75.00 | 85.00 |
| ed. remarqued . . . . . . . . . . . . . . . . . . . . . . . . . . . . . . . . . . . . . . . . . . . . | 160.00 | — |
| ☐ **AFTER THE STORM - PINTAILS,** rel. 1978. ed. 850, s/n, 17½" x 23", pub WWI. . . . . . . . . . . . . . . . . . . . . . . . . . . . . . . . . . . . . . . . . . . . . . . . . . . | 85.00 | — |
| ed. 50 remarque . . . . . . . . . . . . . . . . . . . . . . . . . . . . . . . . . . . . . . . . . . | 185.00 | — |
| ☐ **EVENING SOLITUDE - BIG HORNS,** rel. 1978. ed. 850, s/n, 25" x 17 ¹/₈", pub WWI. . . . . . . . . . . . . . . . . . . . . . . . . . . . . . . . . . . . . . . . . . . . . . . . . . | 85.00 | — |
| ☐ **THE RENDEZVOUS - MALLARDS,** rel, 1979. ed. 850 s/n, 24¾" x 17 ¹/₈", pub WWI. . . . . . . . . . . . . . . . . . . . . . . . . . . . . . . . . . . . . . . . . . . . . . . . . . | 85.00 | — |
| ed. 40 artists proofs remarqued . . . . . . . . . . . . . . . . . . . . . . . . . . . . . . | 185.00 | — |
| ☐ **AUTUMN TABLEAU - MALLARDS,** rel. 1980. ed. 850, s/n, 16½" x 25", pub WWI. . . . . . . . . . . . . . . . . . . . . . . . . . . . . . . . . . . . . . . . . . . . . . . . . . . | 100.00 | — |
| ed. remarqued . . . . . . . . . . . . . . . . . . . . . . . . . . . . . . . . . . . . . . . . . . . | 200.00 | — |
| ☐ **AVIAN ELITE - PINTAILS,** rel. 1980. ed. 850, s/n, 25" x 16½", pub WWI. . . . | 100.00 | — |
| ed. 40 artists proofs remarqued . . . . . . . . . . . . . . . . . . . . . . . . . . . . . . | 200.00 | — |

| | ISSUE PRICE | CURRENT PRICE |
|---|---|---|
| ☐ **BROOMSEDGE COVER - BOBWHITE**, rel. 1980. ed. 850, s/n, 16½" x 25", pub WWI. | 100.00 | — |
| ed. remarqued | 200.00 | — |
| ☐ **CORNER POCKET - PINTAIL AND CINNAMON TEAL**, rel. 1980. ed. 850, s/n, 25" x 16½", pub WWI. | 100.00 | — |
| ed. 40 artists proofs remarqued | 200.00 | — |
| ☐ **EMPTY BLIND AT SUTTER BUTTES**, rel. 1980. ed. 650, s/n, 22" x 17½"", pub WWI. | 100.00 | — |
| ed. remarqued | 200.00 | — |
| ☐ **GRYFALCON**, rel. 1980. ed. 650, s/n, 22" x 17 ⅝", pub WWI | 100.00 | — |
| ☐ **JERSEY COAST - BLACK DUCKS**, rel. 1980. ed. 850, s/n, 25" x 16", pub WWI. | 100.00 | — |
| ed. 40 remarqued artists proofs | 200.00 | — |
| ☐ **WINTER IDYLL - MALLARDS**, rel. 1980. ed. 850, s/n, 25" x 16½", pub WWI. | 100.00 | — |
| ed. 40 artists proofs remarqued | 200.00 | — |
| ☐ **CALIFORNIA PINTAILS**, rel. 1981. ed. 950, s/n, size N/A, pub WWI | 125.00 | — |
| ☐ **JOURNEY'S END - CANADA GEESE**, rel, 1981. ed. 850 s/n, size N/A, pub WWI. | 125.00 | — |
| ☐ **OCTOBER INTERLUDE - MALLARDS**, rel. 1981. ed. 850, s/n, size N/A, pub WWI. | 125.00 | — |
| ☐ **OVER THE MARSH - SNOW GEESE**, rel. 1981. ed. 950, s/n, size N/A, pub WWI. | 125.00 | — |
| ☐ **STARTLED - MALLARDS**, rel. 1981. ed. 950, s/n, size N/A, pub WWI. | 125.00 | — |
| ☐ **NOVEMBER FANTASY - WIGEON**, rel. 1982. ed. 850, s/n, size N/A, pub WWI. | 125.00 | — |
| ☐ **PULLING OUT - MALLARDS**, rel. 1982. ed. 850, s/n, size N/A, pub WWI. | 100.00 | — |

# MARGI ADEY

| | | |
|---|---|---|
| ☐ **GREAT HORNED OWL**, ed. 1,000, s/n, 16" x 20", pub ALI | 50.00 | — |
| ☐ **OCELOT**, ed. 1,000, s/n, 16" x 20", pub ALI | 50.00 | — |

# J. J. ALEXANDER

J. J. Alexander is a resident of northern Delaware. He has traveled about this area of our country enjoying the natural and man-made settings which give it its character and mark its history. He has recorded this beauty thoughtfully and lovingly for the past thirty years.

Alexander learned to paint in the public schools and art clubs as a boy in Philadelphia. He also studied mechanical and architectural drafting and illustrating. Later, Alexander further developed his technique while studying at the Famous Artists School.

## J. J. ALEXANDER

| | | |
|---|---|---|
| ☐ **MILLINERY SHOP**, ed. 1000, s/n, 13½" x 10", pub SCI* | 30.00 | — |
| ☐ **NEIGHBORS**, ed. 1000, s/n, 14⅞" x 21⅛", pub SCI* | 30.00 | — |
| ☐ **RALEIGH TAVERN**, ed. 1000, s/n, 13⅛" x 22½", pub SCI* | 45.00 | — |

*Represents the Sawyier Collection Inc., and was formed as a subsidiary of Paul Sawyier Galleries, Inc.

NEIGHBORS
J.J. ALEXANDER

**NEIGHBORS** *by J.J. Alexander*

# BETTY ALLISON

|  | ISSUE PRICE | CURRENT PRICE |
|---|---|---|
| ☐ **NATURE'S TRINITY,** rel. 1977. *ed. 800, s/n, 18″ x 24″, pub A&C | 60.00 | 700.00 |
| ed. 25, remarques | 120.00 | 800.00 |
| *400 of edition was destroyed | | |
| ☐ **GRIZZLY,** rel. 1978. ed. 1,00, s/n, 16″ x 20″, pub A&C. | 30.00 | — |
| ☐ **CASCADES IN SHADE,** rel. 1979. ed. 1,000, s/n, 15″ x 30″, pub A&C. | 40.00 | 90.00 |
| ☐ **HE AND HIS LADY,** rel. 1979. | | |
| ed. 1,000 s/n. 18″ x 24″. pub A&C. | 40.00 | 80.00 |
| ed. 1,500 s/o. | 30.00 | — |
| ed. 100, artist proofs. | 50.00 | 125.00 |
| ☐ **CHINA BEAR,** rel. 1979. | | |
| ed. 1,000 s/n. 16″ x 20″. pub A&C. | 40.00 | 80.00 |
| ed. 1,100 s/o. | 30.00 | — |
| ☐ **WINTER'S PEACE,** rel. 1979. | | |
| ed. 1,000 s/n. 12″ x 16″. pub A&C. | 30.00 | 950.00 |
| ☐ **ROSES FOREVER,** rel. 1980. | | |
| ed. 3,000 s/o. 12″ x 16″. pub A&C. | 25.00 | — |
| ☐ **LOS NINOS,** rel. 1980. | | |
| ed. 1,000 s/n. 16″ x 20″. pub A&C. | 50.00 | 200.00 |
| ☐ **CARDINAL,** rel. 1981. | | |
| ed. 3,000 s/o. 12″ x 16″. pub A&C. | 30.00 | — |
| ☐ **IVORY HAZE,** rel. 1981. | | |
| ed. 1,000 s/n. 16″ x 20″. pub A&C. | 55.00 | — |
| ☐ **PROUD HORNS,** rel. 1981. | | |
| ed. 1,000 s/n. 16″ x 20″. pub A&C. | 55.00 | — |
| ☐ **COUGAR CUB,** rel. 1981. | | |
| ed. 1,000 s/n. 12″ x 16″. pub A&C. | 50.00 | — |
| ☐ **SUMMERS JOY,** rel. 1982. | | |
| ed. 1,000 s/n. 12″ x 16″. pub A&C. | 65.00 | — |

**IVORY HAZE** *by Betty Allison*

|  | ISSUE PRICE | CURRENT PRICE |
|---|---|---|
| ☐ **FREEDOM**, ed. N/A, s/n. pub A&C. | — | 200.00 |
| ☐ **ENCOUNTER**, ed. N/A, s/n. pub A&C. | — | 300.00 |
| ☐ **HUNTER'S DELIGHT**, ed. N/A, s/n. pub A&C. | — | 200.00 |
| ☐ **THE CHEETAH**, ed. N/A, s/n. pub A&C. | — | 275.00 |
| ☐ **IVORY HAZE**, ed. N/A, s/n. pub A&C. | 55.00 | 150.00 |
| ☐ **COUGAR CLUB**, ed. N/A, s/n. pub A&C. | 50.00 | — |
| ☐ **MARK OFROYALTY**, ed. N/A, s/n. pub A&C. | — | — |

# AXEL AMUCHASTEGUI

While studying aeronautical engineering, Axel Amuchastegui was introduced to watercolor in required renderings of aircraft sections. Thus began Amuchastegui's love affair with painting, a passion which has grown for four decades.

Family enthusiasm for a career in art was non-existent, and he spent the next few years in the field translating topographical lines into landscape renderings. His break came when a major publisher saw his bird and animal drawings in the state arts and crafts gallery and hired the artist as a book illustrator. He spent twenty years in this position becoming well-known throughout Argentina.

Later he came to New York with his paintings and was given a show at Kennedy Galleries. Next Tryon Galleries in London published three limited edition books of his work showing birds and mammals of South America, North America and Africa. He is also the author and illustrator of a three-volume work titled *Birds of the World*.

**NESTING ~ CANADA GOOSE** *by Axel Amuchastegui*

| AXEL AMUCHASEGUI | ISSUE PRICE | CURRENT PRICE |
|---|---|---|
| ☐ **JAGUAR RESTING**, rel. 1982. | | |
| ed. 950 s/n. 31¾" x 24½". pub MPPI. . . . . . . . . . . . . . . . . . . . . . . . . . . . . | 245.00 | — |
| ☐ **NESTING - CANADA GOOSE**, rel. 1982. | | |
| ed. 950 s/n. 31⅝"" x 24". pub MPPI. . . . . . . . . . . . . . . . . . . . . . . . . . . . | 265.00 | — |

# BARNEY ANDERSON

For the past twenty-five years, Barney Anderson has served as an art teacher and as chairman of the art department at Owatonna High School in Owatonna, Minnesota. While fulfilling his educational duties there he has further developed his skill in the fine art of pen and ink drawing.

This highly skilled technique is accomplished by making countless cross-hatchings with a needle-point pen on fabric-like paper. Much like the technique of dry point etching, this art form combines finely sketched detail with a remarkable range of values.

A lifelong resident of southern Minnesota, Anderson has spent a great deal of time hunting and fishing the marshes and lakes of that area. His pen and ink drawings are a direct result of such observations and experiences and capture on paper many moods and scenes typically experienced by the waterfowler.

| BARNEY ANDERSON | ISSUE PRICE | CURRENT PRICE |
|---|---|---|
| ☐ BLUEBILLS, rel. 1981. | | |
| ed. 580 s/n. size N/A, pub WWI. | 40.00 | — |
| ☐ MALLARDS, rel. 1981. | | |
| ed. 580 s/n. size N/A, pub WWI. | 40.00 | — |

# TROY ANDERSON

Sensitivity would probably be the best way to describe the essence of Troy Anderson's paintings. He uses a traditional technique to create paintings that reflect a style of contemporary realism, while also portraying the reverence for life inherent in the spirit of the American Indian.

Anderson, of Cherokee descent, was raised in Arkansas and Oklahoma. He studied art at West Texas State University where he earned his Bachelor of Science degree.

Anderson was recipient of the 1978 Heritage Grand Award and took first in the 1978 Cherokee Division from the Five Civilized Tribes Museum at Muskogee, Oklahoma. Anderson's work has been shown in many prestigious galleries.

## TROY ANDERSON

| | | |
|---|---|---|
| ☐ ON THE MOVE, rel. 1979. ed. 500, s/n, 32″ x 19⅝″, pub AIAC | 100.00 | — |
| ☐ SUMAC LEAVES "REMADE", ed. 1,500, s/n, 17″ x 23″, pub AIAC | 35.00 | — |

# HARRY ANTIS

Harry Antis spent more than seven years as a commercial illustrator painting automobiles, space vehicles and numerous other products, but nearly all of his spare time was still occupied with studying and painting of wildlife subjects. In 1970, he became a freelance artist.

"I find each new painting to be a stimulus for the next one and my field trips, whether it be a walk in the woods behind our home or an excursion to vast plains of East Africa, flood my mind with more ideas than I can find time to express. To portray each new subject as accurately as possible requires a considerable amount of research since details are not readily observed in the wild. This preparation for each individual painting also limits me to only twelve to fifteen finished works in a year's time," said Antis.

**BLACK BEAR** *by Harry Antis*

| HARRY ANTIS | ISSUE PRICE | CURRENT PRICE |
|---|---|---|
| ☐ **WHITETAIL BUCK,** rel. 1970. ed. 500, s/n, 24″ x 30″, pub GNAW. | 25.00 | 60.00 |
| ed. 2,500, s/o | 15.00 | 50.00 |
| ☐ **WHITETAIL DOE & FAWN,** rel. 1970. ed. 500, s/n, 24″ x 30″, pub GNAW. | 25.00 | 50.00 |
| ed. 2,500, s/o | 15.00 | 40.00 |
| ☐ **AMERICAN ELK,** rel. 1971. ed. 500, s/n, 24″ x 30″, pub GNAW. | 25.00 | 35.00 |
| ed. 2,500, s/o | 15.00 | 25.00 |
| ☐ **BLACK BEAR,** rel. 1971. ed. 500, s/n, 18″ x 24″, pub GNAW. | 25.00 | 60.00 |
| ed. 2,500, s/o | 15.00 | 50.00 |
| ☐ **RACCOONS AND CORN,** rel. 1971. ed. 500, s/n, 20″ x 24″, pub GNAW. | 30.00 | 75.00 |
| ed. 2,500, s/o | 20.00 | 65.00 |
| ☐ **COUGAR,** rel. 1971. ed. 500, s/n, 24″ x 30″, pub GNAW. | 75.00 | 250.00 |
| ☐ **CHIPMUNK,** rel. 1972. ed. 500, s/n, 10″ x 12″, pub GNAW. | 12.00 | 30.00 |
| ed. 2,500, s/o | 10.00 | 25.00 |
| ☐ **BOBCAT,** rel. 1972. ed. 500, s/n, 20″ x 24″, pub GNAW. | 30.00 | 90.00 |
| ed. 2,500, s/o | 20.00 | 75.00 |
| ☐ **TIMBER WOLF,** rel. 1972. ed. 500, s/n, 18″ x 24″, pub GNAW. | 30.00 | 90.00 |
| ed. 2,500, s/o | 20.00 | 75.00 |
| ☐ **BIG HORN SHEEP,** rel. 1972. ed. 1,000, s/n, 22″ x 26″, pub GNAW. | 50.00 | 85.00 |
| ☐ **BALD EAGLE,** rel. 1972. ed. 500, s/n, 24″ x 30″, pub GNAW. | 75.00 | 250.00 |
| ☐ **BEAR CUBS,** rel. 1973. ed. 500, s/n, 16″ x 20″, pub GNAW. | 30.00 | 40.00 |
| ed. 2,500, s/o | 20.00 | — |
| ☐ **AMERICAN JAGUAR,** rel. 1973. ed. 500, s/n, 20″ x 30″, pub GNAW. | 40.00 | 60.00 |
| ed. 2,500, s/o | 30.00 | — |
| ☐ **OLD AMERICAN (BUFFALO),** rel. 1973. ed. 500, s/n, 20″ x 24″, pub GNAW. | 35.00 | 50.00 |
| ed. 2,500, s/o | 25.00 | Sold Out |
| ☐ **PROUD AMERICAN,** rel. 1973 (COUGAR). ed. 500, s/n, 20″ x 24″, pub GNAW. | 35.00 | 70.00 |
| ed. 2,500, s/o | 25.00 | 40.00 |

| | ISSUE PRICE | CURRENT PRICE |
|---|---|---|
| ☐ **CARDINALS,** rel. 1973. ed. 3,000, s/o, 16″ x 20″, pub GNAW. . . . . . . . . . . | 20.00 | 50.00 |
| ☐ **BOBWHITE QUAIL,** rel. 1973. ed. 3,000, s/o, 16″ x 20″, pub GNAW. . . . . . . . . . . . . . . . . . . . . . . . . . . . . . . . . . . . . . . . | 20.00 | 90.00 |
| ☐ **MALLARD DRAKE,** rel. 1973. ed. 3,000, s/o, 16″ x 20″, pub GNAW. . . . . . . . . . . . . . . . . . . . . . . . . . . . . . . . . . . . . . | 20.00 | 65.00 |
| ☐ **A REFRESHING PAUSE (EASTERN BLUEBIRDS),** rel. 1973. ed. 3,000, s/o, 16″x 20″, pub GNAW. . . . . . . . . . . . . . . . . . . . | 20.00 | 40.00 |
| ☐ **SAW-WHAT? (SAW-WHET OWL).** rel. 1974. ed. 2,000, s/n, 12″ x 14″, pub GNAW. . . . . . . . . . . . . . . . . . . . . . . . . . . . . | 20.00 | 50.00 |
| ☐ **THE PATRIARCH (AFRICAN LIONS),** rel. 1974. ed. 500, s/n, 24″ x 36″, pub GNAW. . . . . . . . . . . . . . . . . . . . . . . . . . . | 75.00 | 275.00 |
| ☐ **ALWAYS UNDERFOOT (EMPEROR PENGUIN & CHICK),** rel. 1974. 1,500, s/n, 16″ x 20″, pub GNAW. . . . . . . . . . . . . . . | 25.00 | — |
| ☐ **THE NEW LANDLORD (GOSHAWK),** rel. 1974. ed. 1,500, s/n, 16″ x 20″, pub GNAW. . . . . . . . . . . . . . . . . . . . . . . . . . | 25.00 | — |
| ☐ **OCTOBER MORNING (PHEASANT),** rel. 1975. ed. 950, s/n, 20″ x 32″, pub GNAW. . . . . . . . . . . . . . . . . . . . . . . . . . . | 65.00 | — |
| ☐ **WATCHING AND WAITING (CHEETAH),** rel. 1975. ed. 2,000, s/n, 20″ x 24″, pub SG. . . . . . . . . . . . . . . . . . . . . . . . . | 50.00 | — |
| ☐ **PLAYING CAT & MOUSE (COUGAR CUBS),** rel. 1974. ed. 500, s/n, 20″ x 22″, pub GNAW. . . . . . . . . . . . . . . . . . . . . . . | 35.00 | 50.00 |
| ed. 750, s/o . . . . . . . . . . . . . . . . . . . . . . . . . . . . . . . . | 25.00 | 40.00 |
| ☐ **BREAKING THE COVER (WHITETAIL DEER),** rel. 1976. ed. 2,000, s/n, 20″ x 24″, pub SG. . . . . . . . . . . . . . . . . . . . . . | 50.00 | — |
| ☐ **THE HIGH COUNTRY (BALD EAGLE),** rel. 1976. ed. 1,500, s/n, 24″ x 30″, pub SG. . . . . . . . . . . . . . . . . . . . . . . . . . . | 60.00 | — |
| ☐ **THE MATRIARCH (ELEPHANT),** rel. 1977. ed. 1,250, s/n, 23½″ x 37½″, pub SG. . . . . . . . . . . . . . . . . . . . . . . . . . | 75.00 | — |
| ☐ **LEOPARD'S DOMAIN,** rel. 1977. ed. 2,000, s/n, 23″ x 29″, pub SG. . . . . . . . | 50.00 | — |
| ☐ **THE STALKER (COUGAR),** rel. 1978. ed. 1,000, s/n, 16¼″ x 20″, pub SG. . . . | 75.00 | — |
| ☐ **COUGAR COUNTRY,** rel. 1978. ed. 1,000, s/n, 16″ x 20″, pub SG. . . . . . . . . | 40.00 | Sold Out |
| ☐ **CLOSE ENCOUNTER,** rel. 1978. ed. 1,000, s/n, 18½″ x 24″, pub SG. . . . . . . | 50.00 | — |
| ☐ **WAPITI,** rel. 1978. ed. 1,000, s/n, 18″ x 29″, pub SG. . . . . . . . . . . . . . . | 60.00 | — |
| ☐ **OLD BANANA HORN,** rel. 1979. ed. 1,000, s/n, 20″ x 29″, pub SG. . . . . . . . | 75.00 | — |
| ☐ **FREE TRAPPERS,** rel. 1979. ed. 650, s/n, 16½″ x 29″, pub SG. . . . . . . . . | 75.00 | Sold Out |
| ☐ **PASSING IN WINTER SILENCE,** rel. 1979. ed. 500, s/n 19″ x 29″, pub SG. . . . | 75.00 | — |

Publishers listed . . . GNAW and SG are no longer in business. Further information available at a later date.

# JACK APPLETON

Jack Appleton graduated from the American Academy of Art in Chicago. His paintings are in private collections, public buildings and offices. He was selected one of Indiana's outstanding artists by the Indiana State Museum. He has participated in and won awards in the Hoosier Art Salon, the Michigan Biennial and the Union Art League of Chicago, in addition to his one-man exhibit at Marshall Field's Picture Galleries.

Attention to detail is persistent in his midwest landscapes and architecture, whether pencil, pen and ink, dry-brush gouache or egg tempera.

| **JACK APPLETON** | ISSUE PRICE | CURRENT PRICE |
|---|---|---|
| ☐ **THE HORSE STALL,** ed. 950, s/n, 23″ x 15″, pub CGAL. . . . . . . . . . . . . . | 50.00 | — |
| ed. 12, Artist accented, s/n . . . . . . . . . . . . . . . . . . . | 100.00 | — |
| ☐ **THE FARM PORCH,** ed. 950, s/n, 23″ x 16½″, pub CGAL. . . . . . . . . . . . . | 50.00 | — |
| ☐ ed. 12, Artist accented, s/n . . . . . . . . . . . . . . . . . . . | 100.00 | — |
| ☐ **GLAZED SILO,** ed. 95. s/n, 22″ x 14½″, pub CGAL. . . . . . . . . . . . . . . . | 50.00 | — |
| ed. 12, Artist accented, s/n . . . . . . . . . . . . . . . . . . . | 100.00 | — |
| ☐ **GOING HOME,** rel. 950, s/n, 22″ x 14½″, pub CGAL. . . . . . . . . . . . . . . . | 50.00 | — |
| ed 12, Artist accented, s/n . . . . . . . . . . . . . . . . . . . | 100.00 | — |

# CLYDE ASPEVIG

A burning desire to capture the essence of the landscape of the northwestern United States characterizes the art of Clyde Aspevig. His dramatic landscapes have won him acclaim and awards throughout the West.

As a 1975 graduate of Eastern Montana College in Billings, Aspevig sketches the layout of his painting on canvas while afield. He then takes a series of photographs and notes which will accompany him to his studio for completion of his work.

Aspevig's one-man shows have been consistent sellouts. At the 1981 Western Rendezvous of Art his "30 minute quick draw sketch" sold for $3,500. In 1980 one of his paintings won one of only six awards of merit which were given at the Rendezvous Show.

| CLYDE ASPEVIG | ISSUE PRICE | CURRENT PRICE |
|---|---|---|
| ☐ TOUNGE RIVER COUNTRY, rel. 1981. ed. N/A, s/n, 24″ x 16″, distr. SGL. . . . | 75.00 | |
| ☐ PASSAGE, rel. 1981. ed. N/A, s/n, 24″ x 16″, distr. SGL. . . . . . . . . . . . . . . . | 65.00 | |
| ☐ THE VALLEY, rel. 1981. ed. N/A, s/n, 25″ x 17″, distr. SGL. . . . . . . . . . . . . . | 65.00 | |
| ☐ TONGUE RIVER COUNTRY, rel. 1983. ed. 1,000, s/n, 26″ x 16″, distr. SGL. . . | 75.00 | |

# ANTHONY AUTORINO

| | | |
|---|---|---|
| ☐ APRES, rel. 1977. ed. 100, s/n, etching, pub MMGI . . . . . . . . . . . . . . . . . . . . . | 30.00 | — |
| ☐ AUGUST HAT, rel. 1977. ed. 100, s/n, etching, pub MMGI . . . . . . . . . . . . . . . | 50.00 | — |
| ☐ NATURES WAY, rel. 1978. ed. 200, s/n, litho, pub MMGI . . . . . . . . . . . . . . . . | 50.00 | — |

# ANDREY AVINOFF

| | | |
|---|---|---|
| ☐ AVINOFF ORCHIDS, rel. 1960. | | |
| *Sold only as a pair | | |
| ☐ Pair #1 - The Baroness - Plate No. 9 | | |
| Truffautiana 'Aurea' - Plate No. 10 . . . . . . . . . . . . . . . . . . . . . . . . | 25.00* | — |
| ☐ Pair #2 - Cliftonil 'Magnifica' - Plate No. 21 | | |
| David Adams - Plate No. 22 . . . . . . . . . . . . . . . . . . . . . . . . . . . . . | 25.00 | — |
| ☐ Pair #3 - Hybrid from Bic. Xanthea - Plate No. 39 | | |
| C. Mossiae - Plate No. 40 . . . . . . . . . . . . . . . . . . . . . . . . . . . . . | 25.00 | — |
| ☐ Pair #4 - Lc. Marie Dobrott - Plate No. 41 | | |
| C. Empress Frederick - Plate No. 42 . . . . . . . . . . . . . . . . . . . . . | 25.00 | — |
| ☐ FIRESTONE ROSE, rel. 1976. ed. 1,250, 11″ x 14″, pub NHI . . . . . . . . . . . . . . | 12.50 | — |
| ☐ TULIP, rel. 1976. ed. 1,250, 11″ x 14″, pub NHI . . . . . . . . . . . . . . . . . . . . . . . | 12.50 | — |
| ☐ PINK ROSE/YELLOW ROSE, rel. 1976. ed. 1,250, 11″ x 14″, pub NHI . . . . . . . | 30.00* | — |
| *Sold only as a set of two. | | |
| ☐ FLEMISH BOUQUET, rel. 1976. ed. 1,250, 16″ x 20″, pub NHI . . . . . . . . . . . . . | 30.00 | — |

**FLEMISH BOUQUET** *by Andrey Avinoff*

## WILLIAM C. BAGGETT, JR.

William C. Baggett, Jr. studied and taught at Auburn University and the University of Mississippi. A charter member of the Southern Watercolor Society, Mr. Baggett has exhibited in several national exhibitions including the American Watercolor Society and the Rocky Mountain National Watermedia Exhibition. He has won numerous awards in the South, and his prints and watercolors are represented in public and private collections throughout the country and in thirteen foreign nations.

**WILLIAM C. BAGGETT, JR.**

| | ISSUE PRICE | CURRENT PRICE |
|---|---|---|
| ☐ **STANDING ROOM ONLY,** ed. 900, s/n, 24″ x 15″, pub NG . . . . . . . . . . . . . . . | 40.00 | — |

## WAYNE BAIZE

Native Texan Wayne Baize enjoys his life as a western artist because it enables him to combine ranching and painting into a profitable career.

Under the artistic influence of his older brother, Baize began drawing, taking his first art lessons at age 12. He had no formal art training after high school; his education as a western artist took the form of incessant practice. Years of observing horses and cattle yielded a profound anatomical knowledge of these animals. His full time artistic career began as a portrait painter in a Western goods store. Baize now lives on a 400 acre ranch near Ft. Davis, Texas, where he raises herefords, mix-breeds and quarter horses. His subjects are drawn from his surroundings, the environment and lifestyle he understands and loves.

**FRISKY FILLY** *by Wayne Baize*

## WAYNE BAIZE

| | ISSUE PRICE | CURRENT PRICE |
|---|---|---|
| ☐ LAZY SUMMER DAYS, rel. 1974. ed. 2,500, s/o, 27" x 15", pub FHG. | 30.00 | 125.00 |
| ☐ LIMPIA CREEK CROSSING, rel. 1975. ed. 1,500, s/n, 28" x 21½", pub FHG. | 40.00 | 300.00 |
| ☐ WINTER STAGE, rel. 1976. ed. 1,000, s/n, 11½" x 22", pub FHG. | 30.00 | 125.00 |
| ☐ COWBOY CAMP, rel. 1977. ed. 500, s/n, 20" x 28", pub FHG. | 40.00 | 200.00 |
| ☐ HER GIFT, rel. 1977. ed. 500, s/n, 20" x 28", pub FHG. | 40.00 | 300.00 |
| ☐ HER PRIDE, rel. 1978. ed. 500, s/n, 28" x 22", pub FHG. | 50.00 | 250.00 |
| ☐ RANGE BABY, rel. 1978. ed. 500, s/n, 18" x 24", pub FHG. | 50.00 | 1,600.00 |
| ☐ HER TENDER LOVING CARE, rel. 1979. ed. 750, s/n, 22" x 28", pub FHG. | 50.00 | 75.00 |
| ☐ THE GOAT KEEPER/WASHDAY, rel. 1979. ed. 750, s/n, 15" x 18", pub FHG. | *40.00 | — |
| *Sold as a pair. | | |
| ☐ THE HITCHHIKER, rel. 1979. ed. 750, s/n, 17" x 30", pub FHG. | 55.00 | 100.00 |
| ☐ THE NEW BORN, rel. 1979. ed. 750, s/n, 22" x 28", pub FHG. | 50.00 | 130.00 |
| ☐ THE WATERHOLE, rel. 1979. ed. 750, s/n, 26" x 20", pub FHG. | 55.00 | 100.00 |
| ☐ NATURE'S BLESSING, rel. 1981. ed. 1,000, s/n, 16½" x 21½", pub TAP. | 90.00 | 120.00 |
| ☐ SPRING, rel. 1981. ed. 1,000, s/n, 16¾" x 21½", pub TAP. | 60.00 | 200.00 |
| ☐ FIT TO BE HITCHED, rel. 1982. ed. 1,000, s/n, 16½" x 21½", pub TAP. | 90.00 | — |
| ☐ IN THE LEAD, rel. 1982. ed. 1,000, s/n, 15¾" x 25", pub TAP. | 90.00 | — |
| ☐ WAITIN' UP, rel. 1982. ed. 1,000, s/n, 29" x 14¾", pub TAB. | 90.00 | — |
| ☐ A ROYAL BREED, rel. 1983. ed. 1,000, s/n, 16½" x 21¼", pub TAP. | 90.00 | — |
| ☐ FRISKY FILLY, rel. 1983. ed. 1,000, s/n, 12" x 16", pub TAP. | 80.00 | — |
| ☐ FROSTY MORN, rel. 1983. ed. 1,000, s/n, 12" x 16", pub TAP. | 80.00 | — |
| ☐ HIDING OUT, rel. 1983. ed. 1,000, s/n, 17" x 22½", pub TAP. | 90.00 | — |

## FELICIE BALAY

| | ISSUE PRICE | CURRENT PRICE |
|---|---|---|
| ☐ **HOMMAGE**, ed. 225, s/n, 33″ x 28¼″, original color lithograph, pub FI . . . . . . | **175.00** | **500.00** |

## DON BALKE

Don Balke has the ability to make a bird or animal come to life. With autonomical accuracy, clarity, attention to detail and fine brushwork, he creates a scene of vital realism. Working in transparent and opaque watercolor, he brings brilliance to his paintings with a highly developed sense of color.

Balke has illustrated the covers of various magazines and his paintings hang in many corporate and private collections. He is presently at work on an extensive commission sanctioned by the National Audubon Society involving birds and flowers.

The artist personally supervises every step of the printing process and is present at the press for every proofing and the entire run. Each print is then inspected by him before it is signed and numbered. This careful attention has been rewarded many times with the prestigious Blue Ribbon awards from the Printing Industries of America in their annual competition. His reproductions have been displayed in the International Print Show in Dusseldorf, Germany, as examples of the finest in printing quality.

**RED FOX** *by Don Balke*

## DON BALKE

| | ISSUE PRICE | CURRENT PRICE |
|---|---|---|
| **BIRDS OF PREY SERIES** | | |
| ☐ BARN OWL, rel. 1976. ed. 1,000, s/n, 20" x 26", distr. MMFC............ | 40.00 | — |
| ☐ BALD EAGLE, rel. 1977. ed. 1,000, s/n, 27" x 35½", distr. MMFC......... | 75.00 | 150.00 |
| ☐ OSPREY, rel. 1979. ed. 1,000, s/n, 23¼" x 30¾", distr. MMFC.......... | 55.00 | Sold Out |
| ☐ SNOWY OWL, rel. 1979. ed. 1,000, s/n, 22" x 28", distr. MMFC.......... | 55.00 | Sold Out |
| **FLEETWOOD SERIES** | | |
| ☐ CANADA GOOSE, rel. 1979. ed. 1,000, s/n, 17½" x 20½", distr. MMFC..... | 45.00 | Sold Out |
| ☐ THE INVESTIGATOR, rel. 1979. ed. 1,000, s/n, 19½" x 20½", distr. MMFC.. | 45.00 | Sold Out |
| **HERITAGE SERIES** | | |
| ☐ RUFFED GROUSE, rel. 1977. ed. 1,000, s/n, 20" x 26", distr. MMFC....... | 45.00 | — |
| ☐ SUMMER BOBWHITES, rel. 1977. ed. 1,000, s/n, 23¾" x 34½", distr. MMFC............................... | 55.00 | — |
| ☐ WILD TURKEY, rel. 1977. ed. 1,000, s/n, 24" x 34½", distr. MMFC....... | 60.00 | 120.00 |
| ☐ GRAY FOX, rel. 1978. ed. 1,000, s/n, 21¼" x 33", distr. MMFC.......... | 75.00 | 200.00 |
| ☐ TIMBER WOLVES, rel. 1978. ed. 1,000, s/n, 24" x 32", distr. MMFC....... | 75.00 | — |
| ☐ COUGAR, rel. 1980. ed. 1,000, s/n, 24" x 32", distr. MMFC............. | 75.00 | — |
| ☐ RED FOX FAMILY, rel. 1980. ed. 1,000, s/n, 27" x 35½", distr. MMFC..... | 95.00 | — |
| **HOMESTEADING SERIES** | | |
| ☐ AUTUMN DAY, rel. 1982. ed. 1,000, s/n, 18¾" x 23", distr. MMFC....... | 75.00 | — |
| ☐ ESCAPE, rel. 1982. ed. 1,000, s/n, 14¾" x 20", distr. MMFC............ | 75.00 | — |
| ☐ GOLD FINCHES, rel. 1982. ed. 1,000, s/n, 12" x 15½", distr. MMFC....... | 65.00 | — |
| **MASTERPIECE SERIES** | | |
| ☐ BOBWHITE QUAIL, rel. 1976. ed. 1,000, s/n, 24" x 32", distr. MMFC...... | 50.00 | 300.00 |
| ☐ RED FOX, rel. 1976. ed. 1,000, s/n, 24" x 34½", distr. MMFC............ | 50.00 | 350.00 |
| ☐ WHITE-TAILED DEER, rel. 1976. ed. 1,000, s/n, 24" x 32", distr. MMFC..... | 50.00 | — |
| **NATURE SERIES - (Black and White)** | | |
| ☐ BARRED OWL, ed. 450, s/n, 11" x 14", distr. MMFC.................... | 6.00 | 60.00 |
| ☐ BOBWHITE QUAIL, ed. 450, s/n, 11" x 14", distr. MMFC............... | 6.00 | 25.00 |
| ☐ CANADIAN LYNX, ed. 450, s/n, 11" x 14", distr. MMFC............... | 6.00 | 15.00 |
| ☐ CARDINALS, ed. 450, s/n, 11" x 14", distr. MMFC................... | 6.00 | 25.00 |
| ☐ GRAY SQUIRREL, ed. 450, s/n, 11" x 14", distr. MMFC............... | 6.00 | 25.00 |
| ☐ MALLARDS, ed. 450, s/n, 11" x 14", distr. MMFC.................... | 6.00 | 60.00 |
| ☐ PHEASANT, ed. 450, s/n, 11" x 14", distr. MMFC.................... | 6.00 | 25.00 |
| ☐ RACCOONS, ed. 450, s/n, 11" x 14", distr. MMFC................... | 6.00 | 60.00 |
| ☐ RED-TAILED HAWK, ed. 450, s/n, 11" x 14", distr. MMFC.............. | 6.00 | 25.00 |
| ☐ SMALL MOUTH BLACK BASS, ed. 450, s/n, 11" x 14", distr. MMFC........ | 6.00 | 15.00 |
| ☐ WHITE-TAILED DEER, ed. 450, s/n, 11" x 14", distr. MMFC............. | 6.00 | 25.00 |
| **NORTH AMERICAN SERIES** | | |
| ☐ AMERICAN BADGER, rel. 1974. ed. 950, s/n, 22" x 28", distr. MMFC....... | 35.00 | — |
| ☐ AMERICAN ROBIN, rel. 1974. ed. 950, s/n, 14" x 18", distr. MMFC........ | 20.00 | 60.00 |
| ☐ BLACK-CAPPED CHICKADEE, rel. 1974. ed. 950, s/n, 14" x 18", distr. MMFC. | 20.00 | — |
| ☐ GRAY FOX, rel. 1974. ed. 950, s/n, 22" x 28", distr. MMFC............ | 35.00 | 175.00 |
| ☐ RACCOON, rel. 1974. ed. 950, s/n, 18" x 23", distr. MMFC............. | 25.00 | 115.00 |
| ☐ RUFFED GROUSE, rel. 1974. ed. 950, s/n, 22" x 28", distr. MMFC........ | 35.00 | — |
| ☐ BOBCAT KITTEN, rel. 1975. ed. 750, s/n, 10¾" x 13⅝", distr. MMFC....... | 25.00 | — |
| ☐ BOBWHITES, rel. 1975. ed. 600, s/n, 20" x 28", distr. MMFC.......... | 45.00 | 200.00 |
| ☐ BROWN PELICAN, rel. 1975. ed. 600, s/n, 20" x 28", distr. MMFC........ | 45.00 | — |
| ☐ CARDINALS, rel. 1975. ed. 950, s/n, 16⅝" x 21", distr. MMFC.......... | 35.00 | 225.00 |
| ☐ COUGAR CUB, rel. 1975. ed. 750, s/n, 10¾" x 13⅝", distr. MMFC........ | 25.00 | — |
| ☐ GRAY SQUIRRELS, rel. 1975. ed. 950, s/n, 18" x 23", distr. MMFC........ | 35.00 | 150.00 |
| ☐ HOMESTEADING, rel. 1975. ed. 750, s/n, 20" x 28", distr. MMFC........ | 60.00 | Sold Out |
| ☐ MALLARDS, rel. 1975. ed. 950, s/n, 22" x 28", distr. MMFC........... | 45.00 | — |
| ☐ RING-NECKED PHEASANT, rel. 1975. ed. 600, s/n, 24" x 32", distr. MMFC. . | 45.00 | 210.00 |
| ☐ WHITE-TAILED FAWN, rel. 1975 (Plate 18). ed. 750, s/n, 15¾" x 19¾", distr. MMFC............................... | 30.00 | — |
| ☐ WHITE-TAILED FAWN, rel. 1975 (Plate 19). ed. 750, s/n, 15¾" x 19¾", distr. MMFC............................... | 30.00 | — |
| NOTE: The two fawn prints could be sold as a pair...................... | 50.00 | — |
| ☐ WOOD DUCKS, rel. 1975. ed. 950, s/n, 22" x 26", distr. MMFC.......... | 45.00 | 145.00 |
| ☐ SHIPWRECK, rel. 1976. ed. 950, s/n, 20" x 28", distr. MMFC........... | 50.00 | 125.00 |
| **SEA AND SHORE BIRD SERIES** | | |
| ☐ SANDPIPERS, rel. 1978. ed. 1,000, s/n, 18" x 23", distr. MMFC.......... | 45.00 | — |

| | ISSUE PRICE | CURRENT PRICE |
|---|---|---|
| **SONG BIRDS SERIES** | | |
| ☐ **RUBY THROATED HUMMINGBIRD,** rel. 1980. ed. 1,000, s/n, 14″ x 19″, distr. MMFC. | 40.00 | — |
| ☐ **RUFOUS HUMMINGBIRD,** rel. 1980. ed. 1,000, s/n, 14″ x 19″, distr. MMFC. | 40.00 | — |
| ☐ **CARDINALS IN SPRINGTIME,** rel. 1982. ed. 1,000, s/n, 16″ x 19½″, distr. MMFC. | 65.00 | — |
| **VEIN MOUNTAIN SERIES** | | |
| ☐ **CARDINAL FAMILY,** rel. 1978. ed. 1,000, s/n, 18″ x 23″, dist. by MMFC. | 45.00 | 175.00 |
| ☐ **CHIPMUNKS,** rel. 1978. ed. 1,000, s/n, 17″ x 21″, dist. by MMFC. | 40.00 | — |
| ☐ **COTTONTAILS,** rel. 1978. ed. 1,000, s/n, 18″ x 23″, dist. by MMFC. | 45.00 | — |
| ☐ **LITTLE BANDITS,** rel. 1978. ed. 1,000, s/n, 18″ x 23″, dist. by MMFC. | 45.00 | 175.00 |
| ☐ **A PAIR OF QUAIL,** rel. 1978. ed. 1,000, s/n, 17″ x 21″, dist. by MMFC. | 40.00 | — |
| ☐ **RED FOX PUP,** rel. 1978. ed. 1,000, s/n, 17″ x 21″, dist. by MMFC. | 40.00 | 175.00 |
| ☐ **YOUNG SKUNKS,** rel. 1978. ed. 1,000, s/n, 18″ x 23″, dist. by MMFC. | 45.00 | — |
| ☐ **BLUEBIRD FAMILY,** rel. 1979. ed. 1,000, s/n, 18″ x 23″, dist. by MMFC. | 45.00 | 140.00 |
| ☐ **GRAY SQUIRREL FAMILY,** rel. 1979. ed. 1,000, s/n, 18″ x 23″, dist. by MMFC. | 45.00 | 175.00 |
| ☐ **SCREECH OWL,** rel. 1980. ed. 1,000, s/n, 17⅜″ x 23½″, distr. MMFC. | 55.00 | — |
| ☐ **THE ENCOUNTER,** rel. 1981. ed. 1,000, s/n, 22″ x 29″, distr. MMFC. | 110.00 | — |

# JAMES BAMA

Born in 1926 and endowed with natural ability as an artist, James Bama attended the specialized High School of Music and Art in New York and then went on to the Art Student's League. He free lanced briefly before going to work for the Charles E. Cooper Studios where he remained for nearly fifteen years. He did illustrations for *The Saturday Evening Post* and Bantam Books, painted portraits of the

**DAVILLA BROTHERS** *by Jim Bama*

"greats" for the New York Football Giants and the Baseball Hall of Fame, and made trips abroad to paint for the U.S. Air Force.

His work hangs in many prestigious collections. He has been represented in major exhibitions throughout the West and has had two one-man shows in New York City. A book, *The Western Art of James Bama*, was published in 1975. He has, indeed, cut a wide swath through American art.

## JAMES BAMA

| | ISSUE PRICE | CURRENT PRICE |
|---|---|---|
| ☐ KEN HUNDER, WORKING COWBOY, rel. 1974. ed. 1,000, s/n, 21" x 24", pub GW. | 55.00 | 375.00 |
| ☐ SHOSHONE CHIEF, rel. 1974. ed. 1,000, s/n, 20" x 26", pub GW. | 65.00 | 485.00 |
| ☐ CHUCK WAGON IN THE SNOW, rel. 1975. ed. 1,000, s/n, 18½" x 16", pub GW. | 50.00 | 300.00 |
| ☐ SAGE GRINDER, rel. 1976. ed. 1,000, s/n, 20" x 24", pub GW. | 65.00 | 850.00 |
| ☐ A CROW INDIAN, rel. 1977. ed. 1,000, s/n, 22½" x 18", pub GW. | 65.00 | 225.00 |
| ☐ TIMBER JACK JOE, rel. 1977. ed. 1,000, s/n, 19" x 24", pub GW. | 65.00 | 365.00 |
| ☐ A MOUNTAIN UTE, rel. 1978. ed. 1,000, s/n, 19¼" x 24", pub GW. | 75.00 | 300.00 |
| ☐ CONTEMPORARY SIOUX INDIAN, rel. 1978. ed. 1,000, s/n, 32" x 22", pub GW. | 75.00 | 190.00 |
| ☐ MOUNTAIN MAN, rel. 1978. ed. 1,000, s/n, 19" x 24", pub GW. | 75.00 | 475.00 |
| ☐ ROOKIE BRONC RIDER, rel. 1978. ed. 1,000, s/n, 22" x 17½", pub GW. | 75.00 | 150.00 |
| ☐ HERITAGE, rel. 1979. ed. 1,500, s/n, 23½" x 23½", pub GW. | 75.00 | 185.00 |
| ☐ INDIAN AT CROW FAIR, rel. 1979. ed. 1,500, s/n, 17" x 22¼", pub GW. | 75.00 | 130.00 |
| ☐ LITTLE STAR, rel. 1979. ed. 1,500, s/n, 15" x 19", pub GW. | 80.00 | 375.00 |
| ☐ PRE-COLUMBIAN INDIAN WITH ATLATL, rel. 1979. ed. 1,500, s/n, 22" x 18", pub GW. | 75.00 | 130.00 |
| ☐ KEN BLACKBIRD, AN ASSINIBOIN SIOUX, rel. 1980. ed. 1,500, s/n, 22" x 20½", pub GW. | 95.00 | 130.00 |
| ☐ MOUNTAIN MAN 1820-1840 PERIOD, rel. 1980. ed. 1,500, s/n, 17½" x 24½", pub GW. | 115.00 | 175.00 |
| ☐ MOUNTAIN MAN AND HIS FOX, rel. 1980. ed. 1,500, s/n, 21½" x 26", pub GW. | 90.00 | 375.00 |
| ☐ OLD SADDLE IN THE SNOW, rel. 1980. ed. 1,500, s/n, 21" x 15", pub GW. | 75.00 | 80.00 |
| ☐ OLD SOD HOUSE, rel. 1980. ed. 1,500, s/n, 23" x 13", pub GW. | 80.00 | 115.00 |
| ☐ SHEEP SKULL IN DRIFT, rel. 1980. ed. 1,500, s/n, 20" x 16", pub GW. | 75.00 | 80.00 |
| ☐ YOUNG PLAINS INDIAN, rel. 1980. ed. 1,500, s/n, 25½" x 26¼", pub GW. | 125.00 | 225.00 |
| ☐ AT A MOUNTAIN MAN WEDDING, rel. 1981. ed. 1,500, s/n, 22" x 22", pub GW. | 145.00 | 180.00 |
| ☐ AT THE BURIAL OF GALLAGER AND BLIND BILL, rel. 1981. ed. 1,500, s/n, 26½" x 21½", pub GW. | 135.00 | Sold Out |
| ed. 150, s/n, proceeds to Old Trail Town, Cody, Wyoming. | 135.00 | 175.00 |
| ☐ CROW INDIAN DANCER, rel. 1982. ed. 1,250, s/n, 22¾" x 23½", pub GW. | 150.00 | — |
| ☐ OLD ARAPAHO STORY-TELLER, rel. 1981. ed. 1,500, s/n, 22¼" x 23¼", pub GW. | 35.00 | Sold Out |
| ☐ PORTRAIT OF A SIOUX, rel. 1981. ed. 1,500, s/n, 22½" x 23", pub GW. | 135.00 | 225.00 |
| ☐ WINTER TRAPPING, rel. 1981. ed. 1,500, s/n, 20" x 24", pub GW. | 150.00 | 175.00 |
| ☐ OLDEST LIVING CROW INDIAN, rel. 1982. ed. 1,500, s/n, 22" x 26¼", pub GW. | 135.00 | Sold Out |
| ☐ MOUNTAIN MAN WITH RIFLE, rel. 1982. ed. 1,250, s/n, 16" x 25", pub GW. | 135.00 | — |
| ☐ SIOUX INDIAN WITH EAGLE FEATHER, rel. 1982. ed. 1,500, s/n, 17¼" x 21½", pub GW. | 135.00 | Sold Out |
| ☐ DON WALKER — BAREBACK RIDER, rel. 1983. ed. 1,250, s/n, 12½" x 17", pub GW. | 85.00 | — |
| ☐ THE DAVILLA BROTHERS — BRONC RIDERS, rel. 1983. ed. 1,250, s/n, 23" x 19⅛", pub GW. | 145.00 | — |
| ☐ SOUTHWEST INDIAN FATHER AND SON, rel. 1983. ed. 1,250, s/n, 17½" x 23½", pub GW. | 145.00 | — |

# JOHN M. BARBER

While still a young man growing up in southern Virginia, John M. Barber became enchanted with the sea. With sketch pad and paints, he explored the shifting Atlantic shoreline and remote inlets of the Chesapeake Bay. His artistic talents won him a fellowship from the Virginia Museum of Fine Arts to pursue his education at Virginia Commonwealth University, from which he graduated in 1969 with a Bachelor of Fine Arts.

Since then, Barber has been in Richmond, Virginia, gaining a national reputation as one of today's most sensitive painters of the life and places on the Chesapeake Bay. Known for the precision in his work, Barber captures the feeling of the Bay Country through exceptional composition and coloration. He is a Charter Member of the American Society of Marine Artists and was featured in their 1978 exhibit at the World Trade Center in New York. His work has been viewed by thousands in shows and galleries in Virginia, Georgia, Maryland, Massachusetts, New York, North Carolina, Ohio and Connecticut.

**DISTANT THUNDER** *by John Barber*

## JOHN BARBER

| | ISSUE PRICE | CURRENT PRICE |
|---|---|---|
| ☐ "ATLANTIC SENTINEL," ed. 750, s/n, 18″ x 28″, dist. CAP | 40.00 | 200.00 |
| ☐ "AT THE NETS," ed. 500, s/n, 15½″ x 11⅜″, dist. CAP | 25.00 | 25.00 |
| ☐    ed. 25, Artist Proofs | 45.00 | 100.00 |
| ☐ "BOAT SHED," ed. 750, s/n, 18″ x 28″, dist. CAP | 40.00 | 100.00 |
| ☐ "BUTLER'S BOAT YARD," ed. 500, s/n, 18″ x 28″, dist. CAP | 40.00 | 150.00 |
| ☐ "CAPT. WALTER'S WHARF," ed. 950, s/n, 18″ x 28″, dist. CAP | 40.00 | 125.00 |
| ☐    ed. 50, Artist Proofs, remarque | 125.00 | 400.00 |
| ☐ "CHESAPEAKE BAY SKIPJACK," ed. 750, s/n, 18″ x 28″, dist. CAP | 40.00 | 350.00 |
| ☐ "CHESAPEAKE OYSTER TONGERS," ed. 500, s/n, 15½″ x 11¾″, dist. CAP | 25.00 | 25.00 |
| ☐    ed. 25, Artist Proofs | 45.00 | 100.00 |
| ☐ "DISTANT THUNDER," ed. 950, s/n, 24½″ x 13¾″, dist. CAP | 75.00 | 75.00 |
| ☐    ed. 50, Artist Proofs, remarque | 225.00 | 450.00 |
| ☐ "ELSWORTH," ed. 950, s/n, 18″ x 28″, dist. CAP | 40.00 | 275.00 |
| ☐ "GOOD DAYS CATCH," ed. 950, s/n, 17⅞″ x 26″, dist. CAP | 55.00 | 55.00 |
| ☐    ed. 50, Artist Proofs, remarque | 175.00 | 350.00 |
| ☐ "HAMPTON CREEK DERELICT," ed. 500, s/n, 18″ x 28″. dist. CAP | 40.00 | 125.00 |
| ☐ "MAGGIE LEE," ed. 950, s/n, 24½″ x 13¾″, dist. CAP | 55.00 | 55.00 |
| ☐    ed. 50, Artist Proofs, remarque | 175.00 | 400.00 |

|  | ISSUE PRICE | CURRENT PRICE |
|---|---|---|
| ☐ "MARTHA LEWIS," ed. 950, s/n, 18" x 28", dist. CAP | 40.00 | 200.00 |
| ☐ ed. 50, Artist Proofs, remarque | 125.00 | 400.00 |
| ☐ "MORNING AT BELL BUOY #12," ed. 500, s/n, 15½" x 11⅜", dist. CAP | 25.00 | 25.00 |
| ☐ ed. 25, Artist Proofs | 45.00 | 100.00 |
| ☐ "NELLIE CROCKETT" OYSTER BOAT, ed. 750, s/n, 18" x 28", dist. CAP | 40.00 | 200.00 |
| ☐ "PARRAMORE ISLAND GUARDIAN," ed. 250, s/n, 15" x 25", dist. CAP | 250.00 | 500.00 |
| ☐ "SIGSBEE," ed. 500, s/n, 15½" x 11⅜", dist. CAP | 25.00 | 25.00 |
| ☐ ed. 25, Artist Proofs, remarque | 45.00 | 100.00 |
| ☐ "SIGSBEE," ed. 950, s/n, 14⅛" x 26", dist. CAP | 55.00 | 55.00 |
| ☐ ed. 50, Artist Proofs, remarque | 175.00 | 350.00 |
| ☐ "THE SKIPJACK 'LADY KATIE'," ed. 950, s/n, 18" x 28", dist. CAP | 40.00 | 100.00 |
| ☐ ed. 50, Artist Proofs, remarque | 125.00 | 400.00 |
| ☐ "SPRING PAINTING," ed. 500, s/n, 18" x 28", dist. CAP | 40.00 | 40.00 |
| ☐ "WILD DUCK" ROUNDING HOOPER STRAIT LIGHTHOUSE, ed. 500, s/n, 18" x 28", dist. CAP | 40.00 | 350.00 |
| ☐ "WILLIAM B. TENNISON," ed. 950, s/n, 17⅞" x 26", dist. CAP | 40.00 | 55.00 |
| ☐ ed. 50, Artist Proofs, remarque | 150.00 | 300.00 |

## AL BARNES

|  | | |
|---|---|---|
| ☐ THE BLUE MARAUDER, rel. 1982. ed. 600, s/n, size N/A, pub WWI | 47.50 | 95.00 |

## GERTRUDE BARRER

|  | | |
|---|---|---|
| ☐ EVENING SONG, rel. 1976. ed. 150, s/n, serigraph, pub MMGI | 60.00 | — |
| ☐ SUMMER GARDEN, rel. 1976. ed. 150, s/n, serigraph, pub MMGI | 60.00 | — |
| ☐ WHITE VASE, rel. 1976. ed. 150, s/n, serigraph, pub MMGI | 50.00 | — |

# MILDRED BARRETT

The Manhattan-born Mildred Barrett is a woman to whom painting is capturing the mood of the subject with an exceptional use of color. Barrett's training includes the Art Student's League, the National Academy of Fine Arts, and the Brooklyn Museum Art School. She has traveled extensively through which the theme and style of her work was created and developed.

Barrett has had numerous one-woman shows on Madison Avenue in New York and in galleries on Long Island and her works have been sold and are collected all over the United States, Canada and Europe. Her paintings are also on permanent display at Bergdorf Goodman's Nena's Choice Gallery.

There is a simplicity and charm in Barrett's work which is enhanced by her remarkable feeling for color. Her impressionistic style captures the mood of the subject — figures which are unique in themselves in certain poses and expressions. Her canvases glow with flowers which look as though they have just been picked.

## MILDRED BARRETT

|  | | |
|---|---|---|
| ☐ FLOWER CHILD, ed. 300, s/n, 36" x 30", original color silkscreen, pub FI | 150.00 | 200.00 |
| ☐ FLOWER MARKET, ed. 300, s/n, 36" x 30", original color silkscreen, pub FI | 150.00 | 200.00 |
| ☐ PARASOLS, ed. 300, s/n, 36" x 30", original color silkscreen, pub FI | 150.00 | 200.00 |
| ☐ SPRING CHILDREN, ed. 300, s/n, 36" x 30", original color silkscreen, pub FI | 150.00 | 200.00 |
| ☐ SWINGING, ed. 300, s/n, 36½" x 30", original color silkscreen, pub FI | 200.00 | — |

## FRED TAYLOR BARTLETT

Born in Asbury Park, New Jersey in 1935, Fred Bartlett has dedicated his life to the pursuit of excellence in the art world. Bartlett executes works in all graphics and painting mediums, with his favorite mediums being lithography, etching, and watercolor.

After graduating from Kutztown State College, with a Bachelor of Science degree in Art Education and studying at the renowned Art Student's League, Bartlett taught art for the next 15 years. He was subsequently selected by the Hunt Pen Company to demonstrate and lecture their paints. For the last eight years, Bartlett has pursued a successful career as a free lance artist with a growing reputation among serious collectors for his original graphics.

Bartlett has won numerous state and local awards including many "Best of Show" for his paintings and pottery.

| FRED TAYLOR BARTLETT | ISSUE PRICE | CURRENT PRICE |
|---|---|---|
| ☐ **WICKER**, ed. 180, s/n, 25″ x 31″, litho, pub EG ........................ | 60.00 | — |

## LARRY BARTON

Larry Barton was an award winning editorial cartoonist. His work often appeared in *Time Magazine,* the *Washington Post* and the *New York* and *Los Angeles Times.*

Currently, he is a full time wildlife artist.

**THE LOW FLYERS** *by Larry Barton*

## LARRY BARTON

| | ISSUE PRICE | CURRENT PRICE |
|---|---|---|
| ☐ "THE LOW FLYERS", ed. 800, s/n, 16" x 24½", pub. PP | 75.00 | — |
| remarqued, s/n | 165.00 | — |
| ☐ "THE MORNING WATCH", ed. 800, s/n, 25" x 17½", pub. PP | 75.00 | — |
| remarqued, s/n | 165.00 | — |

# ROBERT BATEMAN

Canadian artist Robert Bateman, born and schooled in Toronto, filled his youthful days with a myriad of out-door experiences involving nature.

He majored in geography and studied art at the University of Toronto, received his teaching certificate, and in Ontario taught both geography and art. It was during a two-year teaching stint in Africa that he began his serious African wildlife painting.

He travels extensively on field trips feeling his most important tool is first hand observation.

The focus on environment is the essence of Bateman's paintings. His drawings and paintings are direct from nature and realistic in style. His works have been exhibited worldwide and are in collections on three continents.

**ROYAL FAMILY – MUTE SWANS** *by Robert Bateman*

## ROBERT BATEMAN

| | | |
|---|---|---|
| ☐ **BY THE TRACKS - KILLDEER**, rel. 1978. ed. 950, s/n, 20" x 27½", pub MPPI. | 75.00 | 150.00 |
| ☐ **CHEETAH WITH CUBS**, rel. 1978. ed. 950, s/n, 21" x 27½", pub MPPI | 95.00 | 175.00 |
| ☐ **DOWNEY WOODPECKER ON GOLDENROD GALL**, rel. 1978. ed. 950, s/n, 21" x 14", pub MPPI. | 50.00 | 450.00 |
| ☐ **LION CUBS**, rel. 1978. ed. 950, s/n, 21" x 28", pub MPPI | 125.00 | 150.00 |
| ☐ **MAJESTY ON THE WING - BALD EAGLE**, rel. 1978. ed. 950, s/n, 24" x 36", pub MPPI. | 150.00 | 1,200.00 |
| ☐ **WINTER CARNIVAL**, rel. 1978. ed. 950, s/n, 20¼" x 14", pub MPPI | 75.00 | 1,200.00 |
| ☐ **WOLF PACK IN MOONLIGHT**, rel. 1978. ed. 950, s/n, 21" x 27½", pub MPPI | 95.00 | 825.00 |
| ☐ **YOUNG BARN SWALLOW**, rel. 1978. ed. 950, s/n, 27½" x 20½", pub MPPI. | 75.00 | 175.00 |
| ☐ **AFTERNOON GLOW - SNOWY OWL**, rel. 1979. ed. 950, s/n, 21½" x 27½", pub MPPI. | 125.00 | 250.00 |

| | ISSUE PRICE | CURRENT PRICE |
|---|---|---|
| ☐ AMONG THE LEAVES - COTTONTAIL RABBIT, rel. 1979. ed. 950, s/n, 16" x 20", pub MPPI | 75.00 | 325.00 |
| ☐ BULL MOOSE, rel. 1979. ed. 950, s/n, 23" x 29½", pub MPPI | 125.00 | 325.00 |
| ☐ COUNTRY LANE - PHEASANT, rel. 1979. ed. 950, s/n, 19½" x 23", pub MPPI | 85.00 | 175.00 |
| ☐ EVENING SNOWFALL - AMERICAN ELK, rel. 1979. ed. 950, s/n, 21½" x 31½", pub MPPI | 150.00 | 425.00 |
| ☐ GOLDEN EAGLE, rel. 1979. ed. 950, s/n, 24½" x 37¼", pub MPPI | 150.00 | 175.00 |
| ☐ GREAT BLUE HERON, rel. 1979. ed. 950, s/n, 22" x 28", pub MPPI | 125.00 | 325.00 |
| ☐ HIGH COUNTRY - STONE SHEEP, rel. 1979. ed. 950, s/n, 22½" x 29", pub MPPI | 125.00 | 150.00 |
| ☐ KING OF THE REALM, rel. 1979. ed. 950, s/n, 20½" x 27½", pub MPPI | 125.00 | 200.00 |
| ☐ MASTER OF THE HERD - AFRICAN BUFFALO, rel. 1979. ed. 950, s/n, 22½" x 31½", pub MPPI | 150.00 | 275.00 |
| ☐ SURF AND SANDERLINGS, rel. 1979. ed. 950, s/n, 18" x 23", pub MPPI | 65.00 | 125.00 |
| ☐ UP IN THE PINE - GREAT HORNED OWL, rel. 1979. ed. 950, s/n, 24½" x 35", pub MPPI | 150.00 | 175.00 |
| ☐ WILD AND WARY - RED FOX, rel. 1979. ed. 950, s/n, 22½" x 28½", pub MPPI | 125.00 | 410.00 |
| ☐ WINTER CARDINAL, rel. 1979. ed. 950, s/n, 20½" x 14⅛", pub MPPI | 75.00 | 1,250.00 |
| ☐ WINTER — SNOWSHOE HARE, rel. 1979. ed. 950, s/n, 18" x 25½", pub MPPI | 95.00 | 300.00 |
| ☐ YELLOW-RUMPED WARBLER, rel. 1979. ed. 950, s/n, 14" x 18½", pub MPPI | 50.00 | 140.00 |
| ☐ AFRICAN AMBER - LIONESS PAIR, rel. 1980. ed. 950, s/n, 24½" x 38", pub MPPI | 175.00 | 200.00 |
| ☐ ANTARCTIC ELEMENTS, rel. 1980. ed. 950, s/n, 22¾" x 27", pub MPPI | 125.00 | 150.00 |
| ☐ ARCTIC FAMILY - POLAR BEARS, rel. 1980. ed. 950, s/n, 22¼" x 30½", pub MPPI | 150.00 | 200.00 ` |
| ☐ ASLEEP ON THE HEMLOCK - SCREECH OWL, rel. 1980. ed. 950, s/n, 25" x 17", pub MPPI | 125.00 | 225.00 |
| ☐ AUTUMN OVERTURE - MOOSE, rel. 1980. ed. 950, s/n, 24½" x 36¼", pub MPPI | 245.00 | 300.00 |
| ☐ BARN OWL IN THE CHURCHYARD, rel. 1980. ed. 950, s/n, 20" x 24", pub MPPI | 125.00 | 150.00 |
| ☐ BLUFFING BULL - AFRICAN ELEPHANT, rel. 1980. ed. 950, s/n, 22¾" x 26¾", pub MPPI | 135.00 | 175.00 |
| ☐ BROWN PELICAN AND PILINGS, rel. 1980. ed. 950, s/n, 34½" x 25", pub MPPI | 165.00 | 325.00 |
| ☐ CHAPEL DOORS, rel. 1980. ed. 950, s/n, 29½" x 23", pub MPPI | 135.00 | — |
| ☐ COYOTE IN WINTER SAGE, rel. 1980. ed. 950, s/n, 24½" x 34½", pub MPPI | 245.00 | 850.00 |
| ☐ CURIOUS GLANCE - RED FOX, rel. 1980. ed. 950, s/n, 18¾" x 27½", pub MPPI | 135.00 | 260.00 |
| ☐ EVENING GROSBEAK, rel. 1980. ed. 950, s/n, 24⅛" x 19⅛", pub MPPI | 125.00 | 195.00 |
| ☐ FALLEN WILLOW-SNOWY OWL, rel. 1980. ed. 950, s/n, 25" x 38", pub MPPI | 200.00 | 275.00 |
| ☐ FLYING HIGH - GOLDEN EAGLE, rel. 1980. ed. 950, s/n, 31½" x 23¼", pub MPPI | 150.00 | 225.00 |
| ☐ HERON ON THE ROCKS, rel. 1980. ed. 950, s/n, 13½" x 22", pub MPPI | 75.00 | 125.00 |
| ☐ KITTIWAKES GREETING, rel. 1980. ed. 950, s/n, 20" x 16", pub MPPI | 75.00 | 150.00 |
| ☐ LEOPARD IN A SAUSAGE TREE, rel. 1980. ed. 950, s/n, 24¾" x 30¼", pub MPPI | 150.00 | 175.00 |
| ☐ LION AT TSAVO, rel. 1980. ed. 950, s/n, 21½" x 31½", pub MPPI | 150.00 | 150.00 |
| ☐ MISCHIEF ON THE PROWL - RACCOON, rel. 1980. ed. 950, s/n, 14" x 23", pub MPPI | 85.00 | 150.00 |
| ☐ MISTY COAST GULLS, rel. 1980. ed. 950, s/n, 23¼" x 29¼", pub MPPI | 135.00 | 200.00 |
| ☐ ON THE ALERT-CHIPMUNK, rel. 1980. ed. 950, s/n, 12" x 16³/₈", pub MPPI | 60.00 | 275.00 |
| ☐ PRAIRIE EVENING-SHORTEARED OWL, rel. 1980. ed. 950, s/n, 23" x 31½", pub MPPI | 150.00 | — |
| ☐ ROCKY WILDERNESS - COUGAR, rel. 1980. ed. 950, s/n, 24¾" x 31¼", pub MPPI | 175.00 | 340.00 |
| ☐ SPRING CARDINAL, rel. 1980. ed. 950, s/n, 18" x 24½", pub MPPI | 125.00 | 215.00 |
| ☐ SPRING THAW-KILLDEER, rel. 1980. ed. 950, s/n, 16½" x 22", pub MPPI | 85.00 | 125.00 |
| ☐ THE AWESOME LAND - AMERICAN ELK, rel. 1980. ed. 950, s/n, 24½" x 38", pub MPPI | 245.00 | 300.00 |
| ☐ VANTAGE POINT, rel. 1980. ed. 950, s/n, 24½" x 38", pub MPPI | 245.00 | 450.00 |
| ☐ WHITE ENCOUNTER, rel. 1980. ed. 950, s/n, 24¾" x 31¾", pub MPPI | 245.00 | 400.00 |

| | ISSUE PRICE | CURRENT PRICE |
|---|---|---|
| ☐ **WHITE-FOOTED MOUSE IN WINTERGREEN**, rel. 1980. ed. 950, s/n, 11¾" x 13¼", pub MPPI. | 60.00 | 175.00 |
| ☐ **WINTER ELM - AMERICAN KESTREL**, rel. 1980. ed. 950, s/n, 20" x 37½", pub MPPI. | 135.00 | 175.00 |
| ☐ **WINTER - SNOWSHOE HARE**, rel. 1980. ed. 950, s/n, 18" x 25½", pub MPPI. | 95.00 | 250.00 |
| ☐ **WINTER SONG - CHICKADEES**, rel. 1980. ed. 950, s/n, 17¼" x 14", pub MPPI. | 95.00 | 225.00 |
| ☐ **ABABI ROYAL FAMILY - MUTE SWANS**, rel. 1981. ed. 950, s/n, 24⅝" x 37¼", pub MPPI. | 245.00 | 260.00 |
| ☐ **ABOVE THE RIVER - TRUMPETER SWANS**, rel. 1981. ed. 950, s/n, 21⅛" x 32¼", pub MPPI. | 200.00 | — |
| ☐ **BRIGHT DAY - ATLANTIC PUFFINS**, rel. 1981. ed. 950, s/n, 22¾" x 25⅝", pub MPPI. | 175.00 | — |
| ☐ **CANADA GEESE - NESTING**, rel. 1981. ed. 950, s/n, 24" x 31", pub MPPI. | 295.00 | 550.00 |
| ☐ **CLEAR NIGHT - WOLVES**, rel. 1981. ed. 950, s/n, 24⅝" x 32½", pub MPPI. | 245.00 | 675.00 |
| ☐ **COURTING PAIR - WHISTLING SWANS**, rel. 1981. ed. 950, s/n, 22¾" x 29½", pub MPPI. | 245.00 | 375.00 |
| ☐ **COURTSHIP DISPLAY - WILD TURKEY**, rel. 1981. ed. 950, s/n, 24⅝" x 26¾", pub MPPI. | 175.00 | 200.00 |
| ☐ **EDGE OF THE ICE - ERMINE**, rel. 1981. ed. 950, s/n, 17¾" x 21½", pub MPPI. | 175.00 | 290.00 |
| ☐ **EVENING LIGHT - WHITE GYRFALCON**, rel. 1981. ed. 950, s/n, 24⅝" x 32½", pub MPPI. | 245.00 | 275.00 |
| ☐ **GALLINULE FAMILY**, rel. 1981. ed. 950, s/n, 20⅝" x 31½", pub MPPI. | 135.00 | — |
| ☐ **GALLOPING HERD - GIRAFFES**, rel. 1981. ed. 950, s/n, 29¾" x 24½", pub MPPI. | 175.00 | 215.00 |
| ☐ **GENTOO PENGUINS & WHALE BONES**, rel. 1981. ed. 950, s/n, 24½" x 37¼", pub MPPI. | 205.00 | — |
| ☐ **GRAY SQUIRREL**, rel. 1981. ed. 950, s/n, 21½" x 29¾", pub MPPI. | 180.00 | 275.00 |
| ☐ **HIGH CAMP AT DUSK**, rel. 1981. ed. 950, s/n, 24¼" x 38", pub MPPI. | 245.00 | — |
| ☐ **IN FOR THE EVENING**, rel. 1981. ed. 950, s/n, 21¼" x 25", pub MPPI. | 150.00 | 190.00 |
| ☐ **LAST LOOK - BIGHORN SHEEP**, rel. 1981. ed. 950, s/n, 24⅜" x 38", pub MPPI. | 195.00 | 200.00 |
| ☐ **LAUGHING GULL & HORSESHOE CRAB**, rel. 1981. ed. 950, s/n, 14½" x 22⅛", pub MPPI. | 125.00 | 150.00 |
| ☐ **LITTLE BLUE HERON**, rel. 1981. ed. 950, s/n, 19¼" x 12¾", pub MPPI. | 95.00 | 125.00 |
| ☐ **KINGFISH AND ASPEN**, rel. 1981. ed. 950, s/n, 24½" x 29¼", pub MPPI. | 225.00 | 250.00 |
| ☐ **MISTY MORNING - LOONS**, rel. 1981. ed. 950, s/n, 20" x 27½", pub MPPI. | 150.00 | Sold Out |
| ☐ **PAIR OF SKIMMERS**, rel. 1981. ed. 950, s/n, 15⅜" x 27½", pub MPPI. | 150.00 | 175.00 |
| ☐ **PIONEER MEMORIES - MAGPIE PAIR**, rel. 1981. ed. 950, s/n, 18⅝" x 24½", pub MPPI. | 175.00 | — |
| ☐ **RED-TAILED HAWK BY THE CLIFF**, rel. 1981. ed. 950, s/n, 24½" x 34⅛", pub MPPI. | 245.00 | 285.00 |
| ☐ **RED-WINGED BLACKBIRD AND RAIL FENCE**, rel. 1981. ed. 950, s/n, 22¾" x 29½", pub MPPI. | 195.00 | 200.00 |
| ☐ **ROUGH-LEGGED HAWK IN THE ELM**, rel. 1981. ed. 950, s/n, 22¾" x 29½", pub MPPI. | 175.00 | — |
| ☐ **ROYAL FAMILY - MUTE SWANS**, rel. 1981. ed. 950, s/n, 24⅝" x 37¼", pub MPPI. | 245.00 | 275.00 |
| ☐ **SHEER DROP - MOUNTAIN GOATS**, rel. 1981. ed. 950, s/n, 32" x 24½", pub MPPI. | 245.00 | 325.00 |
| ☐ **SWIFT FOX**, rel. 1981. ed. 950, s/n, 15" x 24½", pub MPPI. | 175.00 | 275.00 |
| ☐ **THE ARTIST AND HIS DOG**, rel. 1981. ed. 950, s/n, 19¼" x 28½", pub MPPI. | 150.00 | Sold Out |
| ☐ **THE OSPREY FAMILY**, rel. 1981. ed. 950, s/n, 24½" x 34", pub MPPI. | 245.00 | 250.00 |
| ☐ **THE SARAH E. WITH GULLS**, rel. 1981. ed. 950, s/n, 30½" x 24½", pub MPPI. | 245.00 | 400.00 |
| ☐ **WATCHFUL REPOSE - BLACK BEAR**, rel. 1981. ed. 950, s/n, 24⅝" x 30", pub MPPI. | 245.00 | 250.00 |
| ☐ **WHITE WORLD - DALL SHEEP**, rel. 1981. ed. 950, s/n, 24⅝" x 28½", pub MPPI. | 200.00 | 225.00 |
| ☐ **WINTER MIST - GREAT HORNED OWL**, rel. 1981. ed. 950, s/n, 38" x 24½", pub MPPI. | 245.00 | 325.00 |
| ☐ **WINTER WREN**, rel. 1981. ed. 950, s/n, 20⅝" x 20⅝", pub MPPI. | 135.00 | 200.00 |

| | ISSUE PRICE | CURRENT PRICE |
|---|---|---|
| ☐ **WRANGLER'S CAMPSITE - GRAY JAY,** rel. 1981. ed. 950, s/n, 28½" x 20⅝", pub MPPI | 195.00 | 225.00 |
| ☐ **ABOVE THE RIVER — TRUMPETER SWANS,** rel. 1982. ed. 950, s/n, 21⅛" x 32¼", pub MPPI | 200.00 | — |
| ☐ **ARTIC EVENING - WHITE WOLF,** rel. 1982. ed. 950, s/n, 24⅝" x 20", pub MPPI | 185.00 | 225.00 |
| ☐ **ARTIC PORTRAIT - WHITE GYRAFALCON,** rel. 1982. ed. 950, s/n, 16¾" x 22¼", pub MPPI | 175.00 | 200.00 |
| ☐ **AT THE ROADSIDE - RED-TAILED HAWK,** rel. 1982. ed. 950, s/n, 21⅝" x 29½", pub MPPI | 185.00 | — |
| ☐ **BAOBAB TREE AND IMPALA,** rel. 1982. ed. 950, s/n, 30¼" x 24½", pub MPPI | 245.00 | — |
| ☐ **BARN SWALLOWS IN AUGUST,** rel. 1982. ed. 950, s/n, 24½" x 34¾", pub MPPI | 245.00 | — |
| ☐ **CHEETAH PROFILE,** rel. 1982. ed 950, s/n, 24½" x 35", pub MPPI | 245.00 | — |
| ☐ **DIPPER BY THE WATERFALL,** rel. 1982. ed. 950, s/n, 17¾" x 26¼", pub MPPI | 165.00 | — |
| ☐ **EDGE OF THE WOODS — WHITETAIL DEER,** rel. 1982. ed. 950, s/n, 24½" x 35", pub MPPI | 745.00 | 800.00 |
| ☐ **FOX AT THE GRANARY,** rel. 1982. ed. 950, s/n, 20½" x 27¾", pub MPPI | 165.00 | — |
| ☐ **FROSTY MORNING — BLUE JAY,** rel. 1982. ed. 950, s/n, 23¾" x 19¾", pub MPPI | 185.00 | 375.00 |
| ☐ **GALLINULE FAMILY,** rel. 1982. ed. 950, s/n, 20⅝" x 31½", pub MPPI | 135.00 | — |
| ☐ **GENTOO PENGUINS AND WHALE BONES,** rel. 1982. ed. 950, s/n, 24½" x 37¼", pub MPPI | 205.00 | — |
| ☐ **GOLDEN CROWNED KINGLET AND RHODODEND,** rel. 1982. ed. 950, s/n, 16½" x 20⅛", pub MPPI | 150.00 | 550.00 |
| ☐ **KINGFISHER IN WINTER,** rel. 1982. ed. 950, s/n, 28½" x 24½", pub AA, distr. MPPI | 175.00 | 325.00 |
| ☐ **LEOPARD AMBUSH,** rel. 1982. ed. 950, s/n, 24½" x 32", pub MPPI | 245.00 | — |
| ☐ **LIVELY PAIR - CHICKADEES,** rel. 1982. ed. 950, s/n, 14¾" x 18¾", pub MPPI | 160.00 | 250.00 |
| ☐ **MEADOW'S EDGE - MALLARD,** rel. 1982. ed. 950, s/n, 20¼" x 27⅜", pub MPPI | 175.00 | — |
| ☐ **MERGANSER FAMILY IN HIDING,** rel. 1982. ed. 950, s/n, 21½" x 31½", pub MPPI | 200.00 | 215.00 |
| ☐ **PILEATED WOODPECKER ON BEECH TREE,** rel. 1982. ed. 950, s/n, 24½" x 18¼", pub MPPI | 175.00 | 200.00 |
| ☐ **PIONEER MEMORIES — MAGPIE PAIR,** rel. 1982. ed. 950, s/n, 18⅝" x 24½", pub MPPI | 175.00 | — |
| ☐ **POLAR BEAR PROFILE,** rel. 1982. ed. 950, s/n, 24½" x 35", pub MPPI | 210.00 | 235.00 |
| ☐ **POLAR BEARS AT BAFFIN ISLAND,** rel. 1982. ed. 950, s/n, 31¾" x 24½", pub MPPI | 245.00 | 275.00 |
| ☐ **QUEEN ANNE'S LACE AND AMERICAN GOLDFINCH,** rel. 1982. ed. 950, s/n, 16½" x 20¼", pub MPPI | 150.00 | 550.00 |
| ☐ **READY FOR THE HUNT - SNOWY OWL,** rel. 1982. ed. 950, s/n, 24½" x 36", pub MPPI | 245.00 | 275.00 |
| ☐ **RED SQUIRREL,** rel. 1982. ed. 950, s/n, 16⅜" x 22¼", pub MPPI | 175.00 | 215.00 |
| ☐ **SPRING MARSH - PINTAIL PAIR,** rel. 1982. ed. 950, s/n, 22¾" x 29½", pub MPPI | 200.00 | 215.00 |
| ☐ **STILL MORNING - HERRING GULLS,** rel. 1982. ed. 950, s/n, 22" x 31¼", pub MPPI | 200.00 | 215.00 |
| ☐ **WHITE-FOOTED MOUSE ON ASPEN,** rel. 1982. ed. 950, s/n, 13½" x 14⅜", pub MPPI | 90.00 | 100.00 |
| ☐ **WHITE WORLD-DALL SHEEP,** rel. 1982. ed. 950, s/n, 24⅝" x 28⅛", pub MPPI | 200.00 | 215.00 |
| ☐ **WILLET ON THE SHORE,** rel. 1982. ed. 950, s/n, 18" x 23", pub MPPI | 125.00 | — |
| ☐ **CALL OF THE WILD - BALD EAGLE,** rel. 1983. ed. 950, s/n, 24½" x 31⅛", pub MPPI | 200.00 | 215.00 |
| ☐ **EARLY SPING — BLUEBIRD,** rel. 1983. ed. 950, s/n, 18⅞" x 29½", pub MPPI | 185.00 | — |
| ☐ **GHOST OF THE NORTH — GREAT GRAY OWL,** rel. 1983. ed. 950, s/n, 24½" x 31½", pub MPPI | 200.00 | 215.00 |
| ☐ **GREAT HORNED OWL IN WHITE PINE,** rel. 1983. ed. 950, s/n, 35" x 20⅝", pub MPPI | 225.00 | 230.00 |
| ☐ **OSPREY IN THE RAIN,** rel. 1983. ed. 950, s/n, 19⅝" x 14", pub MPPI | 110.00 | — |

| | ISSUE PRICE | CURRENT PRICE |
|---|---|---|
| ☐ **PHEASANT IN CORNFIELD,** rel. 1983. ed. 950, s/n, 20″ x 29″, pub MPPI . . . . | 200.00 | 215.00 |
| ☐ **RUBY-THROAT AND COLUMBINE,** rel. 1983. ed. 950, s/n, 16½″ x 20¼″, pub MPPI . . . . . . . . . . . . . . . . . . . . . . . . . . . . . . . . . . . . . . . . . . . . . . . . | 150.00 | 550.00 |
| ☐ **TIGER PORTRAIT,** rel. 1983. ed. 950, s/n, 17¼″ x 21″, pub MPPI . . . . . . . . . . | 130.00 | 140.00 |
| ☐ **WINTER BARN,** rel. 1983. ed. 950, s/n, 16″ x 24″, pub MPPI. . . . . . . . . . . . . | 170.00 | — |
| ☐ **WINTER LADY — CARDINAL,** rel. 1983. ed. 950, s/n, 16″ x 19¾″, pub MPPI . | 200.00 | 450.00 |
| ☐ **WOLVES ON THE TRAIL,** rel. 1983. ed. 950, s/n, 21⅛″ x 31½″, pub MPPI . . . | 225.00 | 525.00 |
| ☐ **WOODLAND DRUMMER — PUFFED GROUSE,** rel. 1983. ed. 950, s/n, 14″ x 24″, pub MPPI. . . . . . . . . . . . . . . . . . . . . . . . . . . . . . . . . . . . . . . . . . . | 185.00 | — |
| ☐ **YOUNG ELF OWL — OLD SAGUARD,** rel. 1983. ed. 950, s/n, 12″ x 15½″, pub MPPI . . . . . . . . . . . . . . . . . . . . . . . . . . . . . . . . . . . . . . . . . . . . . . . . | 95.00 | 105.00 |

# TOM BEECHAM

Tom Beecham entered the St. Louis School of Fine Arts at Washington University in Missouri where he was hailed as "the finest natural talent to enter the school in twenty-five years."

This artist's lifelong observation of animals has enabled him to capture in exquisite detail their beauty of form and grace of movement.

He has painted for nearly every major publishing company in the East. His illustrations have appeared in *Reader's Digest, Popular Science, Argosy Magazine, Outdoor Life, Bantam Books, McGraw-Hill Publications* and *Time-Life Books.* In addition, he has received commissions from General Motors and Mercury Motors.

**THE AMERICAN LION** *by Tom Beecham*

His paintings are found in galleries and private collections from New York to Texas and were among those chosen to be shown at the Game Conservation International Show in San Antonio.

## TOM BEECHAM

| | ISSUE PRICE | CURRENT PRICE |
|---|---|---|
| ☐ **BRUSH ROYALTY**, rel. 1980. ed. 1,500, s/n, 32½" x 24⅛", pub ALI | 60.00 | — |
| ☐ **THE AMERICAN LION**, rel. 1980. ed. 1,500, s/n, 29¾" x 25", pub ALI | 60.00 | — |
| ☐ **THE OLD MILL RUN**, rel. 1980. ed. 1,500, s/n, 33½" x 24⅛", pub ALI | 60.00 | — |

# JOE BEELER

Joe Beeler is a graduate of Kansas State Teachers College and attended the Art Center School in Los Angeles. His works have been exhibited in many of the country's leading museums including Gilcrease, Montana Historical Society and the National Cowboy Hall of Fame. A founder of the Cowboy Artists of America, he has served as president of that organization. He has won one gold and five silver medals in CAA competition in the media of drawing and sculpture. He has also been the recipient of the coveted Colt Award for the best exhibit by a single artist.

## JOE BEELER

| | ISSUE PRICE | CURRENT PRICE |
|---|---|---|
| ☐ **DOG SOLDIER**, rel. 1976. ed. 1,000, s/n, 25" x 38", pub FHG | 100.00 | Sold Out |
| ☐ **FINISHING OFF THE DAY**, rel. 1976. ed. 250, s/n, 21½" x 33", pub FHG | 100.00 | Sold Out |
| ☐ **BIDDING FOR A BRIDE**, rel. 1977. ed. 250, s/n, 20¼" x 30", pub FHG | 100.00 | — |

# BRAD BENNETT

Portraying America's cities, Brad Bennett paints a limited number of signed watercolor prints of small towns or large cities.

Bennett works from photographs he takes himself. He has portrayed the cities of Kenosha, Wisconsin, Houston and Chicago.

A well-known book illustrator, Bennett holds a Bachelor of Science Degree in Art Education from the University of Wisconsin. He is a member of the distinguished Society of Illustrators in New York, which limits its membership to 750.

He is also the only artist to have his lithographs registered with the Library of Congress.

## BRAD BENNETT

| | ISSUE PRICE | CURRENT PRICE |
|---|---|---|
| ☐ **BIKE RACES**, rel. 1981. ed. 1,000, s/n, 10½" x 15", pub BBS | 30.00 | — |
| ☐ **COHORAMA**, rel. 1981. ed. 1,000, s/n, 10½" x 15", pub BBS | 30.00 | — |
| ☐ **EVOLUTION OF A SALTWATER PORT**, rel. 1981. ed. 1,000, s/n, 10½" x 15", pub BBS | 30.00 | — |
| ☐ **FIRST SHIP OF THE SEASON**, rel. 1981. ed. 1,000, s/n, 10½" x 15", pub BBS | 30.00 | — |
| ☐ **HARVEST TIME**, rel. 1981. ed. 1,000, s/n, 10½" x 15", pub BBS | 30.00 | — |
| ☐ **KEMPER CENTER**, rel. 1981. ed. 1,000, s/n, 10½" x 15", pub BBS | 30.00 | — |
| ☐ **MONUMENT**, rel. 1981. ed. 1,000, s/n, 10½" x 15", pub BBS | 30.00 | — |
| ☐ **NORTHSHORE TROLLEY**, rel. 1981. ed. 1,000, s/n, 10½" x 15", pub BBS | 30.00 | — |
| ☐ **PETRIFYING SPRINGS**, rel. 1981. ed. 1,000, s/n, 10½" x 15", pub BBS | 30.00 | — |
| ☐ **STORMY HARBOR**, rel. 1981. ed. 1,000, s/n, 10½" x 15", pub BBS | 30.00 | — |
| ☐ **WINTER CANNON**, rel. 1981. ed. 1,000, s/n, 10½" x 15", pub BBS | 30.00 | — |
| ☐ **KENOSHA SERIES PORTFOLIO**, rel. 1981. ed. 1,000, s/n, 16½" x 11½", pub BBS, all twelve prints listed above with narratives and registered with the Library of Congress card catalog number #81-53106. Also includes a 13th print of artist's self portrait. | 240.00 | 300.00 |
| ☐ **ABSOLUTION**, rel. 1982. ed. 1,000, s/n, 10½" x 15", pub BBS | 30.00 | — |

| | ISSUE PRICE | CURRENT PRICE |
|---|---|---|
| ☐ **BAPTISM OF THE BEGGARS**, rel. 1982. ed. 1,000, s/n, 10½″ x 15″, pub BBS | 30.00 | — |
| ☐ **DRESSING FOR BATTLE**, rel. 1982. ed. 1,000, s/n, 10½″ x 15″, pub BBS.... | 30.00 | — |
| ☐ **HUMAN CHESS GAMES**, rel. 1982. ed. 1,000, s/n, 10½″ x 15″, pub BBS ... | 30.00 | — |
| ☐ **KING RICHARD AND HIS COURT**, rel. 1982. ed. 1,000, s/n, 10½″ x 15″, pub BBS | 30.00 | — |
| ☐ **THE JOUST**, rel. 1982. ed. 1,000, s/n, 10½″ x 15″, pub BBS ............ | 30.00 | — |
| ☐ **THE QUEEN'S DANCERS**, rel. 1982. ed. 1,000, s/n, 10½″ x 15″, pub BBS ... | 30.00 | — |
| ☐ **THE SORCERER**, rel. 1982. ed. 1,000, s/n, 10½″ x 15″, pub BBS .......... | 30.00 | — |
| ☐ **TOOTHSOME WENCH**, rel. 1982. ed. 1,000, s/n, 10½″ x 15″, pub BBS ..... | 30.00 | — |
| ☐ **VILLAGE JESTERS**, rel. 1982. ed. 1,000, s/n, 10½″ x 15″, pub BBS........ | 30.00 | — |
| ☐ **KING RICHARD'S FAIRE PORTFOLIO**, rel. 1981. ed. 1,000, s/n, 16½″ x 11½″, pub BBS, all ten prints listed above with narratives and registered with the Library of Congress card catalog number #82-90452................... | 250.00 | 300.00 |
| ☐ **AZALEA TRAIL - BAYOU BEND**, rel. 1983. ed. 1,000, s/n, 10½″ x 15″, pub BBS ........................................ | 30.00 | — |
| ☐ **GREEN TUB CHURNING**, rel. 1983. ed. 1,000, s/n, 10½″ x 15″, pub BBS .... | 30.00 | — |
| ☐ **HIGHWAYS AND SKYWAYS**, rel. 1983. ed. 1,000, s/n, 10½″ x 15″, pub BBS. | 30.00 | — |
| ☐ **HOUSTON FESTIVAL**, rel. 1983. ed. 1,000, s/n, 10½″ x 15″, pub BBS ...... | 30.00 | — |
| ☐ **HOUSTON SHIP CHANNEL**, rel. 1983. ed. 1,000, s/n, 10½″ x 15″, pub BBS.. | 30.00 | — |
| ☐ **LET'S RODEO**, rel. 1983. ed. 1,000, s/n, 10½″ x 15″, pub BBS............ | 30.00 | — |
| ☐ **N.A.S.A.**, rel. 1983. ed. 1,000, s/n, 10½″ x 15″, pub BBS ............... | 30.00 | — |
| ☐ **REFINERY**, rel. 1983. ed. 1,000, s/n, 10½″ x 15″, pub BBS ............. | 30.00 | — |
| ☐ **SAM HOUSTON**, rel. 1983. ed. 1,000, s/n, 10½″ x 15″, pub BBS .......... | 30.00 | — |
| ☐ **THE GALLERIA**, rel. 1983. ed. 1,000, s/n, 10½″ x 15″, pub BBS........... | 30.00 | — |
| ☐ **TRAIL RIDERS**, rel. 1983. ed. 1,000, s/n, 10½″ x 15″, pub BBS .......... | 30.00 | — |
| ☐ **TRANQUILITY PARK**, rel. 1983. ed. 1,000, s/n, 10½″ x 15″, pub BBS ...... | 30.00 | — |
| ☐ **HOUSTON SERIES PORTFOLIO**, rel. 1981. ed. 1,000, s/n, 16½″ x 11½″, pub BBS, all twelve prints listed above with narratives and registered with the Library of Congress card catalog number #83-90043................... | — | — |

# JODY BERGSMA

Jody Bergsma began painting seriously at the age of 13. She had shown some talent as a child and was encouraged by family and educators. The first style that developed is the one she is best known for: her illustrations of big-eyed children and fantasy animals. She originally painted these simple watercolors for gifts and soon found a place to sell them at summer art fairs in the Northwest. Bergsma did hundreds of these paintings between the ages of 13 and 18. When she attended college, she was introduced to traditional art training. From Western Washington University she moved to Canada where she received an art degree from the Vancouver School of Art. She taught painting for two years and free lanced for a Canadian book publishing company. In 1977, Jody went to Europe to further her studies in art. When she returned in 1979, she developed her skills and felt it was time to begin producing paintings for exhibition. Since 1980, Bergsma has had numerous exhibitions.

## JODY BERGSMA

| | ISSUE PRICE | CURRENT PRICE |
|---|---|---|
| ☐ **FIRST BOAT BOY**, rel. 1979. ed. 1,000, s/o, 8″ x 10″, pub Bl ............. | 3.00 | 40.00 |
| ☐ **FIRST BUGGED FROG**, rel. 1979. ed. 1,000, s/o, 8″ x 10″, pub Bl ......... | 3.00 | 40.00 |
| ☐ **FIRST DON'T HURRY**, rel. 1979. ed. 1,000, s/o, 8″ x 10″, pub Bl ......... | 3.00 | 40.00 |
| ☐ **FIRST FLYING HORSE**, rel. 1979. ed. 1,000, s/n, 12″ x 16″, pub Bl........ | 8.00 | 125.00 |
| ☐ **FIRST HUGGING BEARS**, rel. 1979. ed. 1,000, s/o, 8″ x 10″, pub Bl ............................................ | 3.00 | 60.00 |
| ☐ **FIRST PIG IN TUB**, rel. 1979. ed. 1,000, s/n, 12″ x 16″, pub Bl ............ | 8.00 | 120.00 |
| ☐ **FIRST UNICORN**, rel. 1979. ed. 1,000, s/n, 12″ x 16″, pub Bl ............ | 8.00 | 125.00 |
| ☐ **FRIENDS IN TUB**, rel. 1979. ed. 1,000, s/n, 12″ x 16″, pub Bl............. | 8.00 | 70.00 |
| ☐ **FRIENDS WITH CLASS**, rel. 1979. ed. 1,000, s/n, 12″ x 16″, pub Bl ........ | 8.00 | 150.00 |
| ☐ **MIXED FRIENDS**, rel. 1979. ed. 1,000, s/n, 12″ x 16″, pub Bl ............ | 8.00 | 70.00 |
| ☐ **ALONG CAME TODAY**, rel. 1980. ed. 2,500, s/o, 5″ x 7″, pub Bl ........... | 2.00 | 35.00 |

**MOM'S HOLD THEIR CHILDREN'S HANDS FOR AWHILE...
THEIR HEARTS FOREVER** *by Jody Bergsma*

|  | ISSUE PRICE | CURRENT PRICE |
|---|---|---|
| ☐ AMAZING ELF AND DUCK, rel. 1980. ed. 2,500, s/o, 5″ x 7″, pub Bl . . . . . . . . | 2.00 | 25.00 |
| ☐ ANNOYED PIG, rel. 1980. ed. 875, s/n, 12″ x 16″, pub Bl . . . . . . . . . . . . . . . | 9.00 | 100.00 |
| ☐ BE YOURSELF, DRAGON AND STARCHILD, rel. 1980. ed. 1,000, s/o, 8″ x 10″, pub Bl . . . . . . . . . . . . . . . . . . . . . . . . . . . . . . . . . . . . . | 4.00 | 40.00 |
| ☐ BE YOURSELF, PIG AND TOAD, rel. 1980. ed. 2,500, s/o, 5″ x 7″, pub Bl . . . . | 2.00 | 25.00 |
| ☐ BOAT CHILDREN, rel. 1980. ed. 2,500, s/o, 12″ x 16″, pub Bl . . . . . . . . . . . . | 9.00 | 90.00 |
| ☐ BOY, FROG, AND ELF UNDER TREE, rel. 1980. ed. 1,000, s/n, 12″ x 16″, pub Bl. . . . . . . . . . . . . . . . . . . . . . . . . . . . . . . . . . . . . . . . . . . . | 9.00 | 125.00 |
| ☐ BOY IN THE MOUNTAIN, rel. 1980. ed. 2,500, s/o, 8″ x 10″, pub Bl . . . . . . . . | 5.00 | 60.00 |
| ☐ BOY IN WOOD TUB, rel. 1980. ed. 1,000, s/o, 8″ x 10″, pub Bl . . . . . . . . . . . | 4.00 | 50.00 |
| ☐ CAT AND RAT, rel. 1980. ed. 1,000, s/o, 8″ x 10″, pub Bl . . . . . . . . . . . . . . . | 4.00 | 40.00 |
| ☐ COOKIE DOUGH, rel. 1980. ed. 2,500, s/o, 5″ x 7″, pub Bl . . . . . . . . . . . . . . . | 2.00 | 25.00 |
| ☐ ELF CHILDREN UNDER RAINBOW, rel. 1980. ed. 2,500, s/o, 8″ x 10″, pub Bl . | 5.00 | 40.00 |
| ☐ FIRST FLUSH, rel. 1980. ed. 2,500, s/o, 8″ x 10″, pub Bl . . . . . . . . . . . . . . . | 4.00 | 60.00 |
| ☐ FIRST FRIENDSHIP, rel. 1980. ed. 1,000, s/o, 8″ x 10″, pub Bl . . . . . . . . . . . | 4.00 | 60.00 |
| ☐ FIRST GIRL WITH RAINBOW CATS, rel. 1980. ed. 1,000, s/n, 12″ x 16″, pub Bl. . . . . . . . . . . . . . . . . . . . . . . . . . . . . . . . . . . . . . . . . . . . . | 9.00 | 125.00 |
| ☐ FIRST GRANDMA AND GRANDPA, rel. 1980. ed. 1,000, s/o, 8″ x 10″, pub Bl . | 4.00 | 59.00 |
| ☐ FIRST MOM'S HOLD, rel. 1980. ed. 1,000, s/o, 8″ x 10″, pub Bl . . . . . . . . . . | 4.00 | 60.00 |
| ☐ FIRST SISTERS, rel. 1980. ed. 1,000, s/o, 8″ x 10″, pub Bl . . . . . . . . . . . . . | 4.00 | 50.00 |
| ☐ FLYING UNICORN FRIENDS, rel. 1980. ed. 875, s/n, 16″ x 20″, pub Bl . . . . . . . . . . . . . . . . . . . . . . . . . . . . . . . . . . . . . . . . . . . . . . . . . | 25.00 | 100.00 |
| ☐ FRIENDS WITH CLASS, PIG, OWL, AND TOAD, rel. 1980. ed. 1,000, s/o, 8″ x 10″, pub Bl . . . . . . . . . . . . . . . . . . . . . . . . . . . . . . . . . . . . . . . . . . | 5.00 | 40.00 |

| | | | |
|---|---|---|---|
| ☐ | **HAPPINESS SHARED, LION AND LAMB**, rel. 1980. ed. 2,500, s/o, 5″ x 7″, pub Bl | 2.00 | 25.00 |
| ☐ | **HAPPINESS, UNICORN, TOAD AND MOUSE**, rel. 1980. ed. 1,000, s/n, 8″ x 10″, pub Bl | 5.00 | 50.00 |
| ☐ | **HAPPY, FAT PIG**, rel. 1980. ed. 875, s/n, 16″ x 20″, pub Bl | 25.00 | 100.00 |
| ☐ | **HOT TUB**, rel. 1980. ed. 2,500, s/o, 8″ x 10″, pub Bl | 4.00 | 50.00 |
| ☐ | **IT'S RAINING WITH TURTLE AND TOAD**, rel. 1980. ed. 1,000, s/o, 8″ x 10″, pub Bl | 4.00 | 40.00 |
| ☐ | **JOURNEY, BOY IN OLD BOAT**, rel. 1980. ed. 1,000, s/o, 8″ x 10″, pub Bl | 5.00 | 60.00 |
| ☐ | **KANSAS TO OZ**, rel. 1980. ed. 1,000, s/n, 8″ x 10″, pub Bl | 4.00 | 40.00 |
| ☐ | **LOVING YOU**, rel. 1980. ed. 2,500, s/o, 5″ x 7″, pub Bl | 2.00 | 35.00 |
| ☐ | **MAGIC SHORES**, rel. 1980. ed. 1,000, s/n, 12″ x 16″, pub Bl | 9.00 | 100.00 |
| ☐ | **MAGIC**, rel. 1980. ed. 1,000, s/o, 8″ x 10″, pub Bl | 4.00 | 60.00 |
| ☐ | **MAMA CAT**, rel. 1980. ed. 1,000, s/o, 8″ x 10″, pub Bl | 5.00 | 50.00 |
| ☐ | **MR. LARK**, rel. 1980. ed. 1,000, s/n, 12″ x 16″, pub Bl | 9.00 | 70.00 |
| ☐ | **NEVER DO TODAY**, rel. 1980. ed. 2,500, s/o, 5″ x 7″, pub Bl | 2.00 | 25.00 |
| ☐ | **RAINBOW ROAD**, rel. 1980. ed. 1,000, s/n, 12″ x 16″, pub Bl | 9.00 | 70.00 |
| ☐ | **REALITY**, rel. 1980. ed. 2,500, s/o, 8″ x 10″, pub Bl | 4.00 | 30.00 |
| ☐ | **SECOND BUGGED FROG**, rel. 1980. ed. 1,000, s/n, 12″ x 16″, pub Bl | 9.00 | 100.00 |
| ☐ | **SECOND FLYING HORSE**, rel. 1980. ed. 2,500, s/o, 12″ x 16″, pub Bl | 9.00 | 100.00 |
| ☐ | **SECOND HUGGING BEARS**, rel. 1980. ed. 1,000, s/n, 12″ x 16″, pub Bl | 9.00 | 140.00 |
| ☐ | **SECOND PARENT'S HOLD**, rel. 1980. ed. 2,500, s/n, 8″ x 10″, pub Bl | 4.00 | 60.00 |
| ☐ | **SECOND UNICORN**, rel. 1980. ed. 2,500, s/o, 12″ x 16″, pub Bl | 9.00 | 100.00 |
| ☐ | **THANKS**, rel. 1980. ed. 2,500, s/o, 5″ x 7″, pub Bl | 2.00 | 25.00 |
| ☐ | **TURKEY**, rel. 1980. ed. 2,500, s/o, 8″ x 10″, pub Bl | 4.00 | 40.00 |
| ☐ | **UNICORN IN THE GARDEN**, rel. 1980. ed. 2,500, s/o, 5″ x 7″, pub Bl | 2.00 | 35.00 |
| ☐ | **WE'RE NOT PERFECT**, rel. 1980. ed. 2,500, s/o, 5″ x 7″, pub Bl | 2.00 | 25.00 |
| ☐ | **WET BATHROOM WITH TWO CHILDREN**, rel. 1980. ed. 1,000, s/o, 8″ x 10″, pub Bl | 4.00 | 50.00 |
| ☐ | **FRIENDS/SISTERS IN SWING**, rel. 1981. ed. 4,500, s/n, 12″ x 16″, pub Bl | 11.00 | 100.00 |
| ☐ | **I WANT A COOKIE**, rel. 1981. ed. 7,500, s/o, 5″ x 7″, pub Bl | 4.00 | 30.00 |
| ☐ | **MOM'S HOLD WITH BIRD**, rel. 1981. ed. 4,500, s/n, 12″ x 16″, pub Bl | 11.00 | 100.00 |
| ☐ | **SISTERS IN THE GARDEN**, rel. 1981. ed. 7,500, s/o, 5″ x 7″, pub Bl | 4.00 | 30.00 |
| ☐ | **THANKS GRANDMA**, rel. 1981. ed. 7,500, s/o, 5″ x 7″, pub Bl | 4.00 | 30.00 |
| ☐ | **TOGETHER**, rel. 1981. ed. 7,500, s/o, 5″ x 7″, pub Bl | 4.00 | 30.00 |
| ☐ | **ROOTS AND WINGS AND RAINBOW**, rel. 1982. ed. 7,500, s/o, 5″ x 7″, pub Bl | 4.00 | 30.00 |

# LENORE BÉRAN

Lenore Béran, artist, sculptor and printmaker, known for her great versatility in the arts, has lived in California since 1940. Her works are displayed throughout the entire continental United States, Canada and Hawaii, where she has won more than fifty first and second prizes in major competitions, and has been honored with many one-woman shows.

Béran interprets a broad range of subjects with great technical proficiency in a variety of media. Her works range from fragile, almost etheral oil wash paintings through the glowing mosaics of rich color and intricate pattern found in her stained glass like collages to her bold and powerful bronze sculpture.

This same versatility, coupled with a superb sense of design, are the secrets of her success as a fine artist. Her distinctive works have found their way into many fine collections around the world.

## LENORE BÉRAN

| | | | |
|---|---|---|---|
| ☐ | **FLUTIST DREAM**, rel. 1977. ed. 1,000 s/n, 22″ x 22″, pub JBFA. | 45.00 | — |
| ☐ | **MEMORIES OF PAN**, rel. 1977. ed. 1,000 s/n, 22″ x 22″, pub JBFA | 45.00 | — |
| ☐ | **THE CALL OF THE PIPER**, rel. 1977. original lithograph, ed. 100, s/n, 21½″ x 30″, pub JBFA<br>ed. 10 Artist Proofs | 150.00 | — |
| ☐ | **CIRCLE OF ENCHANTMENT**, rel. 1978. ed. 500 s/n, 18″ x 18″, pub JBFA. | 50.00 | — |

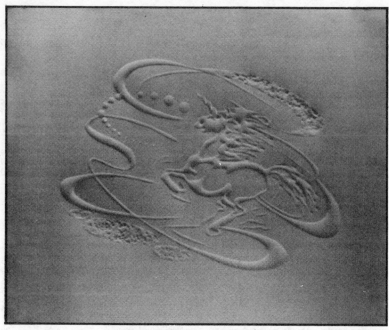

**UNICORN** *by Lenore Béran*

| | ISSUE PRICE | CURRENT PRICE |
|---|---|---|
| ☐ **THE DREAM,** rel. 1978. original lithograph w/embossing, ed. 100 s/n, 21½" x 30", pub JBFA . . . . . . . . . . . . . . . . . . . . . . . . . . . . . . . . . . . . . . . . . . . . . . . . . . ed. 10 Artist Proofs | 200.00 | |
| ☐ **FOR THE LOVE OF A MAIDEN,** rel. 1980. original lithograph w/embossing, ed. 150 s/n, 27" x 22", pub LBA, distr. GBS. . . . . . . . . . . . . . . . . . . . . . . . . . . . . ed. 15 Artist Proofs | 150.00 | — |
| ☐ **LESSONS FROM THE PAST,** rel. 1980. original lithograph w/embossing, ed. 150 s/n, 22" x 30", pub LBA, distr. GBS. . . . . . . . . . . . . . . . . . . . . . . . . . . . . ed. 15 Artist Proofs | 175.00 | — |
| ☐ **PREPARING FOR THE POW POW,** rel. 1980. original lithograph w/embossing, ed. 150 s/n, 26½" x 22", pub LBA, distr. GBS. . . . . . . . . . . . . . . . . . . . . . . ed. 15 Artists Proofs | 150.00 | — |
| ☐ **SACHIKO,** rel. 1980. original lithograph w/hand coloring, ed. 50 s/n, 18" x 26½", pub LBA. . . . . . . . . . . . . . . . . . . . . . . . . . . . . . . . . . . . . . . . . . . . . . ed. 5 Artist Proofs | 175.00 | — |
| ☐ **SPRINGWATER AND THE KACHINA DOLL,** rel. 1980. original lithograph w/embossing. ed. 150 s/n, 26" x 22¼", pub LBS, distr. GBS. . . . . . . . . . . . . . . . | 95.00 | — |
| ☐ **THE GATHERING,** rel. 1980. ed. 500 s/n, 21" x 21", pub LBA. . . . . . . . . . . . . 50 remarques from the edition | 50.00 95.00 | — — |
| ☐ **THE MESSAGE OF THE EAGLE,** rel. 1980. original lithograph w/embossing, ed. 99 s/n, 30" x 22", pub LBA. . . . . . . . . . . . . . . . . . . . . . . . . . . . . . . . . . . . ed. 10 Artist Proofs | 175.00 | — |
| ☐ **VISION,** rel. 1980. original lithograph w/embossing, ed. 99 s/n, 30" x 22", pub LBA. . . . . . . . . . . . . . . . . . . . . . . . . . . . . . . . . . . . . . . . . . . . . . . . . . . ed. 10 Artist Proofs | 175.00 | 195.00 |
| ☐ **FUSION,** rel. 1981. intaglio etching, ed. 42 s/n, 15" x 16", pub LBA. . . . . . . . . ed. 6 Artist Proofs | 95.00 | — |
| ☐ **JAM SESSION,** rel. 1981. intaglio etching, ed. 42 s/n, 15" x 16", pub LBA. . . . ed. 6 Artist Proofs | 95.00 | — |
| ☐ **UP, UP AND AWAY,** rel. 1981. ed. 315 s/n, 25" x 22", pub LBA. . . . . . . . . . . . | 60.00 | — |

| | ISSUE PRICE | CURRENT PRICE |
|---|---|---|
| ☐ **DANCE IN MY FANTACIES,** rel. 1982. intaglio etching, ed. 44 s/n, 30″ x 22″, pub LBA. | 195.00 | — |
|     ed. 6 Artist Proofs | | |
| ☐ **PEGASUS,** rel. 1982. original lithograph w/embossing, ed. 99 s/n, 20″ x 22″, pub LBA. | 40.00 | — |
|     ed. 12 Artist Proofs | | |
| ☐ **UNICORN,** rel. 1982. original lithograph w/embossing, ed. 99 s/n, 20″ x 22″, pub LBA. | 40.00 | — |
|     ed. 12 Artist Proofs | | |
| ☐ **MOONDREAMS,** rel. 1983. intaglio etching, ed. 22 s/n, 19″ x 22″, pub LBA. | 70.00 | — |
|     ed. 3 Artist Proofs | | |
| ☐ **PIMA,** rel. 1983. intaglio etching, ed. 22 s/n, 19″ x 15″, pub LBA. | 60.00 | — |
|     ed. 3 Artist Proofs | | |
| ☐ **SERENADE,** rel. 1983. intaglio etching, ed. 22 s/n, 19″ x 15″, pub LBA. | 60.00 | — |
|     ed. 3 Artist Proofs | | |

# EDWARD J. BIERLY

Edward Bierly was already a successful illustrator when he made the decision to make wildlife art his life's work. His job as designer of natural history exhibits for the National Park Service led to his appointment as consultant to the government of Rhodesia by UNESCO. It was on this assignment that he saw the wildlife of Africa for the first time. Moved by both its grandeur and uncertain future, he decided to use his art to attract attention to the plight of endangered fauna everywhere. He returned home to paint the scenes so vividly etched in his memory, and in 1968 had a one-man show of his work at Abercrombie and Fitch in New York City. The success of this show launched him on a new career as a painter of African and American wildlife. In 1970, he left the National Park Service to devote full time to this new occupation.

**FLIGHT OF FREEDOM (Bald Eagle)** *by Edward J. Bierly*

Today he is recognized as one of the top artists in this field. His paintings have been exhibited at the Royal Ontario Museum, The Smithsonian, The National Audubon Society, The New York Natural History Museum and the National Wildlife Federation in Washington, D.C. He has illustrated several books, including a field guide to the Mammals of Rhodesia, Zambia and Malawi. His art appears in Dr. Bernhard Grzimek's Animal Life Encyclopedia, the largest and most authoritative compendium of animal science ever published. His paintings have been reproduced in such magazines as National Wildlife, International Wildlife, Reader's Digest and The Arts Magazine.

Bierly won the national competition for the Federal Duck Stamp design in 1956, 1963 and 1970. He is a member of the Society of Animal Artists.

## EDWARD J. BIERLY

| | ISSUE PRICE | CURRENT PRICE |
|---|---|---|
| ☐ **AMERICAN MERGANSERS,** rel. 1956-7. Federal Duck Stamp Print, ed. 325 s/o, 10″ x 11½″, pub EJB. | 15.00 | 1,000.00 |
| *ed. 125, s/o, 10″ x 11½″, rel. 1967, pub EJB. | 40.00 | 675.00 |
| *2nd. printing, etching plate now canceled | | |
| ☐ **AMERICAN BRANT,** rel. 1963-4. Federal Duck Stamp Print, ed. 550 s/o, 12½″ x 14″, pub EJB. | 20.00 | 1,000.00 |
| *ed. 125, s/o, 12½″ x 14″, rel. 1967, pub EJB. | 40.00 | 700.00 |
| *2nd. printing, etching plate now canceled | | |
| ☐ **ROSS GEESE,** rel. 1970-71. Federal Duck Stamp Print, ed. 700 s/n, 13″ x 15″, pub EJB. | 60.00 | 2,200.00 |
| ed. 300, remarqued, 13″ x 15″, rel. 1970, pub EJB. | 100.00 | 3,200.00 |
| ed. 2,150, s/n, 13″ x 15″, rel. 1976, pub EJB | 100.00 | 150.00 |
| ☐ **LIONS AT WANKIE (Lion and Lioness),** rel. 1968. ed. 500, s/n, 20¼″ x 27½″, dist. EJB | 50.00 | — |
| ☐ **THE AFRICAN QUEEN (Lioness and Cubs),** rel. 1968. ed. 750, s/n, 23″ x 27″, dist. EJB | 50.00 | — |
| ☐ **MOHINI & CUB (White Tigress and Cubs),** rel. 1971. ed. 1,000, s/n, 22¾″ x 29½″, dist. EJB. | 100.00 | — |
| *Commissioned for the Smithsonian ''Save The Tiger Fund'' | 100.00 | |
| ☐ **EMPEROR GEESE PITCHING,** rel. 1972. ed. 500, s/n, 19½″ x 25½″, pub SEL. | 50.00 | — |
| ☐ **GIANT PANDAS,** rel. 1972. ed. 500, s/n, 19¾″ x 27¾″, pub SEL | 50.00 | 100.00 |
| ed. 50, remarqued | 125.00 | 250.00 |
| ☐ **THE SURVIVOR (Wolf),** rel. 1974. ed. 250, s/n, 21″ x 27″, dist. EJB | 60.00 | 200.00 |
| ☐ **BREAKING THE TRAIL (Bison),** rel. 1976. ed. 375, s/n, 24″ x 32″, pub EJB | 100.00 | — |
| ☐ **CHALBI STAMPEDE (Zebra),** rel. 1976. ed. 375, s/n, 24″ x 32″, pub EJB | 100.00 | — |
| *Commissioned by the Buffalo Zoological Society. | | |
| ☐ **SNOW LEOPARD,** rel. 1976. ed. 500, s/n, 24¾″ x 35″, dist. EJB | 150.00 | 450.00 |
| ☐ **FLAGS UP (White-tailed deer),** rel. 1977. ed. 800, s/n, 21¾″ x 29″, pub PP, distr. EJB. | 60.00 | — |
| ☐ **READY FOX,** rel. 1977. ed. 800, s/n, 21″ x 26¼″, pub PP, distr. EJB. | 60.00 | 150.00 |
| ☐ **WINTER WOODS (White-tailed deer),** rel. 1977. ed. 600, s/n, 24″ x 32″, pub EJB | 100.00 | 350.00 |
| ☐ **BENGAL SUNSET (Tiger),** rel. 1978. ed. 800, s/n, 22¾″ x 26″, pub PP, distr. EJB. | 60.00 | — |
| ☐ **FLORIDA BASS,** rel. 1978. ed. 950, s/n, 21″ x 26½″, pub EJB | 45.00 | — |
| ☐ **LEOPARD'S POOL,** rel. 1978. ed. 800, s/n, 22¾″ x 26″, pub PP, distr. EJB. | 60.00 | — |
| ☐ **A CLOSE CALL (Red Fox and Ruffed Grouse),** rel. 1979. ed. 800, s/n, 22¾″ x 29″, pub PP, distr. EJB. | 60.00 | — |
| ☐ **GREATER KUDU,** rel. 1979. ed. 500, s/n, 22″ x 30½″, pub EJB | 100.00 | — |
| ☐ **THE NIGHT HARVESTERS (Canada Geese),** rel. 1979. ed. 800, s/n, 23″ x 27″, pub PP, distr. EJB. | 60.00 | — |
| ☐ **CLOUDED LEOPARD,** rel. 1980. ed. 600, s/n, 24½″ x 32½″, pub EJB. | 100.00 | — |
| ☐ **FOUR FLUSHED (Grey Fox & Quail),** rel. 1980. ed. 950, s/n, 22¾″ x 27″, pub EJB. | 75.00 | — |
| ☐ **DEN MOTHER (Red Fox & Cubs),** rel. 1981. ed. 950, s/n, 22¼″ x 25¼″, pub EJB. | 85.00 | — |
| ☐ **HAPPY HOUR (White-tailed Deer & Fawns),** rel. 1981. ed. 950, s/n, 19¾″ x 23½″, pub EJB. | 75.00 | — |
| ☐ **MASAI WARRIOR,** rel. 1981. ed. 500, s/n, 20¼″ x 27″, pub EJB. | 100.00 | — |
| ☐ **TRANQUILITY (Giraffes),** rel. 1981. ed. 500, s/n, 21¼″ x 28″, pub EJB. | 100.00 | — |

|  | ISSUE PRICE | CURRENT PRICE |
|---|---|---|
| ☐ **FLIGHT OF FREEDOM (Bald Eagle)**, ed. 950, s/n, 24" x 28", pub EJB. . . . . . . | 150.00 | — |
| ed. 50 remarqued . . . . . . . . . . . . . . . . . . . . . . . . . . . . . . . . . . . . . . . . . . . | 300.00 | Sold Out |
| ☐ **THE CHALLENGE (White-Tailed Deer)**, rel. 1982. ed. 1,500, s/n, 12" x 14", pub SGL. . . . . . . . . . . . . . . . . . . . . . . . . . . . . . . . . . . . . . . . . . . . . . . . . | 130.00 | — |
| 1982 Deer Unlimited Stamp Print, includes stamp. | | |
| ☐ **BLUEBIRDS (Western, Eastern and Mountain)**, rel. 1983. ed. 950, s/n, 15" x 19½", pub EJB. . . . . . . . . . . . . . . . . . . . . . . . . . . . . . . . . . . . . . . . . . . . | 150.00 | — |
| rel. 1983, ed. 3,000, i/o, 15" x 19½", pub EJB . . . . . . . . . . . . . . . . . . . . . | 75.00 | — |
| Commissioned by Campfire, Inc. | | |
| Sold only as a portfolio of three prints. | | |

## RICHARD BISHOP

|  | | |
|---|---|---|
| ☐ **BLUE WINGS**, no information available, distr. WWI. . . . . . . . . . . . . . . . . . . . . | 35.00 | 250.00 |
| ☐ **FLOODED TIMBER - MALLARDS**, no information available, distr. WWI. . . . . . . | 40.00 | 400.00 |
| ☐ **GOOD CALLING - MALLARDS**, no information available, distr. WWI. . . . . . . . . | 60.00 | 400.00 |
| ☐ **IN THE BAG - MALLARDS**, no information available, distr. WWI. . . . . . . . . . . . | 35.00 | 250.00 |
| ☐ **IN THE STOCKS - MALLARDS**, no information available, distr. WWI. . . . . . . . . | 60.00 | 300.00 |
| ☐ **OVERFLOW - MALLARDS**, no information available, distr. WWI. . . . . . . . . . . . | 64.00 | 400.00 |
| ☐ **SAFE RETURN - MALLARDS**, no information available, distr. WWI. . . . . . . . . . | 52.00 | 300.00 |

## BEN BLACK

As a still life artist, Ben Black brings a marvelous combination of resonant color, free-flowing texture and disciplined pattern to his works. As a portraitist, he conceives striking character studies, filled with pathos, humor, and great sympathy.

Born in Boston, Black began his career as an artist just before World War II, when he graduated from the Massachusetts College of Art. After military service, he began working as an art director for one of Boston's leading advertising agencies. Later, he headed his own studio, and contributed work to leading national magazines, including The New Yorker, The Saturday Evening Post, and Reader's Digest. Today, his art appears in collections in cities throughout the world, including Florence, Rome, Vienna, and Sao Paulo, as well as major cities in this country. He is also the winner of the coveted Richard Minton Juror's Award, in the Annual Exhibition of Contemporary New England Artists.

### BEN BLACK

|  | | |
|---|---|---|
| ☐ **BIRDS AND FAN**, rel. 1980. ed. 275, s/n, 26½" x 20½", pub EEI . . . . . . . . . | 200.00 | — |
| ☐ **LOVELY VICTORIANA**, rel. 1980. ed. 275, s/n, 24" x 20", pub EEI . . . . . . . . . | 200.00 | — |
| ☐ **MOMENT FOR THE CLOWN**, rel. 1980. ed. 275, s/n, 27" x 19", pub EEI . . . . . | 200.00 | — |
| ☐ **SWEET ALICE DOLL**, rel. 1980. ed. 275, s/n, 24" x 20", pub EEI . . . . . . . . . . | 200.00 | — |

## NORMAN BLACK

One of Britain's leading surrealists, Black was born in Glasgow in 1920. He now resides in Brighton, England.

After completing his studies and spending many years as a successful designer in glass, ceramics, and metal, he now concentrates solely on his painting.

## NORMAN BLACK

| | ISSUE PRICE | CURRENT PRICE |
|---|---|---|
| ☐ **JOKER TAKES ALL**, ed. 950, s/n, 23″ x 17½″, pub CGAL | 74.00 | 85.00 |
| ed. 12, Artist Accented, s/n | 310.00 | 420.00 |
| ☐ **THE ENTERTAINER**, ed. 950, s/n, 23″ x 18¾″, pub CGAL | 100.00 | — |
| ed. 12, Artist Accented, s/n | 290.00 | — |
| ☐ **THE QUEEN RISING**, General run, 12″ x 16″, pub CGAL | 10.00 | — |
| Signed in plate only | | |
| ed. 12, Artist Accented, s/n | 310.00 | — |
| ☐ **SAFE ARRIVAL**, General run, 12″ x 16″, pub CGAL | 10.00 | — |
| Signed in plate only | | |
| ed. 12, Artist Accented, s/n | 310.00 | — |
| ☐ **THE WRECK**, ed. 950, s/n, 21½″ x 17½″, pub CGAL | 100.00 | — |
| ed. 12, Artist Accented, s/n | 290.00 | — |

# CAROLYN BLISH

Carolyn Blish is an artist who captures with her paintbrush a single fleeting moment in the onward rush of time. It may be a moment of discovery in a child's world of wonder, or the beat of a bird's wing in mid-flight. Her purpose is always to communicate her love for her subject matter. "Without love a painting is sterile."

**MAKE A WISH** *by Carolyn Blish*

Born in Washington, D.C., in 1928, she attended Bradford Junior College in Massachusetts, where she studied psychology, philosophy and comparative religion, taking all of one art course in the process. Her formal art education consisted of two weeks studying under watercolorist Edgar A. Whitney, from whom she learned how to construct and design a painting. In 1965 she began to exhibit nationally. Today, she is a member of the American Watercolor Society and the Allied Artists of America. She has won numerous awards, including Gold Medals of Honor at the National Arts Club in New York City and top awards in the annual shows of the American Watercolor Society. She has served on juries for many national art exhibitions.

## CAROLYN BLISH

| | ISSUE PRICE | CURRENT PRICE |
|---|---|---|
| ☐ **BEACHED,** rel. 1973. ed. 1,500, s/n, 31″ x 21″, pub GW | 65.00 | 115.00 |
| ☐ **ROADSIDE DAISIES,** rel. 1973. ed. 1,000, s/n, 34″ x 24″, pub GW | 65.00 | 200.00 |
| ☐ **SIMPLICITY,** rel. 1973. ed. 1,500, s/n, 26″ x 18¼″, pub GW | 45.00 | 70.00 |
| ☐ **WONDERMENT,** rel. 1973. ed. 1,000, s/n, 28″ x 22″, pub GW | 45.00 | 230.00 |
| ☐ **MISTY SEA,** rel. 1975. ed. 1,000, s/n, 35″ x 15½″, pub GW | 65.00 | 185.00 |
| ☐ **SHORE BIRDS,** rel. 1974. ed. 1,000, s/n, 26″ x 18″, pub GW | 55.00 | 220.00 |
| ☐ **SEASONS** (Portfolio of 4 Prints), rel. 1975. ed. 1,000, s/n, 9″ x 11″, pub GW | 60.00 | 85.00 |
| ☐ **AFTER THE STORM,** rel. 1976. ed. 1,000, s/n, 35″ x 19″, pub GW | 65.00 | 100.00 |
| ☐ **BLUEBELLS AND DAFFODILS,** rel. 1976. ed. 1,000, s/n, 31″ x 22½″, pub GW | 65.00 | 170.00 |
| ☐ **DISCOVERY,** rel. 1976. ed. 1,000, s/n, 31″ x 18½″, pub GW | 65.00 | 140.00 |
| ☐ **STORM'S EDGE,** rel. 1977. ed. 1,000, s/n, 34″ x 18″, pub GW | 65.00 | 100.00 |
| ☐ **FLIGHT,** rel. 1977. ed. 1,000, s/n, 40″ x 26″, pub GW | 75.00 | 300.00 |
| ☐ **THE HIGHEST DUNE,** rel. 1977. ed. 1,500, s/n, 22″ x 29″, pub GW | 55.00 | 140.00 |
| ☐ **FLIGHT II,** rel. 1978. ed. 1,500, s/n, 18″ x 28″, pub GW | 65.00 | 185.00 |
| ☐ **DAY DREAM,** rel. 1978. ed. 1,500, s/n, 14½″ x 22½″, pub GW | 65.00 | 140.00 |
| ☐ **TIDE'S EDGE,** rel. 1978. ed. 1,500, s/n, 34″ x 17¼″, pub GW | 65.00 | — |
| ☐ **WASHDAY,** rel. 1978. ed. 1,500, s/n, 32″ x 22″, pub GW | 65.00 | Sold Out |
| ☐ **WINDSURF,** rel. 1978. ed. 1,500, s/n, 32″ x 20″, pub GW | 65.00 | — |
| ☐ **A CLOSER LOOK,** rel. 1979. ed. 1,500, s/n, 21½″ x 27″, pub GW | 65.00 | — |
| ☐ **A QUIET PLACE,** rel. 1979. ed. 1,500, s/n, 32″ x 22″, pub GW | 65.00 | — |
| ☐ **RAGGEDY ANN,** rel. 1979. ed. 1,500, s/n, 18″ x 20″, pub GW | 75.00 | — |
| ☐ **BRIGHT ENCOUNTER,** rel. 1980. ed. 1,500, s/n, 28″ x 20″, pub GW. | 75.00 | — |
| ☐ **LAST LEAVES,** rel. 1980. ed. 1,500, s/n, 32″ x 21¾″, pub GW | 75.00 | — |
| ☐ **REMEMBER A SWING,** rel. 1980. ed. 1,500, s/n, 32″ x 21½″, pub GW. | 75.00 | — |
| ☐ **MAKE A WISH,** rel. 1982. ed. 1,000, s/n, 17⅝″ x 22⅝″, pub GW. | 125.00 | — |
| ☐ **SAND TREASURES,** rel. 1981. ed. 1,000, s/n, 28″ x 22½″, pub GW. | 125.00 | — |
| ☐ **WIND BORNE,** rel. 1981. ed. 1,500, s/n, 22½″ x 29½″, pub GW. | 85.00 | — |

# SEAN BOLLAR

As a farm boy Sean Bollar enjoyed spending hours observing and drawing wildlife, but by the time he entered college his interest had taken a scientific turn and he received degrees in biology and chemistry. Bollar worked as a Marine Research Biologist, but it was later, as a teacher of Marine Science, that his love of drawing surfaced again. Stimulated by the diverse Florida wildlife, he set out to depict it in precise detail.

Sean enjoys thoroughly researching the behavior of each animal he paints. Even when he portrays his subject at rest, the vibrant life and constant awareness upon which the survival of any wild creature depends is unmistakably conveyed.

## SEAN BOLLAR

| | | |
|---|---|---|
| ☐ **FLORIDA SCREECH OWL,** rel. 1973. ed. 800, s/n, 16″ x 22″, pub PGL | 25.00 | 180.00 |
| ed. 1,200, s/o | 15.00 | 105.00 |
| ☐ **RED-SHOULDERED HAWK,** rel. 1973. ed. 1,000, s/n, pub PGL | 25.00 | 130.00 |
| ed. 2,000, s/o | 15.00 | 75.00 |
| ☐ **FLORIDA PANTHER,** rel. 1974. ed. 1,000, s/n, 16″ x 17″, pub PGL | 25.00 | 160.00 |
| ed, 2,000, s/o | 15.00 | 80.00 |

**JAGUAR** *by Sean Bollar*

| | ISSUE PRICE | CURRENT PRICE |
|---|---|---|
| ☐ RED-HEADED WOODPECKER, rel. 1975. ed. 800, s/n, 12″ x 16″, pub PGL . . . . | 24.00 | 30.00 |
| ed. 1,200, s/o . . . . . . . . . . . . . . . . . . . . . . . . . . . . . . . . . . . . . . . . . . . . . | 14.00 | 20.00 |
| ☐ JAGUAR PORTRAIT, rel. 1976. ed. 900, s/n, 16″ x 20″, pub PGL . . . . . . . . . . | 45.00 | 55.00 |
| ed. 1,000, s/o . . . . . . . . . . . . . . . . . . . . . . . . . . . . . . . . . . . . . . . . . . . . . | 35.00 | 45.00 |
| ☐ ROYAL BENGAL TIGER, rel. 1977. ed. 900, s/n, 19½″ x 25½″, pub PGL . . . . . | 60.00 | 75.00 |
| ed. 1,000, s/o . . . . . . . . . . . . . . . . . . . . . . . . . . . . . . . . . . . . . . . . . . . . . | 50.00 | 60.00 |
| ☐ SQUIRREL TREEFROG, rel. 1977. ed. 900, s/n, 12″ x 16″, pub PGL . . . . . . . . . | 30.00 | — |
| ed. 1,000, s/o . . . . . . . . . . . . . . . . . . . . . . . . . . . . . . . . . . . . . . . . . . . . . | 20.00 | — |
| ☐ BENGAL TIGER PORTRAIT, rel. 1979. ed. 900, s/n, 16″ x 20″, pub PGL . . . . . . | 55.00 | — |
| ☐ EL TIGRE GRANDE (Full Jaguar), rel. 1980. ed. 900, s/n, 17″ x 26½″, pub PGL . . . . . . . . . . . . . . . . . . . . . . . . . . . . . . . . . . . . . . . . . . . . . . . . . . . | 75.00 | — |
| ☐ PESKY PANTHER (Juvenile Florida Panther), rel. 1980. ed. 900, s/n, 16″ x 20″, pub PGL . . . . . . . . . . . . . . . . . . . . . . . . . . . . . . . . . . . . . . . . . . . . . . | 55.00 | — |
| ☐ SILENT FLIGHT (Barred Owl), rel. 1980. ed. 900, s/n, 23″ x 25½″, pub PGL . . | 75.00 | — |

# BRUCE BOMBERGER

For many people, the unique appeal of a Bruce Bomberger lithograph is the feeling of de ja vu it gives the viewer. As critic Barnaby Conrad recently enthused in Southwest Art magazine: "A Bomberger street scene, for example, is not just any street, but a particular one, observed and recorded by the artist with true appreciation and tender, loving attention . . . if his images don't take you back to places where you've been, they take you to places you'd love to have been."

Beginning his painting career at the tender age of eight, Bomberger first studied art at the Berkeley (CA) School of Arts and Crafts, and at the Art Center School in Los Angeles. After selling his first major story illustration (at age 20) to Good Housekeeping, he soon developed into one of America's leading illustrators — a career he pursued for over 25 years. Currently, Bomberger is a fulltime fine artist.

Says Bomberger, "I know many people like my pictures for the same reason that I create them — because they love the real places I'm depicting."

**RUE LE JOUR** *by Bruce Bomberger*

## BRUCE BOMBERGER

| | ISSUE PRICE | CURRENT PRICE |
|---|---|---|
| ☐ **BASTILLE DAY,** rel. 1977. ed. 250, s/n, litho, arches, 30″ x 24½″, pub EEI... | 150.00 | 500.00 |
| ed. 50, japon . . . . . . . . . . . . . . . . . . . . . . . . . . . . . . . . . . . . . . . . . . . . | 175.00 | 525.00 |
| ☐ **BUTTER, EGGS & CHEESE,** rel. 1977. ed. 250, s/n, litho, arches, 28″ x 22¾″, pub EEI. . . . . . . . . . . . . . . . . . . . . . . . . . . . . . . . . . . . . . . . . . . . . . . . . . | 150.00 | 450.00 |
| ed. 50, japon . . . . . . . . . . . . . . . . . . . . . . . . . . . . . . . . . . . . . . . . . . . . | 175.00 | 475.00 |
| ☐ **RUE LE JOUR,** rel. 1977. ed. 250, s/n, litho, arches, 28½″ x 23½″, pub EEI. . | 175.00 | 300.00 |
| ed. 50, japon . . . . . . . . . . . . . . . . . . . . . . . . . . . . . . . . . . . . . . . . . . . . | 200.00 | 325.00 |
| ☐ **ART DIRECTOR,** rel. 1978. ed. 250, s/n, litho, arches, 31″ x 25″, pub EEI. . . . | 200.00 | 450.00 |
| ed. 50, japon . . . . . . . . . . . . . . . . . . . . . . . . . . . . . . . . . . . . . . . . . . . . | 225.00 | 475.00 |

| | ISSUE PRICE | CURRENT PRICE |
|---|---|---|
| ☐ **BOOKSTALLS,** rel. 1978. ed. 250, s/n, litho, arches, 27″ x 23″, pub EEI. . . . | 250.00 | 325.00 |
| ed. 50, japon | 275.00 | 350.00 |
| ☐ **ENGLISH PUBS PORTFOLIO,** rel. 1978. ed. 250, s/n, litho, arches, 29″ x 24″, pub EEI. | 1,200.00 | 1,400.00 |
| ed. 50, japon | 1,400.00 | 1,600.00 |
| ☐ **L'ESCARGOT,** rel. 1978. ed. 250, s/n, litho, arches, 32″ x 27″, pub EEI. . . . . | 175.00 | 425.00 |
| ed. 50, japon | 200.00 | 450.00 |
| ☐ **PONT ROYALE,** rel. 1978. ed. 250, s/n, litho, arches, 27″ x 21½″, pub EEI. . . | 175.00 | 250.00 |
| ed. 50, japon | 200.00 | 275.00 |
| ☐ **FLEA MARKET,** rel. 1979. ed. 250, s/n, litho, arches, 34″ x 24″, pub EEI. . . . | 275.00 | 300.00 |
| ed. 50, japon | 300.00 | 325.00 |
| ☐ **GREENGROCER,** rel. 1979. ed. 250, s/n, litho, arches, 29¼″ x 23¾″, pub EEI. | 250.00 | 300.00 |
| ed. 50, japon | 275.00 | 325.00 |
| ☐ **SACRE COEUR,** rel. 1979. ed. 250, s/n, litho, arches, 29¼″ x 24″, pub EEI. . . | 250.00 | 300.00 |
| ed. 50, japon | 275.00 | 325.00 |
| ☐ **PARIS METRO,** rel. 1980. ed. 250, s/n, litho, arches, 24″ x 34″, pub EEI. . . . | 275.00 | 325.00 |
| ed. 50, japon | 300.00 | 350.00 |

# HERB BOOTH

Herb Booth was born in Colorado Springs, Colorado, on June 15, 1942, but grew up in La Junta, Colorado. La Junta is located in the middle of the Colorado-Arkansas River Valley. He began to hunt with a friend and his father when he was in the seventh grade . . . a very serious project every weekend in the fall of the year continuing until he graduated from high school.

He attended the University of Arizona for one year, and then continued on to receive his B.A. degree in Economics and Journalism in 1965 from the University of Colorado.

Booth's art education has been very minimal, consisting of a few drawing courses in college, and a short study of watercolor with Clayton Staples during his high school years. He does not like to consider himself "self-taught" as an artist, but rather having been taught by every artist who's work he has studied . . . namely, Remington, Russell, Homer, Rungius, Ripley, Pleissner, Bishop, Hagerbaumer, Weiler, Cowan and others.

## HERB BOOTH

| | | |
|---|---|---|
| ☐ **BLOWIN' IN,** rel. 1982. ed. 600, s/n, size NA, pub WWI. . . . . . . . . . . . . . . . | 95.00 | — |
| ☐ **BREAK AWAY,** rel. 1982. ed. 600, s/n, size NA, pub WWI. . . . . . . . . . . . . . . . | 85.00 | 95.00 |
| ☐ **BRUSHLAND BOB,** ed. 600, s/n, 22″ x 28½″, pub MLC . . . . . . . . . . . . . . . . . | 85.00 | 125.00 |
| ☐ **CALLING 'EM IN,** rel. 1980. ed. 600, s/n, size NA, pub WWI. . . . . . . . . . . . . | 95.00 | — |
| ☐ **DOWN AND BACK,** ed. 600, s/n, 22″ x 28½″, pub MLC . . . . . . . . . . . . . . . . . | 85.00 | 85.00 |
| ☐ **GOOD SPORT,** ed. 600, s/o, 22″ x 28½″, pub MLC . . . . . . . . . . . . . . . . . . | 60.00 | 85.00 |
| ☐ **HOME PLACE,** ed. 600, s/o, 22″ x 28½″, pub MLC . . . . . . . . . . . . . . . . . . | 50.00 | 250.00 |
| ☐ **SEPTEMBER,** rel. 1980. ed. 600, s/n, 27″ x 20″, pub WWI. . . . . . . . . . . . . . | 85.00 | 250.00 |
| ☐ **SPLIT COVEY,** ed. 600, s/o, 22″ x 28½″, pub MLC . . . . . . . . . . . . . . . . . . | 60.00 | 85.00 |
| ☐ **THE THREE WISE MEN,** ed. 600, s/o, 22″ x 28½″, pub MLC . . . . . . . . . . . . . | 50.00 | 250.00 |

# JIM BOOTH

| | | |
|---|---|---|
| ☐ **AUTUMN RUN,** rel. 1977. ed. 500, s/n, litho, pub FWSG. . . . . . . . . . . . . . . | — | 50.00 |
| ☐ **CHURCH STREET,** rel. 1977. ed. 500, s/n, litho, pub FWSG. . . . . . . . . . . . . | — | 50.00 |
| ☐ **COTTON CLIPPER,** rel. 1977. ed. 500, s/n, litho, pub FWSG. . . . . . . . . . . . . | — | 50.00 |
| ☐ **MORNING FLIGHT,** rel. 1977. ed. 500, s/n, litho, pub FWSG. . . . . . . . . . . . | — | 50.00 |
| ☐ **MORNING LIGHT,** rel. 1977. ed. 500, s/n, litho, pub FWSG. . . . . . . . . . . . . | — | 50.00 |

| | ISSUE PRICE | CURRENT PRICE |
|---|---|---|
| ☐ **COUNTRY ROAD,** rel. 1978. ed. 250, s/n, litho, pub FWSG. | — | 125.00 |
| ☐ **SOUTH BATTERY,** rel. 1978. ed. 500, s/n, litho, pub FWSG. | — | 25.00 |
| ☐ **WINGS OF AUTUMN,** rel. 1978. ed. 2,000, s/n, litho, pub FWSG. | — | 35.00 |

## STAN BORACK

**DAWN'S LIGHT** *by Stan Borack*

| | | |
|---|---|---|
| ☐ **DAWN'S LIGHT,** rel. 1981. ed. 950, s/n, 18″ x 27″, pub SCI*. | 65.00 | — |
| ☐ **AWAITING THE SIGNAL,** rel. 1982. ed. 350, s/n, size NA, pub SCI*. | 65.00 | — |

*Represents the Sawyier Collection, Inc., and was formed as a subsidiary of Paul Sawyier Galleries, Inc.

## JAMES BOREN

James Boren, has a Master of Fine Arts degree granted jointly by the Kansas City Art Institute and Kansas City University. His background in education and in life brings classical richness to his paintings.

Born in Wazahachie, Texas, Boren grew up in small towns in west Texas where his father was a preacher. In 1942, he joined the Navy, became a medical corpsman and served with the First Marine Raider Battalion in the Pacific.

After the war, Boren attended Kansas City Art Institute. After graduation, he taught in the Fine Arts Department at St. Mary College, Leavenworth, Kansas. In 1956, Boren moved to Denver where he spent eight years as a "concept illustrator" for the Martin Company. Ready to paint full time, he accepted the position of Art Director for the National Cowboy Hall of Fame in 1965.

**REST STOP AT A WARM KITCHEN** *by James Boren*

Four years later, after a two-man show at the Cowboy Hall of Fame, he resigned as Art Director and became a full-time western artist. He maintained his studio in Oklahoma City until 1971 when he moved to a ranch near Clifton, Texas.

He has served for two terms as president of the Cowboy Artists of America. He was named Texas State Artist in 1976 and has won many medals and awards for his paintings.

## JAMES BOREN

| | ISSUE PRICE | CURRENT PRICE |
|---|---|---|
| ☐ RAINY DAY AT HILLSBORO, rel. 1977. ed. 950, s/n, 20½″ x 27½″, pub MPPI | 75.00 | 185.00 |
| ☐ FIRST LIGHT OF A WINTER'S MORNING, rel. 1978. ed. 2,250, s/n, 14″ x 22″, pub TAP | 85.00 | 150.00 |
| ☐ FIRST LIGHT OF A WINTER'S MORNING, rel. 1979. ed. 2,250, s/n, 14″ x 22″, pub TAP | 85.00 | — |
| ☐ IN LATE APRIL, rel. 1979. ed. 2,250, s/n, 16″ x 22″, pub TAP | 85.00 | — |
| ☐ REST STOP AT A WARM KITCHEN, rel. 1979. ed. 950, s/n, 21″ x 28¾″, pub MPPI | 95.00 | 150.00 |
| ☐ A WET MORNING, rel. 1980. ed. 2,250, s/n, 14″ x 22″, pub TAP | 100.00 | — |
| ☐ PRAYER MEETIN' TIME, rel. 1980. ed. 2,250, s/n, 20″ x 28″, pub TAP | 100.00 | — |
| ☐ WINTER IN THE ROCKIES, rel. 1980. ed. 2,250, s/n, 21″ x 28″, pub TAP | 100.00 | — |
| ☐ WINTER IN STEPHENVILLE, rel. 1980. ed. 2,250, s/n, 20½″ x 22″, pub TAP | 100.00 | — |
| ☐ EARLY TEXAS OIL, rel. 1981. ed. 1,050, s/n, 17″ x 26½″, pub TAP | 100.00 | — |
| ☐ EARLY TEXAS WINTER, rel. 1981. ed. 750, s/n, 16″ x 22″, pub TAP | 100.00 | — |
| ☐ 'NEATH A WARM WINTER SUN, rel. 1981. ed. 950, s/n, 21¾″ x 32¼″, pub MPPI | 150.00 | — |
| ☐ WINTER AT THE PUEBLO, rel. 1981. ed. 550, s/n, 23″ x 28¾″, pub MPPI | 125.00 | — |
| ☐ LAZY DAY AT LUCKENBACH, rel. 1982. ed. 1,000, s/n, 20″ x 29″, pub TAP | 100.00 | — |
| ☐ MENDING WALL, rel. 1982. ed. 1,250, s/n, 18¾″ x 25″, pub TAP | 100.00 | — |
| ☐ AFTER THE SPRING STORM, rel. 1983. ed. 950, s/n, 17½″ x 23⅞″, pub MPPI | 75.00 | — |

# JODIE BOREN

Jodie Boren is a westerner who paints a West that is peaceful and tranquil with natural people who have real feelings.

Boren attended the Art Institute in Kansas City majoring in commercial art and eventually became an art director for an advertising agency. At night he taught at Abilene Christian College. Perhaps spurred by his continuing interest in all elements of Western life, Boren turned to a career in fine art documenting Western life.

Rather than telling a story with each painting, Boren creates a mood. He believes that "each person looks at a painting relative to his own background and experience. It is my desire to furnish the stage and the setting; you create the play".

**RENDEZVOUS WITH THE 707** by Jodie Boren

| JODIE BOREN | ISSUE PRICE | CURRENT PRICE |
|---|---|---|
| ☐ **MAC'S TRADING POST**, rel. 1982. ed. 975, s/n, 24" x 34", pub FHG . . . . . . . . | 75.00 | — |
| ☐ **MAIN STREET, DODGE CITY**, rel. 1982. ed. 975, s/n, 16" x 32", pub FHG . . . . | 75.00 | — |
| ☐ **RETURNING HUNTER**, rel. 1982. ed. 975, s/n, 20" x 25½", pub FHG . . . . . . . | 75.00 | — |
| ☐ **THE LITTLE BROWN CHURCH**, rel. 1983. ed. 750, s/n, 18½" x 20", pub FHG . | 90.00 | — |
| ☐ **RENDEZVOUS WITH THE 707**, rel. 1983. ed. 750, s/n, 30" x 18½", pub FHG . | 90.00 | — |

# GEORGE BOUTWELL

"I love everything about nature, it has a beauty that we humans are incapable of equaling. There are so many things that I want to paint, I wish that there were more hours in a day," said George Boutwell.

His watercolors are not typical. They have a richness of color, a sharp focus and an attention to detail not usually found in watercolor paintings. Having no formal art education, he discovered his techniques on his own.

"I tried several other mediums, but I just kept going back to watercolor, so I decided to explore its possibilities for painting with the detail and control I had in mind."

**WAITING FOR THE BUS** *by George Boutwell*

Boutwell's philosophy about his work is simple and straightforward. "I like people and I want those who view my work to feel relaxed and refreshed. I see beauty all around me and I try to share it."

His work has been collected throughout the United States and several foreign countries. Prints of his work are available in shops and galleries in every state and Canada and Europe. Boutwell's work has been the subject of feature articles in Texas Highways, October 1979; "Prints Magazine, Fall 1979"; Art Voices South, Sept.-Oct. 1979; Southwest Art, May '77; North Light, May-June '77; Southwestern Art, Fall '76; in addition to many newspapers and special publications.

## GEORGE BOUTWELL

| | ISSUE PRICE | CURRENT PRICE |
|---|---|---|
| ☐ **FENCE LINE**, rel. 1970. ed. 1,000, s/n, 5" x 7", offset lithograph, pub BGL ... | 1.00 | 15.00 |
| ☐ **GOLD MINER**, rel. 1970. ed. 500, s/n, 15½" x 13½", offset lithograph, pub BGL. | 3.00 | 20.00 |
| ☐ **MISSOURI PACIFIC RAILROAD**, rel. 1970. ed. 500, s/n, 8" x 20", offset lithograph, pub BGL | 4.00 | 80.00 |
| ☐ **RED-SHOULDERED HAWK**, rel. 1970. ed. 500, s/n, 11¼" x 12¾", offset lithograph, pub BGL. | 2.00 | 50.00 |
| ☐ **ROADRUNNER**, rel. 1970. ed. 500, s/n, 11¼" x 10¼", offset lithograph, pub BGL. | 2.00 | 60.00 |
| ☐ **STEAM ENGINE**, rel. 1971. ed. 25, signed on Plate and Hand Numbered Engraving, 11" x 14", pub BGL. | 90.00 | 500.00 |
| ☐ **WILD TURKEYS**, rel. 1971. ed. 25, signed on Plate and Hand Numbered Engraving, 11" x 14", pub BGL. | 90.00 | 500.00 |
| ☐ **BRONC RIDER**, rel. 1972. ed. 25, signed on Plate and Hand Numbered Engraving, 5" x 7", pub BGL. | 15.00 | 75.00 |

| | ISSUE PRICE | CURRENT PRICE |
|---|---|---|
| ☐ **MOUNTAIN CABIN**, rel. 1972. ed. 25, signed on Plate and Hand Numbered Engraving, 5" x 7", pub BGL | 15.00 | 75.00 |
| ☐ **OWL**, rel. 1972. ed. 25, signed on Plate and Hand Numbered Engraving, 8" x 10", pub BGL | 40.00 | 200.00 |
| ☐ **BREMOND HOUSE**, rel. 1973. ed. 17, signed on Plate and Hand Numbered Engraving, 16" x 20", pub BGL | 125.00 | 600.00 |
| ☐ **BREMOND HOUSE**, rel. 1973. ed. 1,000, s/n, 8½" x 11", offset lithograph, pub WPC | * | 40.00 |
| *Special Promotion Editions, used as Christmas Gifts and Sales Incentives. | | |
| ☐ **HOUGHTON HOUSE**, rel. 1973. ed. 13, signed on Plate and Hand Numbered Engraving, 16" x 20", pub BGL | 125.00 | 500.00 |
| ☐ **HOUGHTON HOUSE**, rel. 1973. ed. 1,000, s/n, 8½" x 11", offset lithograph, pub WPC | * | 40.00 |
| *Special Promotion Editions, used as Christmas Gifts and Sales Incentives. | | |
| ☐ **ST. MARY'S CATHEDRAL**, rel. 1973. ed. 14, signed on Plate and Hand Numbered Engraving, 16" x 20", pub BGL | 125.00 | 500.00 |
| ☐ **ST. MARY'S CATHEDRAL**, rel. 1973. ed. 1,000, s/n, 8½" x 11", offset lithograph, pub WPC | * | 20.00 |
| *Special Promotion Editions, used as Christmas Gifts and Sales Incentives. | | |
| ☐ **SOUTHERN PACIFIC**, rel. 1973. ed. 1,000, s/n, 4" x 9", offset lithograph, pub BGL | * | 30.00 |
| *Special Promotion Editions, used as Christmas Gifts and Sales Incentives. | | |
| ☐ **ANTLER HOTEL**, rel. 1974. ed. 76, s/n, 16" x 20", engraving, pub HLNB | * | 200.00 |
| *Special Promotion Editions, used as Christmas Gifts and Sales Incentives. | | |
| ☐ **BIBLE HOUSE**, rel. 1974. ed. s/n, 16" x 20", engraving, pub HLNB | * | 150.00 |
| *Special Promotion Editions, used as Christmas Gifts and Sales Incentives. | | |
| ☐ **DRISKILL HOTEL**, rel. 1974. ed. 17, signed on Plate and Hand Numbered Engraving, 16" x 20", pub BGL | 150.00 | 600.00 |
| ☐ **DRISKILL HOTEL**, rel. 1974. ed. 1,000, s/n, 8½" x 11", offset lithograph, pub BGL | * | 35.00 |
| *Special Promotion Editions, used as Christmas Gifts and Sales Incentives. | | |
| ☐ **FORT CROGAN**, rel. 1974. ed. 76, s/n, 16" x 20", engraving, pub HLNB | * | 175.00 |
| *Special Promotion Editions, used as Christmas Gifts and Sales Incentives. | | |
| ☐ **GRANITE MOUNTAIN**, rel. 1974. ed. 76, s/n, 16" x 20", engraving, pub HLNB | * | 175.00 |
| *Special Promotion Editions, used as Christmas Gifts and Sales Incentives. | | |
| ☐ **LBJ RANCH HOUSE**, rel. 1974. ed. 76, s/n, 16" x 20", engraving, pub HLNB | * | 200.00 |
| *Special Promotion Editions, used as Christmas Gifts and Sales Incentives. | | |
| ☐ **LITTLEFIELD HOUSE**, rel. 1974. ed. 13, signed on Plate and Hand Numbered Engraving, 16" x 20", pub BGL | 150.00 | 500.00 |
| ☐ **LITTLEFIELD HOUSE**, rel. 1974. ed. 1,000, s/n, 8½" x 11", offset lithograph, pub WPC | * | 55.00 |
| *Special Promotion Editions, used as Christmas Gifts and Sales Incentives. | | |
| ☐ **LLANO HIGH SCHOOL**, rel. 1974. ed. 76, s/n, 16" x 20", engraving, pub HLNB | * | 125.00 |
| *Special Promotion Editions, used as Christmas Gifts and Sales Incentives. | | |
| ☐ **MASON COURTHOUSE**, rel. 1974. ed. 76, s/n, 16" x 20", engraving, pub HLNB | * | 150.00 |
| *Special Promotion Editions, used as Christmas Gifts and Sales Incentives. | | |
| ☐ **SOUTHWESTERN UNIVERSITY**, rel. 1974. ed. 76, s/n, 16" x 20", engraving, pub HLNB | * | 175.00 |
| *Special Promotion Editions, used as Christmas Gifts and Sales Incentives. | | |
| ☐ **TEXAS CAPITOL**, rel. 1974. ed. 76, s/n, engraving, pub HLNB | * | 250.00 |
| *Special Promotion Editions, used as Christmas Gifts and Sales Incentives. | | |
| ☐ **TEXAS GOVERNOR'S MANSION**, rel. 1974. ed. 76, s/n, 16" x 20", engraving, pub HLNB | * | 200.00 |
| *Special Promotion Editions, used as Christmas Gifts and Sales Incentives. | | |
| ☐ **WINDMILL**, rel. 1974. ed. 1,250, s/n, 4" x 9", offset lithograph, pub BGL | 5.00 | 25.00 |
| ☐ **ARMADILLO**, rel. 1975. ed. 250, s/n, 7" x 13", offset lithograph, pub BGL | 5.00 | 40.00 |
| ☐ **BOB WHITE**, rel. 1975. ed. 150, s/n, 8" x 10", offset lithograph, pub BGL | 5.00 | 20.00 |
| ☐ **CANADA GEESE**, rel. 1975. ed. 150, s/n, 7" x 14", offset lithograph, pub BGL | 5.00 | 25.00 |
| ☐ **CASWELL HOUSE**, rel. 1975. ed. 6, signed on Plate and Hand Numbered Engraving, 16" x 20", pub BGL | 150.00 | 500.00 |
| ☐ **CASWELL HOUSE**, rel. 1975. ed. 1,000, s/n, 8½" x 11", offset lithograph, pub WPC | * | 20.00 |
| *Special Promotion Editions, used as Christmas Gifts and Sales Incentives. | | |

| | | ISSUE PRICE | CURRENT PRICE |
|---|---|---|---|
| ☐ | **DeWITT CLINTON RAILROAD**, rel. 1975. ed. 250, s/n, 10" x 20", offset lithograph, pub BGL ... | 5.00 | 10.00 |
| ☐ | **DONNAN HOUSE**, rel. 1975. ed. 5, signed on Plate and Hand Numbered Engraving, 16" x 20", pub BGL... | 150.00 | 500.00 |
| ☐ | **DONNAN HOUSE**, rel. 1975. ed. 1,000, s/n, 8½" x 11", offset lithograph, pub WPC ... | * | 15.00 |
| | *Special Promotion Editions, used as Christmas Gifts and Sales Incentives. | | |
| ☐ | **ONE ROW PLANTER**, rel. 1975. ed. 1,750, s/n, 4" x 6", offset lithograph, pub BGL... | 5.00 | 10.00 |
| ☐ | **PELICAN**, rel. 1975. ed. 150, s/n, 5" x 12½", offset lithograph, pub BGL .... | 5.00 | 30.00 |
| ☐ | **SQUIRREL**, rel. 1975. ed. 150, s/n, 8" x 10", offset lithograph, pub BGL ..... | 5.00 | 25.00 |
| ☐ | **WILD TURKEYS**, rel. 1975. ed. 150, s/n, 12" x 16", offset lithograph, pub BGL | 10.00 | 20.00 |
| ☐ | **WINDMILL TANK**, rel. 1975. ed. 250, s/n, 9" x 12", offset lithograph, pub BGL | 5.00 | 35.00 |
| ☐ | **GAP GATE**, rel. 1975. ed. 1,000, s/n, 6" x 9", offset lithograph, pub BGL .... | 2.00 | 5.00 |
| ☐ | **GAIL TEXAS**, rel. 1975. ed. 1,000, s/n, 11" x 16", offset lithograph, pub BGL . | 10.00 | 40.00 |
| ☐ | **THE ENCOUNTER**, rel. 1975. ed. 1,000, s/n, 19" x 25", offset lithograph, pub BGL... | 20.00 | 40.00 |
| ☐ | **FREEDOM REGAINED**, rel. 1975. ed. 1,000, s/n, 11" x 25", offset lithograph, pub BGL... | 15.00 | 90.00 |
| ☐ | **A PLAY OF LIGHT**, rel. 1975. ed. 1,000, s/n, 13" x 17", offset lithograph, pub BGL... | 15.00 | 25.00 |
| ☐ | **BACK PORCH ANNIE**, rel. 1976. ed. 750, s/n, 11" x 16", offset lithograph, pub BGL... | 15.00 | 150.00 |
| ☐ | **BOUTWELL HOME**, rel. 1976. ed. 2,400, s/n, 8½" x 11", offset lithograph, pub BGL... | 10.00 | 25.00 |
| ☐ | **CHRISTMAS EVE**, rel. 1976. ed. 750, s/n, 11" x 25", offset lithograph, pub BGL... | 20.00 | 40.00 |
| ☐ | **HILL COUNTY**, rel. 1976. ed. 750, s/n, 13" x 17", offset lithograph, pub BGL . | 20.00 | 35.00 |
| ☐ | **MARTIN CABINESS HOUSE**, rel. 1976. ed. 4, signed on Plate and Hand Numbered Engraving, 16" x 20", pub BGL... | 150.00 | 500.00 |
| ☐ | **MARTIN CABINESS HOUSE**, rel. 1976. ed. 1,000, s/n, 8½" x 11", offset lithograph, pub WPC ... | * | 20.00 |
| | *Special Promotion Editions, used as Christmas Gifts and Sales Incentives. | | |
| ☐ | **ST. EDWARDS UNIVERSITY**, rel. 1976. ed. 4, signed on Plate and Hand Numbered Engraving, 16" x 20", pub BGL... | 150.00 | 500.00 |
| ☐ | **ST. EDWARDS UNIVERSITY**, rel. 1976. ed. 1,000, s/n, 8½" x 11", offset lithograph, pub WPC ... | * | 25.00 |
| | *Special Promotion Editions, used as Christmas Gifts and Sales Incentives. | | |
| ☐ | **I'VE CROSSED THAT BRIDGE BEFORE**, rel. 1977. ed. 500, s/n, 12" x 17", offset lithograph, pub BGL... | 20.00 | 75.00 |
| ☐ | **MARTHAS FANTASY**, rel. 1977. ed. 500, s/n, 13" x 22", offset lithograph, pub BGL... | 20.00 | 40.00 |
| ☐ | **MY BACK YARD**, rel. 1977. ed. 310, pub BGL ... | 10.00 | 25.00 |
| ☐ | **NEIL COCHRAN HOUSE**, rel. 1977. ed. 2, signed on Plate and Hand Numbered Engraving, 16" x 20", pub BGL... | 150.00 | 500.00 |
| ☐ | **NEIL COCHRAN HOUSE**, rel. 1977. ed. 1,000, s/n, 8½" x 11", offset lithograph, pub WPC ... | * | 20.00 |
| | *Special Promotion Editions, used as Christmas Gifts and Sales Incentives. | | |
| ☐ | **A NICE TREE**, rel. 1977. ed. 750, s/n, 19" x 25", offset lithograph, pub BGL .. | 25.00 | 175.00 |
| ☐ | **PRAIRIE DELL TEXAS**, rel. 1977. ed. 500, s/n, 13" x 23", offset lithograph, pub BGL... | 20.00 | 100.00 |
| ☐ | **LAZY AFTERNOON**, rel. 1978. ed. 500, s/n, 17" x 17", offset lithograph, pub BGL... | 25.00 | 150.00 |
| ☐ | **LUNCHLINE AT THE ANCHOR**, rel. 1978. ed. 500, s/n, 9" x 21", offset lithograph, pub BGL... | 20.00 | 175.00 |
| ☐ | **MEMORIES**, rel. 1978. ed. 500, s/n, 13" x 16", offset lithograph, pub BGL ... | 20.00 | 60.00 |
| ☐ | **MUDDY ROAD**, rel. 1978. ed. 4,400, s/n, 8½" x 8½", offset lithograph, pub BGL... | 10.00 | 40.00 |
| ☐ | **TEXAS CLASSIC**, rel. 1978. ed. 500, s/n, 13" x 25", offset lithograph, pub BGL... | 25.00 | 250.00 |
| ☐ | **A TRIBUTE TO TWO TREES**, rel. 1978. ed. 500, s/n, 17½" x 23", offset lithograph, pub BGL... | 25.00 | 200.00 |
| ☐ | **THE BROWN LIZARD**, rel. 1979. ed. 500, s/n, 13" x 17", offset lithograph, pub BGL... | 25.00 | 75.00 |

| | ISSUE PRICE | CURRENT PRICE |
|---|---|---|
| ☐ **A HERO THAT WOULDN'T DIE**, rel. 1979. ed. 500, s/n, 12" x 16", offset lithograph, pub BGL. | 25.00 | 125.00 |
| ☐ **PASSING BY**, rel. 1979. ed. 500, s/n, 19" x 25", offset lithograph, pub BGL. | 35.00 | 400.00 |
| ☐ **WEST TEXAS MORNING**, rel. 1979. ed. 500, s/n, 12" x 25", offset lithograph, pub BGL. | 25.00 | 70.00 |
| ☐ **WINGS OF IMAGINATION**, rel. 1979. ed. 6,700, s/n, 8½" x 8½", offset lithograph, pub BGL. | 10.00 | 10.00 |
| *Special Promotion Editions, used as Christmas Gifts and Sales Incentives. | | |
| ☐ **BRIGHT COLORED BIRD**, rel. 1980. ed. 7,600, s/n, 8½" x 5½", offset lithograph, pub BGL. | 10.00 | 10.00 |
| ☐ **BRUSH COUNTRY**, rel. 1980. ed. 500, s/n, 16" x 24", offset lithograph, pub BGL. | 35.00 | 75.00 |
| ☐ **COUNTRY CANTINA**, rel. 1980. ed. 500, s/n, 16" x 20", offset lithograph, pub BGL. | 35.00 | 400.00 |
| ☐ **HIGHLIGHT OF THE DAY**, rel. 1980. ed. 500, s/n, 16" x 20", offset lithograph, pub BGL. | 35.00 | 200.00 |
| ☐ **McKINNEY FALLS**, rel. 1980. ed. 500, s/n, 16" dia., offset lithograph, pub BGL. | 25.00 | 40.00 |
| ☐ **THE LUCKY ONE**, rel. 1981. ed. 9,300, s/n, size N/A, offset lithograph, pub BGL. | 10.00 | 10.00 |
| ☐ **MUD ISLAND**, rel. 1981. ed. 500, s/n, 12" x 24", offset lithograph, pub BGL. | 45.00 | 75.00 |
| ☐ **MY FRONT YARD**, rel. 1981. ed. 500, s/n, 12" x 16", offset lithograph, pub BGL. | 30.00 | 30.00 |
| ☐ **TEXAS BLUE NORTHER**, rel. 1981. ed. 500, s/n, 8½" x 24", offset lithograph, pub BGL. | 40.00 | 75.00 |
| ☐ **HAVEN OF THORNS**, rel. 1982. ed. 1,000, s/n, offset lithograph, pub GB. | 35.00 | 60.00 |
| ☐ **IN THE NICK OF TIME**, rel. 1982. ed. 500, s/n, offset lithograph, pub GB. | 45.00 | 75.00 |
| ☐ **JANUARY 14th**, rel. 1982. ed. 500, s/n, offset lithograph, pub GB. | 45.00 | 125.00 |
| ☐ **PECAN STREET FESTIVAL POSTER**, rel. 1982. ed. 1,000, s/n, size N/A, offset lithograph, pub BGL. | 25.00 | 35.00 |
| ☐ **ROOSTER**, rel. 1982. ed. 10,600, s/n, offset lithograph, pub GB. | 10.00 | 10.00 |
| ☐ **SHADY LANE**, rel. 1982. ed. 500, s/n, offset lithograph, pub GB. | 60.00 | 75.00 |
| ☐ **WAITING FOR THE BUS**, rel. 1982. ed. 500, s/n, 16" x 20", offset lithograph, pub BGL. | 45.00 | 50.00 |
| ☐ **PRIDE OF THE OPEN RANGE**, rel. 1983. ed. 500, s/n, offset lithograph, pub GB. | 50.00 | 50.00 |
| ☐ **STAR GAZERS**, rel. 1983. ed. 500, s/n, offset lithograph, pub GB. | 40.00 | 40.00 |
| ☐ **A TIME FOR DECISION**, rel. 1983. ed. 500, s/n, offset lithograph, pub GB. | 40.00 | 45.00 |
| ☐ **WHERE THEY PRAY FOR COTTON**, rel. 1983. ed. 500, s/n, offset lithograph, pub GB. | 50.00 | 50.00 |
| ☐ **YEARS OF SERVICE**, rel. 1983. ed. 500, s/n, offset lithograph, pub GB. | 30.00 | 30.00 |

*Represents prints used for special purposes; Christmas Gifts and Sales Incentives.

*Special Promotion Editions, due to demand they have become collectibles.

# BENNETT BRADBURY

Bennett Bradbury portrays the majesty and power of the ocean in his paintings. He is considered by leading art critics, connoisseurs and collectors of art, as the greatest living painter of the sea.

### BENNETT BRADBURY

| | | |
|---|---|---|
| ☐ **POST MERIDIAN, XIX**, ed. 950, s/n, 24½" x 16", pub CGAL. | 150.00 | — |
| ed. 12, Artist accented, s/n | 420.00 | — |
| ☐ **CARMEL HIGHLANDS**, ed. 950, s/n, 24" x 16", pub CGAL. | 150.00 | — |
| ed. 12, Artist accented, s/n | 420.00 | — |
| ☐ **IN THE CASCADES**, ed. 950, s/n, 24" x 15½", pub CGAL. | 150.00 | — |
| ed. 12, Artist accented, s/n | 420.00 | — |

# MARGE BRICHLER

Marge Brichler is fascinated with people, countryside and seaside. When her inspiration comes she captures it with brushes and paints in a brilliant blend of colors — from shocking pink of Italian architecture to the delicate blue of a child's eyes.

She has been teaching since 1959, and began formal art training at the St. Louis Museum of Fine Art in 1944. From the beginning she has been a regular exhibitor in national exhibitions consistently winning awards. Her paintings are part of private collections internationally.

She is at ease in painting and teaching all medias and subject matter simultaneously including watercolors, oils, charcoal, pastel, pencil and pen and ink.

In addition to formal training at Southwest High School as an Art Major for four years, and Washington University she graduated from William Woods College. Since then she has studied with some of the nation's finest artists including Ramon Froman, Bud Biggs, Ed Whitney, Ray Loos, Robert E. Wood, Chen Chi, E. Raymond Kinstler and Charles Reid.

She has been a demonstrator, lecturer and instructor for leading art organizations in Houston, Dallas, St. Dallas, Corpus Christi, Cincinnati, Kennebunkport, Maine and Florence, Italy.

| MARGE BRICHLER | ISSUE PRICE | CURRENT PRICE |
|---|---|---|
| ☐ THREE TO MAKE READY, rel. 1980. ed. 1,500, s/n, 32½″ x 25″, pub ALI .... | 60.00 | — |
| ☐ FRANKIE MAE, rel. 1981. ed. 1,500, s/n, 31⅝″ x 25″, pub ALI ............ | 60.00 | — |

# PENNY BRITTAIN

Penny Brittain's own interest in art developed early. She won her first awards in the eighth grade and in high school won some college-level competitions.

During her professional development she worked as a technical illustrator in advertising art and in a national illustration studio. She later did architectural renderings, worked as a art director for a magazine in Florida and as an illustrator on a space shuttle.

| PENNY BRITTAIN | | |
|---|---|---|
| ☐ AMONG THE WISPERINGS, ed. 100, s/n, etching, dist. by MMFC.......... | 98.00 | — |
| ☐ BEGINNINGS, ed. 200, s/n, 25″ x 32″, etching, dist. by MMFC. ........... | 98.00 | — |
| ☐ BLACKBERRY WINTER, ed. 250, s/n, 11¾″ x 15″, etching, dist. by MMFC. ... | 140.00 | — |
| ☐ DIGNITY, ed. 250, s/n, etching, dist. by MMFC. ..................... | 108.00 | — |
| ☐ DREAMS AND SCHEMES, ed. N/A, s/n, etching, dist. by MMFC.......... | 28.00 | — |
| ☐ EDWARD AND LEROY, ed. N/A, s/n, etching, dist. by MMFC............ | 108.00 | — |
| ☐ GOAT ROPER, ed. N/A, s/n, etching, dist. by MMFC................... | 54.00 | — |
| ☐ GRANDMOTHER'S PORCH, ed. 100, s/n, etching, dist. by MMFC. ....... | 86.00 | — |
| ☐ HOPE, ed. 250, s/n, etching, dist. by MMFC. ...................... | 108.00 | — |
| ☐ INSIDE STRAIGHT, ed. N/A, s/n, etching, dist. by MMFC. ............. | 50.00 | — |
| ☐ LILLIAN, ed. 200, s/n, etching, dist. by MMFC. .................... | 22.00 | — |
| ☐ MONDAY'S CHILD, ed. 200, s/n, etching, dist. by MMFC. ............. | 28.00 | — |
| ☐ MYRENA'S BABY, ed. 200, s/n, etching, dist. by MMFC................ | 22.00 | — |
| ☐ MOVING ON, ed. N/A, s/n, etching, dist. by MMFC. ................. | 50.00 | — |
| ☐ OLD JOE BROWN HOME, ed. N/A, s/n, etching, dist. by MMFC. .......... | 86.00 | — |
| ☐ ROSE OF SHARON, ed. 175, s/n, etching, dist. by MMFC. ............. | 54.00 | — |
| ☐ SATURDAY'S CHILD, ed. 200, s/n, 4¾″ x 6¼″, etching, dist. by MMFC. .... | 28.00 | — |
| ☐ SECRET GARDENS, ed. 250, s/n, 11¾″ x 15″, etching, dist. by MMFC. ..... | 140.00 | — |
| ☐ STOUT-HEARTED FRIENDS ON SATURDAY, ed. N/A, s/n, etching, dist. by MMFC. ................................................ | 54.00 | — |
| ☐ SWEET LILLIAN JAMES, ed. 140, s/n, etching, dist. by MMFC. ......... | 86.00 | — |
| ☐ TAXI DANCER, ed. 200, s/n, 12⅞″ x 17⅞″, etching, dist. by MMFC. ........ | 98.00 | — |

**ROSE OF SHARON** *by Penny Brittain*

| | ISSUE PRICE | CURRENT PRICE |
|---|---|---|
| ☐ **THURSDAY'S CHILD,** ed. 200, s/n, etching, dist. by MMFC. . . . . . . . . . . . . . | 28.00 | — |
| ☐ **TUESDAY'S CHILD,** ed. 200, s/n, etching, dist. by MMFC. . . . . . . . . . . . . . . | 28.00 | — |
| ☐ **WEDNESDAY'S CHILD,** ed. N/A, s/n, etching, dist. by MMFC. . . . . . . . . . . . . | 28.00 | — |

# STAN BROD

Stan Brod is an established graphic designer and adjunct professor at University of Cincinnati.

His quiet enthusiasm and dedication to graphic design have been a part of his life for a long time. "I can remember that I was drawing when I was five years old . . . and I've been interested in graphic art since the middle of high school," recalls the artist. "I work in a graphic design office part of the day and teach it the other part. It's a good contrast for me," he continued. "I can learn something from the students and also give something."

A native of Cincinnati, Brod has contributed much to the city's visual appeal. He designed a mural for a ten-story office building, he has also created posters for a United Appeal campaign and to help promote sites in the greater Cincinnati area. He has developed promotional materials for Playhouse in the Park, the city's symphony orchestra and ballet company.

Brod designed six seven-foot by nineteen-foot "urban banners" for the Contemporary Art Center. They were exhibited in the UNS Pavilion in Sao Paulo, Brazil. He has exhibited other works internationally in Japan, Ireland, Australia, India, and Canada.

| STAN BROD | ISSUE PRICE | CURRENT PRICE |
|---|---|---|
| ☐ CAT AND RAINBOW, rel. 1978. ed. 750, s/n, 16″ x 16″, pub FHG | 45.00 | — |
| ☐ CIRCLE CAT, rel. 1978. ed. 500, s/n, 15¼″ x 19″, pub FHG | 45.00 | Sold Out |
| ☐ OVAL OWL, rel. 1978. ed. 750, s/n embossed, 17¾″ x 13″, pub FHG | 45.00 | — |
| ☐ SWAN LAKE, rel. 1979. ed. 5,000, s/o, 8½″ x 9⅜″ | 10.00 | — |

## KIM BROOKS

| | | |
|---|---|---|
| ☐ AMBER GLOW, ed. 650, s/n, 14½″ x 29″, distr. GI | 75.00 | — |
| ☐ VIGILANT LEOPARD, ed. 650, s/n, 16″ x 24″, distr. GI | 65.00 | — |

## D. CROSBY BROWN

| | | |
|---|---|---|
| ☐ PATCHES, rel. 1978. ed. 750, s/n, 19¾″ x 26½″, pub FHG | 50.00 | — |

## LEE BRUBAKER

Lee Brubaker's early interest and talent in drawing was first noticed and encouraged by his mother, who was also a talented artist. It was her encouragement and advice that helped to channel his efforts toward a professional career in art. He enrolled in the Art Center School of Los Angeles where he studied illustration and fine art for four years.

His commercial work has been seen in *Fortune, Time, Newsweek, Playboy, Sports Illustrated,* and other popular magazines. He has worked with several major companies such as 7-Up, Anheuser Busch, Ralston Purina, and Monsanto.

Although the commercial field has been exciting and rewarding, Brubaker is a painter. His range of interest is quite varied; however, his first love is western art, specifically subject matter dealing with the American Indian.

Brubaker has won many awards and has participated in several one man shows all over the country. He has been commissioned for special works by many collectors and has several of his past work permanently hung by various societies and galleries.

### LEE BRUBAKER

| | | |
|---|---|---|
| ☐ SHOWING OFF, ed. 1000, s/n, 18″ x 27¼″, pub SCI* | 65.00 | — |
| ☐ SOUIX WAR PARTY, ed. 1000, s/n, 18″ x 27¼″, pub SCI* | 65.00 | — |

*represents the Sawyier Collection Inc., and was formed as a subsidiary of Paul Sawyier Galleries, Inc.

## RUTH BRUNNER-STROSSER

After attending art school, Ruth Brunner-Strosser illustrated children's books and annual reports. This work influenced her fine art paintings.

Brunner-Strosser finds that "coming up with the idea for a painting is the easiest part; I never have to worry about it. In fact, there are hundreds of ideas I've

**THE GOLDEN SPIKE** *by Ruth Brunner-Strosser*

never had the time to develop.'' Then, after the concept for a painting is chosen, she researches the subject carefully and thoroughly.

Once she has a good working knowledge of her subject, she begins to concentrate on the composition and details of the piece.

Rather than trying to represent a 'moment' in history, complete in every detail, Brunner-Strosser tries to portray the 'event' and the 'tradition' that surrounds it. She admits "I sometimes take artistic liberties to make the story come alive. That's the important thing, I call it 'authenticity with a flair'!"

| RUTH BRUNNER-STROSSER | ISSUE PRICE | CURRENT PRICE |
|---|---|---|
| ☐ **THE AMERICAN WAY**, rel. 1982. ed. 975, s/n, 20″ x 24″, pub FHG. . . . . . . . . | 75.00 | — |
| ed. 300 Exclusive First Day Issue | | |
| ☐ **THE GOLDEN SPIKE**, rel. 1982. ed. 975, s/n, 20″ x 24″, pub FHG. . . . . . . . . . | 75.00 | — |
| ☐ **WRIGHT FLIGHT**, rel. 1982. ed. 975, s/n, 20″ x 24″, pub FHG. . . . . . . . . . . | 75.00 | — |
| ed. 300, s/n, Exclusive First Day Issue | | |

# LINDA BUDGE

| | ISSUE PRICE | CURRENT PRICE |
|---|---|---|
| ☐ **ANTELOPE COUNTRY**, rel. 1978. ed. 750, s/n, 14″ x 20″, pub SGL. . . . . . . . . | 45.00 | — |
| Remarqued, s/n . . . . . . . . . . . . . . . . . . . . . . . . . . . . . . . . . . . . . . . . . . . . . | 75.00 | — |
| ☐ **PRAIRIE BABIES**, rel. 1978. ed. 750, s/n, 12″ x 16″, pub SGL. . . . . . . . . . . | 45.00 | — |
| Remarqued, s/n . . . . . . . . . . . . . . . . . . . . . . . . . . . . . . . . . . . . . . . . . . . . . | 75.00 | — |

# AL BUELL

Al Buell's canvases portray the sky, sea, birds and translucent green gulf waters. His best known portrait is famous *Katherine Hepburn,* commissioned by *Reader's Digest.*

Buell studied at the Art Institute of Chicago and the Art Students League in New York before starting a career in illustration which resulted in commissions from leading American magazines including *Saturday Evening Post, Ladies Home Journal, McCall's, Redbook, Cosmopolitan, Sports Afield* and others. His style had universal appeal and brought assignments from magazines in England, Germany, Italy, Spain, Scandinavia, South America, and Canada.

As a member of the New York Society of Illustrators, he was invited to participate in the U.S. Air Force program, traveling the world to make sketches for large paintings which became a part of its permanent collection at the Air Force Academy. The Space Age brought the privilege of covering the First Man in Space—Alan Shepard.

Buell moved to Florida's Gulf Coast in the 1950's and has in the ensuing decades developed a oneness with the surf, sand and sky which makes his oils and acrylic seascapes, the next best thing to being there.

An accomplished craftsman as well as a sensitive painter, Al Buell received many awards and honors in the world of illustration and has been featured in *American Artist, Redbook,* and the *National Geographic Magazine.*

**LADY WITH A HAT** *by Al Buell*

| AL BUELL | ISSUE PRICE | CURRENT PRICE |
|---|---|---|
| ☐ **JUST THE SEA AND ME,** rel. 1982. ed. 950, s/n, 24" x 19½", pub MPPI. .... | 85.00 | — |

# E. HOWARD BURGER

The paintings of versatile artist E. Howard Burger portray a peaceful way of life that many of us are too young to remember. This North Carolina artist was commissioned by the 1982 World's Fair to create the official World's Fair Collector series of art. His original painting "Granny" was recently presented to President Ronald Reagan.

**DAY OF REST** *by E. Howard Burger*

| E. HOWARD BURGER | ISSUE PRICE | CURRENT PRICE |
|---|---|---|
| ☐ **BACK HOME**, rel. 1975. ed. 1000, s/n, 18″ x 20″, pub PSGI | 30.00 | 250.00 |
| ed. 25, remarqued | 100.00 | 550.00 |
| ☐ **BE THANKFUL**, rel. 1975. ed. 1000, s/n, 16″ x 20″, pub PSGI | 30.00 | 280.00 |
| ed. 25, remarqued | 100.00 | 400.00 |
| ☐ **AUTUMN IN WALKER VALLEY**, rel. 1976. ed. 1000, s/n, 17″ x 24¾″, pub PSGI | 30.00 | 275.00 |
| ed. 25, remarqued | 100.00 | 350.00 |
| ☐ **CHIEF DANIEL BOON HORNBUCKLE**, rel. 1976. ed. 1000, s/n, 16″ x 20″, pub PSGI | 30.00 | 175.00 |
| ed. 25, remarqued | 100.00 | 275.00 |
| ☐ **BRADY'S TENANT HOUSE**, rel. 1977. ed. 1000, s/n, 17″ x 24¾″, pub PSGI | 30.00 | 100.00 |
| ed. 25, remarqued | 100.00 | 225.00 |
| ☐ **MELTON'S BARN & LAST DAYS (Pair)**, rel. 1977. ed. 2000, i/o, 11″ x 14″, pub PSGI | 20.00 | — |
| ed. 25, Hand Colored | 60.00 | 650.00 |
| ☐ **BENDABOUT**, rel. 1978. ed. 1500, s/n, 16″ x 29¾″, pub PGSI | 35.00 | 65.00 |
| ed. 25, remarqued | 100.00 | 200.00 |
| ☐ **WHEN DAY IS DONE**, rel. 1978. ed. 1000, s/n, 16″ x 20″, pub PSGI | 55.00 | 350.00 |
| ed. 25, remarqued | 100.00 | 450.00 |
| ☐ **WHERE IS THE MASTER**, rel. 1978. ed. 1500, s/n, 16″ x 20″, pub PSGI | 35.00 | 125.00 |
| ed. 25, remarqued | 100.00 | 200.00 |
| ☐ **BLESS MOMMY & DADDY**, rel. 1979. ed. 1000, s/n, 16″ x 20″, pub PSGI | 55.00 | 125.00 |
| ed. 25, remarqued | 100.00 | 225.00 |
| ☐ **THE LOOKOUT**, rel. 1979. ed. 1000, s/n, 15½″ x 18½″, pub PSGI | 55.00 | — |
| ed. 25, remarqued | 100.00 | 130.00 |
| ☐ **YESTERDAY**, rel. 1979. ed. 1000, s/n, 16″ x 20″, pub PSGI | 55.00 | 70.00 |
| ed. 25, remarqued | 100.00 | 140.00 |
| ☐ **CONCENTRATION**, rel. 1980. ed. 1250, s/n, 16″ x 20″, pub PSGI | 55.00 | — |
| ed. 25, remarqued | 100.00 | — |

| | ISSUE PRICE | CURRENT PRICE |
|---|---|---|
| ☐ **GRACE,** rel. 1981. ed. 1,250, s/n, 16″ x 20″, pub PSGI. | 55.00 | 75.00 |
| ed. 25, remarked | 100.00 | 195.00 |
| ☐ **"OOPS",** rel. 1981. ed. 1,250, s/n, 16″ x 20″, pub PSGI. | 55.00 | — |
| ed. 25, remarked | 100.00 | — |
| ☐ **A VIEW FROM THE PAST,** rel. 1982. ed. 1,250, s/n, 16″ x 20″, pub BG. | 55.00 | — |
| ☐ **GRANNY,** rel. 1982. ed. 1,250, s/n,126″ x 20″, pub BG. | 55.00 | — |
| ed. 25, remarked | 100.00 | 175.00 |
| ☐ **DAY OF REST,** rel. 1983. ed. 1,000, s/n, 21″ x 32″, pub BG. | 75.00 | — |

# PAUL CALLE

Paul Calle is equally skilled at oil paintings and pencil drawings. His drawings are notable for the incredible control and sensitivity they show, giving them the quality of fine etchings.

His selection as an official artist of the National Aeronautics and Space Administration's Fine Art Program gave him the unique opportunity to paint Neil Armstrong's first step on the the moon. He was commissioned by The United States Postal Service to design the stamp capturing that historic moment. He has designed other stamps including the recently released "International Year of the Child" commemorative.

**SOMETHING FOR THE POT** *by Paul Calle*

To Calle, the portrayal of Western Art is not a romantic adventure but a realistic challenge, a personal commitment to portray America's past with the same sense of history that guided his hand in depicting our nation's space explorations. As chairman of the Department of Interior's "Artist in the Parks" program, Calle traveled widely throughout the West. His imagination was stimulated by the majesty of the Western scene. He knows that space exploration and the Western experience are both part of our heritage, a heritage to be set down in paint.

In addition to major corporate and private collections, his work is in the permanent collections of the Phoenix Museum of Fine Arts, Phoenix, Arizona; Pacific Northwest Indian Center, Spokane, Washington; George Phippen Museum, Prescott, Arizona; and The National Aeronautics and Space Administration Collection, Washington, D.C.; among others.

Paintings and drawings have been exhibited at many galleries and museums including The Museum of the Southwest, Midland, Texas; The National Gallery of Art, Washington, D.C.; The Stamford Museum, Stamford, Connecticut; The Hudson River Museum Yonkers, New York; and the U.S. Embassy, Stockholm, Sweden.

Under the auspices of the United States Information Office his work has been shown at museums in Krakow, Poland; Moscow, U.S.S.R.; Tbilisi, U.S.S.R.; and in Leningrad, U.S.S.R. He is the recipient of the Franklin Mint Gold Medal for Distinguished Western Art.

Calle is the author of *"The Pencil"* published by Watson-Guptill, now in its fifth printing. The book records his odyssey as "an artist with a pencil."

## PAUL CALLE

| | ISSUE PRICE | CURRENT PRICE |
|---|---|---|
| ☐ **PAUSE FOR A DRINK,** ed. 275, s/n, 30" x 24", pub ALI | 50.00 | — |
| ed. 25, Artist's proofs | 50.00 | Sold Out |
| ☐ **THE LONELY WATCH,** ed. 275, s/n, 30" x 24", pub ALI | 50.00 | — |
| ed. 25, Artist's proofs | 50.00 | Sold Out |
| ☐ **THE TRAIL BOSS,** ed. 275, s/n, 30" x 24", pub ALI | 50.00 | — |
| ed. 25, Artist's proofs | 50.00 | Sold Out |
| ☐ **CARING FOR THE HERD,** rel. 1980. ed. 950, s/n, pencil, 22⅛" x 29", pub. MPPI. | 110.00 | 135.00 |
| ☐ **CHIEF HIGH PIPE,** rel. 1980. ed. 950, s/n, pencil, 22¾" x 29", pub MPPI | 75.00 | 150.00 |
| ☐ **CHIEF JOSEPH - MAN OF PEACE,** rel. 1980. ed. 950, s/n, pencil, 24½" x 30¾", pub. MPPI. | 135.00 | 155.00 |
| ☐ **PRAYER TO THE GREAT MYSTERY,** rel. 1980. ed. 950, s/n, color, 24¾" x 32¼", pub. MPPI. | 245.00 | 375.00 |
| ☐ **SIOUX CHIEF,** rel. 1980. ed. 950, s/n, pencil, 29⅜" x 22", pub MMPI. | 85.00 | 100.00 |
| ☐ **SOMETHING FOR THE POT,** rel. 1980. ed. 950, s/n, color, 24¾" x 33¾", pub MPPI. | 175.00 | 875.00 |
| ☐ **THE LANDMARK TREE,** rel. 1980. ed. 950, s/n, pencil, 24½" x 30¾", pub. MPPI. | 125.00 | 240.00 |
| ☐ **THE WINTER HUNTER,** rel. 1980. ed. 950, s/n, pencil, 29½" x 22", pub MPPI | 65.00 | 475.00 |
| ☐ **VIEW FROM THE HEIGHTS,** rel. 1980. ed. 950, s/n, color, 24⅝" x 32½", pub. MPPI. | 245.00 | 350.00 |
| ☐ **WHEN SNOW CAME EARLY,** rel. 1980. ed. 950, s/n, pencil, 22⅛" x 29", pub. MPPI. | 85.00 | 235.00 |
| ☐ **ALMOST HOME,** rel. 1981. ed. 950, s/n, color, 20¼" x 25½", pub MPPI. | 150.00 | 160.00 |
| ☐ **AND STILL MILES TO GO,** rel. 1981. ed. 950, s/n, color, 24⅝" x 30", pub. MPPI. | 245.00 | 350.00 |
| ☐ **ANDREW AT THE FALLS,** rel. 1981. ed. 950, s/n, 24½" x 32", pencil, pub MPPI. | 150.00 | 175.00 |
| ☐ **CHIEF HIGH PIPE,** rel. 1981. ed. 950, s/n, color, 24⅝" x 32¼", pub MPPI. | 265.00 | 275.00 |
| ☐ **END OF A LONG DAY,** rel. 1981. ed. 950, s/n, pencil, 24¼" x 31¾", pub MPPI. | 150.00 | 175.00 |
| ☐ **FRIENDS,** rel. 1981. ed. 950, s/n, 18½" x 22¼", pub MPPI. | 150.00 | — |
| ☐ **FRESH TRACKS,** rel. 1981. ed. 950, s/n, pencil, 24½" x 31¾", pub MPPI. | 150.00 | 175.00 |
| ☐ **JUST OVER THE RIDGE,** rel. 1981. ed. 950, s/n, color, 24½" x 38", pub. MPPI. | 245.00 | 300.00 |

| | ISSUE PRICE | CURRENT PRICE |
|---|---|---|
| ☐ **ONE WITH THE LAND,** rel. 1981. ed. 950, s/n, color, 24⅝" x 37", pub MPPI | 245.00 | 300.00 |
| ☐ **PAUSE AT THE LOWER FALLS,** rel. 1981. ed. 950, s/n, pencil, 31¾" x 20¼", pub MPPI | 110.00 | 125.00 |
| ☐ **TETON FRIENDS,** rel. 1981. ed. 950, s/n, pencil, 24½" x 30¾", pub MPPI | 150.00 | 215.00 |
| ☐ **THE WINTER HUNTER,** rel. 1981. ed. 950, s/n, 36¼" x 24½", pub MPPI | 245.00 | 550.00 |
| ☐ **EMERGING FROM THE WOODS,** rel. 1982. ed. 950, s/n, 23¼" x 30¾", pub MPPI | 110.00 | — |
| ☐ **GENERATIONS IN THE VALLEY,** rel. 1982. ed. 950, s/n, 24½" x 35½", pub. MPPI | 245.00 | — |
| ☐ **RETURN TO CAMP,** rel. 1982. ed. 950, s/n, 24⅝" x 37⅛", pub MPPI | 245.00 | 325.00 |
| ☐ **THE BREATH OF FRIENDSHIP,** rel. 1982. ed. 950, s/n, 24½" x 32", pub MPPI | 225.00 | — |
| ☐ **TWO FROM THE FLOCK,** rel. 1982. ed. 950, s/n, 24½" x 36½", pub MPPI | 245.00 | 315.00 |
| ☐ **FREE SPIRITS,** rel. 1983. ed. 950, s/n, 27" x 24½", pub MPPI | 195.00 | — |
| ☐ **IN SEARCH OF BEAVER,** rel. 1983. ed. 950, s/n, 25½" x 38½", pub MPPI | 225.00 | 250.00 |
| ☐ **STRAYS FROM THE FLYWAY,** rel. 1983. ed. 950, s/n, 22¾" x 28¾", pub MPPI | 195.00 | 235.00 |

## JOHN CAMPBELL

John Campbell majored in fine art at Louisiana State University, studied at the Hans Wang Art School and the Paris Conservatory of Fine Art on a scholarship.

For his efforts in founding the Art Students League of New Orleans, opening an art school under his name, and contributions to the city's cultural welfare he was awarded the Key to the City.

In 1953, he was invited to the White House to present his portrait of Dwight Eisenhower to the President. Of his paintings he says, "I attempt always to paint life as I see it enveloped in an atmosphere of light and color."

### JOHN CAMPBELL

| | | |
|---|---|---|
| ☐ **THE MARBLE PLAYERS,** rel. 1974. ed. 1,500, s/n, 35" x 24½", pub FHG | 45.00 | 95.00 |
| ☐ **REFLECTIONS AND BLUEBONNETS,** rel. 1974. ed. 1,500, s/n, 29" x 24¼", pub FHG | 45.00 | Sold Out |
| ☐ **MISTY MOUNTAIN,** rel. 1977. ed. 800, s/n, 22" x 32", pub FHG | 50.00 | 90.00 |
| ☐ **SUMMER MORN,** rel. 1977. ed. 800, s/n, 25" x 20", pub FHG | 50.00 | — |

## KEN CARLSON

Since boyhood, Ken Carlson has sketched, painted and concentrated on observing his subjects firsthand. Born in a small town in Minnesota, he was encouraged by a school teacher to draw. At 16, Carlson started his formal art training under the personal tutelage of the late Walter J. Wilwerding.

Carlson continued his studies at the Minneapolis Art Institute. From there, like other artists, Carlson began his career as a commercial illustrator working for an advertising agency and a newspaper before moving to California to do free-lance illustrating. As an illustrator, he devoted many hours each day to his primary interest of either drawing, painting or photographing animal subjects. In 1970, Carlson gave up the security of his commercial work to devote full time to painting.

Spring and fall research trips are spent by Carlson in the Canadian Rockies or some remote area of his favorite state, Wyoming, where he is able to observe, sketch, and photograph his subjects in their natural habitat.

Carlson's paintings are executed in oil with attenton to details which capture the special character of each animal in its natural surroundings.

The artist has been published in *Audubon, The Naturalist* and *Ducks Unlimited.* An unusual collection of 50 Carlson watercolor plates appears in the recently-published book *Birds of Western North America*. In 1978, he accepted a commission for General Motors to do a series of twelve mammal and bird paintings. Carlson won the 1979-80 National Wild Turkey stamp design competition.

## KEN CARLSON

| | ISSUE PRICE | CURRENT PRICE |
|---|---|---|
| ☐ **PINTAILS**, rel. 1974. ed. 580, s/n, 19½" x 21", pub WWI | 60.00 | 75.00 |
| ed. 50 remarque artist proof | 125.00 | – |
| ☐ **BALD EAGLE**, rel. 1975. ed. 580, s/n, 22" x 17½", pub WWI | 60.00 | 75.00 |
| ed. 50. remarque artist proof | 130.00 | – |
| ☐ **WOODCOCK**, rel. 1976. ed. 600, s/n, 14½" x 17¾", pub WWI | 50.00 | 100.00 |
| ed. 50, remarque artist proof | 130.00 | – |
| ☐ **SAND FLATS - PINTAILS**, rel. 1977. ed. 580, s/n, 15" x 26", pub WWI | 65.00 | 75.00 |
| ☐ **DOMESTIC RABBITS**, rel. 1979. ed. 950, s/n, 13½" x 19", pub MPPI | 50.00 | – |
| ☐ **MONARCH OF THE PLAINS - BISON**, rel. 1979. ed. 950, s/n, 18" x 29½", pub MPPI | 95.00 | – |
| ☐ **PYGMY GOATS**, rel. 1979. ed. 950, s/n, 13½" x 19", pub MPPI | 50.00 | – |
| ☐ **RAINBOW TROUT**, rel. 1979. ed. 300, s/n, size N/A, pub WWI | 85.00 | – |
| ☐ **TETON WINTER - TRUMPETERS**, rel. 1979. ed. 850, s/n, 25" x 16⅝", pub WWI | 75.00 | – |
| ☐ **WINTER RAMS**, rel. 1980. ed. 950, s/n, 22¾" x 28", pub MPPI | 135.00 | – |
| ☐ **ARTIC NOMADS**, rel. 1981. ed. 950, s/n, 20¾" x 28", pub MPPI | 150.00 | – |
| ☐ **CATCHING A SCENT - RED FOX**, rel. 1981. ed. 550, s/n, 20" x 27½", pub MPPI | 125.00 | – |
| ☐ **EVENING SHADOWS**, rel. 1981. ed. 950, s/n, 20" x 27½", pub MPPI | 95.00 | – |
| ☐ **IN WINTER COAT - SNOWSHOE HARE**, rel. 1981. ed. 950, s/n, 14¾" x 24", pub MPPI | 75.00 | – |
| ☐ **MASKED BANDIT - RACCOON**, rel. 1981. ed. 950, s/n, 24" x 14½", pub MPPI | 75.00 | – |
| ☐ **WINGS OF NOBILITY - BALD EAGLE**, rel. 1981. ed. 950, s/n, 19⅞" x 29½", pub MPPI | 95.00 | – |
| ☐ **OPENING DAY - MALLARDS**, rel. 1982. ed. 950, s/n, size unavailable, pub MPPI | 150.00 | – |
| ☐ **RIO GRANDE VIGIL - WHITETAIL DEER**, rel. 1982. ed. 950, s/n, 21½" x 32", pub MPPI | 150.00 | – |
| ☐ **THREE RAMS**, rel. 1982. ed. 950, s/n, 16½" x 20", pub MPPI | 65.00 | – |

# BOB CARNEY

Bob Carney is a highly versatile artist whose works have included murals, landscapes, still lifes, portraits of people, prize winning walking horses and championship dogs. Carney's art training began in high school, and as a selected gifted student, he received instruction at Peabody College during the same period. Later he was privately tutored, and also studied through correspondence courses from a nationally recognized art school.

He won first place among state pastel artists for his rendition of a Tennessee walking horse, and he has been commissioned by country music entertainer Tom T. Hall and his wife, Dixie, to do portraits of thirty of their championship bassett hounds.

Carney is becoming one of the best known domestic animal artists in the nation. His dog portraits, in particular, have won acclaim from expert dog trainers and handlers as well as pet owners.

## BOB CARNEY

| | | |
|---|---|---|
| ☐ **PUPPY LOVE**, ed. 1,250, signed/donated to National Ducks Unlimited ed. 750, s/n, 16" x 20", pub BCS | 50.00 | – |
| ☐ **OPENING DAY**, rel. 1976. ed. 980, s/n, 16" x 20", pub BCS | 25.00 | – |
| ☐ **DADDY'S MULE**, rel. 1976. ed. 2,000, s/n, 16" x 20", pub BCS | 25.00 | 100.00 |
| ☐ **KENNEL COUSINS**, rel. 1977. | | |
| **BLACK LABRADOR/YELLOW LABRADOR**. ed. 1,500, s/n, 16" x 20", pub BCS *Priced for EACH PRINT | *20.00 | |
| **Priced as a SET | **35.00 | – |

| | ISSUE PRICE | CURRENT PRICE |
|---|---|---|
| ☐ **SMOKEY,** rel. 1977. ed. 3,500, s/n, 16″ x 20″, pub BCS . . . . . . . . . . . . . . . | 20.00 | — |
| ☐ **TENNESSEE-WALKER,** rel. 1978. ed. 2,000, s/n, 16″ x 20″, pub BCS . . . . . . . | 30.00 | — |
| ☐ **GRANDADDY'S MULES,** rel. 1979. ed. 2,000, s/n, 19″ x 23¾″, pub BCS . . . . | 35.00 | — |
| ☐ **POINT OF INDECISION,** rel. 1979. ed. 1,200, s/n, 16″ x 20″, pub BCS . . . . . . | 40.00 | — |
| ☐ **MAMA'S MULE,** rel. 1980. ed. 2,000, s/n, 16″ x 20″, pub BCS . . . . . . . . . . . | 35.00 | — |

# GREG CARON

| | | |
|---|---|---|
| ☐ **BIRCH COVER - RUFFED GROUSE,** rel. 1979. ed. 400, s/n, size N/A, pub WWI | 50.00 | — |

# CHARLES CARROLL

| | | |
|---|---|---|
| ☐ **MORNING MISCHIEF,** rel. 1978. ed. 950, s/n, 19″ x 15″, pub FHG . . . . . . . | 25.00 | — |

# JAMES A. CARSON

| | | |
|---|---|---|
| ☐ **BLACK-CAPPED CHICKADEE,** rel. 1975. ed. 250, s/n, 18″ x 24″, litho, pub PHFA . . . . . . . . . . . . . . . . . . . . . . . . . . . . . . . . . . . . . . . . . . . . . | 75.00 | — |
| ☐ **LOGGERHEAD SHRIKE,** rel. 1975. ed. 250, s/n, 18″ x 24″, litho, pub PHFA . . . | 75.00 | — |
| ☐ **GREAT-HORNED OWL,** rel. 1976. ed. 250, s/n, 25″ x 32″, litho, pub PHFA . . . | 85.00 | — |
| ☐ **LONG-EARED OWL,** rel. 1976. ed. 250, s/n, 22″ x 30″, litho, pub PHFA . . . . . . | 85.00 | — |
| ☐ **SCREECH OWLS,** rel. 1976. ed. 250, s/n, 24″ x 33″, litho, pub PHFA . . . . . . . | 85.00 | — |
| ☐ **SAW-WHET OWL,** rel. 1977. ed. 250, s/n, 20″ x 29″, litho, pub PHFA . . . . . . . | 150.00 | — |

# JOHN L. CARTER

John L. Carter's watercolors bring a new dimension of sensitivity to wildlife art. Several of his paintings hang in the Wildlife World Museum in Monument, Colorado. His originals have received wide acclaim at the Safari Club International, the Mzuri Safari Foundation, and in Game Conservation International convention art shows. Carter is also a member of the Department of Interior's Snake River Expedition to do study counts on hawks and other birds of prey in that area.

Carter's work has been reproduced in Ducks Unlimited, Ruffed Grouse Society, Sports Afield, and North American Decoy. In addition to being selected for the cover of the United States Department of the Interior's Mallard Study, his work won first place in the Ducks Unlimited Midwest Art Show.

## JOHN L. CARTER

| | | |
|---|---|---|
| ☐ **AN EARLY COVEY,** ed. 800, s/n, 16″ x 22″, litho, pub PP . . . . . . . . . . . . . . . | 60.00 | 80.00 |
| ☐ **RUFFS ON THE EDGE,** ed. 450, s/n, 12¾″ x 25½″, litho, pub PP . . . . . . . . . . | 50.00 | 80.00 |
| ☐ **OLD CHANNEL WALDPORT GEESE,** ed. 450, s/n, 17¾″ x 25½″, litho, pub PP. | 50.00 | 80.00 |
| ☐ **BACKWATER WOODIES,** ed. 800, s/n, 16″ x 22″, litho, pub PP . . . . . . . . . . . | 60.00 | — |
| ☐ **MORNING FLIGHT,** ed. 800, s/n, 18″ x 25″, litho, pub PP . . . . . . . . . . . . . . . | 60.00 | — |
| ☐ **AUTUMN WINGS,** ed. 800, s/n, 17″ x 23½″, litho, pub PP . . . . . . . . . . | 60.00 | — |
| ☐ **MALLARDS AND MASONS,** ed. 800, s/n, 18½″ x 22″, litho, pub PP . . . . . . . . | 60.00 | — |
| ☐ **COVEY RISE,** ed. 800, s/n, 18″ x 24″, litho, pub PP . . . . . . . . . . . . . . . . . . . | 60.00 | — |

# DAVE CHAPPLE

Without losing the realism and scientific accuracy of his paintings, Dave Chapple's works are action bird scenes.

Chapple's interest in birds led him to study taxidermy, a technical skill that is reflected in his etchings and paintings. His love for fine line work led Chapple to explore etching as a medium.

His works have become internationally recognized. He has exhibited at the Leigh Yawkey Woodson Art Museum and the Easton Waterfowl Festival.

He has had numerous one-man shows and is an enthusiastic supporter of Ducks Unlimited.

**COVEY BREAK** *by Dave Chapple*

## DAVE CHAPPLE

| | ISSUE PRICE | CURRENT PRICE |
|---|---|---|
| ☐ BACKWATER MALLARDS, rel. 1978. ed. 150, etching, pub EE | 90.00 | 150.00 |
| ☐ BLACK DUCK, rel. 1978. ed. 150, etching, pub EE | 90.00 | 150.00 |
| ☐ BLUEBILLS, rel. 1978. ed. 150, etching, pub EE | 90.00 | 150.00 |
| ☐ BLUE-WINGED TEAL, rel. 1978. ed. 150, etching, pub EE | 90.00 | 150.00 |
| ☐ CANADA GEESE, rel. 1978. ed. 150, etching, pub EE | 90.00 | 200.00 |
| ☐ CANVASBACKS, rel. 1978. ed. 150, etching, pub EE | 90.00 | 150.00 |
| ☐ IN TO FEED-CANADA GEESE, rel. 1978. ed. 150, etching, pub EE | 90.00 | 150.00 |
| ☐ MALLARDS, rel. 1978. ed. 150, etching, pub EE | 90.00 | 150.00 |
| ☐ NIGHT OWLS, rel. 1978. ed. 150, etching, pub EE | 200.00 | 300.00 |
| ☐ OVER THE MARSH-PINTAILS, rel. 1978. ed. 150, etching, pub EE | 90.00 | 150.00 |
| ☐ PINTAILS, rel. 1978. ed. 150, etching, pub EE | 90.00 | 150.00 |
| ☐ SETTING DOWN-RED HEADS, rel. 1978. ed. 150, etching, pub EE | 90.00 | 150.00 |
| ☐ WOOD DUCK, rel. 1978. ed. 150, etching, pub EE | 90.00 | 200.00 |
| ☐ CANADA GOOSE, rel. 1979. ed. 150, etching, pub EE | 200.00 | 400.00 |
| ☐ PEREGRINE FALCON, rel. 1979. ed. 150, etching, pub EE | 200.00 | 750.00 |
| ☐ SPRINGER SPANIEL/PHEASANT, rel. 1979. ed. 150, etching, pub EE | 200.00 | 750.00 |
| ☐ MALLARDS-COLOR, rel. 1980. ed. 150, etching, pub EE | 200.00 | 375.00 |
| ☐ PINTAILS, rel. 1980. ed. 150, etching, pub EE | 150.00 | 225.00 |
| ☐ CALIFORNIA QUAIL, rel. 1981. ed. 150, etching, pub EE | 150.00 | 175.00 |
| ☐ GREEN-WINGED TEAL, rel. 1981. ed. 150, etching, pub EE | 150.00 | 225.00 |

| | ISSUE PRICE | CURRENT PRICE |
|---|---|---|
| ☐ **PHEASANT**, rel. 1981. ed. 150, etching, pub EE ........................ | 150.00 | 175.00 |
| ☐ **WOOD DUCK**, rel. 1981. ed. 150, etching, pub EE ..................... | 150.00 | 225.00 |
| ☐ **JUMPING-WOODDUCKS**, rel. 1982. ed. 250, 18" x 24", hand-colored etching, pub EE........................................... | 250.00 | — |
| ☐ **CARDINAL**, rel. 1983. ed. 250, s/n, size unavailable, etching, pub FHG ..... | 150.00 | — |
| ☐ **COVEY BREAK - BOBWHITE**, rel. 1983. ed. 250, s/n, size unavailable, etching, pub FHG ............................................... | 225.00 | — |
| ☐ **HEDGEROW - PHEASANT**, rel. 1983. ed. 250, s/n, size unavailable, etching, pub FHG ............................................... | 150.00 | Sold Out |
| ☐ **PEERING OUT**, rel. 1983. ed. 250, s/n, size unavailable, etching, pub FHG ... | 225.00 | — |
| ☐ **THE ARENA**, rel. 1983. ed. 975, s/n, size unavailable, litho, pub FHG ....... | 80.00 | — |
| ☐ **THE LOOKOUT**, rel. 1983. ed. 250, s/n, size unavailable, etching, pub FHG ... | 95.00 | — |
| ☐ **TRANQUIL - WOODIES**, rel. 1983. ed. 250, s/n, size unavailable, etching, pub FHG ............................................... | 120.00 | — |
| ☐ **VALLEY QUAIL**, rel. 1983. ed. 240, s/n, size unavailable, etching, pub FHG .. | 150.00 | — |

# HERB CHIDLEY

Herb Chidley, a renowned wildlife artist with over fifty years experience, is represented in industrial and private collections throughout the United States and Canada.

His paintings reflect his exceptional artistry as well as the authenticity of a hunter and fisherman.

Chidley's numerous commissions include the World Book Encyclopedia, covers for all leading outdoor magazines and wildlife collections for the oldest and largest calendar houses.

## HERB CHIDLEY

| | | |
|---|---|---|
| ☐ **BOBWHITE QUAIL - AIRBORN**, rel. 1977. ed. 575, s/n, 16½" x 22", pub HC .. | 55.00 | — |
| Remarqued ....................................................... | 115.00 | — |
| ☐ **SPECIAL DELIVERY - SPRINGER WITH PHEASANT**, rel. 1977. ed. 575, s/n, 17" x 20½", pub HC........................................... | 55.00 | — |
| Remarqued ....................................................... | 115.00 | — |
| ☐ **TOUCHDOWN - MALLARDS**, rel. 1977. ed. 575, s/n, 16½" x 25", pub HC ... | 55.00 | — |
| Remarqued ....................................................... | 115.00 | — |

# RAYMOND CHING

Raymond Ching was born in Brooklyn Wellington, New Zealand in 1939. His paintings were first seen in Auckland in 1966, with a showing of thirty watercolors and gouaches of birds.

These early paintings and a later collection shown the following year, firmly established his reputation in New Zealand and formed the basis of work that was, by 1972, recognized among the finest of its kind in the world.

Late in 1966, *The Reader's Digest* commissioned Ching to illustrate their now famous book, *The Book Of British Birds*.

Ching authored and illustrated the book, *The Bird Paintings*. This large volume (released in November, 1978) contains 26 full color paintings and 50 drawings and is acclaimed as one of the finest publications on bird art.

Many of Ching's paintings have been exhibited at the prestigious Tyron Gallery in London.

**EARLY SNOW – MOURNING DOVES** *by Raymond Ching*

## RAYMOND CHING

| | ISSUE PRICE | CURRENT PRICE |
|---|---|---|
| ☐ **KESTREL,** rel. 1978. ed. 850, s/n, 23″ x 18⅝″, pub RAF | 100.00 | 250.00 |
| ☐ **TREASURE CHEST,** rel. 1980. ed. 850, s/n, 24⅞″ x 18½″, pub RAF | 100.00 | 250.00 |
| ☐ **SWALLOW,** rel. 1981. ed. 850, s/n, 26″ x 20″, distr. RAF | 175.00 | — |
| ☐ **WINTER WREN,** rel. 1981. ed. 850, s/n, size not available, distr. RAF | 70.00 | — |
| ☐ **EARLY SNOW-MOURNING DOVES,** rel. 1982. ed. 850, s/n, size not available, distr. RAF | 150.00 | — |

# ROBERT CHRISTIE

Robert A. Christie's interest in animals and painting goes back to his early teens. During those years, he seemed destined to take up veterinarian medicine as a career, but the lure of brush and canvas, and an already apparent artistic talent, dictated otherwise. After graduation from high school, he studied fine arts at Ohio Wesleyan University and at Pratt Institute and Art Students League in New York.

Currently, Christie is a full time fine artist who primarily paints sporting and hunting dogs.

## ROBERT CHRISTIE

| | ISSUE PRICE | CURRENT PRICE |
|---|---|---|
| ☐ **AUTUMN ELEGANCE**, ed. 2,000, s/n, 17″ x 21¼″, pub CSI | 35.00 | — |
| ☐ **AT THE BEAVER POND**, ed. 2,000, s/n, 17″ x 21¼″, pub CSI | 35.00 | — |
| ☐ **GOLDEN SHORES**, ed. 2,000, s/n, 17″ x 21¼″, pub CSI | 35.00 | — |
| ☐ **GUS AND BLUE**, rel. 1973. ed. 1,000, s/n, 17″ x 21¼″, pub CSI | 35.00 | 110.00 |
| ☐ **MY TWO FAVORITES**, rel. 1973. ed. 1,000, s/n, 17″ x 21¼″, pub CSI | 35.00 | 85.00 |
| ☐ **POINT AND HONOR**, rel. 1979. ed. 950, s/n, 17″ x 21¼″, pub CSI | 50.00 | — |
| ☐ **THE SEEKERS**, rel. 1979. ed. 950, s/n, 16″ x 20″, pub CSI | 40.00 | — |
| ☐ **STEADY AND STYLISH**, rel. 1979. ed. 950, s/n, 17″ x 21¼″, pub CSI | 45.00 | — |

# ROBERT CLARK

A landscape, a piece of the past, or an intimate look at homely, everyday objects painted with beauty and tenderness are the arresting subjects of Robert Clark's art.

Peace and serenity painted with a refreshing clarity emerge from Clark's own philosophy of art and his masterful use of that most difficult of all mediums: egg tempera.

Clark's paintings are strikingly distinguished by a glowing luminosity and perspective rendering of detail, intricately blended and softened. A discriminating use of texture dramatically accented by light and dark, intensifies certain elements.

He received his formal art training at the Minneapolis School of Art and the Walker Art Center School. Later, after moving to California, he was on the staff of the Los Angeles County Museum where he executed large scale backgrounds for natural history dioramas which furthered his interest in portraying nature. In 1965, he finished a magnificent 45″ x 75″ mural of *The Resurrection* for Forest Lawn Memorial Park.

Since then he has concentrated on easel paintings which have been shown in museums throughout the United States and are in many fine private collections. He has been the subject of a documentary film produced by William F. Taylor; *Robert Clark: An American Realist.*

**NESTING SWANS** *by Robert Clark*

| ROBERT CLARK | ISSUE PRICE | CURRENT PRICE |
|---|---|---|
| ☐ **AUGUST STILL LIFE**, rel. 1980. ed. 950, s/n, 23″ x 16″, pub MPPI ......... | 50.00 | — |
| ☐ **INDIAN SUMMER**, rel. 1980. ed. 950, s/n, 23″ x 16″, pub MPPI ........... | 50.00 | — |

# SANDY CLOUGH

| | | |
|---|---|---|
| ☐ **SOUTHERN WINTER**, rel. 1979. ed. 1,000, s/n, 14½″ x 29⅓″, distr. MMFC . | 40.00 | — |

# FRANCOIS CLOUTIER

As an artist of international stature, Francois Cloutier finds inspiration for his paintings in his travels throughout the world. His relaxed, muted and simply stated themes reveal his love of life and nature. Cloutier came to the United States as an art director and designer. His dazzling creations took top international awards for seven consecutive years. His credits include stage and scenic designs for many national extravaganzas in everything from musical comedy to ballet. His paintings can be found in many important private collections throughout the world.

**THE PROPOSAL** *by Francois Cloutier*

**FRANCOIS CLOUTIER**

| | | |
|---|---|---|
| ☐ **MOMENT IN TIME**, ed. 500, s/n, 20⅛″ x 37⅝″, pub EHC ................ | 60.00 | — |
| ☐ **MORNING RISE**, ed. 500, s/n, 25″ x 37¼″, pub EHC ................... | 60.00 | — |
| ☐ **THE PROPOSAL**, ed. 500, s/n, 22¾″ x 37¼″, pub EHC ................ | 60.00 | — |

# JOHN CLYMER

John Clymer lives on the side of a mountain in the Grand Tetons of Wyoming, where he is surrounded by wildlife and Western scenes. He has had a long distinguished career as an artist. A masterful and talented painter, Clymer is famous for his portrayals of North American mammals and great Northwestern historical subjects.

Born and raised in Ellensburg, Washington, Clymer started his art training while still in high school. His talents were further developed in Canada at the Ontario College of Art and the Vancouver School of Decorative and Applied Art. He returned to the States to study at the Grand Central School of Art in New York, and later at the Wilmington Academy of Art in Delaware.

A forty year career as an illustrator yielded many commercial creations. Best known may be the ninety-eight covers he painted for *The Saturday Evening Post* during a twenty year period.

Since 1964, Clymer's winters are dedicated to work at his easel, and the summers saved for extensive research and field trips.

Clymer is a member of many art associations including the Cowboy Artists of America, the National Academy of Western Art, and the Society of Animal Artists. He has won a many honors for his paintings at shows and exhibitions, and for his contribution in the field of fine arts for the preservation of Western history.

| JOHN CLYMER | ISSUE PRICE | CURRENT PRICE |
|---|---|---|
| ☐ **HIDING PLACE,** rel. 1976. ed. 950, s/n, 20″ x 27½″, pub MPPI . . . . . . . . . . . . | 100.00 | 150.00 |
| ☐ **BY THE TUNDRA POND,** rel. 1979. ed. 750, s/n, size not available, pub WWI . . | 200.00 | — |

# GUY COHELEACH

"He turned vagabond in his last two high school summers. Thumbed westward from his Long Island home, saw Canada, then Mexico, climbing mountains in the Rockies and Tetons in between. He caught rattlesnakes and sidewinders, encountered bears and moonshiners, and raced autos in Erie, Pa." In these words, Les Line describes the teenage years of Guy Coheleach.

In 1976 the African Safari Club of Washington voted Guy Coheleach "Conservationist of the Year" for his outstanding contributions to conservation. Some of the groups that have received donations of Coheleach prints and originals include National Wildlife Federation; National Audubon Society; Game Conservation International; The Fund for Animals Inc.; Holy Land Conservation Fund; National Foundation for Conservation and Environmental Officers and many universities and other worthwhile organizations.

Before working full time as an artist, Coheleach was employed in the advertisting field where he met Don Eckelberry. When a publisher asked Eckelberry to do a bird calendar, he declined but suggested Coheleach. Coheleach has been painting wildlife ever since.

In 1972 at an auction for the World Wildlife Fund, two of his paintings brought more than all the other art put together. Coheleach's *American Eagle* was chosen by the State Department which presents the prints to visiting heads of state while an elephant painting hangs in the White House.

**DOUBLE TROUBLE** *by Guy Coheleach*

## GUY COHELEACH

| | ISSUE PRICE | CURRENT PRICE |
|---|---|---|
| ☐ **LONG-EARED OWL**, rel. 1967. ed. 400, s/n, 11″ x 14″ . . . . . . . . . . . . . . . . . | 30.00 | 950.00 |
| Printed in New York prior to affiliation with Frame House Gallery. Not considered part of the Gallery collection. Highly valued by Coheleach collectors. | | |
| ☐ **BALD EAGLE "Endangered Species"**, rel. 1968. ed. 1,000, s/n, 32″ x 40″ . . . | 75.00 | 650.00 |
| Released through National Wildlife Federation | | |
| ☐ **PURPLE GALLINULE**, rel. 1968. ed. 19,500, s/o, 11¼″ x 14¾″, pub FHG . . . . | * | 50.00 |
| *Obtainable only with membership to National Audubon Society during 1968-69 Florida membership campaign. | | |
| ☐ **GREAT BLUE HERON,** rel. 1968. ed. 2,500, s/o, 22½″ x 26½″, pub FHG . . . . | 40.00 | 75.00 |
| ed. 500, s/n . . . . . . . . . . . . . . . . . . . . . . . . . . . . . . . . . . . . . . . . . . . . . | 50.00 | 100.00 |
| ☐ **RED-TAILED HAWK,** rel. 1968. ed. 3,500, s/o, 22″ x 18″, pub FHG . . . . . . . . | 20.00 | 90.00 |
| ☐ **GOLDEN EAGLE,** rel. 1968. ed. 1,000, s/n, 28″ x 35″, pub FHG . . . . . . . . . . . | 75.00 | 400.00 |
| ☐ **SNOWY EGRETS,** rel. 1968. ed. 500, signed/numbered donated to National Audubon Society to raise money for Corkscrew Swamp Sanctuary . . . . . . . . . . | 100.00 | 360.00 |
| ed. 2,500, unsigned and unnumbered, 24″ x 31″, pub FHG . . . . . . . . . . . . . | 50.00 | 300.00 |
| ☐ **BARN SWALLOW,** rel. 1968. ed. 3,500, s/o, 18″ x 22″, pub FHG . . . . . . . . . . | 20.00 | 35.00 |
| ☐ **CARDINAL,** rel. 1969. ed. 4,200, s/o, 18″ x 22″, pub FHG . . . . . . . . . . . . . . . | 20.00 | 85.00 |
| Also offered as a free bonus to new membership during the 1969-70 Audubon Society membership campaign in North Carolina. | | |
| ☐ **AMERICAN ELK,** rel. 1968. ed. 3,500, s/o, 22″ x 18″, pub FHG . . . . . . . . . . . | 15.00 | 50.00 |
| ☐ **GRIZZLY BEAR,** rel. 1968. ed. 3,500, s/o, 22″ x 18″, pub FHG. . . . . . . . . . . . | 15.00 | 50.00 |
| ☐ **BLACK CRAPPIE,** rel. 1968. ed. 3,500, s/o, 22″ x 18″, pub FHG . . . . . . . . . . | 15.00 | 50.00 |
| ☐ **STRIPPED BASS,** rel. 1968. ed. 3,500, s/o, 22″ x 18″, pub FHG . . . . . . . . . . | 15.00 | 50.00 |
| ☐ **GREAT HORNED OWL,** rel. 1970. ed. 1,000 signed, numbered and imprinted with the college seal, printed exclusively for the alumni of Transylvania University, Lexington, Kentucky . . . . . . . . . . . . . . . . . . . . . . . . . . . . . . . . . . | 65.00 | 275.00 |
| ed. 2,000, s/o, 24″ x 31″, pub FHG . . . . . . . . . . . . . . . . . . . . . . . . . . . . . | 50.00 | 210.00 |

| | ISSUE PRICE | CURRENT PRICE |
|---|---|---|
| ☐ **KIRTLAND'S WARBLER,** rel. 1970. ed. 5,000, s/o, 10" x 14", pub FHG . . . . . . | 12.50 | — |
| This print also offered as a free bonus during the 1970 Audubon Society membership campaign in Michigan, to new members. | | |
| ☐ **WOOD THRUSH,** rel. 1970. ed. 3,500, s/o, 12" x 16", pub FHG . . . . . . . . . . . . | 15.00 | 35.00 |
| ☐ **BLACK-CAPPED CHICKADEE,** rel. 1970. ed. 3,500, s/o, 12" x 16", pub FHG . . | 15.00 | 400.00 |
| ☐ **LEOPARD,** rel. 1970. ed. 650, s/n, 31½" x 25", pub FHG . . . . . . . . . . . . . . . | 75.00 | 525.00 |
| ☐ **PEREGRINE FALCON,** rel. 1970. ed. 3,500, s/o, 18" x 22", pub FHG . . . . . . . . | 20.00 | 110.00 |
| ☐ **SAW-WHET OWL,** rel. 1969. ed. 5,000, s/o, 12¼" x 16½", pub FHG . . . . . . . | 10.00 | 135.00 |
| ☐ **AMERICAN KESTREL,** rel. 1971. ed. 5,000, s/o, 16" x 20", pub FHG . . . . . . . . | 20.00 | — |
| ☐ **SIBERIAN TIGER,** rel. 1971. ed. 3,500, s/o, 20½" x 25", pub FHG . . . . . . . . . | 30.00 | 250.00 |
| ☐ **ELEPHANT,** rel. 1971. ed. 1,000, s/n, 31½" x 25", pub FHG . . . . . . . . . . . . . . | 75.00 | 150.00 |
| ed. 1,500, s/o . . . . . . . . . . . . . . . . . . . . . . . . . . . . . . . . . . . . . . . . . . . . | 60.00 | 125.00 |
| ☐ **KILLDEER PLOVER,** rel. 1971. ed. 5,000, s/o, 14" x 20", pub FHG . . . . . . . . . | 20.00 | — |
| ☐ **IVORY-BILLED WOODPECKER,** rel. 1971. ed. 1,000, s/n, 22" x 29¾", pub FHG . . . . . . . . . . . . . . . . . . . . . . . . . . . . . . . . . . . . . . . . . . . . . | 65.00 | — |
| ed. 3,000, s/o . . . . . . . . . . . . . . . . . . . . . . . . . . . . . . . . . . . . . . . . . . . . | 50.00 | — |
| ☐ **AFRICAN LION,** rel. 1971. ed. 5,000, s/o, 20½" x 25", pub FHG . . . . . . . . . . | 30.00 | 90.00 |
| ☐ **COMMON EGRET,** rel. 1972. ed. 5,000, s/o, 30" x 23", pub FHG . . . . . . . . . . . | 35.00 | — |
| ☐ **LEOPARD STARE,** rel. 1972. ed. 1,000, s/n, 24" x 29", pub FHG . . . . . . . . . . . | 75.00 | 225.00 |
| ed. 3,000, s/o . . . . . . . . . . . . . . . . . . . . . . . . . . . . . . . . . . . . . . . . . . . . | 60.00 | 165.00 |
| *ed. 1,000 donated to National Wildlife Federation to raise funds for conservation work. . . . . . . . . . . . . . . . . . . . . . . . . . . . . . . . . . . . . . . . . . . | *60.00 | 140.00 |
| ☐ **KOALA BEAR,** rel. 1972. ed. 5,000, s/o, 12" x 16", pub FHG . . . . . . . . . . . . . | 15.00 | 125.00 |
| ☐ **WAPITI STAG,** rel. 1972. ed. 1,000, s/n, 22¾" x 29⅞", pub FHG . . . . . . . . . . | 75.00 | 225.00 |
| ed. 3,000, s/o . . . . . . . . . . . . . . . . . . . . . . . . . . . . . . . . . . . . . . . . . . . . | 60.00 | 200.00 |
| *ed. 1,500 signed special edition bearing the official seal of the Benevolent and Protective Order of Elks . . . . . . . . . . . . . . . . . . . . . . . . . . . . . . . . . | *60.00 | — |
| ☐ **BEWARE,** rel. 1972. ed. 5,000, s/o, 23" x 19", pub FHG . . . . . . . . . . . . . . . . | *20.00 | 160.00 |
| *500 donated to African Wildlife Leadership Foundation to raise funds for research and education projects. | | |
| ☐ **GIANT PANDA,** rel. 1972. ed. 5,000, s/o, 16" x 20", pub FHG . . . . . . . . . . . . . | 20.00 | 100.00 |
| ☐ **SNOW LEOPARD,** rel. 1972. ed. 1,000, s/n, 31⅝" x 25", pub FHG . . . . . . . . . . | 75.00 | 475.00 |
| ed. 3,000, s/o . . . . . . . . . . . . . . . . . . . . . . . . . . . . . . . . . . . . . . . . . . . . | 60.00 | 380.00 |
| *ed. 1,000 Fund for Animals, Inc. . . . . . . . . . . . . . . . . . . . . . . . . . . . . . . | *60.00 | — |
| ☐ **THE CHASE,** rel. 1973. ed. 5,000, s/o, 25¾" x 20½", pub FHG . . . . . . . . . . . | 35.00 | 165.00 |
| ☐ **SNOWY OWL,** rel. 1973. ed. 1,000, s/n, 34" x 24½", pub FHG . . . . . . . . . . . . | 75.00 | — |
| ed. 4,000, s/o . . . . . . . . . . . . . . . . . . . . . . . . . . . . . . . . . . . . . . . . . . . . | 60.00 | — |
| ☐ **WINTER CARDINALS,** rel. 1973. ed. 5,000, s/o, 16" x 20", pub RHAI . . . . . . . | 20.00 | 90.00 |
| ☐ **LEOPARD HEAD,** rel. 1973. ed. 5,000, s/o, 16" x 20", pub RHAI . . . . . . . . . . . | 20.00 | 290.00 |
| ☐ **JUNGLE JAGUAR,** rel. 1973. ed. 5,000, s/o, 26" x 21", pub RHAI . . . . . . . . . . | 40.00 | 220.00 |
| ☐ **RED-SHAFTED FLICKER,** rel. 1973. ed. 5,000, s/o, 16" x 20", pub RHAI . . . . . | 20.00 | 50.00 |
| ☐ **CLOUDED LEOPARD,** rel. 1973. ed. 5,000, s/o, 20" x 26", pub RHAI . . . . . . . . | 40.00 | 125.00 |
| ☐ **GOLDEN EAGLE,** rel. 1974. ed. 5,000, s/o, 21" x 26", pub RHAI . . . . . . . . . . . | 40.00 | 90.00 |
| ☐ **CATS OF THE AMERICAS,** rel. 1974. Portfolio of six prints. ed. 5,000, i/o, 14½" x 18", pub RHAI . . . . . . . . . . . . . . . . . . . . . . . . . . . . . . . . . . . . . . . . | 80.00 | 200.00 |
| ☐ **SCREECH OWLS,** rel. 1974. ed. 5,000, i/o, 16" x 20", pub RHAI . . . . . . . . . . . | 20.00 | 200.00 |
| ☐ **FOX DEN,** rel. 1974. ed. 1,000, s/n, 26" x 35", pub RHAI . . . . . . . . . . . . . . . | 100.00 | 300.00 |
| ed. 500, s/o . . . . . . . . . . . . . . . . . . . . . . . . . . . . . . . . . . . . . . . . . . . . . | 80.00 | 225.00 |
| ed. 500, s/o, donated to Fox Den Village . . . . . . . . . . . . . . . . . . . . . . . . . . | — | — |
| ☐ **IMPERIAL EAGLE,** rel. 1974. ed. 5,000, i/o, 11" x 14", pub RHAI . . . . . . . . . . | 10.00 | 50.00 |
| ☐ **CHARGING ELEPHANT,** rel. 1974. ed. 4,500, s/o, 26" x 19", pub RHAI . . . . . . | 40.00 | 125.00 |
| ed. 500 donated to Game Conservation International . . . . . . . . . . . . . . . . . . | 80.00 | 125.00 |
| ☐ **BLACK BEAR CUBS,** rel. 1974. ed. 4,500, i/o, 16" x 20", pub RHAI . . . . . . . . . | 20.00 | 90.00 |
| ed. 500 donated to the University of Tennessee . . . . . . . . . . . . . . . . . . . . . | 50.00 | 80.00 |
| ☐ **CARIBOU,** rel. 1974. ed. 3,000, s/o, 20¼" x 26", pub RHAI . . . . . . . . . . . . . . | 40.00 | 135.00 |
| ☐ **THE LOOKOUT,** rel. 1974. ed. 1,000, s/n, 35" x 28", pub RHAI . . . . . . . . . . . . | 100.00 | 425.00 |
| ed. 1,000, s/o . . . . . . . . . . . . . . . . . . . . . . . . . . . . . . . . . . . . . . . . . . . . | 80.00 | 350.00 |
| ☐ **SHORT EARED OWL,** rel. 1974. ed. 3,000, i/o, 16" x 20", pub RHAI . . . . . . . . | 30.00 | 50.00 |
| ed. 500 Obtainable only with membership to National Audubon Society . . . . . . | — | — |
| ☐ **JAGUAR HEAD,** rel. 1975. ed. 3,500, i/o, 16" x 20", pub RHAI . . . . . . . . . . . . | 30.00 | 150.00 |
| ☐ **MUTE SWANS,** rel. 1975. ed. 4,000, s/n, 25" x 19¾", pub RHAI . . . . . . . . . . . | 50.00 | — |
| ☐ **LONG BILLED MARSHWREN,** rel. 1975. ed. 4,000, i/o, 11" x 14", pub RHAI . . | 20.00 | 40.00 |
| ☐ **TIGER HEAD,** rel. 1975. ed. 4,000, i/o, 16" x 20", pub RHAI . . . . . . . . . . . . . | 30.00 | 225.00 |
| ☐ **BICENTENNIAL EAGLE,** rel. 1975. ed. 1,000, s/n, 32⅞" x 25½", pub RHAI . . | 100.00 | 170.00 |
| ed. 2,000, s/o . . . . . . . . . . . . . . . . . . . . . . . . . . . . . . . . . . . . . . . . . . . . | 80.00 | 150.00 |

| | ISSUE PRICE | CURRENT PRICE |
|---|---|---|
| ☐ **RACCOONS**, rel. 1975. ed. 3,500, s/o, 20″ x 26″, pub RHAI | 60.00 | 200.00 |
| ☐ **CAPE BUFFALO**, rel. 1975. ed. 2,000, s/o, 26″ x 20¼″, pub RHAI | 60.00 | Sold Out |
| ☐ **DUSK**, rel. 1975. ed. 189, s/n, 15″ x 18″, stone lithograph, pub RHAI | 150.00 | 470.00 |
| ☐ **DAWN**, rel. 1975. ed. 147, s/n, 15″ x 18″, stone lithograph, pub RHAI | 200.00 | 510.00 |
| ☐ **REFLECTIONS**, rel. 1976. ed. 156, s/n, 15″ x 11″, stone lithograph, pub RHAI | 200.00 | 250.00 |
| ☐ **SCARLET TANAGER & WHIP-POOR-WILL**, rel. 1976. ed. 5,000, i/o, 12″ x 15″, pub RHAI | 20.00 | Sold Out |
| ☐ **WILD TURKEY**, rel. 1976. ed. 1,000, s/n, 25½″ x 34″, pub RHAI | 100.00 | Sold Out |
|     ed. 1,500, s/o | 80.00 | Sold Out |
|     ed. 500, s/o, donated National Foundation for Conservation & Environmental Officers | — | — |
| ☐ **GREAT WHITE SHARKS**, rel. 1976. ed. 4,000, i/o, 16″ x 20″, pub RHAI | 30.00 | 45.00 |
| ☐ **YOUNG GREAT HORNED OWLS**, rel. 1976. ed. 5,000, s/o, 20″ x 26″, pub RHAI | 50.00 | 90.00 |
| ☐ **SNOW LEOPARD HEAD**, rel. 1976. ed. 5,000, i/o, 16″ x 20″, pub RHAI | 30.00 | 100.00 |
| ☐ **BLACK WATCH**, rel. 1976. ed. 1,000, s/n, 34″ x 25½″, pub RHAI | 100.00 | 175.00 |
|     ed. 1,000, s/o | 80.00 | 150.00 |
| ☐ **WOOD DUCKS**, rel. 1976. ed. 5,000, s/o, 26″ x 20″, pub RHAI | 50.00 | 50.00 |
| ☐ **INDIAN ROLLERS**, rel. 1977. ed. 5,000, i/o, 16″ x 21″, pub RHAI | 30.00 | Sold Out |
| ☐ **MOUNTAIN STALK**, rel. 1977. ed. 1,000, s/n, 32½″ x 25½″, pub RHAI | 100.00 | 150.00 |
|     ed. 1,000, s/o | 80.00 | 130.00 |
| ☐ **BOBCAT**, rel. 1977. ed. 3,500, s/o, 21″ x 26″, pub RHAI | 60.00 | Sold Out |
| ☐ **WHITE TIGER HEAD**, rel. 1977. ed. 4,500, i/o, 16″ x 20″, pub RHAI | 30.00 | 100.00 |
|     ed. 500, s/n, donated to New Paltz Peregrine Falcon Foundation | 65.00 | — |
| ☐ **WHITE TAILED DEER**, rel. 1977. ed. 1,000, s/n, 25¼″ x 20¾″, pub RHAI | 75.00 | 90.00 |
|     ed. 2,000, s/o | 60.00 | 60.00 |
| ☐ **AT EASE**, rel. 1977. ed. 1,000, s/n, 32¾″ x 25½″, pub RHAI | 100.00 | 170.00 |
|     ed. 1,000, s/o | 80.00 | 150.00 |
| ☐ **KOALA BEAR**, rel. 1977. ed. 5,000, i/o, 16″ x 20″, pub RHAI | 30.00 | 50.00 |
| ☐ **AUTUMN DUO**, rel. 1977. ed. 149, s/n, 18¼″ x 14¾″, stone lithograph, pub RHAI | 200.00 | 260.00 |
| ☐ **LION HEAD**, rel. 1978. ed. 5,000, i/o, 16″ x 20″, pub RHAI | 30.00 | Sold Out |
| ☐ **AMBUSH**, rel. 1978. ed. 1,000, s/n, 25½″ x 35″, pub RHAI | 100.00 | 225.00 |
|     ed. 1,000, s/o | 80.00 | 150.00 |
| ☐ **BOBWHITE**, rel. 1978. ed. 5,000, i/o, 16″ x 20″, pub RHAI | 30.00 | — |
| ☐ **AFFIRMED**, rel. 1978. ed. 1,000, s/n, 20″ x 26″, pub RHAI | 100.00 | Sold Out |
| ☐ **1978 BELMONT STAKES**, rel. 1978. ed. 1,000, s/n, 11″ x 14″, pub RHAI | *100.00 | Sold Out |
|     *Portfolio of four prints. | | |
| ☐ **PEREGRINES' RETURN**, rel. 1978. ed. 1,000, s/n, 25½″ x 35″, pub RHAI | 100.00 | — |
|     ed. 1,000, s/o | 80.00 | — |
| ☐ **DOUBLE TROUBLE**, rel. 1978. ed. 221, s/n, 12″ x 20¾″, stone lithograph, pub RHAI | 200.00 | — |
| ☐ **BABY SNOW LEOPARD** (Pair-Set), rel. 1978. ed. 4,000, i/o, 11″ x 14″, pub RHAI | 40.00 | — |
| ☐ **SNOW LEOPARD (Mother and Cubs)**, rel. 1978. ed. 2,000, s/o, 26″ x 20″, pub RHAI | 60.00 | 125.00 |
| ☐ **SPOTTED OWL**, rel. 1979. ed. 2,000, s/o, 20″ x 26″, pub RHAI | 60.00 | 75.00 |
| ☐ **BACHELOR PAIR**, rel. 1979. ed. 1,000, s/n, 30¼″ x 22¾″, pub RHAI | 100.00 | 75.00 |
|     ed. 1,000, s/o | 80.00 | 150.00 |
| ☐ **CHINESE LEOPARD HEAD**, rel. 1979. ed. 5,000, i/o, 16″ x 20″, pub RHAI | 30.00 | 105.00 |
| ☐ **CANADIAN GEESE**, rel. 1979. ed. 3,000, s/o, 20″ x 26″, pub RHAI | 60.00 | — |
| ☐ **BABY BUBO**, rel. 1979. ed. 168, s/n, 12¼″ x 20¾″, stone litho, pub RHAI | 200.00 | 240.00 |
| ☐ **SIBERIAN CHASE**, rel. 1979. ed. 850, s/n, 15″ x 26″, pub RHAI | 180.00 | 300.00 |
| ☐ **EARLY WARNING**, rel. 1979. ed. 5,000, i/o, 20″ x 16″, pub RHAI | 30.00 | — |
| ☐ **COUGAR & CUBS**, rel. 1979. ed. 2,500, s/o, 20″ x 26″, pub RHAI | 60.00 | — |
| ☐ **MALLARDS**, rel. 1979. ed. 3,000, s/o, 20″ x 26″, pub RHAI | 60.00 | — |
| ☐ **PANDA & CUB**, rel. 1980. ed. 5,000, i/o, 16″ x 20″, pub RHAI | 30.00 | 45.00 |
| ☐ **WHITE GYRFALCON**, rel. 1980. ed. 3,500, s/o, 20″ x 26″, pub RHAI | 60.00 | Sold Out |
| ☐ **LIONESS HEAD**, rel. 1980. ed. 5,000, i/o, 16″ x 20″, pub RHAI | 30.00 | 60.00 |
| ☐ **RACCOON MOTHER & CUB**, rel. 1980*. ed. 5,000, i/o, 11″ x 14″, pub RHAI | 70.00 set | — |
|     *Sold as a Set with print "RACCOON". | | |
| ☐ **RACCOON**, rel. 1980*. ed. 5,000, s/o, 20″ x 26″, pub RHAI | 70.00 set | — |
|     *Sold as a Set with print "RACCOON MOTHER & CUB". | | |
| ☐ **LEOPARD'S LAIR**, rel. 1980. ed. 4,000, s/o, 26″ x 15″, pub RHAI | 60.00 | — |

| | ISSUE PRICE | CURRENT PRICE |
|---|---|---|
| ☐ BENGAL BRACE, rel. 1980. ed. 1,000, s/n, 31⅝" x 24½", pub RHAI ........ | 100.00 | 125.00 |
| ed. 1,000, s/o ......................................... | 80.00 | 100.00 |
| ☐ ROCKY MOUNTAIN LION, rel. 1980. ed. 1,500, s/n, 33½" x 25", pub RHAI .. | 100.00 | 130.00 |
| ed. 1,000, s/o ......................................... | 80.00 | 110.00 |
| ☐ HAREE MOMENT, rel. 1980. ed. 850, s/n, 26" x 17¼", pub RHAI ......... | 180.00 | 270.00 |
| ☐ SIBERIAN TIGER HEAD, rel. 1981. ed. 3,700, s/o, 20" x 26", pub RHAI ...... | 60.00 | Sold Out |
| ☐ ROCKY MOUNTAIN CHASE, rel. 1981. ed. 1,500, s/n, 26" x 20", pub RHAI .. | 70.00 | — |
| ed. 500, s/o .......................................... | 50.00 | — |
| ☐ BABY SAW-WHET OWLS, rel. 1981. ed. 5,000, i/o, 16" x 20", pub RHAI .... | 30.00 | — |
| ☐ WOLF PACK, rel. 1981. ed. 1,500, s/n, 26" x 20", pub RHAI ............. | 70.00 | — |
| ed. 500, s/o .......................................... | 50.00 | — |
| ☐ CHEETAH HEAD, rel. 1981. ed. 5,000, i/o, 16" x 20", pub RHAI ......... | 30.00 | Sold Out |
| ☐ LONG SHADOWS, rel. 1981. ed. 850, s/n, 20" x 15", pub RHAI ........... | 180.00 | Sold Out |
| ☐ STORM FLIGHT, rel. 1981. ed. 850, s/n, 26" x 15", pub RHAI ............ | 180.00 | — |
| ☐ CLOUDED SIESTA, rel. 1981. ed. 1,500, s/n, 25½" x 34", pub RHAI ....... | 100.00 | — |
| ed. 1,500, s/o ........................................ | 80.00 | — |
| ☐ MANCHURIAN CHASE, rel. 1982. ed. 850, s/n, size not available, distr. WWAM ............................................... | 180.00 | Sold Out |
| ☐ BARRIER BEACH CHASE, rel. 1982. ed. 850, s/n, 15" x 32", distr. WWAM ... | 180.00 | — |
| ☐ BARRED OWL, rel. 1982. ed. 1,000, s/n, 27" x 32", distr. WWAM .......... | 120.00 | — |
| ☐ PRIMA HEAD, rel. 1982. ed. 5,000, i/o, 16" x 20", distr. WWAM .......... | 30.00 | — |
| ☐ BABY HARP SEALS, rel. 1982. ed. 5,000, i/o, 16" x 20", distr. WWAM ...... | 30.00 | — |
| ☐ WOLF HEAD, rel. 1983. ed. 4,000, i/o, 16" x 20", distr. WWAM .......... | 35.00 | — |
| ☐ BLACK JAGUAR, rel. 1983. ed. 5,000, s/n, 20" x 36", distr. WWAM ........ | 150.00 | — |
| ☐ SURVIVORS, rel. 1983. ed. 950, s/n, 20" x 26", distr. WWAM ............ | 200.00 | — |

# SIMON COMBES

Simon Combes has spent most of his life in close communication with the wild animals of the African bush, a first-hand experience that makes him outstanding as a wildlife painter. "No animal in captivity," he explains, "has the lean, hard muscles and alert eyes of one fending for itself in the wild." Combes is able to capture on canvas the subtle essence of the truly wild beast.

After formal schooling, he spent thirteen years in the military, during which he became commander of the Kenyan airborne forces and attained the rank of Lieutenant Colonel before being released in 1974 as the last European in that country's army.

It was not until 1966, during a long involvement with Somali guerrillas in northeast Kenya, that Combes first decided to paint. To occupy his spare time, he painted and sketched the local tribesmen. When his work sold readily, he was inspired to do more. While attending Army Staff College in England in 1970, he was commissioned to paint H.R.H. Prince of Wales, and the portrait now hangs in the college. He next became interested in animal painting, and by 1972 realized that he should devote full time to his art.

Combes had a one-man show in Nairobi in 1979. He exhibited at the first World Wilderness Congress in Johannesburg, South Africa, in 1977 and has participated in three shows at the Game Conservation International in San Antonio, Texas, in 1975, '77 and '79. His illustrated *Cheetahs of Samburu* which was published in 1976 to help raise funds for the Chicago Zoological Society's "Waterhole Exhibit".

## SIMON COMBES

| | ISSUE PRICE | |
|---|---|---|
| ☐ FACING THE WIND, rel. 1980. ed. 1,500, s/n, 32" x 22", pub GW .......... | 75.00 | — |
| ☐ INTERLUDE, rel. 1980. ed. 1,500, s/n, 31" x 21½", pub GW .............. | 85.00 | Sold Out |
| ☐ MANYARA AFTERNOON, rel. 1980. ed. 1,500, s/n, 25¾" x 20⅛", pub GW ... | 75.00 | — |
| ☐ SERENGETI MONARCH, rel. 1980. ed. 1,500, s/n, 28¼" x 22½", pub GW ... | 85.00 | — |
| ☐ THE SOLITARY HUNTER, rel. 1980. ed. 1,500, s/n, 28½" x 22½", pub GW .. | 75.00 | — |

| | ISSUE PRICE | CURRENT PRICE |
|---|---|---|
| ☐ **ALERT**, rel. 1981. ed. 1,000, s/n, 30" x 21¼", pub GW . . . . . . . . . . . . . . . . . | 95.00 | — |
| ☐ **LEOPARD CUBS**, rel. 1981. ed. 1,000, s/n, 25½" x 20", pub GW . . . . . . . . . | 95.00 | — |
| ☐ **CHUI**, rel. 1983. ed. 275, s/n, 23¼" x 23¾", hand-drawn lithograph, pub GW | 250.00 | — |

## ART COOK

Art Cook is as concerned about preserving the wildfowl he paints as he is of accurately depicting the anatomy of his subjects.

An interest in drawing at an early age preceded some formal training in high school and college before enrolling in a local art school. A talented student, Cook was urged to seek a career in commercial art. A long period of illustrative work followed, during which time he became industrial art director for a large mid-west corporation.

Winning the Federal Duck Stamp design in 1972 with his colorful and striking portrayal of Emperor Geese was Cook's cue to leave the business world and become a full time wildlife artist.

A hard working conservationist, he is active in both the National and International Wildlife Federations, Ducks Unlimited, The National Audubon Society and Trout Unlimited.

**THE TRAVELER RESTS, ARTIC TERN** *by Art Cook*

**ART COOK**

| | ISSUE PRICE | CURRENT PRICE |
|---|---|---|
| ☐ **THE TRAVELER RESTS -ARTIC TERN**, rel. 1974. ed. 450, s/n, 15" x 21", pub WWI . . . . . . . . . . . . . . . . . . . . . . . . . . . . . . . . . . . . . . . . . . . . . . | 50.00 | 75.00 |
| ed. 75 remarque artist proof . . . . . . . . . . . . . . . . . . . . . . . . . . . . . . . . . . | 100.00 | — |

# ROGER COOKE

Roger Cooke paints Western history with a difference. Instead of Indian wars and the hostilities of frontier life, Cooke's paintings tell of human beings living in a beautiful land. "My interest in the early history of Oregon goes back to my childhood," he says. "For many years I lived on a ranch located on the Oregon Trail and listened to the stories my grandfather told about Chief Joseph and the Nez Perce Indians. I developed a desire to paint the people involved in those events," he said.

Cooke acquired his education and formal art training at Portland State College and the Art Center College of Design in Los Angeles. In 1968, he embarked on a dual career of illustration and fine art painting. It was the latter that he really enjoyed, however, and he made the decision that painting should become his life's work. He is represented in numerous public and private collections and has been the subject of articles in *Southwest Art* and *The Illustrator*.

Cooke paints against a background of beautiful mountains, streams, forests and deserts provided by his native Oregon. His favorite subjects are horses and Indians, for whose culture and way of life he has empathy and respect. He does careful research with sketch pad and camera, and creates moods and impressions by a technique of diluting oils so they run like watercolors.

| ROGER COOKE | ISSUE PRICE | CURRENT PRICE |
|---|---|---|
| ☐ **GATHERING FOR THE HUCKLEBERRY FEAST,** rel. 1979. ed. 1,000, s/n, 27″ x 22″, pub GW | 75.00 | — |
| ☐ **PEACEFUL SUMMER,** rel. 1980. ed. 1,000, s/n, 31¼″ x 21¾, pub GW | 75.00 | — |

# ANN COOPER

A native of New Orleans, Ann Cooper's work has been exhibited in galleries throughout the nation including Circle Gallery of New Orleans, Lord and Taylor Fine Art Gallery in New York, Merrill-Chase Galleries in Chicago, and Fisher Galleries in Washington, D.C.

| ANN COOPER | | |
|---|---|---|
| ☐ **GOTHAM CITY,** rel. 1978. ed. 300, s/n, 30″ x 26″, pub FHG | 125.00 | — |
| ☐ **PARTICULAR PARROTS,** ed. 275, s/n, 28″ x 24″, pub CFAC | 125.00 | — |

# WAYNE COOPER

| | | |
|---|---|---|
| ☐ **TUESDAY,** ed. 300, s/n, 30″ x 22″, lithograph, pub CFAC | — | 400.00 |
| ☐ **BOSSY'S HOUSE,** ed. 300, s/n, 28″ x 18″, lithograph, pub CFAC | — | 400.00 |
| ☐ **BRUNCH,** ed. 300, s/n, 19″ x 26″, lithograph, pub CFAC | — | 175.00 |
| ☐ **PAPA LEON,** ed. 300, s/n, 18″ x 26″, lithograph, pub CFAC | — | 175.00 |
| ☐ **SEVEN SEAS,** ed. 300, s/n, 24″ x 34″, lithograph, pub CFAC | — | 250.00 |
| ☐ **DECEMBER NINE,** ed. 300, s/n, 20″ x 27″, lithograph, pub CFAC | — | 250.00 |
| ☐ **ENJOY,** ed. 300, s/n, 24″ x 34″, lithograph, pub CFAC | — | 375.00 |
| ☐ **RED FORK,** ed. 260, s/n, 12″ x 17″, etching, pub CFAC | — | 225.00 |
| ☐ **BLUE RIDGE,** ed. 300, s/n, 16″ x 22″, lithograph, pub CFAC | — | 200.00 |
| ☐ **STEAM,** ed. 300, s/n, 20″ x 27″, lithograph, pub CFAC | — | 250.00 |
| ☐ **WILLOW SLEW,** ed. 300, s/n, 24″ x 34″, lithograph, pub CFAC | — | 250.00 |
| ☐ **COOPER'S RAINBOW,** ed. 300, s/n, 21″ x 29″, lithograph, pub CFAC | — | 250.00 |
| ☐ **THE SECOND SNOW,** ed. 300, s/n, 21″ x 26″, lithograph, pub CFAC | — | 175.00 |
| ☐ **EVENING MIST,** ed. 350, s/n, 21″ x 28″, lithograph, pub CFAC | — | 175.00 |
| ☐ **BY THE SEA,** ed. 350, s/n, 24″ x 35″, lithograph, pub CFAC | — | 175.00 |

| | ISSUE PRICE | CURRENT PRICE |
|---|---|---|
| ☐ **NORTH**, ed. 300, s/n, 25″ x 28″, lithograph, pub CFAC . . . . . . . . . . . . . . . . . | — | 200.00 |
| ☐ **SPRING ROAD**, ed. 300, s/n, 21″ x 29″ . . . . . . . . . . . . . . . . . . . . . . . . . . . . . . . . | — | 200.00 |
| ed. 35 on Rives Journal paper, lithograph, pub CFAC . . . . . . . . . . . . . . . . . | — | 225.00 |
| ☐ **ONE BULL**, ed. 350, s/n, 21″ x 24″, lithograph, pub CFAC . . . . . . . . . . . . . . . | — | 200.00 |
| ☐ **ABANDONED FARM**, ed. 5,000, s/n, 23″ x 29″, pub CFAC . . . . . . . . . . . . . . . | — | 135.00 |
| ☐ **WINTER MORN**, ed. 5,000, s/n, 23″ x 29″, pub CFAC . . . . . . . . . . . . . . . . . . | — | 135.00 |
| ☐ **LONELY LIGHTHOUSE**, ed. 5,000, s/n, 23″ x 29″, pub CFAC . . . . . . . . . . . . . | — | 135.00 |
| ☐ **COUNTRY ROAD**, ed. 5,000, s/n, 23″ x 29″, pub CFAC. . . . . . . . . . . . . . . . . . | — | 135.00 |
| ☐ **VANISHING IMAGES PORTFOLIO**, Deluxe 4 prints and special pages, ed. 100, s/n, 25″ x 35″, pub CFAC . . . . . . . . . . . . . . . . . . . . . . . . . . . . . . . . . . . . . . . . . . . | — | 875.00 |
| ☐ **TOBACCO ROAD**, ed. 300, s/n, 25″ x 35″, pub CFAC . . . . . . . . . . . . . . . . . . . | — | 350.00 |
| ☐ **WILL CREEK**, ed. 300, s/n, 25″ x 35″, pub CFAC . . . . . . . . . . . . . . . . . . . . . . | — | 350.00 |
| ☐ **STONE VALLEY**, ed. 300, s/n, 25″ x 35″, pub CFAC . . . . . . . . . . . . . . . . . . . | — | 350.00 |
| ☐ **CROW HOLLOW**, ed. 300, s/n, 25″ x 35″, pub CFAC . . . . . . . . . . . . . . . . . . . | — | 350.00 |

# SOPHIE COORS

Sophie Coors has won national fame and success for her Delta paintings that have been shown in New York, Dallas, Atlanta, Nashville, Palm Beach, Colorado and Greenwich, Connecticut.

Coors was born in Houston, Texas, and grew up in Memphis. She began her art training at the Memphis Academy of Arts at the age of eight. She later majored in art at Mt. Vernon College in Washington, D.C.

Former Tennessee Governor Winfield Dunn, Johnny Cash, Debbie Reynolds and Perry Como are among some of the well-known collectors of Sophie Coors' original oils.

## SOPHIE COORS

| | | |
|---|---|---|
| ☐ **TREE TOP HOUSE**, rel. 1974. ed. 500, s/n, 23″ x 19¼″, pub SG . . . . . . . . . . . | 50.00 | — |
| ☐ **AUNT EM'S**, rel. 1974. ed. 500, s/n, 23″ x 19¼″, pub SG . . . . . . . . . . . . . . . | 50.00 | — |
| ☐ **BAYOU BAPTISM**, rel. 1974. ed. 500, s/n, 23″ x 19¼″, pub SG . . . . . . . . . . . | 50.00 | — |
| ☐ **LOVE GAME**, rel. 1975. ed. 300, s/n, 22″ x 18″, pub SG . . . . . . . . . . . . . . . . | 65.00 | — |
| ☐ **NATALIE**, rel. 1978. ed. 1,250, s/n, 16″ x 20″, pub SG . . . . . . . . . . . . . . . . . | 30.00 | — |
| Sovereign Gallery, publisher of Ms. Coors prints, is no longer in business. | | |

# PETER CORBIN

| | | |
|---|---|---|
| ☐ **THE MALLARD HUNTERS**, ed. 800, s/n, 15″ x 25″, pub PP . . . . . . . . . . . . . . . | 75.00 | Sold Out |
| ☐ **FOG BOUND**, ed. 800, s/n, 15″ x 25″, pub PP . . . . . . . . . . . . . . . . . . . . . . . . . | 75.00 | — |
| Remarqued, signed and numbered . . . . . . . . . . . . . . . . . . . . . . . . . . . . . . . . | 165.00 | — |
| ☐ **A CHANCE TO DOUBLE**, rel. 1980. ed. 250, s/n, size not available, pub WWI . . | 90.00 | — |

# MERV CORNING

| | | |
|---|---|---|
| ☐ **CAPTAIN EDDIE**, ed. 300, s/n, 22″ x 25″, lithograph, pub CFAC . . . . . . . . . . | — | 300.00 |
| ☐ **THE RED BARON**, ed. 300, s/n, 23″ x 22″, lithograph, pub CFAC . . . . . . . . . . | — | 325.00 |
| ☐ **FLYING FOOL**, ed. 300, s/n, 22″ x 25″, lithograph, pub CFAC . . . . . . . . . . . . | — | 200.00 |
| ☐ **SET BACKS**, ed. 300, s/n, 22″ x 28″, lithograph, pub CFAC . . . . . . . . . . . . . . | — | 175.00 |
| ☐ **OLD PRO**, ed. 300, s/n, 22″ x 28″, lithograph, pub CFAC . . . . . . . . . . . . . . . . | — | 175.00 |
| ☐ **ON THE LINE**, ed. 300, s/n, 16″ x 20″, lithograph, pub CFAC . . . . . . . . . . . . . | — | 200.00 |
| ☐ **MARINE CORSAIR**, ed. 300, s/n, 24″ x 33″, lithograph, pub CFAC . . . . . . . . . | — | 750.00 |
| ☐ **BLACK FLIGHT**, ed. 300, s/n, 21″ x 26″, lithograph, pub CFAC . . . . . . . . . . . | — | 200.00 |
| ☐ **ARLINGTON HOUSE**, ed. 300, s/n, 22″ x 28″, lithograph, pub CFAC . . . . . . . . | — | 850.00 |

| | ISSUE PRICE | CURRENT PRICE |
|---|---|---|
| ☐ SANTA MAGUERITA, ed. 300, s/n, 31″ x 24″ | — | 700.00 |
| ed. 30 on Rives Journal, lithograph, pub CFAC | — | 750.00 |
| ☐ GREEN RIVER, ed. 300, s/n, 21″ x 28″ | — | 325.00 |
| ed. 30 on Rives Journal, lithograph, pub CFAC | — | 350.00 |
| ☐ SUPER BOWL XI (OFASC - 1977), ed. 600, s/n, 22″ x 28″, lithograph, pub CFAC | — | 275.00 |
| ☐ MIRAMAR HOUSE, ed. 300, s/n, 24″ x 29″ | — | 325.00 |
| ed. 60 on B F K Rives, lithograph, pub CFAC | — | 350.00 |
| ☐ CABINS, ed. 300, s/n, 22″ x 28″ | — | 300.00 |
| ed. 30 on Rives Journal, lithograph, CFAC | — | 350.00 |
| ☐ HIGH COUNTRY, ed. 300, s/n, 22″ x 30″, lithograph, pub CFAC | — | 275.00 |
| ☐ MIRAMAR NOCTURN, ed. 100, s/n, 24″ x 29″, lithograph, pub CFAC | — | 400.00 |
| ☐ OLD BALE MILL, ed. 300, s/n, 24″ x 30″, lithograph, pub CFAC | — | 450.00 |
| ☐ JOYA, ed. 300, s/n, 22″ x 25″, lithograph, pub CFAC | — | 375.00 |
| ☐ DOWN THE ROAD, ed. 300, s/n, 21″ x 24″, lithograph, pub CFAC | — | 300.00 |
| ☐ SUPER BOWL XII (OFASC - 1978), ed. 950, s/n, 23″ x 26″, lithograph, pub CFAC | — | 250.00 |
| ☐ CHAPERONE, ed. 300, s/n, 24″ x 29″, lithograph, pub CFAC | — | 375.00 |
| ☐ PENSIVE, ed. 300, s/n, 21″ x 28″, lithograph, pub CFAC | — | 250.00 |
| ☐ TOY SAILORS, ed. 300, s/n, size not available, lithograph, pub CFAC | — | 250.00 |
| ☐ MAN WITHOUR FEAR, ed. 300, s/n, 26″ x 24″, pub CFAC | — | 650.00 |
| ☐ LOST HILLS RANCH, ed. 300, s/n, 22″ x 30″, pub CFAC | — | 300.00 |
| ☐ FIGUEROA HOUSE, ed. 300, s/n, 26″ x 28″, pub CFAC | — | 525.00 |
| ☐ RAIN POOL, ed. 300, s/n, 21″ x 27″, pub CFAC | — | 325.00 |
| ed. 50 on BFK-Buff paper | — | 375.00 |
| ☐ ANCIENT WARRIOR, ed. 300, s/n, 22″ x 27″, pub CFAC | — | 525.00 |
| ed. 50 on BFK-Buff paper | — | 550.80 |
| ☐ SUPER BOWL XIII/OF ASC 1979, ed. 950, s/n, 26″ x 23″, pub CFAC | — | 250.00 |
| ☐ SUPER BOWL XIV/OF ASC 1980, ed. 950, s/n, 26″ x 23″, pub CFAC | — | 275.00 |
| ☐ SUPER BOWL XV/OF ASC 1981, ed. 950, s/n, 23″ x 26″, pub CFAC | — | 225.00 |
| ☐ SUPER BOWL XVI/OF ASC 1982, ed. 950, s/n, 23″ x 26″, pub CFAC | — | 225.00 |
| ☐ THE GREAT AIRPLANES/1914-1918, 4 pc. suite consisting of Red Knight of Germany, Arizona Balloon Buster Boy Legend and King of the Air Fighters. ed 300, s/n, 21″ x 26″, pub CFAC | — | 1,200.00 |
| Deluxe edition of buff paper, 8 pc. plus special pages | — | 1,750.00 |

# JOSEPH J. CORREALE, JR.

Joseph J. Correale, Jr. has a great love for the scenic flavor of the northeast, having been born and raised in New England. When he chooses a particular theme and transposes it to his painting, he attempts to give the viewer something of the same emotional impact he has felt as the artist.

At the heart of Joseph Correale's painting is a depth of perception into themes we can all relate to and understand. He reaches beyond the chaos of contemporary life and brings to his work those quiet interludes we so often overlook.

Correale is the winner of many regional medals and awards, including the Cultural Arts Workshop's Gold Medal Quarterly. His paintings are exhibited extensively throughout the United States.

## JOSEPH J. CORREALE, JR.

| | ISSUE PRICE | CURRENT PRICE |
|---|---|---|
| ☐ AMERICAN AUTUMN, ed. 300. s/n, 24½″ x 34½″, original color lithograph, pub FI | 200.00 | — |
| ☐ FROSTY SUN, ed. 300. s/n, 21½″ x 29½″, original color lithograph, pub FI | 150.00 | — |
| ☐ LOW TIDE, ed. 300. s/n, 22¼″ x 30″, original color lithograph, pub FI | 150.00 | — |
| ☐ PARIS MARKET, ed. 300. s/n, 24½″ x 35″, original color lithograph, pub FI | 200.00 | 300.00 |
| ☐ PARIS STREET SWEEPER, ed. 300. s/n, 24½″ x 35″, original color lithograph, pub FI | 200.00 | 300.00 |
| ☐ 74th & MADISON, ed. 300. s/n, 22¼″ x 30″, original color lithograph, pub FI | 200.00 | — |
| ☐ TODAY'S SPECIAL, ed. 300. s/n, 29½″ x 21½″, original color lithograph, pub FI | 150.00 | — |

| | ISSUE PRICE | CURRENT PRICE |
|---|---|---|
| ☐ **WHERE THE GULLS FLY,** ed. 300. s/n, 22¼" x 30", original color lithograph, pub Fl | 150.00 | 200.00 |
| ☐ **WINGAERSHEEK & BEYOND,** ed. 300. s/n, 22¼" x 30", original color lithograph, pub Fl | 150.00 | 200.00 |

## DINO COSTANZO

Dino Costanzo's love for nature started when he was four years old, and at age six he became interested in birds, their nests, eggs and habitats. This led to his interest in wildlife art in an attempt to capture his field experiences. He is an avid hunter and conservationist.

From 1972 to 1978 Dino worked at the Cincinnati Museum of Natural History where he was a volunteer in charge of putting together and cataloging bird egg collections which will be used for future references and scientific study. He is currently collecting much-needed waterfowl specimens for the museum and other scientific collections.

Costanzo attended Miami University where he was the recipient of the prestigious William P. Hohmann scholarship. He is presently a student at the University of Cincinnati.

**SCAUP AT REST** by Dino Costanzo

### DINO COSTANZO

| | ISSUE PRICE | CURRENT PRICE |
|---|---|---|
| ☐ **RACCOON,** rel. 1974. ed. 160, s/n, 12" x 16", pub SLA | 6.00 | 200.00 |
| ☐ **BOBWHITE QUAIL,** rel. 1976. ed. 300, s/n, 12" x 16", pub SLA | 6.00 | 130.00 |
| ☐ **FUZZY LITTLE BALL OF OWLET EYES,** rel. 1979. ed. 1,000, s/n, 17" x 22", pub SLA | 20.00 | — |
| ☐ **BLUEGILL SUNFISH CHASING A BEETLE SPIN™,** rel. 1981. ed. 1,500, s/n, 14" x 20", pub SLA | 30.00 | — |
| ☐ ed. 200, s/n, special for Ducks Unlimited, 14" x 20" | 30.00 | 150.00 |
| ☐ **REFRESHING MORNING - CARDINAL,** rel. 1981. ed. 1,500, s/n, 14" x 20", pub SLA | 30.00 | — |
| ☐ **SCAUP AT REST — LESSER SCAUP,** rel. 1981. ed. 1,200, s/n, 19" x 26", pub SLA | 40.00 | — |
| | ed. 300, s/n, special for Ducks Unlimited, 18" x 24" | 40.00 | 150.00 |
| ☐ ed. 200, s/n, special Ducks Unlimited Sponsor edition, 18" x 24" | 40.00 | 150.00 |

| | ISSUE PRICE | CURRENT PRICE |
|---|---|---|
| ☐ SILENT STARE IN STRIPES UNDER THE STARS - BENGAL TIGER, rel. 1981. ed. 1,500, s/n, 27" x 40", pub SLA | 60.00 | — |
| ☐ TRANQUIL PAIR — TRUMPETER SWANS, rel. 1981. ed. 1,500, s/n, 26" x 31", pub SLA | 50.00 | — |

# JOHN P. COWAN

John P. "Jack" Cowan was born in Bristol, Tennessee in 1920. He graduated from the Art School of the Pratt Institute in New York in 1942. After a four year tour of duty in Texas during World War II, he decided to make his home there. During his early years in Texas he engaged in a number of special assignments for Humble Oil, Hughes Tool, Reed, Dowell, Tenneco and Schlumberger, as well as banks and other financial institutions. In these early years, fifty-two of his sporting paintings were reproduced and circulated world-wide by Schlumberger.

In 1960 and 1962 Cowan was awarded two silver medals by the Houston Artists Guild. His paintings were appearing in many national publications. Cowan was honored with a one man exhibition of paintings at the Columbia Museum, Columbia, South Carolina commemorating the 300th Centennial of the State of South Carolina. In 1974 he was one of seven artists selected by the *South Carolina Wildlife* magazine for their article "The Wings of Winter". In September 1976, he participated in the Leigh Yawkey Woodson Museum's exhibit of Birds of the Lakes, Fields and Forest by America's Premier Wildlife Artists.

Cowan's paintings have appeared on the cover and centerfold of the *Ducks Unlimited* magazine. His work was chosen to be on the cover of the *1974 Ducks Unlimited Dinner Program* of the Houston Chapter, which is the largest and most significant of its kind in America. Recently he was named Ducks Unlimited Artist of the Year for 1977.

## JOHN P. COWAN

| | ISSUE PRICE | CURRENT PRICE |
|---|---|---|
| ☐ AT HOME, rel. 1982, ed. 600, s/n, size N/A, distr. WWI | 300.00 | — |
| ☐ BAD ANGLE, rel. 1982, ed. 600, s/n, size N/A, distr. WWI | 85.00 | 500.00 |
| ☐ BAYLEAF BLIND, ed. 600, s/o, 22" x 28½", pub MLC | 60.00 | 500.00 |
| ☐ BOAT BLIND, ed. 600, s/o, 22" x 28½", pub MLC | 50.00 | 500.00 |
| ☐ CREEK BOTTOM, ed. 600, s/o, 22" x 28½", pub MLC | 60.00 | 500.00 |
| ☐ DAWN FLIGHT, ed. 600, s/o, 22" x 28½", pub MLC | 75.00 | 650.00 |
| ☐ DEEP RUN, ed. 600, s/o, 13" x 17", pub MLC | 40.00 | 500.00 |
| ☐ EARLY LIMITS, ed. 600, s/o, 13" x 17", pub MLC | 60.00 | 650.00 |
| ☐ FASTWATER, ed. 600, s/n, 22" x 28½", pub MLC | 60.00 | 125.00 |
| ☐ FOX'S BLIND, rel. 1980, ed. 600, s/n, size N/A, distr. WWI | 85.00 | 500.00 |
| ☐ GETTIN' WELL, ed. 600, s/o, 13" x 17", pub MLC | 25.00 | 750.00 |
| ☐ HEAVY COVER, ed. 600, s/o, 22" x 28½", pub MLC | 60.00 | 1,000.00 |
| ☐ HOT TANK, ed. 600, s/o, 22" x 28½", pub MLC | 60.00 | 1,000.00 |
| ☐ IN THE BROOMWEED - QUAIL, ed. 600, s/o, 22" x 28½", pub MLC | 40.00 | 750.00 |
| ☐ LONGLEAF BOBS, ed. 600, s/o, 22" x 28½", pub MLC | 60.00 | 500.00 |
| ☐ MAGIC MINUTES, rel. 1979, ed. 600, s/n, size N/A, distr. WWI | 60.00 | 750.00 |
| ☐ MALLARDS HIGH, ed. 600, s/o, 22" x 28½", pub MLC | 40.00 | 125.00 |
| ☐ MOVING OUT, ed. 600, s/o, 13" x 17", pub MLC | 25.00 | 250.00 |
| ☐ NEW GUN, ed. 600, s/o, 22" x 28½", pub MLC | 40.00 | 750.00 |
| ☐ NIGHT FEEDERS, ed. 600, s/o, 22" x 28½", pub MLC | 40.00 | 700.00 |
| ☐ OFF BASE, ed. 600, s/o, 22" x 28½", pub MLC | 40.00 | 750.00 |
| ☐ ONE MORE, rel. 1981, ed. 600, s/n, size N/A, distr. WWI | 300.00 | — |
| ☐ PICKING UP PINTAILS, ed. 600, s/o, 22" x 28½", pub MLC | 40.00 | 800.00 |
| ☐ PINE & PALMETTO, ed. 600, s/n, 22" x 28½", pub MLC | 85.00 | 150.00 |
| ☐ PORTABLE BLIND, ed. 600, s/o, 22" x 28½", pub MLC | 40.00 | Sold Out |
| ☐ QUAIL TREE, ed. 600, s/o, 22" x 28½", pub MLC | 40.00 | 800.00 |
| ☐ SWEET WRECK, rel. 1981, ed. 600, s/n, size N/A, distr. WWI | 95.00 | 500.00 |
| ☐ SUNKEN BLIND, ed. 600, s/n, 22" x 28½", pub MLC | 85.00 | 650.00 |

| | ISSUE PRICE | CURRENT PRICE |
|---|---|---|
| ☐ **TEAL HUNT**, ed. 600, s/o, 22" x 28½", pub MLC | 60.00 | 500.00 |
| ☐ **THE FLATS**, ed. 600, s/o, 22" x 28½", pub MLC | 60.00 | 500.00 |
| ☐ **TIDEWATER BASS**, ed. 600, s/o, 22" x 28½", pub MLC | 40.00 | Sold Out |
| ☐ **TOO SOON**, ed. 600, s/o, 22" x 28½", pub MLC | 60.00 | 650.00 |
| ☐ **TWO DOWN**, ed. 600, s/o, 22" x 28½", pub MLC | 40.00 | 650.00 |

## TIM COX

Tim Cox has achieved a remarkable niche for himself in the field of Western American art.

Cox was raised in Duncan in the midst of the cattle ranching area of southeast Arizona.

He says that ranching and "cowboying" have always been an integral part of his life, and from this life-long association and involvement have come the subjects of his paintings.

Cox has studied under the tutelage of William Whitaker, one of the west's finest teachers, at Brigham Young University.

Cox has exhibited his paintings in several art shows. Among them, he has sold pieces in Texas Art Gallery's annual Preview show, and the Western Heritage art show in Houston.

### TIM COX

| | | |
|---|---|---|
| ☐ **NO HELP FROM MOM**, rel. 1979. ed. 2,250, s/n, 12" x 18", pub TAP | 60.00 | — |
| ☐ **BRANDING THE MAVERICK**, rel. 1980. ed. 2,250, s/n, 13¾" x 20⅛", pub TAP | 75.00 | — |
| ☐ **FALL ALONG THE ANIMALS**, rel. 1980. ed. 2,250, s/n, 13⅜" x 20", pub TAP | 75.00 | — |
| ☐ **JINGLIN' HORSES**, rel. 1980. ed. 2,250, s/n, 13½" x 20", pub TAP | 75.00 | — |
| ☐ **MAKING THE CIRCLE**, rel. 1980. ed. 2,250, s/n, 15⅞" x 20⅛", pub TAP | 75.00 | — |
| ☐ **AUTUMN MORNING RIDE**, rel. 1982. ed. 1,000, s/n, 16" x 24", pub TAP | 100.00 | — |
| ☐ **COOLING THE SUMMER HEAT**, rel. 1982. ed. 1,000, s/n, 16" x 25", pub TAP. | 100.00 | — |
| ☐ **SPRING RANGE**, rel. 1982. ed. 1,000, s/n, 16" x 24", pub TAP | 100.00 | — |
| ☐ **WINTER ROUNDUP**, rel. 1982. ed. 1,000, s/n, 16" x 23", pub TAP | 100.00 | — |

## JERRY CRANDALL

Collector of artifacts, researcher of original journals, books and newspapers, as well as student of old photographs, Jerry Crandall travels extensively throughout the West, drinking in the details that he puts on canvas back in his Riverside, California studio. His smaller pieces are painted in acrylics for their quickness, while his works that are 16" x 20" or larger are generally done in oils for their sense of depth and richness.

Crandall is a recognized authority on the American West. He served as technical consultant for the early segments of the television series, *Centennial,* and also for the movie, The Mountain Men, which starred Charlton Heston.

His work is in museums and many private collections including those of Robert Conrad, Jonathan Winters and Charlton Heston.

The paintings of Crandall reflect the richness and rough-hewn beauty of our Western heritage. The clothing and gear of the mountain man, Indians and cavalrymen were etched in vivid, forthright detail, reflecting the artist's lifelong commitment to authenticity.

He is listed in the 15th edition of *Who's Who in American Art;* and *Contemporary Western Artists* by Harold and Peggy Samuels. Also, he donated a percentage of proceeds from sale of his *Solitude* print to the American Indian Center of Columbus, Ohio.

**TROUBLE ON CLEAR CREEK** *by Jerry Crandall*

| JERRY CRANDALL | ISSUE PRICE | CURRENT PRICE |
|---|---|---|
| ☐ **SMOKE UP AHEAD**, rel. 1977. ed. 450, s/n, 20″ x 30″, pub Gl ............. | 60.00 | 450.00 |
| ☐ **"I FOUND THE PASS"**, rel. 1979. ed. 500, s/n, 20″ x 30″, pub Gl .......... | 60.00 | 350.00 |
| ☐ **PURSUED**, rel. 1979. ed. 525, s/n, 22″ x 27½″, pub Gl .................. | 60.00 | — |
| ☐ **ON TO TAOS**, rel. 1980, ed. 650, s/n, 16½″ x 24″, pub Gl ................ | 65.00 | — |
| ☐ **SHRINE TO THE BUFFALO**, rel. 1980. ed. 525, s/n, 21″ x 28″, pub Gl ....... | 65.00 | 450.00 |
| ☐ **CAUTION**, rel. 1981. ed. 650, s/n, 11″ x 14″, pub Gl ................... | 40.00 | Sold Out |
| ☐ **NOT ALONE**, rel. 1981. ed. 650, s/n, 20″ x 14″, pub Gl .................. | 55.00 | 100.00 |
| ☐ **COUREURS DES BOIS**, rel. 1982. ed. 650, s/n, 20½″ x 27½″, pub Gl ....... | 85.00 | — |
| ☐ **SOLITUDE**, rel. 1982. ed. 1,000, s/n, 19″ x 21″, pub Gl ................. | 75.00 | — |
| ☐ **AN EARLY SNOW**, rel. 1983. ed. 650, s/n, 18¾″ x 28″, pub SGL .......... | 85.00 | — |
| ☐ **TROUBLE ON CLEAR CREEK**, rel. 1983. ed. 750, s/n, 18″ x 27″, pub SGL .... | 85.00 | — |

# T. PHILLIP CROWE

"The more I am with nature, the more I am convinced that nothing is unusual in the animal kingdom," says Phillip Crowe. "To paint those memories so others can experience what my eyes have seen is my contribution to the viewer. Painting has to be an emotional experience."

Often honored, Crowe has won numerous Diamond Awards as well as an Addy Award in 1976. His illustrations have appeared on the covers of numerous national magazines.

**MALLARDS AT WINGMEAD** *by Phillip Crowe*

## T. PHILLIP CROWE

| | ISSUE PRICE | CURRENT PRICE |
|---|---|---|
| ☐ JANUARY MUD - **Canvasback,** ed. 300, s/n, 23" x 17½", litho, pub GSP..... | 30.00 | 60.00 |
| ☐ BACKWATER WOOD DUCKS, ed. 1,000, s/n, 18¾" x 22¼", litho, pub GSP... | 40.00 | — |
| 2,000, s/o,.................................................. | 25.00 | — |
| ☐ BEAVER CREEK RED - **Red Fox,** ed. 300, s/n, 24" x 19", litho, pub GSP...... | 30.00 | 45.00 |
| ☐ BUCK COUNTRY - **Deer,** ed. 1,000, s/n, 29" x 27⅞" ................... | 50.00 | |
| ed. 50, a/p, remarqued, litho, pub GSP .......................... | 100.00 | — |
| ☐ REELFOOT WINTER GUESTS - **Mergansers,** ed. 300, s/n, 23½ x 19", litho, pub GSP........................................... | 30.00 | 60.00 |
| ☐ TENNESSEE 1980-1981, **Duck Stamp Print,** rel. 1980. ed. 1,000, s/n, size not available, pub GSP.................................. | 100.00 | 200.00 |
| ed. 250, remarqued ................................... | 250.00 | — |
| ☐ THE OUTLAWS, rel. 1980. ed. 2,000, s/n, size not available, pub GSP ....... | 50.00 | 200.00 |
| ed. 100, remarqued, artist proofs ............................. | 100.00 | N/A |
| ☐ THE BANDITS, rel. 1981. ed. 2,000, s/n, 28" x 29", pub GSP ............. | 50.00 | Sold Out |
| ed. 100, remarqued, artist proofs ............................. | 100.00 | Sold Out |
| ☐ THE OLD MAN AND THE PUP, rel. 1981. ed. 2,000, s/n, 21½" x 28½", pub GSP.................................................. | 50.00 | — |
| ed. 100, remarqued, artist proofs ............................. | 100.00 | — |
| ☐ THE OLD TAYLOR PLACE, rel. 1981. ed. 1,000, s/n, 29½" x 21¾", pub GSP . | 65.00 | — |
| ed. remarqued, artist proofs ................................ | 125.00 | — |
| ☐ DECEMBER MORNING, rel. 1982. ed. 800, s/n, 29½" x 20½", pub GSP ..... | 75.00 | — |
| ed. 100, remarqued, artist proofs ............................. | 125.00 | — |
| ☐ NATIONAL RETRIEVER CLUB STAMP AND PRINT, rel. 1982. ed. N/A, 15" x 15", stamp and print, pub GSP ............................... | 125.00 | 350.00 |
| Watercolor remarques upon request .......................... | 250.00 | 455.00 |
| ☐ THE DUKES OF HAZARD, rel. 1982. ed. 2,500, s/n, 29½" x 20", pub GSP ... | 60.00 | — |
| ed. 100, remarqued, artist proofs ............................. | 110.00 | — |
| ☐ WHITETAILS, rel. 1982. ed. 1,500, s/n, 20½" x 22", pub GSP ........... | 75.00 | — |
| ed. 100, remarqued, artist proofs ............................. | 125.00 | — |

# DONALD V. CROWLEY

Born in Redlands, California, in 1926, Don Crowley has been fascinated by drawing and painting since earliest childhood. Service in the Merchant Marine and Navy enabled Crowley to enroll under the G.I. Bill in Art Center College, Los Angeles, where for five years he pursued a rigorous curriculum under strict discipline. It was here that he met his future wife "B.J." An interior decorator and fine artist in her own right, she takes an active interest in her husband's career.

After completing formal art training, Crowley headed for New York and a successful career in commercial illustration. He became a member of the Society of Illustrators in 1954. In 1973 he accepted an invitation to exhibit in a gallery in Tuscon, Arizona. One look at the Southwest convinced him that this was where he wanted to be. With the wholehearted approval of his family, he sold their Connecticut home and moved to Arizona.

Crowley now paints everything from still lifes to portraits, but concentrates on Paiute and Apache Indian women and children. Several times each year he visits the San Carlos Indian Reservation, making sketches and taking photographs. "I hope that through my work," he says, "these very special people will see in themselves the beauty and dignity that I see in them."

**THE LITTLEST APPACHE** *by Don Crowley*

## DONALD V. CROWLEY

| | ISSUE PRICE | CURRENT PRICE |
|---|---|---|
| ☐ **THE STARQUILT**, rel. 1978. ed. 1,000, s/n, 19" x 25½", pub GW . . . . . . . . . | 65.00 | 315.00 |
| ☐ **DORENA**, rel. 1978 . ed. 1,000, s/n, 23" x 24", pub GW . . . . . . . . . . . . . . . . . | 75.00 | 110.00 |
| ☐ **HUDSON'S BAY BLANKET**, rel. 1978. ed. 1,000, s/n, 20½" x 17", pub GW . . | 75.00 | 110.00 |
| ☐ **DESERT SUNSET**, rel. 1979. ed. 1,500, s/n, 19" x 25½", pub GW . . . . . . . . | 75.00 | 120.00 |
| ☐ **SECURITY BLANKET**, rel. 1979. ed. 1,500, s/n, 12½" x 16½", pub GW . . . . . | 65.00 | Sold Out |
| ☐ **ARIZONA MOUNTAIN MAN**, rel. 1979. ed. 1,500, s/n, 20" x 21", pub GW . . . . | 65.00 | 130.00 |
| ☐ **APACHE IN WHITE**, rel. 1980. ed. 1,500, s/n, 19½" x 32", pub GW . . . . . . . . | 85.00 | 200.00 |
| ☐ **BEAUTY AND THE BEAST**, rel. 1980. ed. 1,500, s/n, 19" x 23½", pub GW . . . | 85.00 | Sold Out |
| ☐ **THE LITTLEST APACHE**, rel. 1980. ed. 275, signed, titled and numbered, 19¹¹⁄₁₆" x 26¾", hand-drawn lithograph, pub GW . . . . . . . . . . . . . . . . . . . . . . | 325.00 | 475.00 |
| ☐ **AFTERGLOW**, rel. 1981. ed. 1,500, s/n, 27" x 22½", pub GW . . . . . . . . . . . . | 110.00 | Sold Out |
| ☐ **SHANNANDOAH**, rel. 1981. ed. 275, signed, titled and numbered, 20" x 25", hand-drawn lithograph, pub GW . . . . . . . . . . . . . . . . . . . . . . . . . . . . . . . . . | 325.00 | — |
| ☐ **THE HEIRLOOM**, rel. 1981. ed. 1,000, s/n, 21¾" x 34¾", pub GW . . . . . . . . | 125.00 | 375.00 |
| ☐ **EAGLE FEATHERS**, rel. 1981. ed. 1,500, s/n, 24½" x 21½", pub GW . . . . . . . | 95.00 | Sold Out |
| ☐ **HOPI BUTTERFLY**, rel. 1982. ed. 275, signed, titled and numbered, 20" x 25", hand-drawn lithograph, pub GW . . . . . . . . . . . . . . . . . . . . . . . . . . . . . . . | 350.00 | — |

# CHARLES T. CRUME, JR.

Charles Crume's illstrated column "Nature Notes" which ran in Kentucky Standard newspaper, caught the attention of Frank H. Bunce, Manager of Bernheim Forest, a 10,000 acre privately operated area in Bullitt and Nelson Counties, and the subsequent offer of a position as Chief Naturalist with Bernheim Forest.

**EASTERN KINGBIRD** *by Charles T. Crume, Jr.*

Crume says, "The association with Bernheim Forest was a major turning point in my life. It allowed me to spend each day close to the things I paint and the opportunity of close and intimate contact with people experienced in the nature fields."

Crume has been a member of the faculty at Western Kentucky University, Bowling Green, Kentucky as Interpretive Naturalist and Lecturer in Residence. He is currently involved in Western Kentucky Heritage Project, which will eventually document much of Kentucky's history and folklore on Educational Television, radio, film strips and tape.

## CHARLES T. CRUME, JR.

| | ISSUE PRICE | CURRENT PRICE |
|---|---|---|
| ☐ **IRONWEED** - Plate I, rel. 1967. ed. 4,500, s/o, 17" x 22", litho, | | |
| pub CCNA/MRH | — | 40.00 |
| ed. 500, s/n | — | 50.00 |
| ☐ **GOLDENROD** - Plate II, rel. 1968. ed. 4,500, s/o, 17" x 22", litho, | | |
| pub CCNA/MRH | — | 40.00 |
| ed. 500, s/n | — | 50.00 |
| ☐ **LARGE MOUTH BASS** - Plate III, rel. 1968. ed. 4,500, s/o, 17" x 22", litho, | | |
| pub CCNA/MRH | — | 65.00 |
| ed. 500, s/n | — | 80.00 |
| ☐ **BLUE JAY** - Plate IV, rel. 1968. ed. 4,500, s/o, 17" x 22", litho, | | |
| pub CCNA/MRH | — | 40.00 |
| ed. 500, s/n | — | 45.00 |
| ☐ **MALE CARDINAL** - Plate V, rel. 1969. ed. 4,500, s/o, 17" x 22", litho, | | |
| pub CCNA/MRH | — | 60.00 |
| ed. 500, s/n | — | 80.00 |
| ☐ **SPARROW** - Plate VI*, rel. 1969. ed. 4,500, s/o, pub CCNA/MRH | — | 40.00 |
| ed. 500, s/n | — | 50.00 |
| (applies to complete set) | | |
| ☐ **WILDFLOWERS** - Plate VII*, rel. 1969. ed. 4,500, s/o, pub CCNA/MRH | — | * |
| ed. 500, s/n | — | * |
| *Sold as a set w/sparrow | | |
| ☐ **WILDFLOWERS** - Plate VIII*, rel. 1969. ed. 4,500, s/o, pub CCNA/MRH | — | * |
| ed. 500, s/n | — | * |
| ☐ **PHEASANT** - Plate IX, rel. 1970. ed. 4,500, s/o, pub CCNA/MRH | — | 65.00 |
| ed. 500, s/n | — | 80.00 |
| ☐ **FEMALE CARDINAL** - Plate X, rel. 1971. ed. 4,500, s/o, 17" x 22", litho, | | |
| pub CCNA/MRH | — | 40.00 |
| ed. 500, s/n | — | 55.00 |
| ☐ **KINGBIRD** - Plate XI, rel. 1972. ed. 4,500, s/o, 17" x 22", litho, | | |
| pub CCNA/MRH | — | 30.00 |
| ed. 500, s/n | — | 35.00 |
| ☐ **SPARROW HAWK** - Plate XII, rel. 1972. ed. 4,500, s/o, 17" x 22", litho, | | |
| pub CCNA/MRH | — | 40.00 |
| ed. 500, s/n | — | 50.00 |
| ☐ **GOLDFINCH** - Plate XIII, rel. 1972. ed. 4,500, s/o, 17" x 22", litho, | | |
| pub CCNA/MRH | — | 20.00 |
| ed. 500, s/n | — | 25.00 |
| ☐ **GREY FOX** - Plate XIV, rel. 1967. ed. 3,000, s/o, 20" x 24", litho, | | |
| pub CCNA/MRH | — | 35.00 |
| ed. 500, s/n | — | 45.00 |
| ☐ **CARDINAL PAIR** - Plate XV, rel. 1973. ed. 4,500, s/o, 17" x 22", litho, | | |
| pub CCNA/MRH | — | 50.00 |
| ed. 500, s/n | — | 70.00 |
| ☐ **MEADOW LARK** - Plate XVI, rel. 1973. ed. 3,000, s/o, 17" x 22", litho, | | |
| pub CCNA/MRH | — | 20.00 |
| ed. 500, s/n | — | 25.00 |
| ☐ **PLATED WOODPECKER** - Special Plate**, rel. 1973. ed. 3,000, s/o, 20" x 24", | | |
| litho, pub CCNA/MRH | — | 110.00 |
| ed. 500, s/n | — | 120.00 |
| ☐ **SPORTSMAN SERIES (QUAIL)** - Plate I, rel. 1974. ed. 1,500, s/n, 20" x 24", | | |
| litho, pub CCNA/MRH | — | 15.00 |

| | ISSUE PRICE | CURRENT PRICE |
|---|---|---|
| ☐ **KENTUCKY WILDCAST** ed. unknown, s/o, 16" x 20", pub MRH . . . . . . . . . . . | — | 25.00 |
| s/n . . . . . . . . . . . . . . . . . . . . . . . . . . . . . . . . . . . . . . . . . . . . . . . . . | — | 30.00 |

**Very rare-printed for Indiana University and sold for a scholarship fund.

# JIM DALY

With a mixture of Indian and Irish blood, Jim Daly is truly a product of America's melting pot, and it shows in his choice of subject matter. From the important events of history to the small incidents of everyday living, from the times when the Indian roamed the continent to the days of the Great Depression, he paints the faces of our people. Sometimes sentimental, at others dramatic, he is always sincere in his love of the land and the people he portrays.

Daly, born in Holdenville, Oklahoma, moved first to California, then to New Mexico and finally back to California. While in high school he won the Bullock Art Award. After graduation came a hitch in the army where he won a welterweight boxing championship in Panama. After the army, he entered the Art Center College of Design with his love of America intact and a strong desire to master the acrylic medium. His success can be judged from his painting.

The artist's desire for authenticity, supported by a large studio collection of costumes and artifacts, is never allowed to obscure his primary purpose in painting. The purpose is to establish an empathy between his canvas characters and the viewer.

**SPRING FEVER** by Jim Daly

Daly has been commissioned to paint covers for a number of magazines oriented toward Western history. He is represented in the permanent collection of the Favell Museum in Klamath Falls, Oregon, and was the 1981 winner of the Mill Pond Press Award at the Northwest Rendezvous in Helena, Montana.

**JIM DALY**

| | ISSUE PRICE | CURRENT PRICE |
|---|---|---|
| ☐ **SPRING FEVER,** rel. 1982. ed. 950, s/n, 20¼" x 24", pub MPPI .......... | 85.00 | — |

# ROBERT B. DANCE

Born in Tokyo, Japan, in 1934, Robert B. Dance moved to the United States, just prior to World War II. He is a graduate of the Philadelphia Museum College of Art, where he studied with among others, Henry C. Pitz, and W. Emerton Heitland.

Dance is regarded as one of the South's foremost realists. His work is included in numerous private and corporate collections. His watercolors have been featured in *American Artist, Southern World, Pace and other magazines. He is also featured in the book, 40 Watercolorists and How They Work* by Watson-Guptill Publications in New York and Sir Issac Pitman & Sons, Ltd. in Great Britain. He is winner of many first place awards in the North Carolina Watercolor Society juried shows, and has been represented in the "Realist Invitational" of the Southeastern Center for Contemporary Art. In 1960 his work was selected for the permanent print collection of the North Carolina Museum of Fine Art.

Dance's paintings are representive of the realistic pure watercolor technique which consits of no opaque white or white mixed with color. Rather, the paper is left clear for the whites, with tonal transitions accomplished by transparent washes of varying density. A sensitive feeling for atmosphere, combined with this intricate technique, forms the basis for these unusual watercolor reproductions.

**HANDY'S WHEEL**
*by Robert B. Dance*

## ROBERT B. DANCE

| | ISSUE PRICE | COLLECTOR PRICE |
|---|---|---|
| ☐ **GEMEIN HAUS**, rel. 1974. ed. 500, s/n, 22" x 28", pub. RI. | 50.00 | 350.00 |
| ☐ **FOLLOWING SUMMER**, rel. 1975. ed. 500, s/n, 22" x 24", pub. RI. | 50.00 | 150.00 |
| ☐ **BLUE RIDGE BREAKDOWN**, rel. 1976. ed. 500, s/n, 22" x 28", pub. RI. | 60.00 | 125.00 |
| ☐ **THE MARSHRIDERS**, rel. 1976. ed. 500, s/n, 19" x 25" (portfolio of 2), pub. RI. | 100.00 | 250.00 |
| ☐ **HANDY'S WHEEL**, rel. 1977. ed. 500, s/n, 20" x 9½", pub. RI. | 75.00 | 75.00 |
| ☐ **THE HOMEPLACE**, rel. 1977. ed. 500, s/n, 23" x 32", pub. RI. | 60.00 | 125.00 |
| ☐ **THE RIG**, rel. 1978. ed. 500, s/n, 17¼" x 17¼", pub. RI. | 50.00 | 150.00 |
| ☐ **CAPE LOOKOUT MORNING**, rel. 1979. ed. 500, s/n, 16⅝" x 25", pub. RI. | 75.00 | 175.00 |

# PETER DARRO

Boldly unique in the field of wildlife art are the paintings of Peter Darro. His rare ability to achieve meticulous accuracy in his subjects, without sacrificing any of their vibrant color and exciting vitality, is the result of a lifetime of intimate observation of nature.

Before finding artistic fulfillment in wildlife painting, his portraiture won him national fame. He painted Senator Everett M. Dirksen and Mrs. Dirksen for the Dirksen Memorial Library and his portrait of Rachel Carson is exhibited in the National Wildlife Hall of Fame.

Darro's animal paintings have led him to the top of his profession as an American artist. Leading publications such as *National Wildlife* and *American Field* regularly feature his works. His paintings and techniques appear in the international *Palette Talk Magazine.* He has been designated official American Field Hall of Fame Artist, and is a member of the eminent Society of Animal Artists. His works have been exhibited at the Cleveland Museum of Natural History, and are included in many prominent collections throughout the world.

As a muralist, his latest achievement is the 120 foot mural at the Glenview State Bank, Glenview, Illinois. This imposing work has as its theme the historical and ethical evolution of the American spirit.

His paintings have won high critical acclaim through exhibitions at fine galleries in such art centers as New York, Los Angeles, Baltimore, Houston and Milwaukee.

## PETER DARRO

| | | |
|---|---|---|
| ☐ **A LOT OF BULL**, ed. 950, s/n, 16" x 24", pub CGAL | 139.00 | 160.00 |
| ed. 12, Artist accented, s/n | 450.00 | 500.00 |
| ☐ **THE SENTINEL**, ed. 950, s/n, 19" x 24", pub CGAL | 139.00 | 160.00 |
| ed. 12, Artist accented, s/n | 450.00 | 500.00 |
| ☐ **INTREPID**, ed. 950, s/n, 19" x 21", pub CGAL | 139.00 | 160.00 |
| ed. 12, Artist accented, s/n | 450.00 | 500.00 |
| ☐ **BEWARE**, ed. 950, s/n, 19" x 21", pub CGAL | 139.00 | 160.00 |
| ed. 12, Artist accented, s/n | 450.00 | 500.00 |
| ☐ **MORNING, KUDU CALF**, ed. 950, s/n, 16½" x 24", pub CGAL | 139.00 | 160.00 |
| ed. 12, Artist accented, s/n | 450.00 | 500.00 |
| ☐ **ON GUARD**, ed. 950, s/n, 12" x 24", pub CGAL | 139.00 | 160.00 |
| ed. 12, Artist accented, s/n | 450.00 | 500.00 |
| ☐ **TRIPLE THREAT**, ed. 950, s/n, 10" x 24", pub CGAL | 139.00 | 160.00 |
| ed. 12, Artist accented, s/n | 450.00 | 500.00 |
| ☐ **CURIOUS, ZEBRA FOAL**, ed. 950, s/n, 24½" x 16½", pub CGAL | 139.00 | 160.00 |
| ed. 12, Artist accented, s/n | 450.00 | 500.00 |
| ☐ **HIS MAJESTY**, ed. 950, s/n, 21" x 17½", pub CGAL | 139.00 | 160.00 |
| ed. 12, Artist accented, s/n | 450.00 | 500.00 |
| ☐ **MASILAND**, ed. 950, s/n, 18" x 21", pub CGAL | 139.00 | 160.00 |
| ed. 12, Artist accented, s/n | 450.00 | 500.00 |
| ☐ **CHARGE**, ed. 950, s/n, 16½" x 24", pub CGAL | 139.00 | 160.00 |
| ed. 12, Artist accented, s/n | 450.00 | 500.00 |

| | ISSUE PRICE | CURRENT PRICE |
|---|---|---|
| ☐ **KING OF THE MOUNTAIN**, ed. 950, s/n, 24″ x 17″, pub CGAL .............. | 160.00 | — |
| ed. 12, Artist accented, s/n ....................................... | 500.00 | — |
| ☐ **SUNNY AFTERNOON**, ed. 950, s/n, 24″ x 12″, pub CGAL ................. | 160.00 | — |
| ed. 12, Artist accented, s/n ....................................... | 500.00 | — |
| ☐ **ON THE PROWL**, ed. 950, s/n, 24″ x 17″, pub CGAL .................... | 160.00 | — |
| ed. 12, Artist accented, s/n ....................................... | 500.00 | — |
| ☐ **FROSTY MORNING**, ed. 950, s/n, 24″ x 17″, pub CGAL ................. | 160.00 | — |
| ed. 12, Artist accented, s/n ....................................... | 500.00 | — |
| ☐ **ALASKAN PARADISE**, ed. 950, s/n, 24″ x 17″, pub CGAL................. | 160.00 | — |
| ed. 12, Artist accented, s/n ....................................... | 500.00 | — |
| ☐ **HUNTING BUDDIES**, ed. 950, s/n, 24⅝″ x 25″, pub CGAL ................ | 160.00 | — |
| ed. 12, Artist accented, s/n ....................................... | 500.00 | — |
| ☐ **KILIMANJAROL**, ed. 950, s/n, 23″ x 15″, pub CGAL..................... | 160.00 | — |
| ☐ **ON THE PLAIN**, ed. 950, s/n, 23″ x 17″, pub CGAL .................... | 160.00 | — |

# RAY DAVENPORT

Although his training was in advertising design at Pratt Institute in New York City, Ray Davenport turned exclusively to fine art after 24 years in the commercial field. Davenport is best known for his meticulous brushwork and attention to fine detail, a result of this early technical training. His work is highly realistic. From nostalgic, rich rural scenes and antique still lifes to complete design studies, his strong realistic style shows.

Davenport has been voted membership in Allied Artists of America and the National Socity of Painters in Casein and Acrylic, both in New York. He is also affiliated with the Guild of South Carolina Artists and the South Carolina Watercolor Society.

**WINTER THAW** by Ray Davenport

## RAY DAVENPORT

| | ISSUE PRICE | CURRENT PRICE |
|---|---|---|
| ☐ **BYGONE SUMMER,** ed. 1,500, s/n, 20″ x 26″, pub FFFAI | 40.00 | — |
| ☐ **GOLDEN AUTUMN,** ed. 1,500, s/n, 20″ x 26″, pub FFFAI | 40.00 | — |
| ☐ **WAY BACK WHEN,** ed. 1,500, s/n, 20″ x 26″, pub FFFAI | 40.00 | — |
| ☐ **WINTER THAW,** ed. 1,500, s/n, 20″ x 26″, pub FFFAI | 40.00 | — |

# LOWELL DAVIS

**BIRTH OF BLOSSOM** *by Lowell Davis*

| | | |
|---|---|---|
| ☐ **PLUM TUCKERED OUT,** rel. 1981. ed. 900, s/n, 19″ x 21½″, pub SB | 75.00 | — |
| ed. 100, remarqued | 100.00 | — |
| ☐ **DUKE'S MIXTURE,** rel. 1981. ed. 900, s/n, 13½″ x 17″, pub SB | 75.00 | — |
| ed. 100, remarqued | 100.00 | — |
| ☐ **SURPRISE IN THE CELLAR,** rel. 1981. ed. 900, s/n, 19″ x 21½″, pub SB | 75.00 | — |
| ed. 100, remarqued | 100.00 | Sold Out |
| ☐ **BIRTH OF BLOSSOM,** rel. 1982. ed. 400, s/n, 15″ x 18″, pub SB | 125.00 | — |
| ed. 50, remarqued | 200.00 | — |
| ☐ **BUSTIN' WITH PRIDE,** rel. 1982. ed. 900, s/n, 13½″ x 17″, pub SB | 75.00 | — |
| ed. 100, remarqued | 100.00 | — |
| ☐ **FOXFIRE FARM,** rel. 1982. ed. 800, s/n, 7″ x 23″, pub SB | 125.00 | — |
| ed. 100, remarqued | 200.00 | — |
| ☐ **SUPPERTIME,** rel. 1982. ed. 400, s/n, 14″ x 18″, pub SB | 125.00 | — |
| ed. 50, remarqued | 200.00 | — |

# RICK DAVIS

| | | |
|---|---|---|
| ☐ **TRIBUTE TO THE KING,** ed. 20,503 | 25.00 | 50.00 |

**TRIBUTE TO THE KING** *by Rick Davis*

# RAY DAY

Ray Day holds a Master of Fine Arts degree in painting and sculpture. His creative experiences abound in diversity as they cross the lines dividing the visual and the performing arts. In addition to teaching art on the secondary level for over seventeen years, Day has continued an interest in theater by staging and directing over thirty-five major musicals and dramas for high school and community theater.

Day has always been charmed by the rustic and lured to the rural areas for his subject matter. His interest in preserving familiar rural scenes of manmade structures and roadside advertising of the past has developed into the *Old Road Series*. His interest in creating tasteful still-life compositions with a touch of the nostalgic has resulted in the *Country Cousins Series*.

Fluid, spontaneous color combined with a keen sense of accuracy of the subject are characteristic of a Day watercolor. Each of the watercolor reproductions is painted "vignette style". The image of the painting is allowed to "float" in the white space of the print permitting no hard edges to form around the painting.

The artists helps us recreate in our "mind's eye" the delights of our youth. Wind, weather and time have taken their toll and a wonderful part of the nation's rural image is nearly gone. *The Old Road* collection captures the end of that era.

**THE OLD MILL** *by Ray Day*

| RAY DAY | ISSUE PRICE | CURRENT PRICE |
|---|---|---|
| **THE OLD ROAD SERIES** | | |
| ☐ **MAIL POUCH BARN, PLATE I**, rel. 1973.ed. 500, s/n, 20″ x 24″, distr. MMFC | 15.00 | 100.00 |
| ed. 2,000, s/o | 10.00 | 75.00 |
| ☐ **ROCK CITY BARN, PLATE II**, rel. 1974. ed. 500, s/n, 20″ x 24″. distr. MMFC . | 15.00 | 75.00 |
| ed. 2,000, s/o | 10.00 | 30.00 |
| ☐ **BURMA SHAVE COUNTRY, PLATE III**, rel 1975. ed. 500, s/n, 16″ x 20″, distr. MMFC | 15.00 | 35.00 |
| ed. 2,000, s/o | 10.00 | — |
| ☐ **COCA-COLA COUNTRY, PLATE IV**, rel. 1977. ed. 750, s/n, 18″ x 24″, distr. MMFC | 20.00 | 100.00 |
| ed. 1,250, s/o | 15.00 | 50.00 |
| ☐ **COUNTRY GENERAL STORE, PLATE V**, rel. 1979. ed. 1,000, s/n, 16″ x 20″, distr. MMFC | 25.00 | — |
| ☐ **THE OLD MILL, PLATE VI**, rel. 1980. ed. 1,000, s/n, 22″ x 17½″, distr. MMFC | 25.00 | 65.00 |
| ☐ **AN OLD COVERED BRIDGE, PLATE VII**, rel. 1981. ed. 1,000, s/n, 17½″ x 22″, distr. MMFC | 35.00 | — |
| ☐ **COUNTRY STATION, PLATE VIII**, rel. 1981. ed. 1,000, s/n, 17½″ x 22″, distr. MMFC | 35.00 | — |
| ☐ **MAIL POUCH, MAIL POUCH, PLATE IX**, rel. 1982. ed. 1,000, s/n, 16″ x 24″, distr. MMFC | 35.00 | — |
| ☐ **COUNTRY CHURCH, PLATE X**, rel. 1982. ed. 1,000, s/n, 17½″ x 22″, distr. MMFC | 35.00 | — |

|  | ISSUE PRICE | CURRENT PRICE |
|---|---|---|
| ☐ **REEL REFRESHING, PLATE XI,** rel. 1983. ed. 1,000, s/n, 22″ x 17″, distr. MMFC | 35.00 | — |
| **THE COUNTRY COUSINS SERIES** | | |
| ☐ **POP'S CORN, PLATE I,** rel. 1976. ed. 500, s/n, 12″ x 14″, distr. MMFC | 10.00 | 30.00 |
| ed. 500, s/o | 7.50 | 30.00 |
| ☐ **MOTHER'S BASKET, PLATE II,** rel. 1976. ed. 500, s/n, 12″ x 14″, distr. MMFC | 10.00 | 30.00 |
| ed. 500, s/o | 7.50 | 30.00 |
| ☐ **STRAWBERRIES AND DAISIES, PLATE III,** rel. 1978. ed. 1,000, s/n, 16″ x 20″, distr. MMFC | 25.00 | 125.00 |
| ☐ **EGGS IN THE BASKET, PLATE IV,** rel. 1979. ed. 1,000, s/n, 14½″ x 18″, distr. MMFC | 25.00 | — |
| ☐ **PUMPKINS AND JUGS, PLATE V,** rel. 1980. ed. 1,000, s/n, 15″ x 15″, distr. MMFC | 30.00 | — |
| ☐ **GERANIUMS, PLATE VI,** rel. 1981. ed. 1,000, s/n, 14″ x 17½″, distr. MMFC. | 30.00 | — |
| ☐ **THE COLLECTION, PLATE VII,** rel. 1981. ed. 1,000, s/n, 15″ x 17″, distr. MMFC | 30.00 | — |
| ☐ **PEACHES ON THE PORCH, PLATE VIII,** rel. 1982. ed. 1,000, s/n, 15″ x 18″, distr. MMFC | 30.00 | — |
| ☐ **HONEYSUCKLE AND ROSES, PLATE IX,** rel. 1983. ed. 1,000, s/n, 12½″ x 17″, distr. MMFC | 30.00 | — |

# CHUCK DEHAAN

Chuck DeHaan's paintings present a purity that is in keeping with the spirit of the West, past and present.

DeHaan's work has appeared on the covers of practically all the major livestock magazines west of the Mississippi. In the past he also illustrated school books and book covers. He turned his attention to the finer arts a few years ago, and since that time his work has been almost exclusively in oils and sculpture.

DeHaan lives on a ranch in West Texas. The ranch is also the setting of most of his paintings. While he rarely uses a model, preferring to paint the life he lives, he does make notes and sketches for later use. He is also a believer in thorough research for greater authenticity.

His works hang in the Western Horseman Art Gallery in Colorado Springs, the Trammell Gallery in Fort Worth, and the Overland Trail Gallery in Scottsdale, Arizona and Jackson, Wyoming.

## CHUCK DEHAAN

| | | |
|---|---|---|
| ☐ **CROSSIN' HORSE CREEK,** ed. 750, s/n, 29″ x 21½″, distr. GI | 100.00 | — |
| ☐ **FOGGY MORNIN' WAIT,** ed. 650, s/n, 24″ x 19¼″, distr. GI | 75.00 | Sold Out |
| ☐ **FORGIN' THE KEECHI,** ed. 650, s/n, 20″ x 30″, distr. GI | 85.00 | Sold Out |
| ☐ **KEEP A MOVIN' DAN,** ed. 750, s/n, 21″ x 17″, distr. GI | 85.00 | — |
| ☐ **MACTAVISH,** ed. 650, s/n, 22½″ x 25½″, distr. GI | 75.00 | Sold Out |
| ☐ **RIDIN' OL' PAINT,** ed. 750, s/n, 21″ x 17″, distr. GI | 85.00 | Sold Out |
| ☐ **STRAWBERRY ROAN,** ed. 750, s/n, 21″ x 17″, distr. GI | 85.00 | — |
| ☐ **SURPRISE ENCOUNTER,** ed. 750, s/n, 22″ x 18″, distr. GI | 85.00 | Sold Out |
| ☐ **TEXAS PANHANDLE,** ed. 650, s/n, 19¼″ x 24″, distr. GI | 75.00 | Sold Out |
| ☐ **THE CIRCLE,** ed. 1,000, s/n, 18½″ x 25″, distr. GI | 30.00 | — |
| ☐ **THREE OF A KIND,** ed. 1,000, s/n, 22½″ x 28½″, distr. GI | 30.00 | — |

# TOM DE JONG

| | | |
|---|---|---|
| ☐ **BIRDS AND BRANCH,** ed. 325, s/o, size not available, silk screen, pub EWG | — | 90.00 |
| ☐ **COUNTRY FAIR,** ed. 325, s/o, size not available, silk screen, pub EWG | — | 90.00 |
| ☐ **DANISH VILLAGE,** ed. 325, s/o, size not available, silk screen, pub EWG | — | 90.00 |

| | ISSUE PRICE | CURRENT PRICE |
|---|---|---|
| ☐ **DOG WALKER,** ed. 150, s/n, 16″ x 24″, silk screen etching, pub EWG . . . . . . | — | 175.00 |
| ☐ **ICE CREAM LADY,** ed. 150, s/n, 16″ x 24″, silk screen etching, pub EWG . . . . | — | 175.00 |
| ☐ **IN THE PARK,** ed. 150, s/n, 16″ x 24″, silk screen etching, pub EWG . . . . . . . | — | 150.00 |
| ☐ **NUTS,** ed. 150, s/n, 11″ x 21″, silk screen etching, pub EWG . . . . . . . . . . . . | — | 125.00 |
| ☐ **STORM AT SEA,** ed. 325, s/o, size not available, silk screen, pub EWG . . . . . . | — | 90.00 |
| ☐ **THE SINGER,** ed. 150, s/n, 16″ x 24″, silk screen etching, pub EWG . . . . . . . | — | 175.00 |

# JACK DeLONEY

Jack DeLoney was born and reared on a farm near Ozark, Alabama, so the bright realistic paintings depicting rural scenes and activities reflect the things with which he is very familiar.

DeLoney spends his studio hours painting well-designed watercolors which demonstrate directness and purity through economy of brushstrokes. Though his watercolors have a definite masculine flair, spontaneous splashes of color yield sparkling transparency and delicacy.

Regional and national juried art competitions have placed significant awards on DeLoney's works. He is a member of the Southern Watercolor Society and is listed in *Who's Who In American Art.* Articles featuring his work have appeared in *Northlight, Grassroots South, Art Voices/South* and other publications.

**NOONDAY SUN** *by Jack DeLoney*

## JACK DeLONEY

| | | |
|---|---|---|
| ☐ **MONDAY'S WASH,** ed. 1,000, s/n, 13″ x 29″, pub CS . . . . . . . . . . . . . . . . . | 25.00 | — |
| ☐ **SUPER PUMPKIN,** ed. 1,000, s/n, 19″ x 25″, pub CS . . . . . . . . . . . . . . . . . | 20.00 | — |
| ☐ **RIVERBOTTOM COTTON,** rel. 1976. ed. 1,000, s/n, 19″ x 25″, pub CS . . . . . . | 20.00 | 200.00 |

| | ISSUE PRICE | CURRENT PRICE |
|---|---|---|
| ☐ **WRAPPED FOR WINTER,** ed. 1,000, s/n, 11″ x 16″, pub CS | 25.00 | — |
| ☐ **NOONDAY SUN,** ed. 1,000, s/n, 19″ x 23¼″, pub CS | 35.00 | 100.00 |
| ☐ **WHEN COTTON WAS KING,** rel. 1979. ed. 1,000, s/n, 20½″ x 26¼″, pub CS . | 45.00 | 150.00 |
| ☐ **END OF AN ERA,** rel. 1982. ed. 800, s/n, pub CS | 65.00 | 130.00 |

## LISETTE DeWINNE

Lisette DeWinne was born in Antwerp, Belgium and received an early art education in Europe, developing out of her Flemish tradition into an impressionistic painter. Her style is figurative with an abstract effect created through the colorful backgrounds of gracefully conceived portraits. She keeps her palette bright and warm and prefers not to blend her strong colors. Because of her powerful brush strokes and assured use of the palette knite, the over all effect is brushy rather than smooth, a quality that the lithographs have faithfully captured.

DeWinne has pursued her career in California since 1957, studying with several contemporary artists. She has developed her talents for evoking the inner warmth and feelings of her subjects in an expansive harmony of color, and capturing those rare private moments, sometimes happy, sometimes sad, that are part of the human experience.

A master in oils, DeWinne's pieces range from portraits to modern semi-representational and non-representational art. DeWinne has had many one woman shows in leading galleries. Her work has been featured in national art magazines and can be found in numerous distinguished private and public collections. The Royal Doulton Company, chose DeWinne's work to be featured on a series of limited edition collectors plates.

### LISETTE DeWINNE

| | | |
|---|---|---|
| ☐ **GYPSY MOTHER,** rel. 1978. ed. 175, s/n, 24″ x 30″, pub WAEL | 125.00 | Sold Out |
| ☐ **MIRELLE,** rel. 1978. ed. 950, s/n, 24″ x 30″, pub WAEL | 125.00 | Sold Out |
| ☐ **MUSICIANS,** rel. 1978. ed. 950, s/n, 24″ x 30″, pub WAEL | 125.00 | Sold Out |
| ☐ **TOM,** rel. 1978. ed. 950, s/n, 20″ x 23″, pub WAEL | 90.00 | — |
| ☐ **VILLAGE CHILD,** rel. 1978. ed. 175, s/n, 24″ x 30″, pub WAEL | 125.00 | Sold Out |
| ☐ **BRIGHTER DAY,** rel. 1979. ed. 950, s/n, 24″ x 30″, pub WAEL | 140.00 | — |
| ☐ **DEBRA,** rel. 1979. ed. 950, s/n, 20″ x 23″, pub WAEL | 90.00 | — |
| ☐ **SCARAMOUCHE,** rel. 1979. ed. 325, s/n, 24″ x 30″, pub WAEL | 100.00 | — |
| ☐ **WE THREE,** rel. 1979. ed. 950, s/n, 20″ x 23″, pub WAEL | 140.00 | — |
| ☐ **AT THE WINDOW,** rel. 1982. ed. 300, s/n, size N/A, pub CIL | 295.00 | — |
| ☐ **GRETCHEN,** rel. 1982. ed. 300, s/n, size N/A, pub CIL | 295.00 | — |

## LARRY DODSON

Larry Dodson traveled throughout the country sketching, drawing, and taking photographs. He knows his subjects, and he paints them as he knows them.

Dodson grew up in an area which is portrayed in most of his art, Trenton, a North Georgia community.

Having had no formal art training, Dodson's style and technique began to develop while he was still in school. The demand for his original art increased to a point where limited edition prints began to be published from his works. Currently there are nearly one hundred of his original works of art in private collections throughout the south.

## LARRY DODSON

| | ISSUE PRICE | CURRENT PRICE |
|---|---|---|
| ☐ **SPRINGTIME IN ELIJAY,** rel. 1975. ed. 1,000, s/n, 18″ x 19″, pub SGL | 20.00 | 175.00 |
| ed. 100 artist proofs | 40.00 | 250.00 |
| ☐ **CURING BARN,** rel. 1976. ed. 1,000, s/n, 16″ x 23″ | 20.00 | 100.00 |
| ed. 100 artist proofs | 40.00 | 150.00 |
| ☐ **MOUNTAIN VIEW ROAD,** rel. 1976. ed. 1,000, s/n, 22″ x 14″, pub SGL | 25.00 | 150.00 |
| ed. 100 artist proofs | 50.00 | 200.00 |
| ☐ **MISTY SUMMER DAY,** rel. 1976. ed. 1,000, s/n, 24″ x 17″, pub SGL | 30.00 | 150.00 |
| ed. 100 artist proofs | 50.00 | 200.00 |
| ☐ **SPRING AWAKENING,** rel. 1977. ed. 1,000, s/n, 23″ x 15″, pub SGL | 30.00 | 250.00 |
| ed. 100 artist proofs | 50.00 | 250.00 |
| ☐ **APRIL MORNING,** rel. 1977. ed. 1,500, s/o, 22¼″ x 15½″, pub SGL | 20.00 | 60.00 |
| ed. 1,000, s/n | 30.00 | 90.00 |
| ed. 100 artist proofs | 50.00 | 125.00 |
| ☐ **AUTUMN MIST,** rel. 1977. ed. 1,500, s/n, 24″ x 14¼″, pub SGL | 20.00 | 60.00 |
| ed. 1,000, s/n | 30.00 | 75.00 |
| ed. 100 artist proofs | 50.00 | 125.00 |
| ☐ **WINTER REFLECTION,** rel. 1977. ed. 1,500, s/o, 22½″ x 17¾″, pub SGL | 25.00 | — |
| ed. 1,000, s/n | 50.00 | 125.00 |
| ed. 100 artist proofs | 75.00 | 125.00 |
| ☐ **MOUNTAIN BREEZE,** rel. 1978. ed. 1,250, s/o, 22¼″ x 14¾″, pub SGL | 25.00 | 50.00 |
| ed. 1,500, s/n | 35.00 | 75.00 |
| ed. 100 artist proofs | 50.00 | 100.00 |
| ☐ **LAUREL RIDGE,** rel. 1978. ed. 1,250, s/o, 22″ x 15¼″, pub SGL | 25.00 | — |
| ed. 1,500, s/n | 35.00 | — |
| ed. 100 artist proofs | 50.00 | — |
| ☐ **TEA KETTLE/WATER PAIL,** rel. 1978. ed. 3,000, s/o, 8″ x 8″, pub SGL | *15.00 | — |
| ed. 100 artist proofs | 25.00 | — |
| *Sold as a pair | | |
| ☐ **YELLOW CREEK,** rel. 1978. ed. 1,250, s/o, 23″ x 15¼″, pub SGL | 25.00 | — |
| ed. 1,500, s/n | 35.00 | — |
| ed. 100 artist proofs | 50.00 | — |
| ☐ **GOLDEN HARVEST,** rel. 1979. ed. 1,500, s/n, 22½″ x 17½″, pub SGL | 45.00 | — |
| ed. 100 artist proofs | 75.00 | — |
| ☐ **SECLUDED TRAIL/TRAIL'S END,** rel. 1979. ed. 1,000, s/o, 9½″ x 12″, pub SGL | *30.00 | — |
| ed. 100 artist proofs | 50.00 | — |
| *Sold as a pair | | |
| ☐ **PEACEFUL MEADOW,** rel. 1979. ed. 1,500, s/n, 23″ x 18½″, pub SGL | 45.00 | Sold Out |
| ed. 100 artist proofs | 75.00 | — |
| ☐ **WINTER AT CHIMNEY TOPS,** rel. 1979. ed. 1,500, s/n, 23″ x 19¼″, pub SGL | 45.00 | — |
| ed. 100 artist proofs | 75.00 | — |

# BEV DOOLITTLE

Bev Doolittle is a Western artist who has never had any doubt about her life's career. Her parents provided the first inspiration. "Somehow they saw promise in my scribbles," she says. Recognition and encouragement followed. "It was a pretty straight road for me."

Doolittle's subject matter is provided by the outdoors. "I love nature," she says. "I try to look beyond the obvious and create unique, meaningful paintings depicting our Western wilderness and its inhabitants. I start with a concept and attempt to convey it through strong design coupled with detailed realism. I want people to *think* when they look at my paintings.

This young artist's talents in the medium of transparent watercolor are winning her a growing following across the West. A member of the National Watercolor Society, she has been active in its exhibitions. She has also participated in two annual shows of the American Watercolor Society in New York City. Her paintings are included in the Favell Museum of Western Art and Indian Artifacts, Klamath Falls, Oregon; the IBM Corporate Art Collection, Tucson, Arizona; and numerous private collections.

**CHRISTMAS DAY, Give Or Take A Week** *by Bev Doolittle*

## BEV DOOLITTLE

| | ISSUE PRICE | CURRENT PRICE |
|---|---|---|
| ☐ **PINTOS,** rel. 1979. ed. 1,000, s/n, 21" x 21", pub GW | 65.00 | 1,375.00 |
| ☐ **BUGGED BEAR,** rel. 1980. ed. 1,000, s/n, 19½" x 19½", pub GW | 85.00 | 110.00 |
| ☐ **THE GOOD OMEN,** rel. 1980. ed. 1,000, s/n, 21⅛" x 32½", pub GW | 85.00 | 900.00 |
| ☐ **WHO!?,** rel. 1980. ed. 1,000, s/n, 12" x 28", pub GW | 75.00 | 100.00 |
| ☐ **SPIRIT OF THE GRIZZLY,** rel. 1981. ed. 1,500, s/n, 21" x 31½", pub GW | 150.00 | 700.00 |
| ☐ **UNKNOWN PRESENCE,** rel. 1981. ed. 1,500, s/n, 31" x 14¼", pub GW | 135.00 | 375.00 |
| ☐ **WOODLAND ENCOUNTER,** rel. 1981. ed. 1,500, s/n, 36" x 20", pub GW | 145.00 | 1,055.00 |
| ☐ **EAGLES FLIGHT,** rel. 1982. ed. 1,500, s/n, 35½" x 19½", pub GW | 185.00 | 900.00 |
| ☐ **CHRISTMAS DAY, GIVE OR TAKE A WEEK,** rel. 1983. s/n, 18½" x 19", pub GW | 80.00 | Sold Out |
| ☐ **ESCAPE BY A HARE,** rel. 1983. ed. 1,500, s/n, 16½" x 13¼", pub GW | 80.00 | 150.00 |
| ☐ **RUSHING WAR EAGLE,** rel. 1983. ed. 1,500, s/n, 28⅛" x 20½", pub GW | 150.00 | 500.00 |
| ☐ **RUNS WITH THUNDER,** rel. 1983. ed. 1,500, s/n, 22¼" x 33⅞", pub GW | 150.00 | Sold Out |
| ☐ **THE ART OF CAMOUFLAGE,** rel. 1983. ed. 2,000, s/n, 24" x 30", poster, pub GW | 55.00 | Sold Out |

# ANNE OPHELIA DOWDEN

Anne Ophelia Dowden has raised botanical drawing to a fine art. Good plant portraiture demands, in addition to a knowledge and love of flowers, great technical skill and deep respect for design.

Though always an ardent student of nature, she turned to botanical painting only after many years in other fields of art. Under her maiden name Anne Ophelia Todd, she was teacher, mural painter, and textile designer until with the publication of her first book in 1961 she changed her professional signature to Dowden.

After a year at the University of Colorado, she graduated from Carnegie Institute of Technology. She taught briefly at Pratt Institute and then at Manhattanville College, where she administered the art department for more than twenty years.

At the same time, she continued as a creative artist, designing high-style fabrics and wallpapers. During a sabbatical, she made a large number of paintings of edible wild plants, some of which were published in *Life* magazine.

**CHRISTMAS PLANTS** *by Anne O. Dowden*

| ANNE O. DOWDEN | ISSUE PRICE | CURRENT PRICE |
|---|---|---|
| ☐ **FLOWERING DOGWOOD,** rel. 1969. ed. 5,000, so, 18″ x 23″, pub FHG . . . . . . . | 20.00 | 65.00 |
| This print was also offered as a free bonus to new members during the 1969-70 Audubon Society membership campaign in North Carolina. | | |
| ☐ **BUTTERFLY WEED,** rel. 1970. ed. 5,000, s/o, 10″ x 14″, pub FHG . . . . . . . . . | | |
| This print was also offered as a free bonus to new members during the 1970 Audubon Society Membership campaign in Michigan. | | |
| ☐ **GOLDENROD,** rel. 1970. ed. 3,500, s/o, 18″ x 22″, pub FHG . . . . . . . . . . . . . | 20.00 | 60.00 |
| ☐ **MUSHROOMS, (PORTFOLIO OF 6),** rel. 1970. ed 5,000, s/o, 6″ x 8″, pub FHG | 20.00 | 75.00 |
| One print signed by the artist constitutes signature for entire portfolio. | | |

| | ISSUE PRICE | CURRENT PRICE |
|---|---|---|
| ☐ SPRING FLOWERS/AUTUMN FLOWERS, pair, rel. 1970. ed. 2,500, s/o, 11" x 14", pub FHG | 20.00 | 85.00 |
| ☐ WILDFLOWERS OF THE PLAINS, rel. 1970. ed. 3,500, s/o, 18" x 22", pub FHG | 20.00 | 40.00 |
| ☐ CRAB APPLE/APRICOT, pair, rel. 1971. ed. 2,500, s/o, 10" x 13", pub FHG | 20.00 | 40.00 |
| ☐ FLAME AZALEA/PIEDMONT AZALEA, rel. 1971. ed. 2,500, s/o, 11" x 15", pub FHG | 20.00 | 75.00 |
| Of the above edition, 500 were with embossed seal printed exclusively for Callaway Gardens, Georgia. | | |
| ☐ PLUMLEAF AZALEA, rel. 1971. ed. 2,500, s/o, 16" x 20", pub FHG | 20.00 | 40.00 |
| Of the above edition, 500 were with embossed seal printed exclusively for Callaway Gardens, Georgia. | | |
| ☐ POMEGRANATE/GRAPE, pair, rel. 1971. ed. 2,500, s/o, 10" x 13", pub FHG | 20.00 | 40.00 |
| ☐ YELLOW BOUQUET, pair, rel. 1971. ed. 2,500, s/o, 11" x 14", pub FHG | 20.00 | 85.00 |
| ☐ HYBRID TEA ROSES/OLD ROSES, pair, rel. 1972. ed. 1,500, s/o, 12" x 18½", pub FHG | 20.00 | 50.00 |
| ☐ CAROLINA ROSE/CHEROKEE ROSE, pair, rel. 1973. ed. 1,500, s/o, 12" x 16", pub FHG | 20.00 | 40.00 |
| ☐ HERBS, (PORTFOLIO OF 6), rel. 1973. ed. 5,000, s/o, 6" x 9", pub FHG | 30.00 | 100.00 |
| One print signed by the artist constitutes signature for portfolio. | | |
| ☐ AMERICAN BEAUTY ROSE, rel. 1974. ed. 3,000, s/o, 14" x 12", pub FHG | 15.00 | — |
| ☐ BLACK-EYED SUSAN, rel. 1974. ed. 3,000, s/o, 14" x 12", pub FHG | 15.00 | 60.00 |
| ☐ FLOWERING DOGWOOD, rel. 1974. ed. 3,000, s/o, 14" x 12", pub FHG | 15.00 | 40.00 |
| ☐ GREAT LAUREL OR ROSE BAY, rel. 1974. ed. 3,000, s/o, 14" x 12", pub FHG | 15.00 | — |
| ☐ HOLDEN RHODODENDRON, rel. 1974. ed. 2,000, s/o, 16" x 20", pub FHG | 20.00 | Sold Out |
| ☐ FLOWERS OF THE FIELD/GARDEN OF HERBS, pair, rel. 1975. ed. 2,000, s/o, 22" x 16", pub FHG | 45.00 | — |
| ☐ FOOD FOR LIFE, rel. 1975. ed. 2,000, s/o, 22" x 30", pub FHG | 40.00 | — |
| ☐ PLANTS FOR THE TEMPLE/TREES OF THE LORD, pair, rel. 1975. ed. 2,000, s/o, 22" x 16", pub FHG | 45.00 | — |
| ☐ PRAIRIE SUNFLOWER, rel. 1977. ed. 600, s/o, 20" x 16", pub FHG | 35.00 | 60.00 |
| ☐ PRICKLY POPPY AND INDIAN PAINTBRUSH, rel. 1977. ed. 600, s/o, 20" x 16", pub FHG | 35.00 | 60.00 |
| ☐ CHRISTMAS PLANTS, rel. 1978. ed. 2,000, s/o, 20" x 16", pub FHG | 30.00 | — |
| ☐ MUSHROOMS FROM A DARK HUMID WOODS/MUSHROOMS FROM A SUNNY FOREST PATH, pair, rel. 1978. ed. 1,500, s/o, 14" x 11", pub FHG | 35.00 | Sold Out |
| ☐ SQUASH BLOSSOM, rel. 1978. ed. 600, s/o, 16" x 20", pub FHG | 40.00 | — |
| ☐ AUTUMN FOLIAGE, rel. 1979. ed. 2,000, s/o, 20" x 16", pub FHG | 35.00 | — |
| ☐ CAMELLIA and FLOWERING QUINCE, rel. 1979. ed. 600, s/o, 16" x 20", pub FHG | 40.00 | — |
| ☐ PEPPERS/ARTICHOKE, pair, rel. 1979. ed. 1,000, s/o, 14" x 11", pub FHG | 30.00 | — |
| ☐ MINIATURE BULB PAIR, pair, rel. 1980. ed. 1,500, i/o, 14" x 11", pub FHG | 40.00 | — |

## JACK DUMAS

| | | |
|---|---|---|
| ☐ MAN TRACKS, rel. 1982. ed. 850, s/o, size N/A, pub WWI | 75.00 | — |

## NOEL DUNN

A true sporting artist, Dunn specializes in watercolor, concentrating mainly on game birds in hunting situations. In addition to being a hunter, photographer and fine painter, he is also an avid decoy collector and an accomplished carver of life-size decoys and Premier mason miniatures. His work has been featured in a number of shows and his paintings and carvings can be found in collections throughout the United States.

## NOEL DUNN

| | ISSUE PRICE | CURRENT PRICE |
|---|---|---|
| ☐ CROSSING THE TOTE ROAD - RUFFED GROUSE, rel. 1981. ed. 500, s/n, size N/A, pub WWI | 65.00 | — |
| ☐ DOWNHILL FLUSH - CHUKAR, rel. 1982. ed. 450, s/n, size N/A, pub WWI | 75.00 | — |
| ☐ STILLWATER MARSH SPRIG, rel. 1982. ed. 450, s/n, size N/A, pub WWI | 75.00 | — |

# TOM DUNNINGTON

Tom Dunnington skillfully blends the sensitivity of the artist with the scientifically detailed accuracy of the ornithologist.

"Many of the impressions I saw and felt twenty and thirty years ago are in my paintings today. Each new work is a culmination of everything that has gone before it," he said.

Dunnington received his art training at the John Herron School of Art in Indianapolis and the American Academy of Art in Chicago. He has taught illustration for four years at Layton School of Art in Milwaukee and drawing at Chicago's Columbia College.

## TOM DUNNINGTON

| | | |
|---|---|---|
| ☐ AMERICAN BALD EAGLE #1, rel. 1971. ed. 4,700, s/o, 32" x 23", pub CHWA . | 30.00 | 60.00 |
| ed. 200, s/n | 100.00 | 225.00 |
| ed. 100 Artist proofs | | 175.00 |
| ☐ BALD EAGLE, rel. 1972. ed. 4,700, s/o, 17" x 23", pub CHWA | 40.00 | 60.00 |
| ed. 200, s/n | 70.00 | 140.00 |
| ed. 100 Artist proofs | | 150.00 |
| ☐ GOLDEN EAGLE, rel. 1972. ed. 4,700, s/o, 23" x 17", pub CHWA | 30.00 | 40.00 |
| ed. 200, s/n | 50.00 | 80.00 |
| ed. 100 Artist proofs | | 125.00 |
| ☐ GREAT PRAIRIE CHICKEN, rel. 1971. ed. 4,700, s/o, 17" x 23", pub CHWA | 20.00 | 40.00 |
| ed. 200, s/n | 70.00 | 140.00 |
| ed. 100 Artist proofs | | 150.00 |
| ☐ MASKED BOB WHITE, rel. 1973. ed. 4,700, s/o, 17" x 23", pub CHWA | 20.00 | 40.00 |
| ed. 200, s/n | 50.00 | 75.00 |
| ed. 100 Artist proofs | | 100.00 |
| ☐ PEREGRINE FALCON, rel. 1971. ed. 4,700, s/o, 23" x 17", pub CHWA | 20.00 | 40.00 |
| ed. 200, s/n | 70.00 | 150.00 |
| ed. 100 Artist proofs | | 175.00 |
| ☐ PILEATED WOODPECKER, rel. 1972. ed. 4,700, s/o, 17" x 23", pub CHWA . . . | 30.00 | 40.00 |
| ed. 200, s/n | 50.00 | 80.00 |
| ed. 100 Artist proofs | | 125.00 |
| ☐ RED TAIL HAWK, rel. 1972. ed. 4,700, s/o, 17" x 23", pub CHWA | 20.00 | 40.00 |
| ed. 200, s/n | 50.00 | 70.00 |
| ed. 100 Artist proofs | | 100.00 |
| ☐ THE OSPREY, rel. 1972. ed. 4,700, s/o, 17" x 23", pub CHWA | 20.00 | 40.00 |
| ed. 200, s/n | 50.00 | 80.00 |
| ed. 100 Artist proofs | | 125.00 |

# GILBERT DURAN

Gilbert Duran has never received any formal art training and owes his increasing mastery of the water-color medium to a very serious dedication to his life's work. He has never stopped his exploration of the different media, techniques and methods that enabled him to grow as an artist.

Duran's wildlife paintings are noted for very fine detail, but, most importantly, for an intense quality about them. One senses a deep feeling on the part of the artist that is reflected in the romantic style of his watercolors. Although one can detect an exactness of life in Duran paintings, it goes much further than a mere cold, illustrative quality that is representative of many artists who recreate wildlife. His works go beyond to the softness of nature, the warmness of life.

## GILBERT DURAN

| | ISSUE PRICE | CURRENT PRICE |
|---|---|---|
| ☐ ALONE, ed. Open, s/o, 24" x 31½" | 45.00 | — |
| ed. Open, unsigned | 25.00 | — |
| ☐ BENGAL TIGER, ed. 1,500, s/n, 30" x 24" | 50.00 | — |
| ed. 1,500, s/o | 40.00 | — |
| ☐ BOB WHITE QUAIL, ed. 500, s/n, 37½" x 24½" | 100.00 | Sold Out |
| ed. 1,500, n/o | 25.00 | Sold Out |
| ☐ DANGER MOMENT, ed. 600, s/n, 28" x 21½" | 40.00 | — |
| ☐ INSTANT OF QUIETNESS, ed. 600, s/n, 28" x 21½" | 40.00 | Sold Out |
| ☐ JAGUAR, ed. 1,500, s/n, 30" x 24" | 50.00 | — |
| ed. 1,500, s/o | 40.00 | — |
| ☐ MORNING DRINK, ed. 600, s/n, 28" x 21½" | 40.00 | Sold Out |
| ☐ MOURNING DOVES, ed. 500, s/n, 24½" x 37½", pub ALI | 100.00 | Sold Out |
| ed. 1,500, n/o | 25.00 | Sold Out |
| ☐ RIO TURKEY, ed. 1,500, s/n, 24" x 30" | 50.00 | — |
| ed. 1,500, s/o | 40.00 | — |
| ☐ SHORT STOP, ed. Open, s/o, 24" x 31½" | 45.00 | — |
| ed. Open, unsigned | 25.00 | — |
| ☐ THE LONELY ONE, ed. 600, s/n, 28" x 21½" | 40.00 | — |
| ☐ TURKEY, ed. 500, s/n, 37½" x 24½" | 100.00 | Sold Out |
| ed. 1,500, n/o | 25.00 | Sold Out |
| ☐ WHITETAIL DEER, ed. 1,500, s/n, 30" x 24" | 50.00 | — |
| ed. 1,500, s/o | 40.00 | — |
| ☐ WHITE WING DOVES, ed. 500, s/n, 24½" x 37", pub ALI | 100.00 | Sold Out |
| ed. 1,500, n/o | 25.00 | Sold Out |
| ☐ WOOD DUCK, ed. 600, s/n, 28" x 21½" | 40.00 | Sold Out |

# BURTON DYE

Burton Dye studied art at Watkins Institute in Nashville. It was from this training plus much study and work on his own that he developed his detailed technique for capturing in oils the warmth of rural America. This realistic style is influenced by his conviction that the splendor of nature is artistry at its best.

Dye's watercolors have been chosen for exhibition in many regional and national exhibits, including the Allied Artist of America Show in New York City. His prints have been sold in galleries in the U.S. and Canada.

## BURTON DYE

| | ISSUE PRICE | CURRENT PRICE |
|---|---|---|
| ☐ FALLS MILL, rel. 1975. ed. 1,000, s/n, 20" x 26", pub BDP | 30.00 | — |
| ed. 2,400, s/o | 20.00 | — |
| ☐ AUTUMN MEMORIES, rel. 1976. ed. 1,000, s/n, 27½" x 21½", pub BDP | 30.00 | 40.00 |
| ☐ COUNTRY AFTERNOON, rel. 1977. ed. 1,000, s/n, 15½" x 22¾", pub BDP | 30.00 | — |
| ☐ LAYNE'S GROCERY, rel. 1977. ed. 1,000, s/n, 15" x 21", pub BDP | 20.00 | — |
| ☐ RUSTY BUCKET, rel. 1978. ed. 3,000, s/o, 10½" x 12½", pub BDP | 7.00 | — |
| ☐ SUMMER DAY, rel. 1978. ed. 1,000, s/n, 15" x 22¾", pub BDP | 30.00 | — |
| ☐ WILD DAISIES, rel. 1978. ed. 3,000, s/o, 10½" x 12½", pub BDP | 7.00 | — |
| ☐ AFTERNOON SHADOWS, rel. 1979. ed. 1,500, s/o, 14" x 18", pub BDP | 15.00 | — |
| ☐ AUNT MATTIE'S PLACE, rel. 1980. ed. 500, s/n, 14½" x 25½", pub BDP | 30.00 | 60.00 |
| ☐ APPLE HARVEST, rel. 1981. ed. 1,000, s/n, 18" x 25", pub BDP | 35.00 | — |
| ☐ PEACEFUL STREAM, rel. 1981. ed. 1,000, s/n, 13½" x 17½", pub BDP | 20.00 | — |
| ☐ SNOWDRIFTS, rel. 1981. ed. 1,000, s/n, 13½" x 17½", pub BDP | 20.00 | — |
| ☐ MISTY MOUNTAIN TRAIL, rel. 1982. ed. 1,000, s/n, 17" x 22½", pub BDP | 30.00 | — |
| ☐ CRIB WATCH, rel. 1983. ed. 1,000, s/n, 18¾" x 24½", pub BDP | 35.00 | — |
| ☐ WINTER SOLITUDE, rel. 1983. ed. 1,000, s/n, 19" x 25", pub BDP | 40.00 | — |

**APPLE HARVEST** *by Burton Dye*

# LARRY DYKE

One does not simply view Larry Dyke's art, one is drawn into it. By combining softness with detail, his prints express an emotion that one can feel as well as see.

His only formal training included twenty hours of art courses at Baylor University, where he received his Bachelor of Arts degree in 1965. Dyke taught in the public schools for ten years and painted part-time for about five years prior to the summer of 1976, at which time he launched into art as a full-time profession. His West Texas roots have instilled in him a respect for the land and its relics, and his beliefs have inspired him to portray his subject matter as symbols embodying the teachings of the Bible. Dyke's philosophy that his artistic talent is a gift explains the most unique feature of his work — a scripture reference included with his signature.

| LARRY DYKE | ISSUE PRICE | CURRENT PRICE |
|---|---|---|
| ☐ COLLECTOR'S SUITE, MATTHEW 11:28, GENESIS 46:32, HEBREWS 8:13, rel. 1979. ed. 1,000, s/n, size varies, pub AMF | 48.00 | 105.00 |
| ed. 1,800, s/o, released in 1980 | 35.00 | 75.00 |
| ☐ DANIEL 2:21 (Racoon), rel. 1982. ed. 1,500, s/n, 16″ x 20″, pub AMF | 70.00 | 85.00 |
| ☐ ed. 2,500, s/o | 45.00 | 55.00 |
| ☐ DEUTERONOMY 28:8 (Barn & Windmill), rel. 1980. ed. 1,000, s/n, 16″ x 20″, pub AMF | 55.00 | 205.00 |
| ed. 1,800, s/o | 37.50 | 150.00 |
| ☐ ECCLESIASTES 3:1 (Turkeys), rel. 1982. ed. 1,500, s/n, 18½″ x 23½″, pub AMF | 70.00 | 90.00 |
| ☐ EZEKIEL 32:14 (Turkeys), rel. 1981. ed. 1,500, s/n, 15″ x 20″, pub AMF | 65.00 | 95.00 |
| ed. 2,500, s/o | 40.00 | 50.00 |
| ☐ EZEKIEL 34:15 (White cows), rel. 1980. ed. 1,000, s/n, 14″ x 24″, pub AMF | 55.00 | 95.00 |
| ed. 1,800, s/o | 37.50 | 85.00 |
| ☐ ISAIAH 40:3 (Stage coach), rel. 1978. ed. 1,000, s/n, 16″ x 20″, pub AMF | 40.00 | 240.00 |
| ed. 1,500, s/o | 30.00 | 125.00 |

|  | ISSUE PRICE | CURRENT PRICE |
|---|---|---|
| ☐ **ISAIAH 45:3 (Oil rig)**, rel. 1982. ed. 1,950, s/n, 18" x 22½", pub AMF . . . . . | 80.00 | 105.00 |
| ☐ **ISAIAH 58:8 (Horizontal windmill)**, rel. 1978. ed. 1,000, s/n, 16" x 20", pub AMF . . . . . . . . . . . . . . . . . . . . . . . . . . . . . . . . . . . . . . . . . . . . . | 35.00 | 285.00 |
| ☐ **JOB 39:8 (Elk)**, rel. 1982. ed. 1,500, s/n, 21" x 27", pub AMF . . . . . . . . . . | 70.00 | 100.00 |
| ☐ **JOHN 3:8 (Vertical windmill)**, rel. 1978. ed. 1,000, s/n, 16" x 20", pub AMF . | 30.00 | 650.00 |
| ☐ **JOHN 8:32 (Mountain panorama)**, rel. 1982. ed. Time-Limited, 1,500, s/n, 16" x 32", pub AMF . . . . . . . . . . . . . . . . . . . . . . . . . . . . . . . . . . . . . . . . | 85.00 | 95.00 |
| ☐ **JOHN 9:4 (Night scene)**, rel. 1979. ed. 1,000, s/n, 18" x 24", pub AMF . . . . . | 45.00 | 115.00 |
| ed. 2,000, s/o, released in 1981 . . . . . . . . . . . . . . . . . . . . . . . . . . . . . . . . | 30.00 | 75.00 |
| ☐ **JOHN 10:27 (Sheep & bluebonnets)**, rel. 1981. ed. 1,000, s/n, 16" x 20", pub AMF . . . . . . . . . . . . . . . . . . . . . . . . . . . . . . . . . . . . . . . . . . . . . . . . . | 60.00 | 115.00 |
| ed. 2,700, s/o . . . . . . . . . . . . . . . . . . . . . . . . . . . . . . . . . . . . . . . . . . . . . | 37.50 | 70.00 |
| ☐ **JOSHUA 2:22 (Mountain man)**, rel. 1982. ed. 1,500, s/n, 18" x 24", pub AMF | 70.00 | — |
| ed. 2,500, s/o . . . . . . . . . . . . . . . . . . . . . . . . . . . . . . . . . . . . . . . . . . . . . | 45.00 | — |
| ☐ **LAMENTATIONS 3:28 (Deer winter scene)**, rel. 1981. ed. 1,500, s/n, 18" x 24", pub AMF . . . . . . . . . . . . . . . . . . . . . . . . . . . . . . . . . . . . . . . . . . . | 68.00 | 115.00 |
| rel. 1982, ed. 2,500, s/o . . . . . . . . . . . . . . . . . . . . . . . . . . . . . . . . . . . . . | 45.00 | 75.00 |
| ☐ **MATTHEW 6:30 (Horse pastoral)**, rel. 1981. ed. Time-limited, s/n, 18" x 24", pub AMF . . . . . . . . . . . . . . . . . . . . . . . . . . . . . . . . . . . . . . . . . . . . . . . | 40.00 | 75.00 |
| ☐ **MATTHEW 9:37 (Corn patch)**, rel. 1981. ed. 1,000, s/n, 16" x 20", pub AMF . | 65.00 | 95.00 |
| ☐ **MATTHEW 18:12 (Sheep at gate)**, rel. 1983. ed. 1,500, s/n, 16" x 20", pub AMF . . . . . . . . . . . . . . . . . . . . . . . . . . . . . . . . . . . . . . . . . . . . . . . . . . . | 75.00 | 80.00 |
| ☐ **PROVERBS 8:25 (Horse)**, rel. 1979. ed. 1,000, s/n, 18" x 24", pub AMF . . . . . | 45.00 | 100.00 |
| ed. 1,800, s/o, released in 1981 . . . . . . . . . . . . . . . . . . . . . . . . . . . . . . . . | 30.00 | 65.00 |
| ☐ **PROVERBS 23:10 (Hereford cows)**, rel. 1981. ed. 1,000, s/n, 18" x 22½", pub AMF . . . . . . . . . . . . . . . . . . . . . . . . . . . . . . . . . . . . . . . . . . . . . . . . | 60.00 | 135.00 |
| ed. 2,200, s/o . . . . . . . . . . . . . . . . . . . . . . . . . . . . . . . . . . . . . . . . . . . . . | 37.50 | 95.00 |
| ☐ **PSALM 27:4 (Mission)**, rel. 1978. ed. 1,000, s/n, 18" x 24", pub AMF . . . . . . | 40.00 | 390.00 |
| ☐ **PSALM 42:1 (Deer & stream)**, rel. 1980. ed. 1,000, s/n, 18" x 24", pub AMF . | 55.00 | 220.00 |
| ed. 1,200, s/o . . . . . . . . . . . . . . . . . . . . . . . . . . . . . . . . . . . . . . . . . . . . . | 37.50 | 135.00 |
| ☐ **PSALM 90:2 (Mountain & lake)**, rel. 1981. ed. 1,500, s/n, 18" x 22½", pub AMF . . . . . . . . . . . . . . . . . . . . . . . . . . . . . . . . . . . . . . . . . . . . . . . . . | 67.50 | 100.00 |
| ed. 2,500, s/o . . . . . . . . . . . . . . . . . . . . . . . . . . . . . . . . . . . . . . . . . . . . . | 45.00 | 65.00 |
| ☐ **PSALM 91:1 (Squirrel)**, rel. 1980. ed. 1,000, s/n, 12" x 16", pub AMF . . . . . . | 45.00 | 65.00 |
| ed. 2,200, s/o . . . . . . . . . . . . . . . . . . . . . . . . . . . . . . . . . . . . . . . . . . . . . | 30.00 | 45.00 |
| ☐ **PSALM 113:3 (Bull)**, rel. 1979. ed. 1,000, s/n, 16" x 20", pub AMF . . . . . . . . | 40.00 | 125.00 |
| ed. 1,500, s/o, released in 1980 . . . . . . . . . . . . . . . . . . . . . . . . . . . . . . . . | 30.00 | 80.00 |
| ☐ **PSALM 147:16 (Christmas print)**, rel. 1979. ed. 1,000, s/n, 16" x 20", pub AMF . . . . . . . . . . . . . . . . . . . . . . . . . . . . . . . . . . . . . . . . . . . . . . . . . . . | 45.00 | 125.00 |
| ed. 1,200, s/o, released in 1980 . . . . . . . . . . . . . . . . . . . . . . . . . . . . . . . . | 30.00 | 95.00 |
| ☐ **REVELATION 21:6 (Waterfall)**, rel. 1980. ed. 1,000, s/n, 20" x 26½", pub AMF . . . . . . . . . . . . . . . . . . . . . . . . . . . . . . . . . . . . . . . . . . . . . . . . . . . | 55.00 | 625.00 |
| ed. 1,800, s/o . . . . . . . . . . . . . . . . . . . . . . . . . . . . . . . . . . . . . . . . . . . . . | 35.00 | 275.00 |
| ☐ **ROMANS 15:32 (Snow scene)**, rel. 1980. ed. 1,000, s/n, 16" x 20", pub AMF | 57.50 | 75.00 |
| ☐ **SONG OF SOLOMON 2:17 (Deer & Cactus)**, rel. 1979. ed. 1,000, s/n, 18" x 24", pub AMF . . . . . . . . . . . . . . . . . . . . . . . . . . . . . . . . . . . . . . . . . . . . . | 45.00 | 135.00 |
| ed. 1,800, s/o, released in 1980 . . . . . . . . . . . . . . . . . . . . . . . . . . . . . . . . | 30.00 | 80.00 |

# EYVIND EARLE

Born in New York, Eyvind Earle was an artist at an early age. He had his first one-man show in France at 14 and at 21 he opened at the Charles Morgan Galleries.

Earle joined Walt Disney Studios as an assistant background painter. Within two years he was promoted to color stylist and was responsible for the styling, background and colors for the successful and highly acclaimed Disney movie *Sleeping Beauty*.

Earle has a totally original perception of landscape. He captures the grandeur and simplicity of the American countryside. His landscapes are remarkable for their suggestion of distances, land masses and weather moods.

**GAVIOTA PASS** *by Eyvind Earle*

In addition to book illustrating, the artist has designed covers for national magazines and produced two television specials created entirely by himself. He is represented in many private collections throughout the country.

| EYVIND EARLE | ISSUE PRICE | CURRENT PRICE |
|---|---|---|
| ☐ **BIG SUR,** ed. 250, s/n, 26″ x 34″, serigraph, pub CFAC | — | 550.00 |
| ☐ **GREEN VALLEY,** ed. 275, s/n, 30″ x 32″, serigraph, pub CFAC | — | 500.00 |
| ☐ **HIDDEN VALLEY,** ed. 300, s/n, 25″ x 36″, serigraph, pub CFAC | — | 500.00 |
| ☐ **LANDSCAPE,** ed. 250, s/n, 34″ x 45″, serigraph, pub CFAC | — | 375.00 |
| ☐ **MIDNIGHT SNOW,** ed. 250, s/n, 28″ x 34″, serigraph, pub CFAC | — | 375.00 |
| ☐ **PRECIPICE,** ed. 275, s/n, 31″ x 36″, serigraph, pub CFAC | — | 450.00 |
| ☐ **RED BARN,** ed. 300, s/n, 24″ x 47″, serigraph, pub CFAC | — | 750.00 |
| ☐ **RED POPPIES,** ed. 250, s/n, 35″ x 46″, serigraph, pub CFAC | — | 600.00 |
| ☐ **SPRING SNOW,** ed. 275, s/n, 30″ x 37″, serigraph, pub CFAC | — | 375.00 |
| ☐ **THE SEA BELOW,** ed. 300, s/n, 25″ x 36″, serigraph, pub CFAC | — | 375.00 |
| ☐ **AUTUMN,** rel. 1979. ed. 300, s/n, 28″ x 22″, serigraph, pub HP | — | Sold Out |
| ☐ **BLACK EVERGREEN FOREST,** rel. 1979. ed. 300, s/n, 30″ x 40″, serigraph, pub HP | — | Sold Out |
| ☐ **BLUE PINE,** rel. 1979. ed. 300, s/n, 28″ x 20″, serigraph, pub HP | — | 550.00 |
| ☐ **MOUNTAIN RISE,** rel. 1979. ed. 300, s/n, 40″ x 20″, serigraph, pub HP | — | 650.00 |
| ☐ **SANTA YNEZ VALLEY,** rel. 1979. ed. 300, s/n, 20″ x 40″, serigraph, pub HP | — | Sold Out |
| ☐ **WINTER QUIET,** rel. 1979. ed. 300, s/n, 24″ x 36″, serigraph, pub HP | — | Sold Out |
| ☐ **ENCHANTED COAST,** rel. 1980. ed. 300, s/n, 40″ x 20″, serigraph, pub HP | — | Sold Out |
| ☐ **GOTHIC FOREST,** rel. 1980. ed. 300, s/n, 24″ x 36″, serigraph, pub HP | — | Sold Out |
| ☐ **AWAKENING,** rel. 1981. ed. 260, s/n, 30″ x 19″, serigraph, pub HP | — | 400.00 |
| ☐ **GIRL WITH RAVEN HAIR,** rel. 1981. ed. 260, s/n, 30″ x 20″, serigraph, pub HP | — | 400.00 |
| ☐ **SPRING,** rel. 1981. ed. 280, s/n, 22″ x 28″, serigraph, pub HP | — | Sold Out |
| ☐ **SUMMER,** rel. 1981. ed. 300, s/n, 22″ x 28½″, serigraph, pub HP | — | Sold Out |
| ☐ **VILLAGE,** rel. 1981. ed. 300, s/n, 20½″ x 16½″, serigraph, pub HP | — | 500.00 |
| ☐ **WINTER,** rel. 1981. ed. 300, s/n, 15″ x 30″, serigraph, pub HP | — | 500.00 |
| ☐ **AMERICAN BARNS,** rel. 1982. ed. 85, s/n, 12″ x 30″, serigraph, pub HP | — | 600.00 |
| ☐ **AUTUMN LEAVES,** rel. 1982. ed. 75, s/n, 12″ x 30″, serigraph, pub HP | — | 600.00 |
| ☐ **BLACK OAK,** rel. 1982. ed. 40, s/n, 20″ x 16″, serigraph, pub HP | — | 600.00 |

|  | ISSUE PRICE | CURRENT PRICE |
|---|---|---|
| ☐ **BIG SUR AND BRANCH,** rel. 1982. ed. 300, s/n, 10" x 8", serigraph, pub HP . | — | 250.00 |
| ☐ **CALIFORNIA SUITE,** a set of four prints, rel. 1982. ed. 100, s/n, 8" x 10", serigraph, pub HP | — | 1,600.00 |
| ☐ **EUCALYPTUS,** rel. 1982. ed. 85, s/n, 22" x 28", serigraph, pub HP | — | Sold Out |
| ☐ **SEVEN WHITE HORSES,** rel. 1982. ed. 40, s/n, 20" x 30", serigraph, pub HP . | — | Sold Out |
| ☐ **VALLEY,** rel. 1982. ed. 300, s/n, 8" x 10", serigraph, pub HP | — | 250.00 |
| ☐ **WINTER BARNS,** rel. 1982. ed. 85, s/n, 15" x 30", serigraph, pub HP | — | 600.00 |
| ☐ **WINTER BONZAI,** rel. 1982. ed. 85, s/n, 28" x 22", serigraph, pub HP | — | Sold Out |
| ☐ **CARMEL HIGHLANDS,** rel. 1983. ed. 85, s/n, 20" x 16", serigraph, pub HP .. | — | Sold Out |
| ☐ **CATTLE COUNTRY,** rel. 1983. ed. 150, s/n, 20" x 30", serigraph, pub HP.... | — | 650.00 |
| ☐ **CENTRAL PARK,** rel. 1983. ed. 200, s/n, 20" x 30", serigraph, pub HP | — | 600.00 |
| ☐ **GAVIOTA PASS,** rel. 1983. ed. 300, s/n, 20" x 30", serigraph, pub HP | — | Sold Out |
| ☐ **GREEN VALLEY,** rel. 1983. ed. 300, s/n, 20" x 30", serigraph, pub HP | — | — |
| ☐ **LAND OF THE MIDNIGHT SUN,** rel. 1983. ed. 85, s/n, 26" x 34", serigraph, pub HP. | — | 800.00 |
| ☐ **MEDIEVAL PROMENADE,** rel. 1983. ed. 85, s/n, 24" x 34", serigraph, pub HP | — | 800.00 |
| ☐ **MIDNIGHT BLUE,** rel. 1983. ed. 80, s/n, 30" x 20", serigraph, pub HP | — | 750.00 |
| ☐ **WINTER BARNS SUITE,** set of four prints, rel. 1983. ed. 100, s/n, 20" x 16", serigraph, pub HP | — | 1,600.00 |

# DON RICHARD ECKELBERRY

At the age of twelve Don Eckelberry began sketching birds with the aid of a pair of binoculars and a dime store bird guide. By the time he was fifteen, Eckelberry had organized a bird club, was writing nature columns for two newspapers, attending summer classes in art and had a one man show in Cleveland.

He studied at the Cleveland Institute of Art, traveling from coast to coast during vacations to "see more birds".

Eckelberry was a National Audubon Society artist when he decided to illustrate the *Audubon Bird Guides* which includes all of the North American birds north of Mexico.

Among his major works are the *Birds of the West Indies,* and *Life Histories of Central American Birds.*

## DON RICHARD ECKELBERRY

| | | |
|---|---|---|
| ☐ **CARIBBEAN HUMMINGBIRDS,** pair, rel. 1968. ed. 5,000, i/o, 14½" x 19", pub FHG | 25.00 | 45.00 |
| ☐ **FULVOUS TREE-DUCK,** rel. 1968. ed. 1,000, i/n, 26" x 23½", canvas, pub FHG | 35.00 | 50.00 |
| ed. 1,000, i/o, canvas | 25.00 | 40.00 |
| ☐ **PALM TANAGER/GRAYISH SALTATOR,** pair, rel. 1968. ed. 2,000, i/o, 22" x 26", pub FHG | 45.00 | 45.00 |
| ☐ **RED-BELLIED WOODPECKER,** rel. 1968. ed. 19,500, i/o, 14¾" x 11¼", pub FHG | — | 35.00 |
| Obtainable only with membership to National Audubon Society during 1968-69 Florida membership campaign. | | |
| ☐ **WHITE-EARED PUFFBIRD,** rel. 1969. ed. 5,000, s/o, 12" x 16", pub FHG .... | 10.00 | 45.00 |
| ☐ **BLUE-GRAY TANAGER,** rel 1970. ed. 2,500, i/o, 22" x 26", pub FHG | 20.00 | 50.00 |
| ☐ **WOOD DUCKS,** rel. 1970. ed. 3,000, s/o, 21" x 26", pub FHG | 20.00 | 30.00 |
| ☐ **BOBWHITE,** rel. 1971. ed. 5,000, i/o, 16" x 20", pub FHG | 20.00 | 50.00 |
| ☐ **MALLARD DRAKES RISING,** rel. 1971. ed. 1,000, i/n, 25" x 30", pub FHG ... | 65.00 | 100.00 |
| ed. 1,500, i/o | 50.00 | 75.00 |
| ☐ **SPRUCE GROUSE,** rel. 1971. ed. 2,000, i/o, 21" x 26", pub FHG | 20.00 | 50.00 |
| ed. 1,500, i/o, offered through Continental Magazine, Lincoln-Mercury Div., Ford Motor Co., to benefit National Wildlife Federation | 20.00 | 50.00 |
| ☐ **"ALERT AND READY",** (White Gyrfalcon), rel. 1972. ed. 1,000, s/n, 23" x 30½", pub FHG | 50.00 | 125.00 |
| ed. 1,500, s/o | 40.00 | 100.00 |
| ed. 1,000 signed and bearing a special insignia for the Association of Graduates, U.S. Air Force Academy | 40.00 | 100.00 |

| | ISSUE PRICE | CURRENT PRICE |
|---|---|---|
| ☐ **BLACK DUCKS OVER THE MARSH,** rel. 1972. ed. 3,000, i/n, 31″ x 23½″, pub FHG | 40.00 | 75.00 |
| ☐ **MOTTLED OWL,** rel. 1972. ed. 3,500, i/o, 18½″ x 23½″, pub FHG | 20.00 | 50.00 |
| ☐ **WOODCOCK AND YOUNG,** rel. 1972. ed. 3,500, i/o, 18″ x 23½″, pub FHG | 20.00 | 30.00 |
| ☐ **YELLOW-CROWNED NIGHT HERON/CAPPED HERON,** pair, rel. 1972. ed. 2,500, i/o, 10⅝″ x 22¼″, pub FHG | 30.00 | Sold Out |
| ☐ **CARDINAL,** rel. 1973. ed. 5,000, i/o, 17″ x 22″, pub FHG | 20.00 | 85.00 |
| ☐ **SKIMMERS,** rel. 1973. ed. 2,000, i/n, 42″ x 14¾″, pub FHG | 50.00 | 80.00 |
| ☐ **TRUMPETER SWAN,** rel. 1973. ed. 2,500, i/o, 31″ x 24½″, pub FHG | 50.00 | Sold Out |
| ☐ **WILD CANARY IN DAISIES,** rel. 1973. ed. 5,000, i/o, 19″ x 15½″, pub FHG | 20.00 | 50.00 |
| ☐ **GREAT BLACK-BACKED GULL,** rel. 1974. ed. 2,000, i/o, 28″ x 22½″, pub FHG | 40.00 | Sold Out |
| ☐ **MEADOWLARK,** rel. 1974. ed. 3,000, i/o, 18″ x 22½″, pub FHG | 35.00 | 70.00 |
| ☐ **GOLDEN-OLIVE WOODPECKER,** rel. 1975. ed. 2,000, i/o, 22″ x 26″, pub FHG | 30.00 | Sold Out |
| ☐ **WILD TURKEY,** rel. 1975. ed. 2,000, i/n, 20″ x 24″, pub FHG | 50.00 | — |
| This limited edition print was released in the AMERICA'S WILDLIFE HERITAGE PORTFOLIO, the portfolio consisting of six prints in all, each by a different Frame House Gallery artist. | | |
| ☐ **CANVASBACK OVER THE BAY,** rel. 1976. ed. 750, i/n, 14½″ x 21″, pub FHG | 50.00 | — |
| ☐ **RUFFED GROUSE,** rel. 1976. ed. 1,000, i/n, 18″ x 24″, pub FHG | 100.00 | — |
| ☐ **UPLAND GAME BIRD PORTFOLIO,** to consist of ten limited edition prints when completed. | | |
| ☐ **CALIFORNIA QUAIL,** rel. 1977. ed. 1,000, i/n, 18″ x 24″, pub FHG | 100.00 | — |
| ☐ **RING-NECK PHEASANT,** rel. 1977. ed. 500, i/n, 18″ x 24″, pub FHG | 100.00 | — |
| ☐ **BLUE GROUSE,** rel. 1978. ed. 500, i/n, 18″ x 24″, pub FHG | 100.00 | — |

## KATALIN EHLING

Katalin Ehling's work reflects the richness of the Southwest, sharing the beauty of the land, its people and their customs. She feels the Indian people of the pueblos are a special subject. "I work primarily with the colors, forms and patterns found in everyday pueblo life. I feel that I would be intruding if I used themes from their religious and ceremonial life." The result is intense colors and a warm, peaceful feeling.

Ehling studied at the American Academy of Art for two years and in Paris for another year.

| **KATALIN EHLING** | ISSUE PRICE | CURRENT PRICE |
|---|---|---|
| ☐ **PUEBLO SONG,** ed. 100, s/n, 22½″ x 30″, pub NWDHG | — | 300.00 |

## STUART EICHEL

Stuart Eichel was born in New York City in 1932 and grew up in Detroit, Michigan. He studied art at Cass Technical High School and The Society of Arts and Crafts in Detroit and graduated with a Bachelor of Fine Arts degree from New York's Pratt Institute. He worked for more than ten years as an art director and illustrator for some of Madison Avenue's top advertising agencies.

Later, he moved his family to Knoxville, Tennessee to become creative director for one of the Southeast's largest advertising agencies.

"Finding what I want to draw is half the fun," he says, "I love this part of the country — its beauty, its peace, the warmth and kindness of the people. Almost any road I go down I can find something I would like to draw."

**FLEA MARKET** *by Stu Eichel*

## STUART EICHEL

| | ISSUE PRICE | CURRENT PRICE |
|---|---|---|
| ☐ **51 YEARS SELLING ON BLOUNT AVE.**, rel. 1971. ed. 350, s/n, 16″ x 20″, pub TRAD | 15.00 | Sold Out |
| ☐ **COUNTRY STORE**, rel. 1972. ed. 500, s/n, 20″ x 16″, pub TRAD | 20.00 | Sold Out |
| ed. 500, s/o | 15.00 | — |
| ☐ **AMERICAN**, rel. 1973. ed. 500, s/n, 16″ x 20″, pub TRAD | 20.00 | Sold Out |
| ed. 500 s/o | 15.00 | — |
| ☐ **MARJORIE**, rel. 1973. ed. 500, s/n, 16″ x 20″, pub TRAD | 20.00 | Sold Out |
| ed. 500 s/o | 20.00 | Sold Out |
| ☐ **SMOKY MTN. 110**, rel. 1973. ed. 500, s/n, 20″ x 16″, pub TRAD | 25.00 | 35.00 |
| ed. 500 s/o | 20.00 | — |
| ☐ **TENNESSEE GOTHIC**, ed. 500, s/n, 16″ x 20″, pub TRAD | 25.00 | — |
| ed. 500 s/o | 15.00 | 35.00 |
| ☐ **WE'VE BEEN MEANING TO DO SOMETHING ABOUT THE GARAGE**, ed. 500, s/n, 20″ x 16″, pub TRAD | 20.00 | 35.00 |
| ed. 500 s/o | 20.00 | — |
| ☐ **CALL HOME**, rel. 1975. ed. 950, s/n, 16″ x 20″, pub TRAD | 25.00 | 35.00 |
| ☐ **THE MEETING PLACE**, rel. 1973. ed. 500, s/n, 20″ x 16″, pub TRAD | 25.00 | Sold Out |
| ed. 500, s/o | 20.00 | — |
| ☐ **GRANDMA'S HOUSE**, rel. 1974. ed. 950, s/n, 16″ x 20″, pub TRAD | 20.00 | Sold Out |
| ed. 500, s/o | 20.00 | — |
| ☐ **SATURDAY AFTERNOON**, ed. 950, s/n, 16″ x 20″, pub TRAD | 25.00 | 35.00 |
| ☐ **SOMEWHERE TO WAIT**, ed. 950, s/n, 16″ x 20″, pub TRAD | 25.00 | 35.00 |
| ☐ **LOW PRICES**, ed. 950, s/n, 20″ x 16″, pub TRAD | 25.00 | 35.00 |
| ☐ **THE LAST ESSO STATION**, ed. 950, s/n, 16″ x 10″, pub TRAD | 25.00 | 35.00 |
| ☐ **PORCH SITTIN'**, ed. 950, s/n, 20″ x 16″, pub TRAD | 25.00 | 35.00 |
| ☐ **BIG VALLEY GRIST MILL**, rel. 1978. ed. 950, s/n, 20″ x 16″, pub TRAD | 25.00 | 35.00 |
| ☐ **JULIA'S GLASS SHOP**, ed. 950, s/n, 20″ x 16″, pub TRAD | 25.00 | — |
| ed. 50, A/P | 25.00 | — |
| ☐ **THE U.S. MAIL**, ed. 350, s/n, 20″ x 16″, pub TRAD | 25.00 | 35.00 |
| ☐ **FLEA MARKET**, ed. 350, 20″ x 16″, pub TRAD | 25.00 | 35.00 |
| ☐ **BLOCKHEAD AND FRIENDS**, ed. 350, 20″ x 16″, pub TRAD | 25.00 | 35.00 |

# JOSEF EIDENBERGER

Josef Eidenberger started his artistic career as a landscape painter, showing great perception for the mood of the local countryside. In 1923 he enrolled in the famed Graphic Academy of Art in Vienna and studied under Professor Alfred Cossman. Starting with copper engraving, Eidenberger soon turned to etching as a medium. His specialized studies and love for subtle color led him to the complicated process of color etching.

His eye for detail and meticulous execution of each plate has brought him many commissions from city officials and members of the business communities throughout Europe, especially in Austria and Germany. In 1973 after visiting the United States for the first time he created a series of California etchings, adding a new dimension to his exquisity European scenes. In commemoration of the United States bicentennial celebration he was commissioned to do a series of color etchings of Williamsburg, Virginia. During the same year he was also commissioned to do etchings of the Utah State Capitol in Salt Lake City and scenes of the East and West Coast.

| JOSEF EIDENBERGER | ISSUE PRICE | CURRENT PRICE |
|---|---|---|
| ☐ SAN FRANCISCO, GOLDEN GATE BRIDGE, (miniature), 5¼″ x 4¾″, pub GI . . . | — | 44.00 |
| ☐ STANFORD UNIVERSITY, 9″ x 7¼″, pub GI . . . . . . . . . . . . . . . . . . . . . . . . . . . | — | 100.00 |
| ☐ CARMEL MISSION, 12¼″ x 9½″, pub GI . . . . . . . . . . . . . . . . . . . . . . . . . . . . | — | 150.00 |
| ☐ SAN FRANCISCO, PANORAMA, 11¾″ x 15¾″, pub GI . . . . . . . . . . . . . . . . . | — | 170.00 |
| ☐ PALACE GATE, AUSTRIA, VIENNA, 13″ x 8″, pub GI . . . . . . . . . . . . . . . . . . . | — | 110.00 |
| ☐ ST. STEPHAN'S INTERIOR, VIENNA, 18″ x 12¾″, pub GI . . . . . . . . . . . . . . . | — | 160.00 |
| ☐ ROOFTOPS OF VIENNA, 19½″ x 13″, pub GI . . . . . . . . . . . . . . . . . . . . . . . . | — | 170.00 |
| ☐ KARL'S CHURCH, VIENNA, 12¾″ x 10½″, pub GI . . . . . . . . . . . . . . . . . . . . . | — | 110.00 |
| ☐ PARLIAMENT - RINGSTRASSE, 18¼″ x 12¼″, pub GI . . . . . . . . . . . . . . . . . | — | 160.00 |
| ☐ CITY HALL - VIENNA, 16½″ x 12¼″, pub GI . . . . . . . . . . . . . . . . . . . . . . . . | — | 160.00 |
| ☐ SCHOENBRUNN CASTLE, 12″ x 8½″, pub GI . . . . . . . . . . . . . . . . . . . . . . . . | — | 90.00 |
| ☐ ST. STEPHAN'S SQUARE, VIENNA, 13¾″ x 10¾″, pub GI . . . . . . . . . . . . . . | — | 140.00 |
| ☐ TECHNOLOGICAL COLLEGE, 10¼″ x 9¾″, pub GI . . . . . . . . . . . . . . . . . . . . | — | 110.00 |
| ☐ SCHUBERT HOUSE, VIENNA, 9¾″ x 6¼″, pub GI . . . . . . . . . . . . . . . . . . . . | — | 46.00 |
| ☐ GENERAL VIEW, VIENNA, 9″ x 12½″, pub GI . . . . . . . . . . . . . . . . . . . . . . . . | — | 140.00 |
| ☐ BURGTHEATER, VIENNA, 11¾″ x 13½″, pub GI . . . . . . . . . . . . . . . . . . . . . . | — | 140.00 |
| ☐ FREYUNG SQUARE, VIENNA, 12½″ x 8¼″, pub GI . . . . . . . . . . . . . . . . . . . . | — | 90.00 |
| ☐ ST. STEPHAN'S INTERIOR, VIENNA, 19½″ x 14½″, pub GI . . . . . . . . . . . . . . | — | 170.00 |
| ☐ OPERA HOUSE, VIENNA, 13¾″ x 11″, pub GI . . . . . . . . . . . . . . . . . . . . . . . | — | 130.00 |
| ☐ GRABEN, VIENNA, 16¼″ x 16″, pub GI . . . . . . . . . . . . . . . . . . . . . . . . . . . . | — | 160.00 |
| ☐ ST. STEPHAN - ROOFTOPS, AUSTRIA, 14″ x 9¾″, pub GI . . . . . . . . . . . . . . | — | 140.00 |
| ☐ UNIVERSITY OF VIENNA, 14½″ x 11″, pub GI . . . . . . . . . . . . . . . . . . . . . . . | — | 140.00 |
| ☐ DACHSTEIN VIEW, AUSTRIA, 16¾″ x 12″, pub GI . . . . . . . . . . . . . . . . . . . . | — | 160.00 |
| ☐ CITY HALL, VIENNA, 4⅞″ x 3⅝″, pub GI . . . . . . . . . . . . . . . . . . . . . . . . . . | — | 44.00 |
| ☐ FIGARO HOUSE, VIENNA, 4⅞″ x 4⅛″, pub GI . . . . . . . . . . . . . . . . . . . . . . | — | 44.00 |
| ☐ BELVEDERE PALACE, VIENNA, 4⅞″ x 4⅛″, pub GI . . . . . . . . . . . . . . . . . . | — | 44.00 |
| ☐ PALACE GATE, VIENNA, 6″ x 3¾″, pub GI . . . . . . . . . . . . . . . . . . . . . . . . . | — | 44.00 |
| ☐ KARL'S CHURCH, VIENNA, 4⅞″ x 4⅛″, pub GI . . . . . . . . . . . . . . . . . . . . . | — | 44.00 |
| ☐ SCHOENBRUNN CASTLE, VIENNA, 4⅞″ x 4⅛″, pub GI . . . . . . . . . . . . . . . | — | 44.00 |
| ☐ OPERA HOUSE, VIENNA, 4⅞″ x 4⅛″, pub GI . . . . . . . . . . . . . . . . . . . . . . . | — | 44.00 |
| ☐ GENERAL VIEW, VIENNA, 4⅞″ x 4⅛″, pub GI . . . . . . . . . . . . . . . . . . . . . . | — | 44.00 |
| ☐ GRAZ, KREBSENKELLER, AUSTRIA, 5″ x 4¼″, pub GI . . . . . . . . . . . . . . . . | — | 44.00 |
| ☐ STALLBURGGASSE, VIENNA, 5¼″ x 3¾″, pub GI . . . . . . . . . . . . . . . . . . . . | — | 44.00 |
| ☐ MARIA AM GESTADE CHURCH, VIENNA, 4¾ x 4⅛″, pub GI . . . . . . . . . . . . | — | 44.00 |
| ☐ RATTENBEG, MINATURE, AUSTRIA, 6¾″ x 4¾″, pub GI . . . . . . . . . . . . . . . | — | 44.00 |
| ☐ MARIA THERESIA STREET, INNSBRUCK, 7¼″ x 5½″, pub GI . . . . . . . . . . . . | — | 50.00 |
| ☐ HEIBLING HOUSE, INNSBRUCK, 7¼″ x 5½″, pub GI . . . . . . . . . . . . . . . . . | — | 50.00 |
| ☐ CITY TOWER, INNSBRUCK, 7¼″ x 5½″, pub GI . . . . . . . . . . . . . . . . . . . . . | — | 50.00 |
| ☐ HERZOG-FRIEDRICH STREET, INNSBRUCK, 7¼″ x 5½″, pub GI . . . . . . . . . . | — | 50.00 |
| ☐ UNDER THE ARCHES, INNSBRUCK, 7¼″ x 5½″, pub GI . . . . . . . . . . . . . . . | — | 50.00 |
| ☐ OTTOBURG CASTLE, INNSBRUCK, 7¼″ x 5½″, pub GI . . . . . . . . . . . . . . . . | — | 50.00 |

| | ISSUE PRICE | CURRENT PRICE |
|---|---|---|
| ☐ ARCHWAY, EPPAN, TYROL, INNSBRUCK, 7½" x 5¼", pub Gl | — | 46.00 |
| ☐ VILLANDERS, AUSTRIA, 7¾" x 5½", pub Gl | — | 58.00 |
| ☐ PUERSTEIN, CHAPEL, AUSTRIA, 7¼" x 5½", pub Gl | — | 50.00 |
| ☐ DUERNSTEIN, MONASTARY, AUSTRIA, 10¼" x 7¼", pub Gl | — | 90.00 |
| ☐ DUERSTERN, MONASTARY, FROM THE DANUBE, AUSTRIA, 10¾" x 9¾", pub Gl | — | 90.00 |
| ☐ KIRCHBERG, AUSTRIA, 10½" x 10¼", pub Gl | — | 90.00 |
| ☐ KLOSTERNEUBERG, AUSTRIA, 11" x 9¼", pub Gl | — | 110.00 |
| ☐ KREMS ON THE DANUBE, 10¾" x 9½", pub Gl | — | 90.00 |
| ☐ POTTENBRUNN CASTLE, AUSTRIA, 12" x 9¾", pub Gl | — | 130.00 |
| ☐ SEEBENSTEIN CASTLE, AUSTRIA, 15¾" x 19½", pub Gl | — | 160.00 |
| ☐ SEMMERING CHAPEL, AUSTRIA, 11½" x 7¼", pub Gl | — | 90.00 |
| ☐ WEISSENKIRCHEN, AUSTRIA, 10½" x 9¾", pub Gl | — | 90.00 |
| ☐ PERCHTOLDSDORF, AUSTRIA, 9¾" x 8¾", pub Gl | — | 90.00 |
| ☐ SCHALLABURG CASTLE, AUSTRIA, 13" x 9¼", pub Gl | — | 90.00 |
| ☐ ST. STEPHAN'S SQUARE, VIENNA (Old), 15½" x 11", pub Gl | — | 110.00 |
| ☐ MELK, MONASTARY, AUSTRIA, 17½" x 13¾", pub Gl | — | 160.00 |
| ☐ ROOFTOPS, LENTZ, AUSTRIA, 14¾" x 10¾", pub Gl | — | 160.00 |
| ☐ STEYR, AUSTRIA, 12½" x 9¾", pub Gl | — | 130.00 |
| ☐ GOSAU GLACIER, AUSTRIA, 11½" x 9¼", pub Gl | — | 90.00 |
| ☐ DACHSTEIN, AUSTRIA, 12¾" x 9¾", pub Gl | — | 90.00 |
| ☐ ST. WOLFGANG, AUSTRIA, 13¾" x 16¾", pub Gl | — | 160.00 |
| ☐ *SAN FRANCISCO, CALIFORNIA STREET, 13" x 9", pub Gl | — | 150.00 |
| ☐ SAN FRANCISCO, GOLDEN GATE BRIDGE, 14¼" x 9½", pub Gl | — | 150.00 |
| ☐ GRAZ, KREBSENKELLER, LANDHOUSE, AUSTRIA, 16½" x 12¼", pub Gl | — | 160.00 |
| ☐ MAUSOLEUM, GRAZ, AUSTRIA, 15" x 11¼", pub Gl | — | 140.00 |
| ☐ ROHRBACH MOUNTAIN, AUSTRIA, 13½" x 9¼", pub Gl | — | 110.00 |
| ☐ LINZ, OLD TOWN, AUSTRIA, 11¾" x 8¾", pub Gl | — | 90.00 |
| ☐ LINZ, HOFGASSE, AUSTRIA, 14½" x 9", pub Gl | — | 90.00 |
| ☐ LANDHAUS, AUSTRIA, 12¼" x 9¼", pub Gl | — | 90.00 |
| ☐ PFARRGASSE, AUSTRIA, 11½" x 9¼", pub Gl | — | 140.00 |
| ☐ HALSTATT, AUSTRIA, 12¾" x 9", pub Gl | — | 90.00 |
| ☐ STEYR, OLD COURTHOUSE, AUSTRIA, 15½" x 13", pub Gl | — | 160.00 |
| ☐ KRUMAU, AUSTRIA, 13¾" x 10½", pub Gl | — | 140.00 |
| ☐ DACHSTEIN, SOUTHWALL, AUSTRIA, 15½" x 20½", pub Gl | — | 170.00 |
| ☐ SALZBURG, CASTLE, AUSTRIA, 9½" x 7½", pub Gl | — | 80.00 |
| ☐ SALZBERG, MARGARETHEN CHURCH, AUSTRIA, 9½" x 6½", pub Gl | — | 80.00 |
| ☐ ST. FLORIAN, MONASTERY, AUSTRIA, 13¼" x 9", pub Gl | — | 140.00 |
| ☐ INNSBRUCK, GOLDEN ROOF, AUSTRIA, 10½" x 8¾", pub Gl | — | 90.00 |
| ☐ INNSBRUCK, MARIO THERESIA STREET, AUSTRIA, 17¼" x 13¾", pub Gl | — | 170.00 |
| ☐ CITY TOWER, INNSBRUCK, 14¼" x 10¼", pub Gl | — | 150.00 |
| ☐ HERZOG-FRIERICH STREET, INNSBRUCK, 14¼" x 10¼", pub Gl | — | 150.00 |
| ☐ STUBEN IN WINTER, AUSTRIA, 10¼" x 8", pub Gl | — | 90.00 |
| ☐ KITZBUEHEL, AUSTRIA, 12¼" x 9½", pub Gl | — | 130.00 |
| ☐ HOETTING, CHURCH, INNSBRUCK, 10½" x 8¾", pub Gl | — | 90.00 |
| ☐ FELDKIRCH MARKET, INNSBRUCK, 11¾" x 9¾", pub Gl | — | 130.00 |
| ☐ EPPAN, SOUTH TYROL, INNSBRUCK, 9½" x 6¾", pub Gl | — | 90.00 |
| ☐ SALZBURG, GENERAL VIEW, AUSTRIA, 10" x 13", pub Gl | — | 140.00 |
| ☐ LANGKOFEL MOUNTAIN, AUSTRIA, 12½" x 15", pub Gl | — | 150.00 |
| ☐ MATTERHORN, SWITZERLAND, 15" x 11½", pub Gl | — | 160.00 |
| ☐ EISENSTADT, HAYDN HOUSE, INNSBRUCK, 11" x 8½", pub Gl | — | 90.00 |
| ☐ FORCHTENSTEIN, INNSBRUCK, 14½" x 11", pub Gl | — | 130.00 |
| ☐ KOTTINGBRUNN CASTLE, AUSTRIA, 11½" x 9¾", pub Gl | — | 140.00 |
| ☐ GOISERN, AUSTRIA, 10½" x 8¾", pub Gl | — | 140.00 |
| ☐ DUERNSTEIN, AUSTRIA, 8¾" x 6½", pub Gl | — | 110.00 |
| ☐ HOETTING, AUSTRIA (Small), 9½" x 7", pub Gl | — | 90.00 |
| ☐ DOLOMITES, WINTER, AUSTRIA, 10½" x 13¾", pub Gl | — | 140.00 |
| ☐ DOLOMITES, SUMMER, AUSTRIA, 10½" x 12/", pub Gl | — | 140.00 |
| ☐ BAD GASTEIN, AUSTRIA, 10" x 13", pub Gl | — | 130.00 |
| ☐ KARL'S CHURCH, VIENNA (Large), 18½" x 15½", pub Gl | — | 170.00 |
| ☐ WEISSENKIRCHEN, AUSTRIA (Large), 14½" x 12½", pub Gl | — | 130.00 |
| ☐ ALT AUSSEE, AUSTRIA, 9" x 12¼", pub Gl | — | 90.00 |
| ☐ SALZBURG, ST. PETER'S GATE, AUSTRIA, 13¾" x 9¾", pub Gl | — | 110.00 |
| ☐ DELFT, SWITZERLAND (Oval), 10½" x 7", pub Gl | — | 140.00 |

| | ISSUE PRICE | CURRENT PRICE |
|---|---|---|
| ☐ ST. WOLFGANG, AUSTRIA (Oval), 10½″ x 7″, pub Gl | — | 140.00 |
| ☐ POTTERY SHOP, AUSTRIA, 12¾″ x 10¼″, pub Gl | — | 130.00 |
| ☐ STUTTGART, GERMANY, 13¼″ x 9¾″, pub Gl | — | 150.00 |
| ☐ BONN, CITY HALL, 9¾″ x 12¾″, pub Gl | — | 150.00 |
| ☐ DUDRSTADT, GERMANY, 12¾″ x 10″, pub Gl | — | 150.00 |
| ☐ BUEDINGEN, TOWN GATE, GERMANY, 13¼″ x 10″, pub Gl | — | 150.00 |
| ☐ DIEPHOLZ CASTLE, GERMANY, 13½″ x 11¼″, pub Gl | — | 150.00 |
| ☐ OLD TOWN DUESSELDORF, 14¾″ x 12¾″, pub Gl | — | 160.00 |
| ☐ HEIDELBERG, ROOFTOPS, 12½″ x 9¾″, pub Gl | — | 150.00 |
| ☐ KAUB ON THE RHINE, GERMANY, 12½″ x 9½″, pub Gl | — | 150.00 |
| ☐ MUNICH, GERMANY, 12¾″ x 9½″, pub Gl | — | 150.00 |
| ☐ NORTHSEA, GREETSIEL, 9¾″ x 12¾″, pub Gl | — | 150.00 |
| ☐ ULM ON THE DANUBE, 10″ x 12¼″, pub Gl | — | 150.00 |
| ☐ XANTEN, GERMANY, 13¾″ x 10½″, pub Gl | — | 150.00 |
| ☐ CASTLE DYCK, GERMANY, 10½″ x 13¾″, pub Gl | — | 150.00 |
| ☐ HAMBURG, HARBOR, GERMANY, 11¾″ x 16¾″, pub Gl | — | 160.00 |
| ☐ SAILBOAT HARBOR, HAMBURG, 12¼″ x 10¼″, pub Gl | — | 150.00 |
| ☐ HEIDELBERG, GERMANY, 12½″ x 10″, pub Gl | — | 150.00 |
| ☐ HEIDELBERG CASTLE COURTYARD, 13″ x 9½″, pub Gl | — | 150.00 |
| ☐ MAIKAMMER, GERMANY, 9½″ x 13″, pub Gl | — | 150.00 |
| ☐ NEUHARDINGSIEL, GERMANY, 10½″ x 14½″, pub Gl | — | 150.00 |
| ☐ OTTENDORF, GERMANY, 10¾″ x 13¼″, pub Gl | — | 150.00 |
| ☐ ROTHENBURG, PLOENLEIN, 12½″ x 10½″, pub Gl | — | 150.00 |
| ☐ ROEDER GATE, TORHENBURG, 12¼″ x 10″, pub Gl | — | 150.00 |
| ☐ BLACKSMITH SHOP, AUGSBURG, 12½″ x 10″, pub Gl | — | 150.00 |
| ☐ CASTLE BENRATH, GERMANY, 13¼″ x 9½″, pub Gl | — | 150.00 |
| ☐ BONN, BEETHOVEN HOUSE, GERMANY, 12¾″ x 9½″, pub Gl | — | 150.00 |
| ☐ DUISBERG, AROUND 1820, 13¾″ x 9¾″, pub Gl | — | 150.00 |
| ☐ CASTLE GEMEN, GERMANY, 9″ x 13¼″, pub Gl | — | 150.00 |
| ☐ MICHEL, HAMBURG, GERMANY, 13½″ x 9½″, pub Gl | — | 150.00 |
| ☐ COLOGNE, PROMENADE, 9½″ x 13″, pub Gl | — | 150.00 |
| ☐ KREUZNACH, GERMANY, 9″ x 13″, pub Gl | — | 150.00 |
| ☐ MARL, GERMANY, 9¼″ x 13½″, pub Gl | — | 150.00 |
| ☐ MICHELSTADT, GERMANY, 13½″ x 9¾″, pub Gl | — | 150.00 |
| ☐ DRESDEN, GERMANY, 11¼″ x 15¼″, pub Gl | — | 150.00 |
| ☐ DUISBERG, AROUND 1850, 11¾″ x 14¾″, pub Gl | — | 150.00 |
| ☐ DUSSELDORF, AROUND 1850, 12¼″ x 16″, pub Gl | — | 160.00 |
| ☐ HILDESHEIM, GERMANY, 13¼″ x 10″, pub Gl | — | 150.00 |
| ☐ COLOGNE, AROUND 1890, 9½″ x 12½″, pub Gl | — | 150.00 |
| ☐ COLOGNE, DEUTZER BRIDGE, 9½″ x 14¼″, pub Gl | — | 150.00 |
| ☐ ST. MARTIN'S 1820, COLOGNE, 9¾″ x 13¾″, pub Gl | — | 150.00 |
| ☐ ROTHENBURG, GERMANY, 13¼″ x 10″, pub Gl | — | 150.00 |
| ☐ TUEBINGER, GERMANY, 12½″ x 10″, pub Gl | — | 150.00 |
| ☐ ZONS, GERMANY, 13¾″ x 10½″, pub Gl | — | 150.00 |
| ☐ VENICE CANAL, ITALY, 14¾″ x 11¾″, pub Gl | — | 160.00 |
| ☐ RIALTO BRIDGE, VIENNA, 9″ x 7½″, pub Gl | — | 90.00 |
| ☐ SAIL BOATS, VENICE, 14″ x 13¼″, pub Gl | — | 160.00 |
| ☐ NUREMBERG, GERMANY, 15″ x 11½″, pub Gl | — | 130.00 |
| ☐ MARKTBREIT, GERMANY, 10″ x 17″, pub Gl | — | 100.00 |
| ☐ ULM ON THE BLAU, GERMANY, 10″ x 7½″, pub Gl | — | 100.00 |
| ☐ REGENSBURG IN WINTER, GERMANY, 9¾″ x 13½″, pub Gl | — | 100.00 |
| ☐ PRAGUE, TYN CHURCH, VENICE, 12½″ x 9″, pub Gl | — | 130.00 |
| ☐ DIEPHOLZ CASTLE, GERMANY, 15¾″ x 12½″, pub Gl | — | 150.00 |
| **THE HERITAGE COLLECTION** | | |
| ☐ PHILADELPHIA, INDEPENDENCE HALL, 20″ x 24″, pub Gl | — | 170.00 |
| ☐ MOUNT VERNON, 21″ x 27″, pub Gl | — | 170.00 |
| ☐ MONTICELLO, 21″ x 27″, pub Gl | — | 170.00 |
| ☐ HERMITAGE, 21″ x 27″, pub Gl | — | 170.00 |
| **SCENES FROM WILLIAMSBURG, VIRGINIA** | | |
| ☐ PUBLIC GOAL, 16″ x 17″, pub Gl | — | 140.00 |
| ☐ BURTON PARISH CHURCH, 19″ x 22″, pub Gl | — | 160.00 |
| ☐ THE CAPITOL, 19″ x 22″, pub Gl | — | 160.00 |
| ☐ WRENN BUILDING, 19″ x 22″, pub Gl | — | 160.00 |
| ☐ GOVERNOR'S PALACE, 19″ x 22″, pub Gl | — | 160.00 |

| | ISSUE PRICE | CURRENT PRICE |
|---|---|---|
| ☐ CARTER'S GROVE PLANTATION, 19" x 22", pub Gl | — | 160.00 |
| ☐ WINTER, 16" x 17", pub Gl | — | 140.00 |
| ☐ HAWAIIAN SUNSET, 6¼" x 8", pub Gl | — | 100.00 |
| ☐ HAWAII, 8¾" x 11", pub Gl | — | 150.00 |
| ☐ SAN FRANCISCO FOG, 8" x 10¾", pub Gl | — | 140.00 |
| ☐ TRACKS IN THE SNOW, 4½" x 6¼", pub Gl | — | 50.00 |
| ☐ ST. OSWALD, 9" x 12¹/₈", pub Gl | — | 140.00 |
| ☐ ROTHENBURG, KLINGER GATE, pub Gl | — | 130.00 |
| ☐ ROTHENBURG STILLER WINKEL, pub Gl | — | 130.00 |
| ☐ IN HOLLAND, MINIATURE, pub Gl | — | 38.00 |
| ☐ SPLIT PERISTYL, pub Gl | — | 100.00 |
| ☐ IERMOSS, AUSTRIA | — | 160.00 |
| ☐ DELFT, HORIZONTAL | — | 150.00 |
| ☐ SCHERMERHORN, HOLLAND | — | 150.00 |
| ☐ MOEDLING, AUSTRIA | — | 140.00 |
| ☐ PRINZENSTEIN, OVAL | — | 140.00 |
| ☐ OLD FARM IN AUSTRIA | — | 140.00 |
| ☐ MUEHLVIERTEL, AUSTRIA | — | 180.00 |
| ☐ DEFREGGEN VALLEY, AUSTRIA, OVAL | — | 140.00 |
| ☐ WEISSENKIRCHEN, COURTYARD | — | 160.00 |
| ☐ KARL'S CHURCH IN WINTER | — | 110.00 |
| ☐ MARIA AM GESTADE, VIENNA | — | 150.00 |
| ☐ WHARF | — | 160.00 |
| ☐ SAN FRANCISCO FISHERMAN'S WHARF | — | 170.00 |
| ☐ WATERFRONT | — | 170.00 |
| ☐ UTAH STATE CAPITOL, SALT LAKE CITY | — | 150.00 |
| ☐ IN WINTER, MINATURE | — | 44.00 |
| ☐ YOSEMITE VALLEY | — | 160.00 |
| ☐ YOSEMITE, EL CAPITAN | — | 160.00 |
| ☐ SEASCAPE, CARMEL BY THE SEA | — | 150.00 |
| ☐ GRAND CANYON | — | 150.00 |
| ☐ GRAND CANYON, LARGE | — | 180.00 |
| ☐ STAGE COACH | — | 170.00 |
| ☐ NEW ORLEANS, BRULATOUR COURTYARD | — | 150.00 |
| ☐ NEW ORLEANS, BRULATOUR COURTYARD, MINIATURE | — | 58.00 |
| ☐ PIRATES ALLEY | — | 150.00 |
| ☐ ACADEMY OF THE SACRED HEART, GRAND COTEU, LA | — | 150.00 |
| ☐ SAN FRANCISCO, CALIFORNIA STREET, SMALL | — | 58.00 |
| ☐ PIEDMONT, CALIFORNIA | — | 160.00 |
| ☐ ROTHENBURG | — | 160.00 |
| ☐ CASTLE TAUFERS | — | 110.00 |
| ☐ SCHATTENBRUG CASTLE | — | 140.00 |
| ☐ NEW ORLEANS, STREETCAR | — | 160.00 |
| ☐ NEW YORK, CENTRAL PARK | — | 160.00 |
| ☐ DENVER | — | 160.00 |
| ☐ LOUISIANA SWAMP | — | 160.00 |
| ☐ AMERICAN OAK GROVE | — | 170.00 |
| ☐ GOISERN | — | 90.00 |
| ☐ NIEDERWALDKIRCHEN | — | 160.00 |
| ☐ DROSENDORF | — | 150.00 |
| ☐ ALPINE CABIN | — | 50.00 |
| ☐ DIEX | — | 160.00 |
| ☐ CASTLE HOCHOSTERWITZ | — | 110.00 |
| ☐ MILLSTADT, OVAL | — | 140.00 |
| ☐ SPITAL, DRAV | — | 58.00 |
| ☐ MILLSTADT | — | 100.00 |
| ☐ MAJORCA, SPAIN | — | 160.00 |
| ☐ WILLIAMSBURG, GOVERNOR'S PALACE, VIEW #2 | 180.00 | — |
| ☐ SAN FRANCISCO VICTORIAN HOUSE | 160.00 | — |
| ☐ ST. PETER | 44.00 | — |
| ☐ THE REDWOODS | 180.00 | — |
| ☐ MARIAZELL | 44.00 | — |
| ☐ YELLOWSTONE CASTLE GEYSER | 80.00 | — |

| | ISSUE PRICE | CURRENT PRICE |
|---|---|---|
| ☐ VIENNA ROOFTOPS .............................................. | 48.00 | — |
| ☐ MILLSTATT MONASTERY ........................................ | 150.00 | — |

*ALL PIECES ARE COLOR ETCHINGS AND CONTAIN NO SPECIFIC EDITION LIMITS.

# PETER ELLENSHAW

Peter Ellenshaw is a man of extraordinary ability who has become one of America's most successful living artists. He is best known for his seascape paintings of Hawaii, California, and Ireland, as well as for his dramatic renderings of the scenic beauty of the Irish landscape. Over the past twelve years his one-man shows at the Hammer Galleries have invariably been sellouts and his paintings have become among the most sought after in the realistic tradition, commanding prices as high as $20,000.00.

Born in London, England in 1913, Ellenshaw began his formal education in art under the tutelage of W. Percy Day, a master of impressionistic realism and member of the Royal Academy. Ellenshaw soon became well known for his work on mattes. Mattes are paintings, which, when photographed, are indistinguishable from the original scene and are used in movie making. They require a high degree of skill, draftmanship and understanding of tone values and lights and shadows. In the late thirties, when Mr. Day was offered a position as production design artist by Sir Alexander Korda, the noted movie director, he took Ellenshaw with him.

After World War II, Walt Disney saw Peter Ellenshaw's work in England and immediately commissioned him to work on the special effects background for "Treasure Island". Then, Mr. Ellenshaw worked on "20,000 Leagues Under the Sea", which not only won an Oscar and a lifelong association with Disney Studios, but also marked the beginning of Ellenshaw's profound study of the sea.

In 1970, at the invitation of one of Ireland's leading art collectors, Ellenshaw journeyed to Ireland. There, he captured the beauty of the Irish countryside in exciting landscape paintings which brought him international acclaim and recognition.

Today, Ellenshaw's paintings are represented in some of the most prestigious private and corporate collections in the United States and Europe. He spends much of his time in Ireland (where he maintains a house), England, Hawaii and California. He now resides in Santa Barbara.

## PETER ELLENSHAW

| | ISSUE | CURRENT |
|---|---|---|
| ☐ CLIPPER SHIPS, rel. 1977. ed. 100, pencil signed by artist, 24″ x 36″ black and white etching, pub HP........................................ | 250.00 | 350.00 |
| ☐ RIVULET, rel. 1977. ed. 300, pencil signed by artist, 24″ x 36″, pub HP...... | 500.00 | 600.00 |
| ☐ ROAD TO COOMCALLEE, rel. 1978. ed. 300, s/n, 24″ x 36″, pub HP ........ ed. 50 Artist proofs | 400.00 | 600.00 |
| ☐ TIDE TURNING, rel. 1978. ed. 300, s/n, 24″ x 36″, pub HP ............... ed. 50 Artist proofs | 400.00 | 750.00 |
| ☐ KERRY SPRINGTIME, rel. 1979. ed. 300, s/n, 24″ x 36″, pub HP ........... | 450.00 | 500.00 |
| ☐ AFTERNOON TIDE, rel. 1980. ed. 200, s/n, 24″ x 20″, pub HP ............. | 400.00 | 500.00 |
| ☐ HYDE PARK, rel. 1980. ed. 200, s/n, 24″ x 20″, pub HP.................. | 400.00 | 500.00 |
| ☐ BOOKHILL KERRY, rel. 1981. ed. 300, s/n, 20″ x 30″, pub HP ............. | 500.00 | — |
| ☐ CRYSTAL STREAM, rel. 1981. ed. 300, s/n, 20″ x 30″, pub HP .......... | 500.00 | — |
| ☐ CALIFORNIA SANDS, rel. 1982. ed. 300, s/n, 20″ x 30″, pub HP ........... | 500.00 | — |
| ☐ MAYFLOWERS, rel. 1982. ed. 300, s/n, 20″ x 30½″, pub HP ........... | 500.00 | — |
| ☐ CRONANIY BURN, rel. 1983. ed. 850, s/n, 16½″ x 12½″, pub GW ........ | 75.00 | — |
| ☐ ERRIGAL MOUNTAIN, rel. 1983. ed. 850, s/n, 16½″ x 12½″, pub GW ...... | 75.00 | — |
| ☐ KNOCKSTOOKA FROM HOGS HEAD, rel. 1983. ed. 850, s/n, 16½″ x 11″, pub GW ............................................................ | 75.00 | — |

# DICK ELLIOTT

Crisp bright watercolors are the hallmark of artist Dick Elliott. He is adept at blending the designs of nature and man into one contemporary piece. His landscapes and life portraits lend a vivid and refreshing style to contemporary subjects.

He is a professional illustrator and designer, and has had years of experience in the art field as a teacher with the University of Tennessee and as a commercial art director for the Methodist Publishing House and Genesco in Nashville. A graduate of Austin Peay State College and Harris School of Art, he is a member of the Tennessee Watercolor Society and has had numerous exhibitions and one-man shows.

Tennessee's first waterfowl stamp design was created by Elliott and appears as the 1979 waterfowl license.

**CATOOSA WHITETAIL** *by Dick Elliot*

| DICK ELLIOTT | ISSUE PRICE | CURRENT PRICE |
|---|---|---|
| ☐ **LOST SPIRIT**, rel. 1978. ed. 500, s/n, 14" x 18", pub CSI | 15.00 | — |
| ☐ **TENNESSEE WATERFOWL STAMP**, rel. 1979-80. ed. 1979, s/n, 11" x 13", pub CSI | 105.00 | 150.00 |
| ☐ **CHESTNUT RAILS**, rel. 1979. ed. 5,000, i/o, 9" x 11", pub CSI | *12.50 | — |
| ☐ **WINTER SHADOWS**, rel. 1979. ed. 5,000, i/o, 9" x 11" pub CSI | *12.50 | — |
| *Set of Chestnut Rails and Winter Shadows | 20.00 | — |

| | ISSUE PRICE | CURRENT PRICE |
|---|---|---|
| ☐ **INDIAN SUMMER,** rel. 1979. ed. 3,000, s/o, 11" x 14", pub CSI . . . . . . . . . . | 15.00 | — |
| ☐ **CATOOSA WHITETAIL,** rel. 1979. ed. 650, s/n, 16" x 20", pub CSI . . . . . . . . | 50.00 | — |

## RUSS ELLIOTT

### TIGERS *by Russ Elliott*

| | ISSUE PRICE | CURRENT PRICE |
|---|---|---|
| ☐ **CURACAO FLOWERS,** ed. 300, s/n, 39½" x 30", original color silkscreen, pub FI. . . . . . . . . . . . . . . . . . . . . . . . . . . . . . . . . . . . . . . . . . . . . . . . . | 200.00 | 300.00 |
| ☐ **LIONS & MONKEYS,** ed. 300, s/n, 30½" x 43", original color silkscreen, pub FI. . . . . . . . . . . . . . . . . . . . . . . . . . . . . . . . . . . . . . . . . . . . . . . . | 300.00 | — |
| ☐ **MARKET,** ed. 300, s/n, 36½" x 31", original color silkscreen, pub FI . . . . . . . | 200.00 | 300.00 |
| ☐ **RED ZINNIAS,** ed. 300, s/n, 36½" x 22½", original color silkscreen, pub FI . . | 250.00 | 300.00 |
| ☐ **TIGERS,** ed. 300, s/n, 31" x 36", original color silkscreen, pub FI . . . . . . . . . | 250.00 | 300.00 |
| ☐ **ZEBRAS,** ed. 300, s/n, 31" x 36", original color silkscreen, pub FI. . . . . . . . . | 200.00 | 300.00 |

## MONTE ELLIS

| | ISSUE PRICE | CURRENT PRICE |
|---|---|---|
| ☐ **HIGH WATER SPRING,** ed. 500, s/n, 38½" x 30", pub NHI . . . . . . . . . . . . . . | 200.00 | — |
| ☐ **MISTY RETURN,** ed. 500, s/n, 30" x 40", pub NHI . . . . . . . . . . . . . . . . . . . . | 200.00 | — |

# RICHARD ELLIS

Richard Ellis is the foremost painter of marine natural history subjects in the United States.

His paintings of the great whales, which originally appeared in the January 1975 issue of *Audubon* magazine, and included the first painting used as an *Audubon* cover illustration since 1961, are considered the most accurate and dramatic color portraits of whales ever painted. In conjunction with the publication of the issue in which these paintings first appeared, a special reception was held at the national headquarters of the Audubon Society. Following the exhibition, the paintings went on tour and were shown at five museums during 1975-76.

Ellis' shark paintings speak for themselves. They are the product of years of meticulous research. After writing numerous articles on the subject, Ellis published a comprehensive non-fiction book on sharks put out by Grosset & Dunlap in 1977.

Ellis' paintings hang in many institutions and private collections. He is active in various conservation organizations and has donated his time and talents to The Animal Welfare Institute, Project Jonah, The Connecticut Cetacean Society and Rare Animal Relief Effort.

| RICHARD ELLIS | ISSUE PRICE | CURRENT PRICE |
|---|---|---|
| ☐ **SPERM WHALE,** rel. 1975. ed. 450, s/n, 22½″ x 18″, pub SEL | 150.00 | — |
| ☐ **TIGER SHARK,** rel. 1975. ed. 450, s/n, 17¾″ x 24½″, pub SEL | 150.00 | — |
| ☐ **GREY NURSE SHARK,** rel. 1977. ed. 975, s/n, 18¼″ x 24″, pub SEL | 150.00 | — |

# NITA ENGLE

A member of the American Watercolor Society since 1969, Engle lives and paints landscapes on the beautiful upper peninsula of northern Michigan. She says Lake Superior has all the advantages of the sea without the tide running out, but that it is a constant challenge to paint with changing lights and different moods.

Although she makes pencil sketches for composition and value in the field and supplements these with black and white photos, Engle is essentially a studio painter. She feels that the artist can be overwhelmed by the subject in on-the-spot painting. In the studio, she can arrive at a controlled design through the objective elimination of non-essentials.

Engle says, "Color is rarely factual but subordinate to the central theme of the watercolor." Therefore, black and white reference and her own mental palette in the studio work best for her. She believes that good decisions exercised by an accomplished painter preserve the original theme and the individuality of the objects of nature.

Engle attended Northern Michigan and Roosevelt Universities and the Art Institute of Chicago. She also studied in England. She worked nine years as an art director for a national advertising agency. She exhibits extensively and is represented in collections here and in England.

Commissions for illustrations have come from *Reader's Digest, Playboy* and other periodicals. She is also in demand as a book illustrator. Her philosophy of art and studio painting preference was carried as a feature of the "Watercolor Page" in *American Artist*.

**QUIET WATERS** *by Nita Engle*

| NITA ENGLE | ISSUE PRICE | CURRENT PRICE |
|---|---|---|
| ☐ **HOUSE BY THE SEA**, rel. 1981. ed. 950, s/n, 24" x 18⅛", pub MPPI . . . . . . . . | 75.00 | — |
| ☐ **WILDERNESS MARSH**, rel. 1981. ed. 950, s/n, 16¾" x 21¾", pub MPPI . . . . | 75.00 | — |
| ☐ **MORNING ON THE YELLOWDOG RIVER**, rel. 1983. ed. 950, s/n, 24" x 17⅞", pub MPPI . . . . . . . . . . . . . . . . . . . . . . . . . . . . . . . . . . . . . . | 75.00 | — |
| ☐ **QUIET WATERS**, rel. 1983. ed. 950, s/n, 17½" x 23¼", pub MPPI . . . . . . . . . | 75.00 | — |
| ☐ **SUMMER RIVER**, rel. 1983. ed. 950, s/n, 17½" x 23⅝", pub MPPI . . . . . . . . . | 75.00 | — |
| ☐ **WILD OCTOBER**, rel. 1983. ed. 950, s/n, 17½" x 22⅛", pub MPPI . . . . . . . . . | 75.00 | — |
| ☐ **WINTER BROOK**, rel. 1983. ed. 950, s/n, 24" x 17½", pub MPPI . . . . . . . . . . | 75.00 | — |

# HANS ERNI

In 1983, Erni was presented with a United Nations Peace Medal by the Secretary-General of the United Nations. Recently, Erni has been commissioned by both the United Nations Postal Administration and by the International Olympics Committee.

In his native Switzerland, Erni, ranks as the national artist, and receives consideration for every commission involving national prestige. His works adorn Swiss museums, government and private office buildings, banks, hotels, communication and transportation center, and even Swiss postage stamps. The most extensive collection of his works is housed in the two-year-old Hans Erni Museum, part of Lucerne's vast Swiss Transport Museum, the largest in Europe. The collection spans more than a half century of Erni's works, 1928-1980, and includes more than 400 of Erni's oil, tempera and acrylic paintings, sculpture, lithographs, drawings, engravings, etchings and ceramics.

A versatile and prolific artist, Erni has created original lithographs and etchings to illustrate more than 200 books from Sophocles to Sartre; designed scenery and costumes for four operas; created medals for the Swiss Mint; and designed more than 30 postage stamps for Switzerland and Liechtenstein.

**MATERNITY, Green / Beige** *by Hans Erni*

He has also authored three books, based on his experiences on research expeditions that explored Mauretania, Guinea, Senegal, India and Israel, and written and lectured extensively on art theory.

## HANS ERNI

| | ISSUE PRICE | CURRENT PRICE |
|---|---|---|
| **ORIGINAL ETCHINGS** | | |
| ☐ **FELIX AND POULO,** rel. 1974. ed. 40, s/n, 12½" x 13", 1 color, distr. EHC ... | 450.00 | 495.00 |
| ☐ **MOTHER AND CHILD, GREEN,** rel. 1979. ed. 90, s/n, 13⅞" x 10", distr. EHC . | 450.00 | 495.00 |
| ☐ **MOTHER PLAYING WITH CHILD ON CHAIR,** rel. 1979. ed. 90, s/n, 13½" x 10¼", 3 colors, distr. EHC . . . . . . . . . . . . . . . . . . . . . . . . . . . . . . . . . . . | 450.00 | 495.00 |
| ☐ **PYGMALION,** rel. 1979. ed. 90, s/n, 8¾" x 8⅞", 3 colors, distr. EHC . . . . . . . | 295.00 | 350.00 |
| ☐ **ASKLEPIOS AND GIRL,** rel. 1980. ed. 90, s/n, 25¼" x 19¼", 1 color, distr. EHC . . . . . . . . . . . . . . . . . . . . . . . . . . . . . . . . . . . . . . . . . . . . . . . | 625.00 | 695.00 |
| ☐ **COUPLE ON CUSHION,** rel. 1980. ed. 90, s/n, 9" x 8¼", 4 colors, distr. EHC . | 450.00 | 495.00 |
| ☐ **COUPLE, RED BACKGROUND,** rel. 1980. ed. 90, s/n, 13" x 10¼", distr. EHC . | 450.00 | 495.00 |
| ☐ **READING SIBYLLE,** rel. 1980. ed. 60, s/n, 15" x 11", 1 color, distr. EHC. . . . . | 450.00 | 495.00 |
| ☐ **THE ARTIST AND HIS MODEL,** rel. 1980. ed. 90, s/n, 11½" x 8", 1 color, distr. EHC . . . . . . . . . . . . . . . . . . . . . . . . . . . . . . . . . . . . . . . . . . . . . . . | 450.00 | 495.00 |
| ☐ **THREE HORSES ON BLUE BACKGROUND,** rel. 1980. ed. 90, s/n, 25¼" x 19½", 3 colors, distr. EHC . . . . . . . . . . . . . . . . . . . . . . . . . . . . . . . . . . . | 625.00 | 695.00 |
| **ORIGINAL STONE LITHOGRAPHS** | | |
| ☐ **CAPRICORN,** rel. 1974. ed. 150, s/n, 14" x 21½", distr. EHC . . . . . . . . . . . . | 435.00 | — |
| ☐ **CAT ON A STOOL,** rel. 1974. ed. 200, s/n, 26½" x 19½", distr. EHC. . . . . . . . | 450.00 | 495.00 |

| | ISSUE PRICE | CURRENT PRICE |
|---|---|---|
| ☐ GEMINI, rel. 1974. ed. 150, s/n, 14" x 21½", distr. EHC | 435.00 | — |
| ☐ LIBRA, rel. 1974. ed. 150, s/n, 14½" x 22", distr. EHC | 435.00 | — |
| ☐ LOVERS, rel. 1974. ed. 150, s/n, 29" x 21", distr. EHC | 750.00 | 850.00 |
| ☐ TAURUS, rel. 1974. ed. 150, s/n, 13¾" x 21½", distr. EHC | 435.00 | — |
| ☐ TIGER, rel. 1974. ed. 150, s/n, 21" x 29", distr. EHC | 625.00 | 695.00 |
| ☐ FOUR IN DISCUSSION, rel. 1975. ed. 150, s/n, 18¼" x 24¼", distr. EHC | 495.00 | 550.00 |
| ☐ FIVE PEOPLE DISCUSSING, rel. 1976. ed. 150, s/n, 18⅜" x 24¾", 5 colors, distr. EHC | 495.00 | 550.00 |
| ☐ PASSIONATE ENGINEER, rel. 1976. ed. 150, s/n, 18¾" x 25¼", distr. EHC | 495.00 | 550.00 |
| ☐ REFLECTING CONSTRUCTOR, rel. 1976. ed. 150, s/n, 19" x 24¾", distr. EHC | 495.00 | 550.00 |
| ☐ THE ARCHITECTS, rel. 1976. ed. 150, s/n, 18¾" x 23", 7 colors, distr. EHC | 495.00 | 550.00 |
| ☐ THE PLANNERS, rel. 1976. ed. 150, s/n, 18¾" x 23", distr. EHC | 495.00 | 550.00 |
| ☐ TWO HORSES, GREEN/YELLOW, rel. 1977. ed. 150, s/n, 21⅛" x 18⅞", 4 colors, distr. EHC | 495.00 | 550.00 |
| ☐ TWO HORSES, VIOLET/OCHRE, rel. 1977. ed. 150, s/n, 21⅛" x 18⅞", 4 colors, distr. EHC | 495.00 | 550.00 |
| ☐ COUPLE WITH MIRROR, rel. 1978. ed. 150, s/n, 23½" x 18⅞", distr. EHC | 450.00 | 550.00 |
| ☐ MOTHER AND CHILD ON GREY BACKGROUND, rel. 1978. ed. 150, s/n, 21" x 16", distr. EHC | 495.00 | 550.00 |
| ☐ J. S. BACH, rel. 1979. ed. 200, s/n, 21¼" x 17½", distr. EHC | 495.00 | 550.00 |
| ☐ ARTIST AND MODEL, rel. 1980. ed. 150, s/n, 25¾" x 21¼", 4 colors, distr. EHC | 495.00 | 550.00 |
| ☐ CHEMIST, rel. 1980. ed. 4,000, s/n, 26" x 19¼", 9 colors, distr. EHC | 525.00 | 575.00 |
| ☐ CHIRALITY, rel. 1980. ed. 150, s/n, 31¾" x 21¾", distr. EHC | 550.00 | 595.00 |
| ☐ COUPLE IN FRONT OF MOON, rel. 1980. ed. 150, s/n, 27" x 20⅜", 4 colors, distr. EHC | 525.00 | 575.00 |
| ☐ COUPLE SITTING ON FIG-BRANCH, rel. 1980. ed. 150, s/n, 18" x 13", distr. EHC | 450.00 | 495.00 |
| ☐ CROUCHING COUPLE, rel. 1980. ed. 150, s/n, 16⅝" x 21", distr. EHC | 495.00 | 550.00 |
| ☐ EUROPE, rel. 1980. ed. 150, s/n, 28" x 20¾", distr. EHC | 495.00 | 550.00 |
| ☐ FATHER-CHILD, rel. 1980. ed. 150, s/n, 17⅝" x 23½", 3 colors, distr. EHC | 495.00 | 550.00 |
| ☐ GIRL AND WINGED BULL, rel. 1980. ed. 150, s/n, 23" x 16½", 4 colors, distr. EHC | 525.00 | 575.00 |
| ☐ GIRL IN GREEN DRESS, rel. 1980. ed. 150, s/n, 33¼" x 13¼", distr. EHC | 595.00 | 650.00 |
| ☐ GIRL IN PINK DRESS, rel. 1980. ed. 150, s/n, 27¼" x 21", 4 colors, distr. EHC | 750.00 | 850.00 |
| ☐ GIRL LEADING HER HORSE, rel. 1980. ed. 150, s/n, 23" x 19", distr. EHC | 495.00 | 550.00 |
| ☐ GIRL SITTING, rel. 1980. ed. 150, s/n, 28½" x 20¼", distr. EHC | 495.00 | 550.00 |
| ☐ KYBERNETES, rel. 1980. ed. 150, s/n, 30⅝" x 21⅝", 5 colors, distr. EHC | 750.00 | 850.00 |
| ☐ MATERNITY, GREEN/BEIGE, rel. 1980. ed. 150, s/n, 23" x 18¾", 4 colors, distr. EHC | 495.00 | 550.00 |
| ☐ MOMENT OF INSTRUCTION, rel. 1980. ed. 150, s/n, 29½" x 21¼", distr. EHC | 750.00 | 850.00 |
| ☐ MOTHER-CHILD, rel. 1980. ed. 150, s/n, 18¼" x 23⅛", 3 colors, distr. EHC | 495.00 | 550.00 |
| ☐ MOTHER WITH CHILD, BLUE BACKGROUND, rel. 1980. ed. 150, s/n, 25¼" x 19", 7 colors, distr. EHC | 525.00 | 575.00 |
| ☐ NIGHTLY DISCUSSION, rel. 1980. ed. 150, s/n, 27" x 24¼", 6 colors, distr. EHC | 495.00 | 550.00 |
| ☐ PLAYING HORSES, rel. 1980. ed. 150, s/n, 18½" x 24½", distr. EHC | 495.00 | 550.00 |
| ☐ REFLECTING MAN, rel. 1980. ed. 150, s/n, 27½" x 21¼", distr. EHC | 750.00 | 850.00 |
| ☐ RIDING COUPLE, rel. 1980. ed. 150, s/n, 16½" x 25¾", distr. EHC | 495.00 | 550.00 |
| ☐ RUNNERS, rel. 1980. ed. 150, s/n, 27¾" x 19¾", 4 colors, distr. EHC | 495.00 | 550.00 |
| ☐ SEMINARY, rel. 1980. ed. 150, s/n, 20½" x 30¼", distr. EHC | 750.00 | 850.00 |
| ☐ SIBYLLE, 1977, rel. 1980. ed. 150, s/n, 22⅝" x 18½", distr. EHC | 495.00 | 550.00 |
| ☐ SITTING GIRL PLAYING WITH HER HAIR, rel. 1980. ed. 150, s/n, 27½" x 21", 5 colors, distr. EHC | 750.00 | 850.00 |
| ☐ SOCRATES AND THE YOUTH, rel. 1980. ed. 150, s/n, 27¾" x 28⅛", 7 colors, distr. EHC | 750.00 | 850.00 |
| ☐ STANDING GIRL, PLAYING WITH HER HAIR, rel. 1980. ed. 150, s/n, 26" x 19½", distr. EHC | 495.00 | 550.00 |
| ☐ TECHNICIAN AND HIS SURROUNDING, rel. 1980. ed. 150, s/n, 31" x 16⅝", distr. EHC | 495.00 | 550.00 |
| ☐ THE PROBLEM, rel. 1980. ed. 150, s/n, 21⅝" x 17½", 4 colors, distr. EHC | 495.00 | 500.00 |
| ☐ THOUGHTS, rel. 1980. ed. 150, s/n, 22" x 17¾", distr. EHC | 495.00 | 550.00 |

| | ISSUE PRICE | CURRENT PRICE |
|---|---|---|
| ☐ **THREE HORSES, GREEN/BROWN,** rel. 1980. ed. 150, s/n, 30⅞" x 21", 10 colors, distr. EHC | 750.00 | 850.00 |
| ☐ **THREE HORSES IN THE MOONLIGHT,** rel. 1980. ed. 150, s/n, 28" x 20", distr. EHC | 750.00 | 850.00 |
| ☐ **THREE HORSES IN THEIR STABLE,** rel. 1980. ed. 150, s/n, 22¾" x 18½", 5 colors, distr. EHC | 750.00 | 850.00 |
| ☐ **TWO HORSES, 1978,** rel. 1980. ed. 150, s/n, 23⅝" x 19⅛", distr. EHC | 525.00 | 575.00 |
| ☐ **TWO YOUNG COUPLES,** rel. 1980. ed. 150, s/n, 21" x 29¼", distr. EHC | 495.00 | 550.00 |
| ☐ **COUPLE IN WINDOW,** rel. 1982. ed. 150, s/n, 20½" x 18½", distr. EHC | 550.00 | — |
| ☐ **MOTHER PEELING POTATOES,** rel. 1982. ed. 150, s/n, 25" x 19", distr. EHC | 550.00 | — |
| ☐ **THE FRAMEMAKER,** rel. 1982. ed. 150, s/n, 25¾" x 19", distr. EHC | 550.00 | — |
| ☐ **THREE CONSTRUCTORS,** rel. 1982. ed. 150, s/n, 23½" x 17½", distr. EHC | 550.00 | — |
| ☐ **COUPLE PLAYING CHESS,** rel. 1983. ed. 150, s/n, 18¼" x 24", distr. EHC | 595.00 | — |
| ☐ **DREAMING MUSICIAN,** rel. 1983. ed. 150, s/n, 24¼" x 24", distr. EHC | 625.00 | — |
| ☐ **PELEUS AND THETIS,** rel. 1983. ed. 150, s/n, 25¼" x 20", distr. EHC | 550.00 | — |
| ☐ **PYTHAGORAS,** rel. 1983. ed. 150, s/n, 26" x 18", distr. EHC | 550.00 | — |
| ☐ **SAINT CHRISTOPHORUS,** rel. 1983. ed. 150, s/n, 16½" x 12⅝", distr. EHC | 340.00 | — |
| ☐ **THE STALLION,** rel. 1983. ed. 150, s/n, 22¼" x 18¼", distr. EHC | 695.00 | — |

# ERTÉ

Romain de Tirtoff was born on the 23rd of November, 1892 in St. Petersburg the capital of Russia. The pseudonym Erté was created from the initials R T when the artist first began his work as a fashion designer.

Erté began his fashion designing in Paris around the year 1912 and about three years later was commissioned by *Harper's Bazaar* to do a cover. That was the beginning of a number of illustrations for this magazine to appear on their covers. About four years later his illustrations began to appear on *Vogue magazine* covers. Some of the artists finest works were done for the Folies-Bergere. He later came to Hollywood and did costume designing. After several years he returned to Paris where he now resides.

## ERTÉ

| | | |
|---|---|---|
| ☐ **SPLENDOR,** ed. 260, serigraph, 34" x 26", pub CFA | — | 2,700.00 |
| ☐ **WINTER RESORT NICE,** ed. 260, serigraph, 30" x 24", pub CFA | — | 650.00 |
| ☐ **FASHIONS,** ed. 260, serigraph, 30" x 24", pub CFA | — | 650.00 |
| ☐ **FURS,** ed. 260, serigraph, 30" x 24", pub CFA | — | 850.00 |
| ☐ **TENNIS,** ed. 260, serigraph, 30" x 24", pub CFA | — | 400.00 |
| ☐ **COMPACT VANITIES,** ed. 260, serigraph, 30" x 24", pub CFA | — | 850.00 |
| ☐ **WINTER RESORTS,** ed. 260, serigraph, 30" x 24", pub CFA | — | 750.00 |
| ☐ **LOVE,** ed. 260, serigraph, 30" x 24", pub CFA | — | 400.00 |
| ☐ **THREE FACES,** ed. 260, serigraph, 30" x 24", pub CFA | — | 1,000.00 |
| ☐ **BROWN BOOT,** ed. 260, serigraph, 20" x 17", pub CFA | — | 650.00 |
| ☐ **MYSTIQUE,** ed. 260, serigraph, 40" x 26", pub CFA | — | 2,400.00 |
| ☐ **BLACK ROSE,** ed. 260, serigraph, 25" x 20", pub CFA | — | 1,500.00 |
| ☐ **TOP HATS,** ed. 260, serigraph, 24" x 19", pub CFA | — | 3,100.00 |
| ☐ **PRINTEMPS,** ed. 260, serigraph, 29" x 23", pub CFA | — | 600.00 |
| ☐ **RENEE,** ed. 260, lithograph, 17" x 11", pub CFA | — | 325.00 |
| ☐ **NICOLE,** ed. 260, lithograph, 17" x 11", pub CFA | — | 325.00 |
| ☐ **YVETTE,** ed. 260, lithograph, 17" x 11", pub CFA | — | 325.00 |
| ☐ **SIMONE,** ed. 260, lithograph, 17" x 11", pub CFA | — | 300.00 |
| ☐ **ZSA ZSA,** ed. 250, lithograph, 35" x 21", pub CFA | — | 1,300.00 |
| ☐ **PREMIER,** ed. 300, lithograph, 16" x 12", pub CFA | — | 465.00 |
| ☐ **BEN SOIR,** ed. 300, lithograph, 16" x 12", pub CFA | — | 275.00 |
| ☐ **ELEGANCE,** ed. 300, lithograph, 16" x 12", pub CFA | — | 275.00 |
| ☐ **TRES CHIC,** ed. 300, lithograph, 16" x 12", pub CFA | — | 275.00 |
| ☐ **THE KISS,** ed. 300, litho/embossment, 12" x 10", pub CFA | — | 850.00 |
| ☐ **SUMMER AND WINTER,** ed. 300, litho/embossment, 11" x 12", pub CFA | — | 500.00 |
| ☐ **THE VEIL,** ed. 300, litho/embossment, 12" x 9", pub CFA | — | 500.00 |
| ☐ **EVENING CREATION,** ed. 175, etching, 15" x 11", pub CFA | — | 475.00 |

| | ISSUE PRICE | CURRENT PRICE |
|---|---|---|
| ☐ FEATHERS, ed. 300, litho/embossment, 12″ x 9″, pub CFA | — | 500.00 |
| ☐ DANCERS, ed. 300, litho/embossment, 6″ x 13″, pub CFA | — | 850.00 |
| ☐ LA BELLE, ed. 300, lithograph, 15″ x 11″, pub CFA | — | 475.00 |
| ☐ FICELLE, ed. 300, lithograph, 15″ x 11″, pub CFA | — | 275.00 |
| ☐ MUFF, ed. 300, lithograph, 15″ x 11″, pub CFA | — | 500.00 |
| ☐ FANTAISIE, ed. 300, lithograph, 15″ x 11″, pub CFA | — | 375.00 |
| ☐ REFLECTIONS, ed. 300, serigraph, 26″ x 24″, pub CFA | — | 850.00 |
| ☐ THE CURTAIN, ed. 300, serigraph/flocking, 26″ x 18″, pub CFA | — | 925.00 |
| ☐ BROADWAY'S IN FASHION, ed. 300, serigraph/embossment, 24″ x 18″, pub CFA | — | 900.00 |
| ☐ WINGS OF VICTORY, ed. 325, serigraph, 32″ x 24″, pub CFA | — | 3,350.00 |
| ☐ SUMMER BREEZE, ed. 300, serigraph, 31″ x 23″, pub CFA | — | 2,200.00 |
| ☐ FLAMES OF LOVE, ed. 300, serigraph, 37″ x 21″, pub CFA | — | 1,300.00 |
| ☐ RIVIERA, ed. 300, serigraph, 24″ x 19″, pub CFA | — | 800.00 |
| ☐ LES POUPEES RUSSES, ed. 300, serigraph, 31″ x 23″, pub CFA | — | 1,250.00 |
| ☐ BAGDAD, ed. 300, lithograph, 16″ x 13″, pub CFA | — | 375.00 |
| ☐ ZOBEIDE, ed. 300, lithograph, 16″ x 13″, pub CFA | — | 400.00 |
| ☐ DINARZADE, ed. 300, lithograph, 16″ x 13″, pub CFA | — | 375.00 |
| ☐ KING'S FAVORITE, ed. 300, lithograph, 26″ x 20″, pub CFA | — | 750.00 |
| ☐ GABY DESLYS, ed. 300, lithograph, 26″ x 20″, pub CFA | — | 900.00 |
| ☐ MANHATTAN MARY I, ed. 300, lithograph, 22″ x 18″, pub CFA | — | 400.00 |
| ☐ LAFAYETTE, ed. 300, serigraph, 32″ x 24″, pub CFA | — | 850.00 |
| ☐ AFTER THE RAIN, ed. 300, serigraph, 31″ x 23″, pub CFA | — | 700.00 |
| ☐ SPRING FASHIONS, ed. 300, serigraph, 31″ x 23″, pub CFA | — | 1,050.00 |
| ☐ BLOSSOM UMBRELLA, ed. 300, serigraph, 30″ x 23″, pub CFA | — | 1,100.00 |
| ☐ THE GOLDEN CLOAK, ed. 300, lithograph, 25″ x 17″, pub CFA | — | 600.00 |
| ☐ MANHATTAN MARY II, ed. 300, litho/seragraph, 24″ x 17″, pub CFA | — | 350.00 |
| ☐ THE BLUE DRESS, ed. 300, serigraph, 25″ x 19″, pub CFA | — | 350.00 |
| ☐ FALL, ed. 300, serigraph, 31″ x 24″, pub CFA | — | 1,850.00 |
| ☐ HEAT, ed. 300, serigraph, 25″ x 19″, pub CFA | — | 1,900.00 |
| ☐ THE CHASTE SUSANNA, ed. 300, serigraph, 24″ x 19″, pub CFA | — | 1,500.00 |
| ☐ FIREFLIES, ed. 300, serigraph, 32″ x 24″, pub CFA | — | 1,800.00 |
| ☐ THE FRENCH ROOSTER, ed. 300, serigraph, 31″ x 22″, pub CFA | — | 2,250.00 |
| ☐ VINTAGE, ed. 300, serigraph, 31″ x 23″, pub CFA | — | 2,600.00 |
| ☐ THE BATH OF THE MARQUISE, ed. 300, serigraph, 24″ x 18″, pub CFA | — | 1,950.00 |
| ☐ LA TOILETTE, ed. 300, serigraph, 11″ x 14″, pub CFA | — | 600.00 |
| ☐ THE WAVE, ed. 300, serigraph, 11″ x 13″, pub CFA | — | 750.00 |
| ☐ THE RIVIERA, ed. 300, serigraph, 10″ x 15″, pub CFA | — | 450.00 |
| ☐ NOON, ed. 300, serigraph, 14″ x 11″, pub CFA | — | 600.00 |
| ☐ QUEEN OF SHEBA, ed. 300, serigraph, 30″ x 22″, pub CFA | — | 1,700.00 |
| ☐ MICHELLE, ed. 300, serigraph, 30″ x 22″, pub CFA | — | 1,200.00 |
| ☐ MYSTERE, ed. 300, serigraph, 32″ x 24″, pub CFA | — | 1,375.00 |
| ☐ PARESSEUSE, ed. 300, serigraph, 31″ x 23″, pub CFA | — | 1,800.00 |
| ☐ RAIN, ed. 300, serigraph/embossment, 10″ x 20″, pub CFA | — | 750.00 |
| ☐ LA MERVEILLEUSE, ed. 300, serigraph, 31″ x 23″, pub CFA | — | 1,100.00 |
| ☐ WOMAN AND SATYR, ed. 300, serigraph, 32″ x 23″, pub CFA | — | 2,400.00 |
| ☐ LOVERS AND IDOL, ed. 300, serigraph, 23″ x 17″, pub CFA | — | 1,100.00 |
| ☐ SAMSON AND DELILAH, ed. 300, serigraph/embossment, 19″ x 24″, pub CFA | — | 1,700.00 |
| ☐ CHARLESTON COUPLE, ed. 300, serigraph, 17″ x 15″, pub CFA | — | 600.00 |
| ☐ TWIN SISTERS, ed. 300, serigraph/embossment, 40″ x 55″, pub CFA | — | 2,700.00 |
| ☐ THE DUEL, ed. 300, serigraph, 31″ x 23″, pub CFA | — | 1,750.00 |
| ☐ FOUR SEASONS FOLIO, four pcs., ed. 260, serigraph, 20″ x 14″, pub CFA | — | 1,500.00 |
| ☐   WINTER or SUMMER ... each | — | 400.00 |
| ☐   AUTUMN | — | 450.00 |
| ☐   SPRING | — | 500.00 |
| ☐ ALPHABET PORTFOLIO, 26 pcs., ed. 350, litho/serigraph, 26″ x 19″, pub CFA | — | 21,000.00 |
| ☐   Pcs. C - H - I - J - N - O - U - V and X ... each | — | 700.00 |
| ☐   Pc. Y | — | 750.00 |
| ☐   Pcs. A - E - Q ... each | — | 800.00 |
| ☐   Pc. S | — | 850.00 |
| ☐   Pcs. K - W ... each | — | 900.00 |
| ☐   Pcs. B - D ... each | — | 1,000.00 |
| ☐   Pc. T | — | 1,050.00 |
| ☐   Pcs. F - G - P ... each | — | 1,100.00 |

| | ISSUE PRICE | CURRENT PRICE |
|---|---|---|
| ☐ Pc. Z | — | 1,350.00 |
| ☐ Pc. R | — | 1,450.00 |
| ☐ Pc. M | — | 1,900.00 |
| ☐ Pc. L | — | 2,900.00 |
| ☐ TWENTIES REMEMBERED FOLIO, eight pcs., ed. 300, serigraph, 24" x 20" and 25" x 22", pub CFA | — | 10,500.00 |
| ☐ BRIDE, 24" x 20" | — | 1,100.00 |
| ☐ AMOUREUSE | — | 600.00 |
| ☐ LES JOLIES DAMES | — | 1,200.00 |
| ☐ RAINBOW IN BLOSSOM | — | 800.00 |
| ☐ BEAUTY OF THE BEAST, 25" x 22" | — | 3,000.00 |
| ☐ AUTUMN SONG | — | 1,200.00 |
| ☐ FISHBOWL | — | 900.00 |
| ☐ DREAM VOYAGE | — | 2,000.00 |
| ☐ TWENTIES REMEMBERED AGAIN FOLIO, eight pcs., ed. 300, serigraph, 24" x 19", pub CFA | — | 9,800.00 |
| ☐ SPRING OPENING | — | 925.00 |
| ☐ LEGERETE | — | 1,150.00 |
| ☐ SELECTION OF A HEART | — | 1,250.00 |
| ☐ TEMPEST | — | 2,000.00 |
| ☐ RUSSIAN FAIRYTALE | — | 1,300.00 |
| ☐ EARTH'S DREAM | — | 1,700.00 |
| ☐ MAKEUP | — | 1,100.00 |
| ☐ FIRST DRESS | — | 1,250.00 |
| ☐ SUITE, three pcs., ed. 300, lithograph, 20" x 16", pub CFA | — | 1,800.00 |
| ☐ ROSE TURBAN | — | 650.00 |
| ☐ YELLOW TURBAN | — | 650.00 |
| ☐ THE MIRROR | — | 700.00 |
| ☐ THE FOUR EMOTIONS FOLIO, four pcs., ed. 300, serigraph, 23" x 18", pub CFA | — | 5,500.00 |
| ☐ NUMBERS PORTFOLIO, 10 pcs. (Numberals 0 through 9), ed. 350, serigraph/embossment, 23" x 17", pub CFA | — | 10,500.00 |
| ☐ Pc. 3 | — | 800.00 |
| ☐ Pcs. 0 - 1 .... each | — | 900.00 |
| ☐ Pc. 2 | — | 950.00 |
| ☐ Pc. 7 | — | 1,000.00 |
| ☐ Pc. 6 | — | 1,100.00 |
| ☐ Pc. 8 | — | 1,300.00 |
| ☐ Pc. 9 | — | 1,500.00 |
| ☐ Pc. 4 | — | 1,700.00 |
| ☐ Pc. 5 | — | 1,800.00 |

# TONY EUBANKS

Tony Eubanks is skilled in a variety of mediums including oil, watercolor, pastels, charcoal, pen and ink, and mixed media, but yet his primary thrust and first love is oil.

Born in Dallas, Texas, Eubanks graduated from North Texas State University and received professional training at the Art Center in Los Angeles. Prior to becoming a full-time painter he was a nationally known illustrator whose work has appeared in *McCall's, Time, Reader's Digest, Ladies Home Journal, TV Guide, National Geographic, Audubon* and other publications.

His talent widely recognized, Eubanks has painted works which hang in the galleries of some of America's finest art collectors. His works have been featured in volumes such as Western Paintings Today and are on permanent display at the Library of Congress.

## TONY EUBANKS

☐ **THE BORROWED MARE**, rel. 1982. ed. 600, s/n, size note available, pub WWI .   **95.00**    —

## CECIL EVERLEY

|  | ISSUE PRICE | CURRENT PRICE |
|---|---|---|
| ☐ **VALLEY OF LUCERAM**, ed. 225, s/n, 26″ x 32″, original color silkscreen, pub Fl | 125.00 | — |
| ☐ **VILLEFRANCHE**, ed. 225, s/n, 26″ x 32″, original color silkscreen, pub Fl . . . . | 125.00 | — |

## CARL EVERS

Carl Evers is a quiet man who paints powerful pictures . . . of thundering waves and towering masts . . . of hulls leaning into the swell . . . of trauma and fury and heroism . . . of peaceful harbors and even the work-a-day tugboat. Evers has built his reputation through hard work — studying blueprints of ships — and through the uncannily realistic waves and water that flow from his brush.

Born in Germany, he painted his way to this country from London and Sweden aboard a freighter through the Panama Canal to San Francisco. On this voyage, he encountered swells at eye level, the best vantage point from which to study and paint them. Evers has painted for the U.S. Naval Institute, for steamship and freightlines, for books and magazines, and for private commission. Today, he is a recognized master whose watercolors are sought worldwide.

| CARL EVERS | ISSUE PRICE | CURRENT PRICE |
|---|---|---|
| ☐ **AMERICA'S CUP 1974**, rel.1975. ed. 750, s/n, 30½″ x 22½″, pub GW . . . . . . | 75.00 | 300.00 |
| *ed. 250, s/n, with three signatures and remarque-like sketches of Ted Hood and Olin Stephens. . . . . . . . . . . . . . . . . . . . . . . . . . . . . . . . | *200.00 | 400.00 |
| ☐ **APPROACHING THE HORN**, rel. 1975. ed. 1,000, s/n, 26″ x 19¼″, pub GW . . | 65.00 | 150.00 |
| ☐ **USS CONSTITUTION**, rel. 1975. ed. 1,000, s/n, 30¼″ x 22″, pub GW . . . . . . . | 75.00 | — |
| ☐ **HURRICANE**, rel. 1976. ed. 1,000, s/n, 26″ x 18¾″, pub GW . . . . . . . . . . . | 65.00 | 130.00 |
| ☐ **SOUTH STREET, NEW YORK, 1879**, rel. 1976. ed. 1,000, s/n, 28¾″ x 18½″, pub GW . . . . . . . . . . . . . . . . . . . . . . . . . . . . . . . . . . . . . . . . . | 65.00 | — |
| ☐ **AMERICA'S CUP 1870**, rel. 1977. ed. 1,000, s/n, 30″ x 19¼″, pub GW . . . . . | 65.00 | — |
| ☐ **THE PRIVATEERS**, rel. 1977. ed. 1,000, s/n, 30″ x 21″, pub GW . . . . . . . . . . | 65.00 | — |
| ☐ **HEAVY SEAS**, rel. 1979. ed. 1,000, s/n, 26″ x 19¼″, pub GW . . . . . . . . . . . . | 65.00 | — |
| ☐ **BATTLE OF THE MONITOR AND MERRIMACK**, rel. 1980. ed. 1,000, s/n, 29″ x 21″, pub GW . . . . . . . . . . . . . . . . . . . . . . . . . . . . . . . . . . . . . . . | 75.00 | — |
| ☐ **FORCE TEN — SURVIVOR**, rel. 1981. ed. 1,000, s/n, 30¼″ x 21″, pub GW . . . | 125.00 | — |
| ☐ **LETTER OF MARQUE 1814**, rel. 1981. ed. 500, s/n, 27″ x 19¼″, pub GW . . . . | 110.00 | — |
| ☐ **EAGLE AT SEA**, rel. 1983. ed. 650, s/n, 28½″ x 21¼″, pub GW . . . . . . . . . . | 135.00 | — |

## BURR FAIRLAMB

Burr Fairlamb feels composition is extremely important in his paintings. He feels the abstract elements must work with the rest of the elements.

After gathering the necessary information and working out a composition, Fairlamb sketches details within the painting, "revising and refining them until I am satisfied. I leave the fine detail for last."

| BURR FAIRLAMB | ISSUE PRICE | CURRENT PRICE |
|---|---|---|
| ☐ **CUTTING GARDEN**, rel. 1980. ed. 700, s/n, 23½″ x 29½″, pub FHG . . . . . . . . | 60.00 | — |

# JOHN FALTER
## (1910-1982)

John Falter was born in Nebraska, and entered the Kansas City Art Institute at the age of 18. Two years later the award of a scholarship to the Art Students League brought him to New York and a career in illustration during its golden years. He produced 185 covers for the *Saturday Evening Post.* Norman Rockwell called him "America's most gifted illustrator."

However, he never allowed his career in illustration to squeeze out his vocation in the fine arts. Lithographs, easel paintings and murals were produced simultaneously with his illustrations. In 1976, John Falter, Harvey Dunn and Winslow Homer were elected to the Illustrators Hall of Fame. It has been correctly said, "he paints America from sea to shining sea".

**THE GUSHER** *by John Falter*

**JOHN FALTER**

<table>
<tr><td></td><td>ISSUE<br>PRICE</td><td>CURRENT<br>PRICE</td></tr>
<tr><td>☐   **THE GUSHER,** rel. 1981. ed. 950, s/n, 28½″ x 22¾″, pub MPPI . . . . . . . . . . .</td><td>**150.00**</td><td>—</td></tr>
</table>

# RON FANER

Ron Faner, who began painting in Michigan, moved to Phoenix, Arizona, in 1973 to continue his study in landscapes and animals of the Southwest. "Eventually, I began to see an interrelationship between animal and man which the Indian has always understood. Therefore, the Indian has become the human subject that fits so well with my feelings for nature."

Faner always includes animals and birds in art because he's "always had a great compassion for wildlife. It's basic to my nature. I try to give animals a voice. What voice do they have other than our compassion?"

**RAVEN'S CALL** by Ron Faner

| RON FANER | ISSUE PRICE | CURRENT PRICE |
|---|---|---|
| ☐ **KEEPER OF THE OWLS**, rel. 1980. ed. 375, s/n, 26" x 33⅓", pub FHG . . . . . . | 100.00 | 185.00 |
| ☐ **THE DEER SLAYER**, rel. 1980. ed. 375, s/n, 20" x 23½", pub FHG . . . . . . . . . | 100.00 | 150.00 |
| ☐ **CUNNING AS THE FOX, SUDDEN AS THE RABBIT**, rel. 1981. ed. 375, s/n, 24" x 24", pub FHG . . . . . . . . . . . . . . . . . . . . . . . . . . . . . . . . . . . . . | 125.00 | — |
| ☐ **LITTLE SPARROW WOMAN**, rel. 1981. ed. 375, s/n, 28" x 24", pub FHG . . . . . | 125.00 | 175.00 |
| ☐ **NIGHT DREAMER**, rel. 1981. ed. 375, s/n, 24" x 24", pub FHG . . . . . . . . . . . | 125.00 | — |
| ☐ **THUNDER GOD AND THE CREATION OF BIRDS**, rel. 1981. ed. 375, s/n, 31¼" x 24½", pub FHG . . . . . . . . . . . . . . . . . . . . . . . . . . . . . . . . . . . . . . . | 125.00 | 225.00 |
| ☐ **MORNING SONG**, rel. 1982. ed. 375, s/n, 24" x 24", pub FHG . . . . . . . . . . . . | 150.00 | — |
| ☐ **SUNBIRD KATCHINA**, rel. 1982. ed. 375, s/n, pub FHG . . . . . . . . . . . . . . . . | 150.00 | — |
| ☐ **WINTER WOLF**, rel. 1982. ed. 375, s/n, 24" x 24", pub FHG . . . . . . . . . . . . . | 150.00 | — |
| ☐ **BUFFALO DREAM**, rel. 1983. ed. 375, s/n, 24½" x 31½", pub FHG . . . . . . . . | 150.00 | — |
| ☐ **SPIRIT WARRIOR**, rel. 1983. ed. 375, s/n, 20" x 37", pub FHG . . . . . . . . . . . | 150.00 | — |
| ☐ **THE RAVEN'S CALL**, rel. 1983. ed. 375, s/n, 23" x 32½", pub FHG . . . . . . . . | 150.00 | — |

# IMOGENE FARNSWORTH

Imogene Farnsworth is recognized as one of America's most talented wildlife artists.

Farnsworth's first print sold out in record time, and in the process won a Printing Industry of America Award that year. Subsequent prints also received PIA awards in 1976, 1978 and 1979.

**LION** *by Imogene Farnsworth*

## IMOGENE FARNSWORTH

| | ISSUE PRICE | CURRENT PRICE |
|---|---|---|
| ☐ **BENGAL TIGER,** rel. 1973. ed. 1,000, s/n, 20″ x 24″, pub II | 35.00 | 750.00 |
| ed. 2,000, s/o | 25.00 | 350.00 |
| ☐ **AFRICAN LION,** rel. 1974. ed. 1,000, s/n, 20″ x 24″, pub II | 35.00 | 350.00 |
| ed. 2,000, s/o | 25.00 | 200.00 |
| ☐ **BROWN BEAR,** rel. 1974. ed. 1,000, s/n, 20″ x 24″, pub II | 35.00 | 150.00 |
| ed. 4,000, s/o | 25.00 | 75.00 |
| ☐ **YOUNG ZEBRA,** rel. 1974. ed. 1,000, s/n, 20″ x 24″, pub II | 35.00 | 100.00 |
| ed. 2,000, s/o | 25.00 | 40.00 |
| ☐ **GIRAFFES,** rel. 1975. ed. 1,000, s/n, 20″ x 24″, pub II | 35.00 | 150.00 |
| ed. 2,000, s/o | 25.00 | 50.00 |
| ☐ **TIGER,** rel. 1975. ed. 3,000, s/n, 20″ x 24″, pub II | 35.00 | 350.00 |
| ☐ **AFRICAN LEOPARD,** rel. 1976. ed. 3,000, s/n, 20″ x 24″, pub II | 45.00 | 350.00 |
| ☐ **AFRICAN LIONNESS & CUBS,** rel. 1976. ed. 3,000, s/n, 24″ x 20″, pub II | 35.00 | 150.00 |
| ☐ **CHEETAH (Head),** rel. 1976. ed. 3,000, s/n, 16″ x 20″, pub II | 35.00 | 75.00 |
| ☐ **THE STALK (Cheetah),** rel. 1976. ed. 3,000, s/n, 29¾″ x 16¾″, pub II | 45.00 | — |
| ☐ **BENGAL TIGER CUBS,** rel. 1977. ed. 3,000, s/n, 22″ x 21½″, pub II | 45.00 | 100.00 |
| ☐ **LION AND PUMA,** rel. 1977. (A & B). ed. 3,000, s/n, size not available, 24″, pub II | 35.00 | 300.00 |
| ☐ **MELANISTIC LEOPARD,** rel. 1977. ed. 3,000, s/n, 26½″ x 21½″, pub II | 50.00 | 150.00 |
| ☐ **PERSIAN LEOPARD & SIBERIAN TIGER,** rel. 1977. (A & B). ed. 3,000, s/n, 11½″ x 11½″, pub II | 40.00 | 120.00 |
| ☐ **COUGAR,** rel. 1978. ed. 3,000, s/n, 20″ x 24″, pub II | 50.00 | — |

|  | ISSUE PRICE | CURRENT PRICE |
|---|---|---|
| ☐ **JAGUAR**, rel. 1978. ed. 3,000, s/n, 22″ x 21½″, pub II | 50.00 | — |
| ☐ **JAGUAR CUBS**, rel. 1978. ed. 3,000, s/n, 20″ x 22″, pub II | 50.00 | — |
| ☐ **CHEETAH KITTENS**, rel. 1979. ed. 3,000, s/n, 20″ x 22″, pub II | 50.00 | — |
| ☐ **THE FOX AND THE FROG**, rel. 1979. ed. 3,000, s/n, 20″ x 24″, pub II | 45.00 | — |
| ☐ **THE RED-TAILED HAWK**, rel. 1979. ed. 3,000, s/n, 20″ x 24″, pub II | 45.00 | — |
| ☐ **SNOW LEOPARDS**, rel. 1979. ed. 1,750, s/n, 18⅜″ x 22″, pub SCI* | 55.00 | — |
| ☐ **WHITE BENGAL TIGER**, rel. 1979. ed. 1,750, s/n, 23″ x 19″, pub SCI* | 55.00 | 300.00 |
| ☐ **LION**, rel. 1980. ed. 2,000, s/n, 19″ x 21″, pub SCI* | 55.00 | — |
| ☐ **PERSIAN LEOPARD**, rel. 1980. ed. 1,750, s/n, 19″ x 21″, pub SCI* | 55.00 | — |
| ☐ **CANEBRAKE**, rel. 1981. ed. 1,750, s/n, 18″ x 22½″, pub SCI* | 55.00 | — |
| ☐ **ENCOUNTER**, rel. 1981. ed. 1,500, s/n, 16″ x 20″, pub SCI* | 55.00 | — |
| ☐ **TIGER CUB AND BOBCAT KITTEN**, rel. 1981. ed. 2,500, s/n, 11″ x 12″, pub SCI* ........pair | 40.00 | — |
| ☐ **BENGAL CUB/FOOTBALL**, rel. 1982. ed. 2,000, s/n, size N/A, pub SCI | 25.00 | — |
| ☐ **PANTHER**, rel. 1982. ed. 1,500, s/n, size not available, pub SCI* | 55.00 | — |

*Represents the Sawyier Collection, Inc., and was formed as a subsidiary of Paul Sawyier Galleries.

# RALPH FASANELLA

Ralph Fasanella's works portray a perception of New York City that is at once joyous and tragic.

His primitive paintings show the working life and political myths of Americans — stickball games on Sunday afternoons, the mosaic of rich and poor, the church spires, tenements, skyscrapers and crowded workshops — the constant motion of millions of people in a small space.

## RALPH FASANELLA

| | | |
|---|---|---|
| ☐ **BASEBALL PARK**, ed. 250, s/n, 31″ x 43½″, original color silkscreen, pub FI | 300.00 | 600.00 |
| ☐ **EMPIRE STATE**, ed. 300, s/n, 45″ x 28″, original color silkscreen, pub FI | 400.00 | 600.00 |
| ☐ **FAMILY SUPPER**, ed. 250, s/n, 41½″ x 30¾″, original color silkscreen, pub FI | 300.00 | 600.00 |
| ☐ **MAY DAY**, ed. 250, s/n, 31″ x 45″, original color silkscreen, pub FI | 300.00 | 500.00 |
| ☐ **NEW YORK GOING TO WORK**, ed. 300, s/n, 31″ x 35⅝″, original color silkscreen, pub FI | 400.00 | — |
| ☐ **NEW YORK SCENE**, ed. 250, s/n, 30″ x 42″, original color silkscreen, pub FI | 300.00 | 1,000.00 |
| ☐ **SAN GENNARO**, ed. 300, s/n, 29″ x 32¾″, original color silkscreen, pub FI | 300.00 | 400.00 |
| ☐ **STICKBALL**, ed. 300, s/n, 29¾″ x 30½″, original color silkscreen, pub FI | 300.00 | 400.00 |

# JAMES FAULKNER

James E. Faulkner is one of the few artists who has mastered the technical and aesthetic nuances of both wildlife and the beautiful landscapes in which they live. To accomplish this, Faulkner found that he had to become part biologist, botanist, geologist, meteorologist and, above all, an artist. Entirely self taught, he has evolved a unique and rich style. This exacting and precise style was developed explicitly to capture the beauty of a single animal in the crisp air of a rocky mountain panorama.

Faulker's original works and limited edition prints have been collected in all fifty states and in several countries.

## JAMES FAULKNER

| | | |
|---|---|---|
| ☐ **RED FOX**, ed. 500, s/n, 16″ x 20″, distr. EHC | 60.00 | — |
| ☐ **OTTER PLAYGROUND**, ed. 500, s/n, 16″ x 20″, distr. EHC | 60.00 | — |
| ☐ **SPRING SNOW**, ed. 500, s/n, 16″ x 20″, distr. EHC | 60.00 | — |

**OTTER PLAYGROUND** *by James Faulkner*

## FRED FELLOWS

"I suppose it was inevitable that my art would be western in nature, I believe most serious artists end up making statements about things that are important to them," said Fred Fellows.

Fellows spent ten years working in the commercial art field as an artist and art director.

Fellows is one of only three contemporary Western artists whose paintings were picked by Phillip Morris to use in world wide advertising of Marlboro. His paintings and sculptures have been featured in many magazines including *Arizona Highways, The Western Horseman, Newsweek, Art West, South West Art, Artist of the Rockies* and *Playboy.*

Fellow's work has won many awards including the Grumbacher Fine Arts Award, Printing Institute of America Award in 1976, Gold medal for the most popular work at the 1975 annual C.A.A. exhibit, and silver medal for drawing at the 1978 C.A.A. annual exhibit.

| FRED FELLOWS | ISSUE PRICE | CURRENT PRICE |
|---|---|---|
| ☐ **MORNING LIGHT ON THE SWAN,** rel. 1976. ed. 1,000, s/n, 26″ x 33″, pub FGH | 100.00 | — |
| ☐ **THE WELCOME COMMITTEE,** rel. 1976. ed. 250, s/n, 20″ x 30″, pub FGH | 100.00 | — |
| ☐ **HIS FIRST SNOW,** rel. 1977. ed. 250, s/n, 18″ x 26″, pub FGH | 100.00 | 200.00 |
| ☐ **FIRST GLIMPSE OF THE ROCKIES,** rel. 1980. ed. 1,000, s/n, 21″ x 32″, pub SCG | 115.00 | — |
| ☐ **SACRED TIMES,** rel. 1980. ed. 1,000, s/n, 30″ x 15″, pub SCG | 115.00 | — |
| ☐ **A WILDERNESS HERITAGE,** rel. 1980. ed. 1,000, s/n, 18¼″ x 35″, pub SCG | 100.00 | — |

| | ISSUE PRICE | CURRENT PRICE |
|---|---|---|
| ☐ **WHEN IT PAYS TO BE MOUNTED,** rel. 1981. ed. 1,000, s/n, 16" x 24", pub SCG | 115.00 | — |
| ☐ **BREAKING THE MORNING TRAIL,** rel. 1982. ed. 1,000, s/n, 17½" x 30", pub SCG | 125.00 | — |

# JUAN FERRANDIZ

Juan Ferrandiz portrays the innocent, honest emotions of children and animals in his art work.

A sensitive and tender world, one filled with goodness, peace and harmony, is the artist's dream. Ferrandiz believes those who know and experience this pure love will forever possess eternal youth within their souls.

Beginning artistic training at the School of Arts in his native Barcelona, recognition of Ferrandiz's art has spread throughout the world. His work can be found on Christmas cards, ornaments, porcelain plates and ANRI woodcarvings.

**HEART OF SEVEN COLORS** *by Juan Ferrandiz*

## JUAN FERRANDIZ

| | | |
|---|---|---|
| ☐ **HE SEEMS TO SLEEP,** rel. 1981. ed. 450, s/n, 17¾" x 10¾", pub SB | 125.00 | 400.00 |
| ☐ **HEART OF SEVEN COLORS,** rel. 1981. ed. 750, s/n, 10¼" x 14½", pub SB | 100.00 | 225.00 |
| ed. 75 (#676-750), remarqued | 175.00 | 550.00 |
| ☐ **MIRROR OF THE SOUL,** rel. 1981. ed. 225, s/n, 15¼" x 10¾", pub SB | 125.00 | 400.00 |
| ☐ **MOST PRECIOUS GIFT,** rel. 1981. ed. 475, s/n, 17" x 27", lithograph, pub SB | 125.00 | 400.00 |
| ed. 50, (#676-750), remarqued | 225.00 | 1000.00 |

|  | ISSUE PRICE | CURRENT PRICE |
|---|---|---|
| ☐ **MY STAR**, rel. 1981. ed. 750, s/n, 10½″ x 17″, pub SB | 100.00 | 250.00 |
| ed. 75, (#676-750), remarqued | 175.00 | 750.00 |
| ☐ **OH SMALL CHILD**, rel. 1981. ed. 475, s/n, 11″ x 15½″, pub SB | 125.00 | 200.00 |
| ed. 100, (#1-50, #426-475), remarqued | 225.00 | 500.00 |
| ☐ **ON THE THRESHOLD OF LIFE**, rel. 1981. ed. 475, s/n, 13½″ x 19″, pub SB | 150.00 | — |
| ed. 50 (#426-475), remarqued | 275.00 | Sold Out |
| ☐ **RIDING THRU THE RAIN**, rel. 1981. ed. 900, s/n, 16″ x 11″, pub SB | 165.00 | — |
| ed. 100 (#801-900), remarqued | 300.00 | Sold Out |
| ☐ **SPREADING THE WORD**, rel. 1981. ed. 725, s/n, 9¾″ x 10½″, pub SB | 125.00 | — |
| ed. 50 (#1-50), 726-750, remarqued | 225.00 | 450.00 |
| ☐ **FRIENDSHIP**, rel. 1982. ed. 475, s/n, pub SB | 165.00 | — |
| ed. 15 (#1-15), remarqued | 1,200.00 | — |

# KEITH FERRIS

The son of a career Air Force officer, Keith Ferris grew up fully expecting to join the Air Force. He majored in aeronautical engineering and enrolled in Air Force ROTC at Texas A&M University. All allergy condition dashed his hopes for a commission, but not his determination to make flying a major part of his life. Employed at the time in the Air Force Training Publications unit at Randolph AFB, Ferris simply channeled his energies into art. From then on, every experience in his life — whether it was an art student, illustrator, graphic arts professional or model builder — served to advance his skill and knowledge as an aviation artist.

Today, in fact, the scope of his career extends beyond art to include important roles as inventor, author, lecturer and historian. He has flown in almost every type of jet aircraft in the Air Force, and done so virtually around the world. He is a major contributor to the Air Force Art Program and is a life member of the Air Force Association. He has painted for almost every major defense contractor and had a variety of commissions for the U.S. Government. A major contribution to the latter is his immense, 25 x 75 foot mural, "Fortresses Under Fire," which covers the entire back wall of the World War II gallery at the National Air and Space Museum in Washington, D.C. Another mural in the same building depicts the history of jet aviation.

**LITTLE WILLIE COMING HOME** *by Keith Ferris*

## KEITH FERRIS

|  |  |  |
|---|---|---|
| ☐ **SUNRISE ENCOUNTER**, rel. 1982. ed. 1,000, s/n, 23″ x 23½″, pub GW | 145.00 | — |
| ☐ **LITTLE WILLIE COMING HOME**, rel. 1983. ed. 1,000, s/n, 37″ x 18¼″, pub GW | 145.00 | — |

## "BLACK JACK" FERRITER

Capturing the beauty and excitement of wildlife and Indian scenes, "Black Jack" Ferriter is a prominent western artist.

He has been a professional artist all of his life. Currently, he conducts workshops for aspiring artists and has been the only instructor to work with Evel Knievel.

**MALLARD DRAKE** *by Black Jack Ferriter*

| "BLACK JACK" FERRITER | ISSUE PRICE | CURRENT PRICE |
|---|---|---|
| ☐ **CUSTER'S LAST STAND**, ed. 2,000, s/n, 16" x 20", pub LC | 200.00 | — |
| ☐ **TIME TO ROOST**, ed. 2,000, s/n, 16" x 20", pub LC | 100.00 | — |
| ☐ **MALLARD DRAKE**, ed. 2,000, s/n, 16" x 20", pub LC | 100.00 | — |
| ☐ **THE HUNTER**, ed. 1,000, s/n, 16" x 20", pub LC | 100.00 | — |
| ☐ **VENISON**, ed. 1,000, s/n, 16" x 20", pub LC | 100.00 | — |
| ☐ **ROUNDUP**, ed. 1,000, s/n, 16" x 20", pub LC | 100.00 | — |
| ☐ **THE DEFENDER**, ed. 1,000, s/n, 16" x 20", pub LC | 200.00 | — |
| ☐ **THE THIEVES**, ed. 1,000, s/n, 16" x 20", pub LC | 200.00 | — |
| ☐ **THE WARRIORS**, ed. 1,000, s/n, 16" x 20", pub LC | 100.00 | — |
| ☐ **PEACEFUL CAMP**, ed. 1,000, s/n, 16" x 20", pub LC | 100.00 | — |

## J. R. FERRITER

Son of "Black Jack" Ferriter, this artist's style is abstract. Ferriter shows a contemporary view of the old west through his unique designs and coloring.

**DESTRUCTION OF AMERICA'S PLAYGROUNDS** *by J.R. Ferriter*

## J. R. FERRITER

| | ISSUE PRICE | CURRENT PRICE |
|---|---|---|
| ☐ **ALL AMERICAN BULL**, ed. 2,000, s/n, 16" x 20", pub LC . . . . . . . . . . . . . . . | 100.00 | — |
| ☐ **STREET WALKER**, ed. 2,000, s/n, 11" x 14", pub LC . . . . . . . . . . . . . . . . . . | 100.00 | — |
| ☐ **PONY GIRL**, ed. 1,000, s/n, 11" x 14", pub LC . . . . . . . . . . . . . . . . . . . . . . . | 100.00 | — |
| ☐ **DESTRUCTION OF AMERICA'S PLAYGROUNDS**, ed. 2,000, s/n, 16" x 20", pub LC. . . . . . . . . . . . . . . . . . . . . . . . . . . . . . . . . . . . . . . . . . . . . . . . . . . . . . | 100.00 | — |
| ☐ **SKILLFUL HUNTER**, ed. 1,000, s/n, 11" x 14", pub LC . . . . . . . . . . . . . . . . | 100.00 | — |
| ☐ **READY FOR WAR**, ed. 1,000, s/n, 16" x 20", pub LC . . . . . . . . . . . . . . . . . . | 100.00 | — |

# CHESTER FIELDS

Chester Fields paints western themes with historical accuracy. Through his art, Fields shares a wealth of knowledge gained during early years spent on ranches in British Columbia and Oregon.

His paintings have been displayed in major western shows and hang in private collections throughout the U.S. and Canada.

## CHESTER FIELDS

| | | |
|---|---|---|
| ☐ **COUGAR COUNTRY**, rel. 1983. ed. 1,000, s/n, 21" x 26¼", pub Washington State Alumni Association will be marketing to their current and past alumni . . . . | 100.00 | — |
| ed. 100 Artist proofs, pub CF. . . . . . . . . . . . . . . . . . . . . . . . . . . . . . . . . . . . . | 200.00 | — |

# DONNY FINLEY

Donny Finley's paintings are designated by rich colors and soft detailing. His paintings achieve the life-like quality that alludes most artists. "I feel that a knowledge of my subject matter is the essence of a realistic painting," says Finley. Consequently, he spends many hours walking in fields and climbing in old haylofts, researching his paintings.

**WALDO BRIDGE** *by Donny Finley*

In the past three years, Finley has won over seventy awards in national shows, including two of the most prestigious, Winter Park and Walt Disney World art shows. He has exhibited with the American Watercolor Society Show in New York and is listed in the current edition of *Who's Who in American Art*.

| DONNY FINLEY | ISSUE PRICE | CURRENT PRICE |
|---|---|---|
| ☐ **BACK PORCH**, ed. 1.000, s/n, 25½″ x 18³/₈″, pub GSP | 50.00 | — |
| ☐ **FRIED PIES**, ed. 1,000, s/n | 40.00 | — |
| ed. 2,000, s/o, 25½″ x 18½″, pub GSP | 30.00 | — |
| ☐ **JIM DANDY**, ed. 1,000, s/n | 40.00 | — |
| ed. 2,000, s/o, 29″ x 21″, pub GSP | 30.00 | — |
| ☐ **MIGHT RAIN**, ed. 1,000, s/n, 20½″ x 29½″, litho, pub GSP | 30.00 | — |
| ☐ **PRINCE ALBERT**, ed. 1,000, s/n | 40.00 | — |
| ed. 2,000, s/o, 22″ x 27½″, pub GSP | 30.00 | — |
| ☐ **MUSCADINE WINE**, rel. 1981. ed. 1,000, s/n, 17″ x 22¼″, pub GSP | 50.00 | — |
| ☐ **SPRING PASTURES**, rel. 1981. ed. 1,000, s/n, 29½″ x 20½″, pub GSP | 60.00 | — |
| ☐ **A FEW DAISIES**, rel. 1982. ed. 1,000, s/n, 29″ x 20½″, pub GSP | 60.00 | — |
| ☐ **PRINCE ALBERT**, rel. 1982. ed. 1,000, s/n, 22″ x 27½″, pub GSP | 40.00 | — |
| ed. 2,000, s/o | 30.00 | — |
| ☐ **WALDO BRIDGE**, rel. 1982. ed. 1,000, s/n, 29½″ x 16½″, pub GSP | 60.00 | — |

# JAMES P. FISHER

Artist James Fisher was born in Wilmington, Delaware in 1912. He attended Howard Pyle School of Illustrators where he was privileged to work under the guidance of three of America's most prominent and finest illustrators: Gayle P. Hoskins, N. C. Wyeth and Frank Schoonover.

During his adult life he has worked as an illustrator and graphic designer ... his preference in painting has always been animals, birds and waterfowl, to which he now devotes his entire time.

Fisher gained much recognition and national prominence by winning the Federal Duck Stamp design competition for 1975. His unique entry of an old shot studded decoy was a most unusual departure from other years.

### JAMES P. FISHER

| | ISSUE PRICE | CURRENT PRICE |
|---|---|---|
| ☐ 1975-76 FEDERAL DUCK STAMP DESIGN (Canvasback Decoy), ed. 3,150 with portion of edition remarqued | reg. | 950.00 |
| size 6½" x 9" plus margins, pub WW | rem. | 1100.00 |
| ☐ BLACK LABRADOR, ed. 450, s/n, 19" x 14½" litho, pub SEL | 55.00 | — |
| ☐ MALLARD DECOY, ed. 950, s/n, 6" x 9" litho, pub WWI | 60.00 | — |
| ☐ CANVASBACK DECOY, ed. 950, s/n, 6" x 9" litho, pub WWI | 25.00 | — |
| ☐ YELLOW LABRADOR, ed. 450, s/n, 19" x 14½" litho, pub SEL | 55.00 | — |
| ☐ WOOD DUCK DECOY, ed. 450, s/n, 10½" x 15½" litho, pub SEL | 50.00 | — |
| ☐ PINTAIL DECOY, ed. 450, s/n, 10½" x 15½" litho, pub SEL | 60.00 | — |
| ☐ AMERICAN GOLDENEYE, ed. 450, s/n, 16" x 20" litho, pub WWI | 50.00 | — |
| ☐ MALLARD DECOY, ed. 450, s/n, 16" x 20" litho, pub WWI | 60.00 | — |
| ☐ RED HEAD DECOY, ed. 450, s/n, 15" x 11" litho, pub WWI | 50.00 | — |
| ☐ PRIMITIVE MALLARD, ed. 450, s/n, 15" x 11" litho, pub WWI | 50.00 | — |
| ☐ CANVAS ON WIRE - CANADA GOOSE, rel. 1978, ed. 450, s/n, 18½" x 16½", pub WWI | 55.00 | — |
| ed. 50, remarque artist proof | 130.00 | — |
| ☐ GREENHEAD DECOY, rel. 1977, ed. 950, s/n, size not available, pub WWI | 25.00 | — |
| ☐ 1948 WARD BLACK DUCK, rel. 1978, ed. 450, s/n, size not available, pub WWI | 55.00 | — |

# JILL FOGELSONG

Living in California for much of her life, Jill Fogelsong has always been fascinated with the beauty of the natural environment. The development of her artistic talent is the result of rigorous study and dedication. At the age of thirteen, Fogelsong exhibited at the 1964 World's Fair in New York. During subsequent travels through Europe, she was greatly influenced by the realism of the Dutch masters. While studying fine art at Stanford University, Fogelsong developed a new watercolor technique which allows her to portray her subjects with meticulous detail by using as many as 400 brush strokes per square inch.

Fogelson believes that it is important for man to live in harmony with nature and has participated in numerous wildlife conferences, donating the proceeds from the sale of her work to benefit wildlife conservation programs. She has also organized fund-raising projects which, through the sale of her prints, have benefited the wildlife collections at children's libraries. Fogelsong's limited edition prints can now be found in private collections in the U.S. and in seventeen foreign countries.

### JILL FOGELSONG

| | | |
|---|---|---|
| ☐ AFRICAN CHEETAH, rel. 1977. ed. 950, s/n, 18" x 22", pub TFC | 36.00 | 50.00 |
| s/n and remarque (on request) | — | 100.00 |
| ☐ AFRICAN LEOPARD, rel. 1976. ed. 1,000, s/n, 18" x 23", pub TFC | 36.00 | 50.00 |
| s/n and remarque (on request) | — | 100.00 |
| ☐ AFRICAN LION, rel. 1977. ed. 950, s/n, 20" x 24", pub TFC | 36.00 | 50.00 |
| s/n and remarque (on request) | — | 100.00 |
| ☐ BENGAL TIGER, rel. 1976. ed. 1,000, s/n, 20" x 22", pub TFC | 36.00 | Sold Out |
| s/n and remarque (on request) | — | Sold Out |
| ☐ GREAT HORNED OWL, rel. 1979. ed. 750, s/n, 16" x 20", pub TFC | 50.00 | 75.00 |
| s/n and remarque (on request) | — | 150.00 |
| ☐ SPECTACLED OWL, rel. 1979. ed. 750, s/n, 16" x 20", pub TFC | 50.00 | 75.00 |
| s/n and remarque (on request) | — | 150.00 |

# BART FORBES

Bart Forbes is an American illustrator, best known for his unique water color paintings. He currently makes his home in Dallas, Texas, where he has established himself as one of the nation's foremost illustrators.

After graduating from the University of North Carolina in 1961, followed by service in the Army, Forbes did graduate study at the Art Center School in Los Angeles. He has guest lectured at many major colleges and universities throughout the country and has been a juror for a gamut of both national and international art exhibitions.

Forbes' editorial illustrations have appeared in *The Saturday Review, Sports Illustrated, Time, TV Guide, Penthouse, Redbook, The Smithsonian, National Geographic, McCalls* and *Seventeen*, among others. His list of commercial clients includes *RCA, Sony, Eastern Airlines, TWA, Exxon, U.S. Navy, American Express, Hart Skis, Proctor & Gamble, NBC, National Football League, Columbia Records*, and others.

Forbes' paintings were included in President Jimmy Carter's White House art collection and illustrated for a series of commemorative postage stamps for the U.S. Postal Service. He has exhibited in a number of one-man shows throughout the United States. As a member of the New York Society of Illustrators, he has been honored with over 40 merit awards in that body's International Exhibition in the past ten years and was selected for inclusion in the Society's show "200 Years of American Illustration". He is also a member of the American Institute of Graphic Arts. His illustrations of award have been published in the *Graphis Annual, CA Annual, CA Art Annual and Creativity*. Bart was also the subject of a feature article in *Communication Arts Magazine*.

## BART FORBES

| | ISSUE PRICE | CURRENT PRICE |
|---|---|---|
| ☐ **STURBRIDGE FARM**, ed. 450, s/n, 25″ x 34″, litho, pub SGC | 110.00 | — |
| ☐ **SHAKER GIRL**, ed. 150, s/n, 22″ x 30″, litho, pub SGC | 150.00 | 250.00 |
| ☐ **1932**, ed. 450, s/n, 18″ x 24″, litho, pub SGC | 60.00 | — |
| ☐ **PHOENIX**, ed. 450, s/n, 18″ x 24″, litho, pub SGC | 68.00 | 200.00 |
| ☐ **SPRING**, ed. 450, s/n, 18″ x 26″, litho, pub SGC | 80.00 | — |
| ☐ **SUMMER**, ed. 450, s/n, 18″ x 26″, litho, pub SGC | 65.00 | 300.00 |
| ☐ **FALL**, ed. 450, s/n, 18″ x 26″, litho, pub SGC | 80.00 | — |
| ☐ **WINTER**, ed. 450, s/n, 18″ x 26″, litho, pub SGC | 120.00 | 150.00 |
| ☐ **BLUE GIRLS**, ed. 700, s/n, 18″ x 24″, litho, pub SGC | 120.00 | — |
| ☐ **WINGS**, ed. 700, s/n, 18″ x 24″, litho, pub SGC | 86.00 | — |
| ☐ **JAZZ SOLO**, ed. 150, s/n, 24″ x 37″, litho, pub SGC | 150.00 | 750.00 |
| ☐ **DAY HERDER**, ed. 50, s/n, 34″ x 44″, litho, pub SGC | 450.00 | 600.00 |
| ☐ **FORT WORTH**, ed. 300, s/n, 26″ x 34″, litho, pub SGC | 80.00 | 150.00 |
| ☐ **WAR HAWK**, ed. 300, s/n, 24″ x 34″, litho, pub SGC | 150.00 | 250.00 |
| ☐ **SEE EES TK**, ed. 750, s/n, 22″ x 28″, litho, pub SGC | 60.00 | — |
| ☐ **SPIRIT WORLD**, ed. 1,500, s/n, 22″ x 28″, litho, pub SGC | 60.00 | — |
| ☐ **TIM-HOO-LAUH**, ed. 1,000, s/n, 22″ x 28″, litho, pub SGC | 100.00 | 75.00 |
| ☐ **OT-WAY**, ed. 450, s/n, 22″ x 30″, litho, pub SGC | 80.00 | — |
| ☐ **TE-MY**, ed. 450, s/n, 22″ x 30″, litho, pub SGC | 80.00 | — |
| ☐ **BRAVE**, ed. 400, s/n, 24″ x 34″, litho, pub SGC | 30.00 | 350.00 |
| ☐ **WESTWARD**, ed. 1,000, s/n, 22″ x 28″, litho, pub SGC | 150.00 | — |
| ☐ **IN-MUT-TOO-YAH-LAT-LAT**, ed. 450, s/n, 22″ x 24″, litho, pub SGC | 50.00 | 300.00 |
| ☐ **OGLALLA SOUIX**, ed. 150, s/n, 24″ x 34″, litho, pub SGC | 40.00 | 750.00 |
| ☐ **RED WING**, ed. 150, s/n, 16″ x 20″, litho, pub SGC | 80.00 | 200.00 |
| ☐ **KIOWA**, ed. 380, s/n, 20″ x 24″, litho, pub SGC | 110.00 | — |
| ☐ **HOO-HA-LA-KIN**, ed. 380, s/n, 16″ x 20″, litho, pub SGC | 80.00 | — |
| ☐ **WAT-CHUM-YUSH**, ed. 450, s/n, 22″ x 23″, litho, pub SGC | 50.00 | 850.00 |
| ☐ **WEP-TES**, ed. 450, s/n, 18″ x 26″, litho, pub SGC | 180.00 | — |
| ☐ **JAZZ DUO**, ed. 500, s/n, 24″ x 35″, litho, pub SGC | 180.00 | — |
| ☐ **HOLDING EAGLE**, ed. 450, s/n, 22″ x 24″, litho, pub SGC | 120.00 | — |
| ☐ **WAR PONY**, rel. 1980. ed. 450, s/n, 22″ x 24″, litho, pub SGC | 120.00 | — |
| ☐ **MOTHER & CHILD**, rel. 1980. ed. 200, s/n, 27″ x 21″, pub SGC | 120.00 | 350.00 |
| ☐ **RANCH HAND**, rel. 1980. ed. 250, s/n, 24″ x 36″, pub SGC | 140.00 | — |
| ☐ **SEA OTTER**, rel. 1980. ed. 450, s/n, 21″ x 25″, pub SGC | 150.00 | — |
| ☐ **TRUMPETER SWAN**, rel. 1980. ed. 450, s/n, 21″ x 23″, pub SGC | 150.00 | 200.00 |
| ☐ **BIG HORN SHEEP**, rel. 1980. ed. 450, s/n, 23″ x 21″, pub SGC | 150.00 | 180.00 |

# STEVE FORBIS

Not since Edward S. Curtis has an artist — working in any medium — revealed the American Indian culture with such sensitivity and craftsmanship. Steve Forbis has developed a precise style that not only documents today's Indian life but also explores the personalities and emotions of the individuals he portrays. His work is enhanced with a special inside into the feeling of people. One senses the rapport that Forbis has with his subjects, many of whom he has known for years.

Alive and vibrant, each of his works is a striking achievement in the subtle balance of light. With delicate shading Forbis captures the richness and depth of forms and textures beyond the limits of photography. He is able to define the sharpest detail of a sunlit bead or to softly shade the gentle contour of a child's face. Our attention is focused on the subjects he depicts through his skillful composition and interpretation of mood.

He combines this native talent with a broad knowledge of Indian cultures. In addition to his first-hand experiences, his training as an anthropologist gives historical accuracy an importance that is reflected in his work. But preservation of Indian life as it is in our time is his special interest.

**IN HER IMAGE** by *Steve Forbis*

## STEVE FORBIS

| | ISSUE PRICE | CURRENT PRICE |
|---|---|---|
| ☐ **TESUQUE SNOWBIRD DANCER**, ed. 100, s/n, size not available, stone lithograph, pub NWDHG | 300.00 | 600.00 |
| ☐ **PASSING TIME AT HUBBELL'S**, ed. 100, s/n, size not available, stone lithograph, pub NWDHG | 300.00 | 600.00 |
| ☐ **BREAD DAY AT TAOS**, ed. 100, s/n, size not available, stone lithograph, pub NWDHG | 260.00 | 300.00 |
| ☐ **DRESSED FOR THE FAIR**, ed. 80, s/n, 13" x 8", stone lithograph, pub NWDHG | 125.00 | — |
| ☐ **SIOUX HEADDRESS**, ed. 80, s/n, 12" x 8", stone lithograph, pub NWDHG | 125.00 | — |
| ☐ **A LOOK AT THE OLD**, ed. 100, s/n, 14" x 19½", stone lithograph, pub NWDHG | 300.00 | — |
| ☐ **IN HER IMAGE**, ed. 100, s/n, 18" x 27", stone lithograph, pub NWDHG | 375.00 | — |

## PAT FORD

| | ISSUE PRICE | CURRENT PRICE |
|---|---|---|
| ☐ **AUTUMN SERENITY**, ed. 750, s/n, 18¾" x 15", distr. GI | 50.00 | — |
| ☐ **MORNING RECESS**, ed. 1,000, s/n, 16" x 20", distr. GI | 35.00 | — |
| ☐ **THE CAROLER**, ed. 750, s/n, 21" x 13¾", distr. GI | 50.00 | — |
| ☐ **THE GATHERING**, ed. 1,000, s/n, 18" x 24", distr. GI | 35.00 | — |

# CHRISTOPHER P. FORREST

Interested in art from the age of 7, Christopher Forrest still speaks fondly of a set of colored pencils presented to him then by his parents. At 11, he won his first award for painting and started exhibiting in galleries. Along with his interest in art, he had a keen attraction for the outdoors and the wildlife which thrived there. After considering schooling in art, Forrest chose to study civil engineering. Upon

**FALL FLIGHT** *by Chris Forrest*

graduation from Virginia Polytechnic Institute, he began a career as a commissioned officer in the United States Army Corps of Engineers. He went to graduate school at North Carolina State University, and it was at this time Forrest started to paint wildlife.
In 1979, Forrest resigned his commission to devote himself to wildlife art. His medium is acrylic, oil and lithography. In 1980, he was elected to membership in the Society of Animal Artists. "Creating a painting or graphic is an adventure and challenge for me. Starting with the observation of the animal in the wilderness, I then approach the painting with the attitude that it will be my finest work."

## CHRISTOPHER P. FORREST

| | ISSUE PRICE | CURRENT PRICE |
|---|---|---|
| ☐ **ARAPAHO CREEK REDTAIL**, rel. 1982. ed. 300, s/n, 22" x 28", litho, pub HUI . | 200.00 | 250.00 |
| ☐ **EVENING'S VIGIL**, rel. 1982. ed. 300, s/n, 21" x 27", litho, pub HUI . . . . . . . . | 200.00 | — |
| ☐ **FALL FLIGHT**, rel. 1982. ed. 300, s/n, 22" x 27", litho, pub HUI . . . . . . . . . . | 200.00 | 250.00 |
| ☐ **FLYING WOODIE**, rel. 1982. ed. 300, s/n, 22" x 28", litho, pub HUI . . . . . . . . | 200.00 | 250.00 |
| ☐ **GOLDEN EAGLE**, rel. 1982. ed. 300, s/n, 21" x 27", litho, pub HUI . . . . . . . . . | 150.00 | 175.00 |
| ☐ **INDIAN PAINTBRUSH**, rel. 1982. ed. 300, s/n, 22" x 27", litho, pub HUI . . . . . | 200.00 | 225.00 |
| ☐ **JOURNEY'S END**, rel. 1982. ed. 300, s/n, 22" x 27", litho, pub HUI . . . . . . . | 200.00 | Sold Out |
| ☐ **LONE TRAVELER**, rel. 1982. ed. 300, s/n, 13" x 19", litho, pub HUI . . . . . . . . | 125.00 | 125.00 |
| ☐ **TIMBER LINE**, rel. 1982. ed. 300, s/n, 22" x 27", litho, pub HUI . . . . . . . . . . . | 150.00 | 175.00 |
| ☐ **DUSK DEPARTURE**, rel. 1983. ed. 300, s/n, 22" x 27", litho, pub HUI . . . . . . | 225.00 | 250.00 |
| ☐ **HAPPY HOVERS**, rel. 1983. ed. 300, s/n, 14" x 20", litho, pub HUI . . . . . . . . | 150.00 | 150.00 |
| ☐ **OCTOBER JOURNEY**, rel. 1983. ed. 300, s/n, 21" x 26", litho, pub HUI . . . . . . | 250.00 | 300.00 |
| ☐ **PINE HAVEN**, rel. 1983. ed. 300, s/n, 13" x 19", litho, pub HUI . . . . . . . . . . . . | 125.00 | 125.00 |
| ☐ **PINTAIL**, rel. 1983. ed. 300, s/n, 22" x 27", litho, pub HUI . . . . . . . . . . . . . | 225.00 | 250.00 |
| ☐ **SPRING STROLL**, rel. 1983. ed. 300, s/n, 22" x 28", litho, pub HUI . . . . . . . . | 250.00 | 300.00 |
| ☐ **SPRING VISITORS**, rel. 1983. ed. 300, s/n, 14" x 20", litho, pub HUI . . . . . . . | 150.00 | 150.00 |
| ☐ **TWILIGHT WANDERS**, rel. 1983. ed. 300, s/n, 21" x 27", litho, pub HUI . . . . . | 250.00 | 300.00 |
| ☐ **WOODY'S REST**, rel. 1983. ed. 300, s/n, 21" x 28", litho, pub HUI . . . . . . . . | 250.00 | 300.00 |

## DON FORREST

| | | |
|---|---|---|
| ☐ **GOLDEN EAGLE**, ed. 500, s/n, 12" x 16", pub RAF . . . . . . . . . . . . . . . . . . . | 30.00 | — |
| ☐ **SPARROW HAWKS**, ed. 500, s/n, 12" x 16", pub RAF . . . . . . . . . . . . . . . . | 30.00 | — |
| ☐ **SPRUCE GROUSE**, ed. 500, s/n, 12" x 16", pub RAF . . . . . . . . . . . . . . . . . | 30.00 | — |

# CHARLES FRACÉ

Charles Fracé graduated from Philadelphia College of Art. He then moved to New York City and became a freelance commercial artist. He illustrated for most of the major publishers, such as *Reader's Digest, McGraw-Hill* and *American Heritage*. He also painted for the National Wildlife Federation and the Audubon Society. Eventually, Fracé became a professional fine art painter. Limited edition prints of his paintings have been published since 1973. Today he is one of the most collected wildlife artists in the world. His wildlife paintings have a unique quality as they capture the spirit of the subjects in addition to keenly depicting the animals appearance.
Fracé is highly regarded in the world of art and has received numerous honors, including a listing in the *Directory of International Biographies, Men of Achievement, Who's Who in American Art* and the *American Cultural Art Register*. He is a dedicated conservationist and a member of the National Audubon Society, the National Wildlife Federation, the Society of Animal Artists, and the Humane Society of the United States.

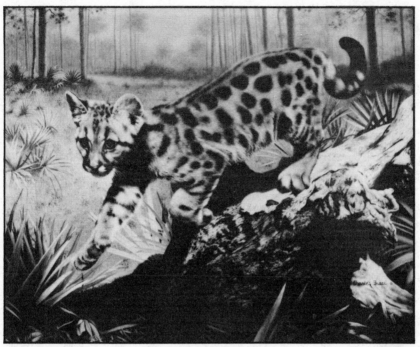

**UNO** *by Charles Fracé*

## CHARLES FRACÉ

| | ISSUE PRICE | CURRENT PRICE |
|---|---|---|
| ☐ **AFRICAN LEOPARD,** rel. 1981. ed. 12,500, s/o, 16″ x 20″, pub AMF........ | 25.00 | 35.00 |
| ☐ **AFRICAN LION,** rel. 1973. ed. 3,000, s/o, 23″ x 23½″, pub FHG ........... | 35.00 | 275.00 |
| ☐ **AMERICAN EAGLE (At Walking Dunes),** rel. 1980. ed. 2,000, s/n, 22½″ x 30″, pub FHG ................................................ | 75.00 | 90.00 |
| ed. 2,000, s/o................................................ | 60.00 | 75.00 |
| ed. 1,000 exclusive | | |
| ☐ **BIGHORN COUNTRY,** rel. 1982. ed. 2,500, s/n, 25″ x 29″, pub AMF ........ | 75.00 | 95.00 |
| ☐ **BISON,** rel. 1975. ed. 2,000, s/n, 20″ x 24″, pub FHG ................... | **50.00 | 90.00 |
| **This limited edition print was released in the AMERICA'S WILDLIFE HERITAGE PORTFOLIO, which consists of six prints in all, each by a different Frame House Gallery artist. | | |
| ☐ **BLACK LEOPARD,** rel. 1978. ed. 3,000, s/o, 28″ x 24″, pub FHG .......... | 50.00 | 300.00 |
| ☐ **BOBCAT,** rel. 1977. ed. 3,000, s/o, 22″ x 18″, pub FHG ................. | 40.00 | 115.00 |
| ☐ **CANADA LYNX,** rel. 1977. ed. 3,000, s/o, 22″ x 24″, pub FHG ........... | 50.00 | 170.00 |
| ☐ **CAVALIER KING CHARLES SPANIELS,** rel. 1976. ed. 1,500, s/n, 20″ x 24″, pub FHG ....................................................... | 35.00 | 85.00 |
| ☐ **CHEETAH,** rel. 1977. ed. 3,000, s/o, 20″ x 26″, pub FHG................ | 50.00 | 90.00 |
| ☐ **CHEETAH KITTEN,** rel. 1974. ed. 5,000, s/o, 24″ x 22½″, pub FHG ...... | 40.00 | 310.00 |
| ☐ **CLOUDED LEOPARD,** rel. 1979. ed. 2,000, s/n, 23″ x 34″ ............... | 65.00 | 110.00 |
| ed. 2,000, s/o, pub FHG ..................................... | 50.00 | 90.00 |
| ☐ **CLOUDED LEOPARD CUB,** rel. 1979. ed. 2,000, s/n, 25″ x 22″ ............ | 75.00 | 110.00 |
| ed. 3,000, s/o, pub FHG .................................... | 60.00 | 80.00 |
| ☐ **COUGAR,** rel. 1978. ed. 1,000, s/n, 25½″ x 30″, pub FHG............... | 90.00 | 550.00 |
| ed. 4,000, s/o ............................................. | 75.00 | 425.00 |
| ☐ **COUGAR CUB,** rel. 1977. ed. 3,000, s/o, 18″ x 22″, pub FHG ............ | 50.00 | 175.00 |
| ☐ **ELEPHANTS AT KILLIMANJARO,** rel. 1976. ed. 1,000, s/n, 21″ x 30″, pub FHG .................................................... | 75.00 | 190.00 |
| ed. 2,000, s/o ............................................. | 60.00 | 140.00 |

| | | | |
|---|---|---:|---:|
| ☐ | **GIANT PANDA,** rel. 1973. ed. 5,000, s/o, 21″ x 24½″, pub FHG | 45.00 | 175.00 |
| ☐ | **GOLDEN EAGLE,** rel. 1973. ed. 1,000, s/n, 30″ x 25¾″, pub FHG | 75.00 | 190.00 |
| | ed. 4,000, s/o | 60.00 | 135.00 |
| ☐ | **GREATER KUDU,** rel. 1977. ed. 3,000, s/o, 21½″ x 20″, pub FHG | 50.00 | 65.00 |
| ☐ | **GYRFALCON,** rel. 1976. ed. 2,000, s/o, 26″ x 20″, pub FHG | 40.00 | 105.00 |
| | ed. 1,000, s/o with the Air Force Emblem | 40.00 | 60.00 |
| ☐ | **HARLAN'S HAWK,** rel. 1977. ed. 1,500, s/n, 20″ x 24″, pub FHG | 60.00 | 110.00 |
| ☐ | **HARP SEAL,** rel. 1980. ed. 2,000, s/n, 23″ x 24″ | 75.00 | 275.00 |
| | ed. 2,000, s/o, pub FHG | 60.00 | 225.00 |
| | ed. 1,500, s/n w/Roman Numerals exclusive for International Fund for Animal Welfare | 100.00 | 300.00 |
| ☐ | **HERRING GULL,** rel. 1974. ed. 5,000, s/o, 21¾″ x 26¾″, pub FHG | 45.00 | 140.00 |
| ☐ | **HIMALAYAN PRINCE,** rel. 1981. ed. 2,000, s/n, 23″ x 28″, pub AMF | 75.00 | 300.00 |
| | ed. 3,000, s/o | 60.00 | 200.00 |
| ☐ | **IMPALA,** rel. 1978. ed. 2,000, s/n, 25½″ x 24″, pub FHG | 60.00 | 80.00 |
| ☐ | **JAGUAR,** rel. 1981. ed. 2,000, s/n, 26¼″ x 31⅛″, pub FHG | 75.00 | 300.00 |
| | ed. 2,000, s/o | 60.00 | 265.00 |
| ☐ | **JAGUAR (Head Series),** rel. 1982. ed. 12,500, s/n, 16″ x 20″, pub AMF | 25.00 | — |
| ☐ | **KOALA BEAR,** rel. 1979. ed. 2,000, s/n, 30″ x 24″ | 65.00 | 175.00 |
| | ed. 2,000, s/o, pub FHG | 50.00 | 145.00 |
| | ed. 1,000 exclusive for Australia | | |
| ☐ | **LEOPARD,** rel. 1977. ed. 1,500, s/n, 20″ x 25″, pub FHG | 75.00 | 300.00 |
| | ed. 1,000, s/n/remarqued | 125.00 | 340.00 |
| ☐ | **LEOPARD CUB,** rel. 1979. ed. 2,000, s/n, 22″ x 28″, pub FHG | 65.00 | 230.00 |
| | ed. 2,000, s/o | 50.00 | 190.00 |
| ☐ | **LION CUB,** rel. 1975. ed. 4,000, s/o, 21½″ x 18½″, pub FHG | 35.00 | 175.00 |
| ☐ | **LOFTY VIEW - RED-TAILED HAWK,** rel. 1981. ed. 2,500, s/n, 24″ x 32″, pub AMF | 75.00 | 90.00 |
| ☐ | **HIS MAJESTY (White-tail Deer),** rel. 1982. ed. 2,500, s/n, 26″ x 29″, pub AMF | 80.00 | 85.00 |
| | ed. 2,000, s/o | 60.00 | — |
| ☐ | **MASAI GIRAFFES AT AMBOSELI,** rel. 1976. ed. 3,000, s/o, 24″ x 18″, pub FHG | 40.00 | 125.00 |
| ☐ | **MORRIS THE CAT,** rel. 1976. ed. 5,000, s/o, 16″ x 20″, pub FHG | 30.00 | 185.00 |
| ☐ | **NORTHERN GOSHAWK,** rel. 1975. ed. 4,000, s/o, 25″ x 27″, pub FHG | 50.00 | 550.00 |
| ☐ | **OCELOT KITTENS,** rel. 1976. ed. 5,000, s/o, 18″ x 20″, pub FHG | 35.00 | 150.00 |
| ☐ | **POLAR BEAR,** rel. 1980. ed. 2,000, s/n, 22″ x 36″, pub AMF | 100.00 | 120.00 |
| | ed. 3,000, s/o | 80.00 | 90.00 |
| ☐ | **PRONGHORN,** rel. 1973. ed. 5,000, s/o, 22″ x 27¼″, pub FHG | 50.00 | 110.00 |
| ☐ | **RACCOON,** rel. 1974. ed. 5,000, s/o, 24″ x 28″, pub FHG | 50.00 | 210.00 |
| ☐ | **RACCOONS (3),** rel. 1978. ed. 5,000, s/o, 24″ x 30″, pub FHG | 50.00 | 350.00 |
| ☐ | **RED SHOULDERED HAWK,** rel. 1975. ed. 2,000, s/n, 28″ x 24″, pub FHG | 60.00 | 110.00 |
| ☐ | **ROYAL PRIDE,** rel. 1982. ed. 2,500, s/n, 25″ x 28″, pub AMF | 100.00 | 115.00 |
| | ed. 2,500, s/o | 80.00 | 90.00 |
| ☐ | **SCREECH OWLS,** rel. 1975. ed. 3,500, s/o, 17″ x 16″, pub FHG | 20.00 | 70.00 |
| ☐ | **SIBERIAN LYNX CUB,** rel. 1980. ed. 2,000, s/n, 22″ x 25″, pub FHG | 75.00 | 130.00 |
| | ed. 2,000, s/o | 60.00 | 80.00 |
| ☐ | **SIBERIAN TIGER,** rel. 1979. ed. 2,000, s/n, 27″ x 33″ | 100.00 | 175.00 |
| | ed. 3,000, s/o, pub FHG | 80.00 | 125.00 |
| ☐ | **SNOW LEOPARD,** rel. 1975. ed. 1,500, s/n, 21⅛″ x 24⅞″, pub FHG | 75.00 | 825.00 |
| | ed. 1,000, s/n/remarqued | 125.00 | 1,200.00 |
| ☐ | **SNOW LEOPARD HEAD,** rel. 1979. ed. 5,000, s/o, 16″ x 20″, pub FHG | 20.00 | 110.00 |
| ☐ | **SNOWY OWLS,** rel. 1979. ed. 2,000, s/n, 23″ x 29″, pub FHG | 65.00 | 95.00 |
| ☐ | **THE LIONS,** rel. 1974. ed. 5,000, s/o, 30½″ x 23½″, pub FHG | 40.00 | 180.00 |
| ☐ | **TIGER,** rel. 1973. ed. 3,000, s/o, 23″ x 23½″, pub FHG | 35.00 | 240.00 |
| ☐ | **TIGER CUB,** rel. 1975. ed. 3,500, s/o, 15″ x 18½″, pub FHG | 35.00 | 195.00 |
| ☐ | **UNO,** rel. 1982. ed. 2,500, s/n, 27″ x 22″, pub AMF | 75.00 | 90.00 |
| | ed. 2,500, s/o | 65.00 | 75.00 |
| | 100 exclusive to Columbus Ohio Zoo. | | |
| ☐ | **WHITE TIGER,** rel. 1976. ed. 1,500, s/n, 26½″ x 34″, pub FHG | 75.00 | 225.00 |
| | ed. 1,000, s/n/remarqued | 125.00 | 265.00 |
| ☐ | **WHITE TIGER HEAD,** rel. 1980. ed. 20,000, s/o, 16″ x 30″, pub FHG | 25.00 | 50.00 |
| ☐ | **LONE HUNTER,** rel. 1982. ed. 2,500, s/n, 22″ x 32″, pub AMF | 100.00 | — |
| | ed. 2,000, s/o | 80.00 | — |
| ☐ | **ZEBRA,** rel. 1975. ed. 4,000, s/o, 39″ x 22¼″, pub FHG | 60.00 | 100.00 |

# THE FRANKLIN MINT

In 1973 The Franklin Mint embarked upon a program of limited edition art with each piece being offered through their Gallery of Art. In the years following most programs were offered in sets.

Inasmuch as their entire offering has been through the Gallery of Art rather than a dealer network it is virtually impossible to determine a collector value as most dealers have neither seen the sets nor know their value and hesitate to offer a customer any secondary market price. This does not necessarily mean they have no value ... it is just that not very many set have been sold on the secondary. There have been a few sets sold through coin shops across the country because they deal exclusively in Franklin Mint material.

| THE FRANKLIN MINT | ISSUE PRICE | CURRENT PRICE |
|---|---|---|
| ☐ **1973 GOLD MEDAL AWARDS**, ed. 4,333, each print individually signed/dated by the artist, series of ten prints, 22″ x 30″ | 500.00 | — |
| APPOINTMENT IN TOWN by Donald Teague; **SELLING THE WHITE STALLION** by Melvin Warren; **AT'EED YAZHI** by Ray Swanson; **DEATH TO LONG KNIVES** by Joe Grandee; **TRIBAL HUNT** by John Clymer; **THE RAIDERS** by Frank McCarthy; **TEXAS LONGHORN** by Robert Summers; **FOGGY MORNING** by Joe Beeler; **CALLING ON NEIGHBORS** by Gordon Phillips; **NOON CHUCK** by James Reynolds | | |
| ☐ **1974 Gold Medal Awards**, ed. 2,908, each print individually signed/dated by the artist, series of twelve prints, 22″ x 30″ | 660.00 | — |
| **TUMBLEWEED SERENADE** by Tom Lovell; **PURSUIT AND ATTACK** by Joe Grandee; **NIGHT RIDER** by Melvin Warren; **MIST OF MORNING** by Ralph Wall; **WOOD GATHERER OF WALPI** by Paul Calle; **LAYING A HEEL TRAP** by Bill Owen; **DUSK ON THE SANTE FE HILLS** by Robert Lougheed; **THE SUPPLY WAGON** by James Reynolds; **WAITING TO GO TO THE POWWOW** by Ray Swanson; **THE GREAT HUNT** by Buck McCain; **CROSSING TRAILS** by Gordon Phillips; **THE NIGHT MAIL** by Donald Teague. | | |
| ☐ **1973 Gallery of American Art** by ten well known entertainers ... Portfolio titled "Celebrity Art Prints", ed. 750, each print individually signed/numbered by the artist, series of ten prints, 22″ x 28″ | 1,500.00 | — |
| **THIRD FLOOR** by Henry Fonda; **MEMORIES OF SUSSEX** by Richard Chamberlain; **NEW YORK** by Tony Bennett; **EVER ONWARD & UPWARD** BY Duke Ellington; **MIGRANT WORKER'S CHILDREN** by Dinah Shore; **SUMMER CREATURES** by Candice Bergen; **THE CLOWN** by Red Skelton; **THE GAMBLERS** by Elke Sommer; **GABY** by Peggy Lee; **THE GULL** by Kim Novak. | | |
| ☐ **1974 - 1977 FLOWERS OF AMERICA ART.** This was a series of eighteen prints from original paintings by the internationally known artist Jeanne Holgate. Each painting portrayed two or more of America's state flowers grouped together as they would be in nature, ed. 2,992, s/n, 22″ x 28″ | 900.00 | — |
| ☐ **1974 BIRD ART PRINTS.** Set consists of 5 prints, each portraying one of America's most beautiful birds, ed. 1,968, signed/dated by the artist, 27″ x 20″ | 300.00 | — |
| **GREAT BLUE HERON, LONG-EARED OWL, WOOD DUCK, BALTIMORE ORIOLE, RED-BELLIED WOODPECKER** | | |
| ☐ **1974 GOLD MEDAL AWARD FOR DISTINGUISHED WATERCOLOR ART.** Consists of twelve prints, signed/dated by the artist. ed. 2,080, 22″ x 30″ | 600.00 | — |
| **BOILING TIME, VERMONT** by Tom Nicholas; **DUSK** by Marion Brown; **DAISIES** by Phillip Jamison; **HEADING HOME** by Paul Rickert; **CHARLIE'S WORLD** by Mel Crawford; **EVENING LIGHT** by Paul Strisik; **NANA'S BOY** by Don Stone; **RAINY TRYST** by John Pike; **WINTER IN CENTRAL PARK** by Bogmoir bogdanovic; **WINDMILLS ON DON QUIXOTE** by Donald Teague; **MILKING TIME** by Guy Fry; **HARBOR SENTINEL** by Rex Brandt. | | |
| ☐ **1974 AMERICA THE BEAUTIFUL ART PRINTS.** Consisting of eight prints by eight distinguished landscape artists, each print is individually signed by the artist, ed. 2,985, 22″ x 30″ | 400.00 | — |
| **O BEAUTIFUL FOR SPACIOUS SKIES** by Wilson Hurley; **FOR AMBER WAVES OF GRAIN** by Ray Hosford; **FOR PURPLE MOUNTAIN MAJESTIES** by Hall Diteman; **ABOVE THE FRUITED PLAIN** by John Chumley; **AMERICA! AMERICA!** by James Fetheroff; **GOD SHED HIS GRACE ON THEE** by Dean Fausett; **AND CROWN THY GOOD WITH BROTHERHOOD** by Robert Sticker; **FROM SEA TO SHINING SEA** by Alex Dzigurski. | | |

| | | ISSUE PRICE | CURRENT PRICE |
|---|---|---|---|

☐ **1975 BIG GAME ART PRINTS.** Consists of ten prints of big game issued by the World Wildlife Fund — U.S. and produced by the Franklin Mint Gallery of Art. The collection was created exclusively for this collection by Gary Swanson, ed. 885, signed/dated by the artist, 22″ x 8″ . . . . . . . . . . . . . . . . . . . . . . . . . . . . . . . . . . **500.00** —
AFRICAN LION, NORTH AMERICAN ELK, GRIZZLY BEAR, GIRAFFES OF KILI-MANHARO, BENGAL TIGER, SHEEP, AFRICAN ELEPHANT, IMPALA, PERSIAN LEOPARD, ROCKY MOUNTAIN GOAT

☐ **1975 SHIPS OF AMERICA ETCHINGS,** Consists of four etchings by well known artist, Alan Jay Gaines, ed. 19,351, signed/dated by the artist, 27³/₈″ x 21¾″ . **300.00** —
THE SCHOONER 'WILLIAM L. WHITE', THE WHALER 'CHARLES W. MORGAN', THE RIVER STEAMBOAT 'ROBERT E. LEE', THE CLIPPER 'SEA WITCH'

☐ **1977 THE FRIGATE 'U.S.S. CONSTITUTION',** ed. 846 . . . special historic ship etching was issued during the Holiday Season . . . . . . . . . . . . . . . . . . . . . . . . **95.00** —

☐ **1976-77 AMERICAN BIRD ENGRAVINGS,** Consists of four engravings. Issued in commemoration of the 150th Anniversary of John James Audubon's Birds of American engravings. Commissioned by the National Audubon Society and drawn by one of our great wildlife artist, Albert Earl Gilbert, ed. 10,253, signed/dated by the artist, 24½″ x 30⁷/₈″ . . . . . . . . . . . . . . . . . . . . . . . . . . . . . **480.00** —
AMERICAN BALD EAGLE, BLUE JAY, SCREECH OWL, CARDINAL

☐ **1976-78 LOCOMOTIVE ETCHINGS,** Consists of four etchings by American Artist Kathleen Cantin, ed. 4,872, signed/dated by the artist, 18″ x 32¼″ . . . . . . . . **360.00** —
THE GREAT LOCOMOTIVE CHASE, EAST MEETS WEST, ENGINE 999, THE TOM THUMB

☐ **1977 SEASCAPES,** Consists of four color lithographs by one of America's most respected seascape artist, Tom Nicholas, ed. 9,189, signed/dated by the artist, 24½″ x 20½″ . . . . . . . . . . . . . . . . . . . . . . . . . . . . . . . . . . . . . . . . . . . . **480.00** —
NEW ENGLAND LIGHTHOUSE, WINTER BEACH (Oregon Coast), ALONG THE GULF COAST (Gulf of Mexico), MONTEREY BEACH (California)

☐ **1977 OLD GEORGIA FARMHOUSE,** Artist Butler Brown. Brown's portrayal of the images of his native Georgia are direct and plain spoken. His inspiration has come from the Georgia midlands where he was born to a farm family, ed. 4,989, signed/remarqued by the artist, 29″ x 25½″ . . . . . . . . . . . . . . . . . . . . . . . . **150.00** —

☐ **1979 LANDSCAPES OF AMERICA,** Artist Butler Brown. This series will consist of four lithographs, with the artist signing and remarquing each edition. Edition size not available at this time because of recent issue size of lithograph will be 25³/₈″ x 22³/₈″ . . . . . . . . . . . . . . . . . . . . . . . . . . . . . . . . . . . . . . . . . . . . . **150.00** —
MILLPOND REFLECTIONS (number one of four)

☐ **1977-78 BIRD LITHOGRAPHS,** Artist Larry Toschik. As accomplished outdoorsman who is widely regarded as one of America's most distinguished wildlife arists. Will consist of four prints when completed, ed. 4,579, signed/dated by the artist, 22³/₈″ x 28½″ . . . . . . . . . . . . . . . . . . . . . . . . . . . . . . . . . . . . . . **380.00** —
WILD CRY OF MORNING (Canada Geese) (number one of four)

☐ **1978-80 COWBOY COLOR LITHOGRAPHS,** Artist Paul Calle. Each of the four lithographs in this series will portray a different moment in the life of the American Cowboy, ed. 2,467, signed/dated by the artist, 21½″ x 25½″ . . . . . . . . . **380.00** —
54 YEARS A COWBOY, MILES TO GO (first two prints in the series)

☐ **1979-80 FLOWERS OF THE YEAR MINIATURES,** Artist Davis Carroll. One of America's most renowned flower artists, he was commissioned by The American Horticultural Society to paint twelve new and original works of flower art . . . these to be issued in authentic limited edition lithographs. Each work to depict the favorite and most captivating flower that blooms during a single month in the gardens of the headquarters of the Society at River Farm. Edition size not available at this time, signed/dated by the artist, 8″ x 9¼″, consists of twelve lithographs . . . . . . . . . . . . . . . . . . . . . . . . . . . . . . . . . . . . . . . . . **420.00** —

☐ **1979-80 CONQUEST OF SPACE COLOR LITHOGRAPH, AND STAMPS,** Artist Paul Calle. Issued to commemorate the tenth anniversary of the first moon landing in 1969. Set will consist of fifteen stamps and color lithographs each providing a pictorial history of America's exploration of space. To preserve its mint condition each stamp is set into a transparent protective capsule with each lithograph specially commissioned to accompany the stamp. Edition size worldwide 15,000, 21¼″ x 18″, signed by the artist . . . . . . . . . . . . . . . . . . . . . . . . . . each **95.00** —
ECHO 1 — COMMUNICATIONS FOR SPACE (1¢ stamp); PROJECT MERCURY (4¢ stamp); ROBERT H. GODDARD (8¢ stamp); APOLLO 8 (6¢ stamp); FIRST

| | ISSUE PRICE | CURRENT PRICE |
|---|---|---|

**MAN ON THE MOON** (10¢ stamp); **U.S. IN SPACE — A DECADE OF ACHIEVE-MENT** (8¢ stamp); **SKYLAB** (10¢ stamp); **PIONEER — JUPITER** (10¢ stamp); **MARINER 10 VENUS/MERCURY** (10¢ stamp); **APOLLO-SOYUZ SPACE TEST PROJECT** (10¢ stamp); **VIKING MISSION TO MARS** (15¢ stamp). There are two in the set untitled as of this writing.

☐ **1979-80 MEL HUNTER LITHOGRAPHS,** This collection of four original color lithographs was created exclusively for this issue by well known artist, Mel Hunter. In the great tradition of American realism, he has chosen to portray the world he knows best — the countryside surrounding his home and studio in Vermont. Edition size not available at this time, signed/dated by the artist, 24½ " x 20¼ "    480.00    —
**CATHERINE'S FARM** (first title of the four)

# ROBERT G. FRANKOWIAK

Bob Frankowiak, Assistant Art Director of the Milwaukee Public Museum, has painted 36 diorama backgrounds depicting wildlife habitat of the United States, the Canadian Arctic, Central America and Africa.

Frankowiak has made several films and given slide lectures on museum expeditions and sport fishing. He has illustrated several fishing books and has done illustrations for magazines like *Trout, International Wildlife,* and *Wisconsin Natural Resources.*

He has exhibited in shows throughout the country and his paintings hang in many private and corporate collections.

**BROWN TROUT** *by Robert Frankowiak*

### ROBERT G. FRANKOWIAK

| | ISSUE PRICE | CURRENT PRICE |
|---|---|---|
| ☐ **BRULE RIVER,** rel. 1976. ed. 300, s/n, 16" x 20", pub RGF, distr. NC . . . . . . | 45.00 | – |
| ☐ **WOLF RIVER,** rel. 1976. ed. 300, s/n, 16" x 20", pub RGF, distr. NC . . . . . . . . | 45.00 | – |
| ☐ **DEER CROSSING,** rel. 1977. ed. 300, s/n, 18" x 24", pub RGF, distr. NC . . . . . | 55.00 | – |
| ☐ **WOOD DUCKS,** rel. 1977. ed. 300, s/n, 18" x 24", pub RGF, distr. NC . . . . . . . | 55.00 | – |
| ☐ **BROWN TROUT,** rel. 1980. ed 600, s/n, 12" x 14", pub NC . . . . . . . . . . . . . . | 85.00 | 35.00 |
| ed. 100 remarqued . . . . . . . . . . . . . . . . . . . . . . . . . . . . . . . . . . . . . . | 160.00 | 600.00 |
| 1980 Wisconsin Trout Stamp print | | |
| ☐ **MUSKELLUNGE,** rel. 1980. ed. 600, s/n, 28" x 22", pub RGF, distr. NC . . . . . | 60.00 | – |
| ☐ **CARDINALS,** rel, 1981. ed. 500, s/n, 22" x 16½", pub RGF, distr. NC . . . . . . | 45.00 | – |
| ☐ **PHEASANTS,** rel. 1981. ed. 500, s/n, 18⅞" x 23", pub RGF, distr. NC . . . . . . | 45.00 | – |

# KENNETH FREEMAN

Kenneth Freeman's artistic talents began to demonstrate themselves at the age of ten. He started painting under the strict training of Joseph DeSalvi. From there he went on to win three one-year scholarships to study art at Stanford University. He continued his studying with William Mosby at the American Academy of Art in Chicago.

The artist has won prizes at the Union League Club, Illinois State Fair, Artist Guild of Chicago, and numerous Art Exhibitions around the country. His paintings have been acquired by people from Hawaii, the Virgin Islands, Mexico, and various private collections throughout the United States.

Freeman has been a Portrait Painter and Illustrator for twenty years. His portrait commissions have included Herbert Hoover, the Mayor of Lincolnwood, Ill., the W. Boyle Family of New Mexico, Presidents of major companies and chairmen of the board of several hospitals in the Chicago area. The subjects come from different occupations; State Senators, School Principals, Actresses, Housewives and Children. He is currently interested in the culture of the American Indian and that of the Cowboy. Travels around the Southwest have acquainted Freeman with their customs and mannerisms. He tries to project on convas the inner depth of the American Heritage. His paintings explore the working Cowboy in modern times and the ageless culture of today's Indians.

Freeman, a native Chicagoan, is married and has two daughters.

### KENNETH FREEMAN

| | | |
|---|---|---|
| ☐ **NUMBER 1 AT PRADO DE SOL,** ed. 950, s/n, 16" x 23½", pub CGAL . . . . . . . . | 150.00 | – |
| ed. 12, Artist accented, s/n . . . . . . . . . . . . . . . . . . . . . . . . . . . . . . . . . | 420.00 | – |
| ☐ **PREPPING FOR THE BRONCS,** ed. 950, s/n, 24" x 18", pub CGAL . . . . . . . . . | 150.00 | – |
| ed. 12, Artist accented, s/n . . . . . . . . . . . . . . . . . . . . . . . . . . . . . . . . . | 420.00 | – |
| ☐ **LONESOME WAIT,** ed. 950, s/n, 18" x 24", pub CGAL . . . . . . . . . . . . . . . . . | 150.00 | – |
| ed. 12, Artist accented, s/n . . . . . . . . . . . . . . . . . . . . . . . . . . . . . . . . . | 420.00 | – |

# LOUIS FRISINO

Deaf since birth, artist Louis Frisino attended the Maryland School for the Deaf, and later attended and graduated from the Maryland Institute of Art, receiving the Peabody Award.

Mr. Frisino recently won the State of Maryland Duck Stamp competition for 1976-77. He placed third in national competition for the Federal Duck Stamp this same year. He also won many awards along the eastern coast.

**RED FOX** *by Louis Frisino*

## LOUIS FRISINO

| | ISSUE PRICE | CURRENT PRICE |
|---|---|---|
| ☐ **SINGLE MALLARD,** ed. 500, s/n, 11″ x 14″, litho, pub RAF | 15.00 | 30.00 |
| ☐ **SINGLE WOOD MALLARD,** ed. 500, s/n, 11″ x 14″, litho, pub RAF | 15.00 | 30.00 |
| ☐ **SINGLE GREEN WING,** ed. 500, s/n, 11″ x 14″, litho, pub RAF | 15.00 | 30.00 |
| ☐ **SINGLE BLUE WING,** ed. 500, s/n, 11″ x 14″, litho, pub RAF | 15.00 | 30.00 |
| ☐ **SINGLE CANADA GOOSE,** ed. 500, s/n, 11″ x 14″, litho, pub RAF | 15.00 | 30.00 |
| ☐ **SINGLE CANVASBACK,** ed. 500, s/n, 11″ x 14″, litho, pub RAF | 15.00 | 30.00 |
| ☐ **REDHEADS - PAIR,** ed. 500, s/n, 14″ x 18″, litho, pub RAF | 30.00 | 60.00 |
| ☐ **CANVASBACKS - PAIR,** ed. 500, s/n, 14″ x 18″, litho, pub RAF | 30.00 | 60.00 |
| ☐ **WOOD DUCKS - PAIR,** ed. 500, s/n, 14″ x 18″, litho, pub RAF | 30.00 | 60.00 |
| ☐ **CANADA GEESE - PAIR,** ed. 500, s/n, 14″ x 18″, litho, pub RAF | 30.00 | 60.00 |
| ☐ **MALLARDS - PAIR,** ed. 500, s/n, 14″ x 18″, litho, pub RAF | 30.00 | 60.00 |
| ☐ **PINTAILS - PAIR,** ed. 500, s/n, 14″ x 18″, litho, pub RAF | 30.00 | 60.00 |
| ☐ **REBEL - GERMAN SHEPHERD,** ed. 600, s/n, 14″ x 18″, litho, pub RAF | 20.00 | 60.00 |
| ☐ **BLACK LAB W/WOOD DUCK,** ed. 500, s/n, 14″ x 18″, litho, pub RAF | 30.00 | 100.00 |
| ☐ **YELLOW LAB W/CANVASBACK,** ed. 500, s/n, 14″ x 18″, litho, pub RAF | 30.00 | 100.00 |
| ☐ **RED FOX,** ed. 950, s/n, 14″ x 18″, litho, distr. MM | — | 35.00 |
| ☐ **CHESAPEAKE W/GOOSE,** ed. 550, s/n, 20″ x 24″, litho, distr. MM | — | 50.00 |
| ☐ **BLACK LAB W/CANVASBACK,** ed. 550, s/n, 20″ x 24″, litho, distr. MM | — | 100.00 |
| ☐ **POINTER HEAD,** ed. 1,000, s/n, 9⅜″ x 12½″, litho, distr. MM | — | 20.00 |
| ☐ **BRITTANY HEAD,** ed. 1,000, s/n, 9⅜″ x 12½″, litho, distr. MM | — | 20.00 |
| ☐ **SPRINGER HEAD,** ed. 1,000, s/n, 9⅜″ x 12½″, litho, distr. MM | — | 20.00 |

| | ISSUE PRICE | CURRENT PRICE |
|---|---|---|
| ☐ **BEAGLE HEAD**, ed. 1,000, s/n, 9⅜" x 12½", litho, distr. MM ............. | — | 20.00 |
| ☐ **BLACK LAB W/PINTAIL**, ed. 1,000, s/n, 18" x 22", litho, distr. MM ........ | — | 100.00 |
| ☐ **GOLDEN RETRIEVER W/MALLARD**, ed. 1,000, s/n, 18" x 22", litho, distr. MM | — | 100.00 |
| ☐ **BLUE BILLS ON WATER**, ed. 550, s/n, 20" x 25", litho, distr. MM ......... | — | 25.00 |
| ☐ **BLACK LAB HEAD**, ed. 1,000, s/n, 9⅜" x 12½", litho, distr. MM .......... | — | 20.00 |
| ☐ **YELLOW LAB HEAD**, ed. 1,000, s/n, 9⅜" x 12½", litho, distr. MM ......... | — | 20.00 |
| ☐ **GOLDEN RETRIEVER HEAD**, ed. 1,000, s/n, 9⅜" x 12½", litho, distr. MM .... | — | 20.00 |
| ☐ **ENGLISH SETTER HEAD**, ed. 1,000, s/n, 9⅜" x 12½", litho, distr. MM ...... | — | 20.00 |
| ☐ **ON THE ALERT**, ed. 950, s/n, 16" x 24", pub RAF..................... | 40.00 | — |
| ☐ **RED FOX**, ed. 950, s/n, 11¼" x 9", pub RAF ....................... | 25.00 | — |

# JERRY GADAMUS

Jerry Gadamus developed an early interest in the outdoors as he trapped, hunted, and fished the Fox River near his home in Green Bay, Wisconsin.

After completing his military service he moved to Stevens Point where he received his formal art training and degree at UW-SP. He is a self-taught taxidermist, which helps him give accurate renderings of wildlife anatomy.

Gadamus is an avid outdoorsman. He has made trips to Alaska and the northwest taking many photographs and collecting materials for his paintings.

Gadamus paints wildlife using an airbrush and through time and experience has been able to achieve detail and fine lines.

His paintings hang in private collections and galleries throughout the United States.

**FLAMING FENCE POST–CARDINALS** by *Jerry Gadamus*

## JERRY GADAMUS

| | ISSUE PRICE | CURRENT PRICE |
|---|---|---|
| ☐ **FIRST DAY ON THE JOB**, rel. 1980. ed. 600, s/n, 28″ x 22″, pub NC . . . . . . . | 60.00 | 250.00 |
| ☐ **KINDERGARTNER**, rel. 1980. ed. 600, s/n, 28″ x 22″, pub NC . . . . . . . . . . . . | 60.00 | — |
| ☐ **ABBY-ALIAS MUD**, rel. 1981. ed. 600, s/n, 22″ x 27¼″, pub NC . . . . . . . . . . | 75.00 | — |
| ☐ **BRULE RIVER MORNING**, rel. 1981. ed. 600, s/n, 35″ x 24″, pub NC . . . . . . . . | 85.00 | — |
| ☐ **FLAMING FENCE POST CARDINALS**, rel. 1983. ed. 600, s/n, 20″ x 24″, pub NC . . . . . . . . . . . . . . . . . . . . . . . . . . . . . . . . . . . . . . . . . . . . . . . . | 75.00 | — |
| ☐ **KILLDEER EGGS**, rel. 1983. ed. 600, s/n, 13⅛″ x 25″, pub NC . . . . . . . . . . . | 55.00 | — |

## LEN GARON

In 1974 Len Garon was awarded the "Most Creative Artist" award in a juried competition for his work with 23 karat gold. Since then, this young artist has been recognized through nomination to *Who's Who in American Art,* 1978, exhibitions in museums, acceptance in major national juried competitions, including the National Academy Galleries in New York City, exhibition at the prestigious Hammer Galleries in New York City, inclusion in many major corporate collections, and through numerous television appearances.

Garon refuses to be typed as an artist who expresses only in one style, one medium, or one subject matter. He is equally at ease with oils, pastel, water color, gold leaf, and lithography. Many of his lithographs are being published by major national publishing firms. His creative, inquisitive mind, skill, and message which he communicates has no limitation for he sets no limitation on himself. Even with his varied technique though, his style exemplifies that "this is a 'Garon'."

He was born in Colorado in 1945 and spent the first 26 years of his life in the West and Southwest prior to moving to Pennsylvania in 1972.

His art can best be described as romantic impressionism. The secret to his skill is that within his paintings of reality the viewer will find hidden abstractions which constantly invite the viewer's eye to look beyond the surface painting to the technique, texture, hidden subtleties, and color which gave three dimensional life and breath to a two dimensional painting.

Garon has studied with the international sculptor and painter Pawel Kontny as well as at the Philadelphia Museum School. He is a member of the national juried Pastel Society of America, the Philadelphia Sketch Club, and the Philadelphia Water Color Club. His works are currently in galleries in Philadelphia, New Jersey, New York, Florida, and California.

## LEN GARON

| | | |
|---|---|---|
| ☐ **BLUE HORIZONS**, ed. 285, s/n, 23″ x 29″, pub EG . . . . . . . . . . . . . . . . . . . . | 75.00 | — |
| ☐ **EARLY FALL**, ed. 285, s/n, 23″ x 29″, pub EG . . . . . . . . . . . . . . . . . . . . . | 75.00 | — |
| ☐ **LOST MEMORIES**, ed. 285, s/n, 23″ x 29″, pub EG . . . . . . . . . . . . . . . . . . . | 75.00 | — |
| ☐ **MASK, THE**, ed. 285, s/n, 23″ x 29″, pub EG . . . . . . . . . . . . . . . . . . . . . . | 75.00 | — |
| ☐ **SUMMER BREEZE**, ed. 285, s/n, 23″ x 29″, pub EG . . . . . . . . . . . . . . . . . . . | 75.00 | — |
| ☐ **SPRING BREEZE**, ed. 250, s/n, 23″ x 29″, pub EG . . . . . . . . . . . . . . . . . . . | 75.00 | — |

## FRANK T. GEE

Frank T. Gee was born in Canton, China, and came to this country when he was six years old. He studied commercial design and watercolors at the Memphis Academy of Arts.

He is renowned as a watercolor for the consummate skill and delicate simplicity of his Oriental brushwork which enables him to unerringly capture the beauty and innocence of nature.

**BABY COTTONTAILS** by Frank T. Gee

Gee's award-winning paintings have been extensively displayed throughout the south, firmly establishing his reputation as an outstanding artist of rare sensitivity and insight.

| FRANK T. GEE | ISSUE PRICE | CURRENT PRICE |
|---|---|---|
| ☐ **MORNING MIST,** rel. 1974. ed. 2,500, s/n, 16″ x 11¾″, pub ALI .......... | **15.00 | — |
| **Some with Chinese signature ............................. | 25.00 | — |
| ☐ **THREE SWALLOWS,** rel. 1974. ed. 2,500, s/n, 18″ x 12½″, pub ALI........ | **15.00 | 160.00 |
| **Some with Chinese signature .................................. | 25.00 | 195.00 |
| ☐ **YOUNG KINGBIRDS,** rel. 1975. ed. 2,000, s/n, 22″ x 16″, pub ALI ......... | **25.00 | 125.00 |
| ed. 500 s/o ................................................ | 15.00 | 60.00 |
| **Some with Chinese signature ........................... | 30.00 | 160.00 |
| ☐ **BABY COTTONTAILS,** rel. 1975. ed. 2,000, s/n, 17½″ x 13½″, pub ALI ..... | **25.00 | — |
| ed. 500, s/o ............................................... | 15.00 | 35.00 |
| **Some with Chinese signature ........................... | 30.00 | — |
| ☐ **SIAMESE KITTENS,** ed. 1,500, s/n, 22″ x 17″, pub ALI ................. | **20.00 | — |
| ed. 1,500, s/o............................................. | 15.00 | — |
| **Some with Chinese signature ........................... | 30.00 | 125.00 |
| ☐ **SNOWBOUND COTTONTAILS,** ed. 2,500, s/n, 26″ x 21½″, pub ALI......... | **25.00 | — |
| **Some with Chinese signature ........................... | 30.00 | 80.00 |
| ☐ **SPAWNING MINNOWS,** ed. 2,500, s/n, 17″ x 22″, pub FTGS.............. | **25.00 | — |
| **Some with Chinese signature ........................... | 30.00 | — |
| ☐ **THREE CHICKADEES,** ed. 2,500, s/n, 16″ x 22″, pub FTGS .............. | **30.00 | — |
| **Some with Chinese signature ........................... | 35.00 | — |
| ☐ **ARKANSAS RIVER,** ed. 2,500, s/n, 17″ x 22″, pub FTGS .............. | 25.00 | — |
| ☐ **TWO SQUIRRELS,** ed. 1,250, s/n, 17½″ x 22″, pub FTGS ............... | **40.00 | — |
| **Some with Chinese signature ........................... | 35.00 | — |
| ed. 1,250, s/n | | |
| ☐ **SPRING SONG,** ed. 1,250, s/n, 17″ x 22″, pub FTGS ................... | **45.00 | — |
| **Some with Chinese signature ......................... | 40.00 | — |
| ed. 1,250, s/n | | |
| ☐ **LITTLE CHIRPERS,** ed. 1,250, s/n, 19″ x 14″, pub FTGS ................ | **40.00 | — |
| **Some with Chinese signature ......................... | 35.00 | — |
| ed. 1,250, s/n | | |

# JOSEPH GETSINGER

Born in Camden, New Jersey in 1948, Joe Getsinger recognized his artistic yearnings in high school where he concentrated on developing a unique and fluid style that has carried through the years in his work. Although he studied law in college, he still pursued training in his spare time under the instruction of George Vail.

Shortly after this, he began to exhibit his work at local group shows, which evolved into several one-man shows in galleries throughout the East Coast. Collecting antique cars as a hobby has provided the stimulus for many nostalgic etchings. The first of these were especially welcomed by the public, and were responsible for his first commissions for advertising illustrations.

As the popularity for his work increases, representation in fine galleries and private collections across the country does as well. His "Center Ring" and the "Artist Poster Print" are in the collection of Red Skelton.

Collectors should note that Getsinger signs his original pieces "J. Gets" with a heart below his name. His editions are signed J. M. Getsinger.

**MARE AND FOAL** by Joseph Getsinger

| JOSEPH GETSINGER | ISSUE PRICE | CURRENT PRICE |
|---|---|---|
| ☐ **ANTIQUE SHOW**, ed. 175, s/n, 10″ x 15″, etching, pub JGE | 20.00 | 30.00 |
| ☐ **ARTIST'S POSTER PRINT (Clown)**, ed. 1,900, s/n, 21″ x 28″, offset litho, pub JGE | 25.00 | 25.00 |
| ☐ **BARN**, ed. 175, s/n, etching, pub JGE | 20.00 | 25.00 |
| ☐ **BARNEGAT LIGHTHOUSE**, ed. 150, s/n, 24″ x 27″, etch, pub JGE | 60.00 | 90.00 |
| ☐ **BIRDWING**, ed. 175, s/n, etch, pub JGE | 45.00 | 70.00 |
| ☐ **1910 BUICK**, ed. 150, s/n, 14″ x 17″, etch, pub JGE | 35.00 | 45.00 |
| ☐ **CENTER RING**, ed. 285, s/n, 24″ x 29″, litho, pub JGE | 50.00 | 110.00 |
| ☐ **28 CHEVROLET**, ed. 175, s/n, 13″ x 16″, etch, pub JGE | 40.00 | 45.00 |
| ☐ **29 CHRYSLER ROADSTER**, ed. 100, s/n, 20″ x 24″, etch, pub JGE | 60.00 | 85.00 |
| ☐ **1936 CORD**, ed. 175, s/n, etch, pub JGE | 40.00 | 50.00 |
| ☐ **53 CORVETTE**, ed. 150, s/n, 10″ x 15″, etch, pub JGE | 35.00 | 45.00 |
| ☐ **DOG FIGHT**, ed. 175, s/n, 17″ x 20″, etch, pub JGE | 40.00 | 45.00 |

| | | ISSUE PRICE | CURRENT PRICE |
|---|---|---|---|
| ☐ | **DRIFTIN' ALONG,** ed. 175, s/n, 11″ x 14″, etch, pub JGE | 20.00 | 35.00 |
| ☐ | **FIRST INDY,** ed. 100, s/n, 10″ x 15″, etch, pub JGE | 30.00 | 35.00 |
| ☐ | **FIRST MOON,** ed. 300, s/n, 8″ x 11″, litho, pub JGE | 25.00 | 30.00 |
| ☐ | **FLYIN',** ed. 100, s/n, 8″ x 8″, etch, pub JGE | 10.00 | 20.00 |
| ☐ | **1903 FORD,** ed. 75, s/n, 16″ x 20″, etch, pub JGE | 40.00 | Sold Out |
| ☐ | **FREE AS THE WIND,** ed. 175, s/n, 20″ x 24″, etch, pub JGE | 35.00 | 70.00 |
| ☐ | **GABLE,** ed. 225, s/n, 17″ x 18″, litho, pub JGE | 20.00 | 30.00 |
| ☐ | **HAPPY,** ed. 175, s/n, 16″ x 19″, etch, pub JGE | 40.00 | 50.00 |
| ☐ | **HERE'S LOOKIN AT YOU KID,** ed. 75, s/n, 15″ x 16″, etching, pub JGE | 35.00 | Sold Out |
| ☐ | **KIKI,** ed. 175, s/n, 19″ x 21″, linoleum, pub JGE | 45.00 | 50.00 |
| ☐ | **LES CHEVAUX,** ed. 175, s/n, 26″ x 33″, litho, pub JGE | 60.00 | 150.00 |
| ☐ | **LE CHEVAUX II,** ed. 300, s/n, 16″ x 20″, litho, pub JGE | 40.00 | 50.00 |
| ☐ | **LE CHEVAUX SUITE,** 25 suites from an edition of 300. A five-piece suite including: Les Chevaux II, First Moon, Moondrift, Luna, and Whispers. | 175.00 | 250.00 |
| ☐ | **LET'S CLOWN AROUND,** ed. 175, s/n, 17″ x 20″, etch, pub JGE | 45.00 | 50.00 |
| ☐ | **LITTLE DOLPHINS,** ed. 175, s/n, 11½″ x 13″, etching, pub JGE | 20.00 | 30.00 |
| ☐ | **LONG ISLAND SOUND,** ed. 150, s/n, 16″ x 17″, etch, pub JGE | 50.00 | 60.00 |
| ☐ | **LOST FRONTIER,** ed. 75, s/n, 14″ x 18″, etching, pub JGE | 45.00 | Sold Out |
| ☐ | **MACAW,** ed. 175, s/n, 14″ x 22″, etching, pub JGE | 40.00 | 50.00 |
| ☐ | **MAIN STREET,** ed. 200, s/n, 23″ x 29″, litho, pub JGE | 70.00 | 90.00 |
| ☐ | **MARE & FOAL,** ed. 175, s/n, 16″ x 19″, etching, pub JGE | 40.00 | 65.00 |
| ☐ | **MOONDRIFT,** ed. 300, s/n, 4″ x 8″, litho, pub JGE | 17.50 | 22.00 |
| ☐ | **MUSHROOMS,** ed. 175, s/n, 15″ x 17″, etching, pub JGE | 30.00 | 45.00 |
| ☐ | **NIGHTCALL,** ed. 2,000, s/n, 21″ x 26″, offset litho, pub JGE | 25.00 | 30.00 |
| ☐ | **OLD FORD PANEL,** ed. 100, s/n, 16″ x 18″, etch, pub JGE | 35.00 | 40.00 |
| ☐ | **1928 PACKARD,** ed. 175, s/n, 17″ x 20″, etch, pub JGE | 50.00 | 75.00 |
| ☐ | **PEGASUS,** ed. 75, s/n, 18″ x 22″, etching, pub JGE | 35.00 | Sold Out |
| ☐ | **RIDING,** ed. 150, s/n, 8″ x 11″, etch, pub JGE | 15.00 | 30.00 |
| ☐ | **31 ROLLS,** ed. 175, s/n, 14″ x 17″, etch, pub JGE | 30.00 | Sold Out |
| ☐ | **RUNNING FREE,** ed. 50, s/n, 8″ x 10″, etching, pub JGE | 20.00 | Sold Out |
| ☐ | **SAVE THE DOLPHINS,** ed. 175, s/n, 16″ x 19″, etching, pub JGE | 30.00 | 45.00 |
| ☐ | **SHORELINE,** ed. 1,900, s/n, 8½″ x 22″, offset litho, pub JGE | 10.00 | 15.00 |
| ☐ | **SPRING,** ed. 175, s/n, 16″ x 18″, etching, pub JGE | 60.00 | 70.00 |
| ☐ | **STUCK,** ed. 25, s/n, 24″ x 30″, litho, pub JGE | 95.00 | Sold Out |
| ☐ | **SUMMER,** ed. 175, s/n, 16″ x 18″, etching, pub JGE | 60.00 | 70.00 |
| ☐ | **THE ROSE,** ed. 75, s/n, 7″ x 10″, etching, pub JGE | 15.00 | Sold Out |
| ☐ | **TOPPY,** ed. 150, s/n, 17″ x 17″, etch, pub JGE | 35.00 | 50.00 |
| ☐ | **T-TOURING,** ed. 100, s/n, 14″ x 17″, etch, pub JGE | 35.00 | 45.00 |
| ☐ | **TUT & AYE,** ed. 285, s/n, 29″ x 34″ litho, foil embossed, pub JGE | 150.00 | 200.00 |
| ☐ | **WHISPERS,** ed. 300, s/n, 8″ x 11″, litho, pub JGE | 25.00 | 30.00 |
| ☐ | **WHITE CLOUD,** ed. 100, s/n, 17″ x 20″, etch, pub JGE | 45.00 | 50.00 |
| ☐ | **YOUNG NUDE,** ed. 75, s/n, 12″ x 16″, etching, pub JGE | 35.00 | Sold Out |

# ALBERT EARL GILBERT

Al Gilbert's work is in the permanent collections of the Carnegie Museum, the National Wildlife Federation, the American Museum of Natural History and many private collections.

Listed in *Who's Who in American Art*, Gilbert is currently President of the Society of Animal Artists and has done much in the way of raising money for conservation organizations, often donating his own work. The artist's highest honor was when he won the 1978-79 Federal Duck Stamp competition.

## ALBERT GILBERT

| | ISSUE PRICE | CURRENT PRICE |
|---|---|---|
| **INTERNATIONAL WILDLIFE SERIES** | | |
| ☐ **AMERICAN BALD EAGLES**, rel. 1973. ed. 1,000, s/n, 24" x 20", pub NWAEI*. | 65.00 | |
| ☐ **CARDINALS ON APPLE BLOSSOM**, rel. 1973. ed. 300, s/n, 20" x 24", pub NWAEI* | 75.00 | 700.00 |
| ☐ **MOCKINGBIRDS ON ORANGE BLOSSOM**, rel. 1973. ed. 750, s/n, 20" x 24", pub NWAEI* | 75.00 | 600.00 |
| ☐ **EASTERN BLUEBIRDS**, rel. 1973. ed. 1,500, s/n, 20" x 24", pub NWAEI*.... | 60.00 | |
| ☐ **COUGAR**, rel. 1973. ed. 3,500, s/n, 24" x 20", pub NWAEI* | 50.00 | |
| ☐ **CARDINALS IN THE SNOW**, rel. 1973. ed. 1,500, s/n, 20" x 24", pub NWAEI* | 60.00 | |
| **THE DECORATOR SERIES** | | |
| ☐ **WILD TURKEY**, rel. 1973. ed. 3,000, s/n, 16" x 20", pub NWAEI* | 30.00 | |
| ☐ **HOODED MERGANSER 1978-79 Federal Duck Stamp Print**, rel. 1978. ed. 5,800, s/n, 13" x 14⁷/₈", pub SRWA | 100.00 | 200.00 |
| ed. 1,350, s/n, remarqued in watercolor | 375.00 | 675.00 |
| ed. 300 Artists proofs | | |
| ☐ **SAW-WHET OWL**, rel. 1978. ed. 950, s/n, 16" x 20", pub SRWA | 50.00 | — |
| ☐ **CHICKADEE ON HOLLY**, rel. 1978. ed. 950, s/n, 16" x 20", pub SRWA | 50.00 | — |
| ☐ **AMAZON JUNGLE JAGUAR & CUB**, rel. 1978. ed. 750, s/n, 32" x 40", pub SRWA | 150.00 | — |
| ☐ **AFRICAN LIONESS & CUBS**, rel. 1978. ed. 750, s/n, 32" x 40", pub SRWA... | 150.00 | — |

*These prints were published by National Wildlife Art Exchange of Florida. This company is no longer in business and because these prints are not actively bought and sold on the collector market at this time we hesitate to place any collector value on these issues.

# H. COBB GILBERT

As a student, H. Cobb Gilbert, entered an international magazine cover-art competition sponsored by Famous Artists Schools of Westpoint, Connecticut and of the over 4,000 entries he received honorable mention. In 1980 his works was selected to be shown at the Second Alaska Wildlife Art Exhibition sponsored by the Audubon Society of Anchorage, Alaska.

**MATCHED WITS** by H. Cobb Gilbert

In 1980, 81 and 82 he received an Awards of Excellence at the Elkhorn Invitational Arts Festival, Sun Valley, Idaho. His Canvasback Ducks entry was selected as a finalist in the Long Island Wetland and Waterfowl League's annual art competition for the Waterfowl Print and Stamp of 1980 . . . entries were received from twenty-six states.

In 1979 his painting of Red-breasted Mergansers was selected for special showing at the Easton Waterfowl Festival in Easton, Maryland and at the Academy of Natural Sciences show in Philadelphia, Pennsylvania. In 1980 his Federal Duck Stamp entry, a painting of Barrows Goldeneyes was selected for a special showing again at the Easton Waterfowl Festival and the Academy of Natural Sciences.

H. Cobb Gilbert has painted cover art for the *Idaho Wildlife Magazine* in both 1981 and 1982, and in 1982 his painting of a Bull Elk was chosen as winner in the State of idaho Archery Stamp competition . . . this being the nation's first bowhunter stamp.

## H. COBB GILBERT

| | ISSUE PRICE | CURRENT PRICE |
|---|---|---|
| ☐ FEMALE BELTED KINGFISHER, rel. 1980. ed. 350, s/n, 12″ x 10″, pub NHFA . | 65.00 | — |
| w/pencil remarque | 130.00 | — |
| w/color remarque | 175.00 | — |
| ☐ RED-BELLIED WOODPECKER, rel. 1980. ed. 250, s/n, 12″ x 13″, pub NHFA .. | 65.00 | — |
| w/pencil remarque | 130.00 | — |
| w/color remarque | 175.00 | — |
| ☐ COAST CANVASBACKS, rel. 1980. ed. 250, s/n, 19″ x 26″, pub NHFA | 65.00 | — |
| w/pencil remarque | 130.00 | — |
| w/color remarque | 175.00 | — |
| ☐ WOOD DUCKS, rel. 1981. ed. 500, s/n, 19″ x 24″, pub NHFA | 85.00 | — |
| w/pencil remarque | 150.00 | — |
| w/color remarque | 195.00 | — |
| ☐ RED-BREASTED MERGANSERS, rel. 1981. ed. 350, s/n, 7″ x 10″, pub NHFA . | 45.00 | — |
| w/pencil remarque | 110.00 | — |
| w/color remarque | 155.00 | — |
| ☐ ELK, rel. 1982. ed. 1,500, s/n, 7″ x 10″, pub NHFA | 125.00 | — |
| w/stamp | 130.50 | — |
| w/pencil remarque | 190.00 | — |
| w/pencil remarque and stamp | 195.50 | — |
| w/color remarque | 235.00 | — |
| w/color remarque and stamp | 240.50 | — |
| ☐ HUNGARIAN PARTRIDGE, rel. 1982. 1st in a Series (5) Idaho Upland Game Birds, ed. 500, s/n, 19″ x 23″, pub NHFA | 75.00 | — |
| w/pencil remarque | 140.00 | — |
| w/color remarque | 185.00 | — |

# GRANT GILDERHUS

Grant Gilderhus learned to enjoy drawing at a young age when his father sat him on his lap and drew pictures for him. His love of the outdoors was nurtured in a family that hiked, hunted and fished.

Both loves have matured into a talent which is now being recognized and honored. His watercolors of field and forest show a unique sensitivity for the drama and beauty of our great land, its heritage and its natural wonders.

A native of Minnesota, Grant is a 1954 graduate from Carthage College, now located in Kenosha, Wisconsin. In 1958 he helped found a publishing firm where he remained as creative director through 1975. In 1976, together with a partner, he began Vista III Design, Inc. where they do commercial design and wildlife illustration.

**GRANT GILDERHUS**

| | ISSUE PRICE | CURRENT PRICE |
|---|---|---|
| ☐ OPENING DAY - LAKE EMMA, rel. 1979. ed. 400, s/n, 28¾" x 22¾", distr. NC . . . . . . . . . . . . . . . . . . . . . . . . . . . . . . . . . . . . . . . . . . . . . . . | 60.00 | — |
| ☐ EARLY MATES - PHEASANTS, rel. 1980. ed. 600, s/n, 29" x 22¾", distr. NC. | 80.00 | — |

## LUNDA HOYLE GILL

By special invitation, Lunda Gill's paintings of the tribal people of Kenya, "*The Kenyans*", were exhibited in the Smithsonian Institution's Museum of Natural History, Washington, D.C., in a one-woman exhibition.

Gill is a Pomona College (California) graduate who studied at the Chouinard Art Institute in Los Angeles, the Art Students League in New York City, and the Academia de Belli Arti in Florence, Italy.

Her paintings have been exhibited in many national, regional, and solo exhibitions from New York to California, including the National Academy of Design and the Mid-America Annual. Among her many awards is the Stacey Fellowship. While a resident of Oklahoma she was appointed by the governor as an art advisor to the Oklahoma Arts and Humanities Council.

Her work is in collections owned by Charlton Heston, Burt Reynolds, and Lyndon B. Johnson, among others. Her paintings hang in prominent galleries in the United States, Canada, Mexico and Europe.

**LUNDY IN THE SAND** by Lunda Hoyle Gill

**LUNDA HOYLE GILL**

| | ISSUE PRICE | CURRENT PRICE |
|---|---|---|
| ☐ LUNDY IN THE SAND, rel. 1972. ed. 1,000, s/n, 31" x 23½", pub FHG . . . . . . | 35.00 | 100.00 |
| ☐ LUNDY IN THE WHEAT, rel. 1973. ed. 1,500, s/n, 25" x 29", pub FHG . . . . . . | 35.00 | Sold Out |
| ☐ LUNDY ON THE ROCK, rel. 1974. ed. 1,000, s/n, 20" x 33½", pub FHG . . . . . | 45.00 | 60.00 |
| ☐ GABRA NAB, rel. 1975. ed. 500, s/n, 18" x 22", pub FHG . . . . . . . . . . . . . . . | 50.00 | Sold Out |
| ☐ NATIVE OF THE NORTH, portfolio of three . . . . . . . . . . . . . . . . . . . . . . . . . . . . | 1,200.00 | Sold Out |
| ☐ Individually, WISE KAKARUK, ed. 300, s/n, 20" x 16", pub HP . . . . . . . . . . | 450.00 | — |

| | ISSUE PRICE | CURRENT PRICE |
|---|---|---|
| ☐ **SEWING MY MUKLUK'S**, ed. 300, s/n, 20" x 23", pub HP | 550.00 | — |
| ☐ **MY LAND**, ed. 300, s/n, 21" x 28", pub HP | 650.00 | — |

## WILLIAM GILLIES

Born in San Francisco in 1911, William Gillies' copious art education included the University of Southern California, the Art Center and Chouinard Art School in Los Angeles and the Grand Central Art School in New York.

He began his professional career in the early 30's as an illustrator and lettering artist, continuing in that capacity for more than twenty years. In 1957, he developed an interest in portrait painting and within two years had founded The Portrait Group, an organization of professional painters. In 1961, he started The Portrait Group School of Painting, an instructional institute specializing in portraits.

Since moving to South Carolina in 1976, Bill has developed a deep interest in painting dogs. Although he is not a hunter himself, he often accompanies friends on hunting trips and field trials, adding to his keen understanding of the technical aspects of a hunting dog's activities.

William Gillies' fine paintings reflect a lifelong interest in art and the outdoors, and his work is now ranked with that of today's foremost sporting artists.

**WILLIAM GILLIES**

| | ISSUE PRICE | CURRENT PRICE |
|---|---|---|
| ☐ **COMING IN - BLACK LAB**, rel. 1981. ed. 850, s/n, size not available, pub WWI | 65.00 | — |
| ☐ **MARK**, rel. 1981. ed. 800, s/n, 18" x 24", pub PP | 75.00 | — |
| s/n, remarqued | 165.00 | — |

## BARBARA GIROUARD

**INDIANA WINTER** *by Barbara Girouard*

| | ISSUE PRICE | CURRENT PRICE |
|---|---|---|
| ☐ **INDIANA WINTER**, rel. 1981. ed. 450, s/n, 22″ x 28″, pub GU . . . . . . . . . . . . | 30.00 | 70.00 |
| ☐ **PONCE DE LEON INLET**, rel. 1981. ed. 300, s/n, 17½″ x 23½″, pub GU . . . . . | 30.00 | 50.00 |
| ☐ **JUST RESTING**, rel. 1981. ed. 300, s/n, 17½″ x 23½″, pub GU . . . . . . . . . . | 30.00 | 50.00 |
| ☐ **THE WINDMILL**, rel. 1981. ed. 300, s/n, 17½″ x 23½″, pub GU . . . . . . . . . . | 30.00 | 50.00 |

# ANDRE GISSON

"There is a dramatic moment in the essence of any scene of life which excludes more than it appears to include. I ask you — the Viewer — to join me in reaching for that moment — in drawing from your life's experiences as you view my paintings."

Gisson was born in 1928 in New York City. A graduate of Pratt Institute, his debt to French Impressionism is most apparent in his earlier works. The landscapes and florals of the period 1952-1960 show his taste for broken color areas and mosaics of color designs, derived from Seurat, and his emphasis on intimacy and form, similar to Renoir. His marked color restraint and subtlely appeared even then, however, and he disregarded the vogues of Post-Impressionism and Fauve's "saturated" color in order to suggest the great power of cool and warm whites, shadings which form the stylistic trademark of so much of his work even to the present day.

Some credit this to his having lived in Japan after the Second World War. The areas of rest and inactivity in contrast to the widely active elements and shapes of the subjects suggests a conscious study of Sesshu and other Sumi-e masters of China and Japan.

In his subject matter, however, Gisson holds to the experienced world of domestic life, the beach, nudes, flowers, and of course the still-life subjects — all seemingly drained of color, yet to the eye and senses aglow with light and the "feeling" of color.

## ANDRE GISSON

| | | |
|---|---|---|
| ☐ **BREEZE AT TRURO**, rel. 1977. ed. 250, s/n, 18″ x 15½″, litho, arches, pub EEI . . . . . . . . . . . . . . . . . . . . . . . . . . . . . . . . . . . . . . . . . | 125.00 | 150.00 |
| ☐ **SHADOW**, rel. 1978. ed. 250, s/n, 38″ x 28½″, litho, arches, pub EEI . . . . . . | 200.00 | 225.00 |
| ☐ **CAROUSEL**, rel. 1979. ed. 250, s/n, 27½″ x 24″, litho, arches, pub EEI . . . . . | 150.00 | 200.00 |
| ed. 50, japon . . . . . . . . . . . . . . . . . . . . . . . . . . . . . . . . . . . . . . . . . . . . . | 175.00 | 225.00 |
| ☐ **PATH**, rel. 1981. ed. 250, s/n, 34″ x 28½″, litho, arches, pub EEI . . . . . . . . . | 200.00 | — |

# NANCY GLAZIER

From her youth, Nancy Glazier has possessed an immense love of both art and animals. Born in Salt Lake City, Utah in 1947, Glazier sketched and painted at every opportunity. Her future in art was shaped in ninth grade when she began taking art lessons from German artist, Adolph Spohr whom she respected and adored. By the age of eighteen she set out on her own, determined to "become and artist".

After living in California for a time, she returned to her native state of Utah and painted the wild animals of Asia and Africa. Yet she remained unsatisfied with her work and has since found the greatest pleasure in painting what she knows best — our North American wildlife.

Glazier expertly and sensitively records on canvas the very spirits of these native American animals, gathering information and inspiration in Yellowstone National Park, The Grand Tetons and the Black Hills of South Dakota. Her works are featured in several galleries.

| NANCY GLAZIER | ISSUE PRICE | CURRENT PRICE |
|---|---|---|
| ☐ THE AMERICANS, rel. 1981. ed. 600, s/n, size not available, pub WWI | 100.00 | — |
| ☐ BEAUTY AND THE BEAST, rel. 1982. ed. 600, s/n, size not available, pub WWI | 85.00 | — |
| ☐ ROYALTY, rel. 1982. ed. 600, s/n, size not available, pub WWI | 85.00 | — |

# DAVID LANCE GOINES

David Lance Goines is an artist, calligrapher and printer of fine books, who lives in Berkeley, California, and heads the Saint Heironymous Press there. He is also a poster maker. The technical excellence with which Goines executes his posters is an inherent part of their appeal. Unlike most contemporary poster makers, who send their designs to commercial printers to be mechanically processed, Goines does all the production work himself. His use of photo-offset lithography is unique; instead of the usual four color separation process of modern offset printing, which results in an overall dot pattern, Goines makes separate solid tone plate for each color he uses, ranging in number from four to as many as fifteen. The colors created in this way are extraordinarily subtle.

Since his first one man exhibition at Thackrey & Robertson (then called The Poster) in 1973, Goines has had numerous one man shows, including major retrospectives at the Achenback Foundation for Graphic Arts at the Fine Arts Museums of San Francisco, 1976-77, and the University Art Museum at the University of California, Berkeley, 1977. Goines' posters have also been included in many group exhibitions, including "Images on an Era: The American Poster 1945-75", an exhibition organized by the Smithsonian Institution which traveled throughout the United States and Europe.

## DAVID LANCE GOINES

| | | |
|---|---|---|
| ☐ THE KITCHEN, rel. 1968. ed. 3,000, 18" x 24", pub DLG | — | N/A |
| ed. 25, hand signed | — | N/A |
| ☐ QUI TACIT CONSENTIT, rel. 1969. ed. 300, 18" x 24", pub DLG | — | N/A |
| ed. 10, hand signed | — | 900.00 |
| ☐ BENNET WEDDING ANNOUNCEMENT, rel. 1969. ed. 250, 18" x 24", pub DLG. | — | N/A |
| ed. 5, hand signed | — | N/A |
| ☐ VELO-SPORT BICYCLES, rel. 1970. ed. 3,000, 18" x 24", 3 colors, pub DLG | — | N/A |
| 13 hand signed | — | N/A |
| ed. 2,000, 5 colors, second edition, pub DLG | — | N/A |
| 100 hand signed | — | 500.00 |
| ed. 4,493, 5 colors, third edition, pub DLG | — | N/A |
| 126 hand signed | — | 400.00 |
| ☐ MIME TROOP, rel. 1970. ed. 1,000, 18" x 24", pub DLG | — | N/A |
| 9 hand signed | — | 900.00 |
| ☐ WOODWORK, rel. 1970. ed. 500, 18" x 24", 2 colors, pub DLG | — | N/A |
| ☐ ANATOLE FRANCE QUOTE, rel. 1970. ed. 500, 15" x 24", 1 color, pub DLG | — | N/A |
| 9 hand signed | — | N/A |
| ☐ RAINBOW-ZENITH, rel. 1970. ed. 200, 17" x 22", 8 colors, pub DLG | — | N/A |
| 4 hand signed | — | N/A |
| ☐ ed. 1,000, 8 colors, second edition, pub DLG | — | N/A |
| 100 hand signed | — | N/A |
| ☐ FOTO-GRAPHIX, rel. 1971. ed. 500, 17" x 24", 3 colors, pub DLG | — | N/A |
| 25 hand signed | — | N/A |
| ed. 1,000, 3 colors, second edition | — | N/A |
| 100 hand signed | — | 150.00 |

| | ISSUE PRICE | CURRENT PRICE |
|---|---|---|
| **HOFFMAN WEDDING ANNOUNCEMENT**, rel. 1971. ed. 200, 18″ x 24″, 3 colors, pub DLG | — | N/A |
| 14 hand signed | — | N/A |
| **BERKELEY ARTS CALENDAR**, rel. 1971. ed. 3,000, 17″ x 24″, pub DLG | — | N/A |
| 18 hand signed | — | N/A |
| **POETRY READING**, rel. 1971. ed. 250, 15″ x 24″, 2 colors, pub DLG | — | N/A |
| 10 hand signed | — | N/A |
| **BERKELEY VD CLINIC**, rel. 1971. ed. 130, 18″ x 24″, 4 colors, no hand signed edition, pub DLG | — | N/A |
| ed. 1,000, 4 colors, second edition, released in 1972 | — | N/A |
| 25 hand signed | — | 2,500.00 |
| **CHEZ PANISSE**, rel. 1972. ed. 1,000, 15″ x 24″, pub DLG | — | N/A |
| 100 hand signed | — | N/A |
| ed. 2,000, 4 colors, second edition | — | N/A |
| 100 hand signed | — | 1,200.00 |
| **ABECEDARIUM BROADSIDE**, rel. 1972. ed. 250, 17″ x 23″, pub DLG | — | N/A |
| 18 hand signed | — | N/A |
| **TYPE SPECIMEN BROADSIDE**, rel. 1972. ed. 100, 18″ x 24″, 1 color, no hand signed prints, pub DLG | — | N/A |
| **DER BLAUE ENGEL**, rel. 1972. ed. 190, 18″ x 24″, 4 colors, pub DLG | — | N/A |
| 25 hand signed | — | N/A |
| ed. 450, 4 colors, second edition | — | N/A |
| 200 copies were to be hand signed, but only a smaller, indeterminate number were in fact inscribed | — | 250.00 |
| **SHERE ANNIVERSARY INVITATION**, rel. 1972. ed. 75, 18″ x 24″, pub DLG | — | N/A |
| 13 hand signed | — | N/A |
| **THE GENERAL**, rel. 1972. ed. 200, 18″ x 24″, 5 colors, pub DLG | — | N/A |
| 12 hand signed | — | N/A |
| ed. 400, 5 colors, second edition | — | N/A |
| 200 hand signed | — | 800.00 |
| ed. 100, 4 colors, third edition released in 1973 | — | N/A |
| 25 hand signed | — | N/A |
| **RUGGLES OF RED GAP**, rel. 1972. ed. 250, 18″ x 24″, 3 colors, pub DLG | — | N/A |
| 25 hand signed | — | 900.00 |
| **EASTMAN HOUSE (Pink)**, rel. 1972. ed. 100, 18″ x 24″, 4 colors, pub DLG | — | N/A |
| 16 hand signed | — | N/A |
| **EASTMAN HOUSE (Silver)**, rel. 1972. ed. 250, 18″ x 24″, 4 colors, pub DLG | — | N/A |
| 23 hand signed | — | 900.00 |
| **OLYMPIA**, rel. 1972. ed. 250, 18″ x 24″, 4 colors, pub DLG | — | N/A |
| 24 hand signed | — | 900.00 |
| **BLUE PRINTS: JM**, rel. 1972. ed. 200, 18″ x 24″, 3 colors, pub DLG | — | N/A |
| **GUINNESS, 1973**, ed. 206, 18″ x 24″, 4 colors, pub DLG | — | N/A |
| 100 hand signed | — | 1,500.00 |
| **BACH**, rel. 1973. ed. 250, 18″ x 24″, 5 colors, pub DLG | — | N/A |
| 25 hand signed | — | N/A |
| ed. 3,749, rel. 1977, second edition | — | N/A |
| 26 artist's proofs | — | N/A |
| ed. 3,389, third edition, no artist's proofs | — | N/A |
| **GOINES: POSTERS**, rel. 1973. ed. 350, 18″ x 24″, 8 colors, pub DLG | — | N/A |
| 150 hand signed | — | 3,000.00 |
| **PAGNOL TRILOGY**, rel. 1973. ed. 300, (three poster set), 13½″ x 24″, 5 colors, pub DLG | — | N/A |
| 100 hand signed ... set | — | 1,400.00 |
| **CHEZ PANISSE 2ND BIRTHDAY**, rel. 1973. ed. 300, 18″ x 24″, 4 colors, pub DLG | — | N/A |
| 100 hand signed | — | 1,000.00 |
| **PIG-BY-THE-TAIL**, rel. 1973. ed. 1,000, 18″ x 24″, 4 colors, pub DLG | — | N/A |
| 100 hand signed | — | 100.00 |
| ed. 1,100, released 1977, second edition, no hand signed | — | N/A |
| **IMAGES MEDIEVALS**, rel. 1973. ed. 500, 18″ x 24″, 10 colors, pub DLG | — | N/A |
| 100 hand signed | — | 700.00 |

| | ISSUE PRICE | CURRENT PRICE |
|---|---|---|
| ☐ **KARL KARDEL**, rel. 1974. ed. 1,850, 18″ x 24″, 8 colors, pub DLG | — | 500.00 |
| 100 hand signed | — | N/A |
| ed. 4,796, released 1978, second edition, no hand signed | — | N/A |
| ed. 208 variant four color printing issued in 1974 | — | N/A |
| 25 hand signed | — | N/A |
| ☐ **BART**, rel. 1974. ed. 600, 21″ x 22″, 5 colors, pub DLG | — | N/A |
| 50 hand signed | — | 200.00 |
| ed. 350, second edition | — | N/A |
| 75 hand signed | — | 150.00 |
| ☐ **THE POSTER, SANTA BARBARA**, rel. 1974. ed. 482, 12¼″ x 24″, 9 colors, pub DLG | — | N/A |
| 100 hand signed | — | 600.00 |
| ed. 948, released in 1977, second edition | — | N/A |
| 26 artist's proofs A-Z | — | N/A |
| ☐ **GOINES: INDIA INK EXHIBITION**, rel. 1974. ed. 484, 13″ x 24″, 6 colors, pub DLG | — | N/A |
| 100 hand signed | — | 250.00 |
| ☐ **DIE NIBELUNDEN**, rel. 1974. ed. 474, 12″ x 24″, 7 colors, pub DLG | — | N/A |
| 100 hand signed | — | 200.00 |
| ☐ **LES ANIMAUX**, rel. 1974. ed. 334, 18″ x 24″, 2 colors, pub DLG | — | N/A |
| 100 hand signed | — | 100.00 |
| ☐ **AMERICA**, rel. 1974. ed. 1,300, 18″ x 24″, 12 colors, pub DLG | — | N/A |
| 200 numbered and 26 artist's proofs | — | 800.00 |
| ☐ **CHEZ PANISSE 3RD BIRTHDAY**, rel. 1974. ed. 417, 18″ x 24″, 6 colors, pub DLG | — | N/A |
| 100 numbered and 26 artist's proofs | — | 1,000.00 |
| ☐ **EARLY MASTERS OF PHOTOGRAPHY**, rel. 1974. ed. 424, 18″ x 24″, 6 colors, pub DLG | — | N/A |
| 100 s/n and 26 artist's proofs | — | 500.00 |
| ☐ **INDIA INK GALLERY**, rel. 1974. ed. 356, 17¼″ x 24″, 3 colors, pub DLG | — | N/A |
| 100 s/n and 26 artist's proofs | — | 250.00 |
| ed. 1,025, released 1977, second edition, no signed edition | — | N/A |
| ☐ **BY HAND**, rel. 1974. ed. 2,398, 18″ x 24″, 5 colors, pub DLG | — | N/A |
| 100 s/n and 26 artist's proofs | — | 500.00 |
| ed. 4,133, released 1977, second edition | — | N/A |
| 26 artist's proofs | — | N/A |
| ☐ **BERKELEY PUBLIC LIBRARY**, rel. 1974. ed. 941, 14″ x 24″, 5 colors, pub DLG | — | N/A |
| 100 s/n and 26 artist's proofs | — | 250.00 |
| ed. 1,060, released 1975, second edition | — | N/A |
| 25 s/n and 26 artist's proofs | — | N/A |
| ed. 2,104, released 1977, third edition, no signed edition | — | N/A |
| ☐ **WEININGER**, rel. 1975. ed. 1,950, 18″ x 24″, 3 colors, pub DLG | — | N/A |
| 100 s/n and 26 artist's proofs | — | 100.00 |
| ☐ **MUSIC AND THE MOVIES**, rel. 1975. ed. 2,745, 10″ x 24″, 7 colors, pub DLG | — | N/A |
| 100 s/n and 26 artist's proofs | — | N/A |
| ☐ **HOFFMAN BIRTH ANNOUNCEMENT**, rel. 1975. ed. 266, 18″ x 24″, 4 colors, pub DLG | — | N/A |
| 100 s/n and 26 artist's proofs | — | 250.00 |
| ☐ **CHEZ PANISSE 4TH BIRTHDAY**, rel. 1975. ed. 834, 18″ x 24″, 9 colors, pub DLG | — | N/A |
| 100 s/n and 26 artist's proofs | — | 1,200.00 |
| ☐ **CHAMPAGNE DEUTZ**, rel. 1975. ed. 320, 18″ x 24″, 7 colors, pub DLG | — | N/A |
| 100 s/n and 26 artist's proofs | — | 800.00 |
| ed. 1,647, released 1976, second edition, no signed edition | — | N/A |
| ed. 1,057, released 1976, third edition, no signed edition | — | N/A |
| ☐ **LOS ANGELES FILM EXPOSITION**, rel. 1975. ed. 1,010, 18″ x 24″, 15 colors, pub DLG | — | N/A |
| 100 s/n and 26 artist's proofs | — | 400.00 |
| ed. 148, 13 colors, printed in the pre-type state | — | N/A |
| 100 s/n and 26 artist's proofs | — | N/A |
| ☐ **PANDORA'S BOX**, rel. 1975. ed. 1,397, 13″ x 24″, 7 colors, pub DLG | — | N/A |
| 100 s/n and 26 artist's proofs | — | 1,000.00 |
| ☐ **BIG MAN**, rel. 1975. ed. 213, 14″ x 24″, 11 colors, pub DLG | — | N/A |
| 100 s/n and 26 artist's proofs | — | 400.00 |

| | ISSUE PRICE | CURRENT PRICE |
|---|---|---|
| ☐ **ANNUNCIATION**, rel. 1975. ed. 398, 15″ x 24″, 8 colors, pub DLG . . . . . . . . . | — | N/A |
| 100 s/n and 26 artist's proofs . . . . . . . . . . . . . . . . . . . . . . . . . . . . . . . | — | 600.00 |
| 15 w/special inscription . . . . . . . . . . . . . . . . . . . . . . . . . . . . . . . . . | — | N/A |
| 25 w/6 colors, s/o . . . . . . . . . . . . . . . . . . . . . . . . . . . . . . . . . . . . | — | N/A |
| ☐ **SAN FRANCISCO SYMPHONY**, rel. 1975. ed. 634, 15¼″ x 24″, 7 colors, pub DLG . . . . . . . . . . | — | N/A |
| 100 s/n and 26 artist's proofs . . . . . . . . . . . . . . . . . . . . . . . . . . . . . | — | 450.00 |
| ed. 689 without the ''Marathon'' type . . . . . . . . . . . . . . . . . . . . . . . . . | — | N/A |
| 100 s/n with 26 artist's proofs . . . . . . . . . . . . . . . . . . . . . . . . . . . . | — | N/A |
| ed. 483, second edition with the type ''Marathon 1977'', none signed . . . . . . | — | — |
| ☐ **ANTIQUE GUILD**, rel. 1976. ed. 2,418, 14½″ x 24″, 4 colors, pub DLG . . . . . . | — | N/A |
| 200 s/n and 26 artist's proofs A-Z and 10 i-x . . . . . . . . . . . . . . . . . . . . | — | 100.00 |
| ed. 2,435, second edition, none signed . . . . . . . . . . . . . . . . . . . . . . . | — | N/A |
| ☐ **THE CARPET CENTER**, rel. 1976. ed. 1,777, 18″ x 24″, 4 colors, pub DLG . . . . | — | N/A |
| 200 s/n and 26 artist's proofs . . . . . . . . . . . . . . . . . . . . . . . . . . . . . | — | 100.00 |
| ☐ **LE MATIN**, rel. 1976. ed. 762, 16¾″ x 24″, 6 colors, pub DLG . . . . . . . . . . . | — | N/A |
| 200 s/n and 26 artist's proofs . . . . . . . . . . . . . . . . . . . . . . . . . . . . . | — | 400.00 |
| ☐ **BOOKSHOP, SANTA CRUZ**, rel. 1976. ed. 2,517, 18″ x 24″, 6 colors, pub DLG | — | N/A |
| 200 s/n and 26 artist's proofs . . . . . . . . . . . . . . . . . . . . . . . . . . . . . | — | 150.00 |
| ☐ **CHEZ PANISSE 5TH BIRTHDAY**, rel. 1976. ed. 2,113, 18″ x 24″, 7 colors, pub DLG . . . . . . . . | — | N/A |
| 200 s/n and 26 artist's proofs . . . . . . . . . . . . . . . . . . . . . . . . . . . . . | — | 250.00 |
| ☐ **GOINES, POSTERS 1968-1976**, rel. 1976. ed. 2,444, 15″ x 24″, 6 colors, pub DLG . . . . . . . . | — | N/A |
| 300 s/n and 26 artist's proofs . . . . . . . . . . . . . . . . . . . . . . . . . . . . . | — | 250.00 |
| ed. 2,000, released 1977 w/text for UC Berkeley, none signed . . . . . . . . . . | — | N/A |
| ed. 683, released in 1977 with no text and none signed . . . . . . . . . . . . . . | — | N/A |
| ☐ **FULL CIRCLE GALLERY**, rel. 1976. ed. 1,404, 18″ x 24″, 6 colors, pub DLG . . | — | N/A |
| 300 s/n and 26 artist's proofs . . . . . . . . . . . . . . . . . . . . . . . . . . . . . | — | 250.00 |
| ed. 2,406, released in 1977, second edition, none signed . . . . . . . . . . . . . | — | N/A |
| ☐ **QUEEN OF HEARTS**, rel. 1977. ed. 1,513, 15″ x 24″, 5 colors, pub DLG . . . . . . | — | N/A |
| 300 s/n and 26 artist's proofs . . . . . . . . . . . . . . . . . . . . . . . . . . . . . | — | 250.00 |
| ☐ **MIRAGE**, rel. 1977. ed. 2,104, 13½″ x 24″, 6 colors, pub DLG . . . . . . . . . . . . | — | N/A |
| 300 s/n and 26 artist's proofs . . . . . . . . . . . . . . . . . . . . . . . . . . . . . | — | 100.00 |
| ☐ **GARLIC**, rel. 1977. ed. 2,380, 18″ x 24″, 7 colors, pub DLG . . . . . . . . . . . . . | — | N/A |
| 300 s/n and 26 artist's proofs . . . . . . . . . . . . . . . . . . . . . . . . . . . . . | — | 100.00 |
| ☐ **FAUST**, rel. 1977. ed. 2,047, 18″ x 24″, 7 colors, pub DLG . . . . . . . . . . . . . | — | N/A |
| 300 s/n and 26 artist's proofs . . . . . . . . . . . . . . . . . . . . . . . . . . . . . | — | 250.00 |
| ☐ **LEVON**, rel. 1977. ed. 1,900, 18″ x 24″, 4 colors, pub DLG . . . . . . . . . . . . . | — | N/A |
| 300 s/n and 26 artist's proofs . . . . . . . . . . . . . . . . . . . . . . . . . . . . . | — | 100.00 |
| ☐ **LETTER FROM AN UNKNOWN WOMAN**, rel. 1977. ed. 1,509, 18″ x 24″, 10 colors, pub DLG . . . . . . | — | N/A |
| 300 s/n and 26 artist's proofs . . . . . . . . . . . . . . . . . . . . . . . . . . . . . | — | 100.00 |
| ☐ **NOSFERATU**, rel. 1977. ed. 2,453, 18″ x 24″, 5 colors, pub DLG . . . . . . . . . . | — | N/A |
| 300 s/n and 26 artist's proofs . . . . . . . . . . . . . . . . . . . . . . . . . . . . . | — | 100.00 |
| ☐ **NEW YEAR'S GREETING**, rel. 1978. ed. 2,615, 16″ x 24″, 8 colors, pub DLG . . | — | N/A |
| 300 s/n and 26 artist's proofs . . . . . . . . . . . . . . . . . . . . . . . . . . . . . | — | 450.00 |
| ☐ **BERKELEY REPERTORY THEATER**, rel. 1977. ed. 3,023, 6 volors, 18″ x 24″, pub DLG . . . . . . . . | — | N/A |
| 300 s/n and 26 artist's proof . . . . . . . . . . . . . . . . . . . . . . . . . . . . . . | — | 250.00 |
| ☐ **UNIVERSITY ARTS CENTER**, rel. 1978. ed. 4,720, 14¼″ x 24″, 5 colors, pub DLG . . . . . . . . . | — | N/A |
| 300 s/n and 26 artist's proofs . . . . . . . . . . . . . . . . . . . . . . . . . . . . . | — | 150.00 |
| ☐ **ORIENTALIA**, rel. 1978. ed. 1,587, 18″ x 24″, 8 colors, pub DLG . . . . . . . . . . | — | N/A |
| 300 s/n and 26 artist's proofs . . . . . . . . . . . . . . . . . . . . . . . . . . . . . | — | 250.00 |
| ☐ **AUGUST, CHEZ PANISSE 7TH BIRTHDAY**, rel. 1978. ed. 1,900, 18″ x 24″, 9 colors, pub DLG . . . . . | — | N/A |
| 300 s/n and 26 artist's proofs . . . . . . . . . . . . . . . . . . . . . . . . . . . . . | — | 100.00 |
| ☐ **WILKEN AND LEVERETT**, rel. 1978. ed. 2,154, 18″ x 24″, 6 colors, pub DLG . . | — | N/A |
| 300 s/n and 26 artist's proofs . . . . . . . . . . . . . . . . . . . . . . . . . . . . . | — | 100.00 |
| ☐ **THACKREY & ROBERTSON**, rel. 1978. ed. 2,130, 16″ x 24″, 5 colors, pub DLG | — | N/A |
| 300 s/n and 26 artist's proofs . . . . . . . . . . . . . . . . . . . . . . . . . . . . . | — | 250.00 |
| ☐ **ASILOMAR**, rel. 1978. ed. 1,952, 18″ x 24″, 7 colors, pub DLG . . . . . . . . . . . | — | N/A |
| 300 s/n and 26 artist's proofs . . . . . . . . . . . . . . . . . . . . . . . . . . . . . | — | 450.00 |

| | ISSUE PRICE | CURRENT PRICE |
|---|---|---|
| ☐ UNPLEASANT SURPRISES, rel. 1978. ed. 2,642, 15½" x 24", 9 colors, pub DLG | — | N/A |
| 300 s/n and 26 artist's proofs | — | 100.00 |
| ☐ MESSIAH, rel. 1978. ed. 2,423, 16¼" x 24", 13 colors, pub DLG | — | N/A |
| 300 s/n and 26 artist's proofs | — | 250.00 |
| ☐ DANCE, rel. 1978. ed. 2,954, 16" x 24", 8 colors, pub DLG | — | N/A |
| 300 s/n and 26 artist's proofs | — | 100.00 |
| ☐ OPTOMETRY, rel. 1979. ed. 2,792, 16$\frac{9}{160}$ x 24", 4 colors, pub DLG | — | N/A |
| 300 s/n and 26 artist's proofs | — | 150.00 |
| ed. 5,136, released 1980, second edition, none signed | — | N/A |
| ☐ DOW AND FROSINI, rel. 1979. ed. 4,305, 18" x 24", 13 colors, pub DLG | — | N/A |
| 300 s/n and 26 artist's proofs | — | 100.00 |
| ☐ RAVENSWOOD, rel. 1979. ed. 1,047, 16" x 24", 5 colors, pub DLG | — | N/A |
| 300 s/n and 26 artist's proofs | — | 100.00 |
| ☐ INTERNATIONAL HOUSE, rel. 1979. ed. 3,327, 16" x 24", 6 colors, pub DLG | — | N/A |
| 300 s/n and 26 artist's proofs | — | 150.00 |
| ☐ A CONSTRUCTED ROMAN ALPHABET, rel. 1979. ed. 1,873, 18" x 24", pub DLG | — | N/A |
| 300 s/n and 26 artist's proofs | — | 250.00 |
| ☐ CAFE, rel. 1980. ed. 2,136, 14⅝" x 24", 9 colors, pub DLG | — | N/A |
| 300 s/n and 26 artist's proofs | — | 400.00 |
| ☐ WINGS, rel. 1980. ed. 2,754, 16$\frac{9}{16}$" x 24", 4 colors, pub DLG | — | N/A |
| 300 s/n and 26 artist's proofs | — | 100.00 |
| ☐ MIRAGE EDITIONS, rel. 1980. ed. 2,872, 18" x 24", 10 colors, pub DLG | — | N/A |
| 300 s/n and 26 artist's proofs | — | 250.00 |
| ☐ EAT, CHEZ PANISSE 9TH BIRTHDAY, rel. 1980. ed. 1,990, 16⅞" x 24", 10 colors, pub DLG | — | N/A |
| 300 s/n and 26 artist's proofs | — | 750.00 |
| ☐ NORTHFACE, rel. 1980. ed. 3,330, 16⅞" x 24", 5 colors, pub DLG | — | N/A |
| 300 s/n and 26 artist's proofs | — | 400.00 |
| ☐ METROPOLIS, rel. 1981. ed. 2,143, 18" x 24", 13 colors, pub DLG | — | N/A |
| 300 s/n and 26 artist's proofs | — | 250.00 |
| ☐ CHEZ PANISSE 10TH BIRTHDAY, rel. 1981. ed. 2,264, 18" x 24", 13 colors, pub DLG | — | N/A |
| 300 s/n and 26 artist's proofs | — | 250.00 |
| ☐ CARDUCCI & HERMAN, LANDSCAPE ARCHITECTS, 1981, ed. 2,783, 12¾" x 24", 7 colors, pub DLG | — | N/A |
| 300 s/n and 26 artist's proofs | — | 250.00 |
| ☐ NEYERS, rel. 1981. ed. 2,141, 15½" x 24", 3 colors, pub DLG | — | N/A |
| 300 s/n and 26 artist's proofs | — | 150.00 |
| ☐ CHEZ PANISSE MENU COOKBOOK, rel. 1981. ed. 1,890, 15½" x 24", 10 colors, pub DLG | — | N/A |
| 300 s/n and 26 artist's proofs | — | 250.00 |
| ☐ QUILT SHOW, rel. 1982. ed. 3,226, 16" x 24", 7 colors, pub DLG | — | N/A |
| 300 s/n and 26 artist's proofs | — | 250.00 |
| ☐ LORD NELSON BEER, rel. 1982. ed. 1,919, 17" x 24", 5 colors, pub DLG | — | N/A |
| 300 s/n and 26 artist's proofs | — | 150.00 |
| ☐ M, rel. 1982. ed. 2,108, 18" x 24", 10 colors, pub DLG | — | N/A |
| 300 s/n and 26 artist's proofs | — | 150.00 |

# FRANCIS GOLDEN

Francis Golden was born in Adams, Massachusetts in 1916. He was trained at the Museum School of Fine Arts in Boston. After a brief career as a muralist, the highlight of which came with work under Salvador Dali, Golden turned to commercial illustration.

Golden is one, among a handful of outdoor painters, who works in watercolors. Goldens' use of watercolor arose through the desire to paint in a free expressive manner. He uses this keenly to create atmosphere. Golden takes black and white photographs as opposed to color, which he enlarges to huge sizes. These show him details of the scene he is painting. He does not want to be confined to the "true" colors of a slide. He wants to create his own.

**TROUT FISHING** *by Francis Golden*

Since 1960, Golden has concentrated on illustration for various magazines, notably *Sports Illustrated, Audubon, National Wildlife, Field & Stream, Gray's Sporting Journal* and *Sports Afield.* Although he is generally known as a sportsman's artist, his watercolors reveal a sensitive appreciation of the gentle side of nature. His skill at capturing the grace of wildlife in its habitat is equalled by his seemingly effortless ability to paint the sportsman in the wild.

## FRANCIS GOLDEN

|  | ISSUE PRICE | CURRENT PRICE |
|---|---|---|
| ☐ **TROUT FISHING,** ed. 750, s/n, 17″ x 25″, pub SEL . . . . . . . . . . . . . . . . . . . . . | 70.00 | — |
| ☐ **CANADAS AND YOUNG,** rel. 1980. ed. 850, s/n, size not available, pub WWI . . | 65.00 | — |

# BARBARA GOLDSTEIN

A native Texan, Barbara Goldstein studied art at the University of Texas, the Palacio de Bella Artes in San Minguel de Allende, Guanajuato, Mexico, and later at the Art Student League of New York and the Froman School of Art in Cloudcroft, New Mexico.

During these years of formal education, she also received individual instruction from prominent artists such as Bror Utter, Bud Biggs, Edgar Whitney, Doug Walton, Daniel Green, John Howard Sanden, David Leffel and Emily Cuthrie Smith. The result was a complex of color and technique which today has distilled into a style singularly her own.

Of her painting, Goldstein says, "It's an emotional turn-on to put down how I feel through my brush. Whatever affects me in life, travel, nature, people I must interpret through the medium of my art. I'm emotionally involved the whole time. I don't even want to quit to eat. It comes from the deepest recesses of my self.

**HILL FLOWERS** by *Barbara Goldstein*

Then, when it's done, I am ready for a new experience to translate from life to paper. That's why I'm able to part with my paintings. Once the actual experience of painting is past, you can't get it back.''

**BARBARA GOLDSTEIN**

| | ISSUE PRICE | CURRENT PRICE |
|---|---|---|
| ☐ **MORNING LACE,** rel. 1981. ed. 1,500, s/n, 32¼" x 25", pub ALI . . . . . . . . . . | 60.00 | — |
| ☐ **WOODLAWN,** rel. 1981. ed. 1,500, s/n, 32½" x 25", pub ALI . . . . . . . . . . . . | 60.00 | — |
| ☐ **HILL FLOWERS,** rel. 1982. ed. 1,500, s/n, 25½" x 19", pub ALI . . . . . . . . . . | 60.00 | — |

# BILL GRANSTAFF

After three years in the Air Corps in World War II, Bill Granstaff attended the Kansas City Art Institute, majoring in painting. Upon graduation he did post-graduate work at the American Academy of Art in Chicago.

Listed in *"Who's Who In American Art"*, and *"The International Biography"*, Cambridge, England, he has worked in art studios, advertising agencies, publishing houses, was an instructor at the Famous Artists School, and spent many years as a free-lance illustrator, doing book covers and children's illustrations.

Bill now maintains his own studio in Princeton, Kentucky and devotes his time to prints and painting.

**VANITY** *by Bill Granstaff*

## BILL GRANSTAFF

| | ISSUE PRICE | CURRENT PRICE |
|---|---|---|
| **MEMENTO SERIES** | | |
| ☐ **AT EASE,** rel. 1973. ed. 200, s/n, 12″ x 16″, pub GPL | 12.00 | 100.00 |
| ed. 800, s/o | 10.00 | 90.00 |
| ed. 25 Artist proof | 25.00 | — |
| ☐ **MONDAY MORN,** rel. 1973. ed. 200, s/n, 12″ x 16″, pub GPL | 12.00 | 100.00 |
| ed. 2,300, s/o | 10.00 | 75.00 |
| ed. 25 Artist proof | 25.00 | — |
| ☐ **EASY AS PIE,** rel. 1974. ed. 300, s/n, 12″ x 16″, pub GPL | 15.00 | 75.00 |
| ed. 2,000, s/o | 10.00 | 65.00 |
| ed. 25 Artist proof | 25.00 | — |
| ☐ **JOHNNY REB,** rel. 1974. ed. 200, s/n, 12″ x 16″, pub GPL | 15.00 | 75.00 |
| ed. 2,300, s/o | 10.00 | 65.00 |
| ed. 25 Artist proof | 25.00 | — |
| ☐ **SUNDAY AFTERNOON,** rel. 1974. ed. 200, s/n, 12″ x 16″, pub GPL | 12.00 | 100.00 |
| ed. 2,300, s/o | 10.00 | 75.00 |
| ed. 25 Artist proof | 25.00 | — |
| ☐ **BABY TALK,** rel. 1975. ed. 350, s/n, 12″ x 16″, pub GPL | 15.00 | 65.00 |
| ed. 1,400, s/o | 10.00 | 55.00 |
| ed. 26 Artist proof | 25.00 | — |
| ☐ **SATURDAY NITE,** rel. 1975. ed. 250, s/n, 12″ x 16″, pub GPL | 15.00 | 75.00 |
| ed. 1,500, s/o | 10.00 | 65.00 |
| ed. 25 Artist proof | 25.00 | — |

| | | ISSUE PRICE | CURRENT PRICE |
|---|---|---|---|
| ☐ | **VANITY,** rel. 1975. ed. 500, s/n, 12″ x 16″, pub GPL | 15.00 | 75.00 |
| | ed. 1,250, s/o | 12.00 | 65.00 |
| | ed. 26 Artist proof | 25.00 | — |
| ☐ | **CANDLES '76,** rel. 1976. ed. 500, s/n, 12″ x 16″, pub GPL | 15.00 | 45.00 |
| | ed. 1,450, s/o | 12.00 | 35.00 |
| | ed. 26 Artist proof | 25.00 | — |
| ☐ | **PLA' LIKE,** rel. 1976. ed. 500, s/n, 12″ x 16″, pub GPL | 17.00 | 45.00 |
| | ed. 2,050, s/o | 12.00 | 35.00 |
| | ed. 50 Artist proof | 25.00 | — |
| ☐ | **PLANTIN' TIME,** rel. 1976. ed. 500, s/n, 12″ x 16″, pub GPL | 15.00 | 45.00 |
| | ed. 1,450, s/o | 12.00 | 35.00 |
| | ed. 26 Artist proof | 25.00 | — |
| ☐ | **MADE FROM SCRATCH,** rel. 1977. ed. 500, s/n, 12″ x 16″, pub GPL | 17.00 | 45.00 |
| | ed. 2,000, s/o | 14.00 | 25.00 |
| | ed. 35 Artist proof | 25.00 | — |
| ☐ | **MILKIN' TIME,** rel. 1977. ed. 500, s/n, 12″ x 16″, pub GPL | 17.00 | 35.00 |
| | ed. 2,000, s/o | 14.00 | 25.00 |
| | ed. 35 Artist proof | 25.00 | — |
| ☐ | **VIOLETS,** rel. 1977. ed. 500, s/n, 12″ x 16″, pub GPL | 17.00 | 75.00 |
| | ed. 1,565, s/o | 12.00 | 65.00 |
| | ed. 35 Artist proof | 25.00 | — |
| ☐ | **BEGONIAS,** rel. 1978. ed. 500, s/n, 12″ x 16″, pub GPL | 17.00 | 25.00 |
| | ed. 2,000, s/o | 14.00 | 20.00 |
| | ed. 35 Artist proof | 25.00 | — |
| ☐ | **KEEP COOL,** rel. 1978. ed. 500, s/n, 12″ x 16″, pub GPL | 17.00 | 25.00 |
| | ed. 2,000, s/o | 15.00 | 20.00 |
| | ed. 35 Artist proof | 25.00 | — |
| ☐ | **TUESDAY MORN,** rel. 1978. ed. 500, s/n, 12″ x 16″, pub GPL | 17.00 | 25.00 |
| | ed. 2,000, s/o | 15.00 | 20.00 |
| | ed. 35 Artist proof | 25.00 | — |
| ☐ | **PUTTIN' BY,** rel. 1979. ed. 500, s/n, 12″ x 16″, pub GPL | 17.00 | 25.00 |
| | ed. 2,000, s/o | 15.00 | 20.00 |
| | ed. 35 Artist proof | 25.00 | 25.00 |
| ☐ | **RAINED OUT,** rel. 1979. ed. 500, s/n, 12″ x 16″, pub GPL | 17.00 | 25.00 |
| | ed. 2,000, s/o | 15.00 | 20.00 |
| | ed. 35 Artist proof | 25.00 | 20.00 |
| ☐ | **DUCK DAYS,** rel. 1980. ed. 500, s/n, 12″ x 16″, pub GPL | 30.00 | — |
| | ed. 1,000, s/o | 25.00 | — |
| | ed. 100 Artist proof | 35.00 | — |
| ☐ | **GERANIUMS,** rel. 1980. ed. 500, s/n, 12″ x 16″, pub GPL | 20.00 | — |
| | ed. 2,000, s/o | 17.00 | — |
| | ed. 35 Artist proof | 25.00 | — |
| ☐ | **OUR DAILY BREAD,** rel. 1980. ed. 500, s/n, 12″ x 16″, pub GPL | 20.00 | — |
| | ed. 1,500, s/o | 17.00 | — |
| | ed. 35 Artist proof | 25.00 | — |
| ☐ | **SCHOOL DAYS,** rel. 1980. ed. 500, s/n, 12″ x 16″, pub GPL | 25.00 | — |
| | ed. 1,500, s/o | 20.00 | — |
| | ed. 35 Artist proof | 35.00 | — |
| ☐ | **SEW SEW,** rel. 1980. ed. 500, s/n, 12″ x 16″, pub GPL | 17.00 | 25.00 |
| | ed. 2,000, s/o | 15.00 | 20.00 |
| | ed. 35 Artist proof | 25.00 | — |
| ☐ | **SUGAR PLUM,** rel. 1980. ed. 500, s/n, 12″ x 16″, pub GPL | 20.00 | — |
| | ed. 1,500, s/o | 17.00 | — |
| | ed. 35 Artist proof | 25.00 | — |
| ☐ | **SUMMERTIME,** rel. 1980. ed. 500, s/n, 12″ x 16″, pub GPL | 20.00 | — |
| | ed. 1,500, s/o | 17.00 | — |
| | ed. 35, Artist proof | 200.00 | — |
| ☐ | **SCHOOL DAYS,** rel. 1981. ed. 850, s/n, pub GPL | 20.00 | — |
| | ed. 1,150, s/o | 25.00 | — |
| | ed. 100 Artist proof | 30.00 | — |
| ☐ | **DUCK DAYS,** rel. 1982. ed. 500, s/n, pub GPL | 25.00 | — |
| | ed. 1,000, s/o | 30.00 | — |
| | ed. 100 Artist proof | 35.00 | — |

|  | ISSUE PRICE | CURRENT PRICE |
|---|---|---|
| ☐ **TOYLAND,** rel. 1982. ed. 500, s/n, pub GPL | 20.00 | — |
| ed. 1,000, s/o | 28.00 | — |
| ed. 100 Artist proof | 30.00 | — |
| ☐ **HOMEMAKER,** rel. 1983. ed. 500, s/n, pub GPL | 20.00 | — |
| ed. Open, s/o | 25.00 | — |
| ed. 100 Artist proof | 30.00 | — |
| **REGULAR SERIES** | | |
| ☐ **OLD CITY HALL,** rel. 1971. ed. 150, s/n, 12" x 16", pub GPL | 12.50 | 225.00 |
| ed. 100, s/o | 10.00 | 190.00 |
| ☐ **TOBACCO LAND,** rel. 1971. ed. 200, s/n, 16" x 20", pub GPL | 12.50 | 200.00 |
| ed. 300, s/o | 10.00 | 190.00 |
| ☐ **OLD FIRE HALL,** rel. 1972. ed. 501, s/n, 12" x 16", pub GPL | 12.00 | 75.00 |
| **RAILROAD SERIES** | | |
| ☐ **SENTIMENTAL JOURNEY,** rel. 1973. ed. 200, s/n, 12" x 16", pub GPL | 12.00 | 110.00 |
| ed. 800, s/o | 10.00 | 100.00 |
| ed. 25 Artist proof | 25.00 | — |
| ☐ **POWDERMAN,** rel. 1977. ed. 900, s/n, 17½" x 23", pub GPL | 25.00 | 75.00 |

# GENE GRAY

|  | ISSUE PRICE | CURRENT PRICE |
|---|---|---|
| ☐ **EASTERN GRAY SQUIRREL,** rel. 1968. ed. 5,000, s/o, 22" x 18", pub AGI.... | 8.00 | 110.00 |
| ☐ **AMERICAN RED FOX,** rel. 1969. ed. 1,000, s/n, 22" x 18", pub AGI | 25.00 | 135.00 |
| 1,500, s/o | 20.00 | 125.00 |
| ☐ **WILDCAT,** rel. 1969. ed. 1,000, s/n, 22" x 17", pub AGI | 25.00 | 385.00 |
| ed. 2,000, s/o | 15.00 | 375.00 |
| NOTE: In addition there were 500 donated to the University of Kentucky, entitled "Kentucky Wildcat" and were sold for $100.00 each to raise $50,000.00 for UK Athletic Dept. They are SOLD OUT. | | |
| ☐ **GREAT HORNED OWL,** rel. 1969. ed. 1,000, s/n, 22" x 26", pub AGI | 25.00 | 425.00 |
| ed. 2,000, s/o | 15.00 | 400.00 |
| ☐ **STRIPED SKUNK,** rel. 1970. ed. 1,000, s/n, 22" x 18", pub AGI | 25.00 | 90.00 |
| ed. 2,000, s/o | 15.00 | 80.00 |
| ☐ **WHITE TAILED DEER,** rel. 1970. ed. 1,000, s/n, 22" x 17", pub AGI | 25.00 | 85.00 |
| ed. 2,000, s/o | 15.00 | 75.00 |
| ☐ **EASTERN COTTONTAIL RABBITT,** rel. 1970. ed. 1,000, s/n, 22" x 17", pub AGI | 25.00 | 70.00 |
| ed. 2,000, s/o | 15.00 | 60.00 |
| ☐ **AMERICAN BALD EAGLE,** rel. 1970. ed. 1,000, s/n, 21" x 25", pub AGI | 25.00 | 235.00 |
| ed. 2,000, s/o | 15.00 | 225.00 |
| NOTE: 2,000 prints comissioned by Morehead State University. Sold for $20.00 each to raise $40,000.00 for scholarships for needy students. | | |
| ☐ **EASTERN CHIPMUNK,** rel. 1971. ed. 1,000, s/n, 20" x 16", pub AGI | 25.00 | 80.00 |
| ed. 2,500, s/o | 15.00 | 70.00 |
| ☐ **EASTERN BELTED KINGFISHER,** rel. 1971. ed. 1,000, s/n, 16" x 20", pub AGI | 25.00 | 65.00 |
| ed. 4,000, s/o | 15.00 | 55.00 |
| ☐ **COUGAR,** rel. 1971. ed. 1,000, s/n, 18" x 24", pub AGI | 25.00 | Sold Out |
| ed. 4,000, s/o | 15.00 | — |
| ☐ **SCREECH OWL,** rel. 1972. ed. 1,000, s/n, 16" x 20", pub AGI | 25.00 | 50.00 |
| ed. 3,000, s/o | 15.00 | 30.00 |
| ☐ **CARDINAL,** rel. 1972. ed. 1,000, s/n, 16" x 20", pub AGI | 25.00 | 65.00 |
| ed. 4,000, s/o | 15.00 | 55.00 |
| ☐ **RACCOON,** rel. 1972. ed. 1,000, s/n, 16" x 20", pub AGI | 25.00 | Sold Out |
| ed. 2,000, s/o | 15.00 | Sold Out |
| NOTE: This print was commissioned by the Tenn. Dept. of Conservation and 2,000 prints were released entitled "Tennessee Raccoon" and sold for $20.00 each to raise $40,000.00 for conservation and wildlife. | | |
| ☐ **AMERICAN OTTER,** rel. 1973. ed. 1,000, s/n, 16" x 20", pub AGI | 25.00 | 50.00 |
| ed. 2,500, s/o | 15.00 | 30.00 |
| ☐ **REDTAIL HAWK,** rel. 1973. ed. 1,000, s/n, 16" x 20", pub AGI | 25.00 | 90.00 |
| 2,500, s/o | 15.00 | 80.00 |
| ☐ **GENERAL GEORGE S. PATTON COMMEMORATIVE AMERICAN BALD EAGLE,** rel. 1973. ed. 2,000, s/o, 22" x 26", pub AGI | 50.00 | 150.00 |
| ed. 3,000, s/o, 18" x 20", pub AGI | 20.00 | — |

| | ISSUE PRICE | CURRENT PRICE |
|---|---|---|
| ☐ **BLACK & WHITE LITHOGRAPHS SET OF FIVE,** rel. 1967. ed. 5,000, s/o, 11" x 14", pub AGI . . . . . . . . . . . . . . . . . . . . . . . . . . . . . . . . . . . . . . . . . . . . . . | 10.00 | 40.00 |
| Mare & Foal, White Tailed Deer Family, Grizzly & Cubs, Raccoon Family, and Big Horn Ram | | |
| ☐ **CHARCOAL FIELD SKETCHED SET OF FOUR,** rel. 1970. ed. 2,000, s/o, 11" x 14", pub AGI . . . . . . . . . . . . . . . . . . . . . . . . . . . . . . . . . . . . . . . . . . . . . . | 15.00 | 45.00 |
| Great Horned Owls, Raccoon Heads, Red Fox Family, and White Tailed Deer | | |
| ☐ **BEAR, CHARCOAL HEAD,** rel. 1971. ed. 5,000, s/o, pub AGI . . . . . . . . . . . . . | 15.00 | Sold Out |
| ☐ **YOUNG BULL BUFFALO, CHARCOAL HEAD,** rel. 1971. ed. 5,000, s/o, pub AGI | 15.00 | Sold Out |
| ☐ **WING COMMANDER,** rel. 1969. ed. 3,000, s/n, 8" x 10", pub AGI . . . . . . . . . | 3.00 | — |
| ☐ **UPLAND GAME BIRDS SET OF THREE,** rel. 1974. ed. 1,000, s/n, 11" x 14", pub AGI . . . . . . . . . . . . . . . . . . . . . . . . . . . . . . . . . . . . . . . . . . . . . . . . . . . | 20.00 | — |
| ed. 1,500, s/o . . . . . . . . . . . . . . . . . . . . . . . . . . . . . . . . . . . . . . . . . . . . . . | 15.00 | — |
| Ruffed Grouse, Morning Dove, and Bob White Quail | | |

## QUINTEN GREGORY

Quinten Gregory, born in 1929 in Topeka, Kansas, drew and painted at every opportunity while working as a sign painter and commercial artist.

In the mid-1960's, Gregory began painting fulltime. His majestic Northwest landscapes and wildlife paintings grace the collections of prominent Idahoans. Gregory works primarily in oils and watercolors for his original paintings.

In the 1970's, the artist began developing his exclusive original lithograph process. Gregory's system involves hand-drawing the images on special vinyl "plates" which are transferred by contact to deep-grained aluminum plates for printing. The artist himself hand-mixes and then applies his inks. The plate is then mounted on the single-sheet press, inked by hand, and a sheet of 100% rag paper takes the image. The artist must repeat this process over 1,000 times to produce an edition of 150 handmade, original lithographs.

Gregory's work is now handled by over eighty galleries nationwide. He was featured in the July/August '83 issue of *Prints* magazine.

### QUINTEN GREGORY

| | ISSUE PRICE | CURRENT PRICE |
|---|---|---|
| ☐ **ASPEN GROVE,** rel. 1980. ed. 45, s/n, 14" x 20", pub WSI . . . . . . . . . . . . . . . | 70.00 | 90.00 |
| ☐ **BUCKSKINS,** rel. 1980. ed. 45, s/n, 14" x 20", pub WSI . . . . . . . . . . . . . . . . . | 70.00 | — |
| ☐ **DOE AND FAWN,** rel. 1980. ed. 100, s/n, 7" x 9", pub WSI . . . . . . . . . . . . . . . | 30.00 | 40.00 |
| ☐ **DUCK HUNTER,** rel. 1980. ed. 95, s/n, 7" x 9", pub WSI . . . . . . . . . . . . . . . . | 30.00 | — |
| ☐ **HEADIN HOME,** rel. 1980. ed. 95, s/n, 7" x 9", pub WSI . . . . . . . . . . . . . . . . | 30.00 | — |
| ☐ **PRONGHORN,** rel. 1980. ed. 95, s/n, 7" x 9", pub WSI . . . . . . . . . . . . . . . . . . | 30.00 | — |
| ☐ **FAWN,** rel. 1980. ed. 95, s/n, 7" x 9", pub WSI . . . . . . . . . . . . . . . . . . . . . . . | 30.00 | 60.00 |
| ☐ **STANLEY LAKE,** rel. 1980. ed. 45, s/n, 20" x 28", pub WSI . . . . . . . . . . . . . . | 150.00 | 350.00 |
| ☐ **THE MILL,** rel. 1980. ed. 45, s/n, 14" x 20", pub WSI . . . . . . . . . . . . . . . . . . | 70.00 | 200.00 |
| ☐ **WOOD DUCKS,** rel. 1980. ed. 100, s/n, 7" x 9", pub WSI . . . . . . . . . . . . . . . . | 30.00 | — |
| ☐ **MT. HOOD,** rel. 1981. ed. 125, s/n, 20" x 28", pub WSI . . . . . . . . . . . . . . . . . | 150.00 | — |
| ☐ **OWYHEE CANYON,** rel. 1981. ed. 95, s/n, 20" x 28", pub WSI . . . . . . . . . . . . | 150.00 | 200.00 |
| ☐ **SAWTOOTH MOUNTAIN FALL,** rel. 1981. ed. 95, s/n, 20" x 28", pub WSI . . . . | 150.00 | 250.00 |
| ☐ **SAWTOOTH MOUNTAIN SHEEP CAMP,** rel. 1981. ed. 95, s/n, 20" x 28", pub WSI . . . . . . . . . . . . . . . . . . . . . . . . . . . . . . . . . . . . . . . . . . . . . . . . . . . . . | 150.00 | 300.00 |
| ☐ **SNAKE RIVER MALLARDS,** rel. 1981. ed. 95, s/n, 20" x 28", pub WSI . . . . . . | 150.00 | 200.00 |
| ☐ **TETON WINTER MORNING,** rel. 1981. ed. 95, s/n, 20" x 28", pub WSI . . . . . . | 150.00 | 325.00 |
| ☐ **SUN VALLEY, IDAHO,** rel. 1982. ed. 140, s/n, 20" x 28", pub WSI . . . . . . . . . | 150.00 | — |
| ☐ **WEST SIDE OF THE TETONS,** rel. 1982. ed. 140, s/n, 20" x 28", pub WSI . . . . | 150.00 | — |
| ☐ **WINTER AT THE RANCH,** rel. 1982. ed. 140, s/n, 20" x 28", pub WSI . . . . . . . | 150.00 | — |
| ☐ **MT. RAINIER,** rel. 1983. ed. 140, s/n, 20" x 28", pub WSI . . . . . . . . . . . . . . . | 150.00 | — |
| ☐ **TROUT PLATE,** rel. 1983. ed. 140, s/n, 20" x 28", pub WSI . . . . . . . . . . . . . . | 175.00 | — |
| ☐ **TETON SHEEP CAMP,** rel. 1983. ed. 150, s/n, 20" x 28", pub WSI . . . . . . . . . | 195.00 | — |

# GERRIT GREVE

Born in Bandung (Java) of Dutch parents, Greve spent the first two years of his life in Indonesia before his family's return to the Netherlands. The Greves then immigrated to the United States when Gerrit was eight. By that time, his talents had become apparent and his artistic creativity was carefully being nurtured by his parents.

Now living and painting in southern California, the great variety of Gerrit Greve's works results from his constant quest for new and vital ways with which to express his creative spontaneity.

His images fall somewhere between the representational and the abstract with areas and shapes that are barely figural; they are the distillation of elements in the world which surrounds them. Areas are blocked out with saturated color thus deepening the figures, the effect of which enriches the importance of the solitary line.

**ELEKTRA** *by Gerrit Greve*

### GERRIT GREVE

| | ISSUE PRICE | CURRENT PRICE |
|---|---|---|
| ☐ **LA BOHEME,** rel. 1981. ed. 350, 22″ x 28½″, litho, arches, pub EEI . . . . . . . . | 275.00 | — |
| ed. 50, japon . . . . . . . . . . . . . . . . . . . . . . . . . . . . . . . . . . . . . . . . . . . . . . . | 300.00 | — |
| ☐ **ELEKTRA,** rel. 1981. ed. 350, 22″ x 28½″, litho, arches, pub EEI . . . . . . . . . . | 275.00 | — |
| ed. 50, japon . . . . . . . . . . . . . . . . . . . . . . . . . . . . . . . . . . . . . . . . . . . . . . . | 300.00 | — |
| ☐ **THOUGHTS,** rel. 1981. ed. 350, 22″ x 28″, litho, arches, pub EEI . . . . . . . . . . | 275.00 | — |
| ed. 50, japon . . . . . . . . . . . . . . . . . . . . . . . . . . . . . . . . . . . . . . . . . . . . . . . | 300.00 | — |
| ☐ **CAT & TOAD,** rel. 1981. ed. 350, 33″ x 22″, litho, arches, pub EEI . . . . . . . . . . | 275.00 | — |
| ☐ **OLD INDIAN,** rel. 1981. ed. 350, 22½″ x 28½″, litho, arches, pub EEI . . . . . . . | 275.00 | — |
| ed. 50, japon . . . . . . . . . . . . . . . . . . . . . . . . . . . . . . . . . . . . . . . . . . . . . . . | 300.00 | — |
| ☐ **INDIGO BUNTING,** rel. 1981. ed. 350, 22½″ x 28½″, litho, arches, pub EEI . . . | 275.00 | — |
| ed. 50, japon . . . . . . . . . . . . . . . . . . . . . . . . . . . . . . . . . . . . . . . . . . . . . . . | 300.00 | — |
| ☐ **DESERT DREAM,** rel. 1981. ed. 350, 22½″ x 28½″, litho, arches, pub EEI . . . | 275.00 | — |
| ed. 50, japon . . . . . . . . . . . . . . . . . . . . . . . . . . . . . . . . . . . . . . . . . . . . . . . | 300.00 | — |

# DOUGLAS GRIER

Doug Grier began drawing and painting as a teenager, selling his first painting at the age of 14. A self taught artist, Grier worked at his painting for ten years while pursuing a career in pharmaceutical sales before leaving that position to open his own gallery in Greenville, South Carolina and paint full time.

A native of New Jersey, Grier exhibited widely in upstate New York while a resident of Syracuse. Since choosing South Carolina as his home in 1975, he has exhibited in numerous group and one-man shows, receiving award recognition for his work. His work is represented by a network of selected galleries and he has paintings in many private and corporate collections. In 1979 The South Carolina Organization of Civitan International chose him to do one painting a year for three years to aid their service projects.

### DOUGLAS GRIER

| | | |
|---|---|---|
| ☐ **PATH TO THE BEACH,** rel. 1978. ed. 500, s/n, 14″ x 20″, pub RLB . . . . . . . . . | 25.00 | 75.00 |
| ☐ **LEO,** rel. 1978. ed. 500, s/n, 14″ x 20″, pub RLB . . . . . . . . . . . . . . . . . . . . . . | 25.00 | — |
| ☐ **ROLLING DUNE,** rel. 1978. ed. 500, s/n, 14″ x 20″, pub RLB . . . . . . . . . . . . . . | 25.00 | — |
| ☐ **TIMELESS,** rel. 1978. ed. 500, s/n, 14″ x 20″, pub RLB . . . . . . . . . . . . . . . . . . | 25.00 | — |
| ☐ **OAK ISLAND PLANTATION,** rel. 1979. ed. 500, s/n, 14″ x 20″, pub RLB . . . . . | 25.00 | — |
| ☐ **STILL IN SERVICE,** rel. 1979. ed. 1,400, s/n, 22½″ x 14¾″, pub RLB . . . . . . | 25.00 | — |
| Commissioned by the South Carolina District Civitan organization. | | |
| ☐ **A MORNINGS' TREASURES,** rel. 1980. ed. 500, s/n, 15″ x 30″, pub RLB . . . . | 35.00 | — |
| ☐ **A NEW DAY,** rel. 1980. ed. 1,000, s/n, 15″ x 30″, pub SIAG . . . . . . . . . . . . . | 25.00 | 75.00 |
| ☐ **EBB TIDE,** rel. 1981. ed. 450, s/n, 11⅞″ x 21⅝″, pub SIAG . . . . . . . . . . . . . | 35.00 | — |
| ☐ **A QUIET MOMENT,** rel. 1981. ed. 450, s/n, 14¾″ x 22″, pub SIAG . . . . . . . . . | 35.00 | — |
| ☐ **LEFT ALONE,** rel. 1981. ed. 1,000, s/n, 17¼″ x 26½″, pub SIAG . . . . . . . . . | 25.00 | — |
| Commissioned by the South Carolina District Civitan organization. | | |

# ROY GRINNELL

| | | |
|---|---|---|
| ☐ **NO CHANCE TO RELOAD,** rel. 1982. ed. 750, 26″ x 14½″, pub SGL . . . . . . . . . | 75.00 | — |
| s/n, remarqued . . . . . . . . . . . . . . . . . . . . . . . . . . . . . . . . . . . . . . . . . . . . . | 150.00 | — |

# BURT GROEDEL

"I've always lived in a kind of fantasy world . . . it's my life . . . my art. Drawing and painting; that's my own personal domain."

His own words serve as an appropriate introduction to a prolific contempoary artist whose work in any medium reveals a truly unique vision. Groedel's stunning style as an illustrator, sculptor, and designer have made him one of the most sought-after talents in the art world today.

A native New Yorker, Groedel began serious art studies at the age of seven with special watercolor and oil painting classes at the city's famed Art Students League. Later he gained what he terms "an incredible background" at another of Manhattan's High School of Music and Art and from there he would go on to graduate from Pratt Institute.

Working as a freelance illustrator, Groedel's efforts caught the eye of Lester Rossin who provided leads to his first important commissions. So distinctive was his figurative graphic style, that it played a key role in the instant success of campaigns for major accounts. At the same time, Groedel's innovative paper sculpture became a regular feature in the display windows at Bergdorf Goodman. And, when his portfolio came to the attention of Edward Fields (the most prominent name in fine rugs and custom wall hangings), the reaction was immediate: "I hired the artist to design a rug — I really did it just for fun. It sold right away — so I asked him for more." The success of Groedel's rug designs has brought a new freshness of ideas to the custom carpet and wall hanging field.

**I'VE GROWN ACCUSTOMED TO YOUR PLACE** *by Burt Groedel*

Groedel has entered a most exciting new area — that of limited edition lithography. Groedel's energy seems unlimited and he looks toward the future with enthusiasm: "The communication here is beauty. Every work is a challenge, each one distinct . . . I don't want to waste time, I want to get as much in as I can."

## BURT GROEDEL

| | ISSUE PRICE | CURRENT PRICE |
|---|---|---|
| ☐ HER SERENE HIGHNESS, rel. 1980. ed. 300, 22" x 28", litho, arches, pub EEl | 225.00 | — |
| ☐ EDIFICE COMPLEX, rel. 1980. ed. 300, 22" x 28", litho, arches, pub EEl . . . . . | 225.00 | — |
| ☐ LADY GO-DIVA, rel. 1980. ed. 300, 22" x 28", litho, arches, pub EEl . . . . . . . | 200.00 | 225.00 |
| ☐ LADY WORTHINGTON'S BIRD, rel. 1980. ed. 300, 22" x 28", litho, arches, pub EEl . . . . . . . . . . . . . . . . . . . . . . . . . . . . . . . . . . . . . . . . . . . . | 200.00 | 225.00 |
| ☐ TAKE ME TO YOUR LEDA, rel. 1980. ed. 300, 22" x 28", litho, arches, pub EEl | 200.00 | 225.00 |
| ☐ I'VE GROWN ACCUSTOMED TO YOUR PLACE, rel. 1980. ed. 300, 22" x 28", litho, arches, pub EEl . . . . . . . . . . . . . . . . . . . . . . . . . . . . . . . . . . . | 200.00 | 300.00 |

# OWEN J. GROMME

Following a lifetime of work at the Milwaukee Public Museum, Owen Gromme retired at 70 to devote full time to painting. Though the midwest has nurtured many fine wildlife artists, few have achieved as much deserved recognition as this notable octogenarian from Wisconsin.

Gromme first gained national acclaim by winning the Federal Duck Stamp competition in 1945. In 1976, he received the First Leigh Yawkey Woodson Art Museum Master Wildlife Artist award, and in 1978 was selected as the Ducks Unlimited Artist of the Year. Later in 1978, Mr. Gromme was chosen to design Wisconsin's first State Duck Stamp and also received an Honorary Doctorate degree from Marian College in Wisconsin. In 1980, his work was displayed at the Smithsonian Institute in Washington, D.C. He was further honored in 1980 when the Milwaukee Public Museum dedicated its new special exhibits hall in his name.

Gromme was among the first of a special breed of modern wildlife painters, highly skilled in science as well as art. In 1941 he began painting a series of 323 American birds and has been acknowledged as one of the greatest living bird painters since the series was published in 1963, with the modest title, BIRDS OF WISCONSIN. He has lived to see the body of his work equal, in the opinions of many art historians, that of Audubon, Wilson and Fuertes, whom he greatly admires. He has been commissioned by some of America's most notable collectors of sporting art, becoming widely recognized for his masterful background treatment and technically perfect birds and animals.

In Gromme's works, you will find recollections of the past, memories treasured by anyone who has ever been afield with a close friend or favorite hunting dog.

Gromme paints with uncommon speed and skill, and is considered to be one of the most prolific of all wildlife artists.

## OWEN J. GROMME

| | | |
|---|---|---|
| ☐ WINTERING QUAIL, rel. 1970. ed. 550, s/n, 17" x 22½", pub WWI . . . . . . . . . | 40.00 | 1,400.00 |
| ☐ BRITTNAY ON POINT - WOODCOCK, rel. 1971. ed. 450, s/n, 17" x 25", pub WWI . . . . . . . . . . . . . . . . . . . . . . . . . . . . . . . . . . . . . . . . . . . . | 50.00 | 900.00 |
| ☐ BACK TO COVER - PHEASANT, rel. 1971. ed. 450, s/n, 18" x 24", pub WWI . . | 50.00 | 575.00 |
| ☐ LATE SEASON - CANVASBACKS, rel. 1972. ed. 450, s/n, 18" x 24", pub WWI | 50.00 | 450.00 |
| ☐ SUNLIT GLADE - RUFFED GROUSE, rel. 1972. ed. 450, s/n, 18" x 22½", pub WWI . . . . . . . . . . . . . . . . . . . . . . . . . . . . . . . . . . . . . . . . . . . . . | 50.00 | 1,200.00 |
| ☐ WINTERING GROSBEAKS, rel. 1973. ed. 600, s/n, 16" x 22½", pub WWI . . . . | 45.00 | 600.00 |
| ☐ BLUE JAY, rel. 1973. ed. 800, s/o, 13¾" x 10¾", pub WWI . . . . . . . . . . . . . | 35.00 | 350.00 |
| ☐ STARTLED GROUSE - GOLDEN RETRIEVER, rel. 1973. ed. 480, s/n, 18" x 22", pub WWI . . . . . . . . . . . . . . . . . . . . . . . . . . . . . . . . . . . . . . . . . . . | 55.00 | 525.00 |

| | ISSUE PRICE | CURRENT PRICE |
|---|---|---|
| ☐ **OVER THE TRIANGLE - PINTAILS,** rel. 1973. ed. 480, s/n, 18" x 25", pub WWI | 55.00 | 125.00 |
| ☐ **ISLAND LAKE - LOON,** rel. 1973. ed. 580, s/n, 16½" x 24¾", pub WWI | 55.00 | 1,000.00 |
| ☐ **EXPECTATION,** rel. 1973. ed. 580, s/n, 18" x 22½", pub WWI | 55.00 | 950.00 |
| ☐ **ENGLISH SETTER,** rel. 1974. ed. 580, s/n, 22" x 17¾", pub WWI | 55.00 | 575.00 |
| ☐ **SACRED CRANES OVER HOKKAIDO,** rel. 1974. ed. 600, s/n, 16" x 26¼", pub WWI | 55.00 | 125.00 |
| ☐ **TAMARACK LAKE - CANADA GEESE,** rel. 1974. ed. 580, s/n, 16" x 24", pub WWI | 60.00 | 300.00 |
| ☐ **PILEATED WOODPECKER,** rel. 1974. ed. 580, s/n, 20" x 15", pub WWI | 50.00 | 100.00 |
| ☐ **CALIFORNIA QUAIL,** rel. 1974. ed. 580, s/n, 17½" x 23½", pub WWI | 60.00 | 125.00 |
| ☐ **HEMLOCK HIDEWAY - RUFFED GROUSE,** rel. 1974. ed. 580, s/n, 16" x 24", pub WWI | 60.00 | 750.00 |
| ☐ **WHISTLING SWANS,** rel. 1974. ed. 580, s/n, 17½" x 23½", pub WWI | 60.00 | 1,000.00 |
| ☐ **EDGE TO FIELD - POINTER,** rel. 1974. ed. 580, s/n, 18" x 24", pub WWI | 60.00 | 75.00 |
| ☐ **DROPPING IN - MORNING DOVES,** rel. 1974. ed. 580, s/n, 16" x 24", pub WWI | 60.00 | 125.00 |
| ☐ **RASCAL'S REVENGE - GREAT HORNED OWL,** rel. 1975. ed. 580, s/n, 17¾" x 23¾", pub WWI | 60.00 | 300.00 |
| ☐ **WINTER AFTERNOON - PHEASANT.** ed. 580, s/n, 16" x 24", pub WWI | 60.00 | 700.00 |
| ☐ **SCURRING GREEN WINGS,** rel. 1975. ed. 580, s/n, 16" x 24", pub WWI | 60.00 | 85.00 |
| ☐ **AMONG THE SHOCKS - PRAIRIE CHICKEN,** rel. 1975. ed. 580, s/n, 16" x 24", pub WWI | 60.00 | 400.00 |
| ☐ **MORNING FROST - RUFFED GROUSE,** rel. 1975. ed. 580, s/n, 16¾" x 22½", pub WWI | 60.00 | 600.00 |
| ☐ **MID-DAY RETREAT - BOBWHITE,** rel. 1975. ed. 580, s/n, 16¾" x 22½", pub WWI | 70.00 | 800.00 |
| ☐ **OUR NATIONAL BIRD - BALD EAGLE,** rel. 1976. ed. 580, s/n, 17¾" x 21", pub WWI | 70.00 | 175.00 |
| ☐ **PRAIRIE SHARP - TAILED GROUSE,** rel. 1976. ed. 580, s/n, 16½" x 25", pub WWI | 70.00 | 85.00 |
| ☐ **EARLY AUTUMN - RUFFED GROUSE,** rel. 1976. ed. 580, s/n, 16¾" x 22½", pub WWI | 70.00 | 850.00 |
| ☐ **EVENING STILLNESS - BARRED OWL,** rel. 1976. ed. 580, s/n, 22" x 17⅝", pub WWI | 60.00 | 325.00 |
| ☐ **RAIL FENCE COVEY - BOBWHITES,** rel. 1976. ed. 580, s/n, 16¾" x 22½", pub WWI | 70.00 | 500.00 |
| ☐ **KILLDEER,** rel. 1976. ed. 800, s/o, 9" x 12", pub WWI | 37.50 | 175.00 |
| ☐ **BY THE ROADSIDE - RUFFED GROUSE,** rel. 1976. ed. 580, s/n, 16¾" x 22½", pub WWI | 70.00 | 425.00 |
| ☐ **HOSTILE SKY - CANVASBACKS,** rel. 1976. ed. 580, s/n, 17¼" x 25", pub WWI | 70.00 | 325.00 |
| ☐ **CARDINALS,** rel. 1976. ed. 800, s/o, 14" x 10", pub WWI | 40.00 | 400.00 |
| ☐ **GROSBEAKS,** rel. 1976. ed. 600, s/n, 22" x 17⅝", pub WWI | 60.00 | 175.00 |
| ☐ **CEDAR SHELTER - BOBWHITES,** rel. 1976. ed. 580, s/n, 16¾" x 22½", pub WWI | 75.00 | 300.00 |
| ☐ **EASING IN - CANADA GEESE,** rel. 1976. ed. 580, s/n, 16½" x 25", pub WWI | 75.00 | 250.00 |
| ☐ **LABRADOR RETREIVER,** rel. 1977. ed. 580, s/n, 16½" x 25", pub WWI | 75.00 | 375.00 |
| ☐ **WINTER MORNING - RUFFED GROUSE,** rel. 1977. ed. 580, s/n, 15" x 26", pub WWI | 75.00 | 800.00 |
| ☐ **SCOLDING BLUE JAY,** rel. 1977. ed. 800, s/n, 13½" x 10", pub WWI | 40.00 | 225.00 |
| ☐ **CORNER COVEY - BOBWHITE,** rel. 1977. ed. 580, s/n, 17½" x 25", pub WWI | 75.00 | 200.00 |
| ☐ **CEDAR CREEK - MALLARDS,** rel. 1977. ed. 580, s/n, 17½" x 22", pub WWI | 75.00 | 275.00 |
| ☐ **WINTER WOODS - WHITETAIL DEER,** rel. 1977. ed. 580, s/n, 17¾" x 23½", pub WWI | 75.00 | 400.00 |
| ☐ **DEPARTURE FROM LAKE KATHERINE,** rel. 1978. ed. 850, s/n, 17¾" x 24¼", pub WWI | 100.00 | 375.00 |
| ☐ **EDGE OF THE THICKET - WOODCOCK,** rel. 1978. ed. 850, s/n, 17¾" x 13¼", pub WWI | 60.00 | 75.00 |
| ☐ **FLUSHED FROM COVER - RINGNECKS,** rel. 1978. ed. 850, s/n, 17¾" x 22¾", pub WWI | 85.00 | 100.00 |
| ☐ **GERMAN SHORT-HAIRED POINTER,** rel. 1978. ed. 850, s/n, 16½" x 25", pub WWI | 85.00 | — |
| ☐ **HIGH COUNTRY - MULE DEER,** rel. 1978. ed. 850, s/n, 17¾" x 23½", pub WWI | 85.00 | — |

| | ISSUE PRICE | CURRENT PRICE |
|---|---|---|
| ☐ SECLUDED POND - WOOD DUCKS, rel. 1978. ed. 850, s/n, 17¾" x 22½", pub WWI | 85.00 | 200.00 |
| ☐ HUMMINGBIRD, rel. 1978. ed. 850, s/o, 10" x 13⅞", pub WWI | 40.00 | 150.00 |
| ☐ GOLDFINCH, rel. 1978. ed. unlimited, 10" x 12½", pub WWI | 40.00 | — |
| ☐ DUKE - AMERICAN WATER SPANIEL, rel. 1978. ed. 850, s/n, 17¾" x 22", pub WWI | 75.00 | 85.00 |
| ☐ STAND OFF - FOX & GOOSE, rel. 1978. ed. 850, s/n, 17¾" x 22", pub WWI | 85.00 | — |
| ☐ STARTLED TRIO - WHITETAIL DEER, rel. 1978. ed. 850, s/n, 16½" x 25", pub WWI | 85.00 | 325.00 |
| ☐ WINTER SHADOWS - RUFFED GROUSE, rel. 1978. ed. 850, s/n, 17¾" x 22¾", pub WWI | 85.00 | 100.00 |
| ☐ WINTERTIME - CARDINAL, rel. 1978. ed. 4,000, s/o, 13½" x 11¾", pub WWI | 40.00 | — |
| ☐ WISCONSIN STATE DUCK STAMP DESIGN - 1978, ed. not available (see Duck Stamp listings), pub WWI | 100.00 | — |
| ☐ A TOUCH OF WHITE - PHEASANTS, rel. 1978. ed. 850, s/n, size not available, pub WWI | 75.00 | 85.00 |
| ☐ AFRICAN ELEPHANTS, rel. 1978. ed. 850, s/n, size not available, pub WWI | 75.00 | 85.00 |
| ☐ CHARGING RHINO - SEREGETI, rel. 1978. ed. 850, s/n, size not available, pub WWI | 75.00 | 85.00 |
| ☐ CONFRONTATION - GAZELLE AND EAGLE, rel. 1978. ed. 850, s/n, size not available, pub WWI | 75.00 | 85.00 |
| ☐ DOUBLE FLUSH - RUFFED GROUSE, rel. 1978. ed. 850, s/n, size not available, pub WWI | 75.00 | 85.00 |
| ☐ EARLY SNOWFALL - WHITETAIL DEER, rel. 1978. ed. 850, s/n, size not available, pub WWI | 75.00 | 500.00 |
| ☐ GOSHAWK AND RUFFED GROUSE, rel. 1978. ed. 850, s/n, size not available, pub WWI | 75.00 | 85.00 |
| ☐ HANGING LOOSE - LEOPARD, rel. 1978. ed. 850, s/n, size not available, pub WWI | 75.00 | 85.00 |
| ☐ MATES - SERENGETI LIONS, rel. 1978. ed. 850, s/n, size not available, pub WWI | 75.00 | 85.00 |
| ☐ STORMY DAY - SERENGETI BUFFALO, rel. 1978. ed. 850, s/n, size not available, pub WWI | 75.00 | 85.00 |
| ☐ SPRING BREAK UP - WHISTLING SWANS, rel. 1979. ed. 850, s/n, 25" x 16½", pub WWI | 85.00 | 125.00 |
| ☐ RETURN TO LAKE DE NEVEU, rel. 1979. ed. 850, s/n, 25" x 16½", pub WWI | 100.00 | — |
| ☐ GOSHAWK AND YOUNG, rel. 1979. ed. 850, s/n, 22" x 17¾", pub WWI | 100.00 | — |
| ☐ EVES OF THE NIGHT - GREAT HORNED OWL, rel. 1979. ed. 850, s/n, 21⅜" x 17¾", pub WWI | 100.00 | — |
| ☐ MORNING HAZE - WOOD DUCKS, rel. 1979. ed. 850, s/n, 16½" x 25", pub WWI | 100.00 | — |
| ☐ AUTUMN SPECTACLE - WOOD DUCKS, rel. 1979. ed. 850, s/n, 25" x 16½", pub WWI | 100.00 | — |
| ☐ ROBIN, rel. 1979. ed. 850, s/n, 13½" x 10⅛", pub WWI | 50.00 | 65.00 |
| ☐ SHARPTAILS ON THE RISE, rel. 1979. ed. 850, s/n, 23½" x 17¾", pub WWI | 100.00 | — |
| ☐ MALLARDS AT SUNSET, rel. 1979. ed. 850, s/n, 25" x 16½", pub WWI | 100.00 | — |
| ☐ SOUTHERN PINES - WILD TURKEYS, rel. 1980. ed. 850, s/n, 17½" x 23", pub WWI | 100.00 | — |
| ☐ EARLY SPRING DRUMMER - RUFFED GROUSE, rel. 1980. ed. 850, s/n, 22" x 17⅜", pub WWI | 125.00 | 250.00 |
| ☐ A PAIR OF CANADAS, rel. 1980. ed. 850, s/n, size not available, pub WWI | 100.00 | — |
| ☐ BARN OWL, rel. 1980. ed. 850, s/n, size not available, pub WWI | 100.00 | — |
| ☐ BLUE JAY AND CARDINAL, rel. 1980. ed. 850, s/n, size not available, pub WWI | 100.00 | — |
| ☐ BLUE JAYS HARASSING SCREECH OWL, rel. 1980. ed. 850, s/n, size not available, pub WWI | 100.00 | — |
| ☐ BUCKING THE STORM - CANVASBACKS, rel. 1980. ed. 850, s/n, size not available, pub WWI | 100.00 | — |
| ☐ DAY'S END - MIXED BAG, rel. 1980. ed. 850, s/n, size not available, pub WWI | 100.00 | — |
| ☐ EVENING GROSBEAKS, rel. 1980. ed. 850, s/n, size not available, pub WWI | 75.00 | 85.00 |
| ☐ EVICTING THE INTRUDER, rel. 1980. ed. 850, s/n, size not available, pub WWI | 100.00 | — |
| ☐ EXPLODING FROM COVER - RUFFED GROUSE, rel. 1980. ed. 850, s/n, size not available, pub WWI | 100.00 | 200.00 |

| | ISSUE PRICE | CURRENT PRICE |
|---|---|---|
| ☐ **FROSTY MORNING - WHISTLING SWANS**, rel. 1980. ed. 850, s/n, size not available, pub WWI | 100.00 | — |
| ☐ **HEN MALLARD BROOD**, rel. 1980. ed. 850, s/n, size not available, pub WWI | 100.00 | — |
| ☐ **KINGFISHER**, rel. 1980. ed. 850, s/n, size not available, pub WWI | 50.00 | — |
| ☐ **MALLARDS AND BLACK DUCKS**, rel. 1980. ed. 850, s/n, size not available, pub WWI | 100.00 | — |
| ☐ **POLAR BEAR - HUDSON'S BAY**, rel. 1980. ed. 850, s/n, size not available, pub WWI | 50.00 | — |
| ☐ **SNOWY OWL**, rel. 1980. ed. 850, s/n, size not available, pub WWI | 100.00 | 200.00 |
| ☐ **TRIO OF BOBWHITES**, rel. 1980. ed. 850, s/n, size not available, pub WWI | 100.00 | — |
| ☐ **YELLOWHEADED BLACKBIRD**, rel. 1980. ed. 850, s/n, size not available, pub WWI | 50.00 | — |
| ☐ **AUTUMN LEAVES - RUFFED GROUSE**, rel. 1981. ed. 950, s/n, size not available, pub WWI | 225.00 | — |
| ☐ **BLUE WING TEAL**, rel. 1981. ed. 850, s/n, size not available, pub WWI | 125.00 | — |
| ☐ **CANVASBACKS**, rel. 1981. ed. 850, s/n, size not available, pub WWI | 125.00 | — |
| ☐ **CARDINALS IN SNOW**, rel. 1981. ed. 800, s/n, size not available, pub WWI | 100.00 | — |
| ☐ **CONNER'S DITCH - HORICON MARSH**, rel. 1981. ed. 850, s/n, size not available, pub WWI | 125.00 | — |
| ☐ **INDIAN SUMMER - RUFFED GROUSE**, rel. 1981. ed. 950, s/n, size not available, pub WWI | 225.00 | — |
| ☐ **PHEASANTS**, rel. 1981. ed. 850, s/n, size not available, pub WWI | 125.00 | — |
| ☐ **PURPLE MARTINS**, rel. 1981. ed. 850, s/n, size not available, pub WWI | 50.00 | — |
| ☐ **RED HEADED WOODPECKER**, rel. 1981. ed. 850, s/n, size not available, pub WWI | 50.00 | — |
| ☐ **RUFFED GROUSE IN WINTER**, rel. 1981. ed. 950, s/n, size not available, pub WWI | 200.00 | 1,000.00 |
| ☐ **SKY PIRACY - EAGLE & OSPREY**, rel. 1981. ed. 950, s/n, size not available, pub WWI | 225.00 | — |
| ☐ **CHANGING OF THE GUARD - COMMON LOON**, rel. 1982. ed. 950, s/n, size not available, pub WWI | 225.00 | — |
| ☐ **EGRETS BELOW THE BRIDGE**, rel. 1982. ed. 980, s/n, size not available, pub WWI | 175.00 | — |
| ☐ **INDIGO BUNTING**, rel. 1982. ed. 850, s/n, size not available, pub WWI | 40.00 | — |
| ☐ **JUMPING BLACKS AND MALLARDS**, rel. 1982. ed. 950, s/n, size not available, pub WWI | 150.00 | — |
| ☐ **LATE SUMMER - MEADOWLARK**, rel. 1982. ed. 950, s/n, size not available, pub WWI | 50.00 | — |
| ☐ **RED SQUIRREL AND BLUE JAY**, rel. 1982. ed. 850, s/n, size not available, pub WWI | 85.00 | — |
| ☐ **RETURNING TO THE REFUGE - CANADA GEESE**, rel. 1982. ed. 950, s/n, size not available, pub WWI | 100.00 | — |
| ☐ **SPRING'S EARLY ARRIVALS**, rel. 1982. ed. 950, s/n, size not available, pub WWI | 85.00 | — |
| ☐ **WHISTLING SWANS - BEYOND THE TEMPEST**, rel. 1982. ed. 950, s/n, size not available, pub WWI | 100.00 | — |

# EARL GUSTAVESON

Earl Gustaveson is a wildlife painter who works in all mediums but prefers acrylics. His work is characterized by a fine sense of color combined with excellent attention to detail.

Gustaveson graduated from the University of Wisconsin where he majored in landscape architecture and design. Gustaveson decided to go into free lance art in 1970. He did commercial and advertising illustration and was art director for a fishing tabloid.

He is an active member of Ducks Unlimited and the National Wildlife Association. His paintings hang in private and corporate collections worldwide.

**MALLARDS** *by Earl Gustaveson*

## EARL GUSTAVESON

| | ISSUE PRICE | CURRENT PRICE |
|---|---|---|
| ☐ **MALLARDS,** rel. 1979. ed. 600, s/n, 26″ x 22″, pub NC | 60.00 | — |
| ☐ **WOOD DUCKS,** rel. 1979. ed. 600, s/n, 22″ x 28″, pub NC | 60.00 | — |
| ☐ **A FINE PAIR,** rel. 1979. ed. 600, s/n, 16″ x 20″, pub NC | 35.00 | — |
| ☐ **NO HUNTING,** rel. 1979. ed. 600, s/n, 16″ x 20″, pub NC | 35.00 | — |

# RON GUTHRIE

An artist from a community south of Chicago, Illinois, Guthrie is head designer for Roper Corporation. He is a strong watercolorist gaining widespread recognition in Illinois and the Midwest.

His works portray some of his many interests and hobbies.

## RON GUTHRIE

| | | |
|---|---|---|
| ☐ **HARD DOWN, WIND BEFORE RAIN,** ed. 300, s/n, 17″ x 24″, pub CGAL | 200.00 | 220.00 |
| ed. 12, Artist accented/signed | 260.00 | 290.00 |
| ed. 38, s/o, artist proofs | 200.00 | 220.00 |
| ed. 600 general print | 55.00 | 60.00 |
| ☐ **THE HIGHLANDS, UPPER PENINSULA,** ed. 950, s/n, 24½″ x 16½″, pub CGAL | 90.00 | 100.00 |
| ed. 12, Artist accented/signed | 260.00 | 290.00 |
| ☐ **MICHIGAN STONE,** ed. 950, s/n, 15″ x 24″, pub CGAL | 90.00 | 100.00 |
| ed. 12, Artist accented/signed | 260.00 | 290.00 |
| ☐ **REEF THE MAIN, DOUSE NUMBER ONE,** ed. 950, s/n, 23″ x 18″, pub CGAL | 90.00 | 100.00 |
| ed. 12, Artist accented/signed | 260.00 | 290.00 |

| | ISSUE PRICE | CURRENT PRICE |
|---|---|---|
| ☐ **PRAIRIE IRON,** ed. 950, s/n, 16″ x 24″, pub CGAL ................. | 90.00 | 100.00 |
| ed. 12, Artist accented/signed ................. | 260.00 | 290.00 |
| ☐ **GIRARD STATION,** ed. 950, s/n, 22″ x 17″, pub CGAL ................. | 90.00 | 100.00 |
| ed. 12, Artist accented/signed ................. | 260.00 | 290.00 |
| ☐ **PASSAGES,** ed. 950, s/n, 24½″ x 17½″, pub CGAL ................. | 90.00 | 100.00 |
| ed. 12, Artist accented/signed ................. | 260.00 | 290.00 |
| ☐ **HARD DOWN, WIND BEFORE RAIN,** ed. 300, s/n, 17″ x 24″, pub CGAL ..... | 200.00 | 220.00 |
| ed. 12, Artist accented/signed ................. | 260.00 | 290.00 |
| ☐ **FIELD HANDS,** ed. 950, s/n, 17″ x 24½″, pub CGAL ................. | 90.00 | 100.00 |
| ed. 12, Artist accented/signed ................. | 260.00 | 290.00 |
| ☐ **SEASON'S OUT,** ed. 950, s/n, 23″ x 18″, pub CGAL ................. | 90.00 | 100.00 |
| ed. 12, Artist accented/signed ................. | 260.00 | 290.00 |
| ☐ **RESURRECTION 1951,** ed. 950, s/n, 16½″ x 25½″, pub CGAL ........... | 90.00 | 100.00 |
| ed. 12, Artist accented/signed ................. | 260.00 | 290.00 |
| ☐ **BURNING OFF,** ed. 950, s/n, 23″ x 17″, pub CGAL ................. | 90.00 | 100.00 |
| ed. 12, Artist accented/signed ................. | 260.00 | 290.00 |
| ☐ **PRAIRIE STATION,** ed. 950, s/n, 16″ x 24½″, pub CGAL ................. | 90.00 | 100.00 |
| ed. 12, Artist accented/signed ................. | 260.00 | 290.00 |
| ☐ **NORTH MANITOU ISLAND, SOUTH POINT,** ed. 950, s/n, 24″ x 18″, pub CGAL | 90.00 | 100.00 |
| ed. 12, Artist accented/signed ................. | 260.00 | 290.00 |
| ☐ **DUNE WAGON,** ed. 950, s/n, 24″ x 18″, pub CGAL ................. | 90.00 | 100.00 |
| ed. 12, Artist accented/signed ................. | 260.00 | 290.00 |

# JAN HAGARA

Jan Hagara, an award-winning, self-taught artist has created a truly individual and unique style that has set her work apart from other artists.

**ADRIANNE AND THE BYE-LO DOLL** *by Jan Hagara*

Hagara's wide-eyed storybook-type children are created totally from real children put into old-style surroundings, using old clothing, dolls, hats and toys. The models, carefully selected are dressed by Hagara in antique costumes and photographed in her studio. The watercolors come from these photographs. She does no children on commission.

The sparkling eyes of Hagara's kids are her trademark along with her familiar blue "hash-marks" in all of her paintings.

Her paintings are sought after by collectors from many parts of the country.

## JAN HAGARA

| | ISSUE PRICE | CURRENT PRICE |
|---|---|---|
| ☐ HATTIE & THE JUMEAU DOLL, rel. 1977. ed. 2,000, s/o, 11" x 14", pub BJAD | 20.00 | — |
| Of this edition 250 s/n | 25.00 | — |
| ☐ JASON & THE RABBITT, rel. 1977. ed. 2,000, s/o, 11" x 14", pub BJAD | 21.00 | — |
| Of this edition 250 s/n | 25.00 | — |
| ☐ LAURIE AND THE POUTY DOLL, rel. 1977. ed. 2,000, s/o, 11" x 14", pub BJAD | 21.00 | — |
| Of this edition 250 s/n | 25.00 | — |
| ☐ MARC & THE TOYBOX, rel. 1977. ed. 2,000, s/o, 11" x 14", pub BJAD | 21.00 | — |
| Of this edition 250 s/n | 25.00 | — |
| ☐ FLOWERS IN THE CAN, rel. 1977. ed. 2,000, s/o, 16" x 20", pub BJAD | 25.00 | 35.00 |
| Of this edition 250 s/n | 30.00 | — |
| ☐ SPRING AND LANCE, rel. 1977. ed. 2,000, s/o, 16" x 20", pub BJAD | 26.00 | 40.00 |
| Of this edition 250 s/n | 30.00 | 45.00 |
| ☐ JODY AND THE TOY HORSE, ed. 2,000, s/n, 16" x 20", pub BJAD | 45.00 | — |
| ☐ JENNY AND THE BYELO DOLL, ed. 2,000, s/o, 16" x 20", pub BJAD | 45.00 | — |
| ☐ OLIVIA, rel. 1978. ed. 600, s/n, 18" x 22", pub BJAD | 55.00 | 350.00 |
| ☐ LISA, rel. 1978. ed. 1,200, s/n, 7" x 9", pub BJAD | 20.00 | — |
| ☐ JUMEAU DOLL, rel. 1978. ed. 1,200, s/n, 7" x 9", pub CGAL | 20.00 | — |
| Above two prints sold as a companion pair. | | |
| ☐ LISA AND THE JUMEAU DOLL, rel. 1978. ed. 900, s/o, 8" x 8", pub CGAL | 20.00 | — |
| ☐ DAISIES FROM MARY BETH, rel. 1978. ed. 900, s/o, 8" x 8", pub BJAD | 20.00 | — |
| ☐ JIMMY, rel. 1979. ed. 750, s/n, 16" x 20", pub BJAD | 45.00 | 100.00 |
| ☐ BETSY AND HER DREAMBABY, rel. 1979. ed. 750, s/n, 16" x 20", pub BJAD | 45.00 | 200.00 |
| ☐ ADRIANNE AND THE BYELO DOLL, rel. 1979. ed. 450, s/n, 16" x 20", pub BJAD | 65.00 | 300.00 |
| ☐ LYDIA AND THE SHIRLEY TEMPLE DOLL, ed. 650, s/n, 16" x 20", pub BJAD | 65.00 | 85.00 |
| ☐ MELANIE AND THE SCARLET O'HARA DOLL, ed. 900, s/n, 16" x 20", pub BJAD | 85.00 | Sold Out |
| ☐ LITTLE SHARICE, ed. 850, s/n, 16" x 20", pub BJAD | 85.00 | — |
| ☐ STORYTIME, ed. 450, s/n, 23" x 28", pub BJAD | 125.00 | 150.00 |
| ☐ VICTORIA'S EASTER, ed. 1,000, s/n, 16" x 20", pub BJAD | 50.00 | — |
| ☐ DAISIES FROM JIMMY, rel. 1979. ed. 900, s/o, 8" x 8", pub BJAD | 20.00 | — |
| ☐ DAISIES FROM MEG, rel. 1980. ed. 900, s/o, 8" x 8", pub BJAD | 20.00 | — |
| ☐ DAISIES FROM MOMMY, rel. 1981. ed. 900, s/o, 8" x 8", pub BJAD | 20.00 | — |
| ☐ CARA AND THE DREAMBABY, ed. 900, s/n, 12" x 12", pub BJAD | 30.00 | — |
| ☐ NATALIE, ed. 900, s/n, 12" x 12", pub BJAD | 40.00 | — |
| ☐ SHARICE, ed. 1,000, s/o, 8" x 10", pub BJAD | 18.00 | — |
| ☐ PARRY, ed. 1,000, s/o, 8" x 10", pub BJAD | 18.00 | — |
| ☐ WENDY, ed. 1,000, s/o, 8" x 10", pub BJAD | 18.00 | — |
| ☐ JULIE, ed. 1,000, s/o, 8" x 10", pub BJAD | 18.00 | — |

# DAVID HAGERBAUMER

David Hagerbaumer was born in Quincy, Illinois and grew up as a sportsman. As a youth he became keenly aware of wildlife in its natural habitat. He is an avid hunter and conservationist.

Hagerbaumer majored in art at San Diego State. He is a knowledgeable and accomplished professional wildlife painter/naturalist.

**MIXED DOUBLE – PHEASANT AND BOBWHITE** *by David Hagerbaumer*

## DAVID HAGERBAUMER

| | ISSUE PRICE | CURRENT PRICE |
|---|---|---|
| ☐ OCTOBER EVENING-PINTAILS, rel. 1963. ed. 400, s/n, 18″ x 27″, pub. see note** | 47.50 | 1200.00 |
| ☐ PLACID MARSH-BLACK DUCKS, rel. 1964. ed. 400, s/n, 17½″ x 27″ | 47.50 | 1200.00 |
| ☐ WOODLOT COVEY-BOBWHITE QUAIL, rel. 1965. ed. 400, s/n, 17½″ x 27″ | 47.50 | 1200.00 |
| ☐ FOGGY MORNING-MALLARDS, rel. 1965. ed. 400, s/n, 17½″ x 27″ | 47.50 | 1200.00 |
| ☐ PORTFOLIO OF FOUR PRINTS, rel. 1967. (Canvasbacks, Pintails, Canada Geese, Mallards). ed. 400, s/n, 12″ x 15½″ | 80.00 | 1000.00 |
| ☐ GREEN WING FLURRY - GREEN WING TEAL, rel. 1969. ed. 600, s/n, 19½″ x 27″ | 47.50 | 450.00 |
| ☐ AUTUMN RUFFS-RUFFED GROUSE, rel. 1969. ed. 600, s/n, 19½″ x 27″ | 47.50 | 500.00 |
| ☐ THE NARROWS-WOOD DUCK, rel. 1971. ed. 450, s/n, 17″ x 23″ | 47.50 | 400.00 |
| ☐ DOUBLE RISE-WOODCOCK, rel. 1971. ed. 450, s/n, 17″ x 23″ | 47.50 | 400.00 |
| ☐ SHANTY, THE, rel. 1972. (PENCIL, w/text), ed. 450, s/n, 12½″ x 16½″ | 25.00 | 75.00 |
| ☐ THRU THE PINE-MOURNING DOVES, rel. 1972. ed. 450, s/n, 17″ x 23″ | 50.00 | 400.00 |
| ☐ HILL COUNTRY GOBLERS-TURKEY, rel. 1972. ed. 450, s/n, 12½″ x 16½″ | 50.00 | 400.00 |
| ☐ GATHERING STORM-PINTAILS, rel. 1972. ed. 450, s/n, 13″ x 17″ | 50.00 | 350.00 |
| ☐ OVER THE RIDGE-PHEASANTS, rel. 1973. ed. 450, s/n, 17″ x 23″ | 60.00 | 450.00 |
| ☐ MINUS TIDE-CANVASBACK, rel. 1973. ed. 450, s/n, 17″ x 23″ | 60.00 | 250.00 |
| ☐ TIMBER POTHOLE-MALLARDS & WIDGEON, rel. 1973. Historical Series #1 w/illustrated text. ed. 350, s/n, 17″ x 23″ | 80.00 | 400.00 |
| ☐ HOG RANCH POINT-BLACK BRANT, rel. 1974. ed. 350, s/n, 19″ x 31″, (rel. w/text) | 80.00 | 125.00 |
| ☐ SINK BOX GUNNING-CANVASBACKS, rel. 1974. Historical Series #2 w/illustrated text. ed. 350, s/n, 17″ x 23″ | 80.00 | 125.00 |
| ☐ TWIN ISLAND MARCH-BLUE WING TEAL, rel. 1974. ed. 450, s/n, 17″ x 23″ | 60.00 | 100.00 |
| ☐ THE OLD DUCK CAMP-MALLARD, rel. 1974. ed. 450, s/n, 17″ x 23″ | 60.00 | 250.00 |
| ☐ GREAT BASIN MARSH-BUFFLEHEADS AND TULE DECOYS, rel. 1975. Historical Series #3 w/illustrated text. ed. 350, s/n, 17″ x 23″ | 80.00 | 200.00 |

| | ISSUE PRICE | CURRENT PRICE |
|---|---|---|
| ☐ **HICKORY GROVE-BOBWHITE QUAIL**, rel. 1975. ed. 450, s/n, 17" x 23"...... | 60.00 | 250.00 |
| ☐ **AFTERNOON SQUALL-CANADA GEESE**, rel. 1975. ed. 450, s/n, 17" x 23".... | 60.00 | 200.00 |
| ☐ **TAMARACK POND-BLACK DUCKS**, rel. 1976. ed. 450, s/n, 17" x 23" ....... | 65.00 | 150.00 |
| ☐ **FIRST SNOW-RUFFED GROUSE**, rel. 1976. ed. 450, s/n, 17" x 23" ......... | 65.00 | 350.00 |
| ☐ **SOUTH BOTTOMS-PINTAILS**, rel. 1976. Historical Series #4 w/illustrated text. ed. 350, s/n, 17" x 23" ........................................ | 80.00 | 200.00 |
| ☐ **MIXED DOUBLE-WOODCOCK & GROUSE**, rel. 1977. ed. 450, s/n, 17" x 23" .. | 65.00 | 450.00 |
| ☐ **MARSHY LAKE-WOOD DUCKS**, rel. 1977. ed. 450, s/n, 17" x 23" .......... | 65.00 | 175.00 |
| ☐ **ARMISTICE DAY STORM-MALLARDS**, rel. 1977. Historical Series #5 w/illustrated text. ed. 350, s/n, 17" x 23"........................... | 85.00 | 250.00 |
| ☐ **MIDDLE FORK-WIGEON, TEAL & SPRIG**, rel. 1978. ed. 450, s/n, 17" x 23" ... | 75.00 | 125.00 |
| ☐ **BEAR CREEK BOTTOMS-PHEASANTS**, rel. 1978. ed. 450, s/n, 17" x 23" .... | 75.00 | 175.00 |
| ☐ **BEECH GROVE-PASSENGER PIGEON**, rel. 1978. Historical Series #6 w/illustrated text. ed. 350, s/n, 17" x 23".......................... | 95.00 | — |
| ☐ **SPRING HILL - BOBWHITE QUAIL**, rel. 1979. ed. 380, s/n, size not available .. | 125.00 | 200.00 |
| ☐ **APPROACHING SPRING - WILD TURKEY**, rel. 1979. ed. 450, s/n, 17" x 23".... | 75.00 | 150.00 |
| ☐ **INDIAN SUMMER - GREEN-WINGED TEAL**, rel. 1979. ed. 450, s/n, 17" x 23" . | 75.00 | 100.00 |
| ☐ **LAST LEAVES OF AUTUMN - RUFFED GROUSE**, rel. 1979. ed. 850, s/n, 17" x 23".............................................. | 95.00 | — |
| ☐ **THE BOTTOMS - PINTAILS**, rel. 1980. ed. 450, s/n, 17" x 23" ............. | 95.00 | — |
| ☐ **EVENING FLIGHT - MOURNING DOVES**, rel. 1980. ed. 450, s/n, 17" x 23" ... | 95.00 | — |
| ☐ **MIXED DOUBLE - MALLARD & BLACK DUCK**, rel. 1980. ed. 450, s/n, 17" x 23".............................................. | 95.00 | — |
| ☐ **FRANK'S PLACE - GREEN-WINGED TEAL**, rel. 1980. ed. 2,000, s/n, size not available, produced by Frank Williams for Ducks Unlimited .................. | — | 125.00 |
| ☐ **AUTUMN SPLENDOR - MALLARD**, rel. 1980. ed. 450, s/n, 17" x 23"........ | 100.00 | — |
| ☐ **MIXED DOUBLE - PHEASANT & BOBWHITE**, rel. 1981. ed. 450, s/n, 17" x 23" | 125.00 | — |
| ☐ **OVAL - MALLARD**, rel. 1981. ed. 450, s/n, 6½" x 9" .................. | 35.00 | 50.00 |
| ☐ **OVAL - PHEASANT**, rel. 1981. ed. 450, s/n, 6½" x 9" .................. | 35.00 | 50.00 |
| ☐ **RUFFED GROUSE SOCIETY #3**, rel. 1981. ed. 1,780, s/n, size not available, produced by Ruffed Grouse Society ............................. | 125.00 | 130.00 |
| ☐ **WINTER NOBILITY - WILD TURKEY**, rel. 1981. ed. 950, s/n, size not available, produced by the National Wild Turkey Federation ...................... | 125.00 | — |
|    ed. 100, s/n ........................................... | 1000.00 | — |
| ☐ **AUTUMN GRANDEUR - PHEASANTS**, rel. 1981. ed. 380 (50 were a/p), s/n, size not available ......................................... | 250.00 | — |
| ☐ **MIXED DOUBLE - WOODCOCK & GROUSE**, rel. 1981. ed. 90, s/n, size not available, etching ......................................... | 125.00 | — |
| ☐ **PINTAILS**, rel. 1981. ed. 90, s/n, size not available, etching .............. | 125.00 | — |
| ☐ **WOODCOCK**, rel. 1981. ed. 90, s/n, size not available, etching .......... | 125.00 | — |
| ☐ **FENCE ROW COVEY - BOBWHITES**, rel. 1981. ed. 90, s/n, size not available, etching ............................................ | 150.00 | — |
| ☐ **RUFFED GROUSE**, rel. 1981. ed. 90, s/n, size not available, etching ......... | 125.00 | — |
| ☐ **PHEASANTS**, rel. 1981. ed. 90, s/n, size not available, etching .......... | 125.00 | — |
| ☐ **VALLEY QUAIL**, rel. 1981. ed. 90, s/n, size not available, etching .......... | 125.00 | — |
| ☐ **JUMPING MALLARDS**, rel. 1981. ed. 90, s/n, size not available, etching ..... | 125.00 | — |
| ☐ **OVAL - GREEN-WINGED TEAL**, rel. 1982. ed. 450, s/n, size not available, etching ............................................. | 40.00 | — |
| ☐ **OVAL - RUFFED GROUSE**, rel. 1982. ed. 450, s/n, 6½" x 9" ............. | 40.00 | — |
| ☐ **HARD ROCK FARM - BOBWHITE**, rel. 1982. ed. 850, s/n, 17" x 23"....... | 95.00 | — |
| ☐ **INDIAN SUMMER - RUFFED GROUSE**, rel. 1982. ed. 450, s/n, 17" x 23"..... | 150.00 | — |
| ☐ **OVAL - LOON**, rel. 1982. ed. 450, s/n, 6½" x 9"....................... | 40.00 | — |
| ☐ **WOODCOCK, BOBWHITE & GROUSE TRIPTYCH**, rel. 1982. ed. 450, s/n, no further information available .................................. | 60.00 | — |

    *Approximately 100 of each edition were remarqued. Add $85.00 or more to the current value for remarqued copies.

    **David Hagerbaumer's prints are available from a number of different sources. Following are the coded listings WWI, SEL and PP.

# BETTY GENE HAILE

Betty Gene Haile was born in San Antonio, Texas. Her interest and talent in art began developing at the early age of five years.

She studied art at the University of Texas, the McNay Art Institute, and later at Trinity University in San Antonio. She has studied with Edgar Whitney, Clay McGaughy, Rex Brandt, Millard Sheets, Robert E. Wood, and many others.

Haile is a member of the Southwestern Watercolor Society, Texas Watercolor Society, San Antonio Watercolor Group, San Antonio Art League, Texas Fine Arts Association, Midwest Watercolor Society, Hill Country Arts Foundation, Kentucky Watercolor Society, River Art Group and the Coppini Academy of Fine Arts.

She has won first place in the Laredo Arts Association, the River Art Show for Acrylic Collage and the Edgar Whitney Award for Watercolor from the Southwestern Watercolor Society.

**EARLY MORNING HAVEN** *by Betty Gene Haile*

| BETTY GENE HAILE | ISSUE PRICE | CURRENT PRICE |
|---|---|---|
| ☐ **EARLY MORNING HAVEN**, rel. 1980. ed. 1,500, s/n, 28″ x 22″, pub ALI . . . . . | 60.00 | — |

# BEN HAMPTON

Ben Hampton is a self taught artist. He is known for his unique style in translating nature into reality on the canvas.

When Hampton was a commercial artist he was awarded fifteen national awards for excellence. Currently, he is a professional fine art painter who was the official artist for the United States Pavilion at the 1982 World's Fair.

**THE RAVEN** *by Ben Hampton*

## BEN HAMPTON

| | ISSUE PRICE | CURRENT PRICE |
|---|---|---|
| ☐ **MONUMENT TO AN ERA**, rel. 1972. ed. 1,000, s/n, 25¾" x 19", pub HHSI... | 22.00 | 1,450.00 |
| ☐ **WINTER REFUGE**, rel. 1972. ed. 1,500, s/n, 13" x 26", pub HHSI .......... | 20.00 | 425.00 |
| ☐ **THE GOOD EARTH**, rel. 1973. ed. 987, s/n, 24" x 15½", pub HHSI ......... | 22.00 | 475.00 |
| ☐ **CLAUDE'S CREEK**, rel. 1973. ed. 992, s/n, 13" x 26", pub HHSI ........... | 22.00 | 300.00 |
| ☐ **PONDERING QUAIL**, rel. 1973. ed. 1,000, s/n, 17½" x 17½", pub HHSI ..... | 30.00 | 475.00 |
| ☐ **THE STUMP**, rel. 1973. ed. 1,000, s/n, 14¼" x 20", pub HHSI ............ | 25.00 | 325.00 |
| ☐ **SAND MOUNTAIN CABIN**, rel. 1973. ed. 1,000, s/n, 16½" x 20", pub HHSI .. | 25.00 | 525.00 |
| ☐ **DAD**, rel. 1973. ed. 1,500, s/n, 16½" x 20", pub HHSI ................. | 20.00 | 125.00 |
| ☐ **APPLACIAN SPRING**, rel. 1974. ed. 1,000, s/n, 18" x 24", pub HHSI........ | 30.00 | 475.00 |
| ed. 2,500, s/o............................................. | 20.00 | 345.00 |
| ☐ **GENTLE MIST**, rel. 1974. ed. 1,000, s/n, 14½" x 21¾", pub HHSI ......... | 30.00 | 175.00 |
| ed. 2,500, s/o............................................. | 20.00 | 125.00 |
| ☐ **AUTUMN WATCH**, rel. 1974. ed. 1,000, s/n, 14¼" x 21¾", pub HHSI ...... | 30.00 | 175.00 |
| ed. 2,500, s/o............................................. | 20.00 | 125.00 |
| ☐ **SUNDAY MORNING**, rel. 1974. ed. 1,000, s/n, 10¾" x 22", pub HHSI ...... | 30.00 | 300.00 |
| ed. 2,500, s/o............................................. | 20.00 | 250.00 |
| ☐ **BRIDGEPORT FERRY**, rel. 1975. ed. 1,000, s/n, 14½" x 21¾", pub HHSI.... | 30.00 | 275.00 |
| ed. 2,500, s/o............................................. | 20.00 | 250.00 |
| ☐ **CAROLINA HAZE**, rel. 1975. ed. 1,500, s/n, 14¼" x 25", pub HHSI ........ | 30.00 | 400.00 |
| ed. 2,500, s/o............................................. | 20.00 | 275.00 |
| ☐ **CRIB HOUSE & CREEK HOUSE**, rel. 1976. ed. 1,500, s/n, 11¾" x 18", pub HHSI .......................................................... | 45.00 | 200.00 |
| ed. 2,500, s/o............................................. | 30.00 | 175.00 |
| ☐ **NANCY WARD**, rel. 1976. ed. 5,000, s/o, 21½" x 20" ................... | 25.00 | 550.00 |
| ☐ **SORGHUM MILL**, rel. 1976. ed. 1,500, s/n, 13" x 26", pub HHSI .......... | 35.00 | 200.00 |
| ed. 3,500, s/o............................................. | 25.00 | 125.00 |
| ☐ **REFLECTING SYCAMORES**, rel. 1977. ed. 1,500, s/n, 13" x 26", pub HHSI .. | 35.00 | 175.00 |
| ed. 3,500, s/o............................................. | 25.00 | 150.00 |

| | | ISSUE PRICE | CURRENT PRICE |
|---|---|---|---|
| ☐ | **WINTER SOUTH,** rel. 1977. SOLD AS A PAIR - North Carolina "Mile in the Sky", Tennessee "Era of the Past", ed. 1,500, s/n, 18" x 11", pub HHSI ... | 60.00 | 175.00 |
| | ed. 6,500, s/o | 45.00 | 125.00 |
| ☐ | **STANDING PROUD,** rel. 1978. ed. 1,500, s/n, 21½" x 20", pub HHSI | 35.00 | 175.00 |
| | ed. 6,500, s/o | 25.00 | 125.00 |
| ☐ | **CASTLE OF CHILLON,** rel. 1978. ed. 1,500, s/n, 13" x 26", pub HHSI | 45.00 | 150.00 |
| | ed. 6,500, s/o | 30.00 | 90.00 |
| ☐ | **SEA OF GALILEE,** rel. 1978. ed. 1,500, s/n, 13" x 26", pub HHSI | 45.00 | 150.00 |
| | ed. 6,500, s/o | 30.00 | 90.00 |
| ☐ | **APPLACIAN SPRING,** rel. 1974. ed. 1,000, s/n, 18" x 24", pub HHSI | 30.00 | 150.00 |
| | ed. 2,500, s/o | 20.00 | 100.00 |
| ☐ | **FAREWELL SUMMERS,** rel. 1979. ed. 1,500, s/n, 23" x 25¾", pub HHSI | 55.00 | 225.00 |
| | ed. 5,000, s/o | 40.00 | 175.00 |
| ☐ | **HIGH SPLENDOR,** rel. 1979. ed. 1,500, s/n, 21½" x 20", pub HHSI | 40.00 | 150.00 |
| | ed. 6,500, s/o | 30.00 | 125.00 |
| ☐ | **NANCY WARD HERITAGE SERIES,** rel. 1979. Set of three - CHOTA ARTIFACTS, POINT LOOKOUT, THE INN. ed. 8,000, i/o, pub HHSI | 30.00 | 45.00 |
| ☐ | **RAMBLING ROSE,** rel. 1980. ed. 1,500, s/n, 20" x 26", pub HHSI | 55.00 | 200.00 |
| | ed. 3,500, s/o | 40.00 | 150.00 |
| | Photo etching of Rambling Rose ed. 500, s/n, 13" x 15", hand coloured by artist | 200.00 | — |
| ☐ | **STEPPING STONES,** rel. 1980. ed. 1,500, s/n, 20" x 26", pub HHSI | 55.00 | 250.00 |
| | ed. 3,500, s/o | 40.00 | 225.00 |
| ☐ | **SPRING PLACE,** rel. 1980. ed. 1,500, s/n, 17¾" x 24", pub HHSI | 55.00 | 125.00 |
| | ed. 3,500, s/o | 40.00 | 65.00 |
| ☐ | **THE BLACKSMITH SHOP,** rel. 1981. ed. 1,500, s/n, 16" x 24", pub HHSI | 65.00 | 125.00 |
| | ed. 4,500, s/o | 45.00 | 100.00 |
| ☐ | **FIVE KILLER HERITAGE SERIES,** rel. 1981. Set of three - CATHERINE'S BASKET, BIG BEND, FORT MARR. ed. 8,000, i/o, pub HHSI | 40.00 | — |
| ☐ | **HISKYTEEHEE (Five Killer),** rel. 1981. ed. 1,500, s/n, 21½" x 20", pub HHSI | 65.00 | 200.00 |
| | ed. 4,000, s/o | 40.00 | 160.00 |
| ☐ | **SHALLOW FORD,** rel. 1982. ed. 1,500, s/n, 16" x 24", pub HHSI | 65.00 | 150.00 |
| | ed. 4,500, s/o | 45.00 | 90.00 |
| ☐ | **SWINGING BRIDGE,** rel. 1982. ed. 1,500, s/n, 20" x 23", pub HHSI | 65.00 | 125.00 |
| | ed. 4,500, s/o | 45.00 | 90.00 |
| ☐ | **THOUGHTS OF SPRING,** rel. 1982. ed. 1,500, s/n, size not available, pub HHSI | 65.00 | 100.00 |
| | ed. 4,500, s/o | 40.00 | 45.00 |
| ☐ | **PLUM THICKET,** rel. 1983. ed. 1,500, s/n, 18" x 21¼", pub HHSI | 65.00 | — |
| | ed. 4,500, s/o | 45.00 | — |
| ☐ | **THE RAVEN,** Nancy Ward's Brother, rel. 1983. ed. 1,500, s/n, 20" x 21½", pub HHSI | 65.00 | — |
| | ed. 4,500, s/o | 45.00 | — |
| | ed. 250, a/p | 100.00 | — |

# ENOCH KELLY HANEY

The goal of Enoch Kelly Haney is to produce the highest quality art available in reproductions.

"Indian art in its finest sense is the ultimate execution of a vision, idea, belief or historic event in an art form of unquestionable quality."

Many hours of research and travel to the native lands of the Seminoles contribute to his art achievements. Kelly's research was enhanced by the teachings of his parents and grandparents through oral teachings of history and folklore. His grandfather Willie Haney contributed numerous legends to the writings of the Smithsonian Institute in Washington, D.C.

He has consulted for twenty years with the most knowledgeable Seminole medicine men.

Kelly has received several national awards. He is one of the masters of the Five Civilized Tribes. One of the highlights of his career was a one-man art show, held

**INDIGNITY OF THE FLAG OF TRUCE** *by Enoch Kelly Haney*

in his honor at the United States Capitol Building in Washington, D.C., which was sponsored by the Honorable Carl Albert, Speaker of the House of Representatives.

Formal training has included study under Cheyenne artist Dr. Richard West, Bacone Junior College; Special Indian Art studies, University of Arizona, Tucson, Arizona; Bachelors Degree from Oklahoma City University, Oklahoma City, Oklahoma; and Business Administration studies, Central State University, Edmond Oklahoma.

## ENOCH KELLY HANEY

| | ISSUE PRICE | CURRENT PRICE |
|---|---|---|
| ☐ **SPIRIT OF OSCEOLA**, ed. 1,500, s/n, size unknown, pub AIAC . . . . . . . . . . . . | 40.00 | 175.00 |
| ☐ **MEKUSUKEY BICENTENNIAL OWL**, ed. 500, s/n, 25⅞" x 32", pub AIAC . . . . . | 200.00 | 1500.00 |
| ☐ **BROKEN PROMISES**, ed. 1,000, s/n, 12" x 22", pub AIAC . . . . . . . . . . . . . . . | 30.00 | 100.00 |
| ☐ **APSAROKE WARRIOR**, ed. 2,000, s/n, 18" x 24", pub AIAC . . . . . . . . . . . . . . | 30.00 | — |
| ☐ **MARK OF THE KNIFE**, ed. 1,000, s/n, 22½" x 38½", pub AIAC . . . . . . . . . . . | 100.00 | — |
| ☐ **INDIGNITY OF THE FLAG OF TRUCE**, ed. 1,500, s/n, 19" x 34", pub AIAC . . . . | 75.00 | 300.00 |
| ☐ **MINIATURE SET** (three prints). | | |
| FLIGHT OF THE OWL, 5" x 7" | | |
| SACRED FEATHERS, 5" x 7" | | |
| AMERICAN INDIAN CHIEF, 5" x 7" | | |
| ed. 2,000, s/n, pub AIAC . . . . . . . . . . . . . . . . . . . . . . . . . . . . . . . . . . . | 30.00 | — |
| ☐ **RED-TAILED HAWK**, ed. 500, s/n, size unknown, pub AIAC . . . . . . . . . . . . . . | 150.00 | 500.00 |
| ☐ **AMERICAN BALD EAGLE**, ed. 500, s/n, size unknown, pub AIAC . . . . . . . . . . | 200.00 | 650.00 |

| | ISSUE PRICE | CURRENT PRICE |
|---|---|---|
| ☐ **THE WOLF, GREAT GRANDPA,** ed. 500, s/n, size unknown, pub AIAC . . . . . . . | 200.00 | 500.00 |
| ☐ **SEMINOLE LIFESTYLE,** ed. 2,000, s/n, 15½" x 21½", pub AIAC . . . . . . . . . | 30.00 | — |
| ☐ **FREEDOM'S END,** ed. 250, s/n, size unknown, pub AIAC . . . . . . . . . . . . . . . | 150.00 | 1200.00 |
| ☐ **SIOUX RAINMAKER,** ed. 1,500, s/n, size unknown, pub NWDHG . . . . . . . . . . . | 100.00 | 150.00 |
| ☐ **WAR CHIEF,** ed. 1,500, s/n, size unknown, pub NWDHG . . . . . . . . . . . . . . . | 40.00 | 90.00 |
| ☐ **SYMBOLS OF INDIAN THEOLOGY,** ed. 1,000, s/n, size unknown, pub AIAC . . . | 30.00 | — |
| ☐ **OWL TRANSFORMATION,** ed. 650, s/n, 18⅞" x 23¼", pub AIAC . . . . . . . . . . | 100.00 | — |
| ☐ **HAWK WARRIOR,** ed. 1,000, s/n, 16" x 20", pub AIAC . . . . . . . . . . . . . . . . . | 40.00 | — |
| ☐ **FLUTE PLAYER,** ed. 750, s/n, 20" x 25½", pub AIAC . . . . . . . . . . . . . . . . . . | 100.00 | 250.00 |

# W. HAROLD HANCOCK

From the early age of 10, when he won his first award in the National Carnegie Library National Book Week Poster Contest, Harold Hancock's world has been filled with a driving desire to capture all the beauty in all subjects and mediums. The pure pleasure of pleasing people has created a great gathering of collectors throughout 43 years of painting. Thousands have collected his prints.

Commissions from various corporations and institutions have given him the opportunity to paint in all parts of the world. Over 100 of his paintings have been chosen as limited editions.

## W. HAROLD HANCOCK

| | | |
|---|---|---|
| ☐ **FOUR SEASONS OF BROWN COUNTY, INDIANA,** rel. 1964. ed. 350, s/n, 12½" x 18", pub HG . . . . . . . . . . . . . . . . . . . . . . . . . . . . . . . . . . . . . | 30.00 | 400.00 |
| ☐ **FOUR WILDLIFE SERIES,** rel. 1973, consisting of Raccoons, Pheasants, Deer, Wild Turkey. ed. 1,200, s/n, 11½" x 15", pub HG . . . . . . . . . . . . . . . . . | 30.00 | 160.00 |
| ☐ **EMMETT WITH WALL STREET JOURNAL,** rel. 1974. ed. 999, s/n, 18" x 14", pub HG . . . . . . . . . . . . . . . . . . . . . . . . . . . . . . . . . . . . . . . . . . | 25.00 | 160.00 |
| ☐ **CUMBERLAND FALLS KENTUCKY,** rel. 1976. ed. 500, s/n, 20" x 26", pub HG | 10.00 | 120.00 |
| ☐ **WESTERN SERIES,** rel. 1976, consisting of Lake Tahoe, Virginia City, Genoa, Carson River. ed. 1,200, s/n, 14" x 18", pub HG . . . . . . . . . . . . . . . . . . | 30.00 | 160.00 |
| ☐ **FIVE CLOWNS,** rel. 1981, consisting of Red Skelton, Indiana Farmer, Emmett Kelly, Happy. ed. 1,000, s/n, 12" x 16", pub HG . . . . . . . . . . . . . . . . . | 50.00 | 120.00 |
| ☐ **BALLOONS,** rel. 1981. ed. 99, s/n, 22" x 28", serigraph, pub HG . . . . . . . . . . | 85.00 | 190.00 |
| ☐ **SAILS,** rel. 1981. ed. 99, s/n, 22" x 28", serigraph, pub HG . . . . . . . . . . . . . | 85.00 | 190.00 |
| ☐ **BIRD SERIES,** rel. 1981, consisting of White Egret, Blue Heron, Pelicans, Sandpipers. ed. 1,000, s/n, 13½" x 21", pub HG . . . . . . . . . . . . . . . . . . . . . . | 35.00 | 65.00 |
| ☐ **4 FAMOUS PARKE COUNTY COVERED BRIDGES,** rel. 1981. ed. 1,000, s/n, 8" x 11", pub HG . . . . . . . . . . . . . . . . . . . . . . . . . . . . . . . . . . . . . . . | 20.00 | 60.00 |
| ☐ **NEW FOUR SEASONS,** rel. 1982. ed. 1,000, s/n, 12" x 16", pub HG . . . . . . . . | 30.00 | 100.00 |
| ☐ **WINTER ON OWL CREEK,** rel. 1983. ed. 750, s/n, 12" x 16", pub HG . . . . . . . . | 85.00 | 165.00 |

# ELDRIDGE HARDIE

| | | |
|---|---|---|
| ☐ **BACK FROM THE CORN - MALLARDS,** rel. 1976. ed. 400, s/n, 28" x 22", pub EH . . . . . . . . . . . . . . . . . . . . . . . . . . . . . . . . . . . . . . . . . . . . . | 60.00 | — |
| ed. 50, s/ and remarque (first fifty) . . . . . . . . . . . . . . . . . . . . . . . . . . . | 135.00 | 275.00 |
| ☐ **BROWN TROUT AND FLIES,** rel. 1970. ed. 1,500, s/n, 22" x 17", pub EH . . . . | 20.00 | — |
| ☐ **BROOK TROUT AND FLIES,** rel. 1970. ed. 1,500, s/n, 22" x 17", pub EH . . . . . | 20.00 | — |
| ☐ **RAINBOW TROUT AND FLIES,** rel. 1970. ed. 1,500, s/n, 22" x 17", pub EH . . | 20.00 | — |
| ☐ **CUTTHROAT TROUT AND FLIES,** rel. 1970. ed. 1,500, s/n, 22" x 17", pub EH | 20.00 | — |
| ☐ **BROWN TROUT AND LIGHT CAHILLS,** rel. 1973. ed. 400, s/n, 25" x 20", pub EH . . . . . . . . . . . . . . . . . . . . . . . . . . . . . . . . . . . . . . . . . . . . . | 50.00 | — |
| ed. 50, s/n and remarque (first fifty) . . . . . . . . . . . . . . . . . . . . . . . . . . | 125.00 | 250.00 |
| ☐ **BROOK TROUT AND BLACKNOSE DACE,** rel. 1974. ed. 400, s/n, 25" x 20", pub EH . . . . . . . . . . . . . . . . . . . . . . . . . . . . . . . . . . . . . . . . . . . . . | 125.00 | — |
| ed. 50, s/n and remarque (first fifty) . . . . . . . . . . . . . . . . . . . . . . . . . . | 125.00 | — |

|  | ISSUE PRICE | CURRENT PRICE |
|---|---|---|
| ☐ **RAINBOW TROUT AND WESTERN OLIVE SEDGES,** rel. 1975. ed. 400, s/n, 25" x 20", pub EH | 50.00 | — |
| ed. 50, s/n and remarque (first fifty) | 125.00 | — |
| ☐ **SPRING CREEK - 1978 Trout Unlimited ''Artist of the Year'' Print,** rel. 1976. ed. 300, s/n, 28" x 22", pub TU | 75.00 | — |
| ed. 25, s/n, remarqued | 135.00 | 350.00 |
| ☐ **NOVEMBER COVEY - BOBWHITE QUAIL,** rel. 1979. ed. 400, s/n, 28" x 22", pub EH | 75.00 | — |
| ed. 50, s/n, remarqued | 155.00 | — |
| ☐ **AUTUMN WINGS - CANADA GEESE,** rel. 1981. ed. 650, s/n, size not available, pub WWI | 100.00 | — |

# H. HARGROVE

A native of southern Italy, Hargrove is a self taught artist. Although interested in art, Hargrove decided to become a wine chemist graduating from the Institute of Wine Technology in Italy.

In his first job after he migrated to the U.S., Hargrove worked as a wine chemist. There he decorated the winery rooms with paintings. Since visitors were impressed with the paintings he decided to become a professional artist.

Hargrove uses a pen name in keeping with the American theme of his work.

**FIRST SNOW** *by H. Hargrove*

## H. HARGROVE

|  | ISSUE PRICE | CURRENT PRICE |
|---|---|---|
| ☐ **FIRST SNOW,** rel. 1982. ed. 770, s/n, pub AG or IG | 150.00 | 300.00 |
| ed. 20, Artist proof | — | — |
| ☐ **TAKING IT EASY,** rel. 1982. ed. 770, s/n, pub AG or IG | 170.00 | 275.00 |
| ed. 20, Artist proof | — | — |
| ☐ **WINDROWING,** rel. 1982. ed. 770, s/n, pub AG or IG | 170.00 | 300.00 |
| ed. 20, Artist proof | — | — |
| ☐ **GENERAL STORE, U.S.A.,** rel. 1983. ed. 770, s/n, pub AG or IG | 225.00 | 275.00 |
| ed. 20, Artist proof | — | — |
| ☐ **THE CIDER MAKER,** rel. 1983. ed. 770, s/n, pub AG or IG | 200.00 | 275.00 |
| ed. 20, Artist proof | — | — |

# RAY HARM

Ray Harm studied at the Cooper School of Art in Cleveland.

While in Cleveland, Wood Hannah, Sr., founder of Frame House Gallery, saw his work and commissioned him to paint twenty eastern species of birds. The results were seen and admired by Dr. Frank G. Dickey, then president of the University of Kentucky, who appointed Ray the first Herman L. Donovan artist-in-residence at the university.

His paintings have drawn accolades including a White House invitation, and honorary doctorate degrees from three colleges. His work has hung at numerous museums and galleries. He is also a nature writer and is widely sought as a lecturer.

**CANADA GEESE** *by Ray Harm*

| RAY HARM | ISSUE PRICE | CURRENT PRICE |
|---|---|---|
| ☐ **AFRICAN SKETCHBOOK**, rel. 1973. ed. 10,000, s/o, 11″ x 15″, pub FHG .... | 50.00 | — |
| ☐ **AMERICAN BISON**, rel. 1978. ed. 1,000, s/n, 24″ x 30″, pub FHG .......... | 60.00 | — |
| *ed. 1,200, s/o Exclusive - the U.S. Field Artillery Association is using a portion of the edition to raise funds for atmospheric control equipment for the building housing the Ft. Sill Museum's Conservation Laboratory. | | |
| 800 will bear the inscription "Monarch of the Plains" and the Field Artillery Museum's seal .......................................................... | *75.00 | — |
| 400 will bear a First Day of Issue seal and the field Artillery Museum seal ... | *100.00 | — |
| ☐ **AMERICAN BUTTERFLIES**, rel. 1966. ed. 5,000, s/o, 22⅝″ x 17″, pub FHG .. | 10.00 | 75.00 |
| ☐ **AMERICAN EAGLE**, rel. 1971. ed. 3,500, s/o, 24″ x 32″, pub FHG .......... | 60.00 | 200.00 |
| ed. 500, s/n ...................................................... | 75.00 | 300.00 |
| ed. 1,000 (West Point Edition), signed and bearing a United States Military Academy shield. Sold exclusively to cadets and members of their families, military personnel and personnel closely affiliated with the Academy. Proceeds of sale donated to U.S.M.A. to further fine arts activities. ................... | — | 325.00 |
| ☐ **AMERICAN GOLDFINCH**, rel. 1966. ed. 5,000, s/o, 16″ x 20″, pub FHG ..... | 10.00 | 90.00 |
| ☐ **AMERICAN KESTREL**, rel. 1982. ed. 1,000, s/n, 21″ x 23¾″, pub FHG ...... | 60.00 | — |
| ☐ **AMERICAN REDSTART**, rel. 1974. ed. 7,500, s/o, 12″ x 15″, pub FHG ...... | 20.00 | 40.00 |
| ☐ **BALD EAGLE**, rel. 1975. ed. 2,000, s/n, 20″ x 24″, pub FHG .............. | **50.00 | — |

| | ISSUE PRICE | CURRENT PRICE |
|---|---|---|
| ☐ **BALD EAGLE (FAMILY)**, rel. 1963. ed. 1,000, s/o, 23″ x 29″, pub FHG . . . . . . | 30.00 | 350.00 |
| ☐ **BALD EAGLE (WINGS SPREAD)**, rel. 1968. ed. 500, s/n, 30½″ x 22½″, pub FHG . . . . . . . . . . . . . . . . . . . . . . . . . . . . . . . . . . . . . . . . . . . . . . . . | 60.00 | 250.00 |
| ☐ ed. 2,500, s/o . . . . . . . . . . . . . . . . . . . . . . . . . . . . . . . . . . . . . . . . . . . . . . | 55.00 | 200.00 |
| ☐ **BALD EAGLE**, rel. 1983. ed. 1,000, s/n, 23½″ x 33½″, pub FHG . . . . . . . . . . | 75.00 | — |
| ☐ ed. 100, s/n . . . . . . . . . . . . . . . . . . . . . . . . . . . . . . . . . . . . . . . . . . . . . . . | — | — |
| ☐ **BALTIMORE ORIOLE**, rel. 1963. ed. 5,000, s/o, 16″ x 20″, pub FHG . . . . . . . . | 10.00 | 100.00 |
| ☐ **BALTIMORE ORIOLE**, rel. 1982. ed. 1,000, s/n, 20″ x 16″, pub FHG . . . . . . . . | 60.00 | — |
| ☐ **BARN SWALLOW** , rel. 1974. ed. 5,000, s/o, 16″ x 20″, pub FHG . . . . . . . . . . | 20.00 | 70.00 |
| ☐ **BARRED OWL**, rel. 1980. ed. 1,000, s/n, 24″ x 20″, pub FHG . . . . . . . . . . . . . | 60.00 | Sold Out |
| ☐ ed. 850, s/n, Exclusive for Oklahoma Christian College Children's Hospital Fnd., Louisville, KY. | | |
| ☐ **BELTED KINGFISHER**, rel. 1966. ed. 5,000, s/o, 16″ x 20″, pub FHG. . . . . . . . | 10.00 | 50.00 |
| ☐ **BIGHORN SHEEP**, rel. 1976. ed. 1,000, s/n, 22″ x 28″, pub FHG . . . . . . . . . . . | 50.00 | — |
| ☐ ed. 3,000, s/o . . . . . . . . . . . . . . . . . . . . . . . . . . . . . . . . . . . . . . . . . . . . . . | 40.00 | Sold Out |
| ☐ ed. 500, s/o exclusive for the Rocky Mountain Nature Association. | | |
| ☐ **BLACK BEAR**, rel. 1974. ed. 1,000, s/n, 21″ x 27″, pub FHG . . . . . . . . . . . . . | 85.00 | Sold Out |
| ☐ ed. 3,500, s/o . . . . . . . . . . . . . . . . . . . . . . . . . . . . . . . . . . . . . . . . . . . . . . | 70.00 | Sold Out |
| ☐ ed. 500, s/o, donated to Pikeville College, Pikeville, Kentucky. | — | Sold Out |
| ☐ **BLACK-BILLED MAGPIE**, rel. 1976. ed. 5,000, s/o, 20″ x 16″, pub FHG . . . . . | 30.00 | Sold Out |
| ☐ **BLACK-CAPPED CHICKADEE**, rel. 1979. ed. 3,000, s/o, 20″ x 16″, pub FHG . . | 40.00 | — |
| ☐ **BLACK-THROATED BLUE WARBLER**, rel. 1974. ed. 7,500, s/o, 15″ x 12″, pub FHG . . . . . . . . . . . . . . . . . . . . . . . . . . . . . . . . . . . . . . . . . . . . . . . . . . | 20.00 | 40.00 |
| ☐ **BLUEBIRD**, rel. 1981. ed. 1,000, s/n, 24″ x 20″, pub FHG . . . . . . . . . . . . . . . | 60.00 | 100.00 |
| ☐ ed. 300, s/n, Exclusive . . . . . . . . . . . . . . . . . . . . . . . . . . . . . . . . . . . . . . . | 60.00 | Sold Out |
| ☐ **BLUEBIRD**, rel. 1982. ed. 5,000, s/o, 15″ x 8″, pub FHG . . . . . . . . . . . . . . . | 25.00 | — |
| ☐ **BLUE JAY**, rel. 1966. ed. 5,000, s/o, 16″ x 20″, pub FHG . . . . . . . . . . . . . . . | 10.00 | 75.00 |
| ☐ **BLUE JAY/AMERICAN ROBIN (Pair)**, rel. 1981. ed. 1,000, s/n, 17″ x 14″, pub FHG . . . . . . . . . . . . . . . . . . . . . . . . . . . . . . . . . . . . . . . . . . . . . . . . . . | 75.00 | Sold Out |
| ☐ **BOBCAT (KENTUCKY WILDCAT)**, rel. 1966. ed. 1,500, 22½″ x 27½″, pub FHG | | |
| *900 prints of this edition were titled ''Kentucky Wildcat'' and furnished to the University of Kentucky Alumni Association for a fund raising drive. Of this number - 400 were signed and numbered . . . . . . . . . . . . . . . . . . . . . . . . . | *35.00 | 350.00 |
| 500 were signed only . . . . . . . . . . . . . . . . . . . . . . . . . . . . . . . . . . . . . . . | *30.00 | 200.00 |
| **600 prints of the edition were titled ''Bobcat'' 100 were signed and numbered . . . . . . . . . . . . . . . . . . . . . . . . . . . . . . . | **35.00 | 350.00 |
| 500 were signed only . . . . . . . . . . . . . . . . . . . . . . . . . . . . . . . . . . . . . . . | **30.00 | 300.00 |
| ☐ **BOBCAT (KITTENS)**, rel. 1981. ed. 1,000, s/n, 29½″ x 23½″, pub FHG . . . . . | 60.00 | — |
| ☐ **BOBWHITE COVEY CIRCLE**, rel. 1982. ed. 1,000, s/n, 28″ x 23″, pub FHG . . . | 60.00 | — |
| ☐ **BRIDLED TITMOUSE**, rel. 1975. ed. 5,000, s/o, 15″ x 12″, pub FHG . . . . . . . . | 20.00 | 30.00 |
| ☐ **BROWN THRASHER**, rel. 1964. ed. 5,000, s/o, 16″ x 20″, pub FHG . . . . . . . . . | 10.00 | 60.00 |
| ☐ **CACTUS WREN**, rel. 1979. ed. 750, s/n, 20″ x 16″, pub FHG . . . . . . . . . . . . . | 40.00 | — |
| ☐ ed. 250, s/n, Exclusive for Arizona Nature Conservancy. . . . . . . . . . . . . . | — | Sold Out |
| ☐ **CALIFORNIA GROUND SQUIRREL**, rel. 1969. ed. 5,000, s/o, 16″ x 20″, pub FHG . . . . . . . . . . . . . . . . . . . . . . . . . . . . . . . . . . . . . . . . . . . . . . . . . . | 20.00 | 50.00 |
| ☐ **CALIFORNIA QUAIL**, rel. 1973. ed. 5,000, s/o, 16″ x 20″, pub FHG . . . . . . . . | 20.00 | 125.00 |
| ☐ **CAPE BUFFALO**, rel. 1976. ed. 1,000, s/n, 19½″ x 29½″, pub FHG . . . . . . . . | 75.00 | Sold Out |
| ☐ ed. 2,500, s/o . . . . . . . . . . . . . . . . . . . . . . . . . . . . . . . . . . . . . . . . . . . . . . | 60.00 | — |
| ☐ **CANADA GOOSE**, rel. 1968. ed. 3,000, 31″ x 24″, pub FHG . . . . . . . . . . . . . | — | — |
| *2,500 unsigned and unnumbered. . . . . . . . . . . . . . . . . . . . . . . . . . . . . . | *50.00 | 125.00 |
| **500 signed and numbered donated to National Audubon Society to raise money for Corkscrew Swamp Sanctuary. . . . . . . . . . . . . . . . . . . . . . . . . . | **100.00 | 250.00 |
| ☐ **CANADA GOOSE**, rel. 1983. ed. 1,000, s/n, 23½″ x 33½″, pub FHG . . . . . . . . | 75.00 | — |
| ☐ **CARDINAL**, rel. 1979. ed. 5,000, s/o, 14″ x 11″, pub FHG . . . . . . . . . . . . . . . | 20.00 | — |
| ☐ **CARDINAL (DOGWOOD)**, rel. 1963. ed. 5,000, s/o, 20″ x 16″, pub FHG . . . . . . | 10.00 | 300.00 |
| ☐ **CARDINAL (DOGWOOD)**, rel. 1983. ed. 1,000, s/n, 24″ x 20″, pub FHG . . . . . . | 75.00 | — |
| ☐ ed. 550, s/n . . . . . . . . . . . . . . . . . . . . . . . . . . . . . . . . . . . . . . . . . . . . . . . | — | — |
| ☐ **CARDINAL (SUNFLOWER)**, rel. 1969. ed. 5,000, s/o, 16″ x 20″, pub FHG . . . . | 20.00 | 100.00 |
| ☐ **CARDINAL (WITH YOUNG)**, rel. 1975. ed. 5,000, s/o, 26″ x 22″, pub FHG . . . | 40.00 | 125.00 |
| ☐ **CAROLINA WREN**, rel. 1970. ed. 5,000, s/o, 16″ x 20″, pub FHG . . . . . . . . . . | 20.00 | 50.00 |
| ☐ **CEDAR WAXWING**, rel. 1968. ed. 5,000, s/o, 16″ x 20″, pub FHG . . . . . . . . . | 20.00 | 50.00 |
| ☐ **CHEETAH**, rel. 1975. ed. 1,000, s/n, 22½″ x 30″, pub FHG . . . . . . . . . . . . . . | 75.00 | 90.00 |
| ☐ ed. 2,500, s/o . . . . . . . . . . . . . . . . . . . . . . . . . . . . . . . . . . . . . . . . . . . . . . | 60.00 | 75.00 |

| | | ISSUE PRICE | CURRENT PRICE |
|---|---|---|---|
| ☐ | CHIPMUNK, rel. 1979. ed. 1,500, s/n, 18" x 28", pub FHG . . . . . . . . . . . . . | 45.00 | 70.00 |
| ☐ | COTTONTAIL RABBIT, rel. 1979. ed. 2,000, s/o, 16" x 20", pub FHG . . . . . . . | 40.00 | 90.00 |
| ☐ | COUGAR, rel. 1977. ed. 3,000, s/o, 20" x 16", pub FHG . . . . . . . . . . . . . . . | 40.00 | Sold Out |
| ☐ | DOWNY WOODPECKER, rel. 1967. ed. 5,000, s/o, 16" x 20", pub FHG . . . . . . | 20.00 | 50.00 |
| ☐ | DOWNY WOODPECKER, rel. 1982. ed. 1,000, s/n, 24" x 20", pub FHG . . . . . . | 65.00 | — |
| ☐ | EAGLE AND OSPREY, rel. 1964. ed. 500, s/n, 43¼" x 30¼", pub FHG . . . . . . | 75.00 | 2000.00 |
| ☐ | EASTERN BLUEBIRD, rel. 1966. ed. 5,000, s/o, 16" x 20", pub FHG . . . . . . . . | 10.00 | 100.00 |
| ☐ | EASTERN BOBWHITE, rel. 1966. ed. 5,000, s/o, 16" x 20", pub FHG . . . . . . . . | 10.00 | 200.00 |
| ☐ | EASTERN BOBWHITE, rel. 1980. ed. 1,000, s/n, 24" x 20", pub FHG . . . . . . . | 50.00 | 80.00 |
| ☐ | ELF OWL, rel. 1977. ed. 3,500, s/o, 15" x 12", pub FHG . . . . . . . . . . . . . . . | 20.00 | Sold Out |
| ☐ | EVENING GROSBEAK, rel. 1973. ed. 5,000, s/o, 16" x 20", pub FHG . . . . . . . . | 20.00 | 45.00 |
| ☐ | FEEDER GROUP, rel. 1963. ed. 5,000, s/o, 16" x 20", pub FHG . . . . . . . . . . . | 10.00 | 60.00 |
| ☐ | THE FLEDGLINGS, rel. 1983. ed. 1,000, s/n, 17" x 30", pub FHG . . . . . . . . . . | 75.00 | — |
| ☐ | FLICKER, rel. 1966. ed. 5,000, s/o, 16" x 20", pub FHG . . . . . . . . . . . . . . . | 10.00 | 60.00 |
| ☐ | GAMBEL'S QUAIL, rel. 1979. ed. 3,000, s/o, 16" x 20", pub FHG . . . . . . . . . . | 40.00 | — |
| ☐ | GOLDEN EAGLE, rel. 1977. ed. 1,000, s/n, 24" x 30", pub FHG . . . . . . . . . . . | 60.00 | 120.00 |
| | ed. 2,000, signed only, The General Creighton W. Abrams Commemorative Golden Eagle, First Day Issue, The Patton Museum, Fort Knox, Kentucky. | | |
| ☐ | GOLDFINCH, rel. 1978. ed. 3,000, s/n, 15" x 12", pub FHG . . . . . . . . . . . . . . | 20.00 | — |
| ☐ | GRAY FOX, rel. 1980. ed. 1,500, s/n, 26" x 22", pub FHG . . . . . . . . . . . . . . | 50.00 | — |
| ☐ | GRAY SQUIRREL, ed. 1,500, s/n, 27½" x 23", pub FHG . . . . . . . . . . . . . . . | 60.00 | 90.00 |
| ☐ | GREAT HORNED OWL, rel. 1972. ed. 1,000, s/n, 21" x 27", pub FHG . . . . . . . | 75.00 | 135.00 |
| | ed. 3,000, s/o . . . . . . . . . . . . . . . . . . . . . . . . . . . . . . . . . . . . . . . . . . . . | 60.00 | 115.00 |
| | *ed. 1,000 signed and bearing a distinctive seal, donated to Kentucky Bankers Assn. to raise funds for Trooper Island, Kentucky State Police summer camp project for underprivileged boys . . . . . . . . . . . . . . . . . . . . . . . . . . . | *100.00 | Sold Out |
| ☐ | GREAT HORNED OWL, rel. 1981. ed. 1,000, s/n, 24" x 20", pub FHG . . . . . . . | 60.00 | — |
| ☐ | HOUSE WREN, rel. 1963. ed. 5,000, s/o, 16" x 20", pub FHG . . . . . . . . . . . . | 10.00 | 50.00 |
| ☐ | HUMMINGBIRDS AND CARDINAL FLOWERS, rel. 1968. ed. 7,500, 9" x 12", pub FHG | | |
| | Donated to Kentucky Chapter, The Nature Conservancy to raise funds for the preservation of Murphey's Pond, Kentucky's last Cypress Swamp (1968-69); and to the Alabama Conservancy for a 1971 membership campaign. | | |
| ☐ | IMPALA, rel. 1973. ed. 5,000, s/o, 18" x 24", pub FHG . . . . . . . . . . . . . . . . | 45.00 | 85.00 |
| ☐ | INDIGO BUNTING, rel. 1966. ed. 5,000, s/o, 16" x 20", pub FHG . . . . . . . . . . | 10.00 | 40.00 |
| ☐ | KENTUCKY WARBLER, rel. 1972. ed. 5,000, s/o, 16" x 20", pub FHG . . . . . . . | 20.00 | 40.00 |
| ☐ | KESTREL (SPARROW HAWK), rel. 1967. ed. 5,000, s/o, 16" x 20", pub FHG . | 20.00 | 50.00 |
| ☐ | LATE SUMMER AND FALL WILD FLOWERS, rel. 1978. ed. 5,000, signed one print in each set 14½" x 7½", pub FHG . . . . . . . . . . . . . . . . . . . . . . . . . . . . | 30.00 | — |
| ☐ | LAZULI BUNTING, rel. 1972. ed. 7,500, s/o, 12" x 15", pub FHG . . . . . . . . . . | 15.00 | 35.00 |
| ☐ | LITTLE BLUE HERON, rel. 1967. ed. 5,000, s/o, 16" x 20", pub FHG . . . . . . . . | 10.00 | 40.00 |
| ☐ | MALLARD DUCK, rel. 1971. ed. 5,000, s/o, 16" x 20", pub FHG . . . . . . . . . . . | 20.00 | 90.00 |
| ☐ | MEADOWLARK, rel. 1969. ed. 5,000, s/o, 16" x 20", pub FHG . . . . . . . . . . . . | 20.00 | 90.00 |
| ☐ | MOCKINGBIRD, rel. 1963. ed. 5,000, s/o, 16" x 20", pub FHG . . . . . . . . . . . . | 10.00 | 110.00 |
| ☐ | MOCKINGBIRDS, rel. 1980. ed. 1,000, s/n, 24" x 20", pub FHG . . . . . . . . . . . | 60.00 | 100.00 |
| ☐ | MOUNTAIN CHICKADEE, rel. 1975. ed. 5,000, s/o, 15" x 12", pub FHG . . . . . . | 20.00 | 40.00 |
| ☐ | MOUNTAIN LION, rel. 1972. ed. 1,000, s/n, 31" x 24½", pub FHG . . . . . . . . . | 75.00 | 105.00 |
| | ed. 4,000, s/o . . . . . . . . . . . . . . . . . . . . . . . . . . . . . . . . . . . . . . . . . . . . | 60.00 | 90.00 |
| ☐ | MOUNTAIN QUAIL, rel. 1975. ed. 5,000, s/o, 16" x 20", pub FHG . . . . . . . . . | 30.00 | 60.00 |
| ☐ | MORNING DOVE, rel. 1970. ed. 5,000, s/o, 16" x 20", pub FHG . . . . . . . . . . . | 20.00 | 50.00 |
| ☐ | OVENBIRD, rel. 1972. ed. 7,500, s/o, 12" x 15", pub FHG . . . . . . . . . . . . . . | 15.00 | 45.00 |
| ☐ | PAINTED BUNTING, rel. 1963. ed. 5,000, s/o, 20" x 16", pub FHG . . . . . . . . . | 10.00 | 55.00 |
| ☐ | PELICANS, rel. 1967. ed. 500, s/n, 30½" x 22½", pub FHG . . . . . . . . . . . . . | 60.00 | 100.00 |
| | ed. 4,500, s/o . . . . . . . . . . . . . . . . . . . . . . . . . . . . . . . . . . . . . . . . . . . . | 50.00 | 90.00 |
| ☐ | PEREGRINE FALCON, rel. 1980. ed. 5,000, s/o, 16½" x 14", pub FHG . . . . . . | 25.00 | — |
| ☐ | PHAINOPEPLA, rel. 1974. ed. 5,000, s/o, 12" x 15", pub FHG . . . . . . . . . . . . | 20.00 | Sold Out |
| ☐ | PILEATED WOODPECKER, rel. 1966. ed. 5,000, s/o, 16" x 20", pub FHG . . . . . | 10.00 | 95.00 |
| ☐ | PINTAIL, rel. 1978. ed. 3,000, s/o, 20" x 16", pub FHG . . . . . . . . . . . . . . . . | 40.00 | — |
| ☐ | PURPLE FINCH, rel. 1978. ed. 3,000, s/n, 15" x 12", pub FHG . . . . . . . . . . . | 20.00 | — |
| ☐ | PURPLE MARTIN, rel. 1973. ed. 5,000, s/o, 16" x 20", pub FHG . . . . . . . . . . | 20.00 | 50.00 |
| ☐ | PYRRHLOXIA, rel. 1974. ed. 5,000, s/o, 12" x 15", pub FHG . . . . . . . . . . . . . | 20.00 | Sold Out |
| ☐ | RACCOON (FAMILY), rel. 1968. ed. 500, s/n, 22" x 28", pub FHG . . . . . . . . . | 75.00 | 325.00 |
| | ed. 4,500, s/o . . . . . . . . . . . . . . . . . . . . . . . . . . . . . . . . . . . . . . . . . . . . | 60.00 | 250.00 |
| ☐ | RACCOON, rel. 1976. ed. 5,000, s/o, 20" x 18", pub FHG . . . . . . . . . . . . . . | 35.00 | 100.00 |

| | ISSUE PRICE | CURRENT PRICE |
|---|---|---|
| ☐ **RACCOON**, rel. 1982. ed. 1,500, s/n, 24" x 20", pub FHG | 65.00 | Sold Out |
| ed. 500, Exclusive - Louisville Zoological Gardens. | | |
| ☐ **RED FOX**, rel. 1973. ed. 1,000, s/n, 20" x 24", pub FHG | 75.00 | 150.00 |
| ed. 4,000, s/o | 60.00 | 125.00 |
| ☐ **REDHEADED WOODPECKER**, rel. 1979. ed. 2,000, s/o, 20" x 16", pub FHG | 45.00 | — |
| ☐ **RED-TAILED HAWK**, rel. 1981. ed. 1,000, s/n, 28" x 12", pub FHG | 60.00 | — |
| ed. 100, s/n, Exclusive, St. Lukes Hospital, Fort Thomas Kentucky. | | |
| ☐ **RED-WINGED BLACKBIRD**, rel. 1967. ed. 5,000, s/o, 16" x 20", pub FHG | 20.00 | 50.00 |
| ☐ **RED-WINGED BLACKBIRD**, rel. 1983. ed. 1,000, s/n, 26" x 13", pub FHG | 75.00 | — |
| ☐ **RETICULATED GIRAFFE**, rel. 1973. ed. 1,000, s/n, 20" x 28", pub FHG | 65.00 | 125.00 |
| ed. 4,000, s/o | 50.00 | 100.00 |
| ☐ **RING-NECKED PHEASANT**, rel. 1965. ed. 500, s/n, 29¼" x 21", pub FHG | 35.00 | 300.00 |
| ed. 750, s/o | 30.00 | 250.00 |
| ☐ **RING-NECKED PHEASANT**, rel. 1979. ed. 1,500, s/n, 22" x 30". pub FHG | 50.00 | — |
| ☐ **ROADRUNNER**, rel. 1969. ed. 5,000, s/o, 20" x 16", pub FHG | 20.00 | 40.00 |
| ☐ **ROBIN**, rel. 1963. ed. 5,000, s/o, 16" x 20", pub FHG | 10.00 | 100.00 |
| ☐ **ROSE-BREASTED GROSBEAK**, rel. 1971. ed. 5,000, s/o, 16" x 20", pub FHG | 20.00 | 65.00 |
| ☐ **RUFFED GROUSE**, rel. 1972. ed. 5,000, s/o, 16" x 20", pub FHG | 20.00 | 75.00 |
| ☐ **RUFFED GROUSE**, rel. 1983. ed. 1,000, s/n, 24" x 20", pub FHG | 75.00 | — |
| ed. 100, s/n | — | — |
| ☐ **RUFOUS-SIDED TOWHEE**, rel. 1969. ed. 5,000, s/o, 16" x 20", pub FHG | 20.00 | 60.00 |
| ☐ **SAW-WHET OWL**, rel. 1977. ed. 3,500, s/o, 12" x 15", pub FHG | 20.00 | 50.00 |
| ☐ **SCALED QUAIL**, rel. 1977. ed. 3,000, s/o, 16" x 20", pub FHG | 40.00 | — |
| ☐ **SCARLET TANAGER**, rel. 1963. ed. 5,000, s/o, 16" x 20", pub FHG | 10.00 | 90.00 |
| ☐ **SCREECH OWL**, rel. 1967. ed. 12,500, Free bonus print available only with membership in National Audubon Society during 1967-68 Kentucky membership campaign. | — | 55.00 |
| ☐ **SCREECH OWLS**, rel. 1975. ed. 5,000, s/o, 16" x 20", pub FHG | 20.00 | 75.00 |
| ☐ **SEA OTTER**, rel. 1981. ed. 1,000, s/n, 14" x 24", pub FHG | 60.00 | Sold Out |
| ed. 300, s/n, Exclusive - Friends of the Sea Otter Society. | — | Sold Out |
| ☐ **SPRING WARBLERS**, rel. 1968. ed. 5,000, s/o, 16" x 20", pub FHG | 35.00 | 75.00 |
| Sold only as a pair | | |
| ☐ **SPRING WILDFLOWERS**, rel. 1964. ed. 5,000, s/o, 7" x 16½", pub FHG | 10.00 | 75.00 |
| Set of six, artist's signature on one print of set constitutes signature of entire set. | | |
| ☐ **STRIPED SKUNK**, rel. 1977. ed. 3,000, s/o, 16" x 20", pub FHG | 40.00 | — |
| ☐ **SUMMER TANAGER**, rel. 1963. ed. 5,000, s/o, 16" x 20", pub FHG | 10.00 | 50.00 |
| ☐ **SUMMER WILDFLOWERS**, rel. 1967. ed. 10,000, s/o, 7" x 16½", pub FHG | 10.00 | 50.00 |
| Set of six, artist's signature on one print of set constitutes signature of entire set. | | |
| ☐ **TRUMPETER SWAN**, rel. 1979. ed. 2,000, s/n, 22" x 26", pub FHG | 45.00 | — |
| ☐ **TUFTED TITMOUSE**, rel. 1974. ed. 5,000, s/o, 16" x 20", pub FHG | 20.00 | Sold Out |
| ☐ **UPLAND BIRDS**, rel. 1967. ed. 500, s/n, 30" x 22¼", pub FHG | 60.00 | 100.00 |
| 4,500, s/o | 50.00 | 85.00 |
| ☐ **VERMILION FLYCATCHER**, rel. 1972. ed. 7,500, s/o, 12" x 15", pub FHG | 15.00 | 35.00 |
| ☐ **WESTERN TANAGER**, rel. 1977. ed. 3,000, s/o, 16" x 20", pub FHG | 40.00 | — |
| ☐ **WHITE-BREASTED NUTHATCH**, rel. 1975. ed. 5,000, s/o, 19" x 23½", pub FHG | 30.00 | — |
| ☐ **WHITE-TAILED FAWNS**, rel. 1980. ed. 1,000, s/n, 30" x 23", pub FHG | 60.00 | Sold Out |
| ed. 500, s/n, Exclusive - Bernheim Forest, Clermont Kentucky. | | |
| ☐ **WHITE-THROATED SPARROW**, rel. 1972. ed. 7,500, s/o, 12" x 15", pub FHG | 15.00 | 35.00 |
| ☐ **WHITE-TAILED DEER**, rel. 1970. ed. 500, s/n, 22" x 28", pub FHG | 75.00 | 125.00 |
| 4,500, s/o | 60.00 | 90.00 |
| ☐ **WILDCAT**, rel. 1979. ed. 5,000, s/o, 11" x 14", pub FHG | 20.00 | — |
| ☐ **WILD TURKEY**, rel. 1970. ed. 500, s/n, 20" x 25", pub FHG | 60.00 | 125.00 |
| ed. 4,500, s/o | 45.00 | 100.00 |
| ☐ **WOOD DUCK**, rel. 1966. ed. 500, s/n, 22½" x 27½", pub FHG | 35.00 | 180.00 |
| ed. 2,000, s/o | 30.00 | 150.00 |
| ☐ **WOOD THRUSH**, rel. 1970. ed. 5,000, s/o, 16" x 20", pub FHG | 20.00 | 50.00 |
| ☐ **YELLOW-BILLED CUCKOO**, rel. 1971. ed. 5,000, s/o, 16" x 20", pub FHG | 20.00 | 65.00 |
| ☐ **YELLOW-BREASTED CHAT**, rel. 1973. ed. 7,500, s/o, 12" x 15", pub FHG | 15.00 | 35.00 |
| ☐ **YELLOW-HEADED BLACKBIRD**, rel. 1973. ed. 5,000, s/o, 16" x 20", pub FHG | 20.00 | 60.00 |
| ☐ **YELLOW-THROAT**, rel. 1973. ed. 7,500, s/o, 12" x 15", pub FHG | 15.00 | 35.00 |

# BRETT HARPER

Brett Harper draws and develops his prints from ink drawings because he finds great pleasure in interpreting objects of nature. His medium is silkscreen; his subjects, fruits and flowers.

He received his Bachelor of Arts degree in English from Brown University in 1975 and is employed as a copywriter and creative director with an advertising agency. Harper, who executes every phase in the production of his prints, exhibits regularly in the greater Cincinnati area.

**POTTED PLANTS** *by Brett Harper*

| BRETT HARPER | ISSUE PRICE | CURRENT PRICE |
|---|---|---|
| ☐ **CONSIDER THE LILLIES**, rel. 1975. ed. 250, s/n, 12⅞″ x 20″, pub FHG . . . . . . | 20.00 | 40.00 |
| ☐ **PETUNIA POWER**, rel. 1975. ed. 250, s/n, 13″ x 18½″, pub FHG . . . . . . . . . . | 20.00 | 40.00 |
| ☐ **ZINNIA**, rel. 1975. ed. 250, s/n, 13″ x 19½″, pub FHG . . . . . . . . . . . . . . . . . | 20.00 | 40.00 |
| ☐ **BITTERSWEET**, rel. 1976. ed. 500, s/n, 15⅞″ x 19⅞″, pub FHG . . . . . . . . . . . | 20.00 | 75.00 |
| ☐ **EUCALYPTUS**, rel. 1976. ed. 500, s/n, 24″ x 16″, pub FHG . . . . . . . . . . . . . . | 20.00 | 75.00 |
| ☐ **MELLOW YELLOW**, rel. 1976. ed. 250, s/n, 19⅜″ x 13⅜″, pub FHG . . . . . . . . | 20.00 | 100.00 |
| ☐ **TULIPS**, rel. 1976. ed. 250, s/n, 19¾″ x 15″, pub FHG . . . . . . . . . . . . . . . . | 20.00 | 40.00 |
| ☐ **AMARYLLIS**, rel. 1977. ed. 500, s/n, 20″ x 15½″, pub FHG . . . . . . . . . . . . . | 25.00 | Sold Out |
| ☐ **COUNTRY PICKIN'S**, rel. 1977. ed. 500, s/n, 24″ x 20″, pub FHG . . . . . . . . . | 20.00 | 45.00 |
| ☐ **MUSHROOMS**, rel. 1977. ed. 500, s/n, 12″ x 12″, pub FHG . . . . . . . . . . . . . . | 25.00 | Sold Out |
| ☐ **SENTINEL**, rel. 1977. ed. 500, s/n, 18½″ x 10″, pub FHG . . . . . . . . . . . . . . . | 25.00 | Sold Out |
| ☐ **ANCIENT SYMBOLS**, rel. 1978. ed. 500, s/n, 17⅜″ x 12¾″, pub FHG . . . . . . . | 25.00 | Sold Out |
| ☐ **BEACHCOMBERS' DREAM**, rel. 1978. ed. 300, s/n, 17½″ x 21″, pub FHG . . . | 40.00 | — |
| ☐ **COLLECTIBLES**, rel. 1978. ed. 500, s/n, 14″ x 15¾″, pub FHG . . . . . . . . . . . | 25.00 | — |
| ☐ **HANGING FERN**, rel. 1978. ed. 750, s/n, 30″ x 22″, pub FHG . . . . . . . . . . . . | 25.00 | — |
| ☐ **HOBBY HORSE**, rel. 1978. ed. 500, s/n, 14¾″ x 22¼″, pub FHG . . . . . . . . . . | — | — |

| | ISSUE PRICE | CURRENT PRICE |
|---|---|---|
| ☐ MUSICAL INSTRUMENTS, rel. 1978. ed. 500, s/n, 20½" x 18½", pub FHG .. | 25.00 | — |
| ☐ FINDINGS FROM THE FIELD, rel. 1979. ed. 750, s/n, 23" x 17", pub FHG .... | 25.00 | — |
| ☐ FIREWORKS FROM THE EARTH, rel. 1979. ed. 750, s/n, 26" x 19", pub FHG . | 30.00 | — |
| ☐ OCTOBER GATHERINGS, rel. 1979. ed. 750, s/n, 18" x 21", pub FHG ....... | 25.00 | — |
| ☐ POTTED PLANTS, rel. 1979. ed. 750, s/n, 16" x 20", pub FHG ............. | 25.00 | — |

# CHARLES HARPER

Charles Harper's technique deals with simple suggestions of shape and design based on the fundamentals of nature.

He attended West Virginia Wesleyan College and graduated from the Cincinnati Art Academy, where he taught for many years.

Harper's nature essays on each print are as prized as his non-verbal silk-screened prints. The artist-humorist-naturalist is a highly popular speaker and writer.

Harper has illustrated a number of books for Golden Press on birds, animals and biology; sections in *New World* and *Childcraft* encyclopedias; and articles in magazines including *Look, Ranger Rick* and *National Wildlife.* His ceramic murals adorn the Federal Building and the Convention Center in Cincinnati.

**CONFISKATION** *by Charles Harper*

## CHARLES HARPER

| | ISSUE PRICE | CURRENT PRICE |
|---|---|---|
| ☐ **LADYBUG,** rel. 1968. ed. 500, s/n, 15¼" x 20½", serigraph, pub FHG | 20.00 | 250.00 |
| ☐ **HOUSE WRENS,** rel. 1968. ed. 500, s/n, 20" x 15", serigraph, pub FHG | 20.00 | 135.00 |
| ☐ **PORTFOLIO FOUR PRINTS,** rel. 1968. ed. 500, s/n, 15½" x 20½", serigraph, pub FHG | 60.00 | 200.00 |
| ☐ **ANHINGA,** rel. 1969. ed. 500, s/n, 50" x 24", lithograph on canvas, pub FHG | 50.00 | 225.00 |
| ☐ **HUNGRY EYES,** rel. 1969. ed. 500, s/n, 12⅝" x 20½", serigraph, pub FHG | 20.00 | 350.00 |
| ☐ **WATER STRIDER,** rel. 1969. ed. 500, s/n, 50¼" x 24", serigraph, pub FHG | 40.00 | 350.00 |
| ☐ **BOBWHITE FAMILY,** rel. 1970. ed. 750, s/n, 9½" x 24¾", serigraph, pub FHG | 30.00 | 125.00 |
| ☐ **BURROWING OWL,** rel. 1970. ed. 500, s/n, 20" x 11", serigraph, pub FHG | 30.00 | 100.00 |
| ☐ **CARDINAL (ON CORN),** rel. 1970. ed. 500, s/n, 15¼" x 20½", serigraph, pub FHG | 30.00 | 275.00 |
| ☐ **CRAYFISH MOLTING,** rel. 1970. ed. 750, s/n, 13¼" x 17¼", serigraph, pub FHG | 30.00 | 150.00 |
| ☐ **PILEATED WOODPECKER,** rel. 1970. ed. 750, s/n, 15¼" x 20½", serigraph, pub FHG | 30.00 | 85.00 |
| ☐ **BEAR IN THE BIRCHES,** rel. 1971. ed. 1,500, s/n, 23" x 22⅝", serigraph, pub FHG | 35.00 | 400.00 |
| ☐ **BEETLE BATTLE,** rel. 1971. ed. 750, s/n, 15¼" x 20½", serigraph, pub FHG | 30.00 | 90.00 |
| ☐ **BLUE JAY BATHING,** rel. 1971. ed. 1,500, s/n, 18¾" x 24¼", serigraph, pub FHG | 30.00 | 90.00 |
| ☐ **LADYBUG LOVERS,** rel. 1971. ed. 1,500, s/n, 16¼" x 17½", serigraph, pub FHG | 30.00 | 60.00 |
| ☐ **PUFFIN,** rel. 1971. ed. 750, s/n, 15¼" x 20½", serigraph, pub FHG | 30.00 | 60.00 |
| ☐ **RED-BELLIED WOODPECKER,** rel. 1971. ed. 1,500, s/n, 21⅜" x 15¾", serigraph, pub FHG | 30.00 | 60.00 |
| ☐ **BOX TURTLE,** rel. 1972. ed. 1,500, s/n, 9⅛" x 22⅝", serigraph, pub FHG | 30.00 | 65.00 |
| ☐ **CHIPMUNK,** rel. 1972. ed. 1,500, s/n, 17¼" x 13", serigraph, pub FHG | 30.00 | 60.00 |
| ☐ **FAMILY OWLBUM,** rel. 1972. ed. 1,500, s/n, 11⅜" x 11⅞", serigraph, pub FHG | 30.00 | 80.00 |
| ☐ **LADYBUG,** rel. 1972. ed. 10,000, s/o, 12½" x 12", litho, pub FHG. | 6.00 | 20.00 |
| ☐ **PELICAN IN A DOWNPOUR,** rel. 1972. ed. 1,500, s/n, 16½" x 21½", serigraph, pub FHG | 30.00 | 275.00 |
| ☐ **YELLOW-BELLIED SAPSUCKER,** rel. 1972. ed. 1,500, s/n, 16½" x 16¾", serigraph, pub FHG | 30.00 | 70.00 |
| ☐ **ROUND ROBIN,** rel. 1973. ed. 1,500, s/n, 15" x 20", serigraph, pub FHG | 30.00 | 60.00 |
| ☐ **THE LAST SUNFLOWER SEED,** rel. 1973. ed. 1,500, s/n, 16½" x 21⅝", serigraph, pub FHG | 30.00 | 125.00 |
| ☐ **WATERMELON MOON,** rel. 1973. ed. 1,500, s/n, 15½" x 19⅞", serigraph, pub FHG | 30.00 | 300.00 |
| ☐ **WEDDING FEAST,** rel. 1973. ed. 1,500, s/n, 17½" x 17", serigraph, pub FHG | 30.00 | 65.00 |
| ☐ **WOOD DUCK,** rel. 1973. ed. 1,500, s/n, 21⅞" x 12", serigraph, pub FHG | 30.00 | 250.00 |
| ☐ **BIRDS OF A FEATHER,** rel. 1974. ed. 2,000, s/n, 23½" x 31", serigraph, pub FHG | 50.00 | Sold Out |
| ☐ **COOL CARDINAL,** rel. 1974. ed. 2,000, s/n, 21" x 8½", serigraph, pub FHG | 30.00 | 325.00 |
| ☐ **CROW IN THE SNOW,** rel. 1974. ed. 1,500, s/n, 23½" x 23", serigraph, pub FHG | 35.00 | 125.00 |
| ☐ **FINE FEATHER,** rel. 1974. ed. 1,500, s/n, 23½" x 10", serigraph, pub FHG | 30.00 | 100.00 |
| ☐ **PAINTED BUNTING,** rel. 1974. ed. 1,500, s/n, 19½" x 17", serigraph, pub FHG | 30.00 | 120.00 |
| ☐ **TALL TAIL,** rel. 1974. ed. 2,000, s/n, 21" x 12⅞", serigraph, pub FHG | 30.00 | 75.00 |
| ☐ **BIRDWATCHER,** rel. 1975. ed. 2,000, s/n, 16½" x 13", serigraph, pub FHG | 40.00 | 200.00 |
| ☐ **BLUEBIRDS IN THE BLUE GRASS,** rel. 1975. ed. 2,000, s/n, 23½" x 23", serigraph, pub FHG | 45.00 | Sold Out |
| ☐ **PFWHOOOOOOO,** rel. 1975. ed. 2,000, s/n, 20½" x 15", serigraph, pub FHG | 40.00 | 120.00 |
| ☐ **WHITECOAT,** rel. 1975. ed. 2,000, s/n, 13" x 12½", serigraph, pub FHG | 30.00 | 115.00 |
| ☐ **CLAWS,** rel. 1976. ed. 2,000, s/n, 23½" x 16", serigraph, pub FHG | 40.00 | 85.00 |
| ☐ **CORNPRONE,** rel. 1976. ed. 2,500, s/n, 18¼" x 16½", serigraph, pub FHG | 40.00 | 135.00 |
| ☐ **DEVOTION IN THE OCEAN,** rel. 1976. ed. 2,000, s/n, 17⅞" x 13¼", serigraph, pub FHG | 40.00 | 75.00 |
| ☐ **LOVE FROM ABOVE,** rel. 1976. ed. 2,000, s/n, 31½" x 9¼", serigraph, pub FHG | 40.00 | 250.00 |
| ☐ **SKIMMERSCAPE,** rel. 1976. ed. 2,000, s/n, 24½" x 17½", serigraph, pub FHG | 40.00 | 90.00 |

| | ISSUE PRICE | CURRENT PRICE |
|---|---|---|
| ☐ **BRRRTHDAY**, rel. 1977. ed. 2,500, s/n, 21″ x 16″, serigraph, pub FHG . . . . | 40.00 | 60.00 |
| ☐ **CATNIP**, rel. 1977. ed. 2,500, s/n, 17¾″ x 15¼″, serigraph, pub FHG . . . . . | 50.00 | 100.00 |
| ☐ **DOLFUN**, rel. 1977. ed. 2,500, s/n, 20″ x 15″, serigraph, pub FHG . . . . . . . . | 50.00 | 75.00 |
| ☐ **DOWN UNDER, DOWN UNDER**, rel. 1977. ed. 2,500, s/n, 23″ x 14″, serigraph, pub FHG . . . . . . . . . . . . . . . . . . . . . . . . . . . . . . . . . . . . . . . . | 40.00 | 75.00 |
| ☐ **PHANCY PHEATHERS**, rel. 1977. ed. 2,500, s/n, 30″ x 11¼″, serigraph, pub FHG . . . . . . . . . . . . . . . . . . . . . . . . . . . . . . . . . . . . . . . . . . . | 50.00 | 120.00 |
| ☐ **SEEING RED**, rel. 1977. ed. 2,500, s/n, 17″ x 23″, serigraph, pub FHG . . . . . | 40.00 | 125.00 |
| ☐ **SKIPPING SCHOOL**, rel. 1977. ed. 2,500, s/n, 22¼″ x 20¾″, serigraph, pub FHG . . . . . . . . . . . . . . . . . . . . . . . . . . . . . . . . . . . . . . . . . . . | 50.00 | 75.00 |
| ☐ **BITTERN SUITE**, rel. 1978. ed. 2,500, s/n, 19½″ x 14¼″, serigraph, pub FHG | 50.00 | 75.00 |
| ☐ **CRAWLING TALL**, rel. 1978. ed. 2,500, s/n, 19″ x 18¼″, serigraph, pub FHG | 50.00 | 75.00 |
| ☐ **FROG EAT FROG**, rel. 1978. ed. 2,500, s/n, 18″ x 18″, serigraph, pub FHG . . . | 50.00 | 50.00 |
| ☐ **HARE'S BREADTH**, rel. 1978. ed. 2,500, s/n, 24″ x 19″, serigraph, pub FHG . | 50.00 | 75.00 |
| ☐ **LOVEY DOVEY**, rel. 1978. ed. 2,500, s/n, 18″ x 18″, serigraph, pub FHG . . . . | 50.00 | 75.00 |
| ☐ **RACCROBAT**, rel. 1978. ed. 10,000, s/o, 16″ x 11½″, litho, pub FHG . . . . . . . | 10.00 | — |
| ☐ **BUZZ OFF YOU TURKEY**, rel. 1979. ed. 2,500, s/n, 12¾″ x 27″, serigraph, pub FHG . . . . . . . . . . . . . . . . . . . . . . . . . . . . . . . . . . . . . . . . . . . | 55.00 | — |
| ☐ **COOL CARNIVORE**, rel. 1979. ed. 2,500, s/n, 24″ x 24″, serigraph, pub FHG . | 50.00 | — |
| ☐ **DREAM TEAM**, rel. 1979. ed. 5,000, s/o, 10″ x 14″, serigraph, pub FHG. . . . | 20.00 | — |
| ☐ **FURRED FEEDER**, rel. 1979. ed. 2,500, s/n, 30″ x 11¼″, serigraph, pub FHG | 50.00 | — |
| ☐ **KOALA KOALA**, rel. 1979. ed. 5,000, s/o, 11″ x 14″, serigraph, pub FHG . . . . | 20.00 | — |
| ☐ **SERENGETI SPAGHETTI**, rel. 1979. ed. 2,500, s/n, 21½″ x 28″, serigraph, pub FHG . . . . . . . . . . . . . . . . . . . . . . . . . . . . . . . . . . . . . . . . . . . | 55.00 | — |
| ☐ **HEXIT**, rel. 1980. ed. 1,500, s/n, 20″ x 20″, serigraph, pub FHG. . . . . . . . . . | 60.00 | 100.00 |
| ☐ **JUMBRELLA**, rel. 1980. ed. 1,500, s/n, 16″ x 24″, serigraph, pub FHG . . . . . | 60.00 | Sold Out |
| ☐ **POTLUCK**, rel. 1980. ed. 1,500, s/n, 26″ x 10⅛″, serigraph, pub FHG . . . . . . . | 60.00 | 90.00 |
| ☐ **REDBIRDS AND REDBUDS**, rel. 1980. ed. 1,500, s/n, 19¼″ x 18¾″, serigraph, pub FHG . . . . . . . . . . . . . . . . . . . . . . . . . . . . . . . . . . . . . | 60.00 | 100.00 |
| ☐ **LAST APHID**, rel. 1981. ed. 1,500, s/n, 20″ x 20″, serigraph, pub FHG . . . . . . | 60.00 | — |
| ☐ **RACC AN' RUIN**, rel. 1981. ed. 1,500, s/n, 16″ x 20″, serigraph, pub FHG . . . | 60.00 | — |
| ☐ **RACCPACK**, rel. 1981. ed. 2,000, s/n, 19½″ x 13″, serigraph, pub FHG . . . . . | 35.00 | 100.00 |
| ☐ **ROMANCE ON THE RICHTER SCALE**, rel. 1981. ed. 1,500, s/n, 20″ x 16″, serigraph, pub FHG . . . . . . . . . . . . . . . . . . . . . . . . . . . . . . . . . . . . . | 60.00 | — |
| ☐ **ARMADITTO**, rel. 1982. ed. 1,500, s/n, 17″ x 17″, serigraph, pub FHG . . . . . . | 60.00 | — |
| ☐ **PELICAN PANTRY**, rel. 1982. ed. 1,500, s/n, 18″ x 18″, serigraph, pub FHG . | 60.00 | — |
| ☐ **PRICKLY PAIR**, rel. 1982. ed. 1,500, s/n, 16″ x 16″, serigraph, pub FHG . . . . | 60.00 | — |
| ☐ **TERN, STONES AND TURNSTONES**, rel. 1982. ed. 1,500, s/n, 16″ x 22″, serigraph, pub FHG . . . . . . . . . . . . . . . . . . . . . . . . . . . . . . . . . . . . . | 60.00 | — |
| ☐ **CONFISKATION**, rel. 1983. ed. 1,000, s/n, 17″ x 13½″, serigraph, pub FHG . | 90.00 | — |
| ☐ **FOXSIMILES**, rel. 1983. ed. 1,500, s/n, 21¾″ x 18″, serigraph, pub FHG. . . . | 60.00 | — |
| ☐ **QUAILSAFE**, rel. 1983. ed. 1,000, s/n, 22″ x 16″, serigraph, pub FHG . . . . . . | 90.00 | — |
| ☐ **RACCSNACK**, rel. 1983. ed. 1,000, s/n, 30″ x 12″, serigraph, pub FHG . . . . . | 90.00 | — |
| ☐ **SQUIRREL IN A SQUALL**, rel. 1983. ed. 1,000, s/n, 16″ x 16″, serigraph, pub FHG . . . . . . . . . . . . . . . . . . . . . . . . . . . . . . . . . . . . . . . . . . . | 90.00 | — |

# EDIE HARPER

Edie Harper studied at the Art Academy in Cincinnati. Ironically, on her first day in her first class, she met Charles Harper whom she later married.

Harper is not only a painter, but a photographer and weaver. In one year, she exhibited serigraphs at Mount St. Joseph College, photographs at the Contemporary Arts Center, and weavings at Edgecliff College in Cincinnati.

**MAGNIFICAT** *by Edie Harper*

# EDIE HARPER

| | ISSUE PRICE | CURRENT PRICE |
|---|---|---|
| ☐ **IN THE GARDEN,** rel. 1975. ed. 250, s/n, 16½″ x 14½″, pub FHG | 20.00 | 50.00 |
| ☐ **JONAH,** rel. 1975. ed. 250, s/n, 29″ x 21½″, pub FHG | 20.00 | 250.00 |
| ☐ **NOAZARK,** rel. 1975. ed. 250, s/n, 15¾″ x 16¼″, pub FHG | 20.00 | 210.00 |
| ☐ **DAN'S DEN,** rel. 1976. ed. 750, s/n, 20″ x 8½″, pub FHG | 30.00 | 150.00 |
| ☐ **LITTLE DAVID,** rel. 1978. ed. 750, s/n, 16½″ x 15¾″, pub FHG | 35.00 | 60.00 |
| ☐ **SOLOMON SEZ,** rel. 1976. ed. 750, s/n, 14½″ x 7″, pub FHG | 20.00 | 35.00 |
| ☐ **SONRISE,** rel. 1976. ed. 750, s/n, 17½″ x 15″, pub FHG | 30.00 | 40.00 |
| ☐ **UP, UP AND AWAY,** rel. 1976. ed. 1,000, s/n, 20″ x 24″, pub FHG | 40.00 | Sold Out |
| ☐ **PENNY CANDY,** rel. 1977. ed. 750, s/n, 14½″ x 12″, pub FHG | 35.00 | Sold Out |
| ☐ **THE DISCIPLES,** rel. 1977. ed. 750, s/n, 20″ x 20″, pub FHG | 35.00 | Sold Out |
| ☐ **TREE HOUSE,** rel. 1977. ed. 750, s/n, 21″ x 9⅜″, pub FHG | 35.00 | 60.00 |
| ☐ **ADAM and MS. EVE,** rel. 1978. ed. 750, s/n, 20″ x 16″, pub FHG | 35.00 | Sold Out |
| ☐ **NET PROPHET,** rel. 1976. ed. 750, s/n, 12″ x 20″, pub FHG | 30.00 | 50.00 |
| ☐ **SAMSON AND DELILAH,** rel. 1978. ed. 750, s/n, 13″ x 18¾″, pub FHG | 35.00 | 75.00 |
| ☐ **SUNDAY SCHOOL OUTING,** rel. 1978. ed. 750, s/n, 12¾″ x 17″, pub FHG | 35.00 | Sold Out |
| ☐ **FAMILY PORTRAIT,** rel. 1979. ed. 750, s/n, 15″ x 15″, pub FHG | 40.00 | — |
| ☐ **HERE HE COMES!,** rel. 1979. ed. 705, s/n, pub FHG | 35.00 | — |
| ☐ **POW,** rel. 1979. ed. 750, s/n, 15½″ x 18″, pub FHG | 35.00 | — |
| ☐ **WOW,** rel. 1979. ed. 750, s/n, 20″ x 13″, pub FHG | 35.00 | — |
| ☐ **LOT'S LOT,** rel. 1980. ed. 375, s/n, 15″ x 15″, pub FHG | 40.00 | — |

| | ISSUE PRICE | CURRENT PRICE |
|---|---|---|
| ☐ **PEEPKIN,** rel. 1980. ed. 375, s/n, 12″ x 20″, pub FHG | 40.00 | 70.00 |
| ☐ **SPRING CREEPER,** rel. 1980. ed. 375, s/n, 12″ x 20″, pub FHG | 40.00 | 70.00 |
| ☐ **FISHFUL THINKING,** rel. 1981. ed. 375, s/n, 12⅝″ x 13¼″, pub FHG | 40.00 | 70.00 |
| ☐ **SANDPEEPER,** rel. 1981. ed. 375, s/n, 12″ x 20″, pub FHG | 40.00 | — |
| ☐ **WINTER WATCH,** rel. 1981. ed. 375, s/n, 12″ x 20″, pub FHG | 40.00 | — |
| ☐ **BASKIT,** rel. 1982. ed. 375, s/n, 15″ x 19″, pub FHG | 45.00 | — |
| ☐ **CLEOPETRA,** rel. 1982. ed. 375, s/n, 16″ x 16″, pub FHG | 40.00 | — |
| ☐ **SLEEPYTIMETOM,** rel. 1982. ed. 375, s/n, 13⅞″ x 20″, pub FHG | 40.00 | — |
| ☐ **SUMMER WATCH,** rel. 1982. ed. 375, s/n, 14″ x 19″, pub FHG | 45.00 | — |
| ☐ **MAGNIFICAT,** rel. 1983. ed. 375, s/n, 24″ x 11½″, pub FHG | 60.00 | — |

# JIM HARRISON

Jim Harrison attended the University of South Carolina. Unable to foresee any future in art while in college, his studies turned toward athletics. During eleven years of coaching and teaching at three high schools, his thoughts returned to painting. Summers were filled with art lessons under Zita Mellon who encouraged him to paint full time.

He resigned from coaching in 1970 and took up painting full time.

Harrison prefers to be known as a mood painter, saying that he is really concerned with the "spirit" of a place or thing rather than the object itself.

**MOUNTAIN BRIDGE** *by Jim Harrison*

## JIM HARRISON

| | ISSUE PRICE | CURRENT PRICE |
|---|---|---|
| ☐ **ABANDONED BOAT,** rel. 1974. ed. 1,000, s/n, 13¾″ x 17½″, pub JH | 25.00 | 50.00 |
| ☐ **AMERICAN BYWAYS,** rel. 1975. ed. 1,500, s/n, 28″ x 22″, pub FHG | 40.00 | 225.00 |
| ☐ **BRUSH AND BUCKET,** rel. 1981. ed. 300, s/n, 18¼″ x 26¼″, pub FHG | 300.00 | — |
| ed. 50, a/p | 350.00 | — |
| ☐ **BULL OF THE WOODS,** rel. 1982. ed. 1,500, s/n, 18″ x 21½″, pub FHG | 75.00 | Sold Out |
| ☐ **BURMA SHAVE,** rel. 1977. ed. 1,500, s/n, 13″ x 21½″, pub FHG | 50.00 | 185.00 |
| ☐ **CLABBER GIRL,** rel. 1979. ed. 1,500, s/n, 23″ x 30″, pub FHG | 75.00 | 200.00 |
| ☐ **COASTAL MARSHES,** rel. 1973. ed. 1,000, s/n, 16½″ x 28″, pub JH | 30.00 | 125.00 |
| ☐ **666 COLD TABLETS,** rel. 1978. ed. 1,500, s/n, 22″ x 28″, pub FHG | 50.00 | 150.00 |
| ☐ **COMMUNITY CHURCH,** rel. 1977. ed. 1,500, s/n, 12″ x 20″, pub FHG | 50.00 | 90.00 |

| | ISSUE PRICE | CURRENT PRICE |
|---|---|---|
| ☐ **COUNTRY SEASONIN'**, rel. 1975. ed. 1,500, s/n, 14¾" x 17¾", pub FHG ... | 40.00 | 225.00 |
| ☐ **DISAPPEARING AMERICA**, rel. 1975. ed. 1,500, s/n, 33" x 18½", pub FHG .. | 40.00 | 900.00 |
| ☐ **DR. PEPPER**, rel. 1977. ed. 1,500, s/n, 14¾" x 12", pub FHG ........... | 50.00 | 175.00 |
| ☐ **FALLOW AND FORGOTTEN**, rel. 1977. ed. 1,500, s/n, 16" x 24", pub FHG ... | 50.00 | 75.00 |
| ☐ **FRESH GRITS**, rel. 1983. ed. 1,500, s/n, 17¾" x 30", pub FHG........... | 80.00 | — |
| ☐ **GOLD DUST TWINS**, rel. 1979. ed. 1,500, s/n, 24" x 15½", pub FHG ....... | 55.00 | 75.00 |
| ☐ **GOODY'S**, rel. 1979. ed. 1,500, s/n, 18¾" x 33", pub FHG .............. | 50.00 | 100.00 |
| ☐ **HOUSE AND BARN**, pair, rel. 1981. ed. 1,500, s/n, 12" x 14", pub FHG ..... | 50.00 | 80.00 |
| ☐ **LUCKY STRIKE**, rel. 1979. ed. 1,500, s/n, 12" x 32", pub FHG ........... | 50.00 | 125.00 |
| ☐ **MOUNTAIN BRIDGE**, rel. 1983. ed. 1,500, s/n, 19¾" x 30", pub FHG ....... | 80.00 | — |
| ☐ **OLD DUTCH CLEANSER**, rel. 1981. ed. 1,500, s/n, 20" x 34", pub FHG ...... | 75.00 | 125.00 |
| ☐ **PEANUTS and PEPSI**, pair, rel. 1980. ed. 1,500, s/n, 15" x 18", pub FHG .... | 60.00 | 125.00 |
| ☐ **PHILIP MORRIS**, rel. 1978. ed. 1,500, s/n, 17" x 26", pub FHG ........... | 50.00 | 185.00 |
| ☐ **RAILROAD CROSSING**, rel. 1982. ed. 1,500, s/n, 18" x 32", pub FHG ....... | 75.00 | 115.00 |
| ☐ **RED COVERED BRIDGE**, rel. 1978. ed. 1,500, s/n, 16½" x 30", pub FHG...... | 50.00 | 130.00 |
| ☐ **RURAL AMERICANA**, rel. 1974. ed. 1,500, s/n, 23½" x 15", pub FHG ...... | 40.00 | 250.00 |
| ☐ **RURAL DELIVERY**, rel. 1976. ed. 1,500, s/n, 16½" x 23", pub FHG ........ | 40.00 | 225.00 |
| ☐ **7-UP AND BLACK-EYED SUSANS**, rel. 1981. ed. 1,500, s/n, 20" x 24", pub FHG......... | 75.00 | Sold Out |
| ☐ **SHRINE CIRCUS**, rel. 1983. ed. 1,500, s/n, 21" x 27", pub FHG ........... | 80.00 | — |
| ☐ **TONIC & LINIMENT**, pair, rel. 1980. ed. 1,500, s/n, 10⅞" x 25", pub FHG ... | 85.00 | 125.00 |
| ☐ **TOOLS**, rel. 1978. ed. 300, s/n, serigraph, 19" x 27", pub FHG ........... | 275.00 | 400.00 |
| ed. 50, A/P ......... | 325.00 | 450.00 |
| ☐ **TUBE ROSE SNUFF**, rel. 1980. ed. 1,500, s/n, 18" x 23½", pub FHG ....... | 60.00 | Sold Out |
| ☐ **UNPAINTED COVERED BRIDGE**, rel. 1980. ed. 1,500, s/n, 16¼" x 24", pub FHG ......... | 60.00 | 100.00 |
| ☐ **WINDMILL**, rel. 1982. ed. 1,500, s/n, 22¼" x 20½", pub FHG .......... | 75.00 | Sold Out |
| ☐ **WOODPILE**, rel. 1978. ed. 1,500, s/n, 18" x 18¾", pub FHG .......... | *75.00 | 90.00 |
| *Package includes one color work drawing/two black & white sketches. | | |
| ☐ **YESTERYEAR**, rel. 1976. ed. 1,500, s/n, 12" x 20¾", pub FHG........... | 50.00 | 120.00 |

# JERRY HARSTON

Jerry Harston is an American painter and illustrator working primarily with acrylics and oils.

Harston was born and raised in Wyoming where he came to know his "Western" subjects first hand. He received his degree in fine arts from the University of Utah in 1967 and since then has been preparing art of uncompromising quality for a spectrum of clients.

Harston's illustrations have appeared in *Readers Digest, New Era, English* and *Friend* magazines. He has prepared book cover illustrations for Putnam Books, Desert Books and Readers Digest Books and has illustrated brochures for the U.S. Forest Service, the L.D.S. Church and others.

Harston has received national recognition for his art, including both gold and silver awards from the Salt Lake City Art Director's Club, a certificate of merit from the New York Society of Illustrators, awards from the National Retail Merchant's Association, CA Art Annual and Design West Show.

## JERRY HARSTON

| | | |
|---|---|---|
| ☐ **UTE BRAVE**, ed. 750, s/n, 24" x 34", litho, pub SGC ................... | 80.00 | — |
| ☐ **WA-TA-LO**, rel. 1980. ed. 450, s/n, 22" x 30", litho, pub SGC ............. | 88.00 | — |

# ERNEST H. HART

Ernest H. Hart has authored some twenty books on dogs and pets, illustrated scores of books and magazines, judged fine dogs on five continents and is a widely respected artist and authority on this subject. Hart's Sporting Dogs series

**GERMAN SHORTHAIRED POINTERS** *by Ernest Hart*

are his first collector prints. This series includes six prints featuring pop breeds of North American and Europe.

|  | ISSUE PRICE | CURRENT PRICE |
|---|---|---|
| ☐ **ENGLISH POINTERS**, ed. 2,500, s/n, 22" x 28", pub NHI | 60.00 | — |
| ☐ **ENGLISH SETTER**, ed. 2,500, s/n, 22" x 28", pub NHI | 60.00 | — |
| ☐ **GERMAN SHORT HAIRED POINTERS**, ed. 2,500, s/n, 22" x 28", pub NHI | 60.00 | — |
| ☐ **GORDON AND IRISH SETTERS**, ed. 2,500, s/n, 22" x 28", pub NHI | 60.00 | — |
| ☐ **SPRINGER SPANIELS**, ed. 2,500, s/n, 22" x 28", pub NHI | 60.00 | — |
| ☐ **YELLOW AND BLACK LABS**, ed. 2,500, s/n, 22" x 28", pub NHI | 60.00 | — |

# G. HARVEY

Because Gerald Harvey Jones, who paints under the name of G. Harvey, was born and reared in the ranch country of Texas, his background has given him the desire and the knowledge to paint the West. Even now, he gathers the material for his paintings from first-hand experience — living on ranches, staying in bunk houses with the ranch hands and going on roundups and trail drives where he sketches around the campfire at night.

This artist is beloved, not only for his artistic ability, but for the gentle nature of the man himself. The peaceful tranquility which he brings to his paintings comes from his unhurried life spent in his studio deep in the woods near Austin, Texas, where he surrounds himself with animals who serve as models for his work.

G. Harvey has won the New Master's Award in the American Arts Professional League's Grand National, which is held at Lever House in New York each year. He has been honored with a Life Membership in Grand Central Galleries, whose membership includes many notables and he has exhibited in the National

**ON THE STREETS OF NEW ORLEANS** by G. Harvey

Academy in New York. His works have appeared on the covers of various publications and he has had an impressive number of one-man shows.

## G. HARVEY

| | ISSUE PRICE | CURRENT PRICE |
|---|---|---|
| ☐ **CAREFREE COWHANDS,** ed. 500, s/n, 31″ x 25½″, pub ALI | 50.00 | — |
| ed. 1,000, s/o | 40.00 | — |
| ☐ **POKER PALS,** ed. 500, s/n, 31″ x 25½″, pub ALI | 50.00 | — |
| ed. 1,000, s/o | 40.00 | — |
| ☐ **THE DRIFTING COWHAND,** rel. 1974. ed. 2,000, s/o, 29½″ x 24¾″, pub FHG | 60.00 | 200.00 |
| ☐ **CROSSING THE CANYON,** rel. 1975. ed. 2,000, s/n, 33″ x 23½″, pub FHG | 50.00 | 200.00 |
| ☐ **LEAVIN' THE LINE SHACK,** rel. 1975. ed. 2,000, s/n, 23″ x 28½″, pub FHG | 50.00 | 250.00 |
| ☐ **BOSS' NEW RIG,** rel. 1976. ed. 1,500, s/n, 20″ x 26″, pub FHG | 50.00 | — |
| ☐ **BOOMTOWN DRIFTERS,** rel. 1978. ed. 2,250, s/n, size not available, pub TAP | 100.00 | 600.00 |
| ☐ **CHANGING OF THE RANGELAND,** rel. 1978. ed. 250, s/n, size not available, pub TAP | 150.00 | 1,500.00 |
| ☐ **ALONG THE CANYON WALL,** rel. 1979. ed. 2,250, s/n, 17″ x 20½″, pub TAP | 100.00 | — |
| ☐ **COURTING DAYS,** rel. 1979. ed. 2,250, s/n, 14½″ x 21½″, pub TAP | 100.00 | — |
| ☐ **GRAMPA'S NEIGHBORS,** rel. 1979. ed. 2,250, s/n, 17″ x 21½″, pub TAP | 100.00 | — |
| ☐ **IN THE LAND OF THE BLACKFEET,** rel. 1979. ed. 2,250, s/n, 22″ x 14½″, pub TAP | 100.00 | — |
| ☐ **IN THE LAND OF THE ROCKIES,** rel. 1979. ed. 1,000, s/n, 27″ x 21½″, pub TAP | 125.00 | — |
| ☐ **IN THE LAND OF THE WALKING RAIN,** rel. 1979. ed. 1,000, s/n, 14½″ x 22″, pub TAP | 100.00 | — |
| ☐ **LIGHTS ALONG THE AVENUE,** rel. 1979. ed. 2,250, s/n, 14½″ x 22″, pub TAP | 100.00 | — |
| ☐ **RANCHING - PUMP JACK STYLE,** rel. 1979. ed. 1,000, s/n, 18″ x 27″, pub TAP | 150.00 | — |
| ☐ **RIDING THE SALT RIVER CANYON,** rel. 1979. ed. 1,000, s/n, 16″ x 20″, pub TAP | 100.00 | — |
| ☐ **RIDING WITH GRAMPA,** rel. 1979. ed. 1,000, s/n, 20″ x 27″, pub TAP | 150.00 | 200.00 |
| ☐ **SATURDAY NIGHT POKER PALACE,** rel. 1979. ed. 1,000, s/n, 16″ x 22″, pub TAP | 125.00 | — |
| ☐ **SPRING PALETTE,** rel. 1979. ed. 1,000, s/n, 21″ x 18″, pub TAP | 150.00 | — |
| ☐ **SPRING VIEWS,** rel. 1979. ed. 2,250, s/n, 16½″ x 21⅞″, pub TAP | 100.00 | — |
| ☐ **TAKING TEXAS NORTH,** rel. 1979. ed. 2,250, s/n, 14½″ x 21⅞″, pub TAP | 100.00 | — |
| ☐ **TEXAS - FROM HIDE AND HORN,** rel. 1979. ed. 1,000, s/n, 17″ x 27″, pub TAP | 90.00 | — |

| | ISSUE PRICE | CURRENT PRICE |
|---|---|---|
| ☐ **THE COMING HOME,** rel. 1979. ed. 1,000, s/n, 17½" x 22", pub TAP | 100.00 | — |
| ☐ **THE EARLY RUN,** rel. 1979. ed. 1,000, s/n, 17½" x 22", pub TAP | 125.00 | 225.00 |
| ☐ **THE GOOD LORD WILLIN AND THE CREEK DON'T RISE,** rel. 1979. ed. 1,000, s/n, 15½" x 27", pub TAP | 125.00 | — |
| ☐ **THE KATY DEPOT,** rel. 1979. ed. 2,250, s/n, 14½" x 21⅞", pub TAP | 100.00 | — |
| ☐ **THE NEW FILLY,** rel. 1979. ed. 2,250, s/n, 21½" x 17", pub TAP | 100.00 | — |
| ☐ **THE SILENT HUNTER,** rel. 1979. ed. 1,000, s/n, 22" x 17½", pub TAP | 100.00 | — |
| ☐ **TIMES REMEMBERED,** rel. 1979. ed. 2,250, s/n, 13⅛" x 22", pub TAP | 100.00 | — |
| ☐ **WHEN BANKERS WORE BOOTS,** rel. 1979. ed. 1,000, s/n, 14½" x 22", pub TAP | 75.00 | 200.00 |
| ☐ **WHEN THE LONESOMES SET IN,** rel. 1979. ed. 2,250, s/n, 14⅛" x 22", pub TAP | 100.00 | — |
| ☐ **WINTER'S EVE,** rel. 1979. ed. 2,250, s/n, 14½" x 22", pub TAP | 100.00 | — |
| ☐ **BOOMTOWN DRIFTERS,** rel. 1980. ed. 2,250, s/n, 19⅝" x 28", pub TAP | 100.00 | 600.00 |
| ☐ **BORDER PATROL,** rel. 1980. ed. 2,250, s/n, 26½" x 22⅛", pub TAP | 100.00 | — |
| ☐ **DALLAS,** rel. 1980. ed. 1,200, s/n, size not available, pub TAP | 150.00 | 450.00 |
| ☐ **MAN AMONG NATURE,** rel. 1980. ed. 2,250, s/n, 26½" x 22", pub TAP | 100.00 | — |
| ☐ **THE NEW STALLION,** rel. 1980. ed. 2,250, s/n, 20" x 28", pub TAP | 100.00 | — |
| ☐ **WHEN SNOW MELTS INTO MUSIC,** rel. 1980. ed. 2,250, s/n, 28½" x 20⅞", pub TAP | 100.00 | — |
| ☐ **WHERE EAGLES SOAR,** rel. 1980. ed. 2,250, s/n, 28" x 19½", pub TAP | 100.00 | — |
| ☐ **COWTOWN,** rel. 1981. ed. 1,000, s/n, 17¾" x 27½", pub TAP | 150.00 | 400.00 |
| ☐ **OIL PATCH,** rel. 1981. ed. 1,000, s/n, 22¼" x 30¾", pub TAP | 150.00 | 550.00 |
| ☐ **SUPPLIES FOR THE MISSION,** rel. 1981. ed. 1,000, s/n, 17¾" x 26½", pub TAP | 150.00 | — |
| ☐ **TWENTIETH CENTURY RANCHING,** rel. 1981. ed. 1,000, s/n, size not available, pub TAP | 150.00 | 400.00 |
| ☐ **WALL STREET,** rel. 1981. ed. 1,000, s/n, size not available, pub TAP | 150.00 | 400.00 |
| ☐ **WITH NO INTENTION OF CHANGING,** rel. 1981. ed. 1,000, s/n, size not available, pub TAP | 150.00 | 450.00 |
| ☐ **BOOT TOP DEEP,** rel. 1982. ed. 1,000, s/n, 19½" x 26", pub TAP | 150.00 | Sold Out |
| ☐ **THE COWBOY'S CHRISTMAS BALL,** rel. 1981. ed. 1,000, s/n, 27" x 18", pub TAP | 150.00 | Sold Out |
| ☐ **INDEPENDENT OILMEN,** rel. 1982. ed. 1,000, s/n, 19½" x 26", pub TAP | 150.00 | Sold Out |
| ☐ **ON THE STREETS OF NEW ORLEANS,** rel. 1982. ed. 1,000, s/n, 15¾" x 26½", pub TAP | 150.00 | 225.00 |
| ☐ **THE PLAZA, NEW YORK,** rel. 1982. ed. 1,000, s/n, 19½" x 26", pub TAP | 150.00 | Sold Out |

# DALE HAUCK

Dale Hauck, a native of New Orleans, spent six years in a rustic monastery in St. Tammany Parish, which exposed him to the flora and fauna of Louisiana and gave him a deep appreciation of the exalting loveliness and harmony of nature. In his work, he strives to attain a subjective interpretation of the beauty of wildlife, rather than render a photographic copy of the subject. Tireless research, technical skill and emotion contribute to his unique artistry.

## DALE HAUCK

| | ISSUE PRICE | CURRENT PRICE |
|---|---|---|
| ☐ **BALD EAGLE,** ed. 900, s/n, 29" x 23", pub NG | 40.00 | — |
| ☐ **BROWN PELICAN,** ed. 900, s/n, 20" x 29", pub NG | 45.00 | — |
| ☐ **BROWN TRASHER,** ed. 900, s/n, 12" x 10", pub NG | 20.00 | — |
| ☐ **GOLDEN EAGLE,** ed. 900, s/n, 22" x 30", pub NG | 40.00 | — |
| ☐ **GOLD FINCHES,** ed. 900, s/n, 8" x 12", pub NG | 20.00 | — |
| ☐ **SNOWY OWL,** ed. 900, s/n, 9" x 12", pub NG | 15.00 | — |

# DONALD M. HEDIN

Donald Hedin is not only an artist but a historian and avid collector who is eager to preserve the colorful traditions of the American West. His interest in America's past is reflected in his love for homely utensils and tools that show the years of use and contact with humanity, plus a strong desire to record that feeling.

Hedin paints in acrylics on masonite prepared with a gesso ground. He employs the egg-tempera technique, which allows the artist to achieve great detail and textures. This style of painting is a rigidly disciplined method, designed to achieve a high three-dimensional quality. it demands many long hours of the artist.

A graduate of Pratt Institute, Hedin has been associated with *Reader's Digest* for over thirty years. He is now an Associate Art Editor for the magazine.

Hedin is a member of the American Watercolor Society and the Society of Illustrators. He has been featured in *Southwest Art* and *American Artist*. He was included in the Watson-Guptill book on *Acrylic Painters of America*. The artist is the recipient of numerous awards. His works have been exhibited throughout the U.S. and are found in several private collections.

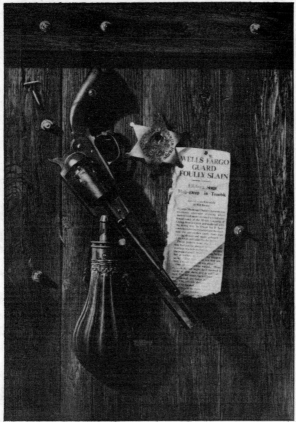

**THE WELLS FARGO GUARD** *by Donald M. Hedin*

**DONALD M. HEDIN**

| | ISSUE PRICE | CURRENT PRICE |
|---|---|---|
| ☐ **A LETTER COMES TO POVERTY BAR,** rel. 1981. ed. 550, s/n, 26¾" x 19¾", pub MPPI | 125.00 | — |
| ☐ **THE WELLS FARGO GUARD,** rel. 1981. ed. 450, s/n, 26¾" x 19½", pub MPPI | 85.00 | — |

## PETER HELCK

Peter Helck is widely regarded as the foremost visual chronicler of the great age of automobile racing. From the time he saw his first race as a boy in New York, he has dedicated his life to recording in paintings and in words the daring, drama and history of the golden age of automobile racing.

Helck's formal art training began at the Art Students League, and was to continue later with Sir Frank Brangwyn, Sidney Dickinson, Harry Wickey and Lewis Daniel. He has received numerous awards, including election to the Society of Illustrators Hall of Fame in 1968. He has published two books on auto racing and his work is in major public and private collections worldwide.

*The Checkered Flag* and *Great Auto Races* are only two of the books that he has authored and painted.

**SAFE ON THE R.R. SIDING** *by Peter Helck*

**PETER HELCK**

| | | |
|---|---|---|
| ☐ **SAFE ON THE R.R. SIDING,** rel. 1983. ed. 475, s/n, 35½" x 19¼", pub GW | 165.00 | — |
| ed. 25, signed, numbered and remarqued | 285.00 | — |

## DR. WILLIAM HEMMERDINGER

William Hemmerdinger is an extraordinarily gifted young artist. Born in 1951, he began drawing and painting at the age of five. By 1966 he was so accomplished that *Los Angeles Times* art critic Henry J. Seldis said ". . . his drawings demonstrate an ability uncommon in one so young."

In 1967 Hemmerdinger was considered to be the finest young watercolorist in the nation. His earliest works demonstrated a high level of technical virtuosity and maturity of concepts and ideas. The young artist received five scholarships to study drawing at the Art Center College of Design in Los Angeles. He attended the Art Center school until 1969.

Diversity of style and enthusiasm for creative invention has always been an aspect of Hemmerdingers work. In the early seventies his work moved in three major directions; A "Representational style", and "experimental mixed-media", Interest; an "expressionist", direction. Pursuing the three approaches at once the works demonstrated a continuity of interest through a devout regard for drawing. Each manner of working developed independently and reaching fruitation found recognition in the quarters of the art establishment.

The artist's work has continued to probe the depths of an aesthetic sensibility Hemmerdinger explores the range of creative possibilities by working in printing, printmaking, sculpture, book and magazine illustrations; producing hand-made books and award winning architectural designs.

Since 1975 he has been included in major exhibitions of painting from Southern California. His work has been exhibited at the National Academy of Design, New York, Whitney Museum of American Art, New York, Los Angeles County Museum of Art, UNESCO Museum, Paris, France; American Watercolor Society and California National Water Color Society Annuals and Traveling Exhibitions, plus many more.

Hemmerdinger graduated from the University of California at Riverside, received a Master of Fine Arts Degree in Painting and Drawing from Claremont Graduate School; recently completed his doctoral dissertation in Philosophy of Education for Claremont. The emphasis of the Ph.D. study was in the discipline of Aesthetics. The artist is a faculty member at the College of the Desert in Palm Desert, California.

| DR. WILLIAM HEMMERDINGER | ISSUE PRICE | CURRENT PRICE |
|---|---|---|
| ☐ **SUNMAID RAISIN,** General run, 18½" x 8½", pub CGAL | 13.00 | — |
| ed. 12, Artist accented, s/n | 100.00 | — |
| ☐ **SAKAI RANCH,** General run, 18" x 8½", pub CGAL | 13.00 | — |
| ed. 12, Artist accented, s/n | 100.00 | — |

# BOB HENLEY

Bob Henley is an artist and conservationist of the highest degree.

Of the seventeen juried shows he has entered, he has won awards in fifteen, including Best of Show, President's Award and the People's Choice Award. The "People's Choice" award seems most appropriate because Henley has certainly become a people's artist. His paintings are collected by individuals as well as corporations and it is not unusual to see as many as fifteen of his paintings in a single collection.

The popularity of his work is due partly to his unbelievable ability to capture detail in his paintings. On gessoed masonite he creates his subjects as he works, with no preliminary sketches, using an oil lift or pickup technique, his animals seem to "grow" their soft coats of fur right before your eyes. Then with multiple color glazes he creates a depth and atmosphere that makes the entire painting come alive.

## BOB HENLEY

| | ISSUE PRICE | CURRENT PRICE |
|---|---|---|
| ☐ **FOREST SECRET,** rel. 1981. ed. 950, s/n, 22" x 16½", pub. Remarqued, Inc. | 50.00 | 50.00 |

# TOM HENNESSEY

A completely self-taught artist, Tom Hennessey was born and raised in Bangor, Maine. An avid sportsman and conservationist, his lifelong exposure to the sportsman's world reflects the accuracy and authenticity of his paintings.

In 1972, he won the Maine Artists Show, and in 1975, the Massachusetts Waterfowl Stamp competition.

Hennessey is an active member and supporter of Ducks Unlimited and is presently involved in the conservation and preservation of the Atlantic Salmon.

His works are represented by the leading galleries of sporting art.

| TOM HENNESSEY | ISSUE PRICE | CURRENT PRICE |
|---|---|---|
| ☐ **LAST CHANCE**, rel. 1973. ed. 400, 23½″ x 15½″, remarque by request, pub Savage Arms Co. | — | 200.00 |
| ☐ **PAYDAY**, rel. 1977. ed. 200, 15″ x 24″, remarque by request, pub T. Hennessey | — | 80.00 |
| ☐ **SALMON POOL**, rel. 1977. ed. 100, 15″ x 24″, remarque by request, pub T. Hennessey | — | 250.00 |
| ☐ **SILVER IN THE SUN**, rel. 1977. ed. 100, 11″ x 15″, remarque none, pub Atlantic Salmon Association of Montreal | — | 150.00 |
| ☐ **EVENING SALMON**, rel. 1978. ed. 100, 11″ x 15″, pub Atlantic Salmon Association of Montreal | — | 150.00 |
| ☐ **SENTINELS AT SUN-UP**, rel. 1978. ed. 800, 16″ x 22½″, signed/numbered, pub Petersen Gallery | — | 60.00 |
| ☐ **PINE CORNER COVERY**, rel. 1978. ed. 800, s/n, 16″ x 22½″, pub Petersen Gallery | — | 60.00 |

# TINA HERRING

Living on the coast in Golden Beach, Florida, Tina Herring is often commissioned by yacht owners to paint scenes for their boats. Not only does she paint scenery, but Herring has a unique talent of capturing expressions in her portraits.

| TINA HERRING | | |
|---|---|---|
| ☐ **HEAVENLY FLIGHT**, ed. 2,000, s/n, 16″ x 20″, pub LC | 200.00 | — |
| ☐ **SEA SHELL**, ed. 1,000, s/n, 11″ x 14″, pub LC | 100.00 | — |
| ☐ **SWEET SIXTEEN**, ed. 1,000, s/n, 11″ x 14″, pub LC | 100.00 | — |
| ☐ **FLOWER POT**, ed. 1,000, s/n, 11″ x 14″, pub LC | 100.00 | — |
| ☐ **COLORED FLOWERS**, ed. 1,000, s/n, 11″ x 14″, pub LC | 100.00 | — |

**COLORED FLOWERS** *by Tina Herring*

# EDNA HIBEL

Edna Hibel is one of America's best loved and most widely acclaimed contemporary artists. Her instantly recognizable and highly individualized style has earned her an international reputation; as a painter and lithographer of extraordinary humanity, sensitivity, and technical virtuosity.

Born in Boston, Massachusetts in January, 1917, she began her formal artistic training as a private student of the noted portrait painter Gregory Michaels. Following her graduation from high school, Hibel studied at the Boston Museum School of Fine Arts under the direction of Karl Zerbe and Alexander Jacovleff, where she was awarded the prestigious Ruth B. Sturtevant Traveling Fellowship in 1939. In 1940, the Boston Museum of Fine Arts purchased one of her paintings for its permanent collection, making her the youngest living artist so honored by a major American museum.

In 1969, the distinguished Craig Collection of Hibel art first went on public display bringing the perspective of time to Hibel's public exhibitions. From the time of her involvement as organizer of the first Boston Arts Festival in 1954, through her 1976 receipt of the New England Region of Hadassah's Citizen's Award, she has maintained her determination to make art the vehicle for enriching the lives of men and women everywhere.

The opening of the Hibel Museum of Art in Palm Beach, Florida, in January 1977, marked an unprecedented recognition of Hibel's unique role in contemporary art. The only museum in the United States devoted to the works of a living woman artist, the Hibel Museum of Art demonstrates both the beauty and the importance of Edna Hibel's singular vision. In 1983, she was honored at the United Nations for her work in helping to launch the United Nation's World Food Program.

**NAVA AND CHILDREN** *by Edna Hibel*

## EDNA HIBEL

| | ISSUE PRICE | CURRENT PRICE |
|---|---|---|
| ☐ **MOTHER & 4 CHILDREN**, ed. 60, s/n, 38¾" x 25½", litho, pub JARP . . . . . . . | 150.00 | 990.00 |
| ☐ **RACHEL & CHILD**, ed. 90, s/n, 20" x 27", litho, pub JARP . . . . . . . . . . . . . . . | 90.00 | 700.00 |
| ☐ **PORTUGAL**, ed. 52, s/n, 24" x 32", litho, pub JARP . . . . . . . . . . . . . . . . . . . | 200.00 | 900.00 |
| ☐ **BRETON WOMAN**, ed. 172, s/n, 17" x 21¼", litho, pub JARP . . . . . . . . . . . | 75.00 | 225.00 |
| ☐ **THREE MUSICIANS**, ed. 65, s/n, 24" x 34", litho, pub JARP . . . . . . . . . . . . | 150.00 | 900.00 |
| ☐ **OBI**, ed. 116, s/n, 25½" x 37¼", litho, pub JARP . . . . . . . . . . . . . . . . . . . . | 225.00 | 1,500.00 |
| ☐ **MOTHER & 2 CHILDREN (Cain & Abel)**, ed. 125, s/n, 24" x 36", litho, pub JARP. . . . . . . . . . . . . . . . . . . . . . . . . . . . . . . . . . . . . . . . . . . . . . | 150.00 | 1,600.00 |
| ☐ **JULIANA**, ed. 51, s/n, 14½" x 21⅛", litho, pub JARP. . . . . . . . . . . . . . . . . . . | 85.00 | 1,000.00 |
| ☐ **THE MOTHER**, ed. 82, s/n, 10" x 13", litho, pub JARP . . . . . . . . . . . . . . . . | 85.00 | 1,000.00 |
| ☐ **MOTHER & BABY**, ed. 235, s/n, 9⅛" x 13½", litho, pub JARP . . . . . . . . . . . | 60.00 | 400.00 |
| ☐ **PICCOLO PLAYER**, one color. ed. 59, s/n, 10¾" x 15⅛", litho, pub JARP . . . . | 75.00 | 600.00 |
| ☐ **PICCOLO PLAYER**, multi-color. ed. 99, s/n, 10¾" x 15", litho, pub JARP . . . . . | 110.00 | 600.00 |
| ☐ **SINGLE NUDE**, ed. 69, s/n, 9" x 12½", litho, pub JARP . . . . . . . . . . . . . . . . | 80.00 | 600.00 |
| ☐ **TORAH**, one color. ed. 135, s/n, 11" x 14¼", litho, pub JARP . . . . . . . . . . . | 65.00 | 1,100.00 |
| ☐ **TORAH**, two color. ed. 47, s/n, 11" x 14¼", litho, pub JARP . . . . . . . . . . . . | 90.00 | 1,100.00 |
| ☐ **RUTH** (Unique only). 5" x 8¾", litho, pub JARP. . . . . . . . . . . . . . . . . . . . . . | 60.00 | 350.00 |
| ☐ **YASUKO** (Unique only). 5¾" x 8", litho, pub JARP . . . . . . . . . . . . . . . . . . . | 60.00 | 450.00 |
| ☐ **DAVID AND BATHSHEBA** (Unique only). 6" x 8⅞", litho, pub JARP . . . . . . . . . | 60.00 | 400.00 |
| ☐ **LOUISE** (Unique only). 5" x 7", litho, pub JARP . . . . . . . . . . . . . . . . . . . . . | 60.00 | 450.00 |
| ☐ **PEASANT WOMAN SMILING**, ed. 45, s/n, 11¼" x 13", litho, pub JARP . . . . . . | 60.00 | 550.00 |
| ☐ **NEW PEASANT WOMAN**, ed. 146, s/n, 11" x 13½", litho, pub JARP . . . . . . . | 75.00 | 400.00 |
| ☐ **PEASANT MAN**, ed. 120, s/n, 14" x 15", litho, pub JARP . . . . . . . . . . . . . . . | 60.00 | 550.00 |
| ☐ **PORTUGUESE FISHERMAN**, ed. 120, s/n, 13½" x 15¼", litho, pub JARP . . . . | 75.00 | 600.00 |
| ☐ **BOUQUET**, one color. ed. 101, s/n, 12¾" x 19⅛", litho, pub JARP . . . . . . . . | 85.00 | 550.00 |
| ☐ **BOUQUET**, three & four color. A-K sections, 12¾" x 19⅛", litho, pub JARP . . . | 125.00 | 550.00 |

**Tea By The Sea**
*by Charles Wysocki*

**General Store U.S.A.**
*by H. Hargrove*

**Plains Madonna**
*by Charles Banks Wilson*

**Tinker**
*by Gregory Perillo*

**An Early Snow**
*by Jerry Crandall*

**Golden — Mountain Man**
*by David Wright*

**The Walleye**
*by Roger Preuss*

**Tomorrows Dreams**
*by Jay Schmidt*

**Sea Otters**
*by Morton Solberg*

**Intruder**
*by Richard Younger*

**Oriental Daydream**
*by Edna Hibel*

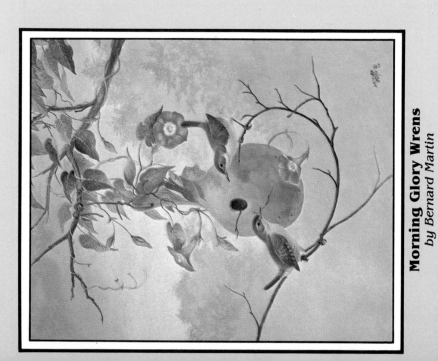

**Morning Glory Wrens**
*by Bernard Martin*

**Deprived Condition**
*by G.H. Rothe*

**My Star**
*by Juan Ferrandiz*

**Center Ring**
*by Joseph Getsinger*

| | ISSUE PRICE | CURRENT PRICE |
|---|---|---|
| ☐ **THREE VASES,** small. ed. 50, s/n, 11" x 14", litho, pub JARP | 75.00 | 495.00 |
| ☐ **GIRL WITH JUG,** ed. 120, s/n, 14" x 20", litho, pub JARP | 75.00 | 600.00 |
| ☐ **VIOLINIST,** two color. ed. 72, s/n, 14" x 18¼", litho, pub JARP | 90.00 | 1,050.00 |
| ☐ **VIOLINIST,** one color. ed. 42, s/n, 14" x 18¼", litho, pub JARP | 70.00 | 1,050.00 |
| ☐ **SAMI,** one color. ed. 116, s/n, 8¾" x 9¾", litho, pub JARP | 75.00 | 1,500.00 |
| ☐ **SAMI THINKING,** ed. 60, s/n, 10⅛" x 12¾", litho, pub JARP | 75.00 | 2,500.00 |
| ☐ **LOVERS,** ed. 170, s/n, 9½" x 12⅝", litho, pub JARP | 60.00 | 600.00 |
| ☐ **MAN & WOMAN,** ed. 75, s/n, 14½" x 22¼", litho, pub JARP | 95.00 | 360.00 |
| ☐ **BAREFOOT CELLIST,** ed. 97, s/n, 14½" x 24¼", litho, pub JARP | 75.00 | 660.00 |
| ☐ **BERET,** ed. 68, s/n, 7¼" x 9¾", litho, pub JARP | 75.00 | 495.00 |
| ☐ **ELEPHANT,** ed. 143, s/n, 15¼" x 11¼", litho, pub JARP | 75.00 | 275.00 |
| ☐ **DUTCH GIRL,** three color. ed. 90, s/n, 14" x 18", litho, pub JARP | 80.00 | 440.00 |
| ☐ **DUTCH GIRL,** one color. ed. 24, s/n, 14" x 18", litho, pub JARP | 60.00 | 385.00 |
| ☐ **MOTHER & 2 CHILDREN,** one color. ed. 120, s/n, 21¾" x 27", litho, pub JARP | 125.00 | 900.00 |
| ☐ **JANET,** ed. 98, s/n, 14½" x 11", litho, pub JARP | 90.00 | 900.00 |
| ☐ **NEW BABY, Regular edition,** three color. ed. 100, s/n, 9" x 12¾" | 80.00 | 550.00 |
| **Special edition,** three color. ed. 58, s/n, 9" x 12¾" | 80.00 | 550.00 |
| **A/E edition,** two color. ed. 50, s/n, 9" x 12¾" | 80.00 | 550.00 |
| litho's, all pub JARP | | |
| ☐ **PLAYING MOTHER & CHILD,** one color. ed. 60, s/n, 11¾" x 14" | 75.00 | 800.00 |
| **Experimental edition,** two color. ed. 15, s/n, 11¾" x 14" | 75.00 | 800.00 |
| lithos, pub JARP | | |
| ☐ **FLUTIST,** ed. 100, s/n, 11½" x 15½", litho, pub JARP | 50.00 | 450.00 |
| ☐ **LOIRE VALLEY,** one color. ed. 49, s/n, 8¾" x 20⅜", litho, pub JARP | 75.00 | 650.00 |
| ☐ **SHIZUE. Regular edition,** ed. 45, s/n, 9½" x 13"; **A/E edition,** ed. 50, s/n, 9½" x 13", lithos, pub JARP | 60.00 | 900.00 |
| ☐ **THREE NUDES,** ed. 87, s/n, 8½" x 12¼", litho, pub JARP | 70.00 | 385.00 |
| ☐ **CELLIST,** one color. **A/E edition,** 9⅝" x 15" | 75.00 | 600.00 |
| **Regular edition,** two color, s/n, 9⅝" x 15" | 70.00 | 600.00 |
| lithos, pub JARP | | |
| ☐ **PROFILE,** ed. 75, s/n, 7" x 8¼", litho, pub JARP | 65.00 | 550.00 |
| ☐ **PAULINE,** edition on silk only, 7" x 10⅞" | — | 3,600.00 |
| ☐ **BEGGAR,** black/white. ed. 70, s/n, 27¾" x 38¼", litho, pub JARP | 150.00 | 1,500.00 |
| ☐ **BEGGAR,** three color, ed. 63, s/n, 27¾" x 38¼", litho, pub JARP | 250.00 | 2,500.00 |
| ☐ **BRETON GIRL,** one color. ed. 140, s/n, 11" x 14" | 75.00 | 700.00 |
| two color, ed. 72, s/n, 11" x 14" | 75.00 | 700.00 |
| litho, pub JARP | | |
| ☐ **BEARDED MAN,** ed. 100, s/n, 13" x 15¾", litho, pub JARP | 75.00 | 650.00 |
| ☐ **FLOWER VENDOR,** ed. 63, s/n, 16" x 22", litho, pub JARP | 125.00 | 495.00 |
| ☐ **JAPANESE GIRL HEAD** (Unique only). s/n, 10" x 10", litho, pub JARP | 90.00 | 550.00 |
| ☐ **FIELDS OF ITALY,** ed. 93, s/n, 22½" x 15", litho, pub JARP | 110.00 | 950.00 |
| ☐ **BETH,** ed. 207, s/n, 9½" x 10⅜", litho, pub JARP | 75.00 | 950.00 |
| ☐ **TWO FLOWER GIRLS,** edition on silk only, 25" x 40" | — | 5,500.00 |
| ☐ **BYRON** (Border). ed. 76, s/n, 12½" x 14½" | 75.00 | 550.00 |
| (No Border), ed. 9, 10¾" x 12¾" | 75.00 | 550.00 |
| lithos, pub JARP | | |
| ☐ **BYRON'S SISTER,** two color. ed. 57, s/n, 11¾" x 13¾", litho, pub JARP | 75.00 | 550.00 |
| ☐ **BYRON'S SISTER,** one color. ed. 9, s/n, 11¾" x 13¾", litho, pub JARP | 75.00 | 550.00 |
| ☐ **TWO FARMERS,** ed. 43, s/n, 9½" x 13¾", litho, pub JARP | 60.00 | 465.00 |
| ☐ **MOTHER & CHILD,** one color. ed. 77, s/n, 12½" x 20" | 75.00 | 495.00 |
| two color, ed. n/a, 12½" x 20" | 75.00 | 495.00 |
| lithos, pub JARP | | |
| ☐ **PORTUGUESE MOTHER & CHILD,** ed. n/a, 11½" x 16", litho, pub JARP | 75.00 | 700.00 |
| ☐ **PRINCESS,** two color. ed. 29, s/n, 13½" x 18" | 75.00 | 700.00 |
| **A/E edition,** one color. ed. 49, s/n, 13⅝" x 18½" | 75.00 | 700.00 |
| lithos, pub JARP | | |
| ☐ **VENICE,** one color. ed. n/a, 15¼" x 20¾", uniques or A/P | — | 540.00 |
| Uniques or A/P w/pastel pencil or Oil Paint | — | 630.00 |
| pub JARP | | |
| ☐ **PEASANT WOMAN,** one color. **Experimental edition,** 12¾" x 15" | — | — |
| ☐ **REBECCA,** two color. ed. n/a, 24" x 36", uniques or A/P | — | 1,400.00 |
| Uniques or A/P w/pastel pencil or Oil Paint | — | 1,400.00 |
| ☐ **BABY LLAMA,** ed. n/a, 12½" x 17½" | 75.00 | 1,100.00 |
| ☐ **MAN WITH WHEELBARROW,** ed. 27, s/n, 16¼" x 14", litho, pub JARP | 75.00 | 385.00 |

| | ISSUE PRICE | CURRENT PRICE |
|---|---|---|
| ☐ **BRITTANY,** ed. 75, s/n, 13½" x 20⅜", litho, pub JARP | 90.00 | 385.00 |
| ☐ **MOTHER & 3 CHILDREN,** ed. 25, s/n, 24" x 35½", litho, pub JARP | 150.00 | 1,200.00 |
| ☐ **FOUR NUDES & 2 CATS,** ed. 8, 22½" x 30½", litho, pub JARP | 125.00 | 560.00 |
| ☐ **TWO NUDES** (Left Side). A/P only, 18" x 24", litho, pub JARP | 75.00 | 560.00 |
| ☐ **TWO NUDES,** 1, 2, 3 color. ed, A/P's only, 18" x 24", litho, pub JARP | 75.00 | 560.00 |
| ☐ **JIMMY BUDDHA,** ed. 25, 15¼" x 23⅛", litho, pub JARP | 90.00 | 800.00 |
| ☐ **ESAU, SARAH & BROS,** ed. 45, 16" x 21¼", litho, pub JARP | 90.00 | 850.00 |
| ☐ **GYPSY VIOLINIST,** one color. ed. 30, 14" x 18" | 75.00 | 440.00 |
| two & three color | 95.00 | 500.00 |
| ed. 103, 14" x 18" | 110.00 | 610.00 |
| litho, pub JARP | | |
| ☐ **THREE GRACES,** ed. 140, 11" x 15", litho, pub JARP | 75.00 | 440.00 |
| ☐ **BETTY'S FIELDS LANDSCAPE,** one color. ed. 33, 14" x 22" | 90.00 | 550.00 |
| two color, ed. 73, 14" x 22" | 75.00 | 550.00 |
| litho, pub JARP | | |
| ☐ **THREE MUSES & VASE,** ed. 40, 14" x 22", litho, pub JARP | 90.00 | 500.00 |
| ☐ **VASES OF FLOWERS** (Lg. Floral). ed. 36 on japon, 22" x 31", litho, pub JARP | 175.00 | 1,100.00 |
| ☐ **VASES OF FLOWERS** (Lg. Floral). ed. 40, 25¼" x 35¾", litho, pub JARP | 175.00 | 1,100.00 |
| ☐ **ONE FARMER WOMAN,** ed. 46, 6½" x 11½" | 60.00 | 385.00 |
| **Keystone** ed. 9, 6½" x 11½" | 60.00 | 385.00 |
| litho, pub JARP | | |
| ☐ **PROVENCE LANDSCAPE,** ed. 48, 14" x 19¼", litho, pub JARP | 85.00 | 650.00 |
| ☐ **WENDY,** no edition, silks only - 11" x 19" | N/A | 4,500.00 |
| ☐ **GERRY,** no edition, silks only - 16" x 20" | N/A | 4,500.00 |
| ☐ **SANTE FE GARDENS,** no edition, silks only - 12½" x 17½" | N/A | 3,300.00 |
| ☐ **WENDY W/FLOWERS,** ed. 118, 24" x 36", litho, pub JARP | 175.00 | 950.00 |
| ☐ **RUTH & CHILD,** line drawing. ed. 33, 14" x 15" | 75.00 | 700.00 |
| one color, ed. 109, 20" x 27" | 85.00 | 700.00 |
| two color, ed. 95, 20" x 27" | 95.00 | 750.00 |
| three color, ed. 95, 20" x 27", pub JARP | 95.00 | 750.00 |
| ☐ **SARAH & CHILDREN,** ed. 185, 24" x 36" | 150.00 | 1,400.00 |
| **Special edition** 7, 24" x 36" | 150.00 | 1,400.00 |
| ☐ **SARAH & CHILDREN** (½ Stone). ed. 57, 20" x 24", litho, pub JARP | 150.00 | 475.00 |
| ☐ **JAPANESE MOTHER & CHILD,** ed. 107, 11⅝" x 14⅝" | 85.00 | 600.00 |
| A/E ed. 45, 11⅝" x 14⅝", litho, pub JARP | 85.00 | 600.00 |
| ☐ **LOVERS OF FLORENCE,** one color, rel. 1975. ed. 11, 24" x 30½" | 90.00 | 700.00 |
| six colors, ed. 140, 27" x 34", litho, pub JARP | 175.00 | 850.00 |
| ☐ **ROCKPORT,** rel. 1975. ed. 50, 16" x 24", litho, pub JARP | 110.00 | 1,000.00 |
| ☐ **LUTE PLAYER,** rel. 1975, two color. ed. 19, 19½" x 37½" | 110.00 | 700.00 |
| four color, ed. 110, 29½" x 37½" | 200.00 | 800.00 |
| ☐ **GAIL & CAT** - long, rel. 1975. ed. 25, 16" x 25½" | 95.00 | 550.00 |
| ☐ **GAIL & CAT** - short. ed. 19, 18¼" x 19", litho, pub JARP | 95.00 | 550.00 |
| ☐ **WENDY W/VEIL,** rel. 1974. ed. 140, 12" x 16¼", litho, pub JARP | 85.00 | 550.00 |
| ☐ **SAMI PAINTING,** rel. 1974. no edition, silks only | N/A | 6,000.00 |
| ☐ **GREEK DANCERS,** rel. 1974. ed. 137, 16½" x 21", litho, pub JARP | 125.00 | 850.00 |
| ☐ **JERUSALEM SCENE,** rel. 1974. no edition, unique - A/P only 9" x 20" | — | 825.00 |
| ☐ **3 VASES,** rel. 1974. no edition, silks only, 30" x 40" | — | 4,500.00 |
| both pub by JARP | | |
| ☐ **MOTHER & 3 CHILDREN** (horiz.), rel. 1974. ed. 132, 26" x 36½", litho, pub JARP | 200.00 | 1,000.00 |
| ☐ **SAMI THE ARTIST,** rel. 1974. ed. 148, 14¼" x 18", litho, pub JARP | 125.00 | 1,000.00 |
| ☐ **OLD MAN HEAD,** rel. 1974. ed. 98, 10¾" x 13", litho, pub JARP | 90.00 | 500.00 |
| ☐ **GIRL W/KERCHIEF (Caroline),** rel. 1974. ed. 115, released in one color, two, three color, 12¼" x 18", litho, pub JARP | 110.00 | 1,200.00 |
| ☐ **JEANNE,** rel. 1974. ed. 85, 12¼" x 16½", litho, pub JARP | 85.00 | 600.00 |
| ☐ **BOY W/DONKEY,** rel. 1974. one, two color, ed. 82, 21½" x 27½", litho, pub JARP | 110.00 | 700.00 |
| ☐ **FAMILY (Mother, Father & 4 Children),** rel. 1974. ed. 150, 27¾" x 39", litho, pub JARP | 150.00 | 1,000.00 |
| ☐ **MOTHER & TWO BOYS,** rel. 1974. ed. 150, 22¾" x 32½", litho, pub JARP | 125.00 | 1,000.00 |
| ☐ **SAMI DANCING,** rel. 1974. ed. 110, 22" x 30", litho, pub JARP | 135.00 | 1,150.00 |
| ☐ **NEW SMALL MOTHER & BABY,** rel. 1974. ed. 149, 7½" x 10¼", litho, pub JARP | 90.00 | 500.00 |
| ☐ **JAN,** rel. 1974. ed. 139, 10" x 14" (a portion was on wood veneer) | 85.00 | 800.00 |
| (a portion was litho) pub JARP | 85.00 | 800.00 |

| | | ISSUE PRICE | CURRENT PRICE |
|---|---|---|---|
| ☐ | **NEW DANCERS** (on wood veneer), rel. 1974. ed. 10, 12½″ x 23″, pub JARP .. | 90.00 | 900.00 |
| ☐ | **BANGKOK,** six color, rel. 1974. ed. 109, 24″ x 33″ .................... | 175.00 | 900.00 |
| | one color, ed. 23, 14″ x 20″, litho, pub JARP ......................... | 90.00 | 450.00 |
| ☐ | **LA TURBIE,** ed. 158, 20″ x 31″, litho, pub JARP ..................... | 175.00 | 550.00 |
| ☐ | **VENICE,** rel. 1974. ed. 56, 16½″ x 25½″, litho, pub JARP ............... | 175.00 | 700.00 |
| ☐ | **HEDDI,** rel. 1974. ed. 290, 16½″ x 25½″, litho, pub JARP ............... | 135.00 | 550.00 |
| ☐ | **SINGLE VASE & FLOWERS,** ed. 250, edition consists of 3 color & 4 color, 9″ x 17″, litho, pub JARP ................................................. | 95.00 | 600.00 |
| ☐ | **MEXICAN MOTHER & BABY,** rel. 1974. ed. 250, editions consist of 3 color & 4 color, 10¾″ x 16″, litho, pub JARP ................................... | 95.00 | 650.00 |
| ☐ | **MAN W/TURBAN,** rel. 1974. ed. 145, 15¾″ x 21″, one color ............ | 90.00 | 400.00 |
| | two color, same size, litho, pub JARP ................................. | 110.00 | 450.00 |
| ☐ | **PETER,** rel. 1974. ed. 250, three color, 10¾″ x 14″ .................. | 95.00 | 500.00 |
| | ed. 250, four color, same size ....................................... | 95.00 | 500.00 |
| ☐ | **ISABEL,** rel. 1974. ed. 250, three color & four color, 10⅛″ x 15½″, litho, pub JARP ............................................................. | 95.00 | 500.00 |
| ☐ | **CHINESE MOTHER & BABY,** rel. 1974. ed. 225, one color, 27″ x 37″ ........ | 175.00 | 1,100.00 |
| | two color, 27″ x 37″ ................................................ | 175.00 | 1,000.00 |
| | three & four color, 27″ x 37″ ........................................ | 195.00 | 1,000.00 |
| | four color, 24″ x 36″ on rice paper ................................... | 215.00 | 1,100.00 |
| ☐ | **HEDDI & CHILDREN,** rel. 1974. ed. 200, 24″ x 35″, litho, pub JARP ......... | 150.00 | 1,250.00 |
| ☐ | **SANDY (Kissing Baby),** rel. 1974. ed. 140, edition in one color & two color, litho, pub JARP ..................................................... | 75.00 | 1,150.00 |
| ☐ | **LINDA & SON,** rel. 1975. ed. 140, one & two color, 14″ x 19″; ed. 30, one color only .............................................................. | 85.00 | 800.00 |
| ☐ | **VILLAGE FIELD,** rel. 1975. ed. 125, issued in one color & two color, 7½″ x 16½″, litho, pub JARP ............................................... | 75.00 | 400.00 |
| ☐ | **DEBBIE & BABY,** rel. 1975. ed. 165, 17½″ x 23½″, wood veneer & one color . | 85.00 | 720.00 |
| | two color & three color, pub JARP .................................... | 110.00 | 780.00 |
| ☐ | **BABS W/FLOWERS,** rel. 1975. ed. 150, 27″ x 37″, litho, pub JARP ......... | 175.00 | 1,000.00 |
| ☐ | **HONG KONG HARBOR,** rel. 1975. ed. 195, 10¼″ x 14½″, one color ......... | 75.00 | 300.00 |
| | three color, litho, pub JARP ......................................... | 95.00 | 350.00 |
| ☐ | **MARY-ANN,** rel. 1975. ed. 195, 8″ x 11¾″, one color.................... | 75.00 | 600.00 |
| | three color, litho, pub JARP ......................................... | 95.00 | 540.00 |
| ☐ | **JOSHUA,** rel. 1975. ed. 195, 7¾″ x 9¾″, one color .................... | 75.00 | 450.00 |
| | three color, litho, pub JARP ......................................... | 90.00 | 425.00 |
| ☐ | **NEW SAMI,** rel. 1975. ed. 195, 7½″ x 9″, one color .................... | 75.00 | 700.00 |
| | three color, litho, pub JARP ......................................... | 90.00 | 650.00 |
| ☐ | **ALBERTO,** rel. 1975. ed. 195, 9″ x 10″, one color .................... | 75.00 | 350.00 |
| | three color, litho, pub JARP ......................................... | 90.00 | 350.00 |
| ☐ | **ELEANOR,** rel. 1975. ed. 195, 9″ x 9″, one color .................... | 75.00 | 420.00 |
| | three color, litho, pub JARP ......................................... | 90.00 | 375.00 |
| ☐ | **RUTH-ANN (Mother & 3 Children),** rel. 1975. ed. 250, 26½″ x 34″, one color . | 150.00 | 950.00 |
| | three color, litho, pub JARP ......................................... | 215.00 | 1,020.00 |
| ☐ | **JAPANESE BOY,** rel. 1975. ed. 250, 9″ x 14″, two, three color .......... | 115.00 | 480.00 |
| | three, four color, litho, pub JARP .................................... | 125.00 | 480.00 |
| ☐ | **JAPANESE GIRL,** rel. 1975. ed. 250, 9″ x 12″, two, three color............ | 115.00 | 480.00 |
| | three, four color, litho, pub JARP .................................... | 125.00 | 480.00 |
| ☐ | **YOU BE KING,** rel. 1975. ed. 98, 25″ x 33½″, one color .................. | 150.00 | 600.00 |
| | two color ......................................................... | 185.00 | 600.00 |
| | three or four color, litho, pub JARP .................................. | 215.00 | 660.00 |
| ☐ | **SWISS MAN,** rel. 1976. ed. 300, 20¼″ x 24″, one color ................. | 85.00 | 225.00 |
| | eight color, litho, pub JARP ......................................... | 150.00 | 375.00 |
| ☐ | **SWISS WOMAN,** rel. 1976. ed. 300, 20¼″ x 24″, one color ............... | 85.00 | 225.00 |
| | eight color, litho, pub JARP ......................................... | 150.00 | 375.00 |
| ☐ | **ELSA & BABY,** rel. 1976. ed. 300, 16½″ x 24″, one color ............... | 85.00 | 2,500.00 |
| | eight color, litho, pub JARP ......................................... | 150.00 | 3,000.00 |
| ☐ | **3 VASES,** rel. 1976. ed. 290, 23½″ x 36″, litho, pub JARP ............. | 250.00 | 1,200.00 |
| ☐ | **OLD MAN HEAD,** rel. 1976. ed. 50, 10″ x 13″, etching, pub JARP.......... | 80.00 | 360.00 |
| ☐ | **GREEK GIRL,** rel. 1976. ed. 50, 10″ x 13″, etching, pub JARP........... | 70.00 | 360.00 |
| ☐ | **DUTCH GIRL & BOY,** rel. 1976. ed. 50, 10″ x 13″, etching, pub JARP ...... | 70.00 | 360.00 |
| ☐ | **MOTHER & BABY,** rel. 1976. ed. 50, 9½″ x 12″, etching, pub JARP......... | 60.00 | 500.00 |
| ☐ | **PICCOLO PLAYER,** rel. 1976. ed. 50, 10½″ x 11½″, etching, pub JARP...... | 60.00 | 360.00 |
| ☐ | **TORSO,** rel. 1970. ed. 50, 2½″ x 2½″, etching, pub JARP ............... | 50.00 | 335.00 |

| | | ISSUE PRICE | CURRENT PRICE |
|---|---|---|---|
| ☐ | **GREEK FIELD**, rel. 1975. ed. 135, 22″ x 30″, litho, pub JARP | 125.00 | 400.00 |
| ☐ | **SAMI NO. 9**, rel. 1976. ed. 250, 17½″ x 25½″ | 125.00 | 1,100.00 |
| | ed. 45, same size but on silk, pub JARP | 175.00 | 1,250.00 |
| ☐ | **CHRIS**, rel. 1975. ed. 150, 13″ x 18¼″, litho, pub JARP | 85.00 | 700.00 |
| ☐ | **CHRYSTAL**, rel. 1975. ed. 120, 12¾″ x 17⅝″, one color | 85.00 | 600.00 |
| | three color | 100.00 | 700.00 |
| | four color, litho, pub JARP | 110.00 | 700.00 |
| ☐ | **GUATEMALA SCENE**, rel. 1976. ed. 295, 13″ x 24⅛″, one color | 95.00 | 550.00 |
| | nine color, litho, pub JARP | 145.00 | 650.00 |
| ☐ | **VIOLIN & FLUTE PLAYER**, rel. 1976. ed. 290, 15½″ x 18″, litho, pub JARP | 90.00 | 700.00 |
| ☐ | **LITTLE LOVERS**, rel. 1976. ed. 280, 5¼″ x 9″, litho, pub JARP | 75.00 | 600.00 |
| ☐ | **GIRL'S HEAD**, rel. 1976. ed. 280, 10¾″ x 13½″, litho, pub JARP | 75.00 | 600.00 |
| ☐ | **CHRISTA IN PIG TAILS**, rel. 1976. ed. 55, 13¼″ x 17⅛″, one color | 85.00 | 600.00 |
| | four color, pub JARP | 95.00 | 600.00 |
| ☐ | **MAYAN WATER CARRIER**, rel. 1976. ed. 300, 11″ x 21¾″, one color | 95.00 | 600.00 |
| | nine color, litho, pub JARP | 145.00 | 600.00 |
| ☐ | **MAYAN WATER CARRIER W/CHILD**, rel. 1976. ed. 300, 11″ x 21¾″ | 95.00 | 700.00 |
| | nine color, litho, pub JARB | 145.00 | 650.00 |
| ☐ | **JAPANESE DOLL**, rel. 1976. ed. 28, 7½″ x 11¼″, one color | 85.00 | 1,500.00 |
| | ed. 52, same size, twelve colors + gold on silk | 160.00 | 2,000.00 |
| | ed. 280, 9″ x 12″, twelve colors + gold on silk, pub JARP | 160.00 | 2,000.00 |
| ☐ | **KIKUE** (Japon), rel. 1976. ed. 150, 11¾″ x 21½″ | 150.00 | 1,550.00 |
| ☐ | **KIKUE** (Silk), rel. 1976. ed. 145, 11¾″ x 21½″, pub JARP | 195.00 | 2,000.00 |
| ☐ | **SWWITZERLAND**, rel. 1976. ed. 270, 24″ x 37″, litho, pub JARP | 350.00 | 1,200.00 |
| ☐ | **MOTHER & 4 CHILDREN**, rel. 1975. ed. 300, 27¼″ x 39¼″, litho, pub JARP | 250.00 | 1,000.00 |
| ☐ | **MAYAN WEAVER** (Japon), rel. 1975. ed. 175, 9″ x 11¾″ | 115.00 | 700.00 |
| ☐ | **MAYAN WEAVER** (Silk), rel. 1975. ed. 105, 9″ x 11¾″, pub JARP | 165.00 | 750.00 |
| ☐ | **MAYAN PRINCESS**, rel. 1975. ed. 300, 26½″ x 40¼″, litho, pub JARP | 250.00 | 650.00 |
| ☐ | **JULIET & BABY** (Japon), rel. 1976. ed. 285, 8½″ x 11″, pub JARP | 115.00 | 1,100.00 |
| ☐ | **COUPLE IN FIELDS**, rel. 1976. ed. 290, 10″ x 13″, litho, pub JARP | 70.00 | 195.00 |
| ☐ | **FARM WOMAN W/BASKET**, rel. 1976. ed. 290, 8″ x 10½″, litho, pub JARP | 70.00 | 195.00 |
| ☐ | **MOTHER & DAUGHTER**, rel. 1976. ed. 290, 7½″ x 11″, litho, pub JARP | 70.00 | 195.00 |
| ☐ | **FISHERMAN**, rel. 1976. ed. 290, 7″ x 12¾″, litho, pub JARP | 70.00 | 195.00 |
| ☐ | **VENICE**, rel. 1976. ed. 290, 11″ x 11″, litho, pub JARP | 70.00 | 195.00 |
| ☐ | **SMALL BRETON WOMAN W/CHILD**, rel. 1976. ed. 290, 9½″ x 10½″, litho, pub JARP | 70.00 | 195.00 |
| ☐ | **THREE WOMEN IN FIELDS**, rel. 1976. ed. 290, 12½″ x 16″, litho, pub JARP | 75.00 | 195.00 |
| ☐ | **TWO DUTCH GIRLS**, rel. 1976. ed. 300, 13″ x 17¼″, litho, pub JARP | 85.00 | 420.00 |
| ☐ | **4 MUSICIANS**, rel. 1976. ed. 300, 13″ x 17″, litho, pub JARP | 85.00 | 500.00 |
| ☐ | **2 DANCERS**, rel. 1976. ed. 300, 7″ x 9½″, litho, pub JARP | 75.00 | 325.00 |
| ☐ | **SAMPAN** (On Silk), rel. 1976. ed. 209, 9″ x 12″, nine colors + gold | 250.00 | 700.00 |
| ☐ | **SAMPAN** (On Japon), ed. 32, 9″ x 12″, nine colors + gold, pub JARP | 225.00 | 700.00 |
| ☐ | **SAMPAN**, ed. 234, 9″ x 12″, pub JARP | 195.00 | 700.00 |
| ☐ | **MAYAN TWIN BOY**, rel. 1976. ed. 290, 15¾″ x 26″, pub JARP | 150.00 | 600.00 |
| ☐ | **MAYAN TWIN GIRL**, rel. N/A, 9″ x 15″ | 100.00 | 550.00 |
| ☐ | **MARCH OF DIMES MOTHER & BABY**, rel. 1976. ed. 190, 7″ x 12½″, litho, pub JARP | 75.00 | 800.00 |
| ☐ | **RENAISSANCE GIRL**, rel. 1976. ed. 300, 9¾″ x 10″, litho, pub JARP | 125.00 w/Bk | 700.00 w/Bk |
| ☐ | **RENAISSANCE BOY** (Book), rel. 1976. ed. 300, 9″ x 12″, pub JARP | 125.00 w/Bk | 800.00 |
| ☐ | **MARGO & CHILD**, One print only; stone unfinished, no edition. | | |
| ☐ | **MOTHER & BABY**, Broken stone | — | — |
| ☐ | **JAPANESE FAMILY**, rel. 1976. ed. 290, 19½″ x 26½″, litho, pub JARP | 165.00 | 275.00 |
| ☐ | **ULLA**, rel. 1976. ed. 295, 13½″ x 19¾″, litho, pub JARP | 150.00 | 300.00 |
| ☐ | **ELLIE & CHILD**, rel. 1976. ed. 295, 12″ x 18¼″, litho, pub JARP | 150.00 | 900.00 |
| ☐ | **SERINA & CHILD** (Japon), rel. 1976. ed. 252, 23½″ x 30½″ | 250.00 | 1,200.00 |
| ☐ | **SERINA & CHILD** (Silk), rel. 1976. ed. 35, 23½″ x 30½″ | 350.00 | 1,200.00 |
| ☐ | **SERINE & CHILD** (Paper), rel. 1976. ed. 10, 23½″ x 30½″, all pub by JARP | 175.00 | 1,200.00 |
| ☐ | **INGRID & CHILD**, rel. 1976. ed. 276, 25½″ x 37¼″, litho, pub JARP | 295.00 | 900.00 |
| ☐ | **SOPHIA & CHILDREN**, rel. 1976. ed. 296, 28″ x 39″ | 325.00 | 2,000.00 |
| ☐ | **ROMANCE** (Japon), rel. 1977. ed. 375, 8½″ x 10¼″, pub JARP | 125.00 | 125.00 |
| ☐ | **SMALL M & B**, rel. 1977. ed. 250, 7″ x 8¼″, litho, pub JARP | 125.00 | 450.00 |
| ☐ | **MAYAN MAN**, rel. 1977. ed. 295, 23½″ x 41¼″, litho, pub JARP | 350.00 | 1,600.00 |
| ☐ | **NEW SINGLE NUDE**, rel. 1977. ed. 250, 9″ x 14″, nine color | 150.00 | 275.00 |
| | two color on silk, 9″ x 14″ | 150.00 | 300.00 |
| | two color, 9″ x 14″, pub JARP | 125.00 | 275.00 |

| | ISSUE PRICE | CURRENT PRICE |
|---|---|---|
| ☐ **MAYAN MOTHER & BABY,** rel. 1977. ed. 250, 7¼" x 10½", litho, pub JARP. . | 125.00 | 700.00 |
| ☐ **MARGARET & CHILD,** rel. 1977. ed. 250, (In Hibel Lithographs, Only), 7½" x 10¼", litho, pub JARP. | 125.00 w/Bk | 600.00 |
| ☐ **LORRIE & CHILD,** rel. 1977. ed. 250, (In Hibel Lithographs, Only), 8" x 10½", litho, pub JARP. | 125.00 w/Bk | 600.00 |
| ☐ **PEARL & CHILD,** rel. 1977. ed. 250, 7" x 9¼", litho, pub JARP. | 125.00 | 600.00 |
| ☐ **JENNIE,** rel. 1977. ed. 398, 9" x 12", litho, pub JARP. | 300.00 | 1,400.00 |
| ☐ **MUSEUM SUITE,** rel. 1977. ed. 375 consists of the following litho: Tamiko, 9" x 12", 16 colors; Friesland, 20" x 10¾", 11 colors; Martha & Iris, 9" x 12", 14 colors; Klassina, 8½" x 11¾", 21 colors; Okasan to Kodoma, 9" x 12", 16 colors; Piazza San Marco, 11¾" x 17¾", 15 colors, pub JARP | 1,900.00 | 8,900.00 |
| ☐ **GIRL WITH EARRING,** rel. 1977. ed. 375, 6" x 8", in Progressions w/Museum Suite only, pub JARP. | — | 150.00 |
| ☐ **GIRL WITH PAINTBRUSH,** rel. 1977. ed. 375, 6" x 8", in Progression book, litho, pub JARP. | 70.00 w/Bk | 150.00 w/Bk |
| ☐ **BOY WITH CHICKEN,** rel. 1977. ed. 375, 7½" x 11", white gold on Japanese rice paper, litho, pub JARP. | 300.00 | 475.00 |
| ☐ **COLETTE & CHILD,** rel. 1977. ed. 275, 14½" x 20", litho, pub JARP. | 195.00 | 1,200.00 |
| ☐ **SHOFAR,** rel. 1977. ed. 275, 11" x 14", litho, pub JARP | 135.00 | 600.00 |
| ☐ **YOUNG RABBI,** rel. 1977. ed. 299, 10" x 14", one color | 100.00 | 600.00 |
| two color, 10" x 14", litho, pub JARP | 100.00 | 500.00 |
| ☐ **LILLIAN & CHILD,** rel. 1977. ed. 150 (I-Japon), 10" x 13½" ed. 152 (II-Japon), same size, litho, pub JARP | 100.00 | 700.00 |
| ☐ **SUZANNA & CHILD,** ed. 290, 14" x 17¼", litho, pub JARP | 125.00 | 600.00 |
| ☐ **KRISTINA & CHILD,** rel. 1977. ed. 290, 22" x 30", eleven colors | 265.00 | 1,100.00 |
| ed. 25, 22" x 30", one color Sec. II | 145.00 | 950.00 |
| ed. 25, 22" x 30", one color Sec. III, litho, all pub by JARP | 145.00 | 950.00 |
| ☐ **DORIS & CHILDREN,** rel. 1977. ed. 295, 19" x 24", litho, pub JARP | 275.00 | 800.00 |
| ☐ **FIELDS NEAR CHARTRES,** rel. 1977. ed. 295, 15" x 21", litho, pub JARP | 295.00 | 450.00 |
| ☐ **PARISIAN FLOWER VENDOR,** rel. 1977. ed. 295, 10" x 14", litho, pub JARP | 165.00 | 375.00 |
| ☐ **MOTHER & CHILD (Childrens Hospital),** rel. 1977. ed. 295, 16" x 20", litho, pub JARP | 195.00 | 900.00 |
| ☐ **DUTCH LANDSCAPE,** rel. 1977. ed. 295 on Japon, except 13 on silk; litho on Japon. | 175.00 | 300.00 |
| on silk, pub JARP. | — | 2,500.00 |
| ☐ **LARGE MOTHER & TWO CHILDREN,** rel. 1978. ed. 295, 30 were proofs, 7 silks, litho on Rives paper | 450.00 | 800.00 |
| proofs | 570.00 | 725.00 |
| silk, pub JARP | N/A | — |
| ☐ **WEDDING OF DAVID AND BATHSHEBA,** rel. 1978. ed. 385, 15" x 18½" litho twelve color + gold, pub JARP | 500.00 | 1,295.00 |
| ☐ **WHO IS RICH?,** rel. 1978. ed. N/A, 15" x 19¾", litho on Japon, pub JARP | 135.00 | 600.00 |
| ☐ **ISRAELI RABBI,** rel. 1978. ed. N/A, litho ten color + gold, pub JARP | 450.00 | 575.00 |
| ☐ **AKKO,** rel. 1978. ed. 294, 18" x 24", litho, pub JARP | 325.00 | 375.00 |
| ☐ **LARGE SINGLE VASE OF FLOWERS,** rel. 1978. ed. 297, 26" x 36", litho, pub JARP | 375.00 | 720.00 |
| ☐ **JERUSALEM SCENE,** rel. 1978. ed, 298, 30" x 40", 18 color + gold, litho, pub JARP. | 500.00 | 800.00 |
| ☐ **WOMAN W/CHILDREN,** rel. 1978. ed. 296, 30" x 40", litho, pub JARP. | 500.00 | 800.00 |
| ☐ **JAPANESE WOMAN,** rel. 1978. ed. 282, 10" x 23½", Torinoko | 235.00 | 850.00 |
| on silk, litho, pub JARP. | 295.00 | 550.00 |
| ☐ **INDIAN BOWL OF FLOWERS,** rel. 1978. ed. 285, 14" x 30¼", litho, pub JARP. | 375.00 | 550.00 |
| ☐ **ANGELINA,** rel. 1978. ed. 295, 12" x 14", two color on Rives | 135.00 | 550.00 |
| one color on Rives, litho, pub JARP | 135.00 | 300.00 |
| ☐ **GRECIAN MOTHER & BABY,** rel. 1978. ed. 425, 18½" x 25", one color | 165.00 | 600.00 |
| ten color, litho, pub JARP | 245.00 | 600.00 |
| ☐ **BOY W/HORN,** rel. 1978. ed. 380, 10¾" x 14½", litho, pub JARP | 245.00 | 395.00 |
| ☐ **SAMI #11,** rel. 1978. ed. 320, 14½" x 18½", one color | 195.00 | 245.00 |
| eleven color, litho, pub JARP | 325.00 | 385.00 |
| ☐ **MORNING BOWL OF FLOWERS,** rel. 1978. ed. 350, 17" x 23", litho, pub JARP | 245.00 | 325.00 |
| ☐ **FELICIA,** rel. 1978. ed. 148, 21" x 30¾", litho, sixteen color + two gold, pub JARP. | 900.00 | 2,500.00 |
| ☐ **ANDREA & CHILD,** rel. 1978. ed. 420, 16¼" x 22½", one color | 165.00 | 500.00 |
| seven colors, same size, litho, pub JARP | 245.00 | 600.00 |

| | ISSUE PRICE | CURRENT PRICE |
|---|---|---|
| ☐ **LENORE,** rel. 1978. ed. N/A, 7½" x 9½", six color + gold porcelain, pub JARP | 600.00 | 1,300.00 |
| ☐ **DAVID SUITE,** rel. 1978. ed. 375 consisting of seven lithographs (one on porcelain) | 3,600.00 | 5,800.00 |
| ☐ **MADCHEN,** rel. 1978. ed. on porcelain, 7¼" x 9½", six colors + one gold, pub JARP | 600.00 | 1,200.00 |
| ☐ **FAMILY - HORIZONTAL,** rel. 1978. ed. 340, s/n, 28" x 39" litho, 2 colors, pub JARP | 300.00 | 600.00 |
| ☐ **THREE BALLERINAS,** rel. 1978. ed. 305, s/n, 17½" x 14½" litho, 9 colors, pub JARP | 210.00 | 475.00 |
| ☐ **BARONESS JOHANNA,** rel. 1978. ed. 310, s/n, 15¼" x 12¼", litho, 2 colors, pub JARP | 135.00 | 600.00 |
| ☐ **MOTHER AND TWO CHILDREN,** rel. 1978. ed. 319, s/n, 27½" x 22", litho, 13 colors, pub JARP | 245.00 | 700.00 |
| ☐ **RITA AND CHILD,** rel. 1978. ed. 365, s/n, 24" x 18", litho, 10 colors, pub JARP | 245.00 | 700.00 |
| ☐ **GREEK FARMERS,** rel. 1978. ed. 310, s/n, 24" x 19", litho, 8 colors, pub JARP | 265.00 | 400.00 |
| ☐ **GIRL WITH LILLIES,** rel. 1978. ed. 375, s/n, 24¾" x 20¼", litho, 11 colors, pub JARP | 275.00 | 800.00 |
| ☐ **LARGE FLORAL,** rel. 1978. ed. 295, s/n, 30" x 40", litho, 15 colors, pub JARP | 525.00 | 1,000.00 |
| ☐ **GIRL WITH HAT,** rel. 1978. ed. 310, s/n, 14" x 12½", litho, 6 colors, pub JARP | 250.00 | 1,050.00 |
| ☐ **MONICA AND CHILD,** rel. 1978. ed. 398, s/n, 24¾" x 20½", litho, 8 colors, pub JARP | 245.00 | 700.00 |
| ☐ **TRIO,** rel. 1979. ed. 360, s/n, 21" x 30¼", litho, 9 colors, pub JARP | 395.00 | 475.00 |
| ☐ **MOTHER & TWO CHILDREN,** rel. 1979. ed. 265, s/n, 17" x 13½", litho, 2 colors, on Rives | 145.00 | 550.00 |
| ☐ on Japon, pub JARP | 175.00 | 575.00 |
| ☐ **TERRE,** rel. 1979. ed. 315, s/n, 12" x 9", pub JARP | 135.00 | 550.00 |
| ☐ **IN MY GARDEN/RAIN THAT FALLS,** rel. 1979. ed. 375, s/n, 25" x 17¾", pub JARP | *1050.00 w/book | 1,150.00 |
| ☐ **SWAYING GRASSES/SNOWMAN,** rel. 1979. ed. 375, s/n, 25" x 17¾", pub JARP | *1050.00 w/book | 1,150.00 |
| ***One set of the above prints were included with the purchase of the book titled ''Sundial Ticking''** | | |
| ☐ **DAVID THE SHEPHERD,** rel. 1979. ed. 150, s/n, 41" x 30" litho, 8 colors + gold, pub JARP | 1,650.00 | 1,850.00 |
| ☐ **MARIA & CHILDREN,** rel. 1979. ed. 352, s/n, 11" x 9½" litho, 3 colors, pub JARP | 135.00 | 400.00 |
| ☐ **SONDRA,** rel. 1979. ed. 314, s/n, 20¾" x 16½", litho, 2 colors on Japon | 325.00 | 650.00 |
| 10 colors on Rives | 295.00 | 800.00 |
| 2 colors on Rives, Barcham, pub JARP | 295.00 | 650.00 |
| ☐ **DAVID BATHSHEBA & SOLOMON,** rel. 1979. ed. 371, s/n, 18" x 16" litho, 10 colors + gold, pub JARP | 500.00 | 950.00 |
| ☐ **AKIKO & CHILDREN,** rel. 1979. ed. 335, s/n, 29¾" x 22" litho, 12 colors + gold | 450.00 | 1,300.00 |
| litho, 3 colors on Rives, pub JARP | 450.00 | 1,300.00 |
| ☐ **MIRIAM & CHILDREN,** rel. 1979. ed. 359, s/n, 38½" x 27", litho 8 colors on Rives | 495.00 | 1,200.00 |
| 3 colors on Rives, pub JARP | 295.00 | 1,050.00 |
| ☐ **INGA,** rel. 1979. ed. 374, s/n, 10" x 8½", pub JARP | 135.00 | 265.00 |
| ☐ **ANNA,** rel. 1979. ed. 310, s/n, 16" x 11", pub JARP | 150.00 | 400.00 |
| ☐ **FRANCESCA,** rel. 1979. ed. 335, s/n, 14⅝" x 12" litho, 6 colors, pub JARP | 195.00 | 550.00 |
| ☐ **PIERRE,** rel. 1979. ed. 335, s/n, 13½" x 12" litho, 6 colors, pub JARP | 195.00 | 550.00 |
| ☐ **MAN WITH HOE,** rel. 1979. ed. 350, s/n, 38⅝" x 27½" litho, 7 colors, pub JARP | 495.00 | 850.00 |

| | ISSUE PRICE | CURRENT PRICE |
|---|---|---|
| ☐ **YOUNG MANCHU,** rel. 1979. ed. 350, s/n, 17¼" x 12" litho, 7 colors plus gold background | 335.00 | 850.00 |
| litho, 11¾" x 9" on Japon | 295.00 | 850.00 |
| litho, 17⅞" x 12", silk background + gold | 375.00 | 850.00 |
| litho 11¾" x 9", silk background only | 350.00 | 900.00 |
| 7 colors plus gold on Bavarian Porcelain, total edition pub JARP | 850.00 | 1,600.00 |
| ☐ **PETRA MIT KINDER,** rel. 1979. ed. 320, s/n, 29¾" x 22", pub JARP | 345.00 | 2,100.00 |
| ☐ **VICTORIA,** rel. 1979. ed. 310, s/n, 17" x 10¾" litho, 3 colors, pub JARP | 165.00 | 450.00 |
| ☐ **VICTORIA,** rel. 1979. size 9¼" x 6½", pub JARP. This litho was not offered for sale Gift - Collectors Society Meeting, Monaco, July 13, 1979. | * | |
| ☐ **NIWA-NO-CHO,** rel. 1979. ed. 300, s/n, 12" x 9", litho, 11 colors + gold on Rives | 375.00 | 850.00 |
| same as above on silk, pub JARP | 395.00 | 525.00 |
| ☐ **KRISTA & CHILD,** rel. 1979. ed. 400, s/n, 13" x 10½" 7 colors + gold on Bavarian Porcelain, pub JARP | 850.00 | 1,150.00 |
| ☐ **INTERNATIONAL YEAR OF THE CHILD SUITE,** rel. 1979. ed. 420, s/n, 11⅞" x 9⅝", CHILD OF SWEDEN, 7 colors + 2 golds; CHILD OF ITALY, 8 colors + 1 gold; CHILD OF THAILAND, 8 colors + 2 golds; CHILD OF PORTUGAL, 7 colors, pub JARP | 900.00 | 2,800.00 |
| ☐ **RENOIR'S GARDEN,** rel. 1980. ed. 330, s/n, 22½" x 19", pub JARP | 350.00 | 550.00 |
| ☐ **VICKIE & CHILDREN,** rel. 1980. ed. 395, s/n, 20½" x 15½", pub JARP | 245.00 | 500.00 |
| ☐ **MICHELLE & NINA,** rel. 1980. ed. 280, s/n, 11¾" x 8¾", pub JARP | 195.00 | 250.00 |
| ☐ **SAMUEL THE KINGMAKER,** rel. 1980. ed. 338, s/n, 23" x 20½", pub JARP | 375.00 | 675.00 |
| ☐ **NORA,** rel. 1980. ed. 394, s/n, 13" x 12¼", pub JARP | 175.00 | 300.00 |
| ☐ **MILDRED,** rel. 1980. ed. 383, s/n, 10¼" x 5¼", pub JARP | 135.00 | 250.00 |
| ☐ **DELORES,** rel. 1980. ed. 383, s/n, 10¼" x 5¼", pub JARP | 135.00 | 250.00 |
| ☐ **HARU,** rel. 1980. ed. 397, s/n, 10¼" x 5¼", pub JARP | 50.00 | — |
| ☐ **UME,** rel. 1980. ed. 390, s/n, 10¼" x 5¼", pub JARP | 135.00 | 175.00 |
| ☐ **JOSEPH,** rel. 1980. ed. 335, s/n, 19" x 14", pub JARP | 495.00 | 800.00 |
| ☐ **FLOWER SONG,** rel. 1980. ed. 289, s/n, 22" x 16", pub JARP | 375.00 | 800.00 |
| ☐ **THAI PRINCESS,** rel. 1980. ed. 395, s/n, 12¼" x 9½", pub JARP | 375.00 | 800.00 |
| ☐ hand applied gold rives | 495.00 | 900.00 |
| ☐ **GUATEMALA MOTHER & BABY,** rel. 1980. ed. 325, s/n, 10" x 8", pub JARP | 295.00 | 350.00 |
| ☐ **PAMELA,** rel. 1980. ed. 395, s/n, 11" x 9", pub JARP | 295.00 | 375.00 |
| ☐ **PRINTEMPS,** rel. 1980. ed. 420, s/n, 15¾" x 10", pub JARP | 250.00 | 300.00 |
| ☐ **ALICIA,** rel. 1980. ed. 400, s/n, 16½" x 15", pub JARP | 275.00 | 500.00 |
| ☐ **TINA,** rel. 1980. ed. 200, s/n, 24" x 19¾", pub JARP | 750.00 | 1,150.00 |
| ☐ **CAROL & JENNIE,** rel. 1980. ed. 428, s/n, 21" x 14", pub JARP | 275.00 | 550.00 |
| ☐ **MATTHEW,** rel. 1980. ed. 392, s/n, 16" x 15", pub JARP | 450.00 | 525.00 |
| ☐ **CHERYLL & WENDY,** rel. 1980. ed. 100, s/n, 24" x 19¼", pub JARP | 3,900.00 | 7,000.00 |
| ☐ **OF WISDOM,** rel. 1980. ed. 385, s/n, consists of FAMILY, 16½" x 8½", CHILDHOOD, 17" x 10½", AGE OF BEAUTY, 17" x 10½", AGE OF WISDOM, 16½" x 8½", pub JARP | 1,200.00 | 2,000.00 |


| | | |
|---|---|---|
| ☐ **UME,** rel. 1980. ed. 390, s/n, 10¼" x 5¼", pub JARP | 135.00 | 175.00 |
| ☐ **JOSEPH,** rel. 1980. ed. 335, s/n, 19" x 14", pub JARP | 495.00 | 800.00 |
| ☐ **FLOWER SONG,** rel. 1980. ed. 289, s/n, 22" x 16", pub JARP | 375.00 | 800.00 |
| ☐ **THAI PRINCESS,** rel. 1980. ed. 395, s/n, 12¼" x 9½", pub JARP | 375.00 | 800.00 |
| ☐ hand applied gold rives | 495.00 | 900.00 |
| ☐ **GUATEMALA MOTHER & BABY,** rel. 1980. ed. 325, s/n, 10" x 8", pub JARP | 295.00 | 350.00 |
| ☐ **PAMELA,** rel. 1980. ed. 395, s/n, 11" x 9", pub JARP | 295.00 | 375.00 |
| ☐ **PRINTEMPS,** rel. 1980. ed. 420, s/n, 15¾" x 10", pub JARP | 250.00 | 300.00 |
| ☐ **ALICIA,** rel. 1980. ed. 400, s/n, 16½" x 15", pub JARP | 275.00 | 500.00 |
| ☐ **TINA,** rel. 1980. ed. 200, s/n, 24" x 19¾", pub JARP | 750.00 | 1,150.00 |
| ☐ **CAROL & JENNIE,** rel. 1980. ed. 428, s/n, 21" x 14", pub JARP | 275.00 | 550.00 |
| ☐ **MATTHEW,** rel. 1980. ed. 392, s/n, 16" x 15", pub JARP | 450.00 | 525.00 |
| ☐ **CHERYLL & WENDY,** rel. 1980. ed. 100, s/n, 24" x 19¼", pub JARP | 3,900.00 | 7,000.00 |
| ☐ **OF WISDOM,** rel. 1980. ed. 385, s/n, consists of FAMILY, 16½" x 8½", CHILDHOOD, 17" x 10½", AGE OF BEAUTY, 17" x 10½", AGE OF WISDOM, 16½" x 8½", pub JARP | 1,200.00 | 2,000.00 |

| | ISSUE PRICE | CURRENT PRICE |
|---|---|---|
| ☐ **SUSAN AND CHILDREN,** rel. 1981. seven colors, ed. 397, s/n, 15¼" x 11¼", II, III on Rives | 335.00 | 335.00 |
| ☐ one color, 12" x 9", I on silk | 265.00 | 325.00 |
| ☐ seven colors, 12" x 9", IV on Bavarian Porcelain, pub EHC | 795.00 | 795.00 |
| ☐ **GLORIA,** rel. 1981. one color, ed. 288, 10¾" x 10¾", I, II on Rives | 195.00 | 195.00 |
| ☐ two colors, 14¾" x 11" on japon | 215.00 | 275.00 |
| ☐ two colors, 14¾" x 11", IV on Rives, pub EHC | 195.00 | 250.00 |
| ☐ **ROBERTA & ROBERTO,** rel. 1981. ed. 344, s/n, 6¾" x 6", pub EHC | 395.00 | 395.00 |
| ☐ **TREE OF LIFE,** rel. 1981. eight colors + gold, ed. 350, s/n, 11½" x 17½", I thru IV on Rives, pub EHC | 395.00 | 395.00 |
| eight colors + gold, VI on Bavarian Porcelain | 1,400.00 | 1,400.00 |
| ☐ **KIMI-NO,** rel. 1981. eleven colors + gold colors, ed. 354, s/n, 17⅞" x 11⅝" thru VIII on Rives, pub EHC | 445.00 | 445.00 |
| eleven colors + gold, IX on Bavarian Porcelain | 1,400.00 | 1,400.00 |
| ☐ **MAID OF KEZAR,** rel. 1981. ed. 385, s/n, 9⅞" x 13¾", bound in Fay Berg's Cookbook, pub EHC | 225.00 | 225.00 |
| ☐ **JOELLE,** rel. 1982. ten colors, ed. 348, 14⅛" x 12", I thru III on Rives, pub EHC | 295.00 | 525.00 |
| three colors, IV on Rives | 265.00 | 500.00 |
| two colors, V on Rives | 225.00 | 475.00 |
| ☐ **KELLY,** rel. 1982. nine colors, ed. 347, 14¼" x 12", I thru III on Rives, pub EHC | 320.00 | 500.00 |
| two colors, IV on Rives | 225.00 | 450.00 |
| ☐ **TRUDY,** rel. 1982. five colors, ed. 305, s/n, 14¾" x 12", I thru VI on Rives, pub EHC | 265.00 | 265.00 |
| two colors, VI-VIII on Rives | 225.00 | 225.00 |
| ☐ **TUSCAN FIELDS,** rel. 1982. eight colors, ed. 394, s/n, 18" x 18¾", I thru VI on Rives, pub EHC | 375.00 | 375.00 |
| eight colors, VII thru XII on japon | 395.00 | 395.00 |
| ☐ **THE FAMILY SUITE 1982,** rel. 1982. ed. 396, s/n consisting of<br>SOWING, nine colors + gold, 12½" x 9"<br>RIPENING, eight colors + gold, 9" x 12½"<br>HARVESTING, nine colors + gold, 12½" x 9"<br>THROUGH THE GENERATIONS, two colors, 9" x 12½", pub EHC | 800.00 | 800.00 |
| ☐ **PORTRAIT OF A FAMILY,** rel. 1982. ed. 330, s/n, 40½" x 28¾", pub EHC | 750.00 | 750.00 |
| ☐ **LITTLE RAJAH AND THE UNICORNS,** rel. 1982. ed. 319, s/n, 41¾" x 29½", pub EHC | 1,000.00 | 1,000.00 |
| ☐ **KATRINA & CHILDREN,** rel. 1982. ed. 329, s/n, 29" x 19½", pub EHC | 345.00 | 500.00 |
| ☐ **ZORINA,** rel. 1982. ed. 329, s/n, 21" x 13¾", pub EHC | 295.00 | 295.00 |
| ☐ **TONI,** rel. 1982. ed. 313, s/n, 16⅜" x 8⅝", pub EHC | 235.00 | 235.00 |
| ☐ **JANUARY,** rel. 1982. ed. 319, s/n, 15½" x 13¼", pub EHC | 295.00 | 295.00 |
| ☐ **RENA AND RACHEL,** rel. 1982. ed. 329, s/n, 15½" x 13¼", pub EHC | 345.00 | 495.00 |
| ☐ **NARO-SAN,** rel. 1982. ed. 322, s/n, 24" x 17¾", pub EHC | 275.00 | 350.00 |
| ☐ **BETTINA AND CHILDREN,** rel. 1982. ed. 300, s/n, 31½" x 18¼", pub EHC | 310.00 | 400.00 |
| ☐ **HELVA,** rel. 1982. ed. 214, s/n, 16⅜" x 8⅝", pub EHC | 235.00 | 235.00 |
| ☐ **WILLA AND CHILD,** rel. 1982. ed. 361, s/n, 8" x 6¾", pub EHC | 850.00 | 850.00 |
| ☐ **LYDIA,** rel. 1982. ed. 298, s/n, 12½" x 11", pub EHC | 195.00 | 275.00 |
| ☐ **FAMILY OF THE MOUNTAIN LAKE,** rel. 1982. ed. 305, s/n, 35" x 24", pub EHC | 395.00 | 595.00 |
| ☐ **FLORA,** rel. 1983. ed. 302, s/n, 30½" x 22", pub EHC | 425.00 | 425.00 |
| ☐ **LOTTE AND HER CHILDREN,** rel. 1983. ed. 358, s/n, 37" x 27", pub EHC | 695.00 | 695.00 |
| ☐ **SONJA AND DIANA,** rel. 1983. ed. 230, s/n, 15" x 10", pub EHC | 215.00 | 215.00 |
| ☐ **NICOLE WITH BABY,** rel. 1983. ed. 297, s/n, 16" x 11", pub EHC | 250.00 | 250.00 |
| ☐ **ROSA AND CHILD,** rel. 1983. ed. 310, s/n, 13" x 18", pub EHC | 175.00 | 175.00 |
| ☐ **BECCA,** rel. 1983. ed. 410, s/n, 12" x 14½", pub EHC | 165.00 | 165.00 |
| ☐ **OLD FRIENDS,** rel. 1983. ed. 300, s/n, 17½" x 12", pub EHC | 215.00 | 215.00 |
| ☐ **VALERIE AND CHILDREN,** rel. 1983. ed. 400, s/n, 13" x 21¼", pub EHC | 295.00 | 295.00 |
| ☐ **MICHAEL'S FAMILY,** rel. 1983. ed. 398, s/n, 36" x 26", pub EHC | 495.00 | 495.00 |
| ☐ **FAMILY ON THE TAKAIDO ROAD,** rel. 1983. ed. 395, s/n, 35" x 25", pub EHC | 550.00 | 675.00 |
| ☐ **NATURE STUDY,** rel. 1983. ed. 330, s/n, 5⅞" x 5½", pub EHC | 100.00 | 100.00 |
| ☐ **SOLO,** rel. 1983. ed. 340, s/n, 6" x 6¼", pub EHC | 100.00 | 100.00 |
| ☐ **MEDItATION,** rel. 1983. ed. 345, s/n, 3¾" x 5½", pub EHC | 100.00 | 100.00 |
| ☐ **TEMPLE VISIT,** rel. 1983. ed. 345, s/n, 6¼" x 5⅜", pub EHC | 100.00 | 100.00 |
| ☐ **AMANDA,** rel. 1983. ed. 340, s/n, 6" x 5⅞", pub EHC | 100.00 | 100.00 |

| | ISSUE PRICE | CURRENT PRICE |
|---|---|---|
| ☐ **SWIFT RIDER**, rel. 1983. ed. 330, s/n, 6⅞″ x 7⅛″, pub EHC | 100.00 | 100.00 |
| ☐ **ORIENTAL DAYDREAM**, rel. 1983. ed. 382, s/n, 16″ x 13½″, pub EHC | 275.00 | 275.00 |
| ☐ **PRIMA**, rel. 1983. ed. 186, s/n, 17″ x 10½″, pub EHC | 165.00 | 165.00 |
| ☐ **CHINESE VASES**, rel. 1983. ed. 366, s/n, 29½″ x 41½″, pub EHC | 595.00 | 595.00 |
| ☐ **NAVA AND CHILDREN**, rel. 1983. ed. 385, s/n, 30″ x 20¼″, pub EHC | 385.00 | 385.00 |

The above listing represents the entire edition of Edna Hibel original lithographs. Recently The Edna Hibel Corporation introduced a line of limited edition reproductions each representing a photo-mechanical reproduction of an original lithograph and each was issued in an edition of 1,000 prints.

The following is a listing of these prints. Prices shown are for framed prints. With each print three different framings were available, therefore, prices may vary depending on the type framing the collector selected.

| | FRAMED PRICE RANGE | |
|---|---|---|
| ☐ **ESTHER**, ed. 1,000, s/n, 35½″ x 23¾″, pub EHC | 195.00 | 325.00 |
| ☐ **MEXICAN BEGGAR**, ed. 1,000, s/n, 39¼″ x 28¼″, pub EHC | 295.00 | 395.00 |
| ☐ **LAMB OF KNOSSOS**, ed. 1,000, s/n, 35¾″ x 25¾″, pub EHC | 195.00 | 225.00 |
| ☐ **JOSEPH**, ed. 1,000, s/n, 47″ x 27″, pub EHC | 295.00 | 335.00 |
| ☐ **CANALE IN VENICE**, ed. 1,000, s/n, 29¾″ x 17¾″, pub EHC | 180.00 | 240.00 |
| ☐ **TOMO**, ed. 1,000, s/n, 30″ x 18″, pub EHC | 155.00 | 185.00 |
| ☐ **BALLERINAS**, ed. 1,000, s/n, 40″ x 25″, pub EHC | | 295.00 |
| ☐ **PATTY**, ed. 1,000, s/n, 22″ x 19″, pub EHC | 175.00 | 185.00 |
| ☐ **BLACK BERET**, ed. 1,000, s/n, 18″ x 31″, pub EHC | 165.00 | 195.00 |
| ☐ **RED BERRIES**, ed. 1,000, s/n, 17½″ x 29½″, pub EHC | 155.00 | 250.00 |
| ☐ **JENNIE**, ed. 1,000, s/n, 9″ x 14″, pub EHC | 100.00 | 130.00 |
| ☐ **SHIZUE**, ed. 1,000, s/n, 28½″ x 19¼″, pub EHC | 250.00 | 375.00 |
| ☐ **ULLA & CHILD**, ed. 1,000, s/n, 9¼″ x 24¼″, pub EHC | 110.00 | 135.00 |
| ☐ **A TALL ROSE**, ed. 1,000, s/n, 30″ x 9¾″, pub EHC | 135.00 | 185.00 |
| ☐ **LOVERS OF FLORENCE**, ed. 1,000, s/n, 15″ x 22½″, on satin | 150.00 | 195.00 |
|   ed. 1,000, s/n, on paper, pub EHC | 95.00 | 150.00 |
| ☐ **THE BLUE VASE**, ed. 1,000, s/n, 25″ x 13½″, pub EHC | 155.00 | 195.00 |
| ☐ **REHERSAL**, ed. 1,000, s/n, 16″ x 12½″, pub EHC | 115.00 | 175.00 |
| ☐ **THE GOLDEN HORN**, ed. 1,000, s/n, 24″ x 19″, pub EHC | 125.00 | 135.00 |
| ☐ **THE FLAUTIST**, ed. 1,000, s/n, 12″ x 15″, on satin | 150.00 | 175.00 |
|   ed. 1,000, s/n, 12″ x 15″, on paper, pub EHC | 115.00 | 160.00 |
| ☐ **LIEVE FROM BELGIUM**, ed. 1,000, s/n, 34″ x 16½″, pub EHC | 145.00 | 255.00 |
| ☐ **VANESSA AND CHILDREN**, ed. 1,000, s/n, 18¾″ x 14½″, pub EHC | 145.00 | 245.00 |
| ☐ **MONIQUE**, ed. 1,000, s/n, 9¼″ x 10¼″, pub EHC | 125.00 | 150.00 |
| ☐ **ORIENTAL CHILD**, ed. 1,000, s/n, 10¼″ x 9¼″, pub EHC | 135.00 | 185.00 |
| ☐ **MARGARET AND NICKI**, ed. 1,000, s/n, 18″ x 10¼″, pub EHC | 150.00 | 175.00 |
| ☐ **DUET**, ed. 1,000, s/n, 15¼″ x 20¼″, pub EHC | 195.00 | |
| ☐ **FLOWER GIRL**, ed. 1,000, s/n, 20″ x 11″, pub EHC | 130.00 | 215.00 |
| ☐ **VOLLRNDAM**, ed. 1,000, s/n, 12¼″ x 18¼″, pub EHC | 135.00 | 195.00 |
| ☐ **KLASINA FROM FRIESLAND**, ed. 1,000, s/n, 10¼″ x 8¼″, pub EHC | 130.00 | 150.00 |
| ☐ **GRANDMOTHER**, ed. 1,000, s/n, 12″ x 9¾″, pub EHC | 135.00 | 150.00 |
| ☐ **MOTHER AND TWO CHILDREN**, ed. 1,000, s/n, 14¾″ x 12″, pub EHC | 125.00 | 170.00 |
| ☐ **MARIANNE AND DANIELLE**, ed. 1,000, s/n, 12¼″ x 11″, pub EHC | 140.00 | 185.00 |
| ☐ **HEIDI**, ed. 1,000, s/n, 10¼″ x 8¼″, pub EHC | 115.00 | 165.00 |
| ☐ **PATRICIA AND BABY**, ed. 1,000, s/n, 9¼″ x 10¼″, pub EHC | 110.00 | 155.00 |
| ☐ **FRENCH FIELDS**, ed. 1,000, s/n, 23¼″ x 30¼″, pub EHC | 185.00 | 210.00 |
| ☐ **FLOWERS**, ed. 1,000, s/n, 20¼″ x 24″, pub EHC | 170.00 | 180.00 |
| ☐ **GRAPE PICKERS OF ALSACE**, ed. 1,000, s/n, 10¼″ x 14¼″, pub EHC | 135.00 | 175.00 |
| ☐ **VIVIAN AND CHILD**, ed. 1,000, s/n, 21″ x 15¾″, pub EHC | 165.00 | 260.00 |
| ☐ **BEATRICE AND BABY**, ed. 1,000, s/n, 30″ x 23½″, pub EHC | 160.00 | 250.00 |
| ☐ **HANNA AND HER TWO CHILDREN**, ed. 1,000, s/n, 30¼″ x 36″, pub EHC | 235.00 | 295.00 |
| ☐ **STEPHANIE AND CHILD**, ed. 1,000, s/n, 37″ x 28″, pub EHC | 435.00 | 450.00 |
| ☐ **MICHIO**, ed. 1,000, s/n, 23½″ x 17½″, pub EHC | 165.00 | 180.00 |
| ☐ **GREECE**, ed. 1,000, s/n, 23½″ x 47″, pub EHC | 325.00 | 375.00 |
| ☐ **LINDA AND ELIZABETH**, ed. 1,000, s/n, 21½″ x 19½″, pub EHC | 185.00 | 195.00 |

# CARDWELL S. HIGGINS
## (? - 1983)

Cardwell Higgins cover and story illustrations have appeared in national magazines such as *Crowell-Collier, Fawcett, Curtis, McFadden, Time-Life* and *Holland's Magazine of the South.*

His serious art studies began when he attended the National Academy of Design in New York. He also studied art anatomy under George Bridgeman, painting and portraiture under Ivan Olinsky at the Art Students' League, and illustration with Harvey Dunn and Dean Cornwell.

Cardwell Higgins served 2½ years in the Corps of Engineers, attached to the Air Force, as an instructor in aviation camouflage during World War II. While in the service, he painted two 60' x 30' murals depicting an aerial battle for the Officers' Service Club at Richmond Air Base, Richmond, Virginia. He also taught art anatomy and figure painting at the Newark School of Fine and Industrial Art.

His portrait commissions included such celebrities as Captain Eddie Rickenbacker, Charles Lindberg, Winston Churchill, Wendell Wilkie, Rudolf Friml (noted composer), Judge Nicholas Castellano, and others.

He is well known for his painting of the famous World War II U.S.O. poster, showing a soldier, a U.S.O. lady, and a sailor marching arm-in-arm.

**THE CIRCLE OF LIFE** *by Cardwell S. Higgins*

| CARDWELL S. HIGGINS | ISSUE PRICE | CURRENT PRICE |
|---|---|---|
| ☐ **SIAMESE DANCERS,** rel. 1980. ed. 500, s/n, 19½″ x 14¼″, pub CSH . . . . . . | 50.00 | — |
| ☐ **DRAGON LADY,** rel. 1980. ed. 500, s/n, 19½″ x 14¼″, pub CSH . . . . . . . . . . | 50.00 | — |
| ☐ **THE CIRCLE OF LIFE,** rel. 1980. ed. 500, s/n, 19½″ x 16½″, pub CSH . . . . . . | 50.00 | *200.00 |
| ☐ **SLAVES OF DESIRE,** rel. 1980. ed. 500, s/n, 19½″ x 16″, pub CSH . . . . . . . . | 50.00 | — |
| ☐ **A DELIGHTFUL PAGE IN THE RECORD OF MY EXISTENCE,** rel. 1980. ed. 500, s/n, 19½″ x 13″, pub CSH . . . . . . . . . . . . . . . . . . . . . . . . . . . . . . . . . . . | 50.00 | — |
| ☐ **THE ELEMENTS INVOLVED,** rel. 1980. ed. 500, s/n, 19½″ x 13″, pub CSH . . . | 50.00 | — |

| | ISSUE PRICE | CURRENT PRICE |
|---|---|---|

☐ **COLLECTORS PORTFOLIO**, containing six prints, one of each design, s/n, all
   prints numbered the same . . . . . . . . . . . . . . . . . . . . . . . . . . . . . . . . . . . . . . . . **300.00**    —
*Bid and sold price for The Circle of Life print at public television Channel 2 art auction, April 12, 1980.

# JACK HINES

Early in life Jack Hines committed himself to an artistic focus on Frontiersmen, Plains Indians and fur traders.

Hines says, "The lives and times of the first Americans, the Indians, are the most fascinating subjects of all the West; their social structure is highly developed. Religion, warfare, crafts, hunting, courtship, family life: all are intriguing and challenging subject matter."

Art training led him through the Los Angeles Center School and the Choinard Art Institute. New York commercial art with its fast-paced rigors of competition developed his discipline and technique.

Moving to Big Timber, Montana, Hines became renowned for depicting mountain men and Indians, sometimes interwoven with words and poetry. An excellent draftsman with a flawless technique, Hines fits media to the subject.

The artist travels and paints in Europe finding many similarities between the Italian and Montana peoples: a devotion to history and art, an agricultural life style and an active interest in art.

**SOFTLY IN THE EAR OF THE WARRIOR** *by Jack Hines*

Involved in the contemporary "Buckskinning" movement of America (dedicated to preserving and recruiting the mountain man tradition), Hines is an avid outdoorsman and frequently packs into the mountain ranges.

### JACK HINES

| | ISSUE PRICE | CURRENT PRICE |
|---|---|---|
| ☐ **MEMORIES OF A MAN,** rel. 1979. ed. 950, s/n, 24½" x 20", pub MPPI . . . . . . | 65.00 | — |
| ☐ **THE FALLEN SHIELD,** rel. 1979. ed. 950, s/n, 29½" x 19", pub MPPI . . . . . . . | 95.00 | — |
| ☐ **THE TASTE OF THE WARRIOR SPIRIT,** rel. 1979. ed. 950, s/n, 20½" x 27½", pub MPPI . . . . . . . . . . . . . . . . . . . . . . . . . . . . . . . . . . . | 75.00 | — |
| ☐ **WHEN THE EAGLE SPOKE,** rel. 1979. ed. 950, s/n, 24½" x 20", pub MPPI . . . | 65.00 | 95.00 |
| ☐ **ETERNITY IS IN THE MOUNTAINS,** rel. 1980. ed. 950, s/n, 20½" x 27½", pub MPPI . . . . . . . . . . . . . . . . . . . . . . . . . . . . . . . . . . . . . | 75.00 | — |
| ☐ **SOFTLY IN THE EAR OF THE WARRIOR,** rel. 1980. ed. 950, s/n, 25½" x 20", pub MPPI . . . . . . . . . . . . . . . . . . . . . . . . . . . . . . . . . . | 70.00 | — |
| ☐ **THE ECHOES SOUND SOFTLY,** rel. 1980. ed. 950, s/n, 25½" x 20", pub MPPI | 70.00 | — |
| ☐ **WHILE YOUNG HANDS LEARN,** rel. 1980. ed. 950, s/n, 25½" x 19¾", pub MPPI . . . . . . . . . . . . . . . . . . . . . . . . . . . . . . . . . . . . . . | 75.00 | — |
| ☐ **EVENING ENCOUNTER AT INDEPENDENCE ROCK,** rel. 1981. ed. 950, s/n, 20" x 30", pub SCG . . . . . . . . . . . . . . . . . . . . . . . . . . . . | 80.00 | — |
| ☐ **FORT LARAMIE . . . GATHERING OF THE TRIBES . . . 1851,** rel. 1981. ed. 950, s/n, 20" x 30", pub SCG . . . . . . . . . . . . . . . . . . . . . | 80.00 | — |
| ☐ **THE PERILS OF JEDIDIAH SMITH,** rel. 1981. ed. 1,350, s/n, 20" x 30", pub SCG . . . . . . . . . . . . . . . . . . . . . . . . . . . . . . . . . . . . . . | 50.00 | Sold Out |
| ☐ **FIRST DAY IN CAMP,** rel. 1982. ed. 1,000, s/o, 13" x 26⅝", pub SCG . . . . . . | 45.00 | — |
| ☐ **PORTUGEE PHILLIP'S RIDE . . . 1866,** rel. 1982. ed. 500, s/n, 20" x 30", pub SCG . . . . . . . . . . . . . . . . . . . . . . . . . . . . . . . . . . . . . . | 85.00 | — |
| ☐ **RIDIN' TO GREENUP,** rel. 1982. ed. 950, s/n, 17⅛" x 22⅞", pub MPPI . . . . . . | 85.00 | — |

# WILLIAM HOLLYWOOD

William Hollywood was born in Lancashire, England in 1923. He graduated from Belfast College of Art.

**WINTERTIME – PHEASANTS** *by William Hollywood*

He joined a commercial design studio, eventually forming his own business which he ran successfully for many years. In 1968, he left the commercial field and concentrated on painting wildfowl and game birds in their natural habitat. He paints wildlife subjects in oils with great feeling and knowledge. He is one of the few overseas members of the Society of Animal Artists. He has exhibited at the Moorland Gallery and Ackerman Gallery on Bond Street, at the Sir Peter Scott annual exhibition in Slimbridge, and practically every important wildlife gallery in the British Isles. His work has also been exhibited at the Country Landowners Association Game Fair in Great Britain over many years.

His paintings are in private collections in Ireland, the United States and Great Britain.

| WILLIAM HOLLYWOOD | ISSUE PRICE | CURRENT PRICE |
|---|---|---|
| ☐ OCTOBER SHOW-WOODCOCK, rel. 1979. ed. 500, s/n, 19½″ x 27½″, pub SEL | 125.00 | — |
| ☐ PINTAILS ON A QUIET INLET, rel. 1976. ed. 510, s/n, 16″ x 24″, pub SEL | 95.00 | — |
| ☐ PHEASANT, rel. 1979. ed. 500, s/n, 19¼″ x 15¼″, pub SEL | 95.00 | — |
| ☐ RISING MALLARDS, rel. 1979. ed. 500, s/n, 18½″ x 27¼″, pub SEL | 125.00 | — |
| ☐ GREENWING TEAL, rel 1980. ed. 750, s/n, 18⅛″ x 27¼″, pub SEL | 150.00 | — |
| ☐ WINTERTIME — PHEASANTS, rel. 1980. ed. 750, s/n, 18⅛″ x 27¼″, pub SEL | 150.00 | — |

# RANCE HOOD

Rance Hood is a self taught artist who has exhibited in group shows and one-man exhibitions in Oklahoma and throughout the United States. He has been awarded many prizes, including three Grand Awards at the Indian Art Exhibit at the American Indian Exposition, and a First Award at the American Indian Artists Exhibition at the Philbrook Art Center.

Hood is also a member of the board of directors of the Oklahoma Indian Arts and Crafts Cooperative.

## RANCE HOOD

| | | |
|---|---|---|
| ☐ WAR CHIEF, ed. 1,500, s/n, 18½″ x 17″, pub NWDHG | 20.00 | 250.00 |
| ☐ WAR ON THE PLAIN, ed. 1,500, s/n, 28″ x 23½″, pub NWDHG | 40.00 | 500.00 |
| remarqued | 100.00 | 600.00 |
| ☐ SIOUX RAINMAKERS, ed. 1,500, s/n, pub NWHG | 100.00 | 450.00 |

# CLAUDE HOWELL

Claude Howell is a mature artist working in his prime. His list of professional and academic honors is endless. He is chairman of the Art Department of the University of North Carolina at Wilmington, a department he established for the old Wilmington College in 1953 and has guided ever since.

"Mending Nets" are a series of four silkscreen prints, the only limited editions the artist has offered for retail sale in his art career. They represent the culmination of years of exploratory efforts and his attempt to closely follow the style of the masters he admired as a student.

## CLAUDE HOWELL

| | | |
|---|---|---|
| ☐ SUNNY DAY, rel. 1976. ed. 300, s/n, 22″ x 27″, pub FFFAI | 100.00 | 375.00 |
| ☐ LATE AFTERNOON, rel. 1977. ed. 300, s/n, 22″ x 27″, pub FFFAI | 100.00 | 375.00 |
| ☐ NOONDAY GLARE, rel. 1978. ed. 300, s/n, 21″ x 28″, pub FFFAI | 100.00 | 300.00 |
| ☐ NORTHEASTER, rel. 1979. ed. 300, s/n, 21″ x 28″, pub FFFAI | 100.00 | 300.00 |
| matched set of above four | 400.00 | 1,500.00 |
| ☐ BALKAN SKETCHBOOK, ed. 500, s/n, 6″ x 9″, 120 page hardcover book of sketches by the artist, pub FFFAI | 25.00 | — |

**NORTHEASTER** *by Claude Howell*

## ALLEN HUGHES, M.D.

Dr. Allen Hughes' art has gained national prominence in a very short period of time. His watercolor style is unique in portraying sporting art.

His paintings have been chosen to appear on more than thirty national and regional publications.

His work has received numerous awards. In 1977, his entry was chosen as the design for Mississippi's waterfowl stamp. He has won ten "Best of Show" ribbons at the Midwest Wildlife Art Show in Kansas City. In addition to being the featured artist in 1972, he became the first person to win top category honors in both painting and woodcarving.

At the 1979 National Wildlife Art Show, Hughes received a plaque naming him the "Most Outstanding Wildlife Artist". This is the largest juried wildlife art show in the country.

At the 1978 Ducks Unlimited National Convention in Winnipeg, Canada, it was reported his prints of "Cypress Swamp Woodies" had raised more than $240,000 for the organization. Others are donated yearly.

Hughes is a self-taught artist who has always loved the outdoors. While still a student at Southwestern College in Memphis, he began practicing taxidermy.

Through his taxidermy efforts, he gained a better knowledge of the anatomy and detail of his subjects which are portrayed in his paintings and woodcarvings.

**GOING FOR COVER** *by Allen Hughes*

## ALLEN HUGHES

| | ISSUE PRICE | CURRENT PRICE |
|---|---|---|
| ☐ **RETURNING WOODIES,** rel. 1975. ed. 750, s/n, 18½" x 23½", pub SGL | 65.00 | 100.00 |
| s/n, remarqued | 100.00 | 150.00 |
| ☐ **FLOODED TIMBER MALLARDS,** rel. 1976. ed. 500, s/n, 16" x 20", pub SGL | 50.00 | 375.00 |
| s/n, remarqued | 75.00 | 425.00 |
| ☐ **CYPRESS SWAMP WOODIES,** rel. 1976. ed. 1,250, s/n, 16" x 20", pub SGL | * | |
| *Were donated to Ducks Unlimited, ed. 100 artists proofs | 75.00 | 300.00 |
| Artist proof remarqued | 100.00 | 375.00 |
| ☐ **MISSISSIPPI WATERFOWL STAMP,** rel. 1977. ed. 500, s/n, 6½" x 9", pub SGL | 65.00 | 500.00 |
| ed. 100 artist proofs remarqued | 100.00 | 550.00 |
| ☐ **DRIFTING IN,** rel. 1977. ed. 750, s/n, 23¾" x 18¾", pub SGL | 65.00 | 150.00 |
| artist proof remarqued | 100.00 | 175.00 |
| ☐ **STARTLED,** rel. 1978. ed. 750, s/n, 23" x 17½", pub SGL | 65.00 | 250.00 |
| ed. 5 artist proofs | 100.00 | 275.00 |
| A portion of the edition s/n remarqued | 125.00 | 200.00 |
| ☐ **RESTING PLACE,** rel. 1978. ed. 950, s/n, 22½" x 17", pub SGL | 65.00 | — |
| s/n remarqued | 100.00 | — |
| ed. 50 artist proofs | 100.00 | — |
| artist proofs remarqued | 125.00 | — |
| ☐ **THE HUSTLERS,** rel. 1979. ed. 750, s/n, 22" x 18¾", pub SGL | 65.00 | 150.00 |
| s/n remarqued | 100.00 | 200.00 |
| ed. 50 artist proofs | 100.00 | 250.00 |
| artist proof remarqued | 125.00 | 275.00 |
| ☐ **THE CHALLENGE,** rel. 1978. ed. 500, s/n, 23" x 18½", pub SGL | 65.00 | 250.00 |
| 50 artist proofs | 100.00 | 300.00 |
| artist proof remarqued | 125.00 | 350.00 |
| ☐ **EARLY ARRIVALS,** rel. 1979. ed. 1,650, s/n, 16" x 20", pub SGL | — | — |
| *Were donated to Ducks Unlimited, ed. 100 artist proofs | 100.00 | 200.00 |
| artist proof remarqued | 150.00 | 275.00 |

|  | ISSUE PRICE | CURRENT PRICE |
|---|---|---|
| ☐ **SPRING FEVER,** rel. 1979. ed. 500, s/n, 16″ x 20″, pub SGL | 65.00 | 200.00 |
| s/n remarqued | 100.00 | 275.00 |
| ed. 50 artist proofs | 100.00 | 275.00 |
| artist proof remarqued | 150.00 | 300.00 |
| ☐ **HEADING SOUTH,** rel. 1979. ed. 750, s/n, 23″ x 18″, pub SGL | 65.00 | — |
| s/n remarqued | 100.00 | — |
| ed. 50 artist proofs | 100.00 | — |
| artist proof remarqued | 150.00 | — |
| ☐ **THE OLD HOMEPLACE,** rel. 1980. ed. 750, s/n, 23½″ x 18½″, pub SGL | 65.00 | — |
| s/n remarqued | 100.00 | — |
| ed. 50 artist proofs | 100.00 | — |
| artist proof remarqued | 150.00 | — |
| ☐ **WINTERS CALLING,** rel. 1980. ed. 500, s/n, 23″ x 17¼″, pub SGL | 75.00 | — |
| s/n remarqued | 125.00 | — |
| ☐ **ATLANTIC FLYWAY,** rel. 1981. ed. 500, s/n, 23″ x 17″, pub SGL | 75.00 | — |
| s/n remarqued | 125.00 | — |
| ☐ **THROUGH THE TIMBER,** rel. 1981. ed. 750, s/n, 23″ x 18″, pub SGL | 75.00 | — |
| s/n remarqued | 150.00 | — |
| ☐ **GOING FOR COVER,** rel. 1981. ed. 750, s/n, 23″ x 15½″, pub SGL | 75.00 | — |
| s/n remarqued | 150.00 | — |
| ☐ **SETTLING IN,** rel. 1980. ed. 2,250, s/n, 16″ x 20″, pub SGL | 100.00 | — |
| ☐ Donated to Ducks Unlimited. | | |
| ☐ **QUAIL CONSERVATION STAMP PRINT,** rel. 1982. ed. 1,500, s/n, 6½″ x 9″, pub SGL | 130.00 | — |
| ☐ **OFF THE ROOST,** rel. 1983. ed. 750, s/n, 19″ x 16″, pub SGL | 75.00 | — |
| ☐ **MORNING FLIGHT,** rel. 1983. ed. 450, s/n, 20″ x 15″, pub SGL | 75.00 | — |
| ☐ **1984-85 TENNESSEE WATERFOWL STAMP PRINT,** rel. 1984. ed. 1,250, s/n, pub SGL | 131.50 | — |

# MEL HUNTER

Mel Hunter's style is realism. His greatest love has been the demanding discipline of drawing. The image is always plainly visible in each subject, no matter how complex the composition, or how delicate the tone.

He is one of a few artists able to sustain a full-time effort in the creation of original graphic prints, and has mastered the difficult techniques of multi-color hand-drawn lithographic printing. Instead of a stone or plate, Hunter uses the Mylar hand-drawn process which he helped to perfect. There is no screen-dot structure since they are not photographed.

Famous for his original lithographs for Circle Galleries, Book of the Month Club, and other organizations, Hunter's works are in public, private and corporate collections all over the worldwide.

## MEL HUNTER

| | | |
|---|---|---|
| ☐ **JANUARY NIGHT,** rel. 1979. ed. 290, s/n, 17½″ x 23″, Mylar Lithograph, pub MPPI | 125.00 | — |
| ☐ **UP AT THE JASPER PLACE,** rel. 1979. ed. 290, s/n, 17½″ x 23″, Mylar lithograph, pub MPPI | 125.00 | — |
| ☐ **HORSE FOLIO,** 10 Pieces, ed. 500, s/n, litho, 30″ x 22″ or 23″ or 24″, pub CFA | — | 1,000.00* |
| The folio contains lithos of Appaloosa, Standard Bred Arabian, Hunter-Jumper, Thoroughbred, Pinto, Tennessee Walker, Morgan, Saddlebred, and Quarter Horse. | | |
| *Each print may be purchased individually, between $125.00 and $150.00. | | |
| ☐ **ALONE TOGETHER,** ed. 200, s/n, litho, 22″ x 19″, pub CFA | — | 175.00 |
| ed. 35, s/n, litho, Rives BFK | — | 225.00 |
| ☐ **U. S. OPEN GOLF/OF ASC-1977,** ed. 600, s/n, litho, 22″ x 28″, pub CFK | — | 200.00 |
| ☐ **STAG HOUND IN FULL GALE** ed. 300, s/n, litho, 22″ x 25″, pub CFA | — | 175.00 |
| ☐ **THE RAVEN AHEAD OFF TIMOR,** ed. 300, s/n, litho, 22″ x 25″, pub CFA | — | 175.00 |
| ☐ **CHALLENGE OFF CHILE,** ed. 300, s/n, litho, 26″ x 19″, pub CFA | — | 250.00 |

| | ISSUE PRICE | CURRENT PRICE |
|---|---|---|
| ☐ DREADNAUGHT, ed. 300, s/n, litho, 24″ x 31″, pub CFA | — | 225.00 |
| ☐ SNOW GEESE OVER CANADIAN ROCKIES, ed. 300, s/n, litho, 20″ x 30″, pub CFA | — | 350.00 |
| ☐ NIGHT WINDS, ed. 300, s/n, litho, 19″ x 29″, pub CFA | — | 350.00 |
| ☐ SNOWIES NESTING, ed. 300, s/n, litho, 22″ x 32″, pub CFA | — | 225.00 |
| ☐ LIGHT AT EMERALD POINT, ed. 300, s/n, litho, 22″ x 36″, pub CFA | — | 300.00 |
| ☐ DAWN MEADOW, ed. 300, s/n, litho, 22″ x 30″, pub CFA | — | 175.00 |
| ☐ DOLL HOUSE, ed. 300, s/n, litho, 22″ x 30″, pub CFA | — | 175.00 |
| ☐ PATRIARCH, ed. 300, s/n, litho, 23″ x 30″, pub CFA | — | 175.00 |
| ☐ PAINTED LADY, ed. 300, s/n, litho, 28″ x 19″, pub CFA | — | 175.00 |

## PETER HURD

| | ISSUE PRICE | CURRENT PRICE |
|---|---|---|
| ☐ APACHE PLUME, ed. 250, s/n, 15″ x 19″, serigraph, pub CFAC | — | 275.00 |
| ☐ A WATERING AT SUNDOWN, ed. 250, s/n, 26″ x 30″, serigraph, pub CFAC | — | 1,000.00 |
| ☐ A PRACTICE GAME, ed. 250, s/n, 32″ x 43″, serigraph, pub CFAC | — | 450.00 |
| ☐ A RACE WITH RAIN, ed. 250, s/n, 32″ x 45″, serigraph, pub CFAC | — | 450.00 |
| ☐ SUNSET THROUGH DUST, ed. 250, s/n, 24″ x 36″, serigraph, pub CFAC | — | 450.00 |
| ☐ DUSTY SUN, ed. 250, s/n, 16″ x 20″ | — | 325.00 |
| ed. 25 on Japon, lithograph, pub CFAC | — | 350.00 |
| ☐ FENCE RIDER, ed. 250, s/n, 11″ x 12″ | — | 275.00 |
| ed. 25 on Japon, lithograph, pub CFAC | — | 325.00 |
| ☐ A FAR AWAY PLACE, ed. 260, s/n, 23″ x 33″, lithograph, pub CFAC | — | 450.00 |
| ☐ NIGHT VISITOR, ed. 260, s/n, 24″ x 20″ | — | 550.00 |
| ed. 25 on Japon, lithograph, pub CFAC | — | 600.00 |
| ☐ A RANCH AT DAWN, ed. 250, s/n, 15″ x 15″ | — | 275.00 |
| ed. 25 on Japon, lithograph, pub CFAC | — | 325.00 |
| ☐ DAY'S END, ed. 260, s/n, 26″ x 26″, serigraph, pub CFAC | — | 550.00 |
| ☐ WINDMILL TROUBLE, ed. 260, s/n, 19″ x 25″ | — | 300.00 |
| ed. 25 on Japon, lithograph, pub CFAC | — | 325.00 |
| ☐ A SURGING CUMULUS, ed. 260, s/n, 25″ x 19″ | — | 300.00 |
| ed. 25 on Japon, lithograph, pub CFAC | — | 375.00 |
| ☐ DOMINIQUEZ WELL, ed. 260, s/n, 14″ x 16″ | — | 300.00 |
| ed. 25 on Japon, lithograph, pub CFAC | — | 350.00 |
| ☐ SHOWER ON THE PRAIRIE, ed. 260, s/n, 20″ x 29″ | — | 350.00 |
| ed. 25 on Japon, lithograph, pub CFAC | — | 400.00 |
| ☐ THE DAY IT RAINED, ed. 260, s/n, 22″ x 29″ | — | 350.00 |
| ed. 35 on Japon, lithograph, pub CFAC | — | 375.00 |
| ☐ WESTWARD INTO NIGHT, ed. 275, s/n, litho, 22″ x 34″, pub CFA | — | 300.00 |

## WILSON HURLEY

Wilson Hurley has been many things in his life . . . student, lawyer and banker. But it is in the role of artist that he will be remembered, and it is in the company of such names as Cole, Catlin, Moran, and Bierstadt that he will be recalled. For like these artists of the past, Hurley paints landscapes with majesty and drama. Indeed, he is called the "Landscapist of Grandeur."

Hurley was born in Tulsa, the son of a lawyer who later became Hoover's secretary of war. The elder Hurley wanted his son to pursue a military career, and sent Wilson to West Point. Even before he graduated, he earned his wings. When he was assigned to duty it was an Army aviator in the South pacific. However, it was 1945 and the war had just ended. Hurley thus flew rescue missions. With him were art supplies that he used to paint the broad panoramas he saw.

After the war he received a law degree from George Washington University, and for the next 13 years he practiced law in Albuquerque. He was unfulfilled by the law, however, and continued to paint. He was drafting a will for a terminally ill young doctor in 1964, and asked himself what he would do if he had 18 months to live. "Paint one really good painting," was the answer he gave himself.

**COLUMBIA AT 30 SECONDS** *by Wilson Hurley*

He closed his practice and became a full-time artist. In the years that have ensued, Hurley has become one of the leading landscapists of our time. His work is disciplined: he has made a virtual science of perspective. But, at the same time, his pictures are filled with emotion born of light and sky. Finally, there is perspective; his years as an aviator gave it to him, along with a comprehension of the land that few painter ever achieve.

**WILSON HURLEY**

| | ISSUE PRICE | CURRENT PRICE |
|---|---|---|
| ☐ **EDGE OF WINTER GRAND CANYON**, ed. 475, s/n, 35¼" x 23⅜", pub GW . . . . | 245.00 | — |
| ☐ **COLUMBIA AT 30 SECONDS**, rel. 1982. ed. 850, s/n, 23¼" x 26", pub GW . . | 150.00 | — |

# JERRY INGRAM

Seldom does one find an artist who blends such a stunning sense of design with such a rich awareness of his cultural heritage. Ingram's work is precise and detailed, yet fluid and free. The natural balance and composition of his work reflect a special sensitivity that reveals a new dimension to even familiar subjects. His work is an outstanding blend of traditional values and contemporary technique.

Ingram was raised on a farm in southeast Oklahoma by his Choctaw mother and his Cherokee father. His great-grandparents had walked to the Indian Territory from North Carolina on the infamous Trail of Tears. Although Ingram's early ambition was to be a lumberjack like his father, his preoccupation with painting and drawing won out and he attended the Institute of American Indian Arts and

**WAR HONORS** *by Jerry Ingram*

Oklahoma State Tech. He had his first one-man show in the council house of the Creek Indian Nation.

The high standards he has set for his work have brought him wide-spread recognition including top awards at the Heard Museum in Phoenix, the Gallup Inter-tribal Ceremonial, the Philbrook Art Center in Tulsa, The Scottsdale National Competition and the Five Tribes Museum.

| JERRY INGRAM | ISSUE PRICE | CURRENT PRICE |
|---|---|---|
| ☐ **PROUD WARRIOR,** edition and size not available, pub NWDHG | 300.00 | 900.00 |
| ☐ **BLACKFOOT MEDICINE,** edition and size not available, pub NWDHG | 300.00 | 600.00 |
| ☐ **BLACKFOOT CHIEFS,** ed. 950, s/n, 14" x 19", pub NWDHG | 60.00 | — |
| ☐ **OUR BATTLES ARE MANY,** ed. 650, s/n, 14" x 18", pub NWDHG | 50.00 | 75.00 |
| ☐ **ELK WOMAN,** ed. 100, s/n, 22" x 30", stone lithograph, pub NWDHG | 300.00 | — |
| ☐ **WAR HONORS,** ed. 90, s/n, 20" x 30", stone lithograph, pub NWDHG | 400.00 | — |

# PHILIP JAMISON

Philip Jamison resides and paints in West Chester, Pennsylvania, and at his summer home on the Isle of Vinalhaven, Maine. He graduated from, and later taught at the Philadelphia College of Art. Among the Museums in which he has exhibited are the Metropolitan Museum of Art in New York City, the Philadelphia Art Museum, the Boston Museum of Art, the Cleveland Institute of Art and the National Academy of Design.

**SUMMER BOUQUET** *by Philip Jamison*

He has won the Dana & Dawson Medals at the Pennsylvania Academy of The Fine Arts; the Gold Medal of Honor, Allied Arts of America; the National Academy of Design Prize, National Academy of Design; as well as numerous awards at the American Watercolor Society, where he is a member. In 1970, Jamison was Academician, National Academy of Design.

Jamison was exhibited in the show "Two Hundred Years of Watercolor Painting in America", held at the Metropolitan Museum of Art in New York. In 1975, he was invited as guest artist by NASA to witness the Apollo-Soyuz space launch. His original paintings of this launch were first exhibited at the West Chester office of the Chester County Federal Savings and Loan, and now hang in the National Air and Space Museum in Washington, D.C.

To his credit are many one-man exhibitions in notable American galleries including his two current dealers—Hirschl and Adler Galleries in New York and the Janet Fleisher Gallery in Philadelphia. Jamison's biography is listed in *Who's Who in America, Who's Who in the East* and *Who's Who in American Art.*

| PHILIP JAMISON | ISSUE PRICE | CURRENT PRICE |
|---|---|---|
| ☐ **RAILROAD CROSSING**, rel. 1980. ed. 950, s/n, 20″ x 32½″, pub MPPI | 75.00 | — |
| ☐ **SUMMER BOUQUET**, rel. 1980. ed. 950, s/n, 22″ x 25½″, pub MPPI | 65.00 | — |

# JEAN JANSEM

| | | |
|---|---|---|
| ☐ **ARLEQUIN AU FOND ROUGE**, ed. 120, s/n, 29½″ x 21″, original color lithograph, pub Fl | 260.00 | — |
| ☐ **ARLEQUIN AU FOND GRIS**, ed. 20, a/p, 29½″ x 21″, Japon, original color lithograph, pub Fl | 300.00 | — |
| ☐ **GRAND ECART A LA TUNIQUE**, ed. 120, s/n, 22″ x 30″, original color lithograph, pub Fl | 260.00 | — |

| | ISSUE PRICE | CURRENT PRICE |
|---|---|---|
| ☐ **DANSEUSE SE CHAUSSANT,** ed. 120, s/n, 25½" x 19¾", original color lithograph, pub Fl | 200.00 | — |
| ☐ **CLOWN,** ed. 120, s/n, 30" x 20", original color lithograph, pub Fl | 260.00 | 280.00 |
| ☐ **MOTHER AND CHILD,** ed. 120, s/n, 30" x 20", original color lithograph, pub Fl | 300.00 | — |

# CHARLEN JEFFERY

For Charlen Jeffery, a resident of Anchorage, Alaska, a paintbrush and pencil have always been a part of her life since her childhood in Corvallis, Oregon. Jeffery obtained a Fine Arts degree from Seattle Pacific University.

Jeffery enjoys painting children and people; however, she is not limited to these subjects alone. Landscapes, seascapes, animals, and still lifes are all portrayed by her.

Her approach to art with different media and subjects, which range from realistic to impressionistic, attest to her versatility and account for her success.

## CHARLEN JEFFERY

| | | |
|---|---|---|
| ☐ **LORD OF THE TUNDRA,** rel. 1980. ed. 750, s/n, 23" x 17", pub SGL | 65.00 | 175.00 |
| s/n remarqued | 175.00 | 250.00 |
| ☐ **EVENING WATCH,** rel. 1980. ed. 750, s/n, 22" x 17", pub SGL | 65.00 | 150.00 |
| s/n remarqued | 125.00 | — |
| ☐ **IN TRAINING,** rel. 1980. ed. 750, s/n, 23" x 16½", pub SGL | 65.00 | — |
| s/n remarqued | 125.00 | — |
| ☐ **WAIT FOR ME MOM,** rel. 1981. ed. 750, s/n, 23" x 19", pub SGL | 75.00 | 250.00 |
| s/n remarqued | 125.00 | 325.00 |
| ☐ **CHECKING THE LINE,** rel. 1981. ed. 750, s/n, 23" x 17", pub SGL | 75.00 | — |
| s/n remarqued | 125.00 | — |
| ☐ **SEPTEMBER IN ALASKA,** rel. 1981. ed. 750, s/n, 23" x 17", pub SGL | 75.00 | — |
| s/n remarqued | 125.00 | — |
| ☐ **JOHN OLIVER CABIN,** rel. 1982. ed. 1,000, s/n, 11" x 14", pub SGL | 25.00 | — |
| ☐ **CADES COVE,** rel. 1982. ed. 1,000, s/n, 11" x 14", pub SGL | 25.00 | — |
| ☐ **NEWFOUND GAP,** rel. 1982. ed. 1,000, s/n, 11" x 14", pub SGL | 25.00 | — |
| ☐ **SMOKY MOUNTAIN POSTER,** rel. 1982. ed. 750, s/o, 23" x 17", pub SGL | 20.00 | — |
| ☐ **LUNCH BREAK,** rel. 1982. ed. 750, s/n, 23" x 17", pub SGL | 75.00 | — |
| s/n remarqued | 125.00 | — |
| ☐ **EVENING CATCH,** rel. 1982. ed. 750, s/n, 11" x 15", pub SGL | 75.00 | — |
| s/n remarqued | 125.00 | — |
| ☐ **ON GUARD,** rel. 1983. ed. 750, s/n, 23" x 19" | 75.00 | — |
| s/n remarqued | 150.00 | — |
| ☐ **"FAMILY FEUD",** rel. 1983. ed. 750, s/n, 23½" x 14" | 75.00 | — |
| ☐ **1983 GAME CONSERVATION STAMP PRINT,** rel. 1983. ed. 950, s/n, 6½" x 9" | 130.00 | — |
| s/n remarqued | 255.00 | — |
| ☐ **PUFFIN,** rel. 1983. ed. 750, s/n, 11" x 13" | 35.00 | — |
| ☐ **SEAGULL,** rel. 1983. ed. 750, s/n, 11" x 13" | 35.00 | — |

# EDNA B. JOHNSON

Long a resident of Texas, Edna Johnson has established a fine clientele not only for her original paintings but also her beautiful plates on which she paints both scenes and portraits. It was only recently that she decided to enter the field of limited edition prints. The following listing represents her first two endeavors. The are printed on heavy rag art paper.

Johnson has taught oil painting twenty years including two at the North Texas College in Ft. Worth. She is a judge of the creative arts at the Dallas State Fair. She often gives painting demonstrations. She has many pieces of her artwork in several art galleries.

**ALTHEAS** *by Edna B. Johnson*

| EDNA B. JOHNSON | ISSUE PRICE | CURRENT PRICE |
|---|---|---|
| ☐ **THE QUAIL HUNT**, rel. 1982. ed. 1,000, s/n, 18″ x 24″, pub Wilson Engraving, distr. EJ . . . . . . . . . . . . . . . . . . . . . . . . . . . . . . . . . . . . . . . . . . . . . . . . . . . . . . . . | 30.00 | 35.00 |
| ☐ **ALTHEAS**, rel. 1982. ed. 1,000, s/n, 19½″ x 24″, pub Wilson Engraving, distr. EJ . . . . . . . . . . . . . . . . . . . . . . . . . . . . . . . . . . . . . . . . . . . . . . . . . . . . . . . . | 30.00 | 35.00 |

# RUSSELL JOHNSON

Russell Johnson's work is well known to serious collectors of original wildlife art. Collectors of fine art at the famed Easton, Maryland Waterfowl Festival and big game enthusiasts at Game Conservation International Art Show in San Antonio were among the first to begin buying Russell Johnson originals. The demand for his originals is so great that at the Sixth Game Coin Art Show all of his paintings were sold before the National Anthem was played at the show's official opening. The sophisticated art buyers instantly recognized Johnson's bold portrayals as statements of an artist of the first rank. His daring subtlety of color, his imaginative and evocative use of background landscapes are the sort of touches that are rarely even attempted by many artists and even few still manage their "rightness" as totally as Russell Johnson.

More so than in most other fields of creative work, wildlife painting instantly offers the viewer a feeling of the artist's ability — both technically and emotionally — to involve him, to enlarge his visions that parallel his own experience. A major painter, as Russell Johnson surely is, takes us from the particular, be it a black duck or an enraged elephant, and transcends that into an expression of universal importance. Mr. Johnson's paintings have that quality of visual growth; they are alive, and they will stay that way . . . gradually revealing more and more to the eye and the mind of the perceptive audience.

**EARLY ARRIVALS** *by Russell Johnson*

A world-wide traveller, Mr. Johnson resides in California working full time at his wildlife painting.

| RUSSELL JOHNSON | ISSUE PRICE | CURRENT PRICE |
|---|---|---|
| ☐ **EARLY ARRIVALS**, ed. 800, s/n, 18″ x 24″, litho, pub PP | 60.00 | 120.00 |
| ☐ **THE UPPER POND**, ed. 800, s/n, 16″ x 24″, litho, pub PP | 60.00 | — |
| ☐ **"UP TO MISCHIEF"**, ed. 800, s/n, 21½″ x 16″, pub PP | 75.00 | — |
| remarqued, signed and numbered | 165.00 | — |
| ☐ **"MORNING"**, ed. 800, s/n, 18″ x 24″, pub PP | 75.00 | — |
| remarqued, signed and numbered | 165.00 | — |
| ☐ **"LAST YEAR'S BLIND—THIS YEAR'S MALLARDS"**, ed. 800, s/n, 16″ x 24″, pub PP | 75.00 | — |
| remarqued, signed and numbered | 165.00 | — |
| ☐ **"OPEN WATER REFUGE"**, ed. 800, s/n, 16″ x 24″, pub PP | 75.00 | — |
| remarqued, signed and numbered | 165.00 | — |
| ☐ **"AMERICAN CLASSICS"**, ed. 800, s/n, 16″ x 24″, pub PP | 75.00 | — |
| remarqued, signed and numbered | 165.00 | — |
| ☐ **TEAL TIME**, ed. 800, s/n, 16″ x 24″, pub PP | 75.00 | — |
| remarqued, signed and numbered | 165.00 | — |

# MARSHALL WOODSIDE JOYCE

On the edge of the marshes of the Jones River in Kingston, Massachusetts, nestles the home and studio of the renowned marine painter, Marshall Woodside Joyce. Joyce, who has lived and worked there since 1947, paints every facet of the sea. His fascination with the sea comes naturally. His father was a sea captain and, as a boy, he sailed on his father's three-masted schooner out of the Mystic River shipyards.

Joyce's talent as an artist developed at an early age. As a young student, his school notebooks were filled with more drawings than notes. After he had completed his art training in a Boston school, he began his professional career as a

**THE SCULLER** *by Marshall Joyce*

free-lance artist in a studio overlooking the Boston Gardens. Even in the commercial world, his talent as a marine illustrator was quickly recognized. For years, he did a series of calendars based on the famous ships of Mystic, Connecticut, and on the whaling industry which was such an important part of seacoast history. He was also commissioned by the Plymouth Plantation to paint the official painting of Mayflower II.

Although Joyce enjoyed the challenge of the art world in Boston, he decided to devote himself marine painting.

Many students have benefited by Joyce's philosophy that knowledge should be shared. For ten years, he devoted two days a week to teaching art at the Butera School in Boston. Now that he has moved to his waterside studio, he conducts classes for adults and is in great demand for marine demonstrations. He has given workshops in New England, Key West, Florida, and at the Museum of Fine Arts of the South in Mobile, Alabama.

Joyce has received numerous awards and honors. His painting of his grandfather's ship, the *Sintram,* won a gold medal in the national competition for marine artists sponsored by the Franklin Mint. Another gold medal of honor was awarded by the Rockport Art Society. Recently, the *American Artist* magazine selected him as one of twenty contemporary American painters to be featured in an anthology, "Twenty Landscape Artist and How They Work."

## MARSHALL WOODSIDE JOYCE

| | ISSUE PRICE | CURRENT PRICE |
|---|---|---|
| ☐ **SEA GHOST**, rel. 1979. ed. 950, s/n, 20″ x 24″, pub MPPI . . . . . . . . . . . . . . . | 85.00 | 110.00 |
| ☐ **SEA MOSS GATHERER**, rel. 1978. ed. 950, s/n, 20″ x 28″, pub MPPI . . . . . . . | 95.00 | 100.00 |
| ☐ **RISING TIDE**, rel. 1980. ed. 950, s/n, 20″ x 25″, pub MPPI . . . . . . . . . . . . . | 65.00 | — |
| ☐ **THE SCULLER**, rel. 1980. ed. 950, s/n, 21″ x 29″, pub MPPI . . . . . . . . . . . . . | 85.00 | — |

# DIANA KAN

Diana Kan brings to her paintings a perfection of brushwork and an affinity for the poetry and tranquility of nature influenced by the teachings of her parents. Born in Hong Kong, she was a student-disciple of Chang Dai-chien. She had her first one-man show at the age of nine.

Kan studied at the Art Students League in New York and at the Beaux Arts and Grande Chaumiere schools in Paris. Her works have been featured world-wide in museums and galleries. She has received innumerable awards including eight from *The Pen and Brush,* four from the American Watercolor Society, and two from the Allied Artists of American.

The Metropolitan Museum of Art, The Philadelphia Museum of Art, Nelson Gallery-Atkins Museum, Kansas City, and the National Historical Museum of Taiwan are among the public institutions which have representative works in their permanent collections.

**SHANGRI-LA** *by Diana Kan*

| DIANA KAN | ISSUE PRICE | CURRENT PRICE |
|---|---|---|
| ☐ **FALLING WATERS,** rel. 1978. ed. 1,500, s/n, 40" x 22", pub FHG . . . . . . . . . | 50.00 | — |
| ☐ **RING AROUND THE ROSEY,** rel. 1978. ed. 750, s/n, 28" x 22", pub FHG . . . . . | 60.00 | — |
| ☐ **LOVE,** rel. 1979. ed. 5,000, s/o, 14" x 14", pub FHG . . . . . . . . . . . . . . . . . . . | 25.00 | — |
| ☐ **SHANGRI LA,** rel. 1983. ed. 475, signed, numbered and titled, 19⅛" x 25¾", pub GW . . . . . . . . . . . . . . . . . . . . . . . . . . . . . . . . . . . . . . . . . . . . . . . . . | 95.00 | — |

# GARY KAPP

|  | ISSUE PRICE | CURRENT PRICE |
|---|---|---|
| ☐ **HUNTING PARTY ON THE SAQUACHE**, rel. 1982. ed. N/A, s/n, 26″ x 15″, distr. SGL | 75.00 | — |

# BARBARA KEEL

Barbara Keel's love for animals shows in each of her works. She portrays this love with a softness, a delicate touch and a keen eye for detail. She has observed, sketched and touched when at all possible, all of her subjects. She knows most of them by name and refers to them in this manner.

Barbara has only been using pastels for a little over five years, having initially received them as a gift from her mother-in-law who said, "Do something with your time." What she has done is win first place in the 1977 Southeastern Wildlife Art Show, and numerous first place awards in shows across the country. She has had her work published in many magazines and has been commissioned by various Wildlife Departments and individuals.

She grew up in Opelika, Alabama and her love for animals began with a cat when she was three days old. She hasn't been without one since. Barbara has traveled to many of the zoos in the Southeast for studies and sketches. Her love for animals comes through in each of her pictures, and now her limited edition prints are being sought in galleries and shops across the country.

## BARBARA KEEL

| | | | |
|---|---|---|---|
| ☐ **ALABAMA DUCK STAMP PRINT**, ed. 1,750, s/n, size not available | | 105.00 | Sold Out |
| ☐ **AUBURN TIGER**, rel. 1982. ed. 500, s/n, 24″ x 20″, pub. SGL | | 225.00 | — |
| ☐ **BABY HARP SEAL**, ed. 1,000, s/n, size not available | | 50.00 | — |
| ☐ **BABY RACCOONS**, ed. 1,000, s/n, 20″ x 24″, distr. SGL | | 45.00 | — |
| ☐ **B J DID IT**, ed. 1,000, s/n, 22″ x 19″, pub. SGL | | 125.00 | — |
|    s/n, remarqued | | 125.00 | — |
| ☐ **B. J. GOOFS AGAIN**, ed. 1,000, s/n, size not available | | 50.00 | — |
| ☐ **BLUE**, ed. 1,000, s/n, 20″ x 18″, distr. SGL | | 45.00 | — |
| ☐ **BOBCAT**, ed. 1,000, s/n, 20″ x 24″, pub MMC | | 35.00 | Sold Out |
| ☐ **CHARLIE**, ed. unknown, s/only, size not available | | 25.00 | — |
| ☐ **CHEETAH**, ed. 1,000, s/n, 20″ x 24″, pub MMC | | 35.00 | Sold Out |
| ☐ **COUGAR**, ed. 900, s/n, 20″ x 24″, pub MMC | | 35.00 | Sold Out |
| ☐ **COUGAR ON A LIMB**, ed. 1,000, s/n, 21″ x 13¼″, distr. SGL | | 45.00 | — |
| ☐ **GIANT PANDAS**, ed. 1,000, s/n, size not available | | 55.00 | — |
| ☐ **GRAY FOXES**, ed. 1,000, s/n, 17½″ x 26½″, pub MMC | | 35.00 | Sold Out |
| ☐ **IT'S MINE**, rel. 1981. ed. 1,000, s/n, 22½″ x 14″, pub. SGL | | 50.00 | — |
|    s/n, remarqued | | 100.00 | — |
| ☐ **LEOPARD CUB**, ed. 1,000, s/n, 19″ x 22″, pub MMC | | 40.00 | — |
| ☐ **MAROBI & BIG MOMA**, ed. 1,000, s/n, 20″ x 24″, distr. SGL | | 45.00 | — |
| ☐ **MISCHIEF**, ed. unknown, s/only, size not available | | 25.00 | — |
| ☐ **SIBAY**, ed. 1,000, s/n, 12″ x 16″, distr. SGL | | 35.00 | — |
| ☐ **SIBERIAN TIGER**, ed. 1,000, s/n, 17″ x 22″, pub MMC | | 35.00 | Sold Out |
| ☐ **SNOW LEOPARDS**, ed. 1,000, s/n, size not available | | 50.00 | — |
| ☐ **THREE BENGAL CUBS**, ed. 900, s/n, 22″ x 28″, pub WAG | | 45.00 | — |
| ☐ **WAR EAGLE**, ed. 500, s/n, size not available | | 250.00 | — |
| ☐ **WHITE SIBERIAN TIGER CUB**, ed. 1,000, s/n, 20″ x 24″, pub MMC | | 40.00 | — |
| ☐ **WILD BOAR**, ed. 1,000, s/n, 20″ x 14″, pub MMC | | 40.00 | — |

# JOHN KELLY

John Kelly was born in Glasgow, Scotland and when he was ten years old, his father brought the family to Vancouver, Canada. It was a childhood in this seaport city that fostered a love for the sea that would evidence itself in his work.

Kelly's early schooling in Canada included extensive artistic training and considerable design experience. Later, he followed in his father's footsteps, putting in time as a merchant seaman, sailing to Alaskan ports on coastal freighters. Here he gained a first-hand knowledge of sea vessels which would become featured subjects in his paintings. Many of these works capture the distinctive mood and atmosphere of the northwest coast. While ashore, Kelly studied Canadian arttist Sidney Baron and Clark Stevenson and with their encouragement continued his education at the famed Art Center School in Los Angeles.

In the years since, Kelly has won numerous honors, taught and lectured widely and established himself as a highly successful artist with a growing, enthusiastic following. His list of collectors includes such prominent names as James Caan, Robert Goulet, Jonathan Winters, Rip Taylor, Don Rickles and Herb Alpert. He has works on permanent display in Malibu Courthouse (lithograph commemorating America's Bicentennial), San Francisco City Hall, and City Hall, Glasgow, Scotland. His "China Suite", inspired by an extensive tour of mainland China, has been widely acclaimed as the first such series done by a visiting American artist.

| JOHN KELLY | ISSUE PRICE | CURRENT PRICE |
|---|---|---|
| ☐ **TIVERTON**, rel. 1977. ed. 250, s/n, 26″ x 20″, litho, arches, pub EEl | 100.00 | 300.00 |
|     ed 25, japon | 120.00 | 350.00 |
| ☐ **VIEW OF THE THAMES**, rel. 1977. ed. 250, s/n, 26″ x 20″, litho, arches, pub EEl | 100.00 | 300.00 |
|     ed. 25, japon | 120.00 | 350.00 |

# MEL KESTER

Although Mel Kester has achieved a high level of success as a commercial designer and packaging executive, he did not start painting until 1969. Twenty months later, he hung forty paintings at the Charlotte public library and nearly all were sold before the show ended.

Since then, Kester has shown his work in fifty-seven exhibits including nineteen one-man shows in ten states from coast to coast. He has won many national and regional awards and his one-artist shows since 1973 have been sell-outs. In his first juried competition, his work was judged Best of Show and earned three of the top four awards. In 1973, in competition with over 1,100 entries from forty-seven states, Mel's painting won national recognition and was awarded Third Prize.

Kester's proficiency as an artist has been phenomenal. Since 1970, he has produced more than four hundred paintings, all of which have been eagerly purchased by art collectors and connoisseurs. One of these hangs in the presidential palace of Honduras. Another decorates an international banking office in Hong Kong. Others have been selected for inclusion in important private and corporate collections in the South as well as in New York, Houston and Los Angeles.

Kester's paintings find their popular appeal in the warmth of his colors, the meticulous detail and the haunting atmospheric perspective he achieves. He works in watercolor and tempera but seldom mixes opaque and transparent colors.

## MEL KESTER

| | | |
|---|---|---|
| ☐ **STABLE STILL LIFE**, ed. 583, s/n, 19″ x 16″, pub Omega Press | 35.00 | — |
| ☐ **RHODODENRON**, ed. 583, s/n, 20¾″ x 25″, pub Omega Press | 40.00 | — |
| ☐ **THE SADDLEMAKER**, ed. 583, s/n, 20⅜″ x 24¾″, pub Omega Press | 35.00 | — |
| ☐ **ROCKING CHAIR**, ed. 583, s/n, 21″ x 27¾″, pub Omega Press | 45.00 | 110.00 |
| ☐ **THE OLD PUSHCART**, rel. 1975. ed. 850, s/n, 19½″ x 15½″, pub AGI | 25.00 | — |
| ☐ **BARN BEE**, rel. 1975. ed. 850, s/n, 24¾″ x 21¾″, pub AGI | 35.00 | — |
| ☐ **OLD FRIENDS**, rel. 1977. ed. 750, s/n, 16″ x 20″, pub FFFAl | 35.00 | 85.00 |

**ROCKING CHAIR** *by Mel Kester*

| | ISSUE PRICE | CURRENT PRICE |
|---|---|---|
| ☐ **ROAD HOME,** rel. 1977. ed. 750, s/n, 20″ x 16″, pub FFFAI . . . . . . . . . . . . . | 35.00 | 75.00 |
| ☐ **SUZY-Q,** rel. 1977. ed. 750, s/n, 24″ x 20″, pub FFFAI . . . . . . . . . . . . . . . | 40.00 | — |
| ☐ **ANOTHER MORNING,** rel. 1977. ed. 750, s/n, 24″ x 20″, pub FFFAI . . . . . . . | 40.00 | — |
| ☐ **ROCK HOUSE,** rel. 1978. ed. 500, s/n, 26″ x 20″, pub FFFAI . . . . . . . . . . . . | 25.00 | — |
| ☐ **THE HAYLOFT,** rel. 1978. ed. 750, s/n, 26″ x 20″, pub FFFAI . . . . . . . . . . . | 40.00 | — |
| ☐ **THE HOUSE DOWN THE ROAD,** rel. 1978. ed. 750, s/n, 26″ x 20″, pub FFFAI . | 40.00 | — |
| ☐ **SUMMER PUMP,** rel. 1980. ed. 1,500, s/n, 26″ x 20″, pub FFFAI . . . . . . . . . . | 45.00 | — |
| ☐ **SUMMER HIDEAWAY & PEACEFUL VALLEY,** rel. 1981. ed. 1,500, s/n, 12″ x 15″, pub FFFAI . . . . . . . . . . . . . . . . . . . . . . . . . . . . . . . . . . . . . . . . . . . | 35.00 | — |

# JAMES H. KILLEN

Jim Killen strives to depict a time when people lived close to the land and its abundant wildlife. His distinctive watercolor paintings often show waterfowl and upland game birds set against rustic backdrops, places where millions of Americans have their roots.

Today Killen ranks among the country's foremost wildlife artists, his memorable watercolors earning acclaim wherever his work is exhibited. He recently earned the "President's Award" as the outstanding artist at the 1980 Ducks Unlimited

**STARTLED** by James Killen

National Wildlife Art Show in Kansas City, Missouri. This comes after winning many other honors and awards at previous Kansas City shows and at the Tulsa Wildlife Art Show. Killen has also exhibited at a number of shows across the country, such as the Easton Waterfowl Festival.

He is active in Ducks Unlimited, Rod and Gun, Sports Afield, National Wildlife, and Turkey Call.

## JAMES H. KILLEN

| | ISSUE PRICE | CURRENT PRICE |
|---|---|---|
| ☐ **QUIET WOODS (Wild Turkey)**, ed. 800, s/n, 16″ x 24″, litho, pub PP | 60.00 | — |
| ☐ **WILDERNESS RETREAT**, ed. 800, s/n, 16″ x 24″, litho, pub PP | 60.00 | Sold Out |
| ☐ **FEEDING TIME - MALLARDS**, ed. 800, s/n, 17″ x 23″, litho, pub PP | 60.00 | — |
| ☐ **PITCHING-IN (Canvasbacks)**, ed. 800, s/n, 18″ x 25″, litho, pub PP | — | — |
| ☐ **THE HOMESTEADERS**, ed. 800, s/n, 16″ x 24″, litho, pub PP | 60.00 | 120.00 |
| ☐ **A NOBLE PAIR**, ed. 800, s/n, 16″ x 24″, litho, pub PP | 60.00 | Sold Out |
| ☐ **STARTLED**, ed. 800, s/n, 16″ x 24″, pub PP | 75.00 | — |
| remarqued, signed and numbered | 165.00 | — |
| ☐ **RUFFLED GROUSE**, ed. 800, s/n, 16¼″ x 25″, pub PP | 75.00 | — |
| remarqued, signed and numbered | 165.00 | — |
| ☐ **MUSKRAT BAY**, ed. 800, s/n, 16″ x 24½″, pub PP | 75.00 | — |
| remarqued, signed and numbered | 165.00 | — |
| ☐ **EARLY SNOW (Canada Goose)**, ed. 800, s/n, 16″ x 24½″, pub PP | 60.00 | — |
| remarqued, signed and numbered | 150.00 | — |
| ☐ **AFTER THE SNOWFALL - MALLARDS**, rel. 1980. ed. 850, s/n, size not available, pub PP | 75.00 | — |
| ☐ **ON THE HIGH PLAINS**, rel. 1981. ed. 990, s/n, size not available, pub PP | 75.00 | — |
| ☐ **WINTER TRIO - WILD TURKEYS**, rel. 1981, ed. 800, s/n, size not available, pub PP | 75.00 | — |

# DONG KINGMAN

Dong Kingman is a Chinese-American artist born in Oakland, California, in 1911. He is a master of the watercolor medium, who paints with a great imagination, story-telling, and a good sense of humor.

Kingman studied art at the Fox and Morgan Studios in Oakland. After a few lessons, the instructor, Mr. Fox, found Kingman's oil paintings hopelessly inadequate, and told him that he would never make it as an artist. But his determination to become an artist overcame his disappointment. Discarding his oil paintings, he began to use watercolor from that time on.

When Kingman put on a one-man exhibition at the Art Center of San Francisco, the critics raved about his work. Kingman became an established artist.

In 1954, the U.S. State Department invited him to go on a cultural exchange program, and for the past 25 years, Kingman has been travelling with the Thurman Hewitt Painting Workshop in the U.S. and abroad.

He taught art at Columbia University and Hunter College. He was also guest lecturer in other universities, and one of the founders of the Famous Artist Schools in Westport, Connecticut.

His work is seen in many major publications, magazines, motion pictures, and television. Over fifty museums and organizations have his paintings in their permanent collections. His new book *Dong Kingman's Watercolors,* was published by Watson-Guptill, Inc.

**DRAGON DANCE** *by Dong Kingman*

| DONG KINGMAN | ISSUE PRICE | CURRENT PRICE |
|---|---|---|
| ☐ **DRAGON DANCE**, rel. 1983. ed. 375, signed, titled and numbered, 28⅜″ x 24″, hand-drawn lithograph, pub GW | 275.00 | — |

# DON KLOETZKE

Don Kloetzke is a prolific painter and an accomplished observer of his surroundings. His painting of Dall sheep earned for him the title "Best of Show" at the 1983 National Art Exhibition of Alaska Wildlife; and his work was featured at the Leigh Yawkey Woodson Bird Art Exhibition in Wausau, Wisconsin.

In 1982, Don was selected as Wisconsin Sportsman Magazine "Wildlife Artist of the Year", and he has demonstrated his versatility by consistently finishing near the top in stamp design competition.

Kloetzke sees wildlife art as a means of stimulating greater interest in preservation of natural resources. He attributes his regard for the natural world to what he describes as "the call of the wild". He says matter-of-factly, "Some people like to go golfing, I like to go to the marsh. When I'm outdoors, I feel more at ease. I feel like a whole human being."

Kloetzke is a veteran of almost twenty years in wildlife art. He is a firm believer in accuracy and realism in his oil paintings.

**SHADOW BOXING** by Don Kloetzke

**DON KLOETZKE**

| | ISSUE PRICE | CURRENT PRICE |
|---|---|---|
| ☐ **SHADOW BOXING,** rel. 1983. ed. 600, s/n, 24" x 20¼", pub NC . . . . . . . . . . . | 95.00 | — |
| ☐ **OUT FOXED,** rel. 1983. ed. 600, s/n, 25" x 18½", pub NC . . . . . . . . . . . . . . | 95.00 | — |

# TERRILL KNAACK

Growing up near the famous Horicon Marsh area was more than an inspiration to this young artist from Wisconsin. A graduate of the University of Wisconsin with a degree in art education, Terrill never seriously considered any vocation

**MORNING STILLNESS - Loon** *by Terrill Knaack*

other than that of a painter. "I felt I would never forgive myself," he said, "if I didn't at least try painting birds as a career."

A short period of free lance work doing scientific illustrations for ornithological journals and zoological publications preceded Terrill's decision to paint full time. Terrill paints in oil on canvas with a very realistic style of portraying birds in impressionistic landscapes. "One must study birds from the inside out in order to paint them well," says Terrell, a fine student of taxidermy as well.

Owen Gromme, dean of American wildlife artists, has been a great inspiration to this young artist as he has given freely his time and knowledge to foster Terrill's career. Said Mr. Gromme, *"Terrell is a very hard working young man with an intense determination to become the best at what he does."* Terrill Knaack has just begun as a wildlife artist.

| TERRILL KNAACK | ISSUE PRICE | CURRENT PRICE |
|---|---|---|
| ☐ **MORNING STILLNESS - LOON,** rel. 1977. ed. 600, s/n, 16½" x 25", pub WWI | 50.00 | 300.00 |
| ed. 50 remarque artist proof .................................... | 100.00 | 300.00 |
| ☐ **BLUE BIRD,** rel. 1978. ed. 850, s/n, 13⅜" x 10¾", pub WWI............. | 40.00 | 45.00 |
| ☐ **OCTOBER DAY - BOBWHITE,** rel. 1978. ed. 850, s/n, 16½" x 25", pub WWI .. | 60.00 | — |
| ed. 50 remarque artist proof .................................. | 130.00 | |
| ☐ **CEDAR WAXWINGS,** rel. 1979. ed. 850, s/n, 10¾" x 13⅜", pub WWI ....... | 40.00 | 45.00 |
| ☐ **LAKE COUNTRY - LOON,** rel. 1979. ed. 850, s/n, 25" x 16½", pub WWI ..... | 75.00 | 85.00 |
| ☐ **CARDINALS,** rel. 1980. ed. 850, s/n, size not available, pub WWI ......... | 45.00 | — |

## EVEL KNIEVEL

Evel Knievel is best known for his daredevil wanderings across the United States, thrilling thousands with his incredible stunts. His name is a household word, and whether the reaction is negative or positive, people have a certain respect for the man who continually defies the laws of man and nature. He is a true folk hero.

Since his early childhood there has been another side of Evel Knievel that is a paradox compared with his public persona. He has always been an artist, putting down his dreams, thoughts and experiences on the canvas. This deeply introspective side of a man who seems to live by his wits shows the double nature that exists in most of us. The affinity that people have for this courageous, impetuous man have caused his prints to have a tremendous impact on the fine arts market.

As early as the age of twelve, Knievel became fascinated by wildlife art. Brought up in rural country, he spent most of his young years hunting and fishing with his grandfather, Ignatius. Now, there is a common theme that runs through his work, and that is the glory of man and animal against the sometimes harsh and always majestic backdrop of nature. His portraits are composed to show not only the soul of the person or animal portrayed but also a broader concept seen in all who possess a proud, adventurous spirit. Perhaps, whether painting man, child or animal, Knievel show us all a little of the stuff of which he is composed — the unrelenting challenger, the will to get up time after time, the ability to face crippling defeat and finally emerge as the victor.

Besides his art and daredevilry, Evel Knievel has used his energy for political activism.

In 1961, he became infuriated and sincerely concerned with the needless slaughter of elk in Yellowstone National Park by government officials and park rangers.

Knievel was the spokesman for thousands of concerned sportsmen in Montana, Wyoming and Idaho concerning the impending extinction of the elk. Through protest activity, he created so much controversy that sportsmen's groups throughout the Pacific northwest financed his program and brought national attention to this worthwhile and vital cause. He hitchhiked to Washington, D.C. carrying with him a huge set of Royal Elk horns to be presented at the White House to the President of the United States, John F. Kennedy.

Through the efforts of the President and the Democratic Majority Leader, Senator Mike Mansfield, and with the assistance of Democratic Congressman from Montana, Arnold Olsen, Knievel delivered a petition of protest of slaughter concerning the elk to the Secretary of the Interior, Stewart Udall, requesting that the government trap and relocate the elk.

Through the efforts of Knievel and thousands of concerned sportsmen, conservationists and wildlife enthusiasts, the President ordered the Secretary of the Interior to stop the slaughter and institute another program. Because of his efforts and those who assisted him, the King of The Big Game animals in North America is still abundant.

Evel Knievel has always been an outspoken man, and some of his opinions have raised much controversy. His outcries against the misuse of the airwaves for religious solicitation caused a storm of protest from people who misunderstood his intentions. Religious appreciation is evident in his prints of "Mother Theresa" and "An Amish Man", along with his admiration for those who are truly good and honest. Portrayals of these qualities incorporated with his talent for capturing the indomitable spirit will survive for future generations.

**FACING DECISION** *by Evel Knievel*

| EVEL KNIEVEL | ISSUE PRICE | CURRENT PRICE |
|---|---|---|
| ☐ **UPSIDE DOWN,** ed. 1,000, s/n, 11″ x 14″, pub LC | 100.00 | — |
| ☐ **BIRDS FLY, WHY CAN'T I,** ed. 1,000, s/n, 11″ x 14″, pub LC | 100.00 | — |
| ☐ **MASTER OF THE HIGH COUNTRY,** ed. 1,000, s/n, 16″ x 20″, pub LC | 200.00 | — |
| ☐ **EAGLE AND PREY,** ed. 5,000, s/n, 16″ x 20″, pub LC | 500.00 | — |
| ☐ **THE SCOUT,** ed. 3,000, s/n, 16″ x 20″, pub LC | 350.00 | — |
| ☐ **FACING DECISION,** ed. 3,000, s/n, 16″ x 20″, pub LC | 350.00 | — |
| ☐ **BEFORE THE STORM,** ed. 3,000, s/n, 16″ x 20″, pub LC | 350.00 | — |
| ☐ **STANDING TALL,** ed. 2,500, s/n, 11″ x 14″, pub LC | 150.00 | — |
| ☐ **PEACEFUL FLIGHT,** ed. 3,000, s/n, 16″ x 20″, pub LC | 200.00 | — |
| ☐ **THE WISE ONE,** ed. 1,000, s/n, 16″ x 20″, pub LC | 150.00 | — |
| ☐ **SPIRIT,** ed. 5,000, s/n, 11″ x 14″, pub LC | 200.00 | — |
| ☐ **GENTLEMAN,** ed. 3,000, s/n, 11″ x 14″, pub LC | 200.00 | — |
| ☐ **THE RED ROOSTER,** ed. 2,500, s/n, 11″ x 14″, pub LC | 100.00 | — |
| ☐ **FIRE,** ed. 5,000, s/n, 16″ x 20″, pub LC | 200.00 | — |
| ☐ **THE KING,** ed. 1,000, s/n, 16″ x 20″, pub LC | 200.00 | — |
| ☐ **BEWARE,** ed. 1,000, s/n, 16″ x 20″, pub LC | 200.00 | — |
| ☐ **BAMBI,** ed. 1,000, s/n, 11″ x 14″, pub LC | 100.00 | — |
| ☐ **SNOW HAWK,** ed. 1,000, s/n, 11″ x 14″, pub LC | 100.00 | — |
| ☐ **SERENITY,** ed. 1,000, s/n, 11″ x 14″, pub LC | 100.00 | — |
| ☐ **HIGH COUNTRY,** ed. 1,000, s/n, 11″ x 14″, pub LC | 100.00 | — |
| ☐ **SAGEBRUSH PRINCE,** ed. 1,000, s/n, 16″ x 20″, pub LC | 200.00 | — |

# HENRY KOEHLER

Henry Koehler, a true sporting painter, combines a thorough mastery of the painting craft with an intimate knowledge of the sports he depicts.

He hunts regularly in Connecticut with the Litchfield County Hounds and in Italy with the Roman Foxhounds while his summers are spent sailing in American and Mediterranean waters.

His paintings of fox hunting, racing, yachting and portraits are in such famous collections as the Duchess of Windsor, John H. Whitney, Edward Kennedy, William S. Paley and the J. B. Speed Museum.

| HENRY KOEHLER | ISSUE PRICE | CURRENT PRICE |
|---|---|---|
| ☐ RACING COLOURS - PORTFOLIO OF FOUR, rel. 1972. ed. 1,500, s/n, 18" x 22½", pub FHG | 75.00 | 225.00 |
| ☐ WARWICKSHIRE STEEPLE CHASE AWAITING START, rel. 1972. ed. 1,500, s/n, 33" x 23½", pub FHG | 40.00 | 85.00 |
| ☐ RIVA RIDGE, rel. 1973. ed. 2,500, s/n, 33" x 23½", pub FHG | 30.00 | 100.00 |
| ☐ SECRETARIAT, rel. 1974. ed. 4,500, s/o, 29" x 21½", pub FHG | 40.00 | 160.00 |
| ☐ RED JOCKEY BELOW, ed. 300, s/n, 31" x 23", litho, pub CFAC | 125.00 | 150.00 |
| ☐ CONSTELLATION BELOW, ed. 300, s/n, 35" x 24", litho, pub CFAC | 125.00 | 275.00 |
| ☐ FIVE ENGLISH JOCKEYS, ed. 300, s/n, 23" x 31", litho, pub CFAC | 125.00 | 250.00 |

# WILLIAM J. KOELPIN

A midwesterner from Wisconsin; artist, woodcarver and sculptor William Koelpin is fast becoming one of the best visual chroniclers of wildlife art in the United States.

Early in life he resolved to capture the look and feel of American wildlife that still inhabits the remaining flyways, waterways and forests of America. He is primarily a visual reporter rather than a studio painter, and tirelessly roams wildlife habitats for ideas.

The historical nature of Koelpin's "Hunters Series" demands that he spend considerable time doing research, part of which involves first hand experience of how these hunters of the past shot their game. "I may paint in one night," he says, "what takes six months of research." Although he gained his early fame in wildlife woodcarvings, he is also a sculptor producing finely cast bronzes in limited edition. The demand for his work has prompted Koelpin to recreate wildlife subject matter in oil paintings and limited edition lithographs.

Koelpin's early works, which began as a part-time hobby, concentrated on bird decoy renderings. On the advice of admirers of his work, Koelpin entered his first competitive show in 1968. In less than a decade he has won four consecutive "Best of Show" awards in the "Midwest Decoy Contest" followed by winning the Decoy Class in the "Central Flyway" and the "International Decoy Contest" (three times) and capped his achievements by winning the "Best in the World" award in decorative life-size wild fowl carvings championship at Salisbury, Maryland. The Birmingham Museum of Art has acclaimed him the "best in the world" and the Leigh Yawkey Woodson Art Museum recently named him one of "America's Premier Artists".

Koelpin won the 1983 Wisconsin Duck Stamp design.

**OFF SEASON** *by William J. Koelpin*

## WILLIAM J. KOELPIN

| | ISSUE PRICE | CURRENT PRICE |
|---|---|---|
| ☐ THE POACHER, rel. 1976. ed. 300, s/n, 24″ x 30″, dist. NC ............. | 60.00 | 2,400.00 |
| ☐ THE BATTERY, rel. 1977. ed. 580, s/n, 24″ x 36″, dist. NC .............. | 60.00 | 350.00 |
| ☐ REFLECTIONS, rel. 1977. ed. 580, s/n, 24″ x 30″, dist. NC ............... | 60.00 | 350.00 |
| ☐ DAMN THE WIND, rel. 1978. ed. 580, s/n, 18″ x 23½″, dist. NC ........... | 75.00 | — |
| ☐ HARD TIMES, rel. 1978. ed. 600, s/n, 18″ x 24″, dist. NC ............... | 45.00 | — |
| ☐ PHEASANTS, rel. 1978. ed. 400, 19″ x 24″, dist. NC .................... | 65.00 | — |
| ☐ THE PLOVER GUN, rel. 1978. ed. 600, s/n, 18″ x 24″, dist. NC ........... | 45.00 | — |
| ☐ FLAMING SUMAC - CARDINALS, rel. 1979. ed. 605, s/n, 14″ x 18″, dist. NC . | 50.00 | — |
|     remarqued print ............................ | 125.00 | — |
| ☐ OFF SEASON, rel. 1979. ed. 600, s/n, 24″ x 30″, dist. NC ............ | 75.00 | — |
|     remarqued print ............................ | 150.00 | — |
| ☐ THE ENTHUSIAST, rel. 1980. ed. 600, s/n, 27½″ x 22¼″, dist. NC ........ | 75.00 | 300.00 |
| ☐ GOOD TIMES, rel. 1980. ed. 600, s/n, 24″ x 30″, dist. NC ............... | 85.00 | — |
|     remarqued print ............................ | 160.00 | — |
| ☐ PRIMEVAL CEREMONY/GREATER PRAIRIE CHICKEN, rel. 1980. ed. 400, s/n, 24″ x 30″, dist. NC ............................ | 75.00 | — |
|     remarqued print ............................ | 150.00 | — |
| ☐ THOU SHALT NOT POACH, rel. 1980. ed. 600, s/n, 24″ x 30″, dist. NC ...... | 85.00 | 450.00 |
| ☐ BARK RIVER WOODIES, rel. 1981. ed. 600, s/n, 24″ x 30″, dist. NC ........ | 100.00 | — |
| ☐ ILLINOIS RIVER CLASSICS, rel. 1981. ed. 600, s/n, 24″ x 20″, dist. NC ..... | 85.00 | — |
|     remarqued print ............................ | 160.00 | — |
| ☐ MAN'S BEST FRIEND, rel. 1981. ed. 800, s/n, 24¼″ x 28¼″, dist. NC ...... | 100.00 | — |
|     remarqued print ............................ | 200.00 | — |

| | ISSUE PRICE | CURRENT PRICE |
|---|---|---|
| ☐ **THE GUN**, rel. 1982. ed. 600, s/n, 20" x 24", dist. NC . . . . . . . . . . . . . . . . . . | 75.00 | — |
| ☐ **PINTAILS**, 1982 Wisconsin Duck Stamp print, rel. 1982. ed. 2,300, s/n, 14" x 12", dist. NC . . . . . . . . . . . . . . . . . . . . . . . . . . . . . . . . . . . . . . . . . . . . . . . | 135.00 | 200.00 |

## LES KOUBA

| | | |
|---|---|---|
| ☐ **LEAVING SHELTER**, rel. 1981. ed. 500, s/n, size not available, pub WWI . . . . . | 175.00 | — |

## JAMES KRAMER

Kramer, an Ohio native, studied painting at the Cleveland Institute of Art and architecture at Ohio State University. He worked for a short while in Ohio and then went to California where architectural design was more exciting.

At that time, Kramer thought of himself as a trained painter who made his living as an architect. He painted evenings and weekends. Donald Teague, an artist of great experience and ability, provided encouragement and help. His confidence in Kramer's ability to solve the problems with which a dynamic painter is faced, was well founded for he has become one of the leading contemporary watercolorists. In 1970, Kramer gave up his architectural practice and became a full-time artist. Field trips for subject matter brought Kramer to Santa Fe several times. He liked it, found land and built a house and studio.

A community of fine painters resides in Santa Fe, and he enjoys the comradery of the professional group. When he is not traveling he paints seven days a week for seven to eight hours a day. Travel freshens Kramer's vision. He has painted in England, France and lately, Mexico.

Kramer is a member of the National Academy of Western Art.

**JAMES KRAMER**

| | | |
|---|---|---|
| ☐ **SPICE MARKET**, rel. 1982. ed. 950, s/n, 16⅛" x 21¾", pub MPPI . . . . . . . . . | 75.00 | — |
| ☐ **FLOWER MARKET**, rel. 1982. ed. 950, s/n, 16⅛" x 21¾", pub MPPI . . . . . . . . | 75.00 | — |

## MILDRED SANDS KRATZ

Mildred Sands Kratz, AWS holds over one hundred art awards with five Gold Medals in National competition. She has exhibited at the National Academy of Design, National Arts Club, Allied Artists, Knickerbocker Artists, New York City and Pennsylvania Academy of Fine Arts. She has had one woman shows from Maine to Florida.

Sands Kratz is an active, vibrant woman whose energies and zest are reflected in her wide range of subject material . . . barns to boats, teddy bears to village streets. Each scene possesses the delicate touch of an artist who thoroughly communicates the ambiance of the scene to the viewer. Listed in *Who's Who of American Artists, Who's Who of the World,* its *Who's Who of American Women* Sands Kratz received the Pennsylvania Senatorial Citation for outstanding artist in 1977.

**REFLECTIONS** *by Mildred Sands Kratz*

| MILDRED SANDS KRATZ | ISSUE PRICE | CURRENT PRICE |
|---|---|---|
| ☐ **THREE ARCH BRIDGE,** ed. 950, s/n, 23¼" x 17", pub WII | 50.00 | — |
| ☐ **VILLAGE WALK,** ed. 950, s/n, 23¼" x 15½", pub WII | 50.00 | — |
| ☐ **BLUE WAGON,** ed. 950, s/n, 26½" x 20", pub WII | 75.00 | — |
| ☐ **SILENT CLOISTERS,** ed. 950, s/n, 18" x 29", pub WII | 60.00 | — |
| ☐ **REFLECTIONS,** ed. 950, s/n, 18" x 29", pub WII | 60.00 | — |
| ☐ **IN PORT,** ed. 950, s/n, 22" x 33", pub WII | 125.00 | — |
| ☐ **SILENT PARADE,** ed. 950, s/n, 22" x 26", pub WII | 125.00 | — |

# DIETMAR KRUMREY

Born in Germany, Dietmar Krumrey emigrated to America with his family at the age of three. After living in the Chicago area for several years, the family discovered the Upper Peninsula of Michigan and decided to make their home there. Krumrey spent the greater part of his youth fishing, hunting and exploring the streams and forests surrounding his home. His deep affection and respect for wildlife is evident in his work.

Krumrey's father, also an artist, encouraged his son to use his senses more completely especially when they camped out or hiked in the wilderness. Upon graduation he worked for Hallmark Cards in Kansas City before leaving to free lance.

In 1981, Krumrey, won the prestigious Michigan Duck Stamp contest.

## DIETMAR KRUMREY

| | | |
|---|---|---|
| ☐ **RACCOONS,** rel. 1973. ed. 172, s/o, 17" x 23", pub CHWA | 20.00 | 60.00 |
| ed. 100, Artist proofs | 50.00 | 120.00 |
| ☐ **RING-NECKED PHEASANT,** rel. 1972. ed. 355, s/o, 23" x 17", pub CHWA | 20.00 | 90.00 |
| ed. 100 Artist proofs | 50.00 | 180.00 |
| ☐ **WOOD DUCK,** rel. 1972. ed. 246, s/o, 23" x 17", pub CHWA | 20.00 | 90.00 |
| ed. 100 Artist proofs | 50.00 | 180.00 |

**GOLDEN RETRIEVER** *by Dietmar Krumrey*

| | ISSUE PRICE | CURRENT PRICE |
|---|---|---|
| ☐ **RUFFED GROUSE,** rel. 1973. ed. 76, s/o, 17″ x 23″, pub CHWA............ | 20.00 | 60.00 |
| ed. 100 Artist proofs ........................................... | 50.00 | 120.00 |
| ☐ **WOODCOCK,** rel. 1973. ed. 46, s/o, 14″ x 11″, pub CHWA............... | 12.00 | 40.00 |
| ed. 100 Artist proofs ........................................... | 30.00 | 80.00 |
| ☐ **GROUSE,** rel. 1975. ed. 300, s/n, pub NWA ........................... | 40.00 | 300.00 |
| ☐ **WOODCOCK,** rel. 1975. ed. 950, s/n, pub NWA ........................ | 40.00 | 120.00 |
| ☐ **BLUE GOOSE,** rel. 1976. ed. 150, s/n, pub NWA ....................... | 70.00 | 100.00 |
| ☐ **BLUE JAYS,** rel. 1976. ed. 300, s/n, pub NWA ........................ | 25.00 | 150.00 |
| ☐ **EASTERN CHIPMUNK,** rel. 1976. ed. 300, s/n, pub NWA ................. | 25.00 | 40.00 |
| ed. 100 Artist proofs ........................................... | 40.00 | — |
| ☐ **EASTERN COTTONTAILS,** rel. 1976. ed. 300, s/n, pub NWA ............... | 40.00 | 120.00 |
| ed. 100 Artist proofs ........................................... | 60.00 | — |
| ☐ **OTTERS,** rel. 1977. ed. 300, s/n, pub NWA .......................... | 60.00 | — |
| ☐ **SCREECH OWL,** rel. 1978. ed. 300, s/n, pub NWA ..................... | 40.00 | 200.00 |
| ☐ **BLUEBILLS,** rel. 1978. ed. 300, s/n, pub NWA ........................ | 50.00 | 200.00 |
| ☐ **EASTERN COTTONTAILS,** rel. 1978. ed. 100 A/P, pub Michigan Conservation Club............................................... | 60.00 | 90.00 |
| ☐ **GROSBEAKS,** rel. 1979. ed. 300, s/n, pub NWA ...................... | 40.00 | 60.00 |
| ☐ **GROUSE,** rel. 1979. ed. 220, s/n, pub NWA ......................... | 60.00 | 100.00 |
| ed. 100 Artist proofs ........................................... | 80.00 | — |
| ☐ **CHICKADEES,** rel. 1980. ed. 300, s/n, pub NWA...................... | 50.00 | 100.00 |
| ed. 100 Artist proofs ........................................... | 80.00 | — |
| ☐ **GOLDEN LABRADOR,** rel. 1980. ed. 850, s/n, pub Artist Portfolio ........... | 60.00 | — |
| ed. 50, s/n, A/P................................................ | 90.00 | — |
| ☐ **GOLDEN RETRIEVER,** rel. 1980. ed. 850, s/n, pub Artist Portfolio ........... | 60.00 | — |
| ed. 50, s/n, A/P................................................ | 90.00 | — |
| ☐ **GROUSE,** rel. 1980. ed. 850, s/n, pub WA*........................... | 80.00 | — |
| ☐ **NUTHATCHES,** rel. 1980. ed. 300, s/n, pub WA ...................... | 50.00 | — |

| | ISSUE PRICE | CURRENT PRICE |
|---|---|---|
| ☐ **TIMBERWOLF,** rel. 1980. ed. 850, s/n, pub WA ...................... | 80.00 | — |
| ☐ **BLACK LABRADOR,** rel. 1981. ed. 850, s/n, pub WWI.................... | 90.00 | — |
| ed. 40, s/n, A/P ...................................................... | 90.00 | — |
| ☐ **BLUE WINGED TEAL,** rel. 1981. ed. 300, s/n, pub WA .................. | 60.00 | — |
| ☐ **BRITTANY,** rel. 1981. ed. 850, s/n, pub WWI .......................... | 60.00 | — |
| ed. 40, s/n, A/P ...................................................... | 90.00 | — |
| *Company name changed from Northwoods Wildlife Art to Wilderness Art. | | |
| ☐ **ERMINE,** rel. 1981. ed. 300, s/n, pub WA ............................. | 40.00 | — |
| ☐ **MALLARDS,** rel. 1981. ed. 300, s/n, pub WA .......................... | 80.00 | — |
| ☐ **CARDINAL,** rel. 1982. ed. 300, s/n, 9" x 11", pub WA .................. | 50.00 | — |
| ☐ **GROUSE WITH CHICKS,** rel. 1982. ed. 200, s/n, 12" x 14½", pub WA, donation to Wildlife Unlimited of Dickinson County, Michigan. .................. | 100.00 | — |
| ed. 50, Artist proofs.................................................. | 100.00 | — |
| ☐ **RIVER OTTER,** rel. 1982. ed. 300, s/n, 6½" x 9½", pub WA ............. | 60.00 | — |
| ☐ **SAWWHET OWL,** rel. 1982. ed. 300, s/n, 10" x 12", pub WA ............. | 60.00 | — |
| ☐ **SNOWSHOE HARE,** rel. 1982. ed. 300, s/n, 7" x 8", pub WA ............. | 40.00 | — |

# BOB KUHN

Since completing his formal study at Brooklyn's Pratt Institute, Bob Kuhn's drawings and paintings have appeared frequently in *Readers Digest, Argosy, Field and Stream, Outdoor Life, Sports Afield* and other national publications. The Remington Arms Company first commissioned him to paint wildlife subjects in 1949 and as "Artist in Residence", his art has been featured in their game art calendars over many years. Each year, his works are sought after at the *Mzuri Safari Club Art Show* as well as at the *Game Conservation International Art Show.*

The book *The Animal Art of Bob Kuhn - A Lifetime of Drawing and Painting,* reflects his ability to capture on canvas the power, grace and innate beauty of these magnificent animals with a remarkable technical mastery.

"Paintbrush Safari" in *Sports Afield Magazine* featured eight pages of his African Masterpieces from private collections, with his comments. During the last decade, his efforts have been strictly devoted to wildlife painting for private collectors.

**DRINKING TIGER** *by Bob Kuhn*

## BOB KUHN

| | ISSUE PRICE | CURRENT PRICE |
|---|---|---|
| ☐ **SOFT TOUCH**, rel. 1972. ed. 1,500, s/n, 30″ x 24″, pub ALI ............. | 80.00 | — |
| ☐ **SUNSHINE AND SHADOWS**, ed. 500, s/n, 32″ x 22½″, pub ALI .......... | 70.00 | Sold Out |
| ☐ **JAGUAR**, ed. 1,000, s/o, 32¾″ x 23¼″, pub ALI ..................... | 60.00 | Sold Out |
| ☐ **HIGH SIESTA - LEOPARD**, rel. 1978. ed. 500, s/n, 15⅞″ x 12⅛″, pub SEL .... | 70.00 | — |
| ☐ **DRINKING TIGER**, rel. 1980. ed. 750, s/n, 15½″ x 30″, pub SEL .......... | 125.00 | Sold Out |
| ☐ **SERENGETI MONARCHS**, rel. 1981. ed. 750, s/n, 18⅛″ x 27¼″, pub EHC ... | 150.00 | Sold Out |

## MORT KÜNSTLER

Whether depicting quiet scenes of yesteryear or interpreting the action filled days of the Old West, artist-illustrator Mort Künstler's paintings convey warmth and reality.

His desire for technical details was enhanced by studies at Pratt Institute. There he studied for a career as an illustrator. Admired for his extreme accuracy, his technical skill won him commissions with such organizations as the American Cyanamid Company, depicting history of the dye industry, and Blair Galleries, Sante Fe, a series on the Kansas Wheat Harvest. The advertising illustrations required extensive research. It was this love of research and art which led him to historical painting.

**BRAVE WARRIOR** *by Mort Künstler*

## MORT KÜNSTLER

| | ISSUE PRICE | CURRENT PRICE |
|---|---|---|
| ☐ **HOLIDAY HOMECOMING**, rel. 1976. ed. 1,000, s/n, 19" x 25", pub FHG . . . . . | *40.00 | 115.00 |
| * A portion of the edition reserved for First Day of Issue, Connecticut Valley Railroad Museum, Essex, Connecticut | | |
| ☐ **STROUD FARM, HUTCHINSON, KANSAS, 1917**, rel. 1976. ed. 2,000, s/n, 22" x 28", pub FHG . . . . . . . . . . . . . . . . . . . . . . . . . . . . . . . . . . . . . . . . | 25.00 | 200.00 |
| ☐ **THIS WE'LL DEFEND**, rel. 1976. ed. 5,000, s/0, pub FHG . . . . . . . . . . . . . . . | 35.00 | Sold Out |
| ☐ **SILVER GHOST, AUTUMN LEAVES**, rel. 1977. ed. 1,000, s/n, 22" x 28", pub FHG . . . . . . . . . . . . . . . . . . . . . . . . . . . . . . . . . . . . . . . . . . . | 40.00 | — |
| ☐ **THAT WAS THE DAY**, rel. 1977. ed. 1,000, s/n, 22" x 28", pub FHG . . . . . . . | 40.00 | — |
| ☐ **TUCSON STAGE**, rel. 1977. ed. 1,000, s/n, 20" x 26", pub FHG . . . . . . . . . . . | 50.00 | — |
| ☐ **AAU/USA INDOOR TRACK & FIELD NATIONALS**, rel. 1978. ed. 600, s/n, pub CFAC . . . . . . . . . . . . . . . . . . . . . . . . . . . . . . . . . . . . . . . . . . . . . . | 165.00 | — |
| ☐ **AMONGST THE SACRED ELDERBERRY**, rel. 1978. ed. 1,000, s/n, 20" x 26", pub FHG . . . . . . . . . . . . . . . . . . . . . . . . . . . . . . . . . . . . . . . . . . . . | 50.00 | — |
| ☐ **EARLY SNOW**, rel. 1978. ed. 300, s/n, 22" x 30", pub CFAC . . . . . . . . . . . . . | 165.00 | 275.00 |
| ☐ **THE KANSAN**, rel. 1978. ed. 300, s/n, 29" x 24", pub CFAC . . . . . . . . . . . . . | 110.00 | 200.00 |
| ☐ **RUNNIN' LATE**, rel. 1978. ed. 300, s/n, pub HPC . . . . . . . . . . . . . . . . . . . . . . | 400.00 | 600.00 |
| ☐ **APACHE RAIDING PARTY**, rel. 1979. ed. 500, s/n, 22½" x 30", pub FHG . . . . | 60.00 | 150.00 |
| ☐ **BRAVE WARRIOR**, rel. 1979. ed. 5,000, s/o, 22" x 18", pub FHG . . . . . . . . . . | 25.00 | — |
| ☐ **EARLY CROSSING**, rel. 1979. ed. 500, s/n, 21" x 30", pub FHG . . . . . . . . . . . | 60.00 | 80.00 |
| ☐ **STORM CLOUDS**, rel. 1980. ed. 300, s/n, silkscreen, 34½" x 25½ " . . . . . . . | 400.00 | 500.00 |
| ☐ **TREATY TALK**, rel. 1979. ed. 500, s/n, 24" x 30", pub FHG . . . . . . . . . . . . . | 65.00 | Sold Out |
| ☐ **WAR CRY**, rel. 1979. ed. 550, s/n, 18½" x 30" . . . . . . . . . . . . . . . . . . . . . | 70.00 | — |
| ed. 150, s/n, remarqued, pub FHG . . . . . . . . . . . . . . . . . . . . . . . . . . . . | 115.00 | — |
| ☐ **BOUNDARY LINE**, rel. 1980. ed. 750, s/n, 30" x 24", pub FHG . . . . . . . . . . . | 70.00 | — |
| ☐ **LONELY NIGHT**, rel. 1980. ed. 750, s/n, 23¼" x 28", pub FHG . . . . . . . . . . . | 70.00 | — |
| ☐ **SURPRISE ATTACK**, rel. 1980. ed. 750, s/n, 24" x 30", pub FHG . . . . . . . . . . | 70.00 | — |
| ☐ **GOING AFTER BIG BULL**, rel. 1981. ed. 300, s/n, 24" x 30", pub HP . . . . . . . | 500.00 | — |
| ☐ **HIS NEW BLUE COAT**, rel. 1981. ed. 300, s/n, 32" x 23", pub HP . . . . . . . . . | 500.00 | — |
| ☐ **CHEYENNE WINTER**, rel. 1983. ed. 500, s/n, size N/A, pub CIL . . . . . . . . . . | 295.00 | — |
| ☐ **MORNING MIST**, rel. 1983. ed. 500, s/n, size N/A, pub CIL . . . . . . . . . . . . . | 295.00 | — |

# HAYDEN LAMBSON

Having painted all his life, 32 year old Hayden Lambson is now receiving recognition as one of the west's outstanding wildlife artists.

The Ramah, New Mexico native has achieved the ability to capture wildlife on canvas with amazing detail and breathtaking scenery. In addition, his portrayals of mountain men and trappers along with the beautiful western landscapes are being commissioned by many serious art collectors.

Lambson has gained his reputation while exhibiting at Safari Club International, Game Conservation International, Foundation for North American Wild Sheep, and the C. M. Russell Art Show.

A graduate of Brigham Young University and Mesa Community College in Mesa, Arizona, Hayden became a full time artist 4½ years ago.

## HAYDEN LAMBSON

| | | |
|---|---|---|
| ☐ **ON THE TRACK**, rel. 1980. ed. 750, s/n, 23" x 25", pub SGL . . . . . . . . . . . . . | 65.00 | — |
| s/n, remarqued . . . . . . . . . . . . . . . . . . . . . . . . . . . . . . . . . . . . . . . . . . . . | 125.00 | — |
| ☐ **DEBATING THE CLEARING**, rel. 1980. ed. 750, s/n, 23" x 15", pub SGL . . . . . | 65.00 | — |
| s/n, remarqued . . . . . . . . . . . . . . . . . . . . . . . . . . . . . . . . . . . . . . . . . . . . | 125.00 | — |
| ☐ **THE HIGHLANDERS**, rel. 1981. ed. 750, s/n, 15½" x 20", pub SGL . . . . . . . . | 65.00 | — |
| s/n, remarqued . . . . . . . . . . . . . . . . . . . . . . . . . . . . . . . . . . . . . . . . . . . . | 125.00 | — |
| ☐ **STAYIN' HIGH**, rel. 1981. ed. 750, s/n, 16" x 20", pub SGL . . . . . . . . . . . . . . | 65.00 | — |
| s/n, remarqued . . . . . . . . . . . . . . . . . . . . . . . . . . . . . . . . . . . . . . . . . . . . | 125.00 | — |
| ☐ **THE APPRENTICE**, rel. 1982. ed. 950, s/n, 24" x 16", pub SGL . . . . . . . . . . . | 50.00 | — |
| s/n, remarqued . . . . . . . . . . . . . . . . . . . . . . . . . . . . . . . . . . . . . . . . . . . . | 125.00 | — |

**THE HIGHLANDERS** *by Hayden Lambson*

## J. FENWICK LANSDOWNE

There is a legendary quality about some artists. J. Fenwick Lansdowne possesses it. His life tells the story.

He was born in Hong Kong in 1937, the son of English parents. With war raging across China, the Lansdowne family fled to Canada. Fen, a victim of polio, was placed in a solarium for crippled children. His father returned to the Far East; his mother, herself a gifted artist, quickly noted Fen's artistic talent and helped nurture his enthusiasm. Soon he was drawing everything from ships to soldiers to pirates. At 13, Lansdowne sketched his first birds. His work came to the attention of the Canadian Audubon Society, and a one-man exhibit was soon arranged at Toronto's Royal Ontario Museum. Instant acclaim followed. Yet, Lansdowne was still a teenager. Equally extraordinary, he was completely self-taught.

By 21, his fame was virtually worldwide. Today, a Lansdowne is a treasured work. His paintings hang in Buckingham Palace and in London's prestigious Tryon Gallery, as well as at the National Wildlife Federation in Washington, D. C. His books have sold more than 150,000 copies; most recently he has published *Birds of the West Coast.* Fen Lansdowne birds are endowed with ornithological accuracy and poetic grace. A bird's ability to fly has always fascinated Lansdowne . . . "perhaps because they can fly and we can't." Although Lansdowne cannot fly, he is soaring into legend with each sure stroke of his brush.

**WILSON'S WARBLER** *by J. Fenwick Lansdowne*

## J. FENWICK LANSDOWNE

| | ISSUE PRICE | CURRENT PRICE |
|---|---|---|
| ☐ **BALD EAGLE**, rel. 1972. ed. 1,500, s/n, 22″ x 28″, pub GW . . . . . . . . . . . . . . . | 100.00 | — |
| ed. 1,000 s/o prints bearing the seal of the Connecticut Audubon Society. Proceeds to their Educational Development Fund. . . . . . . . . . . . . . . . . . . . . . . . | — | — |
| ☐ **BARN OWL**, rel. 1972. ed. 1,500, s/n, 22″ x 28″, pub GW . . . . . . . . . . . . . . | 100.00 | 150.00 |
| ☐ **BARRED OWL**, rel. 1972. ed. 1,500, s/n, 22″ x 28″, pub GW . . . . . . . . . . . . . | 100.00 | 150.00 |
| ☐ **EASTERN MEADOWLARK**, rel. 1972. ed. 1,500, s/n, 20″ x 25″, pub GW . . . . . | 65.00 | — |
| ☐ **SCREECH OWL**, rel. 1972. ed. 850, s/n, 17½″ x 22″, pub GW . . . . . . . . . . . . | N/A | 350.00 |
| ☐ **PINTAIL DUCKS**, rel. 1973. ed. 1,000, s/n, 24″ x 18″, pub GW . . . . . . . . . . . | 75.00 | 140.00 |
| ☐ **WOOD DUCKS**, rel. 1973. ed. 1,000, s/n, 18″ x 24″, pub GW . . . . . . . . . . . . . | 75.00 | 130.00 |
| ☐ **RUFFED GROUSE**, rel. 1976. ed. 1,000, s/n, 18″ x 24″, pub GW . . . . . . . . . . | 75.00 | Sold Out |
| ☐ **KENTUCKY WARBLER**, rel. 1983. ed. 650, s/n, 13⁷⁄₁₆″ x 15¹⁵⁄₁₆″, pub GW . . . . | 75.00 | — |
| ☐ **WILSON'S WARBLER**, rel. 1983. ed. 650, s/n, 13⁷⁄₁₆″ x 15¹⁵⁄₁₆″, pub GW . . . . . | 75.00 | — |

# PHILIP LASZ

Born in Africa in 1933, Philip Lasz early became familiar with the ways of the wilderness in which he was brought up by his missionary parents.

His first love was always art, and when he discovered it might be possible to study under Karle Steele at Wheaton College, Illinois, he made every effort to do so. Those years he considers as the most valuable training he received for his present work.

In 1962, Lasz returned to Africa, this time settling in Kenya. Following the example of his parents he took up his duties as a missionary. Surrounded as he was with the beauty of the abundant wildlife, he found a new challenge and began using it as subject matter for oil and acrylic paintings.

Today he still considers himself a missionary first, but has found further fulfillment in the field of wildlife art, where he attempts to preserve the beauty of these magnificent animals.

## PHILIP LASZ

| | ISSUE PRICE | CURRENT PRICE |
|---|---|---|
| ☐ ELEPHANT HERD ON THE MOVE, ed. 1,000, s/n, 34" x 21", pub PLG ....... | 45.00 | — |
| ☐ HIS MAJESTY, ed. 1,000, s/n, 34" x 21", pub PLG ..................... | 45.00 | — |
| ☐ GREATER KUDU, ed. 1,000, s/n, 34" x 21", pub PLG ................... | 45.00 | — |
| ☐ PEACE BEFORE THE STORM, ed. 1,000, s/n, 34" x 21", pub PLG........... | 45.00 | — |

# LE BA DANG

Le Ba Dang is Vietnamese, living in France since 1939. A painter well-known in the Occident, his art has nevertheless remained extremely oriental.

Thanks to his delicate temperment and his exceptional sensitivity accompanied by an impreccable technique and great skill he has been able to achieve a perfectly balanced synthesis in his work.

Ba Dang was born in Quang-Tri in 1922. After his studies in this town and Hue, he enrolled in the School of Fine Arts in Toulouse, France in 1942. He has lived in Paris since 1948.

His first exhibition in 1950 in a gallery on the Left Bank placed him immediately in the highest rank amongst the young painters of his generation. Ever since, his reputation has soared and at the same time his technique and talent have asserted themselves. His talent which is so sure and individual and for which his art, in spite of belonging indubitably to the School of Paris, does not resemble any other.

The works of Ba Dang, — painting, engraving or lithography, — are of considerable importance and are known all over the world. He is also the first artist to have introduced sculpture to the art of book-printing. He has composed some books in relief, the pages of which are printed neither in colour nor in ink. In form, they resemble the ancient bas-relief.

## LE BA DANG

| | | |
|---|---|---|
| ☐ LOLLIPOP TREE, ed. 120, s/o, lithograph, 20" x 26", pub CFAC ........... | — | 225.00 |
| ☐ ORANGE JUNKS, ed. 120, s/o, lithograph, 20" x 26", pub CFAC .......... | — | 225.00 |
| ☐ AFRIQUE, ed. 180, s/o, lithograph, 19" x 26", pub CFAC .................. | — | 200.00 |
| ☐ LESCHEVAUX ORANGES, ed. 180, s/o, lithograph, 19" x 26", pub CFAC ..... | — | 225.00 |
| ☐ REVE, ed 180, s/o, lithograph, 19" x 26", pub CFAC.................... | — | 150.00 |
| ☐ JUNGLE, ed.180, s/o, lithograph, 19" x 26", pub CFAC ................... | — | 200.00 |
| ☐ PAYSAGE AUX BARQUES, ed. 225, s/o, lithograph, 21" x 29", pub CFAC .... | — | 150.00 |
| ☐ LALUNE ROUGE, ed. 225, s/o, lithograph, 21" x 29", pub CFAC........... | — | 150.00 |
| ☐ LE LAC, ed. 225, s/o, lithograph, 21" x 29", pub CFAC ................. | — | 150.00 |
| ☐ LE CHEVAL, ed. 225, s/o, lithograph, 21" x 29", pub CFAC .............. | — | 150.00 |
| ☐ STALLIONS, ed. 275, s/o, etching, 11" x 15", pub CFAC ................. | — | 150.00 |
| ☐ ARBRE JAUNE, ed. 275, s/o, etching, 11" x 15", pub CFAC ............... | — | 150.00 |
| ☐ FIGURE DE LA LUNE, ed. 275, s/o, etching, 11" x 15", pub CFAC .......... | — | 150.00 |
| ☐ PASSAGE DE LA LUNE, ed. 175, s/o, etching, 11" x 15", pub CFAC........ | — | 150.00 |
| ☐ FEMME NATIVE, ed. 275, s/o, etching, 11" x 15", pub CFAC.............. | — | 150.00 |
| ☐ TRAVAILLE DU MATIN, ed. 275, s/o, etching, 11" x 15", pub CFAC ........ | — | 150.00 |
| ☐ FORET, ed. 175, s/q, etching, 11" x 15", pub CFAC ................... | — | 150.00 |
| ☐ NUE, ed. 175, s/o, etching, 11" x 15", pub CFAC .................... | — | 150.00 |
| ☐ LE CHEVAL CAVALLIER, ed. 175, s/o, etching, 11" x 15", pub CFAC........ | — | 150.00 |
| ☐ MUTHUSWAMY, ed. 275, s/o, etching, 11" x 15", pub CFAC ............. | — | 150.00 |

| | ISSUE PRICE | CURRENT PRICE |
|---|---|---|
| ☐ **GOLDEN ORB**, ed. 275, s/o, lithograph, 26″ x 38″, pub CFAC . . . . . . . . . . . . | — | 1,000.00 |
| ☐ **TEMPEST**, ed. 275, s/o, lithograph, 27″ x 38″, pub CFAC . . . . . . . . . . . . . . | — | 175.00 |
| ☐ **MOONSHADOW**, ed. 275, s/o, lithograph, 21″ x 30″, pub CFAC . . . . . . . . . | — | 175.00 |
| ☐ **IMAGINATIVE LANDSCAPE**, ed. 275, s/o, lithograph, 24″ x 34″, pub CFAC . . . | — | 175.00 |
| ☐ **TEN HORSE FOLIO**, ed. 275, s/o, lithograph, 21″ x 30″, pub CFAC . . . . . . . . . | — | 3,300.00 |
|    ed. 50 on Japon . . . . . . . . . . . . . . . . . . . . . . . . . . . . . . . . . . . . . . . . . . . . . . | — | 4,000.00 |
| ☐ **FANTASIE SUITE**, ed. 200, s/o, remarqued lithograph, 21″ x 29″, pub CFAC . . | — | 3,900.00 |
| ☐ **LES BARQUES A MINUIT**, ed. 200, s/o, remarqued lithograph, 21″ x 29″, pub CFAC . . . . . . . . . . . . . . . . . . . . . . . . . . . . . . . . . . . . . . . . . . . . . . . . . . . . | — | 375.00 |
| ☐ **LA RIVIERE ORANGE**, ed. 200, s/o, remarqued lithograph, 21″ x 29″, pub CFAC . . . . . . . . . . . . . . . . . . . . . . . . . . . . . . . . . . . . . . . . . . . . . . . . . . . . | — | 400.00 |
| ☐ **VERRE DES FLEURS**, ed. 200, s/o, remarqued lithograph, 21″ x 29″, pub CFAC . . . . . . . . . . . . . . . . . . . . . . . . . . . . . . . . . . . . . . . . . . . . . . . . . . . . | — | 400.00 |
| ☐ **BOUQUET DES FLEURS**, ed. 200, s/o, remarqued lithograph, 21″ x 29″, pub CFAC . . . . . . . . . . . . . . . . . . . . . . . . . . . . . . . . . . . . . . . . . . . . . . . . . . . . | — | 450.00 |
| ☐ **COMPOSITION AVEC LES FLEURS**, ed. 200, s/o, remarqued lithograph, 21″ x 29″, pub CFAC . . . . . . . . . . . . . . . . . . . . . . . . . . . . . . . . . . . . . . . . . . . . . . | — | 450.00 |
| ☐ **COMPOSITION**, ed. 200, s/o, remarqued lithograph, 21″ x 29″, pub CFAC . . . . | — | 425.00 |
| ☐ **POT DES FLEURS**, ed. 200, s/o, remarqued lithograph, 21″ x 29″, pub CFAC . . . | — | 400.00 |
| ☐ **LES BARQUES EN BLEU ET ROUGE**, ed. 200, s/o, remarqued lithograph, 21″ x 29″, pub CFAC . . . . . . . . . . . . . . . . . . . . . . . . . . . . . . . . . . . . . . . . . . . . . . | — | 400.00 |
| ☐ **LE SOLEIL ORANGE**, ed. 200, s/o, remarqued lithograph, 21″ x 29″, pub CFAC | — | 400.00 |
| ☐ **LA LUNE MYSTERIEUX**, ed. 200, s/o, remarqued lithograph, 21″ x 29″, pub CFAC . . . . . . . . . . . . . . . . . . . . . . . . . . . . . . . . . . . . . . . . . . . . . . . . . . . . | — | 400.00 |
| ☐ **LA FEMME REPOSEE**, ed. 200, s/o, remarqued lithograph, 15″ x 22″, pub CFAC . . . . . . . . . . . . . . . . . . . . . . . . . . . . . . . . . . . . . . . . . . . . . . . . . . . . | — | 325.00 |
| ☐ **PETITE NATURE MORTE AVEC UNE VERRE**, ed. 200, s/o, remarqued lithograph, 15″ x 22″, pub CFAC . . . . . . . . . . . . . . . . . . . . . . . . . . . . . . . . . . . . | — | 350.00 |
| ☐ **LES FLEURS DE MINUIT**, ed. 200, s/o, remarqued lithograph, 15″ x 22″, pub CFAC . . . . . . . . . . . . . . . . . . . . . . . . . . . . . . . . . . . . . . . . . . . . . . . . . . . . | — | 400.00 |
| ☐ **LA COLOMBE**, ed. 200, s/o, remarqued lithograph, 15″ x 22″, pub CFAC . . . . | — | 400.00 |
| ☐ **LA BRANCHE MORTE**, ed. 200, s/o, remarqued lithograph, 25″ x 41″, pub CFAC . . . . . . . . . . . . . . . . . . . . . . . . . . . . . . . . . . . . . . . . . . . . . . . . . . . . | — | 500.00 |
| ☐ **FANTASIE DU SOIR**, ed. 200, s/o, remarqued lithograph, 26″ x 39″, pub CFAC | — | 500.00 |
| ☐ **NATURE PRAYS WITHOUT WORDS**, ed. 125, s/o, 22″ x 30″, pub EWG . . . . . . | — | *1,800.00 |
|    *Portfolio of 16 original lithographs, ed. 125, on Arches paper with one on Japon Nacre. . . . . . . . . . . . . . . . . . . . . . . . . . . . . . . . . . . . . . . . . . . . . . | — | 2,000.00 |
| ☐ **LES CHEVAUX SUITE**, ed. 125, s/n 11″ x 15″, pub EWG . . . . . . . . . . . . . . | — | *1,800.00 |
|    *Portfolio of 27 original mixed media, ed. 125 Deluxe edition with 7 additional | — | 2,000.00 |
| ☐ **UNWRITTEN WORDS**, ed. 80, s/o, original color lithograph, 20″ x 26″, pub EWG . . . . . . . . . . . . . . . . . . . . . . . . . . . . . . . . . . . . . . . . . . . . . . . . . . | — | 250.00 |
| ☐ **LE SOLEIL BLEU**, ed. 275, s/o, serigraph, 30″ x 22″, pub CFA . . . . . . . . . . | — | 350.00 |
| ☐ **LA MONTAGNE**, ed. 175, s/o, serigraph, 30″ x 22″, pub CFA . . . . . . . . . . . | — | 350.00 |
| ☐ **LE CHEVAL NOIR**, ed. 275, s/o, serigraph, 30″ x 22″, pub CFA . . . . . . . . . . | — | 350.00 |
| ☐ **LE CHEVALIER SOLITAIRE**, ed. 275, s/o, serigraph, 30″ x 22″, pub CFA . . . . | — | 375.00 |
| ☐ **LES VOILIERS**, ed. 275, s/o, serigraph, 30″ x 22″, pub CFA . . . . . . . . . . . . | — | 350.00 |
| ☐ **LA BRANCHE SECHE**, ed. 275, s/o, serigraph, 31″ x 47″, pub CFA . . . . . . . . | — | 550.00 |
| ☐ **LES MONTAGNES DOREES**, ed. 275, s/o, serigraph, 31″ x 47″, pub CFA . . . . . | — | 600.00 |
| ☐ **CHEVEL D'AMTAM**, ed. 275, s/o, serigraph, 31″ x 47″, pub CFA . . . . . . . . . | — | 650.00 |
| ☐ **LA CAVALIERE SOLITAIRE**, ed. 275, s/o, serigraph, 30″ x 22″, pub CFA . . . . | — | 400.00 |
| ☐ **LE ROCHER, LA MERE ET L'ENFANT**, ed. 275, s/o, serigraph, 30″ x 22″, pub CFA . . . . . . . . . . . . . . . . . . . . . . . . . . . . . . . . . . . . . . . . . . . . . . . . . . . | — | 350.00 |
| ☐ **LA MONTAGNE DE LA MERE ET L'ENFANT**, ed. 275, s/o, serigraph, 30″ x 22″, pub CFA | — | 300.00 |
| ☐ **LE ROCHER DE LA GRANDE DAME**, ed. 275, s/o, serigraph, 30″ x 22″, pub CFA. . . . . . . . . . . . . . . . . . . . . . . . . . . . . . . . . . . . . . . . . . . . . . . . . . . | — | 325.00 |
| ☐ **LA MONTAGNE ENSOLEILLEE**, ed. 275, s/o, serigraph, 31″ x 31″, pub CFA . . | — | 400.00 |
| ☐ **LE PRINTEMPS**, ed. 275, s/o, serigraph, 47″ x 21″, pub CFA . . . . . . . . . . . | — | 350.00 |
| ☐ **FLEURS**, ed. 300, s/o, serigraph, 64″ x 48″, pub CFA . . . . . . . . . . . . . . . | — | 1,000.00 |
| ☐ **PLEASURES**, ed. 275, s/o, serigraph, 11″ x 11″, pub CFA . . . . . . . . . . . . . | — | 125.00 |
| ☐ **DREAMS**, ed. 275, s/o, serigraph, 11″ x 11″, pub CFA . . . . . . . . . . . . . . . | — | 125.00 |
| ☐ **MYSTERIEUX**, ed. 275, s/o, serigraph, 11″ x 11″, pub CFA . . . . . . . . . . . . | — | 125.00 |
| ☐ **IMAGINATION**, ed. 275, s/o, serigraph, 11″ x 11″, pub CFA . . . . . . . . . . . . | — | 125.00 |
| ☐ **JOYEUX**, ed. 175, s/o, serigraph, 31″ x 16″, pub CFA . . . . . . . . . . . . . . . | — | 325.00 |

| | ISSUE PRICE | CURRENT PRICE |
|---|---|---|
| ☐ **LE MONUMENT,** ed. 300, s/o, litho embossment, 24″ x 30″, pub CFA . . . . . . | — | 400.00 |
| ☐ **LA PETITE CABANE DU PECHEUR,** ed. 300, s/o, litho embossment, 30″ x 22″, pub CFA. . . . . . . . . . . | — | 425.00 |
| ☐ **LE BOUT DU PASSAGE,** ed. 300, s/o, litho embossment, 30″ x 22″, pub CFA . . | — | 400.00 |
| ☐ **L'AUTRE MONDE,** ed. 300, s/o, litho embossment, 34″ x 25″, pub CFA . . . . . . | — | 425.00 |
| ☐ **LE PAPILLON,** ed. 300, s/o, litho embossment, 25″ x 17″, pub CFA . . . . . . . . | — | 375.00 |
| ☐ **LA BARQUE SOLITAIRE II,** ed. 300, s/o, litho embossment, 30″ x 22″, pub CFA | — | 375.00 |
| ☐ **LA DEMIE LUNE,** ed. 300, s/o, litho embossment, 34″ x 25″, pub CFA . . . . . . | — | 400.00 |
| ☐ **LA BARQUE ET LA LUNE,** ed. 300, s/o, litho embossment, 25″ x 17″, pub CFA | — | 375.00 |
| ☐ **LA BARQUE SOLITAIRE I,** ed. 300, s/o, litho embossment, 25″ x 17″, pub CFA | — | 300.00 |
| ☐ **L'ABERRATION,** ed. 300, s/o, litho embossment, 25″ x 17″, pub CFA . . . . . . | — | 300.00 |
| ☐ **LA LUNE ROUGE ET l'HIVER,** ed. 300, s/o, litho embossment, 24″ x 17″, pub CFA. . . . . . . . . . . | — | 325.00 |
| ☐ **LE PAYSAGE MELANCOLIQUE,** ed. 300, s/o, litho embossment, 24″ x 17″, pub CFA. . . . . . . . . . . | — | 325.00 |
| ☐ **LA COMEDIE HUMAINE #4,** ed. 300, s/o, litho embossment, 35″ x 13″, pub CFA. . . . . . . . . . . | — | 325.00 |
| ☐ **LA COMEDIE HUMAINE #3,** ed. 300, s/o, litho embossment, 35″ x 13″, pub CFA. . . . . . . . . . . | — | 325.00 |
| ☐ **LA COMEDIE HUMAINE #2,** ed. 300, s/o, litho embossment, 24″ x 24″, pub CFA. . . . . . . . . . . | — | 400.00 |
| ☐ **LA COMEDIE HUMAINE #1,** ed. 300, s/o, litho embossment, 24″ x 24″, pub CFA. . . . . . . . . . . | — | 325.00 |
| ☐ **LA COMEDIE HUMAINE #5,** ed. 300, s/o, litho embossment, 30″ x 23″, pub CFA. . . . . . . . . . . | — | 425.00 |
| ☐ **LA LUNE BLANC,** ed. 300, s/o, litho embossment, 30″ x 23″, pub CFA . . . . . . | — | 525.00 |
| ☐ **CE N'EST PAS ENCORE L'HIVER,** ed. 250, s/o, etching embossment, 14″ x 10″, pub CFA. . . . . . . . . . . | — | 225.00 |
| ☐ **UNE PETITE CHANSON DANS L'ESPACE,** ed. 250, s/o, etching embossment, 14″ x 10″, pub CFA. . . . . . . . . . . | — | 225.00 |
| ☐ **UNE PETITE CHANSON,** ed. 250, s/o, etching embossment, 14″ x 10″, pub CFA. . . . . . . . . . . | — | 225.00 |
| ☐ **TRANQUILITE,** ed. 250, s/o, etching embossment, 14″ x 10″, pub CFA . . . . . . | — | 225.00 |
| ☐ **CALME ET DIGNITE,** ed. 250, s/o, etching embossment, 21″ x 10″, pub CFA . . | — | 350.00 |
| ☐ **LA VIE ET LE BONHEUR,** ed. 250, s/o, etching embossment, 32″ x 10″, pub CFA. . . . . . . . . . . | — | 350.00 |
| ☐ **LA NATURE PRIE SANS PAROLE,** ed. 250, s/o, etching embossment, 26″ x 20″, pub CFA . . . . . . . . . . | — | 425.00 |
| ☐ **CALME ET BEAUTE,** ed. 250, s/o, etching embossment, 26″ x 20″, pub CFA . . | — | 425.00 |

# LEE LeBLANC

A man of many talents, Lee LeBlanc retired to his native state of Michigan in 1962 after more than twenty-five years in the motion picture industry. He had been an artist with 20th Century Fox, and later an animator with Disney Productions.

A student of art from early childhood, he attended art schools in New York, Philadelphia and Los Angeles. In 1973, he won the Federal Duck Stamp contest which vaulted him into national prominence, and in 1980 he was honored as the Ducks Unlimited Artist of the Year.

A long-time crusader for the preservation of our wetlands, LeBlanc's awards for his conservation efforts are numerous. In addition to his National Ducks Unlimited award, he has received state honors from Tennessee and Michigan. His efforts to save the Cache River from channelization results in the "Golden Mallard Award" from the Arkansas Wildlife Federation and the Baton Rouge Sportsman's League recognized his efforts to preserve the Atchafalaya Swamp with their "Crawdad Award".

Skilled in both oils and watercolors, LeBlanc depicts his subjects with exacting anatomical accuracy while drawing on his illustrative experience for the colorful and imaginative backdrops which distinguish his work.

**THE GATHERING** *by Lee Leblanc*

**LEE LeBLANC**

| | ISSUE PRICE | CURRENT PRICE |
|---|---|---|
| ☐ OBION RIVER MEMORY, ed. 800, s/n, 16″ x 24″, litho, pub PP . . . . . . . . . . . | 60.00 | 200.00 |
| ☐ HORSESHOE MEMORY - GEESE, ed. 800, s/n, 17½″ x 25″, litho, pub PP . . . . | 60.00 | 120.00 |
| ☐ A LACASSINE MEMORY, ed. 800, s/n, 16″ x 25″, litho, pub PP . . . . . . . . . . . | 60.00 | 100.00 |
| ☐ A CACHE RIVER MEMORY, ed. 800, s/n, 16″ x 25″, pub PP . . . . . . . . . . . . . | 60.00 | 160.00 |
| ☐ A HATCHEE RIVER MEMORY, ed. 800, s/n, 16″ x 25″, pub PP . . . . . . . . . . . | 60.00 | 120.00 |
| ☐ McCULLUM'S FLOODED TIMBER, ed. 800, s/n, 16″ x 25″, litho, pub PP . . . . . | 60.00 | 120.00 |
| ☐ THE GATHERING, ed. 800, s/n, 16″ x 24″, pub PP . . . . . . . . . . . . . . . . . . . . | 75.00 | — |
| remarqued, signed and numbered . . . . . . . . . . . . . . . . . . . . . . . . . . . . . . . | 165.00 | — |
| ☐ SYCAMORE AND BOBWHITES, ed. 800, s/n, 17″ x 25″, pub PP . . . . . . . . . . . | 75.00 | — |
| remarqued, signed and numbered . . . . . . . . . . . . . . . . . . . . . . . . . . . . . . . | 165.00 | — |
| ☐ WHITE TAILS, ed. 800, s/n, 15½″ x 25″, pub PP . . . . . . . . . . . . . . . . . . . . | 75.00 | — |
| remarqued, signed and numbered . . . . . . . . . . . . . . . . . . . . . . . . . . . . . . . | 165.00 | — |
| ☐ WOOD DUCKS AND CYPRESS, ed. 800, s/n, 16″ x 26″, pub PP . . . . . . . . . . . | 75.00 | — |
| remarqued, signed and numbered . . . . . . . . . . . . . . . . . . . . . . . . . . . . . . . | 165.00 | — |
| ☐ ALONG THE BUFFALO, ed. 800, s/n, 16″ x 24″, pub PP . . . . . . . . . . . . . . . . | 75.00 | — |
| remarqued, signed and numbered . . . . . . . . . . . . . . . . . . . . . . . . . . . . . . . | 165.00 | — |
| ☐ A NOBLE PAIR - WILD TURKEYS, rel. 1974. ed. 580, s/n, size note available, pub WWI . . . . . . . . . . . . . . . . . . . . . . . . . . . . . . . . . . . . . . . . . . . . . . . . . . | 60.00 | — |
| ☐ A STATELY PAIR - MALLARDS, rel. 1974. ed. 580, s/n, size not available, pub WWI. . . . . . . . . . . . . . . . . . . . . . . . . . . . . . . . . . . . . . . . . . . . . . . . . . . . . | 60.00 | 300.00 |
| ☐ ARKANSAS MALLARDS, rel 1974. ed. 400, s/n, size not available, pub WWI . . | 45.00 | 150.00 |
| ☐ HONKERS AT HORICON, rel. 1974. ed. 400, s/n, size not available, pub WWI . | 45.00 | 120.00 |
| ☐ A HATCHEE RIVER MEMORY - WOOD DUCKS, rel. 1974. ed. 800, s/n, size not available, pub PP . . . . . . . . . . . . . . . . . . . . . . . . . . . . . . . . . . . . . . . . . . . . | 60.00 | 120.00 |

# MARTHA BLAIR LEONE

Martha Blair Leone earned a Bachelor of Fine Arts degree from the prestigious Rhode Island School of Design. She worked ten years as a commercial artist in New York followed by five years as a free-lance artist. Her style was a solid realistic one until she moved to the country.

Since her way of life had changed drastically, she found her old style of painting no longer suited her.

**SUNSHINE FAIR** *by Martha Blair Leone*

The painter turned to a style which has always charmed her. Using the primitive idiom which had been so innocently and beautifully handled by Rousseau, Grandma Moses and other untrained artists, she added a sophisticated sense of design and color to produce charming and vibrant panels. These wonderfully fresh, exciting paintings throb with the enthusiasm of a sophisticate who had just realized the joy of country life.

| MARTHA BLAIR LEONE | ISSUE PRICE | CURRENT PRICE |
|---|---|---|
| ☐ **COUNTRY CROSSROADS**, rel. 1981. ed. 950, s/n, 16½" x 22¾", pub MPPI . . | 65.00 | — |
| ☐ **SUNSHINE FAIR**, rel. 1981. ed. 950, s/n, 19" x 18⅜", pub MPPI . . . . . . . . . | 75.00 | — |

# MANES LICHTENBERG

Since the 1940's, Manes Lichtenberg has built a distinguished international reputation as a leading contemporary impressionist: an artist who, according to one critic "depicts life not quite as it is, yet chances it not beyond recognition." Whether he paints a serene country scene or the quiet dignity of the city, he captures both the sadness of life and its extraordinary beauty. His work is marked not only by its freshness and vitality, but also by his brilliant use of drawing technique, perspective, color and composition.

Born in New York City in 1920, Lichtenberg's formal training includes schooling in the Art Students League in New York and the Academie de la Grande Chaimiere in Paris. He has been honored with numerous awards in exhibitions both in the United States and Paris.

## MANES LICHTENBERG

| | ISSUE PRICE | CURRENT PRICE |
|---|---|---|
| ☐ **CONNECTICUT SHORE**, rel. 1980. ed. 300, s/n, litho, arches, 23″ x 28″, pub EEI | 250.00 | — |
| ☐ **DOVE COTE**, rel. 1980. ed. 300, s/n, litho, arches, 25″ x 20″, pub EEI | 250.00 | — |
| ☐ **MARCHE AUX FLEURS, PARIS**, rel. 1980. ed. 300, s/n, litho, arches, 23″ x 28″, pub EEI | 250.00 | — |

# LINDA LLOYD

Linda Lloyd pursued her Fine Arts education at LSU in Baton Rouge, and later at the John McCrady School of Art in New Orleans, her native city. Further art studies were accomplished under John C. Pellew N.A., A.W.S., of Westport, Connecticut and Barclay Sheaks A.W.S. of Virginia.

Lloyd spent her childhood summers on a ranch in Texas, where she grew to know and love the animals and wildlife she portrays so beautifully. There is a true lifelike quality in her work, attesting to her intimate knowledge of the habits and instincts of her animal subjects.

**THE CAROLERS** *by Linda Lloyd*

## LINDA LLOYD

| | | |
|---|---|---|
| ☐ **LION CUBS**, ed. 300, s/n, 32″ x 22″, pub NG | — | 75.00 |
| ☐ **HAWK**, ed. 100, s/o, 8¾″ x 3⅞″, etching, dist. MMFC | — | 15.00 |
| ☐ **MUSTANG**, ed. 100, s/o, 8¾″ x 5⅞″, etching, dist. MMFC | — | 15.00 |
| ☐ **THRUSH**, ed. N/A, s/o, 4¼″ x 5¾″, etching, dist. MMFC | — | 15.00 |
| ☐ **OSPREY**, ed. 100, 3⅞″ x 4⅜″, etching, dist. MMFC | — | 15.00 |

| | ISSUE PRICE | CURRENT PRICE |
|---|---|---|
| ☐ FILLY, ed. N/A, s/o, 4¼″ x 5¾″, etching, dist. MMFC | — | 15.00 |
| ☐ ARAB, ed. N/A, s/o, 4¼″ x 6″, etching, dist. MMFC | — | 15.00 |
| ☐ ARANSES (WC), ed. N/A, 4⁷/₈″ x 8¾″, etching, dist. MMFC | — | 15.00 |
| ☐ BUCK, ed. N/A, 5¾″ x 8¾″, etching, dist. MMFC | — | 15.00 |
| ☐ MOUNTAIN QUAIL, ed. N/A, s/o, 5⁷/₈″ x 8⁷/₈″, etching, dist. MMFC | — | 20.00 |
| ☐ PONIES, ed. N/A, 5¾″ x 8¾″, etching, dist. MMFC | — | 15.00 |
| ☐ FIELD MOUSE, ed. N/A, 10¼″ x 7³/₈″, etching, dist. MMFC | — | 40.00 |
| ☐ KOB, ed. N/A, 8¾″ x 11¾″, etching, dist. MMFC | — | 25.00 |
| ☐ IN FLIGHT, ed. N/A, 8¾″ x 4¾″, etching, dist. MMFC | — | 15.00 |
| ☐ TONI, ed. N/A, s/o, 6″ x 9″, etching, dist. MMFC | — | 15.00 |
| ☐ AFRICAN CHILDREN #2 KOB, ed. N/A, 5⁷/₈″ x 8⁷/₈″, etching, dist. MMFC | — | 30.00 |
| ☐ CANADAS, ed. N/A, s/o, 3″ x 9″, etching, dist. MMFC | — | 20.00 |
| ☐ LONG EARED OWL, ed. N/A, s/o, 9¾″ x 4¾″, etching, dist. MMFC | — | 20.00 |
| ☐ KILLDEER, ed. N/A, 6″ x 9″, etching, dist. MMFC | — | 20.00 |
| ☐ SWALLOW TAIL, ed. N/A, 6″ x 9″, etching, dist. MMFC | — | 25.00 |
| ☐ BIRDWING, ed. N/A, 6″ x 9″, etching, dist. MMFC | — | 25.00 |
| ☐ SIMBA I, ed. N/A, 9″ x 7″, etching, dist. MMFC | — | 30.00 |
| ☐ SIMBA II, ed. N/A, 9″ x 7″, etching, dist. MMFC | — | 30.00 |
| ☐ TIGER, ed. N/A, 9″ x 7″, etching, dist. MMFC | — | 30.00 |
| ☐ SYLVESTER, ed. N/A, 11″ x 9″, etching, dist. MMFC | — | 35.00 |
| ☐ SMOKY, ed. N/A, 11″ x 9″, etching, dist. MMFC | — | 35.00 |
| ☐ FLUSHED, ed. N/A, 9″ x 12″, etching, dist. MMFC | — | 30.00 |
| ☐ COVER, ed. N/A, 9″ x 12″, etching, dist. MMFC | — | 30.00 |
| ☐ FIRST BORN, ed. N/A, 9″ x 12″, etching, dist. MMFC | — | 35.00 |
| ☐ PRIDE, ed. N/A, 6″ x 4½″, etching, dist. MMFC | — | 20.00 |
| ☐ FOAL, ed. N/A, s/o, 4½″ x 6″, etching, dist. MMFC | — | 20.00 |
| ☐ COUGAR KIT, ed. N/A, 6″ x 9″, etching, dist. MMFC | — | 25.00 |
| ☐ CHEETAH KIT, ed. N/A, 6″ x 4½″, etching, dist. MMFC | — | 20.00 |
| ☐ SPIRIT OF 76, ed. N/A, 9″ x 12″, etching, dist. MMFC | — | 35.00 |
| ☐ BISON 76, ed. N/A, 9″ x 12″, etching, dist. MMFC | — | 35.00 |
| ☐ CUB, ed. N/A, 4½″ x 6″, etching, dist. MMFC | — | 20.00 |
| ☐ JAQUAR, ed. N/A, 6″ x 4½″, etching, dist. MMFC | — | 20.00 |
| ☐ COONS 76, ed. N/A, 9″ x 12″, etching, dist. MMFC | — | 35.00 |
| ☐ FULL MOON I, ed. N/A, 8″ circle, etching, dist. MMFC | — | 25.00 |
| ☐ FULL MOON II, ed. N/A, 8″ circle, etching, dist. MMFC | — | 25.00 |
| ☐ SCAUP, ed. N/A, 2¾″ x 5″, etching, dist. MMFC | — | 15.00 |
| ☐ COMING IN, ed. N/A, 12″ x 6″, etching, dist. MMFC | — | 25.00 |
| ☐ WOODIES, ed. N/A, 12″ x 6″, etching, dist. MMFC | — | 25.00 |
| ☐ MALLARDS, ed. N/A, 12″ x 6″, etching, dist. MMFC | — | 25.00 |
| ☐ LANDING, ed. N/A, 12″ x 6″, etching, dist. MMFC | — | 25.00 |
| ☐ MOTHER GOOSE, ed. N/A, 12″ x 6″, etching, dist. MMFC | — | 25.00 |
| ☐ QUINTS, ed. N/A, 12″ x 9″, etching, dist. MMFC | — | 35.00 |
| ☐ COUGAR, ed. N/A, 12″ x 9″, etching, dist. MMFC | — | 35.00 |
| ☐ FORREST PRINCE, ed. N/A, 12″ x 9″, etching, dist. MMFC | — | 35.00 |
| ☐ KINGS RESTING, ed. N/A, 12″ x 9″, etching, dist. MMFC | — | 35.00 |
| ☐ SCAMP, ed. N/A, 5″ x 8″, etching, dist. MMFC | — | 25.00 |
| ☐ LIONESS, ed. N/A, s/o, 6″ x 9″, etching, dist. MMFC | — | 30.00 |
| ☐ LION, ed. N/A, 9″ x 7″, etching, dist. MMFC | — | 30.00 |
| ☐ LEOPARD, ed. N/A, 9″ x 7″, etching, dist. MMFC | — | 30.00 |
| ☐ COUGAR, ed. N/A, 9″ x 7″, etching, dist. MMFC | — | 30.00 |
| ☐ LYNX, ed. N/A, 9″ x 7″, etching, dist. MMFC | — | 30.00 |
| ☐ PRONGHORN, ed. N/A, 11¾″ x 8¾″, etching, dist. MMFC | — | 25.00 |
| ☐ NESTING, ed. N/A, 9″ x 12″, etching, dist. MMFC | — | 35.00 |
| ☐ TRIPLETS, ed. N/A, 9″ x 12″, etching, dist. MMFC | — | 35.00 |
| ☐ HOVERING, ed. N/A, 9″ x 12″, etching, dist. MMFC | — | 30.00 |
| ☐ EYES LEFT, ed. N/A, 6″ x 12″, etching, dist. MMFC | — | 25.00 |
| ☐ HIBISCUS, ed. N/A, 9″ x 12″, etching, dist. MMFC | — | 35.00 |
| ☐ LITTLE OWL II, ed. N/A, 7″ x 9″, etching, dist. MMFC | — | 30.00 |
| ☐ BIG CATS VII CHEETAH, ed. N/A, 6¾″ x 9″, etching, dist. MMFC | — | 30.00 |
| ☐ THE INNOCENTS, ed. N/A, 4″ x 5″, etching, dist. MMFC | — | 20.00 |
| ☐ AFFECTION, ed. N/A, 4½″ x 6″, etching, dist. MMFC | — | 20.00 |
| ☐ HUSKY PUPS, ed. N/A, 3″ x 6″, etching, dist. MMFC | — | 15.00 |
| ☐ YOUNG ROYALTY, ed. N/A, 4½″ x 9″, etching, dist. MMFC | — | 25.00 |
| ☐ WHOOO, ed. N/A, 3″ x 9″, etching, dist. MMFC | — | 20.00 |

| | ISSUE PRICE | CURRENT PRICE |
|---|---|---|
| ☐ AFRICAN CHILDREN #2 CHEETAH, ed. N/A, 6" x 9", etching, dist. MMFC.... | — | 30.00 |
| ☐ AFRICAN CHILDREN #7 GIRAFFI, ed. N/A, 6" x 9", etching, dist. MMFC..... | — | 30.00 |
| ☐ FAMILY GROUP, ed. N/A, 14" x 22", etching, dist. MMFC................ | — | 100.00 |
| ☐ TRUMUIRATE, ed. N/A, 14" x 22", etching, dist. MMFC................. | — | 100.00 |
| ☐ AFRICAN CHILDREN #1 CARACAL, ed. N/A, 5⁷/₈" x 8⁷/₈", etching, dist. MMFC | — | 30.00 |
| ☐ AMERICAN CHILDREN #1 FOXES, ed. N/A, 5⁷/₈" x 8⁷/₈", etching, dist. MMFC. | — | 25.00 |
| ☐ WOODCOCK, ed. N/A, 4⁷/₈" x 7¼", etching, dist. MMFC.................. | — | 25.00 |
| ☐ OWL EYES, ed. N/A, 5⁷/₈" x 8⁷/₈", etching, dist. MMFC................. | — | 25.00 |
| ☐ MICE, ed. N/A, 5⁷/₈" x 8⁷/₈", etching, dist. MMFC.................... | — | 25.00 |
| ☐ CARDINAL, ed. N/A, 4¼" x 5¾"", etching, dist. MMFC................. | — | 25.00 |
| ☐ BLUE JAY, ed. N/A, 4¼" x 5¾", etching, dist. MMFC.................. | — | 25.00 |
| ☐ DOLPHIN, ed. N/A, 8⁷/₈" x 11⁷/₈", etching, dist. MMFC................ | — | 40.00 |
| ☐ AMERICAN CHILDREN #2 FOXY LADY, ed. N/A, 5⁷/₈" x 8⁷/₈", etching, dist. MMFC........................................... | — | 25.00 |
| ☐ COTTONTAILS, ed. N/A, 5⁷/₈" x 8⁷/₈", etching, dist. MMFC............. | — | 25.00 |
| ☐ AMERICAN CHILDREN #3 MULE DEER, ed. N/A, 5⁷/₈" x 8⁷/₈", etching, dist. MMFC................................................. | — | 25.00 |
| ☐ BLACKBIRDS, ed. N/A, 8⁷/₈" x 11⁷/₈", etching, dist. MMFC............. | — | 40.00 |
| ☐ LITTLE OWL I, ed. N/A, 6⁷/₈" x 8⁷/₈", etching, dist. MMFC............ | — | 30.00 |
| ☐ NBC PEACOCK, ed. 81/200, 2⁷/₈" x 8⁷/₈", etching, dist. MMFC.......... | — | 20.00 |
| ☐ WADERS, ed. 64/200, 2⁷/₈" x 8⁷/₈", etching, dist. MMFC.............. | — | 20.00 |
| ☐ HERON, ed. 80/200, 5⁷/₈" x 8⁷/₈", etching, dist. MMFC............... | — | 25.00 |
| ☐ DROPPING IN, ed. 140/200, 5⁷/₈" x 8⁷/₈", etching, dist. MMFC......... | — | 25.00 |
| ☐ BLUE CRAB, ed. 40/200, 5⁷/₈" x 8⁷/₈", etching, dist. MMFC........... | — | 25.00 |
| ☐ STONE CRAB, ed. 40/200, 5⁷/₈" x 8⁷/₈", etching, dist. MMFC.......... | — | 25.00 |
| ☐ CANVASBACK (Sepia). ed. 95/200, 8⁷/₈" x 13⁷/₈", etching, dist. MMFC..... | — | 40.00 |
| ☐ REDHEAD (Sepia). ed. 95/200, 8⁷/₈" x 13⁷/₈", etching, dist. MMFC........ | — | 40.00 |
| ☐ CAROUSEL HORSE, ed. 20/100, 8⁷/₈" x 11⁷/₈", etching, dist. MMFC....... | — | 35.00 |
| ☐ TWO PELICAN, ed. 56/200, 5⁷/₈" x 8⁷/₈", etching, dist. MMFC......... | — | 25.00 |
| ☐ BLACKBIRD II, ed. 103/200, 3⁷/₈" x 8⁷/₈", etching, dist. MMFC......... | — | 25.00 |
| ☐ TRASH, ed. 78/200, 2⁷/₈" x 2⁷/₈", etching, dist. MMFC.............. | — | 20.00 |
| ☐ SAM, ed. 128/200, 2⁷/₈" x 2⁷/₈", etching, dist. MMFC............... | — | 20.00 |
| ☐ GREEN WING TEAL, ed. N/A, 5⁷/₈" x 11⁷/₈", etching, dist. MMFC....... | — | 30.00 |
| ☐ RING NECKS, ed. N/A, 5⁷/₈" x 11⁷/₈", etching, dist. MMFC............. | — | 30.00 |
| ☐ BLUE WING TEAL, ed. N/A, 5⁷/₈" x 11⁷/₈", etching, dist. MMFC......... | — | 30.00 |
| ☐ SQUIRRELS #2, ed. N/A, 5⁷/₈" x 8⁷/₈", etching, dist. MMFC........... | — | 30.00 |
| ☐ PINTAILS, ed. N/A, 5⁷/₈" x 11⁷/₈", etching, dist. MMFC.............. | — | 30.00 |
| ☐ BOBWHITE #2, ed. N/A, 8⁷/₈" x 11⁷/₈", etching, dist. MMFC........... | — | 35.00 |
| ☐ TREED, ed. N/A, 8⁷/₈" x 11⁷/₈", etching, dist. MMFC................ | — | 35.00 |
| ☐ BARN OWL #2, ed. N/A, 11⁷/₈" x 15⁷/₈", etching, dist. MMFC.......... | — | 50.00 |
| ☐ EAGLE OWL #2, ed. N/A, 11⁷/₈" x 15⁷/₈", etching, dist. MMFC......... | — | 50.00 |
| ☐ DUO, ed. N/A, 6" x 9", etching, dist. MMFC...................... | — | 20.00 |
| ☐ PEACE, ed. 250, 3⁵/₈" x 4½", etching, dist. MMFC................. | — | 20.00 |
| ☐ CANADIAN, ed. 250, 3⁵/₈" x 4½", etching, dist. MMFC.............. | — | 20.00 |
| ☐ THE CAROLERS, ed. 250, 3⁵/₈" x 4½", etching, dist. MMFC........... | — | 20.00 |
| ☐ CANVAS BACK DRAKE, ed. 150, 6" x 9", etching, dist. MMFC......... | — | 30.00 |
| ☐ CADEWALL DRAKE, ed. 150. 6" x 9", etching, dist. MMFC............ | — | 30.00 |
| ☐ PINTAIL DRAKE, ed. 150, 6" x 9", etching, dist. MMFC............. | — | 30.00 |
| ☐ TURNSTONES, ed. 200, 7" x 12", etching, dist. MMFC.............. | 46.00 | — |
| ☐ EGRETS, ed. 200, 7" x 12", etching, dist. MMFC................. | 46.00 | — |
| ☐ WE TWO, ed. 200, 5⅞" x 3⅞", etching, dist. MMFC............... | 26.00 | — |
| ☐ SANDERLINGS, ed. 200, 4½" x 12", etching, dist. MMFC............ | 40.00 | — |
| ☐ FLOTILLA, ed. 200, 4" x 6", etching, dist. MMFC................. | 26.00 | — |
| ☐ SHORE BIRDS, ed. 150, 9" x 6", etching, dist. MMFC.............. | 34.00 | — |
| ☐ ALERT, ed. 150, 9" x 6", etching, dist. MMFC................... | 34.00 | — |
| ☐ BANDITS II, ed. 150, 15" x 11", etching, dist. MMFC.............. | 66.00 | — |
| ☐ ARTIC CHILDREN, ed. 200, 9" x 12", etching, dist. MMFC........... | 54.00 | — |
| ☐ MALLARDS AWAY, ed. 200, 9⅞" x 10", etching, dist. MMFC.......... | 40.00 | — |
| ☐ TIGER CUBS, ed. N/A, 6" x 9", etching, dist. MMFC............... | 40.00 | — |
| ☐ MUREX, ed. N/A, 5" x 7", etching, dist. MMFC................... | 28.00 | — |
| ☐ NAUTILUS, ed. N/A, 5" x 7", etching, dist. MMFC................ | 28.00 | — |
| ☐ WHELK, ed. N/A, 5" x 7", etching, dist. MMFC................... | 28.00 | — |

# DAVID G. LOCKHART

Born in New York City, David Lockhart was educated and received his art training both here and in Europe.

Skilled in both watercolor and oil, he offers such varied subjects as hunting, fly fishing and yachting scenes in familiar and nostalgic moods. He was commissioned by the America's Cup Committee to do the official paintings of the last two races.

Widely traveled, his works reflect that of the sportsman in action, often capturing the outdoor setting at its finest.

| DAVID G. LOCKHART | ISSUE PRICE | CURRENT PRICE |
|---|---|---|
| ☐ COVEY POINT - QUAIL, rel. 1973. ed. 480, s/n, size not available, pub WWI .. | 40.00 | — |
| ☐ PUDDLE JUMPERS, rel. 1978. ed. 490, s/n, size not available, pub WWI ..... | 65.00 | — |
| ☐ AUTUMN CALM - BLACK DUCKS, rel. 1980. ed. 850, s/n, size not available, pub WWI ........ | 70.00 | — |
| ☐ DOVE CLUB AT WEBER'S, rel. 1980. ed. 600, s/n, size not available, pub WWI ........ | 50.00 | — |

# ART LONG

Art Long was born in northern Wisconsin and has spent his entire life close to nature. During his early years he worked in his father's taxidermy shop which he feels gave him first hand information and skills to paint wildlife. He now devotes all his time to painting.

Long works primarily in oils, although he does some work with watercolors and acrylics. He also does wood carving and sculpture. He has had some formal training but is basically self-taught and he feels that practice and more practice is the key to successful painting.

His work appears in private collections and galleries across the country. He has done illustrations for Sporting magazines, nationally distributed calendars, and designs for wrapping paper. He has also participated in wildlife art shows throughout the midwest.

Being an avid hunter and fisherman, Long knows the importance of proper resource management and good habitat. He has donated many originals and prints to raise funds for wildlife. He has contributed to Ducks Unlimited, Foundation for North American Wild Sheep, the Ruffed Grouse Society and the new Northwoods Wildlife Hospital and Rehabilitation Center started in his local area, as well as other wildlife organizations.

## ART LONG

| | | |
|---|---|---|
| ☐ WINTERY AFTERNOON - RUFFED GROUSE, rel. 1979. ed. 300, s/n, 28¼" x 22½", distr. NC ........ | 50.00 | 400.00 |
| ☐ EAGLE WITH NORTHERN PIKE, rel. 1980. ed. 480, s/n, 17¼" x 21½", distr. NC ........ | 35.00 | — |
| ☐ FIGHTING MUSKY, rel. 1980. ed. 480, s/n, 24¼" x 20", distr. NC ........ | 45.00 | — |
| ☐ QUIET POND - WOOD DUCKS, rel. 1980. ed. 350, s/n, 27¼" x 19½", distr. NC ........ | 50.00 | — |
| ☐ LOONS AT DUSK, rel. 1981. ed. 150, s/n, 29" x 23", distr. NC ........ | 100.00 | 200.00 |
| ☐ MAJESTIC MOUNTAINS - ELK, rel. 1981. ed. 500, s/n, 28" x 21", distr. NC .. | 60.00 | — |
| ☐ NEW YEARS DAY, rel. 1981. ed. 500, s/n, 37" x 25½", distr. NC ........ | 85.00 | — |
| ☐ BACKYARD BUDDY - BARRED OWL, rel. 1982. ed. 500, s/n, 11¾" x 15¾", distr. NC ........ | 30.00 | — |
| ☐ SPIRIT OF THE NORTH - LOON, rel. 1982. ed. 480, s/n, 17⅛" x 21¼", distr. NC ........ | 40.00 | — |
| ☐ SPRINGTIME SPLENDOR, rel. 1983. ed. 480, s/n, 29" x 23", distr. NC ...... | 60.00 | — |

| | ISSUE PRICE | CURRENT PRICE |
|---|---|---|
| ☐ **STONY BROOK - GREAT BLUE HERON,** rel. 1983. ed. 480, s/n, 17⅛″ x 21¼″, distr. NC . . . . . . . . . . . . . . . . . . . . . . . . . . . . . . . . . . . . . . . . . . . . . . | 80.00 | — |
| ☐ **UNDER THE BALSAM,** rel. 1983. ed. 480, s/n, 29″ x 23″, distr. NC . . . . . . . . | 40.00 | — |

# ROBERT LONG

The pursuit of knowledge is one of life's essential ingredients. There is nothing, perhaps, which provides us more gratification. For this artist, painting is a part of his thirst for learning. One's philosophy of living is a constantly developing evolving phenomenon. This may be the reason that painting did not begin early in his life. Instead, Long spent many years in another profession before realizing his necessity to express his inner feelings visually. But his paintings have a meaning beyond the visual image. He feels a good painting and the thought behind it should be, for the viewer, what a grain of sand is to the oyster. His decision to paint had its roots in a quotation from philosopher Will James: "The best use of life is to spend it for something which will outlast it."

Long's watercolors have hung in juried exhibits across the country. He has had more than fifty one-artist exhibits. His paintings hang in selected galleries throughout the United States. He paints in transparent watercolor and is a member of the Midwest Watercolor Society.

Eight signed and numbered limited edition prints have been published from his paintings and are sold to more than 600 dealers in 48 states and Canada. He is widely known for his remarques which are painted in original watercolor.

**NUZZLIN'** *by Robert Long*

## ROBERT LONG

| | ISSUE PRICE | CURRENT PRICE |
|---|---|---|
| ☐ **A HERITAGE PASSING**, rel. 1975. ed. 1,000, s/n, litho, pub SAG | 25.00 | — |
| ed. 1,000, s/o | 15.00 | — |
| ☐ **NATURE'S LATTICEWORK**, rel. 1975. ed. 250, s/n, litho, pub SAG | 25.00 | — |
| ed. 250 | 15.00 | — |
| ☐ **RETIREMENT**, rel. 1978. ed. 1,150, s/n, litho, pub SAG | 25.00 | — |
| ed. 100, s/n, remarqued in watercolor | 50.00 | 105.00 |
| ☐ **HUB**, rel. 1979. ed. 750, s/n, litho, pub SAG | 40.00 | — |
| ed. 100, s/n, remarqued in watercolor | 75.00 | 135.00 |
| ☐ **AUTUMN'S SUBTLE BEAUTY**, rel. 1982. ed. 550, s/n, litho, pub SAG | 65.00 | — |
| ed. 300, s/n, remarqued in watercolor | 100.00 | 120.00 |
| ☐ **BLACK GINGER AND HOMEMAKE SIN**, rel. 1983. ed. 950, s/n, litho, pub SAG | 42.50 | — |
| ed. 50, s/n, remarqued in watercolor | 95.00 | 130.00 |
| ☐ **NUZZLIN'**, rel. 1983. ed. 950, s/n, litho, pub SAG | 42.50 | — |
| ed. 50, s/n, remarqued in watercolor | 95.00 | 130.00 |
| ☐ **SOMEONE'S PRINCE**, rel. 1983. ed. 950, s/n, litho, pub SAG | 85.00 | — |
| ed. 300, s/n, remarqued in watercolor | 150.00 | — |

# TED LONG

Ted Long has been interested in art since his first artistic attempts at the age of six. Although having no formal training in the classroom, he has received his inspiration from the world around him. And what a rich environment it has been.

According to Long, "I have been fortunate to have grown up in a place where I could experience the uniqueness of western history."

Long's career prior to becoming a full time artist included being a movie director and a television Art Director. Obviously, those experiences have helped shape his attitude and sharpen his eye for the details he knows are important to a viewer.

In addition to his painting, Long added sculpture to his repertoire of artistic expression.

The late John Wayne owned a large collection of Long's artwork, including both paintings and sculpture. Other collectors include Catherine Ross, Ken Curtis, Ben Johnson, Amanda Blake, and the late Henry Fonda.

## TED LONG

☐ **IN SEARCH OF BEAVER**, ed. 500, s/n, 21" x 17", distr. GI .......... **65.00** —

# ROBERT LOUGHEED

For several years, Robert Lougheed and his wife Cordy lived high above the Santa Fe Trail in New Mexico's Sangre de Cristo mountain range. During the spring and fall Lougheed painted and gathered subject materials on several of the large cattle ranches in the area.

He traveled widely throughout the West sketching grizzly bears, deer, moose, elk, caribou, and antelope from life. From his studio in his adobe home, he could view winter-hungry deer munching leaves off rose bushes and apple trees. They were so close that Lougheed could paint them from his window.

Brought up on a farm in central Canada, Robert Lougheed started drawing animals and wildlife at an age when he was learning to read and write. His models were his father's horses and cattle, as well as the wildlife that he and his friends captured.

His formal art training began at the Ontario College of Arts and the 'Ecole des Beaux Arts' in Montreal. Later, after working for the *Toronto Star* newspaper, he went to New York to study with Frank Vincent DuMond and Dean Cornwell at the Art Student's League.

**IN THE QUIET OF WINTER** *by Robert Lougheed*

Lougheed then entered the New York art market. During his thirty-year commercial career, he received commissions to do *Reader's Digest* covers, and illustrations for many of the major national magazines including: *True, National Geographic, Colliers,* and *Sports Afield.* One of his most memorable and visible commercial art creations was the "Flying Red Horse" for Mobil Oil, and also the steeplechase horses for Texaco. He was commissioned to design the Buffalo Stamp, the last six-cent stamp in its series for the United States Post Office Department.

During his illustrating and commercial art period, he successfully continued to do fine art for the American and Canadian art galleries. He devoted one year to painting a one-man show for the Continental Gallery in Montreal.

The Lougheeds lived in Westport and in Newtown, Connecticut during the New York portion of his career. However, regular field trips were scheduled to reacquaint the artist with the West. He recalled, "Every fall, the day after Labor Day, Cordy and I would start out in our camper headed for the West. For two months I would paint in Texas, Colorado, Arizona, Utah, and New Mexico. By the time I returned to Connecticut in November, I would have enough paintings and reference material to carry me through until the next fall."

He painted illustrations for Marguerite Henry's book, *Mustang,* and the original oils hang in the permanent collection of the National Cowboy Hall of Fame in Oklahoma City. The new Henry book, *San Domingo,* was recently published using Lougheed's paintings as illustrations.

For twenty-five years, Lougheed was a member of the eminent Salmagundi Club, and for ten years he was a member of the Society of Animal Artists. He was a charter member of the National Academy of Western Art and a member of the Cowboy Artists of America.

Three of his originals were included in the international "Animals in Art" exhibition at the Royal Ontario Museum in Toronto in 1975. This was the largest collection of wildlife art ever assembled.

His paintings hang in major public and private collections in the United States, Canada and Europe.

Lougheed passed away June 1982.

**ROBERT LOUGHEED**

| | ISSUE PRICE | CURRENT PRICE |
|---|---|---|
| ☐ **IN THE QUIET OF WINTER,** rel. 1977. ed. 950, s/n, 18" x 30", pub MPPI . . . . . | 85.00 | — |
| ☐ **DUST TRAIL OF THE BELL REMUDA,** ed. 800, s/n, 16½" x 33", pub PP . . . . . | 125.00 | — |

| | | ISSUE PRICE | CURRENT PRICE |
|---|---|---|---|
| ☐ | OPEN RANGE ENCOUNTER, rel. 1980. ed. 1,000, s/n, 20½" x 35", pub SCG . | 150.00 | Sold Out |
| ☐ | SUNSET IN THE HIGH COUNTRY, rel. 1980. ed. 1,000, s/n, 18" x 36", pub SCG . . . . . . . . . . . . . . . . . . . . . . . . . . . . . . . . . . . . . . . . . . . | 115.00 | — |
| ☐ | NAVAJO TAPESTRY, rel. 1982. ed. 950, s/n, 19¼" x 32½", pub MPPI . . . . . . | 115.00 | — |

# CHARLES LOVATO

Artist, poet, jeweler, craftsman — Charles Lovato is an amazingly talented individual. And yet for all of his skill one can sense in each of his creations an unparalleled humility and a deep respect for the earth — for the beauty of the nature that surrounds us.

Lovato lives between the Santo Domingo and Cochiti Pueblos in the majestic Rio Grande valley of Northern New Mexico. He takes inspiration for his work from his ancestry and the land around him, and combines these with a unique style that conveys, in an ethereal way, man's age-old alliance with the earth and all living things. His works seem to reach back in time, into the farthest reaches of our subconcious memory and awaken our senses with an exploration of the abstract designs of pueblo pottery. Many of these ancient designs are used in his striking contemporary images. Often a shard of prehistoric pottery, found on one of his walks around the area of his home, will be the seed of an idea for a new painting or lithograph.

The list of honors Lovato has received is impressive, including top awards at the Philbrook Annual, the Gallup Inter Tribal Ceremonial, the Pine Ridge Arts and Crafts Show in South Dakota, the Heard Museum's Annual Arts and Crafts Exhibit, and the Scottsdale National Indian Arts Exhibition. Of special note is his winning, in both 1969 and 1971, the Avery Memorial Award for the Most Outstanding Painting at the Heard Museum Exhibit. Another distinction is that he is the only artist to have emerged from the conservative Santo Domingo Pueblo.

In his work Lovato uses the colors to be found in his beautiful country; deep umber and terra cotta, sandy colored beiges and brown, warm yellows and an occasional touch of brilliant green or the bright blue of the sky.

## CHARLES LOVATO

| | | | |
|---|---|---|---|
| ☐ | SONG FROM THE EARTH & MAN, ed. 100, stone lithograph, pub NWDHG . . . . . | 300.00 | 750.00 |
| ☐ | I HAVE GIVEN YOU REASONS TO LIVE, ed. 100, stone lithograph, pub NWDHG | 300.00 | 650.00 |
| ☐ | HE WILL HAVE LEFT HIS MARK, ed. 100, stone lithograph, pub NWDHG . . . . . | 250.00 | 500.00 |
| ☐ | ORIGINS, ed. 100, stone lithograph, pub NWDHG . . . . . . . . . . . . . . . . . . . . . . | 300.00 | 500.00 |
| ☐ | NOW ONLY MEMORIES, editions and size not available, pub NWDHG . . . . . . . | 80.00 | 140.00 |
| ☐ | THE HANDS OF MAN, ed. 100, s/n, 18" x 26", stone lithograph, pub NWDHG . | 300.00 | — |
| ☐ | CHILD OF THE EARTH, ed. and size not known . . . . . . . . . . . . . . . . . . . . . . . . | 50.00 | 75.00 |
| ☐ | NOW ONLY MEMORIES, ed. and size not known . . . . . . . . . . . . . . . . . . . . . . . | 80.00 | 350.00 |

# RALPH LOVE

A thorough knowledge of his subject, plus a natural feeling for beauty, and backed up by years of careful study of the skills necessary to express himself, has made Ralph Love one of the top landscape painters of the country.

A famous teacher once said that to learn all the words of the dictionary was not enough to make you a short story writer; that unless you had something to say the words are useless.

Love has served on many art juries, including the S.W.A.M.H. DeYoung Museum Show and the Leguna Art Festival. He has lectured and demonstrated in most of the major art associations in Southern California. As art instructor he has served on the faculty of the School of Art and Design at Laguna Beach, and guest instructor at the art school at Pescadero under the late Dr. Marque Reitzel.

## RALPH LOVE

| | ISSUE PRICE | CURRENT PRICE |
|---|---|---|
| ☐ **SONATA IN COLOR**, ed. 950, s/n, 24″ x 16½″, pub CGAL | 150.00 | — |
| ed. 12, Artist accented, s/n | 420.00 | — |
| ☐ **PACIFIC GRANDEUR**, ed. 950, s/n, 24½″ x 16½″, pub CGAL | 150.00 | — |
| ed. 12, Artist accented, s/n | 420.00 | — |
| ☐ **SENTINEL OF THE WEST**, ed. 950, s/n, 24″ x 16½″, pub CGAL | 150.00 | — |
| ed. 12, Artist accented, s/n | 420.00 | — |
| ☐ **AFTER THE GOLDRUSH**, ed. 950, s/n, 24½″ x 16½″, pub CGAL | 150.00 | — |
| ed. 12, Artist accented, s/n | 420.00 | — |
| ☐ **MOMENTS OF GOLD**, ed. 950, s/n, 24½″ x 16½″, pub CGAL | 150.00 | — |
| ed. 12, Artist accented, s/n | 420.00 | — |
| ☐ **EARLY NEW MEXICO**, ed. 950, s/n, 23½″ x 16½″, pub CGAL | 150.00 | — |
| ed. 12, Artist accented, s/n | 420.00 | — |
| ☐ **LAND OF THE APACHE**, ed. 950, s/n, 24″ x 16″, pub CGAL | 150.00 | — |
| ed. 12, Artist accented, s/n | 420.00 | — |
| ☐ **FISHING VILLAGE**, ed. 950, s/n, 24″ x 16″, pub CGAL | 150.00 | — |
| ed. 12, Artist accented, s/n | 420.00 | — |
| ☐ **DESERT THUNDER**, ed. 950, s/n, 24″ x 15½″, pub CGAL | 150.00 | — |
| ed. 12, Artist accented, s/n | 420.00 | — |
| ☐ **LITTLE RANCHO**, General run, 24″ x 15½″, pub CGAL | 19.00 | — |
| ed. 12, Artist accented, s/n | 420.00 | — |
| ☐ **TETON MEADOW**, General run, 23½″ x 16″, pub CGAL | 19.00 | — |
| ed. 12, Artist accented, s/n | 420.00 | — |
| ☐ **AUTUMN IN CALIFORNIA**, ed. 950, s/n, 24″ x 16″, pub CGAL | 150.00 | — |
| ed. 12, Artist accented, s/n | 420.00 | — |

# TOM LOVELL

"I try to place myself back in time and imagine situations that would make interesting and appealing pictures." Tom Lovell's words portray his work almost as well as the pictures themselves. His paintings are rooted in fact, but it is his imagination, his interpretation, and his ability to create the strongest and simplest design commensurate with the required elements of the subject, that lifts his work to the classic level.

**SUGAR IN THE COFFEE** *by Tom Lovell*

Lovell's love of books, museums and pictures led him to enroll in the College of Fine Arts at Syracuse University. He received his degree in 1931, but actually his career as an illustrator while still in college. In 1944 he enlisted in the Marines and found himself working for *Leatherneck* and other Marine Corps publications. After the war he resumed his career as a highly successful illustrator. With a major commission in 1969, Lovell turned solely to the American West for his painting inspiration. In the ensuing years, he has carved a solid place for himself as a leader in the field of contemporary Western art. He is a much-feted member of the Cowboy Artists of America, the National Academy of Western Art, and the Society of Illustrators Hall of Fame.

## TOM LOVELL

| | ISSUE PRICE | CURRENT PRICE |
|---|---|---|
| ☐ CARSON'S BOATYARD, rel. 1981. ed. 1,000, s/n, 27" x 18½", pub GW . . . . . | 150.00 | — |
| ☐ THE DECEIVER, rel. 1981. ed. 1,000, s/n, 30" x 18½", pub GW . . . . . . . . . . . | 150.00 | — |
| ☐ FIRES ON THE OREGON TRAIL, rel. 1981. ed. 1,000, s/n, 22" x 26½", pub GW . . . . . . . . . . . . . . . . . . . . . . . . . . . . . . . . . . . . . . . . . . . . | 150.00 | — |
| ☐ INVITATION TO TRADE, rel. 1982. ed. 1,000, s/n, 22" x 29", pub GW . . . . . . | 150.00 | — |
| ☐ THE WHEELSOAKERS, rel. 1982. ed. 1,000, s/n, 30¼" x 19¾", pub GW . . . . | 150.00 | — |
| ☐ SUGAR IN THE COFFEE, rel. 1983. ed. 650, s/n, 30½" x 18⅞", pub GW . . . . . | 165.00 | — |
| ☐ WALKING COYOTE AND THE BUFFALO ORPHANS, rel. 1983. ed. 650, s/n, 22½" x 28", pub GW . . . . . . . . . . . . . . . . . . . . . . . . . . . . . . . . . . . . . . . | 165.00 | — |

# RICHARD LUCE

Richard Luce's work is a tribute to his enthusiasm and love for painting and the West.

Luce attended Dutches Community College in Poughkeepsie, and found his first job in Manhattan as a commercial illustrator.

"I feel that my work is primarily landscape," says Luce. "I also realize that the Indians, the mountain men, the weapons, the very life I portray, must be authentic. And, of course, I must travel the West; it is so spacious, so clean, so unspoiled in many areas. It is an inspiration in itself."

## RICHARD LUCE

| | | |
|---|---|---|
| ☐ A TRAPPER'S WEALTH, rel. 1981. ed. 975, s/n, 24" x 34½", pub FHG . . . . . . | 80.00 | 130.00 |
| ☐ EAGLE COUNTRY, rel. 1981. ed. 975, s/n, 22" x 30", pub FHG . . . . . . . . . . . | 80.00 | 160.00 |
| ☐ QUIET PAUSE, rel. 1981. ed. 975, s/n, 22" x 30", pub FHG . . . . . . . . . . . . . | 65.00 | 160.00 |
| ☐ THE SCOUTS, rel. 1981. ed. 975, s/n, 24" x 36¾", pub FHG . . . . . . . . . . . . . | 80.00 | 130.00 |
| ☐ BREAKING THE SKYLINE, rel. 1982. ed. 975, s/n, 21" x 35", pub FHG . . . . . . | 80.00 | 130.00 |
| ☐ DOWNWIND, rel. 1982. ed. 975, s/n, 20" x 38", pub FHG . . . . . . . . . . . . . . . | 80.00 | — |
| ☐ LAST CROSSING, rel. 1982. ed. 975, s/n, 24" x 34", pub FHG . . . . . . . . . . . | 80.00 | — |
| ☐ PRIMING THE PIECE, rel. 1982. ed. 975, s/n, 32" x 24", pub FHG . . . . . . . . . | 80.00 | — |
| ☐ PRAYER TO THE FOUR WINDS, rel. 1983. ed. 975, s/n, 24" x 26½", pub FHG | 80.00 | — |
| ☐ THE TROPHY, rel. 1983. ed. 975, s/n, 22" x 32", pub FHG . . . . . . . . . . . . . . . | 80.00 | — |

**PRAYER TO THE FOUR WINDS** *by Richard Luce*

## GARY LUCY

| | ISSUE PRICE | CURRENT PRICE |
|---|---|---|
| ☐ **MERRIAM'S WILD TURKEY**, rel. 1980. ed. 750, s/n, size not available, pub WWI | 45.00 | — |

## STEPHEN E. LYMAN

Stephen E. Lyman is one with the wilderness, in his art and in his life.

Lyman was raised in the Pacific Northwest, regularly hiking with his family into the Snake River Country. He always intended to be an artist, eventually receiving his training at the Art Center School of Design in Pasadena. After graduation, he worked in commercial illustration in Los Angeles, but found the big city lifestyle not to his liking. He returned to his native state, Idaho, there devoting two years to discovering and developing the type of art that he was to call his own.

Lyman prefers his own keen senses and the camera for his field work, confining his sketching and painting to the studio. He has a penchant for detail, which leads the viewer to study his work for what seems to be hours, searching out and enjoying each subtlety.

**EARLY WINTER IN THE MOUNTAINS** *by Steve Lyman*

## STEPHEN E. LYMAN

|  | ISSUE PRICE | CURRENT PRICE |
|---|---|---|
| ☐ **EARLY WINTER IN THE MOUNTAINS,** rel. 1983. ed. 850, s/n, 30½" x 18¾", pub GW | 95.00 | — |
| ☐ **END OF THE RIDGE,** rel. 1983. ed. 850, s/n, 30½" x 19⅜", pub GW | 95.00 | — |
| ☐ **THE PASS,** rel. 1983. ed. 850, s/n, 30½" x 16⅞", pub GW | 95.00 | — |

# DAVID MAASS

Born and raised in Minnesota, David Maass has had ample opportunity to study the ways of nature firsthand. He spent much of his youth exploring the Mississippi River bottoms, and he took full advantage of the numerous migrating waterfowl which frequent that great flyway.

After high school, Maass became a professional illustrator but his interest in wildlife art remained strong, and in the late fifties he was invited to display his work at galleries in New York and Chicago.

In 1974, Maass won the Federal Duck Stamp Design competition with his stunning portrayal of wood ducks. Later in 1974, he was further honored as the Ducks Unlimited Artist of the Year.

In 1977, he was asked by the Department of Natural Resources to design the state's first waterfowl stamp; and in 1979, his striking design of a pair of pintails was selected as the third Minnesota State Duck Stamp Print.

He was selected by the National Wild Turkey Federation as their Conservationist of the Year.

The Ruffed Grouse Society of North America selected Maass to design their 1980 print, and the Minnesota Wildlife Heritage Foundation named him their first Minnesota Wildlife Artist of the Year.

He was further honored by being selected for the prestigious Leigh Yawkey Woodson Bird Art Show in Wausau, Wisconsin.

A true conservationist, Maass has donated a number of original paintings and more than 1,000 limited edition prints to Ducks Unlimited Chapters throughout the country.

## DAVID A. MAASS

| | ISSUE PRICE | CURRENT PRICE |
|---|---|---|
| ☐ MISTY MORNING - WOODCOCK, rel. 1972. ed. 450, s/n, 20″ x 17″, pub WWI . | 50.00 | 1,250.00 |
| ed. 100 remarque artist proof . . . . . . . . . . . . . . . . . . . . . . . . . . . . . . . . . | 125.00 | 1,350.00 |
| ☐ BACK BAY - MALLARDS, rel. 1973. ed. 600, s/n, 11″ x 15½″, pub WWI . . . . . | 40.00 | 750.00 |
| ed. 100 remarque artist proof . . . . . . . . . . . . . . . . . . . . . . . . . . . . . . . . . | 110.00 | 900.00 |
| ☐ MISTY MORNING - RUFFED GROUSE, rel. 1973. ed. 580, s/n, 20″ x 17″, pub WWI . . . . . . . . . . . . . . . . . . . . . . . . . . . . . . . . . . . . . . . . . . . . . . . . | 55.00 | 1,300.00 |
| ed. 190 remarque artist proof . . . . . . . . . . . . . . . . . . . . . . . . . . . . . . . . . | 135.00 | 1,400.00 |
| ☐ BREAKING IN BLUEBILLS, rel. 1973. ed. 480, s/n, 16″ x 25″, pub WWI . . . . . | 55.00 | 725.00 |
| ed. 131 remarque artist proof . . . . . . . . . . . . . . . . . . . . . . . . . . . . . . . . . | 125.00 | 825.00 |
| ☐ AMONG THE PINES - QUAIL, rel. 1973. ed. 600, s/n, 11″ x 16″, pub WWI . . . . | 40.00 | 500.00 |
| ed. 100 remarque artist proof . . . . . . . . . . . . . . . . . . . . . . . . . . . . . . . . . | 110.00 | 600.00 |
| ☐ MISTY MORNING - WOOD DUCKS, rel. 1974. ed. 580, s/n, 30″ x 17″, pub WWI . . . . . . . . . . . . . . . . . . . . . . . . . . . . . . . . . . . . . . . . . . . . . . . . | 55.00 | 1,200.00 |
| ed. 161 remarque artist proof . . . . . . . . . . . . . . . . . . . . . . . . . . . . . . . . . | 125.00 | 1,300.00 |
| ☐ BREAKING WEATHER - CANADA GEESE, rel. 1973. ed. 580, s/n, 16″ x 25″, pub WWI . . . . . . . . . . . . . . . . . . . . . . . . . . . . . . . . . . . . . . . . . . . . . . . . | 55.00 | 800.00 |
| ed. 111 remarque artist proof . . . . . . . . . . . . . . . . . . . . . . . . . . . . . . . . . | 125.00 | 900.00 |
| ☐ ONE THE MOVE - CANVASBACKS, rel. 1974. ed. 580, s/n, 16″ x 25″, pub WWI . . . . . . . . . . . . . . . . . . . . . . . . . . . . . . . . . . . . . . . . . . . . . . . . | 60.00 | 550.00 |
| ed. 100 remarque artist proof . . . . . . . . . . . . . . . . . . . . . . . . . . . . . . . . . | 145.00 | 650.00 |
| ☐ RIVER FLATS - PINTAILS, rel. 1974. ed. 580, s/n, 16″ x 25″, pub WWI . . . . . | 60.00 | 550.00 |
| ed. 70 remarque artist proof . . . . . . . . . . . . . . . . . . . . . . . . . . . . . . . . . | 145.00 | 700.00 |
| ☐ RIDGE LINE - RUFFED GROUSE, rel. 1974. ed. 580, s/n, 15½″ x 25″, pub WWI . . . . . . . . . . . . . . . . . . . . . . . . . . . . . . . . . . . . . . . . . . . . . . . . | 70.00 | 775.00 |
| ed. 101 remarque artist proof . . . . . . . . . . . . . . . . . . . . . . . . . . . . . . . . . | 150.00 | 875.00 |
| ☐ AUTUMN BIRCH - WOODCOCK, rel. 1974. ed. 580, s/n, 16″ x 25″, pub WWI . | 70.00 | 850.00 |
| ed. 64 remarque artist proof . . . . . . . . . . . . . . . . . . . . . . . . . . . . . . . . . | 150.00 | 950.00 |
| ☐ RED HEAD BAY, rel. 1975. ed. 580, s/n, 16½″ x 25″, pub WWI . . . . . . . . . . . | 70.00 | 400.00 |
| ed. 75 remarque artist proof . . . . . . . . . . . . . . . . . . . . . . . . . . . . . . . . . | 150.00 | 550.00 |
| ☐ DUSK IN THE BAY - CANADA GEESE, rel. 1975. ed. 600, s/n, 11″ x 15″, pub WWI . . . . . . . . . . . . . . . . . . . . . . . . . . . . . . . . . . . . . . . . . . . . . . . . | 50.00 | 350.00 |
| ed. 75 remarque artist proof . . . . . . . . . . . . . . . . . . . . . . . . . . . . . . . . . | 145.00 | 500.00 |
| ☐ MISTY MORNING - MALLARDS, rel. 1975. ed. 580, s/n, 20″ x 17″, pub WWI . | 85.00 | 750.00 |
| ed. 156 remarque artist proof . . . . . . . . . . . . . . . . . . . . . . . . . . . . . . . . . | 175.00 | 850.00 |
| ☐ TWISTING THROUGH - BLUE WING TEAL, rel. 1975. ed. 580, s/n, 16½″ x 25″, pub WWI . . . . . . . . . . . . . . . . . . . . . . . . . . . . . . . . . . . . . . . . . . | 70.00 | 500.00 |
| ed. 75 remarque artist proof . . . . . . . . . . . . . . . . . . . . . . . . . . . . . . . . . | 150.00 | 675.00 |
| ☐ MISTY MORNING - QUAIL, rel. 1975. ed. 580, s/n, 20″ x 17″, pub WWI . . . . . | 85.00 | 750.00 |
| ed. 154 remarque artist proof . . . . . . . . . . . . . . . . . . . . . . . . . . . . . . . . . | 175.00 | 850.00 |
| ☐ WINTER WINDS - BLUEBILLS, rel. 1976. ed. 580, s/n, 16¼″ x 25″, pub WWI | 70.00 | 250.00 |
| ed. 75 remarque artist proof . . . . . . . . . . . . . . . . . . . . . . . . . . . . . . . . . | 150.00 | 350.00 |
| ☐ OVER THE POND - RUFFED GROUSE, rel. 1976. ed. 600, s/n, 11″ x 16″, pub WWI . . . . . . . . . . . . . . . . . . . . . . . . . . . . . . . . . . . . . . . . . . . . . . . . | 52.50 | 200.00 |
| ed. 75 remarque artist proof . . . . . . . . . . . . . . . . . . . . . . . . . . . . . . . . . | 150.00 | 300.00 |
| ☐ HASTY DEPARTURE - RUFFED GROUSE, rel. 1976. ed. 580, s/n, 16½″ x 25″, pub WWI . . . . . . . . . . . . . . . . . . . . . . . . . . . . . . . . . . . . . . . . . . | 70.00 | 600.00 |
| ed. 75 remarque artist proof . . . . . . . . . . . . . . . . . . . . . . . . . . . . . . . . . | 150.00 | 700.00 |
| ☐ MISTY MORNING - GREEN WINGS, rel. 1976. ed. 580, s/n, 20″ x 17″, pub WWI . . . . . . . . . . . . . . . . . . . . . . . . . . . . . . . . . . . . . . . . . . . . . . . . | 85.00 | 500.00 |
| ed. 75 remarque artist proof . . . . . . . . . . . . . . . . . . . . . . . . . . . . . . . . . | 175.00 | 600.00 |
| ☐ PLACID BACKWATERS - WOODDUCKS, rel. 1976. ed. 580, s/n, 16½″ x 25″, pub WWI . . . . . . . . . . . . . . . . . . . . . . . . . . . . . . . . . . . . . . . . . . | 70.00 | 350.00 |
| ed. 75 remarque artist proof . . . . . . . . . . . . . . . . . . . . . . . . . . . . . . . . . | 150.00 | 500.00 |
| ☐ SWEEPING THE NARROWS - CANVASBACKS, rel. 1976. ed. 580, s/n, 16½″ x 25″, pub WWI . . . . . . . . . . . . . . . . . . . . . . . . . . . . . . . . . . . . . . . . . . | 70.00 | 300.00 |
| ed. 75 remarque artist proof . . . . . . . . . . . . . . . . . . . . . . . . . . . . . . . . . | 150.00 | 450.00 |
| ☐ WESTERN MARSH - PINTAILS, rel. 1976. ed. 580, s/n, 16½″ x 25″, pub WWI | 70.00 | — |
| ed. 75 remarque artist proof . . . . . . . . . . . . . . . . . . . . . . . . . . . . . . . . . | 150.00 | — |
| ☐ RIVERS EDGE - MALLARDS, rel. 1977. ed. 580, s/n, 16½″ x 25″, pub WWI . . | 75.00 | 350.00 |
| ed. 75 remarque artist proof . . . . . . . . . . . . . . . . . . . . . . . . . . . . . . . . . | 160.00 | 450.00 |
| ☐ INTO THE SHALLOWS - CANADA GEESE, rel. 1977. ed. 580, s/n, 15½″ x 25″, pub WWI . . . . . . . . . . . . . . . . . . . . . . . . . . . . . . . . . . . . . . . . . . | 75.00 | 150.00 |
| ed. 75 remarque artist proof . . . . . . . . . . . . . . . . . . . . . . . . . . . . . . . . . | 160.00 | 250.00 |

| | ISSUE PRICE | CURRENT PRICE |
|---|---|---|
| ☐ **COVEY BREAK - QUAIL,** rel. 1977. ed. 580, s/n, 16½″ x 25″, pub WWI . . . . . | 75.00 | 225.00 |
| ed. 75 remarque artist proof . . . . . . . . . . . . . . . . . . . . . . . . . . . . . . . . . . . . | 160.00 | 350.00 |
| ☐ **AUTUMN MARSH - MALLARDS,** rel. 1977. ed. 580, s/n, 16½″ x 25″, pub WWI . . . | 75.00 | 425.00 |
| ed. 75 remarque artist proof . . . . . . . . . . . . . . . . . . . . . . . . . . . . . . . . . . . . | 160.00 | 550.00 |
| ☐ **BACK COUNTRY - RUFFS,** rel. 1977. ed. 580, s/n, 16½″ x 25″, pub WWI . . . . | 75.00 | 150.00 |
| ed. 75 remarque artist proof . . . . . . . . . . . . . . . . . . . . . . . . . . . . . . . . . . . . | 160.00 | 250.00 |
| ☐ **AUTUMN DAY - RUFFED GROUSE,** rel. 1977. ed. 850, s/n, 24″ x 20″, pub WWI . . . | 100.00 | 700.00 |
| ed. 75 remarque artist proof . . . . . . . . . . . . . . . . . . . . . . . . . . . . . . . . . . . . | 185.00 | 800.00 |
| ☐ **EARLY ARRIVALS - MALLARDS,** rel. 1977. ed. 850, s/n, 11″ x 16½″, pub WWI . . . | 55.00 | 150.00 |
| ed. 75 remarque artist proof . . . . . . . . . . . . . . . . . . . . . . . . . . . . . . . . . . . . | 115.00 | 275.00 |
| ☐ **DECEMBER SQUALL - PHEASANT,** rel. 1978. ed. 850, s/n, 16½″ x 25″, pub WWI . . . | 75.00 | 85.00 |
| ed. 75 remarque artist proof . . . . . . . . . . . . . . . . . . . . . . . . . . . . . . . . . . . . | 160.00 | — |
| ☐ **CAUTIOUS TRIO - TURKEY,** rel. 1978. ed. 850, s/n, 16½″ x 25″, pub WWI . . . | 75.00 | 85.00 |
| ed. 75 remarque artist proof . . . . . . . . . . . . . . . . . . . . . . . . . . . . . . . . . . . . | 160.00 | |
| ☐ **FIRST PASS - MALLARDS,** rel. 1978. ed. 850, s/n, 16½″ x 25″, pub WWI . . . | 85.00 | 100.00 |
| ed. 75 remarque artist proof . . . . . . . . . . . . . . . . . . . . . . . . . . . . . . . . . . . . | 185.00 | — |
| ☐ **NEW SNOW - RUFFED GROUSE,** rel. 1978. ed. 850, s/n, 16½″ x 15⅛″, pub WWI . . . | 85.00 | 225.00 |
| ed. 75 remarque artist proof . . . . . . . . . . . . . . . . . . . . . . . . . . . . . . . . . . . . | 185.00 | 325.00 |
| ☐ **SWINGING THE CHANNEL - CANVASBACKS,** rel. 1978. ed. 850, s/n, 16½″ x 25″, pub WWI . . . | 85.00 | 100.00 |
| ed. 75 remarque artist proof . . . . . . . . . . . . . . . . . . . . . . . . . . . . . . . . . . . . | 185.00 | — |
| ☐ **WOODLAND REPOSE - RUFFED GROUSE,** rel. 1978. ed. 850, s/n, 16½″ x 25″, pub WWI . . . | 100.00 | 650.00 |
| ed. 75 remarque artist proof . . . . . . . . . . . . . . . . . . . . . . . . . . . . . . . . . . . . | 200.00 | 750.00 |
| ☐ **WORKING THE BAY - BLUEBILLS,** rel. 1978. ed. 850, s/n, 16½″ x 25″, pub WWI . . . | 85.00 | 100.00 |
| ed. 75 remarque artist proof . . . . . . . . . . . . . . . . . . . . . . . . . . . . . . . . . . . . | 185.00 | — |
| ☐ **DEADWOOD CORNER - MALLARDS,** rel. 1978. ed. 850, s/n, 25″ x 16½″, pub WWI . . . | 85.00 | 175.00 |
| ed. 25 artist proofs remarqued . . . . . . . . . . . . . . . . . . . . . . . . . . . . . . . . . | 185.00 | 275.00 |
| ☐ **MARSHLAND - CANADA GEESE,** rel. 1978. ed. 850, s/n, 25″ x 16½″, pub WWI . . . | 75.00 | 150.00 |
| ed. 25 artist proofs remarqued . . . . . . . . . . . . . . . . . . . . . . . . . . . . . . . . . | 160.00 | 250.00 |
| ☐ **AUTUMN DAY - WOODCOCK,** rel. 1979. ed. 850, s/n, 20″ x 24″, pub WWI . . . | 100.00 | 150.00 |
| ed. 25 artist proofs remarqued . . . . . . . . . . . . . . . . . . . . . . . . . . . . . . . . . | 200.00 | — |
| ☐ **REELFOOT VISITORS AT MIDDLEFORK CLUB,** rel. 1979. ed. 850, s/n, 25″ x 16¼″, pub WWI . . . | 100.00 | — |
| ed. 30 artist proofs remarqued . . . . . . . . . . . . . . . . . . . . . . . . . . . . . . . . . | 200.00 | — |
| ☐ **GROUSE COVER,** rel. 1979. ed. 850, s/n, 25″ x 16½″, pub WWI . . . . . . . . . | 100.00 | 200.00 |
| ed. 30 artist proofs remarqued . . . . . . . . . . . . . . . . . . . . . . . . . . . . . . . . . | 200.00 | — |
| ☐ **HEAVY WEATHER - REDHEADS,** rel. 1979. ed. 850, s/n, 25″ x 16½″, pub WWI . . . | 100.00 | — |
| ed. 30 artist proofs remarqued . . . . . . . . . . . . . . . . . . . . . . . . . . . . . . . . . | 200.00 | — |
| ☐ **PINTAILS IN AUTUMN,** rel. 1979. ed. 950, s/n, 15⅝″ x 11⅛″, pub WWI . . . . | 50.00 | 65.00 |
| ☐ **MALLARDS IN AUTUMN,** rel. 1980. ed. 950, s/n, 15⅝″ x 11⅛″, pub WWI . . . . | 50.00 | 65.00 |
| ☐ **COMING IN - CANADA GEESE,** rel. 1969. ed. 400, s/n, size not available, pub WWI . . . | 50.00 | 850.00 |
| ☐ **MALLARDS,** rel. 1972. ed. 600, s/n, size not available, pub WWI . . . . . . . . . . . | 60.00 | 850.00 |
| Artists proofs, remarqued . . . . . . . . . . . . . . . . . . . . . . . . . . . . . . . . . . . . | N/A | 1,100.00 |
| ☐ **QUAIL,** rel. 1971. ed. 600, s/n, size not available, pub WWI . . . . . . . . . . . . . | 60.00 | 1,100.00 |
| Artists proofs, remarqued . . . . . . . . . . . . . . . . . . . . . . . . . . . . . . . . . . . . | N/A | 1,100.00 |
| ☐ **ABANDONED ORCHARD - RUFFED GROUSE,** rel. 1980. ed. 850, s/n, pub WWI. | 125.00 | 250.00 |
| Artists proofs, remarqued . . . . . . . . . . . . . . . . . . . . . . . . . . . . . . . . . . . . | N/A | 350.00 |
| ☐ **AFTER THE RAIN - BOBWHITE,** rel. 1980. ed. 850, s/n, 16″ x 25″, pub WWI . . | 100.00 | — |
| Artists proofs, remarqued . . . . . . . . . . . . . . . . . . . . . . . . . . . . . . . . . . . . | 200.00 | — |
| ☐ **CANVASBACKS IN AUTUMN,** rel. 1980. ed. 950, s/n, 16″ x 11″, pub WWI . . . | 50.00 | 65.00 |
| ☐ **INTO QUIET WATERS - MALLARDS,** rel. 1980. ed. 850, s/n, 25″ x 18″, pub WWI . . . | 100.00 | — |
| remarqued . . . . . . . . . . . . . . . . . . . . . . . . . . . . . . . . . . . . . . . . . . . . . . . | 200.00 | — |

| | ISSUE PRICE | CURRENT PRICE |
|---|---|---|
| ☐ **NORTH SHORE - GOLDENEYES,** rel. 1980. ed. 850, s/n, 25" x 17", pub WWI . | 100.00 | — |
| remarqued . . . . . . . . . . . . . . . . . . . . . . . . . . . . . . . . . . . . . . . . . . . . . . . . | 200.00 | — |
| ☐ **RUFFED GROUSE IN AUTUMN,** rel. 1980. ed. 950, s/n, 16" x 11", pub WWI . . | 50.00 | 65.00 |
| ☐ **TWO AWAY - WOODCOCK,** rel. 1980. ed. 850, s/n, 15" x 18", pub WWI . . . . . | 85.00 | — |
| remarqued . . . . . . . . . . . . . . . . . . . . . . . . . . . . . . . . . . . . . . . . . . . . . . . . | 185.00 | — |
| ☐ **BACKWATER HIDEAWAY - WOOD DUCKS,** rel. 1981. ed. 950, s/n, size not available, pub WWI . . . . . . . . . . . . . . . . . . . . . . . . . . . . . . . . . . . . . . . . . | 150.00 | — |
| ☐ **EARLY WINTER MORNING - BOBWHITE,** rel. 1981. ed. 850, s/n, size not available, pub WWI . . . . . . . . . . . . . . . . . . . . . . . . . . . . . . . . . . . . . . | 150.00 | 400.00 |
| remarqued . . . . . . . . . . . . . . . . . . . . . . . . . . . . . . . . . . . . . . . . . . . . . . . . | N/A | 425.00 |
| ☐ **FARM POND - GREEN WINGED TEAL,** rel. 1981. ed. 850, s/n, size not available, pub WWI . . . . . . . . . . . . . . . . . . . . . . . . . . . . . . . . . . . . . . . . | 125.00 | — |
| ☐ **JIMMY'S POINT - DELTA MARSH BLUEBILLS,** rel. 1981. ed. 950, s/n, size not available, pub WWI . . . . . . . . . . . . . . . . . . . . . . . . . . . . . . . . . . . | 125.00 | — |
| ☐ **LOW CEILING - CANADA GEESE,** rel. 1981. ed. 850, s/n, size not available, pub WWI . . . . . . . . . . . . . . . . . . . . . . . . . . . . . . . . . . . . . . . . . . . . . . | 100.00 | — |
| ☐ **SUNLIT MARSH - MALLARDS,** rel. 1981. ed. 950, s/n, size not available, pub WWI . . . . . . . . . . . . . . . . . . . . . . . . . . . . . . . . . . . . . . . . . . . . . . . . | 125.00 | — |
| ☐ **TIMBER'S EDGE - RUFFED GROUSE,** rel. 1981. ed. 950, s/n, size not available, pub WWI . . . . . . . . . . . . . . . . . . . . . . . . . . . . . . . . . . . . . . . . | 150.00 | — |
| ☐ **WILD WINGS LOGO - GREENWING TEAL,** rel. 1981. ed. 950, s/n, size not available, pub WWI . . . . . . . . . . . . . . . . . . . . . . . . . . . . . . . . . . . . . | 75.00 | 100.00 |
| ☐ **WINDSWEPT MARSH - CANVASBACKS,** rel. 1982. ed. 950, s/n, size not available, pub WWI . . . . . . . . . . . . . . . . . . . . . . . . . . . . . . . . . . . . . . | 150.00 | — |

# FRED MACHETANZ

Fred Machetanz is an artist who portrays Alaska. He first went to Alaska in 1935, painting its people, animals, and seasons. His art hangs in collections from East to West. A complete collection of his 49 stone lithographs hangs at the University of Alaska in Fairbanks.

Machetanz was appointed a "Distinguished Associate of Art" in 1963 from the University of Alaska, Fairbanks. He was elected to the Alaska Hall of Fame in 1966 and awarded an honorary Doctorate in Fine Arts in 1973 at the University of Alaska, Anchorage.

**TENDER ARCTIC** *by Fred Machetanz*

A book of his paintings, *The Alaskan Paintings of Fred Machetanz,* was published in 1977. Also that year, Machetanz was named "Alaskan of the Year", based on his significant contribution to the character and growth of Alaska in the arts.

| FRED MACHETANZ | ISSUE PRICE | CURRENT PRICE |
|---|---|---|
| ☐ **FACE TO FACE,** rel. 1978. ed. 950, s/n, 36" x 24", pub MPPI | **150.00** | **1,150.00** |
| ☐ **HUNTER'S DAWN,** rel. 1978. ed. 950, s/n, 22" x 25", pub MPPI | **125.00** | **550.00** |
| ☐ **INTO THE HOME STRETCH,** rel. 1978. ed. 950, s/n, 25" x 37½", pub MPPI | **175.00** | **550.00** |
| ☐ **BEGINNINGS,** rel. 1979. ed. 950, s/n, 23" x 27", pub MPPI | **175.00** | **410.00** |
| ☐ **DECISION ON THE ICE FIELD,** rel. 1979. ed. 950, s/n, 22½" x 32½", pub MPPI | **150.00** | **410.00** |
| ☐ **PICK OF THE LITTER,** rel. 1979. ed. 950, s/n, 22¾" x 27", pub MPPI | **165.00** | **375.00** |
| ☐ **REACHING THE CAMPSITE,** rel. 1979. ed. 950, s/n, 25" x 37½", pub MPPI | **200.00** | **375.00** |
| ☐ **KING OF THE MOUNTAIN,** rel. 1980. ed. 950, s/n, 25" x 29", pub MPPI | **200.00** | **310.00** |
| ☐ **NELCHINA TRAIL,** rel. 1980. ed. 950, s/n, 24½" x 30", pub MPPI | **245.00** | **360.00** |
| ☐ **SOURDOUGH,** rel. 1980. ed. 950, s/n, 24½" x 30", pub MPPI | **245.00** | **375.00** |
| ☐ **WHEN THREE'S A CROWD,** rel. 1980. ed. 950, s/n, 24¾" x 35", pub MPPI | **225.00** | **375.00** |
| ☐ **GOLDEN YEARS,** rel. 1981. ed. 950, s/n, 24½" x 35½", pub MPPI | **245.00** | **410.00** |
| ☐ **MIDDAY MOONLIGHT,** rel. 1981. ed. 950, s/n, 23" x 27", pub MPPI | **265.00** | **390.00** |
| ☐ **WHAT EVERY HUNTER FEARS,** rel. 1981. ed. 950, s/n, 24½" x 30", pub MPPI | **245.00** | **350.00** |
| ☐ **WHERE MEN & DOGS SEEM SMALL,** rel. 1981. ed. 950, s/n, 29¾" x 24½", pub MPPI | **N/A** | **Sold Out** |
| ☐ **WINTER HARVEST,** rel. 1981. ed. 950, s/n, 24½" x 37½", pub MPPI | **265.00** | **325.00** |
| ☐ **MIGHTY HUNTER,** rel. 1982. ed. 950, s/n, 24⅝" x 35¼", pub MPPI | **265.00** | **375.00** |
| ☐ **MOOSE TRACKS,** rel. 1982. ed. 950, s/n, 24⅝" x 31", pub MPPI | **265.00** | **300.00** |
| ☐ **MOONLIT STAKEOUT,** rel. 1982. ed. 950, s/n, 24½" x 37¾", pub MPPI | **265.00** | **350.00** |
| ☐ **THE TENDER ARCTIC,** rel. 1982. ed. 950, s/n, 24½" x 37¾", pub MPPI | **265.00** | **360.00** |

# ALDERSON MAGEE

After a fifteen-year career in the field of aviation, Alderson Magee resigned to pursue an interest in fine arts, concentrating on the unique medium of scratchboard engraving.

Magee learned the fascinating technique of scratchboard engraving in Europe, while a technical representative for one of America's largest corporations. He has spent the last nine years seeking to master this century-old art form.

Striving for extremely fine detail and brilliant contrasting effects, he uses engraver's tools to cut through a dense India ink surface to a pure white underlayer of China clay. His skillful handling of this medium is well-suited to the depiction of wildlife and his accomplishments include the 1976-77 Federal Duck Stamp Print award.

He has gained national recognition for his unique wildlife portrayals, and is currently listed in *Who's Who in American Art.*

| ALDERSON MAGEE | | |
|---|---|---|
| ☐ **COACHMAN'S CONQUEST - BROOK TROUT,** rel. 1975. ed. 450, s/n, 7⅞" x 9⅞", pub SEL | **45.00** | **400.00** |
| ☐ **FIRST HATCHED - CANADA GEESE,** rel. 1978. ed. 580, s/n, 10" x 8", pub WWI | **75.00** | **85.00** |
| ☐ **PROFESSOR PRIZE - RAINBOW TROUT,** rel. 1978. ed. 580, s/n, 8" x 10", pub WWI | **75.00** | **100.00** |
| ☐ **JUMPING MALLARD,** rel. 1976. ed. 600, s/n, 16" x 20", pub WWI | **100.00** | **125.00** |
| ☐ **BOBCAT,** rel. 1982. ed. 600, s/n, 16" x 20", pub WWI | **85.00** | **—** |

# BETTY MALONE

Betty Malone has been drawing and painting practically all her life.

Since her initial one-woman show in 1973, Malone has sold hundreds of her memory-evoking originals across the country. She has received numerous awards and has had work accepted in an international show in Paris. In 1975, her first limited edition print was published.

Malone was born and reared in Charleston, Mississippi, a small town on the edge of the Delta. She received her education at Harding University and Memphis State University and worked for several years as a commercial artist.

She is a member of the Germantown Art League, the Tennessee Watercolor Society and the American League of Penwomen.

| BETTY MALONE | ISSUE PRICE | CURRENT PRICE |
|---|---|---|
| ☐ **NARY A NIBBLE,** rel. 1975. ed. 1,250, s/n, 16″ x 20″, pub SG . . . . . . . . . . . . | 30.00 | — |
| ☐ **CURIOSITY,** rel. 1976. ed. 1,250, s/n, 16″ x 20″, pub SG . . . . . . . . . . . . . . . | 30.00 | — |
| ☐ **GATEWAY TO A LEGEND,** rel. 1978. ed. 500, s/n, 16″ x 20″, pub SG . . . . . . . . | 30.00 | 60.00 |
| ed. 4,500, s/o . . . . . . . . . . . . . . . . . . . . . . . . . . . . . . . . . . . . . . . . . . . . . . . . | 20.00 | — |
| ☐ **THE WAY HOME,** rel. 1979. ed. 1,250, s/n, 18½″ x 24″, pub SG . . . . . . . . . . | 40.00 | — |
| ☐ **PLAYING UNDER THE HOUSE.** rel. 1980. ed. 750, s/n, 16″ x 20″, pub MS . . . | 30.00 | — |

# DON MARCO

With his ultra realistic style, Don Marco's detailed portraits of Indians and Western subjects draws immediate attention because of their unusual medium — crayon.

Born in Minnesota, Marco spent most of his work life in government service, living in Hawaii for twenty-seven years. He began to draw with crayon after his retirement five years ago.

His works are created on construction paper and consist primarily of 19th century Indians. He does not draw the Indian without carefully researching every detail of their lives. Occasionally Marco depicts a rugged ranch hand. Marco has developed his own crayon improvements and has a few secret techniques which give his portraits their unique appearance.

| DON MARCO | | |
|---|---|---|
| ☐ **APACHE,** rel. 1979. ed. 350, s/n, 18″ x 23″, pub ALL . . . . . . . . . . . . . . . . . . | 95.00 | — |
| ☐ **CHEYENNE HUNTER,** rel. 1979. ed. 350, s/n, 18″ x 23″, pub ALL . . . . . . . . . | 95.00 | — |
| ☐ **CHIEF LITTLE WOUND,** rel. 1979. ed. 350, s/n, 18″ x 23″, pub ALL . . . . . . . . | 95.00 | — |
| ☐ **BEAR BULL,** rel. 1979. ed. 1,150, s/n, 18″ x 24″ . . . . . . . . . . . . . . . . . . . . . | 60.00 | — |

# CAROLYN MARSHALL

Carolyn Marshall's work ranges from realism to abstraction and from pen and ink drawing to oil and acrylic paintings. Her drawings of sailboats have an authenticity not often seen in marine art, but her desire for strong design and expressive color always brings her back to abstract painting.

Marshall's abstracts have a wide range of color and design, with each painting suggesting its basis in the natural world. Her study of color has been extensive and her paintings reflect this knowledge in their richness and subtlety of color variations.

Marshall began painting at an early age and her continuing interest in art resulted in many awards, including the art prize upon graduation from high school. She also won the art award upon receipt of her B.F.A. degree from Newcomb College of Tulane University.

After further study in New York at the Art Student's League and Columbia University, Marshall moved to Texas where she taught drawing and design for three years at the University of Houston. In 1967 she moved to Austin where she obtained a Master of Fine Arts Degree from the University of Texas. She then taught for two years at Laguna Gloria Museum Art School and later conducted private classes in painting. For the past several years, Marshall has been a self-employed artist devoting all of her time to painting and graphics.

| CAROLYN MARSHALL | ISSUE PRICE | CURRENT PRICE |
|---|---|---|
| ☐ **SAILING SHIP "A"**, ed. 950, s/o, 16" x 20", pub HC, | 10.00 | — |
| black and white, hand colored | 25.00 | — |
| ☐ **SAILING SHIP "A"**, ed. 950, s/o, 16" x 20", pub HC, | 10.00 | — |
| black and white, hand colored | 25.00 | — |
| ☐ **SAILING SHIP "C"**, ed. 950, s/o, 16" x 20", pub HC, | 10.00 | — |
| black and white, hand colored | 25.00 | — |
| ☐ **SAILING SHIP "D"**, ed. 950, s/o, 16" x 20", pub HC, | 10.00 | — |
| black and white, hand colored | 25.00 | — |
| ☐ **SUNFISH**, ed. 950, s/o, 12" x 16", pub HC, | 9.00 | — |
| black and white, hand colored | 20.00 | — |
| ☐ **SNIPE**, ed. 950, s/o, 12" x 16", pub HC, | 9.00 | — |
| black and white, hand colored | 20.00 | — |
| ☐ **HOBIE 16**, ed. 950, s/o, 12" x 16", pub HC, | 9.00 | — |
| black and white, hand colored | 20.00 | — |
| ☐ **LIGHTNING**, ed. 950, s/o, 12" x 16", pub HC, | 9.00 | — |
| black and white, hand colored | 20.00 | — |
| ☐ **SAILING YACHT**, ed. 950, s/o, 17" x 23", pub HC | 44.00 | — |

# BERNARD MARTIN

Bernard Martin is widely recognized for his limited edition prints and original paintings. He was the first featured artist for the Midwest Wildlife Art Show, now known as National Wildlife Art Show. In both the 1981 and 1982 shows he was awarded the Judges Order of Merit. Sixteen of twenty-two released prints have sold out and become collector's items.

Martin was selected as a feature artist for the September/October 1981 wildlife issue of *Prints* magazine. Early this year he was commissioned to paint a large poster for the Missouri Conservation Department, depicting eight species of wildlife, once threatened, but now abundant in Missouri woodlands.

Martin is a devoted follower of *Ducks Unlimited.* He has been a featured artist for many chapters. He completed a supplemental print for DU titled "Over The Cattails," which raised over $150,000 for waterfowl projects.

The artist has written and illustrated hundreds of nature features for Sunday magazines and book publishers. He has illustrated over forty books.

## BERNARD MARTIN

| | | |
|---|---|---|
| ☐ **SPRING IS THE ROBIN**, rel. 1972. ed. 1,500, s/n, 14" x 16½", pub BM | 20.00 | 20.00 |
| ☐ **EASTERN BLUEBIRD**, rel. 1974. ed. 500, s/n, 16" x 18⅜", pub BM | 20.00 | 200.00 |
| ☐ **RING-NECKED PHEASANT**, rel. 1974. ed. 500, s/b, 17" x 19", pub BM | 25.00 | 60.00 |
| ☐ **CARDINAL**, , rel. 1975. ed. 500, s/n, 16" x 18⅜", pub BM | 20.00 | 200.00 |
| ☐ **MALLARDS & PINTAILS**, rel. 1975. ed. 500, s/n, 16" x 18⅜", pub BM | 20.00 | 60.00 |
| ☐ **BALTIMORE ORIOLE**, rel. 1976. ed. 350, s/n, 16" x 18⅜", pub BM | 20.00 | 60.00 |
| ☐ **BOBWHITE**, rel. 1976. ed. 350, s/n, 16" x 18⅜", pub BM | 20.00 | 60.00 |
| ☐ **GOLDFINCH**, rel. 1977. ed. 350, s/n, 16" x 18⅜", pub BM | 25.00 | 60.00 |

**OVER THE CATTAILS** by Bernard Martin

|  | ISSUE PRICE | CURRENT PRICE |
|---|---|---|
| ☐ CANADA GOOSE, rel. 1977. ed. 350, s/n, 16″ x 18⅜″, pub BM | 25.00 | 60.00 |
| ☐ OZARKS GOBBLER, rel. 1977. ed. 500, s/n, 18″ x 24″, pub BM | 35.00 | 75.00 |
| ☐ BLUE JAY, rel. 1978. ed. 350, s/n, 16″ x 18⅜″, pub BM | 25.00 | 60.00 |
| ☐ CARDINAL FAMILY, rel. 1980. ed. 500, s/n, 16″ x 18⅜″, pub BM | 30.00 | 60.00 |
| ☐ MALLARDS, rel. 1980. ed. 500, s/n, 16″ x 18⅜″, pub BM | 30.00 | — |
| ☐ SPORTSMAN'S SET, rel. 1972. ed. 350, s/n, 16″ x 18⅜″, pub BM | 39.00 | 60.00 |
| ☐ STRANGER ON THE TRAIL, rel. 1980. ed. 350, s/n, 19½″ x 28″, pub BM | 40.00 | 60.00 |
| ☐ WOOD DUCK, rel. 1978. ed. 350, s/n, 16″ x 18⅜″, pub BM | 25.00 | 100.00 |
| ☐ MEADOWLARK, rel. 1979. ed. 500, s/n, 16″ x 18⅜″, pub BM | 30.00 | 60.00 |
| ☐ GREEN-WINGED TEAL, rel. 1979. ed. 500, s/n, 16″ x 18⅜″, pub BM | 30.00 | — |
| ☐ SUNDAY MORNING BLUEBIRDS, rel. 1981. ed. 500, s/n, 16″ x 18⅜″, pub BM | 35.00 | 60.00 |
| ☐ STONY POINT COVEY, rel. 1981. ed. 500, s/n, 16″ x 18⅜″, pub BM | 35.00 | 35.00 |
| ☐ ROOST TREE, rel. 1981. ed. 350, s/n, 16″ x 18⅜″, pub BM | 40.00 | 40.00 |
| ☐ MORNING GLORY WRENS, rel. 1982. ed. 500, s/n, 16″ x 18⅜″, pub BM | 35.00 | 35.00 |
| ☐ OVER THE CATTAILS, rel. 1982. ed. 1,850, s/n, 18″ x 25″, pub BM | 40.00 | 40.00 |

# LARRY K. MARTIN

Larry Martin is similar to many other artists in the sense that a compulsion to paint has gradually eclipsed other endeavors. In his case this irresistable drive to portray wildlife and human subjects overcame the appeal of professions which are fascinating in their own right — Tropical Medicine, which involved travels to exotic areas and live-in experiences with stone-age tribes, and employment as a Curator at a natural history museum, with a variety of creative projects. Even his hobbies — including a decade of collecting and reassembling antique log cabins — have been put on "hold" during the past few years of concentrated painting.

**WINTER WHITETAILS** *by Larry Martin*

Each exquisitely detailed drawing or painting by Martin involves a combination of experiments, and many works require as much as 200 hours to complete. In response to artists and art critics who decry the incorporations of detail into works of art, Martin makes the point that beauty occurs at *all* levels of natural creation — whether in the distant blur of wingbeats of a bird in motion, or in the microstructure of a feather. No artist, he maintains, is ever able to capture, or flatter, or improve on nature itself. We can only offer an individual interpretation of a subject.

This attitude of absolute respect for nature permeates Martin's philosophy about the traditional human disregard for nature. He finds comfort in the fact that the Art profession in general involves relatively little adverse effect on the environment or other living creatures. In fact, by the contribution of art works to a wide variety of conservation causes, he finds a second pleasure in his artistic efforts.

## LARRY K. MARTIN

| | ISSUE PRICE | CURRENT PRICE |
|---|---|---|
| ☐ **IN PURSUIT (Bass)**, rel. 1978. ed. 1,150, s/n, 20″ x 27″, pub TCG . . . . . . . . . | 30.00 | 40.00 |
| ed. 100 remarque . . . . . . . . . . . . . . . . . . . . . . . . . . . . . . . . . . . . . . . . . . . . . | 60.00 | 75.00 |
| ☐ **INTRUDER (Squirrel & Jay)**, rel. 1978. ed. 1,150, s/n, 20″ x 27″, pub TCG . . . | 30.00 | 40.00 |
| ed. 100 remarqued . . . . . . . . . . . . . . . . . . . . . . . . . . . . . . . . . . . . . . . . . . . | 60.00 | 75.00 |

| | ISSUE PRICE | CURRENT PRICE |
|---|---|---|
| ☐ **DE N'OVE SERIES** | | |
| This set consists of six prints were sold in singles, pairs or sets of six BLUEBIRDS, BARN OWLS, PINTAILS, MALLARD, BOBWHITE QUAIL, GREAT BLUE HERON; rel. 1979. ed. 1,000, s/n, 8" x 10", pub WGN . . . . . . . . . . . . . | 20.00 ea. | — |
| | 34.00 pr. | — |
| | 105.00 seven | — |
| remarqued prints available at . . . . . . . . . . . . . . . . . . . . . . . . . . . . . . . . . . . . | 50.00 | 90.00 |
| ☐ **WINTER WHITETAILS**, rel. 1979. ed. 950, s/n, 18" x 24", pub WNG . . . . . . . . | 45.00 | 65.00 |
| ed. 100 remarqued . . . . . . . . . . . . . . . . . . . . . . . . . . . . . . . . . . . . . . . . . . . | 100.00 | 125.00 |
| **BI-LEVEL SERIES** | | |
| ☐ **BUFFLEHEADS, RUDDY DUCKS**, rel. 1980. ed. 950, s/n, 12" x 16", pub WNG | 36.00 | Sold Out |
| | 60.00 pr. | Sold Out |
| ed. 25 remarqued . . . . . . . . . . . . . . . . . . . . . . . . . . . . . . . . . . . . . . . . . . . | 90.00 | 110.00 |
| ☐ **MALLARDS**, rel. 1982. ed. 950, s/n, 12" x 19", pub WNG . . . . . . . . . . . . . . | 50.00 | — |
| ☐ **PINTAILS**, rel. 1983. ed. 950, s/n, 22" x 19", pub WNG . . . . . . . . . . . . . . . . | 50.00 | — |
| ed. 12 remarqued . . . . . . . . . . . . . . . . . . . . . . . . . . . . . . . . . . . . . . . . . . . | 90.00 pr. | — |
| | 175.00 | Sold Out |
| ☐ **BARN OWLS**, rel. 1980. ed. 950, s/n, 25" x 22", pub WNG . . . . . . . . . . . . . | 55.00 | 65.00 |
| ed. 25 remarqued . . . . . . . . . . . . . . . . . . . . . . . . . . . . . . . . . . . . . . . . . . . | 110.00 | 125.00 |
| ☐ **AFRICAN ELEPHANTS**, rel. 1981. ed. open, 18" x 12", pub WNG . . . . . . . . . | 10.00 | — |
| ed. 2,000, s/o . . . . . . . . . . . . . . . . . . . . . . . . . . . . . . . . . . . . . . . . . . . . . . | 12.00 | — |
| ed. 50 s/n . . . . . . . . . . . . . . . . . . . . . . . . . . . . . . . . . . . . . . . . . . . . . . . . | 45.00 | Sold Out |
| ☐ **BIGHORN RAM**, rel. 1981. ed. open, 16" x 12", pub WNG . . . . . . . . . . . . . . . | 8.00 | — |
| ed. 2,000, s/o . . . . . . . . . . . . . . . . . . . . . . . . . . . . . . . . . . . . . . . . . . . . . . | 10.00 | — |
| ed. 50 s/n . . : . . . . . . . . . . . . . . . . . . . . . . . . . . . . . . . . . . . . . . . . . . . . . | — | Sold Out |
| ☐ **CHIPMUNKS**, rel. 1981. ed. open, 16" x 8", pub WNG . . . . . . . . . . . . . . . . . | 8.00 | — |
| ed. 2,000, s/o . . . . . . . . . . . . . . . . . . . . . . . . . . . . . . . . . . . . . . . . . . . . . . | 10.00 | — |
| ed. 50, s/n . . . . . . . . . . . . . . . . . . . . . . . . . . . . . . . . . . . . . . . . . . . . . . . | — | Sold Out |
| ☐ **KEEPERS OF THE MILL**, rel. 1981. ed. open, 22" x 19", pub WNG . . . . . . . . . | 15.00 | — |
| ed. 2,000, s/o . . . . . . . . . . . . . . . . . . . . . . . . . . . . . . . . . . . . . . . . . . . . . . | 20.00 | — |
| ed. 100, s/n . . . . . . . . . . . . . . . . . . . . . . . . . . . . . . . . . . . . . . . . . . . . . . . | 45.00 | Sold Out |
| ☐ **MANDARIN DUCKS**, rel. 1981. ed. 950, s/n, 30" x 22", pub WNG . . . . . . . . . | 60.00 | 75.00 |
| ed. 25 remarqued . . . . . . . . . . . . . . . . . . . . . . . . . . . . . . . . . . . . . . . . . . . | 110.00 | 125.00 |
| ☐ **MR. VICTOR CHADWICK, AMERICAN HOBO**, rel. 1981. ed. open, 16" x 25", pub WNG . . . . . . . . . . . . . . . . . . . . . . . . . . . . . . . . . . . . . . . . . . . . . . . . . . | 16.00 | — |
| ed. 2,000, s/o . . . . . . . . . . . . . . . . . . . . . . . . . . . . . . . . . . . . . . . . . . . . . . | 20.00 | — |
| ed. 50, s/n . . . . . . . . . . . . . . . . . . . . . . . . . . . . . . . . . . . . . . . . . . . . . . . | 45.00 | Sold Out |
| ☐ **PARKER ISLAND RACCOONS**, rel. 1981****. ed. open, 14" x 11", pub WNG . . | 8.00 | — |
| ed. 2,000, s/o . . . . . . . . . . . . . . . . . . . . . . . . . . . . . . . . . . . . . . . . . . . . . . | 10.00 | — |
| ed. 50, s/n . . . . . . . . . . . . . . . . . . . . . . . . . . . . . . . . . . . . . . . . . . . . . . . | — | Sold Out |
| ****1,000 prints donated for "Save Parker Island" fund. | | |
| ☐ **SCREECH OWLS**, rel. 1981****. ed. open, 11" x 14", pub WNG . . . . . . . . . . | 8.00 | — |
| ed. 2,000, s/o . . . . . . . . . . . . . . . . . . . . . . . . . . . . . . . . . . . . . . . . . . . . . . | 10.00 | — |
| ed. 50, s/n . . . . . . . . . . . . . . . . . . . . . . . . . . . . . . . . . . . . . . . . . . . . . . . | — | Sold Out |
| ****500 prints donated for fund raising by Wildlife Rescue Service, Birmingham, Alabama. | | |
| ☐ **WHITETAIL DOE**, rel. 1981. ed. open, 8" x 10", pub WNG . . . . . . . . . . . . . . . | 5.00 | — |
| ed. 2,000, s/o . . . . . . . . . . . . . . . . . . . . . . . . . . . . . . . . . . . . . . . . . . . . . . | 7.00 | — |
| ed. 50, s/n . . . . . . . . . . . . . . . . . . . . . . . . . . . . . . . . . . . . . . . . . . . . . . . | — | Sold Out |
| ☐ **WHITETAIL MATURE BUCK**, rel. 1981. ed. open, 8" x 10", pub WNG . . . . . . . . | 5.00 | — |
| ed. 2,000, s/o . . . . . . . . . . . . . . . . . . . . . . . . . . . . . . . . . . . . . . . . . . . . . . | 7.00 | — |
| ed. 50, s/n . . . . . . . . . . . . . . . . . . . . . . . . . . . . . . . . . . . . . . . . . . . . . . . | — | Sold Out |
| ☐ **WHITETAIL YOUNG BUCK**, rel. 1981. ed. open, 8" x 10", pub WNG . . . . . . . . . | 5.00 | — |
| ed. 2,000, s/o . . . . . . . . . . . . . . . . . . . . . . . . . . . . . . . . . . . . . . . . . . . . . . | 7.00 | — |
| ed. 50, s/n . . . . . . . . . . . . . . . . . . . . . . . . . . . . . . . . . . . . . . . . . . . . . . . | — | Sold Out |
| ☐ **WINTER RACCOONS**, rel. 1981. ed. open, 11" x 14", pub WNG . . . . . . . . . . . | 8.00 | — |
| ed. 2,000, s/o . . . . . . . . . . . . . . . . . . . . . . . . . . . . . . . . . . . . . . . . . . . . . . | 10.00 | — |
| ed. 50, s/n . . . . . . . . . . . . . . . . . . . . . . . . . . . . . . . . . . . . . . . . . . . . . . . | 25.00 | Sold Out |
| ☐ **YOUNG COTTONTAIL**, rel. 1981. ed. open, 10" x 8", pub WNG . . . . . . . . . . . . | 5.00 | 8.00 |
| ed. 2,000, s/o . . . . . . . . . . . . . . . . . . . . . . . . . . . . . . . . . . . . . . . . . . . . . . | 10.00 | — |
| ed. 50, s/n . . . . . . . . . . . . . . . . . . . . . . . . . . . . . . . . . . . . . . . . . . . . . . . | — | Sold Out |
| ☐ **EVERGREEN BOUGH, BALD EAGLES**, rel. 1982. ed. 950, s/n, 32" x 25½", pub WNG . . . . . . . . . . . . . . . . . . . . . . . . . . . . . . . . . . . . . . . . . . . . . . . . . . | 80.00 | 80.00 |
| ed. 12 remarqued . . . . . . . . . . . . . . . . . . . . . . . . . . . . . . . . . . . . . . . . . . . | 200.00 | Sold Out |

| | ISSUE PRICE | CURRENT PRICE |
|---|---|---|
| ☐ **AMERICA'S GOAT MAN, MR. CHES MCCARTNEY,** rel. 1983. ed. open, 18" x 25", pub WNG | 15.00 | — |
| ed. 2,000, s/o | 20.00 | — |
| ed. 100, s/n | 45.00 | Sold Out |
| ☐ **JUVENILE GRAY SQUIRREL,** rel. 1983. ed. open, 15" x 12", pub WNG | 10.00 | — |
| ed. 2,000, s/o | 12.00 | — |
| ed. 50, s/n | — | Sold Out |
| ☐ **SUE ALSTON, GUARDIAN ANGEL OF HAMPTON,** rel. 1983. ed. open, 24" x 19", pub WNG | 15.00 | — |
| ed. 2,000, s/o | 20.00 | — |
| ed. 100, s/n | 45.00 | Sold Out |
| ☐ **TRUMPETER SWANS,** rel. 1983. ed. 950, s/n, 9" x 8", pub WNG | 26.00 | 26.00 |
| ed. 12 remarqued | 175.00 | Sold Out |
| ☐ **YOUNG KILLDEER,** rel. 1983. ed. open, 10" x 8", pub WNG | 5.00 | — |
| ed. 2,000, s/o | 12.00 | — |
| ed. 50, s/n | — | Sold Out |

*The de n'ovo series of bird-in-egg design was introduced with the first half-dozen subjects, and marks a continuing series which incorporates the egg outline, an inner circle and the bird subject, reflecting the symbolism of egg as environment and circular yolk as location for developing bird embryo.

# FRANCISCO J. J. C. MASSERIA

Francisco J. J. C. Masseria was born in Parana, Argentina on April 7, 1926. He began to draw at a very early age and at fourteen won his first gold medal in the "Salon Annuale De Entre Rios".

In the years to follow this self taught artist criss-crossed the Americas with a series of successful exhibitions that established him as a serious artist with a devoted following. Perhaps the turning point in his career was his decision to move to Europe where for the first time he could observe at first hand the fascinating world of the Spanish and Italian Renaissance masters. He studied the delicate brush work of Raffaelo, Masaccio, Velasquez and the ethereal expression of Fra Angelico's Madonnas. The result was the emergence of a complex and unique painting style.

Masseria does not use models for his paintings. His subjects are the product of his imagination, of his idealized perception of children and the deeply felt religious mysticism that guides his brush. The absorbing expressions of his children are not planned but are the result of a purely spontaneous emotional process that matures as the painting progresses.

The prestigious English company, Royal Doulton, has chosen Masseria to paint six original works of art for their limited edition plate series called "Portraits of Innocence". This major artistic effort sponsored by one of the world's leading china companies will undoubtedly catapult Masseria into international fame.

**JAMIE** *by Francisco Masseria*

# FRANCISCO J. J. C. MASSERIA

| | | ISSUE PRICE | CURRENT PRICE |
|---|---|---|---|
| ☐ | **EDUARDO,** rel. 1980. ed. 300, s/n, size N/A, pub WAEL | 275.00 | 2,000.00 |
| ☐ | **FIRST KISS,** rel. 1980. ed. 300, s/n, size N/A, pub WAEL | 375.00 | 900.00 |
| ☐ | **NINA,** rel. 1980. ed. 300, s/n, size N/A, pub WAEL | 325.00 | 1,000.00 |
| ☐ | **ROSANNA,** rel. 1980. ed. 300, s/n, size N/A, pub WAEL | 275.00 | 2,000.00 |
| ☐ | **ELEANOR,** rel. 1981. ed. 300, s/n, size N/A, pub WAEL | 375.00 | 550.00 |
| ☐ | **ELISA WITH FLOWER,** rel. 1981. ed. 300, s/n, size N/A, pub WAEL | 325.00 | 750.00 |
| ☐ | **FIRST FLOWER,** rel. 1981. ed. 300, s/n, size N/A, pub WAEL | 325.00 | 1,000.00 |
| ☐ | **JESSICA,** rel. 1981. ed. 300, s/n, size N/A, pub WAEL | 375.00 | 750.00 |
| ☐ | **JULIE,** rel. 1981. ed. 300, s/n, size N/A, pub WAEL | 375.00 | 500.00 |
| ☐ | **SELENE,** rel. 1981. ed. 300, s/n, size N/A, pub WAEL | 325.00 | 900.00 |
| ☐ | **SOLANGE,** rel. 1980. ed. 300, s/n, size N/A, pub WAEL | 325.00 | 700.00 |
| ☐ | **SUSAN SEWING,** rel. 1981. ed. 300, s/n, size N/A, pub WAEL | 375.00 | 1,300.00 |
| ☐ | **AMY,** rel. 1982. ed. 300, s/n, size N/A | 425.00 | — |
| ☐ | **JAMIE,** rel. 1982. ed. 300, s/n, 18″ x 22″, pub WAEL | 425.00 | 450.00 |
| ☐ | **JILL,** rel. 1982. ed. 300, s/n, 18″ x 22″, pub WAEL | 425.00 | 450.00 |
| ☐ | **JODIE,** rel. 1982. ed. 300, s/n, 18″ x 22″, pub WAEL | 425.00 | 450.00 |
| ☐ | **JUDITH,** rel. 1980. ed. 300, s/n, size N/A | 425.00 | 450.00 |
| ☐ | **ROBIN,** rel. 1982. ed. 300, s/n, 18″ x 22″, pub WAEL | 425.00 | 450.00 |
| ☐ | **YASMIN,** rel. 1982. ed. 300, s/n, size N/A | 425.00 | 450.00 |
| ☐ | **YVETTE,** rel. 1982. ed. 300, s/n, size N/A | 425.00 | 450.00 |
| ☐ | **ANTONIO,** rel. 1983. ed. 300, s/n, size N/A | 450.00 | — |
| ☐ | **CHRISTOPHER,** rel. 1983. ed. 300, s/n, size N/A, pub CIL | 450.00 | — |
| ☐ | **MEMOIRS,** rel. 1983. ed. 300, s/n, 20″ x 24″, pub CIL | 450.00 | — |
| ☐ | **TARA,** rel. 1983. ed. 300, s/n, size N/A | 450.00 | — |

## JAY MATTERNES

|  | ISSUE PRICE | CURRENT PRICE |
|---|---|---|
| ☐ **FIRST RETRIEVE**, ed. 950, s/n, 18" x 27", pub RAF | 80.00 | — |
| ☐ **FIELD PARTNERS**, ed. 950, s/n, 17" x 21", pub RAF | 80.00 | — |

## IKKI MATSUMOTO

Born in Tokyo, Japan, Matsumoto came to the United States to attend John Herron Art Institute in Indianapolis, Indiana. The second summer he took a course at Cincinnati Art Academy taught by Charles Harper. After graduating, Matsumoto worked for different advertising agencies and studios in Cincinnati as a graphic designer, and at the same time kept up his own interest in book illustration. "I was able to expand my book and newspaper illustration, so in 1972 I quit my job, and had my own studio until 1975 when," he adds happily, "I left advertising all together, and started drawing what I wanted to draw."

He illustrated the book, *Animal Rides,* published by World Library of Sacred Music, and collaborated with Charles Harper on a two volume book of punch out paper sculpture for children, titled *Zoo it Yourself,* published by Rand McNally.

### IKKI MATSUMOTO

| | | |
|---|---|---|
| ☐ **BLUEBIRD IN RED BERRIES**, ed. 200, s/n | 30.00 | — |
| ☐ **BLUE HERON**, ed. 50, s/n | N/A | 150.00 |
| ☐ **BUTTERFLY**, ed. 200, s/n | 20.00 | Sold Out |
| ☐ **GO FLY A KITE**, ed. 130, s/n | N/A | 100.00 |
| ☐ **FISHY**, ed. 200, s/n | 30.00 | Sold Out |
| ☐ **FLY TO THE MOON**, ed. 200, s/n | 20.00 | Sold Out |
| ☐ **LITTLE GIRL BLUE**, ed. 200, s/n | 40.00 | Sold Out |
| ☐ **MAILMAN OF AUTUMN**, ed. 200, s/n | 20.00 | Sold Out |
| ☐ **PELICAN**, ed. 100, s/n | N/A | 100.00 |
| ☐ **RAINBOW DROPS**, ed. 150, s/n | N/A | 125.00 |
| ☐ **SANDPIPERS**, ed. 100, s/n | N/A | 1,100.00 |
| ☐ **STRANGER ON THE BEACH**, ed. 130, s/n | N/A | 100.00 |
| ☐ **BUTTERFLY TREE**, rel. 1977. ed. 250, s/n, 22" x 22", pub FHG | 40.00 | 250.00 |
| ☐ **POPPY FIELD**, rel. 1977. ed. 750, s/n, 26½" x 22", pub FHG | 40.00 | 75.00 |
| ☐ **UP, UP BUTTERFLY**, rel. 1977. ed. 750, s/n, 26½" x 20", pub FHG | 40.00 | 85.00 |
| ☐ **ANHINGA**, rel. 1978. ed. 750, s/n, 30" x 21", pub FHG | 75.00 | 120.00 |
| ☐ **COMMON EGRET**, rel. 1978. ed. 750, s/n, 30" x 24", pub FHG | 75.00 | 120.00 |
| ☐ **FLY BY NIGHT**, rel. 1978. ed. 750, s/n, 25" x 20", pub FHG | 50.00 | 65.00 |
| ☐ **GREAT BLUE HERON**, rel. 1978. ed. 750, s/n, 21" x 30", pub FHG | 75.00 | 120.00 |
| ☐ **SAND CASTLE**, rel. 1978. ed. 750, s/n, 20" x 28", pub FHG | 40.00 | — |
| ☐ **OVER THE BUTTERFLY HILLS**, rel. 1979, ed. 750, s/n, 22½" x 22", pub FHG | 55.00 | — |
| ☐ **PELICAN**, rel. 1979. ed. 750, s/n, 30" x 33", pub FHG | 75.00 | 120.00 |
| ☐ **SWANS**, rel. 1979. ed. 750, s/n, 15" x 30", pub FHG | 55.00 | — |
| ☐ **YOU'LL NEVER MAKE IT OVER THE ATLANTIC WITH THAT THING/AHH, YOU CAN'T LIVE ON SEASHELLS ALONE**, pair, rel. 1979. ed. 2,500, s/o, 12¼" x 12¾", pub FHG | 20.00 | — |
| ☐ **BAMBOO TIGER**, rel. 1980. ed. 750, s/n, 20" x 30", pub FHG | 80.00 | — |
| ☐ **BLUE AND GOLD MACAW**, rel. 1980. ed. 750, s/n, 30" x 18", pub FHG | 80.00 | — |
| ☐ **TOUCANS**, rel. 1980. ed. 750, s/n, 17" x 30", pub FHG | 80.00 | — |

## BRUCE MATTESON

| | | |
|---|---|---|
| ☐ **LAB WITH CANVASBACK**, rel. 1980. ed. 950, s/n, size not available, pub WWI | 85.00 | — |
| ☐ **GOLDEN RETRIEVER**, rel. 1980. ed. 950, s/n, size not available, pub WWI | 100.00 | — |
| ☐ **MARSH MONTAGE**, rel. 1980. ed. 950, s/n, size not available, pub WWI | 100.00 | — |
| ☐ **THE POACHER**, rel. 1980. ed. 950, s/n, size not available, pub WWI | 100.00 | — |

# ARTHUR McCALL

Equally at home using acrylics or oils, Arthur McCall has chosen the south Texas ranch country for the subjects of his paintings. The barns, windmills, houses, cowpens, wildlife and horses are his subjects.

| ARTHUR McCALL | ISSUE PRICE | CURRENT PRICE |
|---|---|---|
| ☐ **SANDY CREEK QUAIL**, rel. 1981. ed. 1,500, s/n, 23⅛" x 31¾", pub ALI . . . . | 60.00 | — |

# IRISH McCALLA

Irish McCalla was always interested in art and at the age of 14, one of her watercolors was chosen for an exhibit by the Joslyn Art Museum in Omaha, Nebraska.

At 17, McCalla moved to California where she became an actress. She had the starring role in the TV series "Sheena, Queen of the Jungle" and traveled extensively around the world on personal appearances, always painting and taking pictures. She also continued to study art from the famed illustrator, Fritz Willis, portrait with Carlo Buonora and palette knife with Grace Harvey. When she discovered she was making such a good living with her art and winning awards in juried shows, she immediately gave up acting, since art has always been her first love.

Her list of clients are varied from celebrities such as Jamie Farr, Edgar Bergen, Marty Allen, Producer E. Jack Neuman to the Federal Bank's Collection of American Artists and the permanent collection of the Bell Telephone Company. Her paintings have hung in the Western White House, the Los Angeles Museum of Science and Industry and the Cowgirl Hall of Fame. She is an officer of the highly acclaimed *"Women Artists Of the American West"*.

| IRISH McCALLA | ISSUE PRICE | CURRENT PRICE |
|---|---|---|
| ☐ **MAIL ORDER BRIDE**, ed. 500, s/n, size not available, pub MEI . . . . . . . . . . . . | 75.00 | Sold Out |
| ed. 25, a/p . . . . . . . . . . . . . . . . . . . . . . . . . . . . . . . . . . . . . . . . . . . . . . . . . . | 75.00 | Sold Out |
| ☐ **HIGH COUNTRY CABIN**, ed. 750, s/n, 14" x 25", pub MEI . . . . . . . . . . . . . . . | 55.00 | — |
| ed. 50, a/p . . . . . . . . . . . . . . . . . . . . . . . . . . . . . . . . . . . . . . . . . . . . . . . . . . | 55.00 | Sold Out |
| ☐ **WHO BE YA CALLIN A RUNT**, ed. 900, s/n, 14¾" x 19½", pub MEI . . . . . . . . | 35.00 | — |
| ed. 50, a/p . . . . . . . . . . . . . . . . . . . . . . . . . . . . . . . . . . . . . . . . . . . . . . . . . . | 35.00 | — |
| ed. 45, remarqued . . . . . . . . . . . . . . . . . . . . . . . . . . . . . . . . . . . . . . . . . . . . | 125.00 | — |
| ☐ **PLENTY MUCH FIREWATER**, ed. 900, s/n, 14¾" x 19½", pub MEI . . . . . . . . . | 35.00 | — |
| ed. 50, a/p . . . . . . . . . . . . . . . . . . . . . . . . . . . . . . . . . . . . . . . . . . . . . . . . . . | 35.00 | — |
| ed. 45, remarqued . . . . . . . . . . . . . . . . . . . . . . . . . . . . . . . . . . . . . . . . . . . . | 125.00 | — |
| ☐ **MOUNTAIN MEN**, (rel. as a pair). ed. 950, s/n, size N/A, pub MEI . . . . . . . . . . | 65.00 | — |
| ed. 45, remarqued . . . . . . . . . . . . . . . . . . . . . . . . . . . . . . . . . . . . . . . . . . . . | 125.00 | — |
| ed. 50, singly . . . . . . . . . . . . . . . . . . . . . . . . . . . . . . . . . . . . . . . . . . . . . . . . | 35.00 | — |
| ☐ **FIRST LIGHT OF DAWN**, ed. 350, s/n, size N/A, pub MEI . . . . . . . . . . . . . . . . | 35.00 | — |
| available on canvass . . . . . . . . . . . . . . . . . . . . . . . . . . . . . . . . . . . . . . . . . . | 95.00 | — |
| ed. 25, a/p . . . . . . . . . . . . . . . . . . . . . . . . . . . . . . . . . . . . . . . . . . . . . . . . . . | 60.00 | — |
| ☐ **THE LETTER**, ed. 500, s/n, size N/A, pub MEI . . . . . . . . . . . . . . . . . . . . . . . | 95.00 | — |

# D. MICHAEL McCARTHY

D. Michael McCarthy calls himself "an artist of the mountains." His magnificent landscapes reveal that his self-description is accurate beyond question. These works are not mere pictures, however, but expressions of something deeper: "What I seek to do in my painting is to capture people's imagination, not their attention. To make people truly feel the sensation of nature in my painting is a deeply felt conviction."

**THE GRAND TETONS** *by D. Michael McCarthy*

McCarthy's own story began in Los Angeles in 1951. His love of art blossomed in childhood, nurtured by frequent visits with his parents. He entered college intending to pursue a career in business. But he soon realized his talents lay in the arts. He considered writing first, but his love of art dominated. He graduated from Fontbonne College in St. Louis with a B.F.A. He has participated in numerous one-man and group shows, and has been the subject of magazine articles. In 1976, his kinship with nature led him to settle in Sedona, Arizona, where he makes his home today.

McCarthy's art is strongly reminiscent of the Hudson Valley School. And like those artists of a century ago, his emphasis is on color and light. Using water colors to finish his sketches, McCarthy works out the interplay of these powerful sources. Detailed notes and his own uncanny ability to recall colors exactly, help him achieve the effect he wants. While his innate talent allows McCarthy to work his miracles on canvas, intense practice and hours spent studying the work of the "Old Masters" have shaped and developed that talent. With youth on his side, Michael is creating a body of work that will one day be placed alongside those "Masters" he so diligently studies.

| D. MICHAEL McCARTHY | ISSUE PRICE | CURRENT PRICE |
|---|---|---|
| ☐ **THE MOUNTAIN OF THE HOLY CROSS**, rel. 1981. ed. 500, s/n, 22½" x 29½", pub GW | 125.00 | — |
| ☐ **MT. ROBSON**, rel. 1983. ed. 100, s/n, 24½" x 19¾", stone lithograph pulled at the Tamarind Institute, pub GW | 225.00 | — |
| ☐ **THE GRAND TETONS**, rel. 1983. ed. 650, s/n, 25" x 19⅝", pub GW | 125.00 | — |

# FRANK McCARTHY

Viewing a McCarthy painting of the Old West is like walking in on an Indian raid or chasing bandits or riding with the cavalry in a column of two's.

Born in 1924 in New York City, Frank McCarthy has been drawn to the West ever since he read Will James novels as a boy and was excited by N. C. Wyeth's illustrations in classics such as *Robin Hood* and *Treasure Island.* His formal education was acquired at Pratt Institute and the Art Student's League where he studied under the eminent painters George Bridgeman and Reginald Marsh. A successful career in commercial art and illustration followed, including book covers for major publishers and advertising art for movie studios and large corporations.

The lure of the West was strong, however, and in 1974 McCarthy settled in Sedona, Arizona, where he has blazed a trail of accomplishments ever since. He is a member of the Cowboy Artists of America; has had retrospective shows at the Museum of the Southwest in Midland, Texas, and the Norton Museum in Shreveport, Louisiana; and exhibits his paintings in galleries in Dallas and Sedona. Articles about his work have appeared in many national magazines, and his book *The Western Paintings of Frank C. McCarthy* (Ballantine Books, 1974) is in its fourth printing.

**OUT OF THE MIST THEY CAME** *by Frank McCarthy*

| FRANK McCARTHY | ISSUE PRICE | CURRENT PRICE |
|---|---|---|
| ☐ **LONE SENTINEL,** rel. 1974. ed. 1,000, s/n, 20″ x 25½″, pub GW . . . . . . . . . | 55.00 | 1,350.00 |
| ☐ **LONG COLUMN,** rel. 1974. ed. 1,000, s/n, 30½″ x 21½″, pub GW . . . . . . . . | 75.00 | 825.00 |
| ☐ **THE HUNT,** rel. 1974. ed. 1,000, s/n, 30½″ x 19½″, pub GW . . . . . . . . . . . . | 75.00 | 700.00 |
| ☐ **THE NIGHT THEY NEEDED A GOOD RIBBON MAN,** rel. 1974. ed. 1,000, s/n, 24″ x 27″, pub GW . . . . . . . . . . . . . . . . . . . . . . . . . . . . . . . . . . . . . . . . . . . | 65.00 | 335.00 |
| ☐ **RETURNING RAIDERS,** rel. 1975. ed. 1,000, s/n, 30″ x 17¼″, pub GW . . . . . . | 75.00 | 500.00 |
| ☐ **SMOKE WAS THEY ALLY,** rel. 1975. ed. 1,000, s/n, 26″ x 18¾″, pub GW . . . | 75.00 | 460.00 |
| ☐ **THE SURVIVOR,** rel. 1975. ed. 1,000, s/n, 26″ x 20″, pub GW . . . . . . . . . . . . | 65.00 | 450.00 |
| ☐ **WAITING FOR THE ESCORT,** rel. 1975. ed. 1,000, s/n, 30½″ x 21½″, pub GW . . . . . . . . . . . . . . . . . . . . . . . . . . . . . . . . . . . . . . . . . . . . . . . . . . . . . . | 75.00 | 335.00 |
| ☐ **PACKING IN,** rel. 1976. ed. 1,000, s/n, 18″ x 22½″, pub GW . . . . . . . . . . . . . | 65.00 | 300.00 |
| ☐ **SIOUX WARRIORS,** rel. 1976. ed. 650, s/n, 20″ x 16″, pub GW . . . . . . . . . . . | 55.00 | 425.00 |
| ☐ **THE HOSTILES,** rel. 1976. ed. 1,000, s/n, 30½″ x 21½″, pub GW . . . . . . . . . | 75.00 | 625.00 |

| | ISSUE PRICE | CURRENT PRICE |
|---|---|---|
| ☐ **THE WARRIOR,** rel. 1976. ed. 650, s/n, 20″ x 20½″, pub GW | 55.00 | 470.00 |
| ☐ **AN OLD-TIME MOUNTAIN MAN,** rel. 1977. ed. 1,000, s/n, 16″ x 19¼″, pub GW | 65.00 | 325.00 |
| ☐ **COMANCHE MOON,** rel. 1977. ed. 1,000, s/n, 30½″ x 20½″, pub GW | 75.00 | 315.00 |
| ☐ **DISTANT THUNDER,** rel. 1977. ed. 500, s/n, 30″ x 22″, pub GW | 75.00 | 650.00 |
| *ed. 1,000 prints bearing the embossed Old Trooper seal. Proceeds to ongoing restoration of the United States Cavalry Museum, Ft. Riley, Kansas. | *75.00 | 290.00 |
| ☐ **DUST-STAINED POSSE,** rel. 1977. ed. 1,000, s/n, 30″ x 22″, pub GW | 75.00 | 625.00 |
| ☐ **ROBE SIGNAL,** rel. 1977. ed. 850, s/n, 18″ x 23″, pub GW | 60.00 | 400.00 |
| ☐ **THE BEAVER MEN,** rel. 1977. ed. 1,000, s/n, 26½″ x 18½″, pub GW | 75.00 | 425.00 |
| ☐ **BEFORE THE NORTHER,** rel. 1978. ed. 1,000, s/n, 30″ x 18″, pub GW | 90.00 | 525.00 |
| ☐ **NIGHT CROSSING,** rel. 1978. ed. 1,000, s/n, 22″ x 13″, pub GW | 75.00 | 275.00 |
| ☐ **SINGLE FILE,** rel. 1978. ed. 1,000, s/n, 13″ x 22″, pub GW | 75.00 | 325.00 |
| ☐ **THE FORDING,** rel. 1978. ed. 1,000, s/n, 30″ x 16½″, pub GW | 75.00 | 400.00 |
| ☐ **TO BATTLE,** rel. 1978. ed. 1,000, s/n, 30½″ x 21″, pub GW | 75.00 | 325.00 |
| ☐ **IN THE PASS,** rel. 1979. ed. 1,500, s/n, 30″ x 21″, pub GW | 90.00 | 245.00 |
| ☐ **ON THE WARPATH,** rel. 1979. ed. 1,000, s/n, 20″ x 15½″, pub GW | 75.00 | 250.00 |
| ☐ **RETREAT TO HIGHER GROUND,** rel. 1979. ed. 1,000, s/n, 32″ x 22″, pub GW | *90.00 | 325.00 |
| *ed. 1,000, s/n bearing the embossed Old Trooper seal proceeds to U.S. Cavalry Museum Ft. Riley, Kansas | | — |
| ☐ **THE AMBUSH,** rel. 1979. ed. 1,000, s/n, 40″ x 21½″, pub GW | 125.00 | 300.00 |
| ☐ **THE LONER,** rel. 1979. ed. 1,000, s/n, 25½″ x 21″, pub GW | 75.00 | 375.00 |
| ☐ **THE PRAYER,** rel. 1979. ed. 1,500, s/n, 33½″ x 20¾″, pub GW | 90.00 | 550.00 |
| ☐ **A TIME OF DECISION,** rel. 1980. ed. 1,000, s/n, 32″ x 22″, pub GW | 125.00 | 290.00 |
| ed. 150, signed and numbered, proceeds to the Red Rock Volunteer Ambulance Service of Sedona, Arizona | 125.00 | Sold Out |
| ☐ **BEFORE THE CHARGE,** rel. 1980. ed. 1,000, s/n, 31″ x 21½″, pub GW | 115.00 | 250.00 |
| ☐ **BURNING THE WAY STATION,** rel. 1980. ed. 1,000, s/n, 32″ x 22″, pub GW | 125.00 | 360.00 |
| ☐ **FORBIDDEN LAND,** rel. 1980. ed. 1,000, s/n, 32″ x 32″, pub GW | 125.00 | 275.00 |
| ☐ **ROAR OF THE NORTHER,** rel. 1980. ed. 1,000, s/n, 16″ x 20¼″, pub GW | 90.00 | 300.00 |
| ☐ **SNOW MOON,** rel. 1980. ed. 1,000, s/n, 32″, x 22″, pub GW | 115.00 | 460.00 |
| ☐ **THE TROOPER,** rel. 1980. ed. 1,000, s/n, 16″ x 20¼″, pub GW | 90.00 | 275.00 |
| ☐ **HEADED NORTH,** rel. 1981. ed. 1,000, s/n, 32½″ x 19½″, pub GW | 150.00 | 240.00 |
| ☐ **RACE WITH THE HOSTILES,** rel. 1981. ed. 1,000, s/n, 15″ x 26¾″, pub GW | 135.00 | Sold Out |
| ☐ **SURROUNDED,** rel. 1981. ed. 1,000, s/n, 30″ x 21½″, pub GW | 150.00 | Sold Out |
| ☐ **THE COUP,** rel. 1981. ed. 1,000, s/n, 24½″ x 19¾″, pub GW | 125.00 | 200.00 |
| ☐ **UNDER HOSTILE FIRE,** rel. 1981. ed. 1,000, s/n, 30″ x 21½″, pub GW | 150.00 | 335.00 |
| ☐ **ALERT,** rel. 1982. ed. 1,000, s/n, 23/″ x 11″, pub GW | 135.00 | — |
| ☐ **APACHE SCOUT,** rel. 1982. ed. 1,000, s/n, 29½″ x 19¾″, pub GW | 165.00 | — |
| ☐ **ATTACK ON THE WAGON TRAIN,** rel. 1982. ed. 1,000, s/n, 31¾″ x 22 11/16″, pub GW | 150.00 | — |
| ed. 400, s/n, donated to Arizona Kidney Foundation. | — | — |
| ☐ **THE CHALLENGE,** rel. 1982, ed. 1,000, s/n, 26″ x 18⅞″, pub GW | 175.00 | 230.00 |
| ☐ **THE WARRIORS,** rel. 1982. ed. 1,000, s/n, 32″ x 18″, pub GW | 150.00 | — |
| ☐ **WHIRLING, HE RACED TO MEET THE CHALLENGE,** rel. 1982, ed. 1,000, s/n, 26″ x 18⅞″, pub GW | 175.00 | 250.00 |
| ☐ **BLACKFOOT RAIDERS,** rel. 1983, ed. 1,000, s/n, 13 5/16″ x 15 15/16″, pub GW | 90.00 | 150.00 |
| ☐ **IN THE LAND OF THE SPARROW HAWK PEOPLE,** rel. 1983, ed. 1,000, s/n, 30″ x 16¾″, pub GW | 165.00 | Sold Out |
| ☐ **MOONLIT TRAIL,** rel. 1983, ed. 1,000, s/n, 16½″ x 10¾″, pub GW | 90.00 | Sold Out |
| ☐ **OUT OF THE MIST THEY CAME,** rel. 1983, ed. 1,000, s/n, 21″ x 20⅝″, pub GW | 165.00 | 250.00 |
| ☐ **UNDER ATTACK,** rel. 1983, ed. *, s/n, 35″ x 18¼″, pub GW | 125.00 | Sold Out |
| *This is a Personal Commission print and edition size will be determined by number of orders received by September 30, 1983. | | |

## JAMES McCLELLAND

Attracted at an early age to plants and animals, Jim McClelland grew up surrounded by the natural beauty of the rich, Michigan farm country. He was particularly fascinated by the birds inhabiting that country. Drawing and painting were his way of recording his impressions and experiences. Today, he strives to share that experience with those who view his work.

An art and English major at Andrews University in Michigan, he has taught on the elementary, secondary and university levels and is currently an associate professor of art at Union College in Lincoln, Nebraska.

McClelland was selected as the winner of the 1980 Nebraska Habitat Stamp contest and has captured numerous Best-of-Show awards. His paintings of each hummingbird species found in America appear in the book, *Hummingbirds of North America,* authored by Dr. Paul Johnsgard, of the University of Nebraska and published by Smithsonian Press in 1981.

| | | ISSUE PRICE | CURRENT PRICE |
|---|---|---|---|
| **JAMES McCLELLAND** | | | |
| ☐ **CHICADEE FAMILY,** rel. 1981. ed. 600, s/n, size not available, pub WWI . . . . . | | 65.00 | — |

## RALPH J. McDONALD

Ralph McDonald's immense talent has been recognized nationwide. His wildlife art has appeared on such magazines as *Ducks Unlimited, Southern Outdoors* and various other outdoor and conservation publications. He has been commissioned by the governors of Tennessee and South Carolina, Indiana Audubon Society, Bass Anglers Sportsman Society, Knoxville Zoological Park, North Carolina Boys Town and several colleges. He was the featured artist at the National

**GEESE AT GADDY'S POND** *by Ralph McDonald*

Wildlife Art Show in Kansas City in 1978 and won two "best of show" awards. He has shown in the prestigious Waterfowl Festival at Easton, Maryland, and the Safari International Convention. McDonald frequently judges art contests and recently was one of three judges for the Southeast Wildlife Art Show in Atlanta. Success as an artist and businessman is a unique talent indeed. Countryside Studio, his own publishing company, is located in Cottontown, Tennessee, not far from his farm where he lives with his wife, Doris, and two daughters, Karen and Dawn.

## RALPH J. McDONALD

| | ISSUE PRICE | CURRENT PRICE |
|---|---|---|
| ☐ A VIEW FROM THE BUSH. ed. 1,500, s/n, 24" x 31", pub CS | 45.00 | 75.00 |
| ed. 500, s/n donated to Tennessee Lions Club-District 12-1 | | |
| ☐ AMERICAN BALD EAGLE. ed. 1,776, s/n, 23½" x 29½", pub AGI | 40.00 | 600.00 |
| ☐ AMERICAN INDIAN. ed. 1,776, s/n, pub AGI | 30.00 | 225.00 |
| ☐ AMERICAN WILD TURKEY. ed. 1,776, s/n, 20½" x 26½", pub AGI | 40.00 | 250.00 |
| ☐ AMERICAN WHITETAIL DEER. ed. 1,776, s/n, pub AGI | 40.00 | 150.00 |
| ☐ AUTUMN RUST, rel. 1980. ed. 950, s/n, size unavailable, pub CS | 80.00 | 225.00 |
| ☐ BEAVER DAM MALLARDS, rel. 1977. ed. 800, s/n, 16" x 21", pub PPC | 60.00 | 450.00 |
| ☐ BICENTENNIAL SET, rel. 1980. ed. five prints, , pub CS | 180.00 | 1,000.00 |
| ☐ BLUEBIRD. ed. 5,000, s/o, 16" x 20", pub AGI | 20.00 | 150.00 |
| ☐ BOBCAT. ed. 1,000, s/n, 20½" x 26½", pub AGI | 40.00 | 90.00 |
| ☐ BOBWHITE QUAIL. ed. 1,000, s/n, 20½" x 26½", pub AGI | 35.00 | 250.00 |
| ☐ BOBWHITE QUAIL (In Snow), rel. 1978. ed. 5,000, size unavailable, pub AGI | 12.50 | 50.00 |
| ☐ CAHABA 'COON. ed. 2,000, s/n, 21" x 24", pub CS | 35.00 | 150.00 |
| ☐ CAMP BRYAN WHITETAIL. ed. 600, s/n/remarqued, 24" x 31", pub CS | 125.00 | 350.00 |
| signed/numbered | 75.00 | 250.00 |
| ☐ CANADAS AT CAIRO, rel. 1977. ed. 1,250, s/n, pub CS | 55.00 | 125.00 |
| ☐ CARDINAL. ed. 5,000, s/n, 16" x 20", pub AGI | 20.00 | 100.00 |
| ☐ CAROLINA WREN. ed. 2,750, s/o, 12" x 16", pub AGI | 15.00 | 80.00 |
| ☐ CHAIRMAN OF THE BOARD. ed. 4,000, s/o, 16" x 20", pub AGI | 20.00 | 200.00 |
| ☐ CHIPMUNK. ed. 2,750, s/o, 12" x 16", pub AGI | 15.00 | 60.00 |
| ☐ COUGAR, rel. 1981, ed. 500, s/n, size unavailable, pub CS | 95.00 | 150.00 |
| ☐ EASTERN COTTONTAIL. ed. 1,000, s/n, 18" x 24", pub AGI | 30.00 | 200.00 |
| ed. 2,000, s/o | 20.00 | 100.00 |
| ☐ THE FOUR SEASONS PORTFOLIO. ed. 2,000, s/n, 10" x 12", pub CS | *45.00 | 150.00 |
| *This portfolio consists of four prints. | | |
| ☐ FRONTIERSMAN. ed. 1,776, s/n, pub AGI | 30.00 | 175.00 |
| ☐ GEESE AT GADDY'S POND, rel. 1980. ed. 850, s/n, size unavailable, pub CS | 80.00 | 150.00 |
| ☐ GOLDEN DAYS, rel. 1982. ed. 950, s/n, size unavailable, pub CS | 80.00 | 100.00 |
| ☐ GREEN TIMBER GREENHEADS, rel. 1978. ed. 1,250, s/n, 18½" x 26½", pub CS | 55.00 | 200.00 |
| ☐ LARGEMOUTH BASS. ed. 3,500, s/n, 18" x 24", pub AGI | 25.00 | 175.00 |
| ☐ MAJESTIC SILENCE (Deer Stamp), rel. 1980. ed. 1,000, s/n, size unavailable, pub CS | 100.00 | 400.00 |
| ☐ MALLARDS. ed. 1,000, s/n, 20" x 26½", pub AGI | 40.00 | 95.00 |
| ed. 2,000, s/o | 30.00 | 70.00 |
| ☐ MISSISSIPPI FLYWAY, Set of Four, rel. 1977-78. ed. 1,250, s/n, size unavailable, pub CS | 220.00 | 600.00 |
| ☐ MOCKINGBIRD. ed. 500, s/n, 22" x 28", pub AGI | 25.00 | 1,000.00 |
| ed. 2,000, signed and bearing a seal | 25.00 | 500.00 |
| ☐ PINTAILS AND PIROGUES, rel. 1978. ed. 1,250, s/n, size unavailable, pub CS | 55.00 | 200.00 |
| ☐ RACCOONS. ed. 1,000, s/n, 20" x 28", pub AGI | 35.00 | 300.00 |
| ed. 2,000, s/o | 25.00 | 250.00 |
| ☐ SAGE GROUSE. ed. 2,500, s/n, 12½" x 16", pub AGI | 15.00 | 150.00 |
| ☐ SENTINEL. ed. 1,000, s/n, 20" x 24½", pub AGI | 40.00 | 400.00 |
| Released through Ducks Unlimited, 1974. ed. 1,000, s/o | 30.00 | 250.00 |
| ☐ SMALLMOUTH BASS. ed. 2,000, s/n, 18" x 24", pub AGI | 25.00 | 50.00 |
| ☐ SOUTH CAROLINA WHITETAIL DEER. ed. 1,000, s/n, 20½" x 26½", pub AGI | 25.00 | 150.00 |
| ed. 2,000, signed and bearing a seal with the signature of the Governor | 25.00 | 60.00 |
| ☐ SOUTHERN BOUND, rel. 1982. ed. 500, s/n, size unavailable, pub CS | 80.00 | 95.00 |
| ☐ STRIPED BASS. ed. 1,000, s/n, 20½" x 26½", pub AGI | 25.00 | 50.00 |
| ed. 2,000, signed and bearing a seal with South Carolina Governor's signature | 25.00 | — |

|  | ISSUE PRICE | CURRENT PRICE |
|---|---|---|
| ☐ **TENNESSEE BOBWHITE QUAIL.** ed. 3,000, signed and bearing a seal, 20½" x 26½" | 35.00 | — |
| Commissioned by Tennessee Wildlife Resources Agency, pub AGI | | |
| ☐ **THE BAYOU GUIDE.** ed. 1,000, s/n, 26½" x 20½" | **60.00 | — |
| **This print commissioned by Ducks Unlimited is now being offered to the general public through Countryside Studio. | | |
| ☐ **THE BETHEL COLLEGE WILDCAT,** rel. 1978. ed. 1,500, s/n, 18" x 22", pub CS | **— | — |
| **Commissioned by Bethel College, McKenzie, Tennessee special fund raising edition. | | |
| ☐ **THE BIG WHEEL,** rel. 1980. ed. 1,500, s/n, size unavailable, pub CS | 60.00 | 150.00 |
| ☐ **THE CHAMPION,** rel. 1978. ed. 1,500, s/n, size unavailable, pub CS | 65.00 | 95.00 |
| ☐ **THE DAVIDSON WILDCAT.** ed. 1,750, s/n, 16" x 20", pub CS | **37.50 | — |
| **This print was commissioned by the Booster Club of Davidson College, North Carolina, for use in raising funds for the school's athletic program. | | |
| ☐ **THE HARVESTERS,** rel. 1980. ed. 1,500, s/n, size unavailable, pub CS | 60.00 | 150.00 |
| ☐ **THE JUDGE.** ed. 2,000, s/n, 16" x 29", pub CS | 30.00 | 150.00 |
| ☐ **THE REFUGE,** rel. 1978. ed. 1,500, s/n, size unavailable, pub CS | 35.00 | 90.00 |
| ☐ **THE STATESMAN,** rel. 1980. ed. 850, s/n, size unavailable, pub CS | 80.00 | 350.00 |
| ☐ **UNCLE JOHNNY'S COVEY,** rel. 1977. ed. 1,250, s/n, size unavailable, pub CS | 55.00 | 300.00 |
| ☐ **WALKER'S POND BLACK DUCKS,** rel. 1980. ed. 850, s/n, size unavailable, pub PPC | 75.00 | 250.00 |
| ☐ **WALKER'S POND MALLARDS,** rel. 1982. ed. 850, s/n, size unavailable, pub PPC | 95.00 | 350.00 |
| ☐ **WALKER'S POND TEAL,** rel. 1981. ed. 850, s/n, size unavailable, pub PPC | 80.00 | 300.00 |
| ☐ **WALKER'S POND (WOOD DUCKS),** rel. 1976. ed. 800, s/n, 16" x 24¼", pub PPC | 60.00 | 1,500.00 |
| ☐ **WHISTLING SWAN,** ed. 1,000, s/n, 19" x 24", pub AGI | 30.00 | 75.00 |
| ed. 1,000, s/o | 20.00 | 50.00 |
| ☐ **WHITETAIL AND DESCENDING CANVASBACK,** ed. 2,500, s/n, 18" x 24", pub AGI | 25.00 | 300.00 |
| ☐ **WOODIES AT WALNUT LOG,** rel. 1978. ed. 1,250, s/n, 19" x 23½", pub CS | 55.00 | 225.00 |

# CLAY McGAUGHY

Clay McGaughy received his degree in art from the University of Texas. He still resides in San Antonio and has established himself as an outstanding artist of the Southwest.

In addition to his painting, he has done illustration work for a number of nationally known magazines and governmental agencies. He has been singled out for his outstanding talent in the book *"The Cowboy in Art"* by Ed Ainsworth. In addition to numerous awards won in juried exhibitions, he was unanimously elected into the Society of Animal Artists.

## CLAY McGAUGHY

|  | ISSUE PRICE | CURRENT PRICE |
|---|---|---|
| ☐ **BACHELOR,** rel. 1970. ed. 500, s/n, 34" x 27", pub ALI | 50.00 | 300.00 |
| ed. 1,000, s/o | 40.00 | 150.00 |
| ☐ **BIRDS OF A FEATHER,** rel. 1970. ed. 500, s/n, 34" x 27", pub ALI | 50.00 | 300.00 |
| ed. 1,000, s/o | 40.00 | 150.00 |
| ☐ **FOLLOW THE LEADER,** rel. 1970. ed. 500, s/n, 34" x 27", pub ALI | 50.00 | 300.00 |
| ed. 1,000, s/o | 40.00 | 50.00 |
| ☐ **INTRUDER,** rel. 1970. ed. 500, s/n, 34" x 27", pub ALI | 50.00 | 300.00 |
| ed. 1,000, s/o | 40.00 | 150.00 |
| ☐ **AT HOME,** rel. 1971. ed. 500, s/n, 34" x 27", pub ALI | 50.00 | 300.00 |
| ed. 1,000, s/o | 40.00 | 50.00 |
| ☐ **CHECKIN' IN,** rel. 1971. ed. 500, s/n, 34" x 27", pub ALI | 50.00 | 300.00 |
| ed. 1,000, s/o | 40.00 | 150.00 |
| ☐ **SHOW OFF,** rel. 1971. ed. 500, s/n, 34" x 27", pub ALI | 50.00 | 60.00 |
| ed. 1,000, s/o | 40.00 | 50.00 |
| ☐ **ANTELOPE,** rel. 1972. ed. 1,500, s/o, 12¼" x 10¼", pub ALI | 10.00 | — |

| | ISSUE PRICE | CURRENT PRICE |
|---|---|---|
| ☐ **BLUE QUAIL,** rel. 1972. ed. 1,500, s/o, 12¼″ x 10¼″, pub ALI . . . . . . . . . . . | 10.00 | — |
| ☐ **BOBWHITE QUAIL,** rel. 1972. ed. 1,500, s/o, 12¼″ x 10¼″, pub ALI . . . . . . . | 10.00 | — |
| ☐ **LOAFERS,** rel. 1972. ed. 500, s/n, 34″ x 27″, pub ALI . . . . . . . . . . . . . . . . . | 50.00 | 300.00 |
| ed. 1,000, s/o . . . . . . . . . . . . . . . . . . . . . . . . . . . . . . . . . . . . . . . . . . . | 40.00 | 150.00 |
| ☐ **SEA GULL,** rel. 1972. ed. 1,500, s/o, 12¼″ x 10¼″, pub ALI . . . . . . . . . . . | 10.00 | — |
| ☐ **THE ARISTOCRAT,** rel. 1972. ed. 500, s/n, 34″ x 27″, pub ALI . . . . . . . . . . . | 50.00 | 60.00 |
| ed. 1,000, s/o . . . . . . . . . . . . . . . . . . . . . . . . . . . . . . . . . . . . . . . . . . . | 40.00 | 50.00 |
| ☐ **TIME TO MOVE,** rel. 1972. ed. 500, s/n, 34″ x 27″, pub ALI . . . . . . . . . . . . . | 50.00 | 60.00 |
| ed. 1,000, s/o . . . . . . . . . . . . . . . . . . . . . . . . . . . . . . . . . . . . . . . . . . . | 40.00 | 50.00 |
| ☐ **COMMOTION,** rel. 1974. ed. 500, s/n, 16″ x 20″, pub ALI . . . . . . . . . . . . . . | 35.00 | — |
| ed. 1,000, s/o . . . . . . . . . . . . . . . . . . . . . . . . . . . . . . . . . . . . . . . . . . . | 30.00 | — |
| ☐ **HIDE AND SEEK,** rel. 1974. ed. 500, s/n, 16″ x 20″, pub ALI . . . . . . . . . . . . | 35.00 | — |
| ed. 1,000, s/o . . . . . . . . . . . . . . . . . . . . . . . . . . . . . . . . . . . . . . . . . . . | 30.00 | — |
| ☐ **ONE SHOT,** rel. 1975. ed. 500, s/n, 34″ x 27″, pub ALI . . . . . . . . . . . . . . . | 75.00 | 300.00 |
| ed. 1,000, s/o . . . . . . . . . . . . . . . . . . . . . . . . . . . . . . . . . . . . . . . . . . . | 65.00 | — |
| ☐ **TRY AGAIN,** rel. 1975. ed. 500, s/n, 34″ x 27″, pub ALI . . . . . . . . . . . . . . . | 75.00 | — |
| ed. 1,000, s/o . . . . . . . . . . . . . . . . . . . . . . . . . . . . . . . . . . . . . . . . . . . | 65.00 | — |
| ☐ **THE RACE,** rel. 1976. ed. 500, s/n, 34″ x 27″, pub ALI . . . . . . . . . . . . . . . | 75.00 | — |
| ed. 1,000, s/o . . . . . . . . . . . . . . . . . . . . . . . . . . . . . . . . . . . . . . . . . . . | 65.00 | — |
| ☐ **FIRST CAST,** rel. 1980. ed. 1,500, s/n, 31″ x 25″, pub ALI . . . . . . . . . . . . . | 60.00 | — |
| ☐ **RIVAL,** rel. 1980. ed. 1,500, s/n, 31″ x 25″, pub ALI . . . . . . . . . . . . . . . . . . | 60.00 | — |
| ☐ **SHORT CUT,** rel. 1980. ed. 1,500, s/n, 31″ x 25″, pub ALI . . . . . . . . . . . . . | 60.00 | — |
| ☐ **FEATHERLIGHT,** rel. 1981. ed. 1,500, s/n, 31″ x 25″, pub ALI . . . . . . . . . . . | 75.00 | — |
| ☐ **NICE COUPLE,** rel. 1981. ed. 1,500, s/n, 31″ x 22½″, pub ALI . . . . . . . . . . . | 75.00 | — |

# PAUL McGEHEE

Paul McGehee was born in 1960 in Arlington, Virginia, where he still resides. He is a self-taught artist and has been painting oils since the age of five.

Many of McGehee's paintings have a rich flavor of the olden days, for he is an inveterate researcher and collector of memorabilia. All of these energies are channeled into creating his accurate portrayals of hunting scenes and waterfowl, as well as the historical port scenes and marine paintings for which he is widely

**NANTUCKET** *by Paul McGehee*

known. He travels to the actual sites of his paintings but usually finds their present-day appearance vastly different from the time period in which he portrays them.

McGehee's works can be seen in numerous corporate and private collections, as well as in galleries throughout the United States and Canada.

He is a charter member of the American Society of Marine Artists (A.S.M.A.), and has exhibited at the World Trade Center, The Grand Central Galleries in New York City, and the U.S. Congress in Washington, D.C.

He is also a member of the Salmagundi Club in New York, The Steamship Historical society of America, and Ducks Unlimited, to which he contributes his work to aid in their waterfowl conservation efforts.

### PAUL McGEHEE

| | ISSUE PRICE | CURRENT PRICE |
|---|---|---|
| ☐ CHESEPEAKE BAY HARBOR, rel. 1979. ed. 850, s/n, 19″ x 30½″, pub ARI ... | 100.00 | — |
| ed. 100, s/n, remarqued . . . . . . . . . . . . . . . . . . . . . . . . . . . . . . . . . . | 150.00 | 200.00 |
| ☐ DOWN THE BAY, rel. 1979. ed. 850, s/n, 19″ x 30½″, pub ARI . . . . . . . . . . . | 100.00 | — |
| ed. 100, s/n, remarqued . . . . . . . . . . . . . . . . . . . . . . . . . . . . . . . . . . | 150.00 | 200.00 |
| ☐ BAY COUNTRY LANDING, rel. 1979. ed. 850, s/n, 19″ x 30½″, pub ARI . . . . . | 100.00 | — |
| ed. 100, s/n, remarqued . . . . . . . . . . . . . . . . . . . . . . . . . . . . . . . . . . | 150.00 | 200.00 |
| ☐ END OF THE LINE, rel. 1979. ed. 1,000, s/n, 16″ x 24″, pub ARI . . . . . . . . . . | 35.00 | — |
| ed. N/A, s/o, remarqued . . . . . . . . . . . . . . . . . . . . . . . . . . . . . . . . | 85.00 | — |
| ☐ SKIPJACKS IN TANGIER SOUND, rel. 1979. ed. 850, s/n, 17″ x 20½″, pub ARI . . . . . . . . . . . . . . . . . . . . . . . . . . . . . . . . . . . . . . . . . . . . . . . . | 80.00 | — |
| ed. 200, s/n, remarqued . . . . . . . . . . . . . . . . . . . . . . . . . . . . . . . . . . | 130.00 | 180.00 |
| ☐ WINTER IN HEIDELBERG, rel. 1980. ed. 750, s/n, 19″ x 25⅜″, pub ARI . . . . . . | 100.00 | — |
| ed. 200, s/n, remarqued . . . . . . . . . . . . . . . . . . . . . . . . . . . . . . . . . . | 150.00 | — |
| ☐ STORMY PASSAGE, rel. 1980. ed. 750, s/n, 19″ x 25⅜″, pub ARI . . . . . . . . . . | 100.00 | — |
| ed. 200, s/n, remarqued . . . . . . . . . . . . . . . . . . . . . . . . . . . . . . . . . . | 150.00 | — |
| ☐ IN TROPICAL WATERS, rel. 1980. ed. 750, s/n, 18¾″ x 30″, pub ARI . . . . . . . | 100.00 | — |
| ed. 200, s/n, remarqued . . . . . . . . . . . . . . . . . . . . . . . . . . . . . . . . . . | 150.00 | — |
| ☐ THE MELON BOAT, rel. 1980. ed. 750, s/n, 24″ x 18″, pub ARI . . . . . . . . . . . | 80.00 | — |
| ed. 200, s/n, remarqued . . . . . . . . . . . . . . . . . . . . . . . . . . . . . . . . . . | 130.00 | — |
| ☐ BALTIMORE, rel. 1980. ed. 750, s/n, 18¾″ x 30″, pub ARI . . . . . . . . . . . . . . | 100.00 | 150.00 |
| ed. 200, s/n, remarqued . . . . . . . . . . . . . . . . . . . . . . . . . . . . . . . . . . | 150.00 | 200.00 |
| ☐ SUNDAY MORNING, rel. 1980. ed. 750, s/n, 16″ x 20″, pub ARI . . . . . . . . . . | 60.00 | — |
| ed. 200, s/n, remarqued . . . . . . . . . . . . . . . . . . . . . . . . . . . . . . . . . . | 110.00 | — |
| ☐ GEORGETOWN, rel. 1980. ed. 750, s/n, 20″ x 24″, pub ARI . . . . . . . . . . . . . . | 80.00 | — |
| ed. 200, s/n, remarqued . . . . . . . . . . . . . . . . . . . . . . . . . . . . . . . . . . | 130.00 | — |
| ☐ MALLARDS AT TILGHMAN ISLAND, rel. 1980. ed. 750, s/n, 16″ x 20″, pub ARI . . . . . . . . . . . . . . . . . . . . . . . . . . . . . . . . . . . . . . . . . . . . . . . . | 60.00 | — |
| ed. 200, s/n, remarqued . . . . . . . . . . . . . . . . . . . . . . . . . . . . . . . . . . | 110.00 | — |
| ☐ NANTUCKET, rel. 1982. ed. 750, s/n, 18¾″ x 30″, pub ARI . . . . . . . . . . . . . . | 100.00 | — |
| ed. 200, s/n, remarqued . . . . . . . . . . . . . . . . . . . . . . . . . . . . . . . . . . | 150.00 | — |
| ☐ EASTERN SHORE MALLARDS, rel. 1982. ed. 750, s/n, 18¾″ x 25″, pub ARI . | 100.00 | — |
| ed. 200, s/n, remarqued . . . . . . . . . . . . . . . . . . . . . . . . . . . . . . . . . . | 150.00 | — |
| ☐ NEW YORK, rel. 1982. ed. 4,700, s/n, 18½″ x 33″, pub ARI . . . . . . . . . . . . . | 100.00 | — |
| ed. 300, s/n, remarqued . . . . . . . . . . . . . . . . . . . . . . . . . . . . . . . . . . | 200.00 | — |
| ☐ LIFTING FOG, rel. 1983. ed. 1,700, s/n, 20″ x 30″, pub ARI . . . . . . . . . . . . . | 100.00 | — |
| ed. 300, s/n, remarqued . . . . . . . . . . . . . . . . . . . . . . . . . . . . . . . . . . | 200.00 | — |
| ☐ THOMAS POINT LIGHTHOUSE, rel. 1983. s/o, 9¼″ x 16⅝″, pub ARI . . . . . . . | 15.00 | — |
| ☐ SKIPJACKS OF THE CHESAPEAKE BAY, rel. 1983. s/o, 9¼″ x 16⅝″, pub ARI . | 15.00 | — |
| ☐ CHESAPEAKE BAY CRAB BOAT, rel. 1983. s/o, 9¼″ x 16⅝″, pub ARI . . . . . . . | 15.00 | — |
| ☐ THE "PRIDE OF BALTIMORE", rel. 1983. s/o, 9¼″ x 16⅝″, pub ARI . . . . . . . . | 15.00 | — |
| ☐ THE HILTON INN, ANNAPOLIS, MD., rel. 1983. s/o, 9¼″ x 16⅝″, pub ARI . . . | 15.00 | — |
| ☐ THE STATE HOUSE FROM EAST ST., ANNAPOLIS, rel. 1983. s/o, 9¼″ x 16⅝″, pub ARI . . . . . . . . . . . . . . . . . . . . . . . . . . . . . . . . . . . . . . . . . . | 15.00 | — |
| ☐ THE CITY DOCK, ANNAPOLIS, MD., rel. 1983. s/o, 9¼″ x 16⅝″, pub ARI . . . . | 15.00 | — |
| ☐ THE ABANDONED WORKBOAT, rel. 1983. s/o, 9¼″ x 16⅝″, pub ARI . . . . . . . . | 15.00 | — |

## BOB McGINNIS

Millions of Americans have seen Bob McGinnis' work without realizing it. National magazines, commercial art, movie productions — they've all had the "McGinnis touch".

McGinnis studied at an art school in Cincinnati. "It was here," he says, "that I learned how to put a picture together." Soon he was doing cartoon work and illustrations for local department stores. "It was good training," McGinnis now says of commercial art. "You had to be precise."

| BOB McGINNIS | ISSUE PRICE | CURRENT PRICE |
|---|---|---|
| ☐ WINTER WHEAT, rel. 1976. ed. 850, s/n, 28" x 16¼", pub GW | 60.00 | Sold Out |
| ☐ SLEEPY HOLLOW, rel. 1977. ed. 1,000, s/n, 25" x 17½", pub GW | 60.00 | — |
| ☐ STEER HORN LANTERN, rel. 1980. ed. 1,000, s/n, 28" x 18¼", pub GW | 75.00 | — |
| ☐ MEMORIES, rel. 1980. ed. 1,000, s/n, 32" x 18", pub GW | 75.00 | — |
| ☐ ETHAN, rel. 1980. ed. 1,000, s/n, 22" x 28½", pub GW | 90.00 | 400.00 |
| ☐ SILENT AND STILL, rel. 1981. ed. 1,000, s/n, 32" x 18½", pub GW | 95.00 | — |

## NANCY McGOWAN

| | ISSUE PRICE | CURRENT PRICE |
|---|---|---|
| ☐ THE SENTINEL, rel. 1973. ed. 500, s/n, 14" x 18", pub ALI | 20.00 | Sold Out |
| ed. 2,500, s/o | 15.00 | — |
| ☐ FIRST SPRING, rel. 1973. ed. 500, s/n, 14" x 18", pub ALI | 20.00 | — |
| ed. 2,500, s/o | 15.00 | — |

## GEORGE McLEAN

| | ISSUE PRICE | CURRENT PRICE |
|---|---|---|
| ☐ CANADA GEESE AND GOSLINGS, rel. 1982. ed. 950, s/n, 14⅝" x 24", pub MPPI | 95.00 | — |
| ☐ CHARLES IN THE GRASS, rel. 1982. ed. 950, s/n, 14" x 20", pub MPPI | 125.00 | — |
| ☐ RED-TAILED HAWK MANTLING, rel. 1982. ed. 950, s/n, 19⅛" x 38", pub MPPI | 245.00 | 325.00 |
| ☐ RED-WINGED BLACK BIRD AND CATTAILS, rel. 1982. ed. 950, s/n, 24" x 17¼", pub MPPI | 90.00 | — |

**CANADA GEESE AND GOSLINGS** *by George McLean*

|  | ISSUE PRICE | CURRENT PRICE |
|---|---|---|
| ☐ SILENT WATCH - GREAT HORNED OWL, rel. 1982. ed. 950, s/n, 24" x 17¾₆", pub MPPI | 90.00 | — |
| ☐ YELLOW LABRADOR RETRIEVER, rel. 1982. ed. 950, s/n, 22" x 38", pub MPPI | 175.00 | — |

## RODGER McPHAIL

| ☐ FIRST LIGHT-WOOD DUCKS, ed. 850, s/n, 17" x 24¾", distr. RAF | 80.00 | |
| ☐ COVEY RISE, ed. 850, s/n, 13¾" x 17", distr. RAF | 80.00 | — |

## WILLIAM N. McPHEETERS

Coupling realism with imagery, the work of William McPheeters captures the very essence of life. Always vital to the artist is his concentration on people. From the warm earthy tones of his watercolors to the precise development of detail in his pencil sketches, McPheeters constantly strives for the best interpretation of his subject.

Reminiscent of times gone by, the *"Life Series"* conveys the intense character of each of McPheeter's subjects. Skillfully captured in pencil, the *"Earth Series"* explores the critical tie between man and earth.

Much in demand as an illustrator, McPheeters has exhibited his work at various one-man shows. His numerous awards include two from the *New York Society of Illustrators.*

### WILLIAM N. McPHEETERS

| ☐ MR. CAGLES SHOP, ed. 2,500, s/n, 29" x 23", litho, pub GSP | 20.00 | — |
|---|---|---|
| ☐ CATCHING BAIT, ed. 1,000, s/n, 19" x 23½", litho, pub GSP | 25.00 | — |
| ed. 1,500, s/o | 20.00 | — |
| ☐ THE SEWING BASKET, ed. 1,000, signed & dated 1976, 12" x 15", pub GSP | 10.00 | — |
| ☐ COMMON SENSE, ed. 1,000, signed & dated, 12" x 15", pub GSP | 10.00 | — |
| ☐ WISDOM, ed. 850, s/n, 27⅞" x 22⅞", pub GSP | 15.00 | 100.00 |
| ☐ MOTHER EARTH, ed. 1,000, s/n, 21" x 24", pub GSP | 20.00 | 40.00 |

## MARGARET MEE

Margaret Mee specializes in orchids. Born in Buckinghamshire, England, she does her scientific and artistic work deep in the Amazon jungle of Brazil where she studies and paints the plants in their native habitat.

She has exhibited throughout the world including the Institute de Botanica, Sao Paulo; Royal Horticultural Society, London; and Botanical Society of South Africa.

Fellowships have included a Guggenheim in 1970 and Honorary Research Fellow in Orchidology at Harvard in 1973. She is author of Flowers of the Brazilian Forests.

### MARGARET MEE

| ☐ FAM. BIGNONIACEAE, rel. 1976. ed. 1,000, s/n, 23" x 17", pub FHG | 35.00 | Sold Out |
|---|---|---|
| ☐ GUSTAVIA, rel. 1976. ed. 1,000, s/n, 23" x 17", pub FHG | 35.00 | Sold Out |

## SUSAN PEAR MEISEL

|  |  | ISSUE PRICE | CURRENT PRICE |
|---|---|---|---|
| ☐ | **PUBLIC LIBRARY**, ed. 175, s/n, 23″ x 28″, silk screen, pub EWG . . . . . . . . . . | — | 300.00 |
| ☐ | **TIMES SQUARE**, ed. 275, s/n, 24″ x 29″, silk screen, pub EWG . . . . . . . . . . . | — | 300.00 |
| ☐ | **FRUIT MARKET**, ed. 275, s/n, 20″ x 40″, litho, pub EWG . . . . . . . . . . . . . . . . | — | 275.00 |
| ☐ | **AMERICAS CUP**, ed. 250, s/n, 20″ x 24″, litho, pub EWG . . . . . . . . . . . . . . . | — | 150.00 |
| ☐ | **SPRING SKATE**, ed. 250, s/n, 20″ x 25″, litho, pub EWG . . . . . . . . . . . . . . . | — | 125.00 |
| ☐ | **MY HOUSE**, ed. 275, s/n, 20″ x 24″, silk screen, pub EWG . . . . . . . . . . . . . | — | 200.00 |
| ☐ | **HAPPY DAYS**, ed. 275, s/n, 20″ x 26″, silk screen, pub EWG . . . . . . . . . . . . | — | 175.00 |
| ☐ | **HOTEL DE ROMA**, ed. 275, s/n, 20″ x 27″, silk screen, pub EWG . . . . . . . . . . | — | 150.00 |
| ☐ | **MOULIN ROUGE**, ed. 275, s/n, 22″ x 30″, silk screen, pub EWG . . . . . . . . . . | — | 200.00 |
| ☐ | **SAN FRANCISCO** - Suite of 3. ed. 250, s/n, lithos, pub EWG . . . . . . . . . . . . . | — | 150.00 |
|  | **GOLDEN GATE**, size 12″ x 20″; **FISHERMAN'S WHARF**, size 9″ x 12″; **CABLE CAR**, 9″ x 12″ |  |  |
| ☐ | **SAN FRANCISCO** - Suite of 3. ed. 500, stone signed only, lithos, pub EWG . . . . | — | 75.00 |
| ☐ | **WASHINGTON MONUMENT**, ed. 325, s/o, 19″ x 24″, litho, pub EWG . . . . . . . . | — | 35.00 |

## STANLEY MELTZOFF

Stanley Meltzoff, born in 1917 in New York City, entered the army in World War II as an art historian and left it as an artist-journalist with *Stars and Stripes*. Publicly, he is known as an illustrator for *Scientific American, Life, Field & Stream* and *National Geographic,* while privately, he was among the first Americans to begin exploring the continental shelf with snorkel and scuba.

Meltzoff is a life-long diver and is proud to hold the spearfishing records for striped bass and bluefish. The determination of Dick Gangel of *Sports Illustrated* to display artist-journalists made it possible for Stanley to connect his life beneath his studio skylights with his life beneath the surface of the sea. He has chosen to represent the salt water game fish which could not be well photographed, because of their speed, rarity or the dimness of their environment. All of the fish painted by Meltzoff have been studied alive in the seas. He has completed a series of Blue Marlin and Sailfish for *Sports Illustrated* and for *National Geographic,* he has followed the bluefin tuna in their annual circumnavigation of the North Atlantic, attempting to record them while they survive in the wild.

He is a highly regarded member of the Society of Animal Artists and was a recipient of an Award of Merit in 1980. He is proud to be a member of the Society of Illistrators from which he continues to receive many awards. Meltzoff has taught in many local New York colleges, as well as having lectured at Harvard University.

**BELOW ON THE FLATS – BONE AND PERMIT FISH** *by Stanley Meltzoff*

## STANLEY MELTZOFF

| | ISSUE PRICE | CURRENT PRICE |
|---|---|---|
| ☐ **\*DOUBLE HEADER #1-BLUE MARLIN,** rel. 1981. ed. 750, s/n, 19¾″ x 27″ . . . | 125.00 | — |
| ☐ **BELOW ON THE FLATS-BONE AND PERMIT FISH,** rel. 1981. ed. 750, s/n, 10¾″ x 27¼″ . . . . . . . . . . . . . . . . . . . . . . . . . . . . . . . . . . . . . . . . . . . . | 85.00 | — |
| ☐ **SHINING SAILFISH AND BALLYHOO,** rel. 1981. ed. 750, s/n, 18½″ x 27¼″ . . | 125.00 | — |
| ☐ **BABY BONES IN A CONCH,** rel. 1982. ed. 750, s/n, 13″ x 10″ . . . . . . . . . . . . | 60.00 | — |

Stanley Meltzhoff prints are distributed through several sources. Please note sources listing under SEL and WWI.

# SALLIE MIDDLETON

Although the artist had formal training at Vesper George School in Boston, her skills spring from a childhood close to nature in the Blue Ridge Mountains of North Carolina and her association with her talented uncle, the watercolorist, Douglas Ellington.

She acquires and actually lives with the live animals or preserved specimens she portrays. She will often spend dozens of hours sitting before the little bit of landscape which embraces these animals, scrutinizing every single thing about it, and then she will patiently reproduce it.

Middleton works exclusively with translucent watercolors, which produces the finest results in brilliance of hue, accuracy of tone, depth of field and precision of imagery.

**SCREECH OWL** *by Sallie Middleton*

## SALLIE MIDDLETON

| | ISSUE PRICE | CURRENT PRICE |
|---|---|---|
| **SPECIAL MINIATURE EDITIONS (DUCK STAMP ENTRIES)** | | |
| ☐ REDHEAD LANDING, rel. 1977. ed. 985, s/n, 8″ x 10″ ............... | 25.00 | 50.00 |
| ☐ AMERICAN GOLDENEYE, rel. 1979. ed. 985, s/n, 8″ x 10″ ............ | 25.00 | 50.00 |
| ed. 250, s/o, exclusive for Nature Society, Asheville, North Carolina. | | |
| ☐ BLUE WINGED TEAL, rel. 1981. ed. 1,500, s/n, 9″ x 10″ ............. | 25.00 | — |
| ☐ MATCHED NUMBER SET OF ALL THREE DUCK MINIATURES .............. | 75.00 | 150.00 |
| **WILDFLOWER SERIES** | | |
| ☐ WILD ROSE AND VIOLET, pair, Plates I & II, rel. 1975. ed. 1,000, s/n, 12″ x 9″ | 35.00 | 75.00 |
| ☐ GENTIAN AND FOAMFLOWER, pair, Plates III & IV, rel. 1976. ed. 1,500, s/n, 12″ x 9″ .................................................. | 45.00 | 65.00 |
| ☐ BLOODROOT AND WILD IRIS, pair, Plates V & VI, rel. 1977. ed. 1,500, s/n, 12″ x 9″ ........................................... | 45.00 | 65.00 |
| ☐ BUTTERCUPS AND BIRDFOOT VIOLETS, pair, Plates VII & VIII, rel. 1981. ed. 1,500, s/n, 12″ x 9″. ...................................... | 50.00 | — |
| ☐ MATCHED NUMBER SET OF ALL FOUR WILDFLOWER PAIRS ............. | 175.00 | 250.00 |
| ☐ SCARLET TANAGER, rel. 1981. ed. 2,500, s/n, 20½″ x 26¼″ ........ | 75.00 | — |
| ☐ THE OTTER AND THE TEAL, rel. 1982. ed. 1,500, s/n, 20½″ x 26½″ ........ | 75.00 | — |
| ☐ A CAT CALLED BOB, rel. 1982. ed. 1,500, s/n, 20″ x 26½″ ........ | 75.00 | — |
| ☐ YOUNG GRAY SQUIRRELS, rel. 1983. ed. 1,500, s/n, 15½″ x 19½″ ........ | 50.00 | — |
| ☐ WARBLER IN SPRING, rel. 1983. ed. 1,500, s/n, 24½″ x 18½″ ........ | 50.00 | — |
| ☐ SCREECH OWL, rel. 1983. ed. 1,500, s/n, 18½″ x 24½″ ............. | 75.00 | — |
| ☐ MALLARD, rel. 1970. ed. 1,000, s/n, 22″ x 27½″ ................. | 35.00 | 350.00 |
| ed. 1,500, s/o ................................................ | 25.00 | 330.00 |
| ☐ GREAT HORNED OWL, rel. 1970. ed. 1,000, s/n, 25½″ x 22″ ........ | 35.00 | 375.00 |
| ed. 1,500, s/o ................................................ | 25.00 | 300.00 |
| ☐ RACCOON, rel. 1971. ed. 1,000, s/n, 25″ x 21½″ ................ | 35.00 | 275.00 |
| ed. 1,500, s/o ................................................ | 25.00 | 200.00 |
| ☐ MOURNING DOVES, rel. 1971. ed. 1,000, s/n, 20″ x 25″ ............. | 35.00 | 150.00 |
| ed. 1,500, s/o ................................................ | 25.00 | 110.00 |
| ☐ ROBIN AND SPARROW, rel. 1971. ed. 1,000, s/n, 17¼″ x 25½″ ........ | 50.00 | 300.00 |
| ☐ CHIPMUNKS IN AUGUST, rel. 1971. ed. 1,000, s/n, 21½″ x 26½″ ........ | 50.00 | 375.00 |
| ☐ CARDINALS IN WINTER, rel. 1971. ed. 1,000, s/n, 26¼″ x 22″ ........ | 35.00 | 300.00 |
| ed. 1,500, s/o ................................................ | 25.00 | 225.00 |
| ☐ TURTLE, rel. 1971. ed. 1,000, s/n, 19″ x 23½″ ................. | 35.00 | 150.00 |
| ed. 1,500, s/o ................................................ | 25.00 | 110.00 |
| ☐ YELLOW SHAFTER FLICKER, rel. 1972. ed. 1,000, s/n, 19½″ x 28½″ ...... | 35.00 | 425.00 |
| ed. 1,500, s/o ................................................ | 25.00 | 375.00 |
| ☐ RABBIT (Single), rel. 1972. ed. 1,000, s/n, 14″ x 19¼″ ............... | 35.00 | 125.00 |
| ed. 1,500, s/o ................................................ | 25.00 | 100.00 |
| ☐ PILEATED WOODPECKER, rel. 1973. ed. 1,000, s/n, 18″ x 25″ ............ | 35.00 | 125.00 |
| ed. 1,500, s/o ................................................ | 25.00 | 75.00 |
| ☐ EASTERN COTTONTAILS (Rabbits in Rhododendron), rel. 1973. ed. 1,000, s/n, 18½″ x 26″. ............................................... | 50.00 | 300.00 |
| ☐ BLUE JAY, rel. 1973. ed. 1,000, s/n, 18½″ x 24″ ................. | 35.00 | 250.00 |
| ed. 1,500, s/o ................................................ | 25.00 | 175.00 |
| ☐ WARBLER IN SPRING, rel. 1983. ed. 1,500, s/n, 24½″ x 18½″ ........... | 50.00 | — |
| ☐ SCREECH OWL, rel. 1983. ed. 1,500, s/n, 18½″ x 24½″ ............. | 75.00 | — |
| ☐ PURPLE FINCHES, rel. 1973. ed. 1,000, s/n, 20″ x 16″ ............. | 35.00 | 60.00 |
| ed. 1,500, s/o ................................................ | 25.00 | — |
| ☐ BOBWHITE QUAIL, rel. 1973. ed. 1,000, s/n, 26¼″ x 20½″ ........... | 50.00 | 250.00 |
| ☐ BARN OWL, rel. 1974. ed. 2,000, s/n, 16½″ x 24″ ................. | 40.00 | 225.00 |
| ☐ CHIPMUNK IN THE SNOW, rel. 1974. ed. 2,000, s/n, 25″ x 18″ ........... | 40.00 | 175.00 |
| ☐ RUFFED GROUSE, rel. 1974. ed. 2,000, s/n, 21½″ x 25″ ............. | 40.00 | 80.00 |
| ☐ WOODCHUCK, rel. 1975. ed. 2,000, s/n, 23″ x 25″ ................ | 40.00 | 100.00 |
| ☐ REDHEADED DUCK, rel. 1975. ed. 2,000, s/n, 22″ x 25½″ ............ | 40.00 | 90.00 |
| ☐ CHAMELEON AND OPOSSUM, pair, rel. 1975. ed. 1,000, s/n, 9½″ x 9½″ ... | 35.00 | 50.00 |
| ☐ INDIGO BUNTING, rel. 1976. ed. 2,000, s/n, 17″ x 22″ ............. | 40.00 | 250.00 |
| ☐ WILLET, rel. 1976. ed. 750, s/n, 21″ x 28½″ ................... | 75.00 | 150.00 |
| ☐ TULIP POPLAR, rel. 1976. ed. 1,776, s/n, 24″ x 20″ .............. | 40.00 | — |
| ed. (200 bearing pencil remarque by the artist) ................... | 75.00 | 100.00 |
| ☐ YOUNG RABBITS IN CLOVER, rel. 1976. ed. 2,000, s/n, 16″ x 20″ ........ | 40.00 | 425.00 |
| ☐ YOUNG RED FOX, rel. 1977. ed. 1,500, s/n, 26″ x 21″ ............. | 75.00 | 425.00 |
| ☐ CHICKADEE, rel. 1977. ed. 1,500, s/n, 20″ x 24″ ................ | 45.00 | 250.00 |
| ☐ RUBY THROATED HUMMINGBIRD, rel. 1977. ed. 1,500, s/n, 25″ x 21″ ..... | 50.00 | 125.00 |
| ☐ WOOD DUCKS, rel. 1,978. ed. 1978, s/n, 20½″ x 26½″ ............. | 125.00 | 425.00 |

# LJUBOMIR MILINKOV

Ljubomir Milinkov is a primitive painter portraying scenes of a small village in Yugoslavia.

He transforms the simple life into a colorful world. Fantastic birds and beasts, panoramic scenes of sowing, harvesting, fishing, or gathering grapes, are topics Milinkov presents with brilliant color.

| LJUBOMIR MILINKOV | ISSUE PRICE | CURRENT PRICE |
|---|---|---|
| ☐ **COUNTRYSIDE**, rel. 1981. ed. 300, s/n, 24" x 28½", litho, arches, pub EEI... | 300.00 | — |
| ☐ **SPRING BLOSSOM**, rel. 1981. ed. 300, s/n, 24" x 28½", litho, arches, pub EEI. | 300.00 | — |
| ☐ **MY MUSTANG**, rel. 1982. ed. 300, s/n, 10¼" x 12½", litho, arches, pub EEI. | 100.00 | — |
| ☐ **BUSY, BUSY**, rel. 1982. ed. 300, s/n, 12½" x 10¼", litho, arches, pub EEI. | 100.00 | — |
| ☐ **HAPPY DAY**, rel. 1982. ed. 300, s/n, 10¼" x 12½", litho, arches, pub EEI. | 100.00 | — |
| ☐ **FLOWER PICKING**, rel. 1982. ed. 300, s/n, 12½" x 10¼", litho, arches, pub EEI. | 100.00 | — |

# GERHARD C. F. MILLER

Gerhard C. F. Miller has had major exhibitions at the Metropolitan Museum, the National Academy and the American Watercolor Society.

In addition to painting, his creative credits also include teaching, lecturing and writing — his book of poetry entitled *"Residue"* was published in 1944.

**THE CHAPEL** *by Gerhard C. F. Miller*

## GERHARD C. F. MILLER

| | ISSUE PRICE | CURRENT PRICE |
|---|---|---|
| ☐ **BOAT HOIST**, ed. 500, s/n, 21½" x 27½", pub CG | 60.00 | 85.00 |
| ☐ **THE CHAPEL**, ed. 375, s/n, 21½" x 27½", pub CG | 60.00 | 300.00 |
| ☐ **JANUARY SHADOWS**, ed. 500, s/n, 21½" x 27½", pub CG | 60.00 | 100.00 |
| ☐ **MARSHMARIGOLDS**, ed. 500, s/n, 21½" x 27½", pub CG | 75.00 | 85.00 |
| ☐ **OLD PINE STUMP**, ed. 500, s/n, 21½" x 27½", pub CG | 75.00 | 85.00 |
| ☐ **OLSON'S BUGGY**, ed. 500, s/n, 21½" x 27½", pub CG | 85.00 | — |
| ☐ **RETURN TO NATURE**, ed. 500, s/n, 21½" x 27½", pub CG | 50.00 | 125.00 |
| ☐ **RETURN OF THE CROWS**, ed. 500, s/n, 21½" x 27½", pub CG | 50.00 | 85.00 |
| ☐ **THE SEEDLING**, ed. 500, s/n, 21½" x 27½", pub CG | 85.00 | — |
| ☐ **SMOKE HOUSE**, ed. 500, s/n, 21½" x 27½", pub CG | 50.00 | 75.00 |
| ☐ **STABLE DOOR**, ed. 500, s/n, 21½" x 27½", pub CG | 50.00 | 125.00 |
| ☐ **SUGAR BUSH**, ed. 500, s/n, 21½" x 27½", pub CG | 60.00 | 100.00 |
| ☐ **SUGAR MAPLE**, ed. 500, s/n, 21½" x 27½", pub CG | 60.00 | 100.00 |
| ☐ **THE VETERAN**, ed. 190, s/n, 21½" x 27½", pub CG | 50.00 | 600.00 |
| ☐ **WILD GRAPES**, ed. 500, s/n, 21½" x 27½", pub CG | 50.00 | 100.00 |

# KATHRYN MILLER

Kathryn Miller paints landscapes, seascapes and other nature scenes. A graduate of the University of North Carolina, Miller is an internationally known realist oil painter. Her limited edition prints hang in galleries worldwide.

**SUMMERTIME** by Kathryn Miller

## KATHRYN MILLER

| | ISSUE PRICE | CURRENT PRICE |
|---|---|---|
| ☐ **GOLDEN SEA OATS**, rel. 1974. ed. 1,500, s/n, 24″ x 36″, pub KMS........ | 30.00 | — |
| ☐ **RIVER SHACK**, rel. 1974. ed. 2,000, s/n, 20″ x 24″, pub KMS............. | 25.00 | — |
| ☐ **COUNTRY HERITAGE**, rel. 1975. ed. 950, s/n, 20″ x 24″, pub KMS ......... | 30.00 | — |
| ☐ **RUSTIC CHARM**, rel. 1975. ed. 950, s/n, 16″ x 20″, pub KMS............. | 20.00 | — |
| ☐ **SUMMER MARSHES**, rel. 1975. ed. 950, s/n, 20″ x 24″, pub KMS ......... | 30.00 | 100.00 |
| ☐ **MOSS CREEK**, rel. 1977. ed. 950, s/n, 20″ x 24″, pub KMS............. | 30.00 | — |
| ☐ **SANDY SHORES**, rel. 1977. ed. 950, s/n, 20″ x 24″, pub KMS ............ | 30.00 | 100.00 |
| ☐ **SOUTHERN BEAUTY**, rel. 1978. ed. 950, s/n, 20″ x 24″, pub KMS ......... | 20.00 | — |
| ☐ **SUMMERTIME**, rel. 1978. ed. 950, s/n, 20″ x 24″, pub KMS.............. | 30.00 | 100.00 |
| ☐ **DAUFUSKIE ISLAND**, rel. 1979. ed. 950, s/n, 22″ x 28″, pub KMS ...... | 50.00 | — |
| ☐ **SOUTHERN LANDSCAPE**, rel. 1979. ed. 950, s/n, 22″ x 28″, pub KMS ...... | 50.00 | — |
| ☐ **LAND OF THE TREMBLING EARTH**, rel. 1980. ed. 950, s/n, 22″ x 28″, pub KMS ............................................. | 50.00 | — |
| ☐ **LOW COUNTRY HAVEN**, rel. 1980. ed. 950, s/n, 22″ x 28″, pub KMS ....... | 50.00 | — |
| ☐ **NIGHTTIME SHELLS**, rel. 1980. ed. 950, s/n, etching, 22″ x 28″, pub KMS... | 20.00 | — |
| ☐ **SUNRISE**, rel. 1980. ed. 950, s/n, 22″ x 28″, pub KMS ................ | 30.00 | — |
| ☐ **BABY BIRDS**, ed. 200, s/n, etching, 8″ x 10″, pub KMS............... | 20.00 | — |
| ☐ **THE BEACHCOMBERS**, ed. 200, s/n, etching, 8″ x 10″, pub KMS........... | 20.00 | — |
| ☐ **BLUE HERON**, ed. 200, s/n, etching, 8″ x 10″, pub KMS.............. | 20.00 | — |
| ☐ **BUTTERFLIES**, ed. 200, s/n, etching, 8″ x 10″, pub KMS.............. | 20.00 | — |
| ☐ **THE CANADIANS**, ed. 200, s/n, etching, 12″ x 16″, pub KMS............... | 60.00 | — |
| ☐ **COASTAL SCENES**, ed. 200, s/n, etching, 11″ x 14″, pub KMS............. | 50.00 | — |
| ☐ **COCKATOO**, ed. 200, s/n, etching, 14″ x 11″, pub KMS............... | 50.00 | — |
| ☐ **COUNTRY BARN**, ed. 200, s/n, etching, 11″ x 14″, pub KMS............. | 40.00 | — |
| ☐ **THE EGRETS**, ed. 200, s/n, etching, 11″ x 15″, pub KMS............... | 60.00 | — |
| ☐ **GEORGIA BACKWATER**, ed. 50, s/n, etching, 14″ x 15″, pub KMS........... | 60.00 | — |
| ☐ **GERANIUMS**, ed. 100, s/n, etching, 8″ x 10″, pub KMS.............. | 30.00 | — |
| ☐ **GOOD MORNING WORLD**, ed. 100, s/n, etching, 8″ x 10″, pub KMS......... | 30.00 | — |
| ☐ **GREEN FROG**, ed. 200, s/n, etching, 8″ x 10″, pub KMS.............. | 20.00 | — |
| ☐ **HANGIN' OUT**, ed. 200, s/n, etching, 8″ x 10″, pub KMS............. | 20.00 | — |
| ☐ **HIGH SOCIETY**, ed. 200, s/n, etching, 18″ x 11″, pub KMS............. | 60.00 | — |
| ☐ **HUMMINGBIRD**, ed. 200, s/n, etching, 8″ x 10″, pub KMS............. | 20.00 | — |
| ☐ **KINGFISHER**, ed. 200, s/n, etching, 11″ x 14″, pub KMS.............. | 40.00 | — |
| ☐ **LIFT OFF**, ed. 200, s/n, etching, 14″ x 11″, pub KMS.............. | 50.00 | — |
| ☐ **LOWCOUNTRY CRABBER**, ed. 50, s/n, etching, 8″ x 10″, pub KMS. ........ | 20.00 | — |
| ☐ **MALLARD**, ed. 200, s/n, etching, 8″ x 10″, pub KMS.............. | 20.00 | — |
| ☐ **MARKET PLACE**, ed. 50, s/n, etching, 8″ x 10″, pub KMS. ............ | 20.00 | — |
| ☐ **PELICAN**, ed. 200, s/n, etching, 8″ x 10″, pub KMS. ............. | 20.00 | — |
| ☐ **POSSUM TIME**, ed. 200, s/n, etching, 11″ x 15″, pub KMS............. | 60.00 | — |
| ☐ **PREENING HERON**, ed. 200, s/n, etching, 15″ x 11″, pub KMS............. | 60.00 | — |
| ☐ **PRELUDE TO SPRING**, ed. 200, s/n, etching, 11″ x 14″, pub KMS. ......... | 40.00 | — |
| ☐ **SAVANNAH GARDEN**, ed. 50, s/n, etching, 14″ x 15″, pub KMS............. | 60.00 | — |
| ☐ **SEA TREASURES**, ed. 200, s/n, etching, 11″ x 14″, pub KMS. ........... | 40.00 | — |
| ☐ **SHELL MEDLEY**, ed. 200, s/n, etching, 12″ x 16″, pub KMS. ........... | 60.00 | — |
| ☐ **SQUIRREL AND ACORNS**, ed. 200, s/n, etching, 8″ x 10″, pub KMS......... | 20.00 | — |
| ☐ **SUN DOWN**, ed. 50, s/n, etching, 14″ x 15″, pub KMS............... | 40.00 | — |
| ☐ **SUN DOWN, SECOND STATE**, ed. 200, s/n, etching, 14″ x 15″, pub KMS. ... | 60.00 | — |
| ☐ **TRITON'S TRUMPET**, ed. 200, s/n, etching, 11″ x 14″, pub KMS............. | 40.00 | — |
| ☐ **THE UNICORN**, ed. 200, s/n, etching, 11″ x 14″, pub KMS.............. | 60.00 | — |
| ☐ **UP AND AWAY**, ed. 200, s/n, etching, 11″ x 16″, pub KMS. ............ | 60.00 | — |
| ☐ **WATER LILY**, ed. 200, s/n, etching, 11″ x 14″, pub KMS. ............ | 50.00 | — |
| ☐ **WINTER MILL**, ed. 200, s/n, etching, 11″ x 14″, pub KMS. ............. | 40.00 | — |
| ☐ **WOOD DUCK**, ed. 200, s/n, etching, 11″ x 14″, pub KMS. .............. | 50.00 | — |

# JOAN MIRO

| | | |
|---|---|---|
| ☐ **SAN LAZARRO ET SES AMIS**, ed. 60, s/n, 29¾″ x 21½″, original color lithograph, pub FI.................................................... | 2,000.00 | 2,500.00 |

# CHUCK MITCHELL

Chuck Mitchell was born and raised in the inner city of Chicago where his creative ability was recognized at an early age. A series of awards during his school years enabled him to receive training in a variety of specialized art programs. He later opened his own studio in Chicago where he achieved success as an illustrator.

His illustrations have appeared in *Sports Afield, Fly Fisherman* and *Outdoor Life* magazines. He is the recipient of many awards including the Society of Illustrators of New York and the Chicago Artists Guild. He was featured in the *American Artist* magazine and has illustrated extensively for *Encyclopedia Brittanica* and *Comptons Encyclopedia*.

**1983 WISCONSIN SALMON** *by Chuck Mitchell*

| CHUCK MITCHELL | ISSUE PRICE | CURRENT PRICE |
|---|---|---|
| ☐ **LAKE TROUT**, rel. 1983. 1983 Wisconsin Great Lakes Salmon & Trout Stamp Print. ed. 600, s/n, 14″ x 12″, pub NC | 200.00 | — |
| ed. 150 remarqued | 350.00 | — |

# HARRY J. MOELLER

Harry Moeller approaches his art with a dedication to portraying the subtle dramas that take place in nature's out-of-doors. His vivid imagination is reflected in the subtle details that often go unnoticed by the casual observer.

A meticulous craftsman, Harry Moeller spends much time in researching an idea. He often tramps through the woodlands of Wisconsin, slow motion camera and sketch book in hand to record the movements of birds and animals.

**FAWN WITH GOLDFINCH** by *Harry J. Moeller*

The idea for painting is first roughed out in a series of preliminary sketches. From a finished pencil sketch the final composition evolves, usually in opaque and transparent watercolor. In contrast to the detailed settings of some of his earlier works, more recent paintings dwell mainly on the wildlife creature, leaving the immediate surroundings briefly detailed and the background hazy or indistinct. "I try to depict what animals are doing, no matter how humorous or odd it may seem to the viewer," said Moeller.

Moeller has exhibited his paintings in Milwaukee, Chicago, Denver, San Antonio, New York and North Carolina. His work is represented in private collections throughout the United States and Europe. Thirty paintings were reproduced and published by Ideals Publishing in a book entitled "Woodland Portraits". Numerous paintings have been used by Child's World Publishing during the past several years, and four paintings were published by National Wildlife Federation, Washington, D.C. He was also one of four artists selected to have his paintings reproduced on Pickard China for the Ghent Bicentennial Collection.

## HARRY J. MOELLER

| | ISSUE PRICE | CURRENT PRICE |
|---|---|---|
| ☐ **BALD EAGLE,** rel. 1969. ed. 1,000, s/n, 18" x 24", dist. NC . . . . . . . . . . . . . . . | 30.00 | — |
| ☐ **MASTER'S PRIDE,** rel. 1970. ed. 1,000, s/n, 18" x 24", dist. NC . . . . . . . . . . | 30.00 | — |
| ☐ **RING-NECKED PHEASANT,** rel. 1970. ed. 1,000, s/n, 18" x 24", dist. NC . . . . | 30.00 | — |
| ☐ **FAWN WITH GOLDFINCH,** rel. 1979. ed. 600, s/n, 22" x 28", pub NC . . . . . . . | 60.00 | — |

| | ISSUE PRICE | CURRENT PRICE |
|---|---|---|
| ☐ **RACCOON WITH CHIPMUNK,** rel. 1979. ed. 600, s/n, 22″ x 28″, pub NC..... | 60.00 | — |
| ☐ **MOOSE,** rel. 1980. ed. 600, s/n, 30″ x 24″, pub NC .................... | 70.00 | — |
| ☐ **WARLORDS,** rel. 1980. ed. 600, s/n, 24″ x 30″, pub NC.................. | 70.00 | — |
| ☐ **WATERFOWL FLIGHTFOLIO,** rel. 1980. ed. 600, s/n, 9″ x 12″, pub NC ...... | 75.00 | — |
| (Portfolio of four prints). | | |
| ☐ **GREAT EXPECTATIONS,** rel. 1981. ed. 600, s/n, 22″ x 28″, pub NC......... | 75.00 | — |
| ☐ **RUFFED GROUSE,** rel. 1981. ed. 600, s/n, 28″ x 21″, pub NC ............. | 75.00 | — |

## WILMA MOHNER-LANGHAMER

Castles, flowers and delicate landscapes of the medieval period are typical of Wilma Mohner-Langhamer's paintings. "I like the earlier times to a certain extent. I have always liked the paintings of the 13th through the 16th centuries . . . but Botticellie and the Florentine school are my favorites," says Mohner-Langhamer.

Born in Germany, Mohner-Langhamer worked in the family knitting factory as a fashion designer for ten years before pursuing her career as a professional artist.

Mohner-Langhamer has been commissioned by companies like Rolls-Royce, BMW, and Neiman-Marcus. Her work has appeared on magazines, calendars and post cards.

**THE FLOWER BALLOON** *by Wilma Mohner-Langhamer*

| WILMA MOHNER-LANGHAMER | ISSUE PRICE | CURRENT PRICE |
|---|---|---|
| ☐ CASTLE SAUMUR-MEDIEVAL GRAPE HARVEST, ed. 950, s/n, 20" x 24", pub GSP | 65.00 | — |
| ed. 50, artist proof | 85.00 | — |
| ☐ FLOWERS-MEDIEVAL SCENE IN TUSCANY, ed. 950, s/n, 20" x 24", pub GSP. | 75.00 | — |
| ed. 50, artist proof | 95.00 | — |
| ☐ HARVEST DANCE-MEDIEVAL SCENE ON THE RHINE, ed. 950, s/n, 20" x 24", pub GSP | 65.00 | — |
| ☐ THE FAIR, ed. 1,000, s/n, 28½" x 22½", pub GSP | 75.00 | — |
| ☐ WINTER DAY-MEDIEVAL SCENE, ed. 950, s/n, 20" x 16", pub GSP | 45.00 | — |

# BOB MOLINE

Bob Moline is a Comanche who was born and grew up in West Texas. As a young man, he learned the art of saddle making and earned a living at it while teaching himself to be an artist. In 1971, Moline devoted his full time to art work. Moline's work portrays both the west and yesteryears of the cattle country. He won the coveted Rand Stephen Awards in 1978. Moline has been featured in numerous magazines and journals and was the 1980 recipient of the Gold Award, Texas Ranger Hall of Fame.

Moline has authored several books including, *XIT — The American Cowboy*, published by Oxmoor Publishing; *Colt Pistols*, published by Jackson Arms; and *Bob Moline — A Cowboy and His Art*, Buffalo Creek Publishing.

## BOB MOLINE

| | | |
|---|---|---|
| ☐ DAY'S END, rel. 1981. ed. 975, s/n, 24" x 30", pub FHG. | 75.00 | — |
| ☐ TALLY GATE, rel. 1981. ed. 975, s/n, 22" x 29", pub FHG. | 75.00 | — |
| ☐ FUR TRAPPER, rel. 1982. ed. 975, s/n, 28" x 22", pub FHG. | 75.00 | — |

# BURTON E. MOORE, JR.

Burton E. Moore, Jr., a native of South Carolina, who spent his formative years in Columbia, enlisted in the U.S. Marines in 1966 and was discharged from the Corps as a Captain of Marine infantry in 1973. His love for the salt marshes, cypress swamps and barrier islands of Carolina led him to choose Charleston as his home and wildlife art as a career.

An avid hunter and conservationist, Moore is a member of Ducks Unlimited, the National Rifle Association and the National Audubon Society.

Moore completed a series of detailed hen and drake illustrations for a duck identification film produced by the South Carolina Wildlife and Marine Resources Department.

## BURTON E. MOORE, JR.

| | | |
|---|---|---|
| ☐ LEE DUDLEY-CANVASBACK, rel. 1979. ed. 950, s/n, 24" x 19", pub MPPI | 65.00 | 125.00 |
| ☐ HARRY SHOURDES REDHEAD, rel. 1979. ed. 950, s/n, 24" x 19", pub MPPI. | 65.00 | — |
| ☐ WARD BROTHERS CANADAS, rel. 1979. ed. 950, s/n, 27½" x 23", pub MPPI. | 85.00 | — |
| ☐ WARD BROTHERS CANVASBACKS, rel. 1980. ed. 950, s/n, 27¼" x 23", pub MPPI | 85.00 | — |
| ☐ JOSEPH LINCOLN PINTAIL ON THE SANTEE, rel. 1981. ed. 950, s/n, 28¾" x 22¾", pub MPPI | 85.00 | — |
| ☐ THE WAITING, rel. 1981. ed. 950, s/n, 27½" x 22¾", pub MPPI | 85.00 | — |
| ☐ THE WIND CALLED HIS NAME, rel. 1981. ed. 950, s/n, 27½" x 22¾", pub MPPI | 85.00 | — |
| ☐ GOLDEN DAWN, rel. 1982. ed. 950, s/n, 27½" x 22¾", pub MPPI | 85.00 | — |

**GOLDEN DAWN** *by Burton E. Moore, Jr.*

## CHARLEYN MOORE

Charleyn Moore is a self-taught artist. She now lives in Ft. Lauderdale, Florida.
At first, she was a portrait artist, spending several years doing charcoal portraits and quick sketches in art shows throughout the Mid-South. As a zoo buff, Moore has traveled nationwide to study and observe exotic animals. It was her interest in these animals that eventually led Moore to wildlife using pastels to achieve the effect of character and strength which she felt was unobtainable with oil paint.

**CARLEYN MOORE**

| | ISSUE PRICE | CURRENT PRICE |
|---|---|---|
| ☐ **AFRICAN LION,** rel. 1976. ed. 2,000, numbered only, 20″ x 24″, pub SG . . . . . | 40.00 | — |
| ☐ **COUGAR CUB,** rel. 1976. ed. 2,000, s/n, 20″ x 24″, pub SG . . . . . . . . . . . . . | 50.00 | — |
| ☐ **SIBERIAN TIGER,** rel. 1976. ed. 2,000, s/n, 20″ x 24″, pub SG . . . . . . . . . . . | 50.00 | — |
| ☐ **BANDIT (RACCOON),** rel. 1977. ed. 2,000, s/n, 20″ x 24″, pub SG . . . . . . . . | 50.00 | — |
| ☐ **KOALA,** rel. 1978. ed. 1,000, s/n, 16″ x 20″, pub SG . . . . . . . . . . . . . . . . . . | 40.00 | — |
| ☐ **MOTHERLY LOVE (JAGUAR & CUB),** rel. 1978. ed. 1,000, s/n, 20″ x 24″, pub SG . . . . . . . . . . . . . . . . . . . . . . . . . . . . . . . . . . . . . . . . . . . | 60.00 | — |
| ☐ **TROUBLES/CUDDLES,** rel. 1979. ed. 2,000, s/n, 14″ x 16″, pub SG . . . . . . . . Priced as a Pair | 45.00 | — |

**BANDIT - RACCOON** *by Charleyn Moore*

## TARA MOORE

A native of Maryland, Tara Moore has traveled the world in search of wildlife reference and artistic inspirations. Her trips have included such far-away places as Kenya, Zambia, Nepal, British Columbia, the Amazon jungles and, most recently, the Canadian Arctic in search of the polar bear.

Moore records her travels with sketches and photographs, later developing them into fullsize oil and acrylic paintings. Her works can be found in books and magazines including *Ducks Unlimited* and *National Wildlife* as well as numerous private collections across the country. She has also participated in juried and member exhibitions of the Society of Animal Artists, the Easton Academy of the Arts, Game Conservation International and the Easton Waterfowl Festival.

| TARA MOORE | ISSUE PRICE | CURRENT PRICE |
|---|---|---|
| ☐ **IN TROUBLE AGAIN,** rel. 1977. ed. 300, s/n, size not available, pub WWI .... | 65.00 | 500.00 |
| ☐ **LAB PUPS AND WATERBUG,** rel. 1979. ed. 850, s/n, 20" x 17", pub WWI .... | 65.00 | 500.00 |
| remarqued .................................................. | N/A | 450.00 |
| ☐ **CHOW TIME,** rel. 1979. ed. 600, s/n, 15" x 20", pub WWI ................ | 65.00 | 450.00 |
| remarqued .................................................. | N/A | 550.00 |
| ☐ **BOX LUNCH,** rel. 1980. ed. 850, s/n, 15" x 20", pub WWI ................ | 65.00 | 150.00 |
| remarqued .................................................. | N/A | 250.00 |
| ☐ **FIRST ADVENTURE,** rel. 1980. ed. 850, s/n, 21" x 17", pub WWI .......... | 65.00 | 200.00 |
| remarqued .................................................. | N/A | 125.00 |
| ☐ **FLIGHT OF THE BUMBLEBEE,** rel. 1980. ed. 840, s/n, 20" x 22", pub WWI ... | 65.00 | 125.00 |
| remarqued .................................................. | N/A | N/A |
| ☐ **FLOUR CHILD,** rel. 1980. ed. 850, s/n, size not available, pub WWI ......... | 65.00 | 125.00 |
| ☐ **ARTIC SPRING,** rel. 1981. ed. 850, s/n, size not available, pub WWI ........ | 65.00 | — |

| | ISSUE PRICE | CURRENT PRICE |
|---|---|---|
| ☐ **PAINT JOB,** rel. 1981. ed. 850, s/n, size not available, pub WWI . . . . . . . . . . . | 65.00 | — |
| ☐ **PRIDE OF THE SHORE,** rel. 1977. ed. 300, s/n, size not available, pub WWI . . . | 75.00 | — |
| ☐ **SOMETHING'S FISHY,** rel. 1981. ed. 850, s/n, size not available, pub WWI . . . | 65.00 | — |
| ☐ **THREE'S A CROWD,** rel. 1981. ed. 850, s/n, size not available, pub WWI . . . . . | 65.00 | 65.00 |

# WAYLAND MOORE

Since Wayland Moore has worked so effectively in the sports idiom, reference to him as an "artistic triple threat" would not be an inappropriate analogy. He is an illustrator, cartoonist and painter.

As an illustrator, he is one of the few Southerners belonging to the Society of Illustrators of New York. In 1967, his work for the Sarasota, Florida Herald-Tribune won him a nomination for a Pulitzer Prize in editorial cartooning.

Moore's specialty is sports, where his facile brush captures the world of motion in all its changing moods — from ballet to calmness to violence.

After graduation from high school in Belton, South Carolina where he received his first art training, Moore majored in commercial design at the Ringling School of Art in Sarasota, Florida. Since graduation he has worked for a design house in Greenville, South Carolina, as art director for an NBC-TV affiliate, art director for the Sarasota Herald-Tribune and as senior illustrator with an Atlanta studio. In 1971 he opened Wayland Moore Studios which is located at Atlanta Stadium where Moore serves as graphics director for the Atlanta Braves, combining his career interests in art with his leisure time love for sports.

Other Moore achievements include a book consisting of his Florida sketches, a front page cartoon that has been included in the permanent collection of Walt Disney Studios in California, a scholarship offered in his name by the Ringling School of Art and a string of artistic assignments that have included coverage of the Indianapolis 500, PGA Golf Tournaments, Can-Am races and, the Billie Jean King-Bobby Riggs tennis match.

## WAYLAND MOORE

| | | |
|---|---|---|
| ☐ **AMERICA'S CHAMPION,** rel. 1977. ed. 500, s/n, 40⅞" x 29¾", original color silkscreen, pub FI . . . . . . . . . . . . . . . . . . . . . . . . . . . . . . . . . . . . . . | 200.00 | 800.00 |
| ☐ **BALLOON,** rel. 1976. ed. 300, s/n, 42" x 30", original color silkscreen, pub FI | 250.00 | 1,200.00 |
| ☐ **BALLOONING,** rel. 1979. ed. 300, s/n, 42½" x 30", original color silkscreen, pub FI . . . . . . . . . . . . . . . . . . . . . . . . . . . . . . . . . . . . . . . . . . . . . . . . | 375.00 | 800.00 |
| ☐ **BASEBALL,** rel. 1979. ed. 300, s/n, 30½" x 24", original color silkscreen, pub FI . . . . . . . . . . . . . . . . . . . . . . . . . . . . . . . . . . . . . . . . . . . . . . . . | 250.00 | 350.00 |
| ☐ **BICYCLE,** rel. 1978. ed. 300, s/n, 27" x 42", original color silkscreen, pub FI . | 250.00 | 350.00 |
| ☐ **BLUE GRASS,** rel. 1978. ed. 300, s/n, 25½" x 36", original color silkscreen, pub FI . . . . . . . . . . . . . . . . . . . . . . . . . . . . . . . . . . . . . . . . . . . . . . . . | 250.00 | — |
| ☐ **BRICKYARD START,** rel. 1977. ed. 300, s/n, 27" x 36", original color silkscreen, pub FI . . . . . . . . . . . . . . . . . . . . . . . . . . . . . . . . . . . . . . . . | 200.00 | 800.00 |
| ☐ **CENTER COURT,** rel. 1978. ed. 300, s/n, 30½" x 42", original color silkscreen, pub FI . . . . . . . . . . . . . . . . . . . . . . . . . . . . . . . . . . . . . . . . | 300.00 | 400.00 |
| ☐ **CHURCHILL DOWNS,** rel. 1979. ed. 300, s/n, 31½" x 40", original color silkscreen, pub FI . . . . . . . . . . . . . . . . . . . . . . . . . . . . . . . . . . . . . . . | 350.00 | 450.00 |
| ☐ **DOWNHILL,** rel. 1979. ed. 300, s/n, 36½" x 28", original color silkscreen, pub FI . . . . . . . . . . . . . . . . . . . . . . . . . . . . . . . . . . . . . . . . . . . . . . . . | 325.00 | 500.00 |
| ☐ **THE EIGHTH FURLONG,** rel. 1976. ed. 300, s/n, 28¾" x 40¾", original color silkscreen, pub FI . . . . . . . . . . . . . . . . . . . . . . . . . . . . . . . . . . . . . | 200.00 | 800.00 |
| ☐ **FLYING ICE,** rel. 1979. ed. 300, s/n, 30" x 42", original color silkscreen, pub FI . . . . . . . . . . . . . . . . . . . . . . . . . . . . . . . . . . . . . . . . . . . . . . . . | 350.00 | 450.00 |
| ☐ **FOOTBALL,** rel. 1978. ed. 300, s/n, 27" x 22", original color lithograph, pub FI | 150.00 | 250.00 |
| ☐ **FRENCH SEAPORT,** rel. 1979. ed. 300, s/n, 18½" x 30", original color silkscreen, pub FI . . . . . . . . . . . . . . . . . . . . . . . . . . . . . . . . . . . . . . . . | 325.00 | 425.00 |

|  | ISSUE PRICE | CURRENT PRICE |
|---|---|---|
| ☐ **GIRAFFE,** rel. 1978. ed. 300, s/n, 44½" x 23¼", original color silkscreen, pub FI | 250.00 | 600.00 |
| ☐ **GOAL POST,** rel. 1979. ed. 300, s/n, 38" x 28", original color silkscreen, pub FI | 350.00 | 450.00 |
| ☐ **GOLF,** rel. 1978. ed. 300, s/n, 28¾" x 36", original color silkscreen, pub FI | 300.00 | 600.00 |
| ☐ **HOCKEY,** rel. 1977. ed. 300, s/n, 25" x 32", original color silkscreen, pub FI | 250.00 | 800.00 |
| ☐ **IN THE PIT,** rel. 1977. ed. 300, s/n, 22" x 30", original color lithograph, pub FI | 150.00 | 250.00 |
| ☐ **JOCKEY,** rel. 1976. ed. 300, s/n, 42" x 24", original color silkscreen, pub FI | 200.00 | 400.00 |
| ☐ **JUMPERS,** rel. 1976. ed. 300, s/n, 36" x 36", original color silkscreen, pub FI | 250.00 | 500.00 |
| ☐ **LEOPARD'S HEAD,** rel. 1977. ed. 300, s/n, 43" x 30", original color silkscreen, pub FI | 250.00 | 450.00 |
| ☐ **LIFT OFF,** rel. 1980. ed. 300, s/n, 36½" x 26", original color silkscreen, pub FI | 475.00 | — |
| ☐ **LION,** rel. 1979. ed. 300, s/n, 22" x 29¾", original color lithograph, pub FI | 200.00 | 300.00 |
| ☐ **LIONS,** rel. 1978. ed. 300, s/n, 28¾" x 36½", original color silkscreen, pub FI | 200.00 | 1,200.00 |
| ☐ **MARATHON,** rel. 1979. ed. 300, s/n, 26" x 36", original color silkscreen, pub FI | 300.00 | 500.00 |
| ☐ **MARDI GRAS,** rel. 1977. ed. 300, s/n, 29½" x 40¾", original color silkscreen, pub FI | 350.00 | 500.00 |
| ☐ **MOTO-X,** rel. 1976. ed. 300, s/n, 28¾" x 40¾", original color silkscreen, pub FI | 200.00 | 350.00 |
| ☐ **OLD PARISIAN,** rel. 1979. ed. 300, s/n, 42½" x 30", original color silkscreen, pub FI | 325.00 | 425.00 |
| ☐ **PARTNERS,** rel. 1979. ed. 300, s/n, 35½" x 29", original color silkscreen, pub FI | 350.00 | 450.00 |
| ☐ **PILE UP,** rel. 1977. ed. 300, s/n, 35" x 29", original color silkscreen, pub FI | 250.00 | 400.00 |
| ☐ **RACQUETBALL (M. HOGAN),** rel. 1979. ed. 300, s/n, 30" x 41", original color silkscreen, pub FI | 375.00 | — |
| (Signed by W. Moore and M. Hogan) | | |
| ☐ **REGATTA,** rel. 1978. ed. 300, s/n, 28½" x 21½", original color lithograph, pub FI | 150.00 | 250.00 |
| ☐ **RODEO,** rel. 1978. ed. 300, s/n, 32" x 28½", original color silkscreen, pub FI | 250.00 | 350.00 |
| ☐ **ROUGH SEAS,** rel. 1976. ed. 300, s/n, 42½" x 30", original color silkscreen, pub FI | 200.00 | 1,200.00 |
| ☐ **SAND TRAP,** rel. 1976. ed. 300, s/n, 46½" x 30", original color silkscreen, pub FI | 200.00 | 600.00 |
| ☐ **SCHOONER,** rel. 1977. ed. 300, s/n, 27¼" x 36", original color silkscreen, pub FI | 150.00 | 500.00 |
| ☐ **SEA BREEZE,** rel. 1977. ed. 300, s/n, 39¾" x 31¼", original color silkscreen, pub FI | 350.00 | 800.00 |
| ☐ **SKIER,** rel. 1977. ed. 300, s/n, 23½" x 29", original color silkscreen, pub FI | 200.00 | 450.00 |
| ☐ **SOCCER,** rel. 1978. ed. 300, s/n, 36" x 30", original color silkscreen, pub FI | 300.00 | 400.00 |
| ☐ **SPINMAKER,** rel. 1979. ed. 300, s/n, 41" x 29¾", original color silkscreen, pub FI | 375.00 | 800.00 |
| ☐ **STORMY WEATHER,** rel. 1979. ed. 300, s/n, 42½" x 30", original color silkscreen, pub FI | 375.00 | 600.00 |
| ☐ **THE TALL SHIP,** rel. 1976. ed. 100, s/n, 20¼" x 15", original etching, pub FI | 80.00 | 300.00 |
| ☐ **TROTTERS,** rel. 1978. ed. 300, s/n, 29½" x 41½", original color silkscreen, pub FI | 300.00 | 400.00 |
| ☐ **UNDEFEATED,** rel. 1977. ed. 300, s/n, 28" x 34", original color silkscreen, pub FI | 250.00 | 800.00 |
| ☐ **WASH ART LITHO,** rel. 1977. ed. 100, s/n, 15¾" x 19½", original lithograph, pub FI | 80.00 | 100.00 |
| ☐ **WHITE WATER CANOE,** rel. 1977. ed. 300, s/n, 29½" x 35", original color silkscreen, pub FI | 200.00 | 300.00 |
| ☐ **WINDSURFER,** rel. 1979. ed. 300, s/n, 36¼" x 29¾", original color silkscreen, pub FI | 475.00 | — |
| ☐ **WINNING VOLLEY,** rel. 1976. ed. 300, s/n, 24" x 18", original color silkscreen, pub FI | 200.00 | 350.00 |

| | ISSUE PRICE | CURRENT PRICE |
|---|---|---|
| ☐ **CIRCUS SUITE**, rel. 1977. ed. 300, s/n, consists of 3 silkscreens . . . . . . . . . . | 700.00 | 1,000.00 |
| **CIRCUS CLOWNS**, 31″ x 29⅛″; **CIRCUS TIGERS**, 29½″ x 40½″; **THE BIG TOP**, 29¾″ x 41⅞″ | | |
| ☐ **PARIS SUITE**, rel. 1977. ed. 250, s/n, consists of 4 lithographs . . . . . . . . . . . . | 320.00 | 400.00 |
| **PARIS KIOSK**, 23¼″ x 16¼″; **LE PONT ALEXANDRE**, 17″ x 23¼″; **PLACE DES VOSGES**, 23¼″ x 16¼″; **VERSAILLES**, 23¼″ x 16¼″ | | |
| ☐ **SAN FRANCISCO SUITE**, rel. 1977. ed. 250, s/n, consists of 4 lithographs . . . . | 320.00 | 400.00 |
| **CHINATOWN**, 17″ x 12″; **CABLE CAR I**, 13¾″ x 17″; **CABLE CAR II**, 13¾″ x 17″; **GOLDEN GATE**, 23¼″ x 16″ | | |
| ☐ **STOCK EXCHANGE SUITE**, rel. 1979. ed. 300, s/n, consists of 2 pieces . . . . . . | 500.00 | 600.00 |
| **BULL AND BEAR**, 30½″ x 24″, original color silkscreen; **WALL STREET**, 24½″ x 35″, original color lithograph. | | |

# C. G. MOREHEAD
## (1921-1979)

A realtor for twenty-four years, and former Kentucky Real Estate Commissioner, C. G. Morehead started painting after he was 40 years of age.

Morehead captured on canvas the image of buildings and real property which have been a significant part of our heritage.

Many of his paintings have been released as limited edition collector prints. His painting "President's Room at the White House" captures the stateliness and importance of the room and the grace and strength of the building.

**SNOW OF '78** *by C. G. Morehead*

## C. G. MOREHEAD

| | ISSUE PRICE | CURRENT PRICE |
|---|---|---|
| ☐ **ANTIQUE SHOP** s/o | 15.00 | 225.00 |
| ed. 5,000, pub MP .........s/n | 25.00 | 270.00 |
| ☐ **THE OLD STONE INN & TALBOTT TAVERN** s/o | 15.00 | 95.00 |
| ed. 5,000, pub MP .........s/n | 25.00 | 130.00 |
| ☐ **TRINITY CHURCH** s/o | 15.00 | 250.00 |
| ed. 1,500, pub MP .........s/n | 25.00 | 270.00 |
| ☐ **RAY HARM'S HOME** s/o | 15.00 | 250.00 |
| ed. 2,500, pub MP .........s/n | 25.00 | 270.00 |
| ☐ **KEENELAND** s/o | 15.00 | 150.00 |
| ed. 2,500, pub MP .........s/n | 25.00 | 175.00 |
| ☐ **CATHEDRAL OF THE ASSUMPTION** s/o | 15.00 | 35.00 |
| ed. 1,500, pub MP .........s/n | 25.00 | 45.00 |
| ☐ **THE PRESIDENT'S OFFICE AT THE WHITE HOUSE** s/o | 15.00 | 85.00 |
| ed. 5,000, pub MP .........s/n | 25.00 | 100.00 |
| ☐ **RAINBOW GARDEN** s/o | 15.00 | 70.00 |
| ed. 1,500, pub MP .........s/n | 25.00 | 80.00 |
| ☐ **OLD SOUTHERN BANK** s/o | 15.00 | 100.00 |
| ed. 5,000, pub MP .........s/n | 25.00 | 120.00 |
| ☐ **MARKET STREET** s/o | 15.00 | 70.00 |
| ed. 2,500, pub MP .........s/n | 25.00 | 85.00 |
| ☐ **AUDUBON HOUSE** s/o | 15.00 | — |
| ed. 5,000, pub MP .........s/n | 25.00 | — |
| ☐ **CHURCHILL DOWNS** s/o | 15.00 | 225.00 |
| ed. 2,500, pub MP .........s/n | 25.00 | 240.00 |
| ☐ **OLD BARN** s/o | 15.00 | 45.00 |
| ed. 2,500, pub MP .........s/n | 25.00 | 60.00 |
| ☐ **OAKHURST**, ed. 5,000, pub MP .........s/o | 20.00 | — |
| ☐ **OLD MULKEY MEETING HOUSE** s/o | 15.00 | 50.00 |
| ed. 2,500, pub MP .........s/n | 25.00 | 60.00 |
| ☐ **GRAND OLE OPRY** s/o | 15.00 | 105.00 |
| ed. 5,000, pub MP .........s/n | 25.00 | 125.00 |
| ☐ **SHAKER HOUSE** s/o | 15.00 | 70.00 |
| ed. 2,500, pub MP .........s/n | 25.00 | 85.00 |
| ☐ **LBJ SCHOOL-HOUSE** s/o | 15.00 | — |
| ed. 5,000, pub MP .........s/n | 25.00 | — |
| ☐ **NO. 10 DOWNING STREET** s/o | 15.00 | 55.00 |
| ed. 2,500, pub MP .........s/n | 25.00 | 70.00 |
| ☐ **UK ADMINISTRATION BUILDING**, ed. 5,000, pub MP .........s/o | 20.00 | — |
| ☐ **OLD CURIOSITY SHOP** s/o | 15.00 | 115.00 |
| ed. 1,500, pub MP .........s/n | 25.00 | 125.00 |
| ☐ **CALUMET BARN** s/o | 15.00 | 90.00 |
| ed. 1,500, pub MP .........s/n | 25.00 | 110.00 |
| ☐ **HAPPY BIRTHDAY U.S.A.** s/o | 15.00 | 60.00 |
| ed. 1,976, pub MP .........s/n | 25.00 | 75.00 |
| ☐ **PINK GARTER THEATER** s/o | 15.00 | 35.00 |
| ed. 1,500, pub MP .........s/n | 25.00 | 50.00 |
| ☐ **COLONNADE** s/o | 15.00 | 55.00 |
| ed. 1,500, pub MP .........s/n | 25.00 | 65.00 |
| ☐ **MOONBEAMS** s/o | 15.00 | 45.00 |
| ed. 1,500, pub MP s/n | 25.00 | 55.00 |
| ☐ **OLDEST HOUSE** s/o | 15.00 | 45.00 |
| ed. 2,000, pub MP .........s/n | 25.00 | 55.00 |
| ☐ **SNOW OF '78** s/o | 15.00 | 150.00 |
| ed. 1,978, pub MP .........s/n | 25.00 | 170.00 |
| ☐ **GATE OF THE SUN** s/o | 15.00 | — |
| ed. 2,000, pub MP .........s/n | 25.00 | — |
| ☐ **MY OLD KENTUCKY HOME** s/o | 15.00 | 150.00 |
| ed. 5,000, pub MP .........s/n | 25.00 | 170.00 |
| ☐ **SUMMER OF 78**, SEAL | 20.00 | 30.00 |
| ed. 2,500, pub MP .........SEAL/N | 30.00 | 40.00 |

# GARY MOSS

After studying art throughout high school Gary attended the Minneapolis College of Art and Design for four years, spending one year studying in Holland. He was a Marine Corps combat artist in Vietnam, where he earned the title of *"Combat Artist of the Year"*, in 1970.

Moss worked as a graphic designer, but now is a full time artist.

Painting mostly in oils but also an accomplished water-colorist, Moss's unique style of portraying waterfowl and game birds attracts the sportsman as well as the housewife. All who view his work are impressed by his vividness and authenticity to his subject matter.

**FAMILY SWANS** *by Gary Moss*

## GARY MOSS

| | ISSUE PRICE | CURRENT PRICE |
|---|---|---|
| ☐ **FAMILY OF SWANS**, rel. 1978. ed. 850, s/n, 16½" x 25", pub WWI | 75.00 | — |
| ed. remarque artist proof | 160.00 | — |
| ☐ **TRIO OF CANADAS**, rel. 1978. ed. 850, s/n, 17½" x 23¾", pub WWI | 75.00 | — |
| ed. remarque artist proof | 160.00 | — |
| ☐ **CANADAS ON THE COAST**, rel. 1979. ed. 850, s/n, 23⅝" x 17¾", pub WWI | 75.00 | — |
| ☐ **SNOWS AND BLUES ON THE COAST**, rel. 1980. ed. 850, s/n, 24" x 18", pub WWI | 75.00 | — |
| ☐ **TRIO OF CANVASBACKS**, rel. 1980. ed. 580, s/n, 23" x 18", pub WWI | 85.00 | — |
| ☐ **LIST OF THE SEASON - GOLDENEYES**, rel. 1981. ed. 580, s/n, size not available, pub WWI | 75.00 | — |
| ☐ **REFLECTIONS - PINTAILS**, rel. 1981. ed. 580, s/n, size not available, pub WWI | 75.00 | — |
| ☐ **ROOSTER TRAIL - RING NECKED PHEASANT**, rel. 1981. ed. 580, s/n, size not available, pub WWI | 75.00 | — |
| ☐ **WATCHFUL TRIO - WILD TURKEYS**, rel. 1982. ed. 580, s/n, size not available, pub WWI | 85.00 | — |

# P. BUCKLEY MOSS

The Amish and Mennonite paintings by P. Buckley Moss have became widely known since she started publishing them in print form in 1978. Today over 1,000 galleries in North American carry Moss prints and overseas sales are expanding rapidly.

Patricia Buckley Moss was born in Staten Island, New York in 1933. She gave her enthusiasm and energies to drawing, ice skating and baseball. When she was ten years old a serious automobile accident kept her out of school for a year, giving her unlimited time for drawing and painting.

Later her portfolio was shown to Margaret Meade, then the principal of Washington Irving high school in Manhattan. An exception was made to allow her to attend. She took four art classes a day. Four years later Pat was awarded a scholarship by the Cooper Union, and subsequently graduated in Fine Arts and Design.

In the early 1960's she moved to Virginia's Shenandoah Valley. A friendship with the Mennonites developed which led to her painting the scenes of their life style. The mother of six children, Moss has used them frequently as her models.

Moss's paintings are a hybrid of abstract and realism. Her first concept is an abstract use of pattern and color within the space of a tonal image. Into the pattern she evolves her symbolic landscapes and figures, bringing realism to the abstract. The combination of her unique style, her talent as a watercolorist and the positive feelings of goodwill that her paintings evoke have already earned her an important place in contemporary American art.

**TOGETHER** *by P. Buckley Moss*

## P. BUCKLEY MOSS

| | | ISSUE PRICE | CURRENT PRICE |
|---|---|---|---|
| ☐ | A WELCOME, rel. 1982. ed. 1,000, s/n, 14″ x 10″, pub MP | 45.00 | — |
| ☐ | ADAM, rel. 1983. ed. 1,000, s/n, size not available, pub MP | 20.00 | — |
| ☐ | ALL IN THE TREE, rel. 1982. ed. 1,000, s/n, 22″ x 15″, pub MP | 80.00 | — |
| ☐ | ALONG THE CANAL, rel. 1982. ed. 1,000, s/n, size not available, pub MP | 80.00 | Sold Out |
| ☐ | AMY, rel. 1983. ed. 1,000, s/n, size not available, pub MP | 20.00 | — |
| ☐ | APPLE DAY, rel. 1983. ed. 1,000, s/n, size not available, pub MP | 80.00 | — |
| ☐ | APPLE GIRL, rel. 1982. ed. 1,000, s/n, 10″ x 9″, pub MP | 30.00 | 60.00 |
| ☐ | APPLE HARVEST, rel. 1979. ed. 1,000, s/n, 21″ x 16″, pub MP | 75.00 | — |
| ☐ | APPLE PICKER, rel. 1978. ed. 1,000, s/n, 10″ x 8″, pub MP | 35.00 | 70.00 |
| ☐ | AUTUMN RIDE, rel. 1982. ed. 1,000, s/n, size not available, pub MP | 80.00 | — |
| ☐ | AWAKE O'EARTH, rel. 1979. ed. 1,000, s/n, 11″ x 13″, pub MP | 50.00 | — |
| ☐ | BALLOON RIDE, rel. 1982. ed. 1,000, s/n, 18″ x 17″, pub MP | 100.00 | — |
| ☐ | BARELIMBED REFLECTIONS, rel. 1978. ed. 1,000, s/n, 8″ x 10″, pub MP | 35.00 | Sold Out |
| ☐ | BECKY, rel. 1983. ed. 1,000, s/n, size not available, pub MP | 20.00 | — |
| ☐ | BECKY AND TOM, rel. 1978. ed. 1,000, s/n, 11″ x 8″, pub MP | 10.00 | Sold Out |
| ☐ | BEHOLD, rel. 1979. ed. 1,000, s/n, 16″ x 11″, pub MP | 35.00 | — |
| ☐ | BETROTHED, rel. 1982. ed. 1,000, s/n, size not available, pub MP | 150.00 | — |
| ☐ | BIRD BOY, rel. 1982. ed. 1,000, s/n, 19″ x 16″, pub MP | 110.00 | — |
| ☐ | BLACK CAT, rel. 1981. ed. 1,000, s/n, 17″ x 14″, pub MP | 50.00 | — |
| ☐ | BLACK CAT ON A PINK CUSHION, rel. 1982. ed. 1,000, s/n, 8″ x 8″, pub MP | 40.00 | — |
| ☐ | BLESSED ASSURANCE, rel. 1979. ed. 1,000, s/n, 16″ x 12″, pub MP | 40.00 | — |
| ☐ | BLUE BALLOON, rel. 1982. ed. 1,000, s/n, 17″ x 11″, pub MP | 60.00 | — |
| ☐ | BLUE BOUQUET, rel. 1981. ed. 1,000, s/n, 5″ x 9″, pub MP | 16.00 | — |
| ☐ | BLUE SHORES, rel. 1982. ed. 1,000, s/n, size not available, pub MP | 35.00 | — |
| ☐ | BLUE WINTER, rel. 1982. ed. 1,000, s/n, 22″ x 17″, pub MP | 100.00 | — |
| ☐ | BROTHERS, rel. 1983. ed. 1,000, s/n, size not available, pub MP | 35.00 | — |
| ☐ | CAMEO GEESE, rel. 1982. ed. 1,000, s/n, 12″ x 12″, pub MP | 40.00 | Sold Out |
| ☐ | CANADA GEESE, rel. 1978. ed. 1,000, s/n, 9″ x 26″, pub MP | 60.00 | Sold Out |
| ☐ | CAPITOL SKATERS, rel. 1980. ed. 1,000, s/n, 22″ x 18″, pub MP | 60.00 | — |
| ☐ | CENTRAL PARK, rel. 1981. ed. 1,000, s/n, 18″ x 19″, pub MP | 80.00 | — |
| ☐ | CHERISHED, rel. 1983. ed. 1,000, s/n, size not available, pub MP | 35.00 | — |
| ☐ | CHICKEN FARMERS, rel. 1983. ed. 1,000, s/n, size not available, pub MP | 40.00 | — |
| ☐ | CHRIS, rel. 1982. ed. 1,000, s/n, 7″ x 10″, pub MP | 25.00 | — |
| ☐ | COLONIAL SLEIGHRIDE, rel. 1983. ed. 1,000, s/n, size not available, pub MP | 125.00 | — |
| ☐ | THE COLT, rel. 1983. ed. 1,000, s/n, size not available, pub MP | 90.00 | — |
| ☐ | COUNTRY CHURCH, rel. 1983. ed. 1,000, s/n, size not available, pub MP | 80.00 | — |
| ☐ | DAILY CHORES, rel. 1978. ed. 1,000, s/n, 10″ x 8″, pub MP | 16.00 | Sold Out |
| ☐ | DANIEL, rel. 1982. ed. 1,000, s/n, 8″ x 10″, pub MP | 20.00 | — |
| ☐ | DASHING AWAY, rel. 1982. ed. 1,000, s/n, size not available, pub MP | 100.00 | — |
| ☐ | DEAR LORD, large, rel. 1979. ed. 1,000, s/n, 22″ x 26″, pub MP | 30.00 | Sold Out |
| | small, rel. 1978. ed. 1,000, s/n, 11″ x 9″ | 35.00 | Sold Out |
| ☐ | DEVOTION, rel. 1983. ed. 1,000, s/n, size not available, pub MP | 50.00 | — |
| ☐ | DONKEY BOY, rel. 1982. ed. 1,000, s/n, size not available, pub MP | 40.00 | — |
| ☐ | EARLY LIGHT, rel. 1982. ed. 1,000, s/n, 14″ x 18″, pub MP | 80.00 | — |
| ☐ | EBONY JET, rel. 1982. ed. 1,000, s/n, 18″ x 27″, pub MP | 150.00 | — |
| ☐ | EQUUS BLUE, rel. 1981. ed. 1,000, s/n, 18″ x 24″, pub MP | 300.00 | — |
| ☐ | EVENING GUESTS, rel. 1983. ed. 1,000, s/n, size not available, pub MP | 60.00 | — |
| ☐ | EVENING RUIN, rel. 1978. ed. 1,000, s/n, 7″ x 24″, pub MP | 55.00 | — |
| ☐ | EVERY BLESSING, rel. 1979. ed. 1,000, s/n, 10″ x 17″, pub MP | 50.00 | — |
| ☐ | FAMILY OUTING, rel. 1978. ed. 1,000, s/n, 17″ x 18″, pub MP | 65.00 | Sold Out |
| ☐ | FANEUIL HALL, rel. 1979. ed. 1,000, s/n, 12″ x 12″, pub MP | 40.00 | — |
| ☐ | FAWN, rel. 1983. ed. 1,000, s/n, size not available, pub MP | 40.00 | — |
| ☐ | FIRST LOVE, rel. 1983. ed. 1,000, s/n, size not available, pub MP | 60.00 | — |
| ☐ | FIVE ON A PONY, rel. 1981. ed. 1,000, s/n, 12″ x 12″, pub MP | 40.00 | — |
| ☐ | FLAG BOY, rel. 1978. ed. 1,000, s/n, 9″ x 6″, pub MP | 16.00 | Sold Out |
| ☐ | FLAG GIRL, rel. 1978. ed. 1,000, s/n, 9″ x 6″, pub MP | 16.00 | Sold Out |
| ☐ | FLOWER GIRL, rel. 1982. ed. 1,000, s/n, 10″ x 8″, pub MP | 20.00 | Sold Out |
| ☐ | FOUR LITTLE GIRLS, rel. 1978. ed. 1,000, s/n, 8″ x 10″, pub MP | 30.00 | Sold Out |
| ☐ | FREE SPIRIT, rel. 1978. ed. 1,000, s/n, 14″ x 37″, pub MP | 110.00 | — |
| ☐ | FRENCH QUARTER, large, rel. 1981. ed. 1,000, s/n, 20″ x 20″, pub MP | 75.00 | — |
| | small, rel. 1981. ed. 1,000, s/n, 8″ x 8″, pub MP | 25.00 | — |
| ☐ | FRESH BOUQUET, rel. 1978. ed. 1,000, s/n, 11″ x 8″, pub MP | 30.00 | Sold Out |
| ☐ | FRIENDLY STEED, rel. 1978. ed. 1,000, s/n, 10″ x 16″, pub MP | 50.00 | — |
| ☐ | FRIENDS, rel. 1978. ed. 1,000, s/n, 12″ x 10″, pub MP | 35.00 | Sold Out |

| | ISSUE PRICE | CURRENT PRICE |
|---|---|---|
| ☐ FROSTY FROLIC, rel. 1978. ed. 1,000, s/n, 22" x 22", pub MP | 75.00 | Sold Out |
| ☐ FRUIT OF THE VALLEY, rel. 1982. ed. 1,000, s/n, 15" x 16", pub MP | 80.00 | Sold Out |
| ☐ FRUIT OF THE VINE I, rel. 1978. ed. 1,000, s/n, 29" x 15", pub MP | 80.00 | — |
| ☐ FRUIT OF THE VINE II, rel. 1978. ed. 1,000, s/n, 29" x 15", pub MP | 80.00 | — |
| ☐ GENTLE DAY, rel. 1982. ed. 1,000, s/n, 28" x 10", pub MP | 75.00 | — |
| ☐ GENTLE HANDS, rel. 1979. ed. 1,000, s/n, size not available, pub MP | 50.00 | — |
| ☐ GINGER, rel. 1983. ed. 1,000, s/n, size not available, pub MP | 40.00 | — |
| ☐ GINNY, rel. 1981. ed. 1,000, s/n, 6" x 4", pub MP | 16.00 | — |
| ☐ GINNY AND CHRIS WITH LAMBS, rel. 1978. ed. 1,000, s/n, 9" x 7", pub MP | 35.00 | Sold Out |
| ☐ GOLDEN WINTER, rel. 1978. ed. 1,000, s/n, 37" x 37", pub MP | 150.00 | Sold Out |
| ☐ GOOD SHEPHERD, rel. 1978. ed. 1,000, s/n, 12" x 6", pub MP | 20.00 | — |
| ☐ GOSSIP, rel. 1978. ed. 1,000, s/n, 9" x 12", pub MP | 45.00 | Sold Out |
| ☐ GOVERNOR'S PALACE, rel. 1983. ed. 1,000, s/n, size not available, pub MP | 50.00 | — |
| ☐ GRANDMOTHER, rel. 1981. ed. 1,000, s/n, 15" x 16", pub MP | 60.00 | — |
| ☐ GRANDPA'S HOUSE, rel. 1982. ed. 1,000, s/n, 12" x 12", pub MP | 40.00 | — |
| ☐ GRANNY'S FAVORITE, rel. 1981. ed. 1,000, s/n, 11" x 8", pub MP | 40.00 | Sold Out |
| ☐ GRANNY'S GIRL, rel. 1983. ed. 1,000, s/n, size not available, pub MP | 50.00 | — |
| ☐ GRANNY'S LESSON, rel. 1981. ed. 1,000, s/n, 8" x 27", pub MP | 35.00 | — |
| ☐ HAIL THE DAY SOLACE, rel. 1979. ed. 1,000, s/n, 22" x 22", pub MP | 75.00 | — |
| ☐ HAND IN HAND, rel. 1982. ed. 1,000, s/n, size not available, pub MP | 40.00 | — |
| ☐ HAPPY DAY, rel. 1979. ed. 1,000, s/n, 13" x 9", pub MP | 25.00 | — |
| ☐ HARK, rel. 1979. ed. 1,000, s/n, 14" x 10", pub MP | 40.00 | — |
| ☐ HAYRIDE, rel. 1982. ed. 1,000, s/n, 9" x 16", pub MP | 50.00 | — |
| ☐ HE LIVES, rel. 1979. ed. 1,000, s/n, 22" x 5", pub MP | 25.00 | — |
| ☐ HELPERS, rel. 1978. ed. 1,000, s/n, 9" x 14", pub MP | 35.00 | — |
| ☐ HER HIGHNESS, rel. 1982. ed. 1,000, s/n, size not available, pub MP | 50.00 | — |
| ☐ HIGHLAND FLING, rel. 1982. ed. 1,000, s/n, size not available, pub MP | 25.00 | — |
| ☐ HOUSE BY THE PARK, rel. 1982. ed. 1,000, s/n, 16" x 12", pub MP | 80.00 | — |
| ☐ HOW CALM THE MORN, rel. 1979. ed. 1,000, s/n, 15" x 30", pub MP | 75.00 | Sold Out |
| ☐ HOW GENTLE, rel. 1978. ed. 1,000, s/n, 7" x 8", pub MP | 20.00 | — |
| ☐ HUNGRY BABY BIRD, rel. 1978. ed. 1,000, s/n, 9" x 5", pub MP | 15.00 | Sold Out |
| ☐ HURRAH!, rel. 1982. ed. 1,000, s/n, 8" x 7", pub MP | 20.00 | — |
| ☐ ICE CREAM PARLOR, rel. 1982. ed. 1,000, s/n, size not available, pub MP | 80.00 | —.00 |
| ☐ INDUSTRIAL REVOLUTIONARY BLDGS, large, rel. 1980. ed. 1,000, s/n, 12" x 12", pub MP | 70.00 | — |
| ☐ INDUSTRIAL REVOLUTIONARY BLDGS, small, rel. 1980. ed. 1,000, s/n, 8" x 8", pub MP | 50.00 | — |
| ☐ JEFFERSON SKATERS, rel. 1980. ed. 1,000, s/n, 16" x 13", pub MP | 60.00 | — |
| ☐ JOHN, rel. 1981. ed. 1,000, s/n, 6" x 6", pub MP | 16.00 | — |
| ☐ JOHN AND MARY, rel. 1981. ed. 1,000, s/n, 36" x 36", pub MP | 200.00 | — |
| ☐ JOY, rel. 1979. ed. 1,000, s/n, 6" x 5", pub MP | 60.00 | Sold Out |
| ☐ JULY 4TH, rel. 1982. ed. 1,000, s/n, 9" x 12", pub MP | 40.00 | — |
| ☐ LANDSCAPE GEESE, BLUE, rel. 1981. ed. 75, s/n, 32" x 51", pub MP | 500.00 | — |
| ☐ LANDSCAPE GEESE, GOLD, rel. 1981. ed. 25, s/n, 32" x 51", pub MP | 500.00 | — |
| ☐ LESSON IN PATIENCE, rel. 1978. ed. 1,000, s/n, 22" x 27", pub MP | 120.00 | — |
| ☐ LILLY AND LIZ, rel. 1982. ed. 1,000, s/n, size not available, pub MP | 40.00 | — |
| ☐ LISA & TIGER, rel. 1982. ed. 1,000, s/n, 9" x 8", pub MP | 30.00 | — |
| ☐ LITTLE APPLES IN A ROW, rel. 1978. ed. 1,000, s/n, 10" x 38", pub MP | 80.00 | — |
| ☐ LITTLE FELLOW, rel. 1978. ed. 1,000, s/n, 20" x 12", pub MP | 57.00 | Sold Out |
| ☐ LITTLE GIRL BLUE, rel. 1981. ed. 1,000, s/n, size not available, pub MP | 16.00 | — |
| ☐ LITTLE GIRL'S PRAYER, rel. 1982. ed. 1,000, s/n, size not available, pub MP | 35.00 | — |
| ☐ LORDS OF THE REALM, rel. 1981. ed. 1,000, s/n, 20" x 20", pub MP | 80.00 | Sold Out |
| ☐ LORDS OF THE VALLEY, rel. 1983. ed. 1,000, s/n, size not available, pub MP | 175.00 | — |
| ☐ LOUISA, rel. 1983. ed. 1,000, s/n, size not available, pub MP | 20.00 | — |
| ☐ LOVE, rel. 1979. ed. 1,000, s/n, 6" x 5", pub MP | 10.00 | Sold Out |
| ☐ MARKET PLACE, rel. 1982. ed. 1,000, s/n, size not available, pub MP | 50.00 | — |
| ☐ MARY'S LAMB, large, rel. 1979. ed. 1,000, s/n, 22" x 22", pub MP | 75.00 | Sold Out |
| small, rel. 1978. ed. 1,000, s/n, size not available, pub MP | 40.00 | Sold Out |
| ☐ MARY AND MAGNOLIA, rel. 1978. ed. 1,000, s/n, 11" x 8", pub MP | 15.00 | Sold Out |
| ☐ ORCHARD GIRL, rel. 1983. ed. 1,000, s/n, size not available, pub MP | 40.00 | — |
| ☐ ORCHARD HELPERS, rel. 1978. ed. 1,000, s/n, 23" x 29", pub MP | 75.00 | Sold Out |
| ☐ OUR LITTLE BROTHER, rel. 1982. ed. 1,000, s/n, size not available, pub MP | 50.00 | — |
| ☐ OUR LITTLE SISTER, rel. 1982. ed. 1,000, s/n, size not available, pub MP | 50.00 | — |
| ☐ PALS, rel. 1982. ed. 1,000, s/n, size not available, pub MP | 25.00 | — |

| | ISSUE PRICE | CURRENT PRICE |
|---|---|---|
| ☐ **PATTI**, rel. 1982. ed. 1,000, s/n, 11″ x 14″, pub MP | 60.00 | — |
| ☐ **PAVILLION AT WOLFBORO**, rel. 1979. ed. 1,000, s/n, 13″ x 10″, pub MP | 40.00 | — |
| ☐ **PEACH HARVEST**, rel. 1980. ed. 1,000, s/n, 22″ x 13″, original lithograph, pub MP | 150.00 | — |
| ☐ **PERFECT PET**, rel. 1978. ed. 1,000, s/n, 9″ x 5″, pub MP | 15.00 | — |
| ☐ **PETER**, rel. 1982. ed. 1,000, s/n, size not available, pub MP | 20.00 | — |
| ☐ **PINK BALLERINA**, rel. 1982. ed. 1,000, s/n, size not available, pub MP | 25.00 | — |
| ☐ **PLEASE GOD**, rel. 1982. ed. 1,000, s/n, size not available, pub MP | 50.00 | — |
| ☐ **PLEASE!**, rel. 1982. ed. 1,000, s/n, 9″ x 9″, pub MP | 35.00 | — |
| ☐ **PONTE VECCHIO**, rel. 1982. ed. 1,000, s/n, size not available, pub MP | 90.00 | — |
| ☐ **POPPA APPLE, BLUE**, rel. 1978. ed. 1,000, s/n, size not available, pub MP | 10.00 | Sold Out |
| ☐ **POPPA APPLE, GOLD**, rel. 1978. ed. 1,000, s/n, size not available, pub MP | 15.00 | Sold Out |
| ☐ **PROMISED**, rel. 1979. ed. 1,000, s/n, 10″ x 12″, pub MP | 40.00 | — |
| ☐ **PUBLIC GARDENS & BEACON STREET**, rel. 1979. ed. 1,000, s/n, 11″ x 9″, pub MP | 50.00 | Sold Out |
| ☐ **THE QUILT**, rel. 1982. ed. 1,000, s/n, size not available, pub MP | 90.00 | — |
| ☐ **QUILTING BEE**, rel. 1978. ed. 1,000, s/n, 16″ x 17″, pub MP | 55.00 | — |
| ☐ **QUILTING DREAMS**, rel. 1981. ed. 1,000, s/n, 10″ x 18″, pub MP | 40.00 | — |
| ☐ **QUILTING LADIES**, rel. 1978. ed. 1,000, s/n, 7″ x 10″, pub MP | 40.00 | Sold Out |
| ☐ **RACHEL AND JACOB**, rel. 1978. ed. 1,000, s/n, 30″ x 37″, pub MP | 150.00 | Sold Out |
| ☐ **RED BIKE**, rel. 1983. ed. 1,000, s/n, size not available, pub MP | 35.00 | — |
| ☐ **RED HOUSE**, rel. 1983. ed. 1,000, s/n, size not available, pub MP | 100.00 | — |
| ☐ **REJOICE**, rel. 1979. ed. 1,000, s/n, 9″ x 6″, pub MP | 16.00 | — |
| ☐ **RELUCTANT BALLERINA**, rel. 1978. ed. 1,000, s/n, 9″ x 5″, pub MP | 15.00 | Sold Out |
| ☐ **RING AROUND A ROSIE**, rel. 1980. ed. 1,000, s/n, 8″ x 17″, pub MP | 40.00 | — |
| ☐ **ROCKING**, rel. 1982. ed. 1,000, s/n, size not available, pub MP | 40.00 | — |
| ☐ **ROTHENBURG**, rel. 1983. ed. 1,000, s/n, size not available, pub MP | 40.00 | Sold Out |
| ☐ **ROTHENBURG II**, rel. 1983. ed. 1,000, s/n, size not available, pub MP | 80.00 | — |
| ☐ **ROYAL STREET**, rel. 1982. ed. 1,000, s/n, size not available, pub MP | 40.00 | Sold Out |
| ☐ **SAM**, rel. 1981. ed. 1,000, s/n, 8″ x 5″, pub MP | 16.00 | — |
| ☐ **SARAH**, rel. 1981. ed. 1,000, s/n, 8″ x 5″, pub MP | 16.00 | Sold Out |
| ☐ **SEASON'S OVER**, rel. 1978. ed. 1,000, s/n, 6″ x 16″, pub MP | 35.00 | Sold Out |
| ☐ **SERENITY IN BLACK & WHITE**, rel. 1978. ed. 1,000, s/n, 29″ x 22″, pub MP | 120.00 | — |
| ☐ **SHENANDOAH HARVEST**, rel. 1982. ed. 1,000, s/n, size not available, pub MP | 60.00 | — |
| ☐ **SHENANDOAH SILHOUETTE**, ed. 1,000, s/n, 10″ x 8″, pub MP | 25.00 | Sold Out |
| ☐ **SHOWALTER'S FARM**, rel. 1978. ed. 1,000, s/n, 14″ x 24″, pub MP | 75.00 | — |
| ☐ **SISTERS**, rel. 1978. ed. 1,000, s/n, 12″ x 16″, pub MP | 20.00 | Sold Out |
| ☐ **SKATING AWAY I**, rel. 1978. ed. 1,000, s/n, 16″ x 30″, pub MP | 70.00 | Sold Out |
| ☐ **SKATING DUET**, rel. 1982. ed. 1,000, s/n, size not available, pub MP | 40.00 | — |
| ☐ **SKATING JOY**, rel. 1981. ed. 1,000, s/n, 36″ x 36″, pub MP | 200.00 | — |
| ☐ **SKATING LESSON**, rel. 1978. ed. 1,000, s/n, 14″ x 20″, pub MP | 150.00 | Sold Out |
| ☐ **SLEIGH RIDE**, rel. 1982. ed. 1,000, s/n, size not available, pub MP | 50.00 | — |
| ☐ **SNOW GOOSE**, rel. 1982. ed. 1,000, s/n, size not available, pub MP | 50.00 | Sold Out |
| ☐ **SNOWY BIRCHES**, rel. 1978. ed. 1,000, s/n, 15″ x 18″, pub MP | 60.00 | Sold Out |
| ☐ **SOLITARY SKATER I**, rel. 1978. ed. 1,000, s/n, 10″ x 8″, pub MP | 35.00 | Sold Out |
| ☐ **SOLITARY SKATER II**, rel. 1981. ed. 1,000, s/n, 9″ x 11″, pub MP | 35.00 | Sold Out |
| ☐ **SOLO**, rel. 1981. ed. 1,000, s/n, 9″ x 6″, pub MP | 15.00 | Sold Out |
| ☐ **SPIRIT OF EQUUS**, rel. 1978. ed. 1,000, s/n, 18″ x 36″, pub MP | 100.00 | — |
| ☐ **SPRING LOVE**, rel. 1981. ed. 1,000, s/n, size not available, pub MP | 25.00 | — |
| ☐ **SPRINGTIME SHEPHERDS**, rel. 1983. ed. 1,000, s/n, size not available, pub MP | 40.00 | — |
| ☐ **STACK OF BOYS**, rel. 1983. ed. 1,000, s/n, size not available, pub MP | 30.00 | — |
| ☐ **STACK OF GIRLS**, rel. 1978. ed. 1,000, s/n, 16″ x 8″, pub MP | 25.00 | Sold Out |
| ☐ **STREET BY THE PARK I**, rel. 1980. ed. 1,000, s/n, 16″ x 22″, pub MP | 200.00 | — |
| ☐ **STREET BY THE PARK II**, rel. 1981. ed. 1,000, s/n, 20″ x 28″, pub MP | 125.00 | Sold Out |
| ☐ **SUGAR VALLEY FARM**, rel. 1978. ed. 1,000, s/n, 22″ x 30″, pub MP | 80.00 | — |
| ☐ **SUNDAY MORNING**, rel. 1981. ed. 1,000, s/n, 15″ x 16″, pub MP | 60.00 | Sold Out |
| ☐ **SUNDAY'S RIDE**, rel. 1981. ed. 1,000, s/n, 14″ x 17″, pub MP | 60.00 | Sold Out |
| ☐ **SUZI**, rel. 1983. ed. 1,000, s/n, size not available, pub MP | 25.00 | — |
| ☐ **SWEET PROMISES**, rel. 1979. ed. 1,000, s/n, 11″ x 12″, pub MP | 40.00 | — |
| ☐ **TAKING TURNS**, rel. 1982. ed. 1,000, s/n, 14″ x 14″, pub MP | 50.00 | — |
| ☐ **TARRY NOT**, rel. 1979. ed. 1,000, s/n, 10″ x 10″, pub MP | 35.00 | Sold Out |
| ☐ **TENDING HER FLOCK**, rel. 1978. ed. 1,000, s/n, 21″ x 28″, pub MP | 80.00 | — |
| ☐ **TIS GRACE**, rel. 1979. ed. 1,000, s/n, 7″ x 10″, pub MP | 20.00 | Sold Out |

| | ISSUE PRICE | CURRENT PRICE |
|---|---|---|
| ☐ **TIS NIGHT**, rel. 1979. ed. 1,000, s/n, 16″ x 9″, pub MP | 50.00 | — |
| ☐ **TO WALK**, rel. 1983. ed. 1,000, s/n, size not available, pub MP | 20.00 | — |
| ☐ **TOGETHER**, rel. 1981. ed. 99, s/n, 30″ x 30″, pub MP | 450.00 | Sold Out |
| ☐ **TOGETHER IN THE PARK**, rel. 1982. ed. 1,000, s/n, 10″ x 14″, pub MP | 80.00 | — |
| ☐ **TREE HOUSE**, rel. 1982. ed. 1,000, s/n, 15″ x 18″, pub MP | 80.00 | — |
| ☐ **TWO LITTLE HANDS**, ed. 1,000, s/n, 11″ x 8″, pub MP | 35.00 | — |
| ☐ **TWO ON A BARRELL**, rel. 1982. ed. 1,000, s/n, size not available, pub MP | 25.00 | — |
| ☐ **TWO ON A SWING**, rel. 1982. ed. 1,000, s/n, size not available, pub MP | 50.00 | — |
| ☐ **VALLEY FARM**, rel. 1980. ed. 1,000, s/n, 15″ x 16″, pub MP | 60.00 | — |
| ☐ **VALLEY VISITORS**, rel. 1982. ed. 1,000, s/n, 47″ x 15″, pub MP | 250.00 | — |
| ☐ **VALLEY WINTER**, rel. 1980. ed. 1,000, s/n, 48″ x 32″, pub MP | 300.00 | — |
| ☐ **VIEW FROM ROOM 48**, rel. 1982. ed. 1,000, s/n, size not available, pub MP | 90.00 | — |
| ☐ **WAITING FOR TOM**, rel. 1981. ed. 1,000, s/n, 8″ x 6″, pub MP | 40.00 | Sold Out |
| ☐ **WAYSIDE INN**, rel. 1980. ed. 1,000, s/n, 15″ x 15″, pub MP | 65.00 | Sold Out |
| ☐ **WEDDING**, rel. 1982. ed. 1,000, s/n, 16″ x 16″, pub MP | 80.00 | Sold Out |
| ☐ **WEDDING II**, rel. 1982. ed. 1,000, s/n, size not available, pub MP | 90.00 | — |
| ☐ **WEDDING III**, rel. 1983. ed. 1,000, s/n, size not available, pub MP | 90.00 | — |
| ☐ **WEDDING DAY**, rel. 1982. ed. 1,000, s/n, size not available, pub MP | 160.00 | — |
| ☐ **WHITE CHURCH**, rel. 1983. ed. 1,000, s/n, size not available, pub MP | 80.00 | — |
| ☐ **WINFIELD FARM**, rel. 1978. ed. 1,000, s/n, 13″ x 33″, pub MP | 100.00 | — |
| ☐ **WINFIELD FARM II**, rel. 1981. ed. 1,000, s/n, 12″ x 20″, pub MP | 100.00 | — |
| ☐ **WINTER AT THE MILL**, rel. 1981. ed. 1,000, s/n, 20″ x 20″, pub MP | 80.00 | Sold Out |
| ☐ **WINTER CAMEO**, rel. 1978. s/n, 12″ x 12″, pub MP | 30.00 | Sold Out |
| ☐ **WINTER DUET**, rel. 1982. ed. 1,000, s/n, 28″ x 11″, pub MP | 60.00 | — |
| ☐ **WINTER SILHOUETTE**, rel. 1981. ed. 1,000, s/n, 28″ x 20″, pub MP | 300.00 | — |
| ☐ **WINTER SKATER**, rel. 1983. ed. 1,000, s/n, size not available, pub MP | 40.00 | — |
| ☐ **WINTER VISITOR**, rel. 1978. ed. 1,000, s/n, 26″ x 14″, pub MP | 80.00 | Sold Out |
| ☐ **WINTER'S DAY**, rel. 1983. ed. 1,000, s/n, size not available, pub MP | 50.00 | — |
| ☐ **WINTER'S GLIMPSE**, rel. 1982. ed. 1,000, s/n, 12″ x 12″, pub MP | 40.00 | — |
| ☐ **WINTER'S HOUSE**, rel. 1980. ed. 1,000, s/n, 29″ x 21″, pub MP | 250.00 | — |
| ☐ **WINTER'S JOY**, rel. 1982. ed. 1,000, s/n, 24″ x 24″, pub MP | 500.00 | — |
| ☐ **WINTER'S MAJESTY**, rel. 1982. ed. 1,000, s/n, 32″ x 48″, pub MP | 300.00 | — |
| ☐ **WOMAN TALK**, rel. 1979. ed. 1,000, s/n, 11″ x 10″, pub MP | 35.00 | Sold Out |
| ☐ **WORKDAY'S O'ER**, rel. 1978. ed. 1,000, s/n, 25″ x 27″, pub MP | 110.00 | Sold Out |
| ☐ **YOUNG NEIGHBORS**, rel. 1982. ed. 1,000, s/n, size not available, pub MP | 30.00 | — |

# RIE MUÑOZ

Alaska became Rie Muñoz's home in 1950. Her first years in Alaska encompassed a wonderful range of experiences. She lived in remote areas and traveled among Native Alaskans. She taught in an isolated picturesque Eskimo village on King Island in the Bering Sea and prospected in the wilderness of Southeast Alaska. Some winters were spent in the wilderness on Prince of Wales Island where the woods teemed with wildlife. At every opportunity, Muñoz sketched. She cruised along the thousands of miles of Southeast Alaska coastline, stopping at every village to visit. All of her experiences were recorded in her sketchbook. For thirteen years, Muñoz entered art shows and sold her paintings.

She then accepted a position as curator of exhibits with the new Alaska State Museum in Juneau. There she grew in her knowledge of Alaska's people, arts, customs, and skills. In 1973, she left the Museum to work full time on her art

Muñoz still makes at least two annual sketching trips to remote areas to paint the lifestyle in the bush which is unique but rapidly changing.

In 1977, Muñoz was nominated outstanding Alaska artist by the Anchorage Fire Arts Museum Association.

**BELUGA WHALE AND CALF** *by Rie Muñoz*

| RIE MUÑOZ | ISSUE PRICE | CURRENT PRICE |
|---|---|---|
| ☐ **BELUGA WHALE AND CALF**, rel. 1978. ed. 950, s/n, 14″ x 22″, pub MPPI ... | 25.00 | 75.00 |
| ☐ **CROW IN A MOUNTAIN ASH TREE**, rel. 1978. ed. 950, s/n, 15″ x 22″, pub MPPI. | 30.00 | — |
| ☐ **RAFT OF DUCKS**, rel. 1978. ed. 950, s/n, 14″ x 22″, pub MPPI | 30.00 | Sold Out |
| ☐ **RIBBON SEALS**, rel. 1978. ed. 950, s/n, 11″ x 14″, pub MPPI | 20.00 | — |
| ☐ **CANNERY WORKER**, rel. 1979. ed. 350, s/n, 18¼″ x 21¾″, pub MPPI | 50.00 | Sold Out |
| ☐ **SEINER**, rel. 1979. ed. 350, s/n, 18¼″ x 21¾″, pub MPPI | 50.00 | Sold Out |

# MARTIN R. MURK

A native of Wisconsin, Martin R. Murk's love of nature and innate artistic ability were the forces that directed him to wildlife art. He studied at the Layton School of Art and then worked with an advertising agency and an art studio before he emerged successfully as a free-lance illustrator and designer, painting wildlife when time permitted.

Winning the 1977 Federal Duck Stamp Competition gave him the coveted opportunity to devote all his time to painting wildlife. He went on to win the 1979 Wisconsin Trout Stamp and the 1980 Wisconsin Duck Stamp Contests. Most recently he was commissioned to do a painting of Canada Geese for Wetlands for Wildlife and the 1982 Wisconsin Great lakes Salmon and Trout Stamp.

Murk's works have been exhibited in numerous galleries, including the Leigh Yawkey Woodson Art Museum, Milwaukee Public Museum, National Museum of American Art-Smithsonian Institution and The Waterfowl Festival.

| MARTIN R. MURK | | |
|---|---|---|
| ☐ **1979 WISCONSIN TROUT STAMP PRINT**, rel. 1979. ed. 500, s/n, 14″ x 12″, dist. NC | 75.00 | 450.00 |
| ed. 100 remarqued | 225.00 | 900.00 |
| ☐ **1982 TIMBERWOLF PRESERVATION SOCIETY STAMP PRINT**, rel. 1982. ed. N/A, s/n, 14¾″ x 12″, distr. NC | 125.00 | — |

# FRANK C. MURPHY

Frank Murphy attended the University of Texas and graduated from the Iowa State University, worked on ranches in Texas and Montana and served in the 23rd (horse) Calvary Brigade of the Texas National Guard.

Following study at the Chicago and American academies, he began a career in the agricultural field, painting and illustrating all types and breeds of livestock for such corporate accounts as The Quaker Oats Company, Swift, Wilson, American Cynamid, Ralston Purina and Successful Farming.

For over 25 years, his work for the American Angus Associaion has achieved national and international recognition. In 1973, his painting of the introduction of the Angus breed to the United States, showing the first Angus bulls with Longhorn cattle on the plains of Kansas, was made the subject of a U.S. Commemorative Postage Stamp. His paintings and illustrations of cattle have won national advertising awards and have appeared on many magazine covers, and are included in private and corporate collections. In 1979, a one man show of his Angus paintings was held at Colorado State University.

| FRANK C. MURPHY | ISSUE PRICE | CURRENT PRICE |
|---|---|---|
| ☐ **BRUSH POPPER,** rel. 1982. ed. 1,500, s/n, 22″ x 28″, pub ALI . . . . . . . . . . . . | 75.00 | — |

# ALAN MURRAY

| | ISSUE PRICE | CURRENT PRICE |
|---|---|---|
| ☐ **TWO FOR TEA,** rel. 1979. ed. 500, s/n, 19″ x 19″, pub ALL . . . . . . . . . . . . . . . | 95.00 | — |
| ed. 50 artist proofs. . . . . . . . . . . . . . . . . . . . . . . . . . . . . . . . . . . . . . . . . . | 95.00 | — |
| ☐ **BISCUITS FOR BOTH,** rel. 1979. ed. 500, s/n, 19″ x 19″, pub ALL. . . . . . . . . | 95.00 | — |
| ed. 50 artist proofs. . . . . . . . . . . . . . . . . . . . . . . . . . . . . . . . . . . . . . . . . . | 95.00 | — |
| ☐ **TEA LEAVES AND MEMORIES,** rel. 1979. ed. 500, s/n, 19″ x 24″, pub ALL . . . | 95.00 | — |
| ed. 50 artist proofs. . . . . . . . . . . . . . . . . . . . . . . . . . . . . . . . . . . . . . . . . . | 95.00 | — |

# SUSAN NEELON

Unlike many artists, Susan Neelon's interest in art developed out of a need to communicate with her sister who is deaf. Neelon would draw a variety of pictures to communicate her feelings. This turned into a lifelong desire to expand on her art and to communicate through this art, the warmth, love and inspiration that her sister had given her.

Neelon was born in the San Fernando Valley and majored in art in high school and college. For three years she studied oils with Irish McCalla and then continuing her art education studied with the famous watercolorist, Jake Lee. Her specialty has been portraits of children.

| SUSAN NEELON | ISSUE PRICE | CURRENT PRICE |
|---|---|---|
| ☐ **PAPER ROSES.** ed. 1,450, s/n, 11″ x 14″, pub MEI . . . . . . . . . . . . . . . . . . . . | 19.50 | — |
| ed. 50 a/p . . . . . . . . . . . . . . . . . . . . . . . . . . . . . . . . . . . . . . . . . . . . . . . . | 19.50 | — |
| ☐ **CAN I KEEP HIM?** ed. 700, s/n, 12″ x 16″, pub MEI . . . . . . . . . . . . . . . . . . . . | 29.50 | — |
| ed. 50, a/p . . . . . . . . . . . . . . . . . . . . . . . . . . . . . . . . . . . . . . . . . . . . . . . . | 29.50 | Sold Out |

# LEROY NEIMAN

| | ISSUE PRICE | CURRENT PRICE |
|---|---|---|
| ☐ **DEUCE**, ed. 275, s/n, 26″ x 32″″, serigraph, pub CFAC | — | 1,500.00 |
| ☐ **SAILING**, ed. 275, s/n, 20″ x 24″, serigraph, pub CFAC | — | 900.00 |
| ☐ **CHIPPING ON**, ed. 275, s/n, 26″ x 32″, serigraph, pub CFAC | — | 900.00 |
| ☐ **MATCHPOINT**, ed. 300, s/n, 36″ x 48″, serigraph, pub CFAC | — | 2,200.00 |
| ☐ **TIGER**, ed. 300, s/n, 36″ x 48″, serigraph, pub CFAC | — | 2,800.00 |
| ☐ **TENNIS PLAYER**, ed. 300, s/n, 18″ x 18″, serigraph, pub CFAC | — | 900.00 |
| ☐ **POOL ROOM**, ed. 350, s/n, 23″ x 26″, serigraph, pub CFAC | — | 850.00 |
| ☐ **THE RACE**, ed. 300, s/n, 17″ x 25″, serigraph, pub CFAC | — | 500.00 |
| ☐ **IN THE STRETCH**, ed. 250, s/n, 26″ x 34″, serigraph, pub CFAC | — | 600.00 |
| ☐ **STOCK MARKET**, ed. 300, s/n, 30″ x 42″, serigraph, pub CFAC | — | 4,000.00 |
| ☐ **JOCKEY**, ed. 300, s/n, 22″ x 26″, serigraph, pub CFAC | — | 800.00 |
| ☐ **CASINO**, ed. 300, s/n, 26″ x 32″, serigraph, pub CFAC | — | 1,000.00 |
| ☐ **PADDOCK**, ed. 300, s/n, 30″ x 30″, serigraph, pub CFAC | — | 800.00 |
| ☐ **PUNCHINELLO**, ed. 250, s/n, 21″ x 30″, serigraph, pub CFAC | — | 300.00 |
| ☐ **PIERROT**, ed. 250, s/n, 20″ x 26″, serigraph, pub CFAC | — | 350.00 |
| ☐ **SLIDING HOME**, ed. 300, s/n, 24″ x 36″, serigraph, pub CFAC | — | 750.00 |
| ☐ **SKIER**, ed. 300, s/n, 18″ x 26″, serigraph, pub CFAC | — | 600.00 |
| ☐ **FOUR ACES**, ed. 300, s/n, 27″ x 36″, serigraph, pub CFAC | — | 600.00 |
| ☐ **SLALOM**, ed. 300, s/n, 26″ x 32″, serigraph, pub CFAC | — | 700.00 |
| ☐ **LEOPARD**, ed. 300, s/n, 38″ x 50″, serigraph, pub CFAC | — | 4,200.00 |
| ☐ **AL CAPONE**, ed. 300, s/n, 30″ x 40″, serigraph, pub CFAC | — | 500.00 |
| ☐ **PIERROT THE JUGGLER**, ed. 200, s/n, 21″ x 30″, lithograph, pub CFAC | — | 350.00 |
| ☐ **HARLEQUIN**, ed. 200, s/n, 18″ x 20″, lithograph, pub CFAC | — | 325.00 |
| ☐ **HARLEQUIN WITH SWORD**, ed. 250, s/n, 19″ x 29″, lithograph, pub CFAC | — | 300.00 |
| ☐ **HOCKEY PLAYER**, ed. 300, s/n, 30″ x 40″, serigraph, pub CFAC | — | 1,800.00 |
| ☐ **PUNCHINELLO WITH TEXT**, ed. 200, s/n, 24″ x 30″, lithograph, pub CFAC | — | 200.00 |
| ☐ **HARLEQUIN WITH TEXT**, ed. 200, s/n, 24″ x 30″, lithograph, pub CFAC | — | 250.00 |
| ☐ **TEE SHOT**, ed. 300, s/n, 24″ x 30″, serigraph, pub CFAC | — | 1,000.00 |
| ☐ **END AROUND**, ed. 300, s/n, 24″ x 30″, serigraph, pub CFAC | — | 750.00 |
| ☐ **LION PRIDE**, ed. 300, s/n, 36″ x 48″, serigraph, pub CFAC | — | 3,500.00 |
| ☐ **MARATHON**, ed. 300, s/n, 26″ x 34″, serigraph, pub CFAC | — | 750.00 |
| ☐ **SCRAMBLE**, ed. 300, s/n, 27″ x 33″, serigraph, pub CFAC | — | 750.00 |
| ☐ **DOWNHILL**, ed. 300, s/n, 17″ x 32″, serigraph, pub CFAC | — | 750.00 |
| ☐ **INNSBRUCK**, ed. 300, s/n, 16″ x 32″, serigraph, pub CFAC | — | 750.00 |
| ☐ **DOUBLES**, ed. 300, s/n, 36″ x 48″, serigraph, pub CFAC | — | 1,500.00 |
| ☐ **TROTTERS**, ed. 300, s/n, 36″ x 48″, serigraph, pub CFAC | — | 900.00 |
| ☐ **GOAL**, ed. 300, s/n, 24″ x 30″, serigraph, pub CFAC | — | 700.00 |
| ☐ **ROULETTE**, ed. 40, s/n, 50″ x 60″, serigraph, pub CFAC | — | 3,500.00 |
| ☐ **BACKHAND**, ed. 300, s/n, 24″ x 31″, serigraph, pub CFAC | — | 800.00 |
| ☐ **SLAPSHOT**, ed. 300, s/n, 30″ x 35″, serigraph, pub CFAC | — | 900.00 |
| ☐ **FOX HUNT**, ed. 300, s/n, 30″ x 26″, serigraph, pub CFAC | — | 800.00 |
| ☐ **SMASH**, ed. 300, s/n, 26″ x 26″, serigraph, pub CFAC | — | 1,000.00 |
| ☐ **OCELOT**, ed. 250, s/n, 30″ x 39″, serigraph, pub CFAC | — | 1,200.00 |
| ☐ **SUDDEN DEATH**, ed. 250, s/n, 31″ x 30″, serigraph, pub CFAC | — | 1,100.00 |
| ☐ **HOMMAGE TO BOUCHER**, ed. 250, s/n, 26″ x 40″, serigraph, pub CFAC | — | 700.00 |
| ☐ **12 METER YACHT RACE**, ed. 250, s/n, 19″ x 30″, serigraph, pub CFAC | — | 900.00 |
| ☐ **BASEBALL PLAYER FOLIO**, ed. 150, s/n, 15″ x 16″ | — | 1,600.00 |
| consisting of ten etchings: Batting Practice, Wind Up, Awaiting The Decision, Warm Up Swings, Next At Bat, The Pitch, The Argument, The Umps, Sliding Home, The Hit, pub CFAC | | |
| ☐ **SKIING FOLIO**, ed. 150, s/n, 15″ x 16″ | — | 1,600.00 |
| consisting of ten etchings: Single Skier, Between Trees, Top Of The Crest, Two Racers, Break, Jump, Village In The Valley, House On The Slopes, Pine Trail, Three Skiers, pub CFAC | | |
| ☐ **HOCKEY FOLIO**, ed. 150, s/n, 15″ x 16″ | — | 1,600.00 |
| consisting of ten etchings: Face Off No. 20, Score No. 22, Fight, Fight With Policeman, Study Of No. 4, 1 Against 1 (Straight Shot), 1 Against 1 (Goalie On Ice), Goalie Down, Goal No. 5, High Stick, pub CFAC | | |

|  | ISSUE PRICE | CURRENT PRICE |
|---|---|---|
| ☐ **ALI-FRAZIER FOLIO,** ed. 150, s/n, 15″ x 20″ . . . . . . . . . . . . . . . . . . . . . . . . consisting of fifteen etchings: Study of Ali, Ali Down, The Introduction, Frazier's Corner, Ali's Corner, The Winner, After The Fight, Study of Frazier and Ali, Rounds 1 and 2, Rounds 3 and 4, Rounds 5 and 6, Rounds 7 through 9, Rounds 10 and 11, Rounds 12 through 14, Round 15, pub CFAC | — | 2,500.00 |
| ☐ **POLAR BEARS** (new release 1979), ed. 300, s/n, 38″ x 28″, serigraph, pub CFAC . . . . . . . . . . . . . . . . . . . . . . . . . . . . . . . . . . . . . . . . . . . . . . . . . | — | 300.00 |

# GARY NIBLETT

Gary Niblett was born and raised in the foothills near Carlsbad, New Mexico. From early childhood he drew pictures of everything he saw. Fascinated by Indian artifacts, he spent hours searching for them. As he grew older he worked on ranches, herding, doctoring and branding. These experiences are reflected in his paintings.

He says his parents never understood his driving desire to be an artist, but they supported him with encouragement and $380 for a correspondence art course, when he was a junior in high school.

Niblett studied at Eastern New Mexico University and the Art Center School in Los Angeles until he was discovered by the Hanna-Barbera animation studios where he worked for nine years as a background artist.

During these years, Niblett continued the development of his easel painting to fulfill his childhood dream of becoming a fine artist. He left the studio and California, moving to Sedona, Arizona, where he profited greatly from his association with Jim Reynolds. He moved to Angel Fire, New Mexico and now keeps a studio there and in Santa Fe.

In 1976, Niblett was the youngest artist ever invited into the prestigious Cowboy Artists of America organization.

**SUNDAY FLOWERS** *by Gary Niblett*

| GARY NIBLETT | ISSUE PRICE | CURRENT PRICE |
|---|---|---|
| ☐ **A DISTANT LIGHT**, rel. 1979. ed. 2,250, s/n, 16″ x 22″, pub TAP . . . . . . . . . . | 100.00 | — |
| ☐ **CONFIRMING THE COUNT**, rel. 1979. ed. 2,250, s/n, 15½″ x 22″, pub TAP . . | 100.00 | — |
| ☐ **SANGRE DE CRISTO AUTUMN**, rel. 1979. ed. 2,250, s/n, 16″ x 22″, pub TAP . | 100.00 | — |
| ☐ **WINTER SUPPLIES**, rel. 1979. ed. 2,250, s/n, 14½″ x 22″, pub TAP . . . . . . . . | 100.00 | — |
| ☐ **COOL WATER**, rel. 1980. ed. 2,250, s/n, 22⅛″ x 28⅛″, pub TAP . . . . . . . . . . | 100.00 | — |
| ☐ **NIGHT VISITOR**, rel. 1980. ed. 2,250, s/n, 18⅛″ x 28⅛″, pub TAP. . . . . . . . . | 100.00 | — |
| ☐ **SUNDAY FLOWERS**, rel. 1980. ed. 2,250, s/n, 21″ x 28⅛″, pub TAP . . . . . . . | 100.00 | — |
| ☐ **THE RABBIT HUNTERS**, rel. 1980. ed. 2,250, s/n, 18½″ x 28″, pub TAP . . . . | 100.00 | — |
| ☐ **WINTER IN THE VERMEJO**, rel. 1980. ed. 2,250, s/n, 22½″ x 27½″, pub TAP | 100.00 | — |
| ☐ **BITTER COLD**, rel. 1982. ed. 950, s/n, 22¾″ x 29½″, pub MPPI . . . . . . . . . . | 135.00 | — |
| ☐ **RAIN OR SHINE**, rel. 1981. ed. 950, s/n, 23″ x 32¼″, pub MPPI . . . . . . . . . . | 150.00 | — |
| ☐ **RABBIT STEW**, rel. 1982. ed. 950, s/n, 19½″ x 24″, pub MPPII. . . . . . . . . . . | 95.00 | — |

# WARD H. NICHOLS

Ward H. Nichols paints rustic old barns, homes and other aging structures in a spirit of deliberate urgency. Deliberate because with his unbelievably detailed technique it often takes him 100 to 200 hours to finish a subject. Urgent because he feels the subjects that he loves to paint are rapidly disappearing.

In the weathered barns, mills and farms, he finds a simple beauty that is seldom captured in modern counterpart structures. Nichols has great admiration for early farmers who designed practical structures and then built them with their own hands. He says that "many older buildings still exist because they still serve the purpose they were designed for. Often a farmer built his barn before he even built his home. Unfortunately, today we often save or restore the home, but allow the barn to fall into ruin. To me, barns have a unique combination of beauty of line and functional design that few other structures have."

As an artist, Nichols exhibits the kind of exacting craftsmanship he so admires in his subjects. His talent as an artist is God-given and then self-developed, as he has had no formal art training. His work has been described as Interpretive Realism. They are "so real they are almost unreal . . . a modern form of trompe-l'oeil that few have the ability, termperament or imagination to do," according to one reviewer. Nichols paints with a style that creates such incredibly fine detail that only a magnifier can capture all of the intricate work.

Though old rural buildings are among his most frequent subjects, Ward actually works on a wide variety of themes. He has a child-like fascination with railroad scenes and steam locomotives; likes to paint complex machinery such as the old time reapers; and creates occasional studies of people and seascapes.

The decision to devote his full-time efforts to painting was a difficult one. His family business depended heavily on him in the daytime, while his evening hours were devoted to painting, a pasttime that began at the age of twelve. Eventually the two endeavors began to take their toll on Ward's health. So in 1967 he devoted all of his efforts to art.

Since that decision fourteen years ago, Ward Nichols' rise to national and international recognition as an artist has been nothing short of phenomenal. His paintings have been presented in exhibits including the National Academy Galleries in New York, The New Horizon Gallery in California, The Springfield Museum of Art in Springfield, Massachusetts and the El Paso Museum of Art. Seventy galleries in 21 states have exhibited his work. He has also shown in 26 National and International Shows.

Nichols has been recognized by *Who's Who in American Art, The International Who's Who in Art and Antiques, The International Directory of the Arts of Cambridge, England, Who's Who in the South, Personalities of the South,* and other prestigious publications. He is represented in numerous private and public collections and is the recipient of many awards. Active in many aspects of the art scene, he has held three Artist In Residencies. Nichols also lectures, judges and presents programs to art and civic groups.

Nichols is a realist with a rare versatility that transforms the commonplace into a visual world of his own creation. His clarity of detail, combined with his enthusiasm, artistic awareness and knowledge of his subject, presents a unique visual interpretation.

Last November Ward Nichols traveled to Mainz, Germany to visit the Gutenberg Museum where he witnessed the creation of the workshop where Johannes Gutenberg invented moveable type. After his visit, Ward was commissioned to create an original oil painting of Gutenberg's workshop, by the Printing Industries of the Carolinas (PICA). The reproductions from this original are being sold in both German and American Editions.

| WARD H. NICHOLS | ISSUE PRICE | CURRENT PRICE |
|---|---|---|
| ☐ BY-PASSED, rel. 1974. ed. 500, s/n, 22″ x 28″, pub RI | 40.00 | Sold Out |
| ☐ EARLY LIGHT, rel. 1975. ed. 500, s/n, 22″ x 28″, pub RI | 40.00 | Sold Out |
| ☐ ADAMS PORCH, rel. 1976. ed. 500, s/n, 17″ x 33″, pub RI | 40.00 | Sold Out |
| ☐ SUPPER TIME, rel. 1976. ed. 500, s/n, 22¼″ x 32½″, pub RI | 50.00 | Sold Out |
| ☐ MICHAEL'S SHIRT, rel. 1976. ed. 500, s/n, 22″ x 28″, pub RI | 30.00 | 30.00 |
| ☐ CASTAWAY, rel. 1976. ed. 500, s/n, 22″ x 28″, pub RI | 50.00 | Sold Out |
| ☐ THE LEGACY, rel. 1977. ed. 500, s/n, 22″ x 28″, pub RI | 50.00 | Sold Out |
| ☐ THE OLD WELL, rel. 1977. ed. 500, s/n, 20″ x 24″, pub RI | 50.00 | Sold Out |
| ☐ BUTLER'S MILL, rel. 1977. ed. 750, s/n, 19½″ x 32½″, pub RI | 50.00 | Sold Out |
| ☐ MEMORABILIA, rel. 1978. ed. 750, s/n, 18½″ x 28½″, pub RI | 50.00 | Sold Out |
| ☐ FARM PORTRAIT, rel. 1978. ed. 750, s/n, 12½″ x 28½″, pub RI | 50.00 | Sold Out |
| ☐ SNOWFALL IN ROCKFORD, rel. 1978. ed. 750, s/n, 18″ x 27½″, pub RI | 50.00 | Sold Out |
| ☐ STEEL, STEAM & SMOKE, rel. 1978. ed. U/L, s/n, (portfolio of 4), 11″ x 18″ and 11″ x 11″, pub RI | 30.00 | 30.00 |
| ☐ AMERICAN TYPE 4-4-0, rel. 1979. ed. 750, s/n, 17″ x 25¾″, pub RI | 75.00 | 75.00 |
| ☐ HAY RAKE, rel. 1979. ed. 500, s/n, 17″ x 17″, pub RI | 50.00 | 50.00 |
| ☐ SHENANDOAH FARM, rel. 1979. ed. 750, s/n, 16″ x 24″, pub RI | 75.00 | 75.00 |
| ☐ A COUNTRY WALK, rel. 1980. ed. 750, s/n, 28″ x 19½″, pub RI | 75.00 | 75.00 |
| ☐ MILKING TIME, rel. 1980. ed. 750, s/n, 15½″ x 28″, pub RI | 75.00 | Sold Out |
| ☐ THE SURVIVOR, rel. 1980. ed. U/L, s/o, 8½″ x 22″, pub RI | 20.00 | 20.00 |
| ☐ STILL LIFE WITH BUTTERFLIES, rel. 1981. ed. 750, s/n, 13¼″ x 22″, pub RI | 75.00 | 75.00 |
| ☐ TOOLS OF FREEDOM, rel. 1981. ed. 2,000, s/n, 15¾″ x 25″, pub for PICA, Scholarship Fund | 75.00 | 75.00 |
| ☐ BEE YARD, rel. 1981. ed. 2,000, s/n, 17″ x 22″, pub for Southern States Beekeepers project | 75.00 | 75.00 |
| ☐ IVEY MOORE RIFLE, rel. 1981. ed. 850, s/n, 17″ x 31″, pub RI | 85.00 | 85.00 |
| ☐ THE 610, rel. 1981. ed. U/L, s/o, 8½″ x 29″, pub RI | 20.00 | 20.00 |
| ☐ GUTENBERG CREATION, rel. 1982. ed. 2,000, s/n, 18″ x 25″, pub for PICA Scholarship Fund | 150.00 | 150.00 |

# ROBERT NIPP

About his paintings Robert Nipp says, "I focus on the characteristics of the animal, the sum total of all those qualities which go to make up its personality as it exists in nature."

Thus, Tennessee black bears may be depicted in play, yet other natural traits such as strength are also clearly imaged. Eastern cottontails may be halted for a frozen moment in the snow, yet their natural agility and alertness are also captured.

What makes these paintings of added interest is often what is *not* depicted. The piercing gaze of the red fox, the guarded stare of the standing bear in the background, the over-the-shoulder look of the cheetah draws us into the paintings. Our natural inclination is to wonder what has captured *their* interest. Our imaginative gaze is cast upon what is *not* depicted in the painting.

Robert Nipp studied at the Ringling School of Art, Sarasota, Florida and is a graduate of the Memphis Academy of Arts. His work has been exhibited in shows and galleries throughout the country. He has won numerous awards for commercial art projects and has gained wide recognition as a creative designer. One of his recent works, *"Bull Cans"* was selected as 'best painting' in the Southern Wildlife Art Festival, sponsored by Ducks Unlimited.

Nipp's interest in Wildlife conservation led to his painting of the *"Wood Duck"*. These prints helped raise a needed $55,000 in two weeks to preserve Radnor Lake, now designated as Tennessee's first Natural Area. Nipp's paintings are regarded by many as an authentic record and preservation of our natural heritage.

**BLUE WINGS OVER YUCATAN** *by Robert Nipp*

## ROBERT NIPP

| | ISSUE PRICE | CURRENT PRICE |
|---|---|---|
| ☐ **THE RED FOX**, ed. 2,500, s/n, 22½" x 28¾", pub RG | 20.00 | Sold Out |
| ☐ **TENNESSEE BLACK BEARS**, ed. 2,500, s/n, 28" x 22¾", pub RG | 20.00 | Sold Out |
| ☐ **EASTERN COTTONTAILS**, ed. 1,000, s/n, 18" x 23", pub RG | 25.00 | — |
| ed. 1,500, s/o | 20.00 | — |
| ☐ **INNOCENCE**, ed. 1,000, s/n, 18" x 22", pub RG | 30.00 | — |
| ☐ **BULL CANS**, ed. 500, s/n, 29" x 23", pub RG | 40.00 | — |
| ed. 1,500, s/o | 25.00 | — |
| ☐ **BOBWHITE QUAIL**, rel. 1977. ed. 500, s/n, 16" x 20", pub RG | 30.00 | — |
| ed. 1,000, s/o | 20.00 | — |
| ☐ **RACCOON FAMILY**, rel. 1977. ed. 500, s/n, 18½" x 25", pub RG | 40.00 | — |
| ed. 1,000, s/o | 25.00 | — |
| ☐ **DAWN FLIGHT**, rel. 1977. ed. 500, s/n, 18" x 23", pub RG | 40.00 | — |
| ed. 1,000, s/o | 25.00 | — |
| ☐ **FLAGS UP**, rel. 1978. ed. 500, s/n, 24" x 18", pub RG | 40.00 | — |
| ed. 1,000, s/o | 25.00 | — |
| ☐ **THE INTRUDER**, ed. 500, s/n, 18½" x 25½", pub RG | 20.00 | — |
| ☐ **SNOWY EGRET**, ed. 400, s/n, 11" x 17", pub RG | 20.00 | — |

|  | ISSUE PRICE | CURRENT PRICE |
|---|---|---|
| ☐ **THE WOOD DUCK,** ed. 650, s/n, 21½" x 27¾", pub RG .................. | **100.00 | Sold Out |
| **This print was proclaimed Tennessee's first Natural Areas Commemorative Edition. This edition was to help raise funds for the Save Radnor Lake Preservation Fund. | | |
| ☐ **BICENTENNIAL EDITION** | | |
| **THE AMERICAN BALD EAGLE, THE AMERICAN WILD TURKEY** | | |
| This series was commissioned by American Advertisers for special promotional distribution by them. | | |
| ed. 1,000 sets, signed and dated by artist, 12" x 15" ................... | 10.00 | — |
| ☐ **OLE BRIGHT EYES,** ed. 500, s/n, 13" x 16", pub RG .................... | 30.00 | — |
| ed. 1,000, s/o ........................................ | 15.00 | — |
| ☐ **BLUE WINGS OVER YUCATAN,** ed. 580, s/n, 19" x 24", pub RG ........... | 40.00 | — |
| ☐ **CHESAPEAKE GOLD,** ed. 580, s/n, 19" x 25", pub RG ................... | 40.00 | — |
| ☐ **BORDER WHITE WINGS,** ed. 580, s/n, 19" x 24", pub RG ................ | 40.00 | — |
| ☐ **MOURNING AT MOMOTOMBO,** ed. 580, s/n, 19" x 24", pub RG ............ | 40.00 | — |

# GUSTAVO NOVOA

| ☐ **GRAND JURY,** rel. 1980. ed. 275, s/n, 24" x 30", pub WAEL .............. | 275.00 | — |
|---|---|---|
| ☐ **PROMENADE,** rel. 1980. ed. 275, s/n, 24" x 30", pub WAEL .............. | 275.00 | — |

# CHERRIE NUTE

Cherrie Nute was born in Philadelphia and lived in Bucks County, Pennsylvania until the age of twelve when her family moved to South Carolina. Nute started drawing at the age of five, partly influenced by her mother who is an accomplished portrait artist.

Nute's first limited edition was the "Governor's Mansion" in Columbia, South Carolina. The original painting was presented to the Governor in 1975 and hung in the Mansion until recently when it was put on public display in the "Lace House" directly across from the Governor's residence.

Clemson University commission Nute to paint a "Tiger" for the athletic department in 1977 of which a limited edition was offered to the alumni.

Nute's popularity blossomed tremendously in 1980 when she started a series of historic scenes centering on Charleston, South Carolina. Each edition has sold out each year and they have gained wide acclaim with each release. Her most frequently used medium is acrylic on canvass using lovely rich colors that enhance most any environment.

## CHERRIE NUTE

| ☐ **GOVERNOR'S MANSION,** rel. 1975. ed. 1,000, s/n, 25½" x 22", pub FFFA, distr. DRN ........................................... | 25.00 | 150.00 |
|---|---|---|
| ☐ **TIGER,** rel. 1977 (through Clemson University Athletic Dept.). ed. 1,500, s/n, 24½" x 35½", pub FFFA, distr. DRN ............................ | 35.00 | 40.00 |
| ☐ **THE BATTERY,** rel. 1980. ed. 950, s/n, 26¼" x 20", pub FFFA, distr. DRN ... | — | — |
| ☐ **RAINBOW ROW,** rel. 1981. ed. 950, s/n, 26¼" x 20", pub FFFA, distr. DRN .. | 40.00 | 225.00 |
| ☐ **CHURCH STREET,** rel. 1982. ed. 950, s/n, 26¼" x 20", pub FFFA, distr. DRN | 45.00 | 125.00 |
| ☐ **SHEM CREEK,** rel. 1982. ed. 950, s/n, 22" x 17", pub FFFA, distr. DRN ..... | 40.00 | 80.00 |
| ☐ **MEETING STREET,** rel. 1983. ed. 950, s/n, 26¼" x 20", pub FFFA, distr. DRN | 50.00 | — |
| ☐ **PAWLEY'S ISLAND,** rel. 1983. ed. 950, s/n, 26¼" x 20", pub FFFA, distr. DRN ........................................... | 50.00 | — |
| ☐ **THE MARKET,** rel. 1983. ed. 950, s/n, 22" x 17", pub FFFA, distr. DRN ..... | 45.00 | — |

# GREG O'BRIEN

Greg O'Brien studied at the Pennsylvania Academy of Fine Arts. He combined his love for ancient history with a desire to express his impressions through etchings, intaglios, and lithographs. He has participated in many group exhibitions as well as several one-man shows. His work has been published in illustrative technique articles across the country. His work is represented by galleries and major corporate collections in the United States.

**THE RESURRECTION** *by Greg O'Brien*

| GREG O'BRIEN | ISSUE PRICE | CURRENT PRICE |
|---|---|---|
| ☐ **BALLOON,** ed. 150, s/n, 19″ x 30″, etch, pub EG | 70.00 | 87.50 |
| ☐ **BLACK KNIGHT, THE,** ed. 75, s/n, 16″ x 21″, intaglio, pub EG | 35.00 | 43.75 |
| ☐ **BREAKFAST IN BED,** ed. 50, s/n, 23″ x 24″, intaglio, pub EG | 40.00 | — |
| ☐ **BUCANNEER,** ed. 75, s/n, 14″ x 16″, intaglio, pub EG | 35.00 | 43.75 |
| ☐ **CAPE HATTERAS LIGHT,** ed. 75, s/n, 20″ x 24″, etch, pub EG | — | — |
| ☐ **CHEETAH,** ed. 75, s/n, 17″ x 22″, etch, pub EG | 30.00 | — |
| ☐ **CLOWN SUN MOON STAR,** ed. 100, s/n, 24″ x 28″, etch, pub EG | 60.00 | — |
| ☐ **80TH DAY, THE,** ed. 100, s/n, 20″ x 28″, intaglio, pub EG | 60.00 | — |
| ☐ **ECCE HOMO,** ed. 75, s/n, 17″ x 22″, intaglio, pub EG | 35.00 | — |
| ☐ **EGYPTIAN,** ed. 100, s/n, 24″ x 30″, etch, pub EG | N/A | — |
| ☐ **EVE,** ed. 75, s/n, 22″ x 26″, etch, pub EG | 60.00 | — |

| | ISSUE PRICE | CURRENT PRICE |
|---|---|---|
| ☐ GIZEH REVISITED, ed. 75, s/n, 18" x 20", etch, pub EG | 35.00 | — |
| ☐ GOING UNDER, ed. 75, s/n, 19" x 22", etch, pub EG | 35.00 | — |
| ☐ HALEY'S COMET, ed. 100, s/n, 20" x 32", intaglio, pub EG | 60.00 | — |
| ☐ HUNT, THE, ed. 295, s/n, 28" x 40", litho, foil embossed, pub EG | 300.00 | 375.00 |
| ☐ HUMMINGBIRD, ed. 75, s/n, 24" x 28", intaglio, pub EG | 35.00 | — |
| ☐ IMPRESSIONS OF THE NIGHT, ed. 75, s/n, 20" x 24", etch, pub EG | 50.00 | — |
| ☐ ISLES OF DESIRE, ed. 50, s/n, 15" x 20", etch, pub EG | 50.00 | — |
| ☐ KEYS TO THE UNIVERSE, ed. 100, s/n, 20" x 24", etch, pub EG | 50.00 | — |
| ☐ LIONS, ed. 100, s/n, 20" x 24", etch, pub EG | 40.00 | — |
| ☐ LOVE BLOSSOMS, ed. 150, s/n, 26" x 38", intaglio, pub EG | 60.00 | — |
| ☐ METASTOPHALIESE, ed. 75, s/n, 12" x 22", etch, pub EG | 30.00 | — |
| ☐ MOMENTS OF VICTORY, ed. 295, s/n, 28" x 40", linoleum cut, pub EG | N/A | - |
| ☐ OBEAH MAN, ed. 50, s/n, 17" x 20", intaglio, pub EG | 25.00 | — |
| ☐ O'MEGACLYPSE, ed. 50, s/n, 18" x 26", intaglio, pub EG | 45.00 | — |
| ☐ OVER THE EARTH, ed. 75, s/n, 24" x 32", intaglio, pub EG | 60.00 | — |
| ☐ RESURRECTION, THE, ed. 295, s/n, 28" x 40", linoleum cut, pub EG | 300.00 | 375.00 |
| ☐ ROMANCE IN DURANGO, ed. 75, s/n, 24" x 30", intaglio, pub EG | 60.00 | — |
| ☐ ROSCOE, ed. 100, s/n, 22" x 25", etch, pub EG | 55.00 | — |
| ☐ SELKET, ed. 100, s/n, 19" x 23", etch, pub EG | 50.00 | — |
| ☐ SENGEN SAMA, ed. 100, s/n, 20" x 23", etch, pub EG | 50.00 | — |
| ☐ SUNRISE OVER GIZEH, ed. 100, s/n, 24" x 30", intaglio, pub EG | 60.00 | — |
| ☐ UP, UP AND AWAY, ed. 100, s/n, 20" x 33", intaglio, pub EG | 60.00 | — |
| ☐ SEA OF JOY, ed. 75, s/n, 20" x 24", intaglio, pub EG | N/A | — |
| ☐ SUNNYSIDE UP, ed. 50, s/n, 19" x 23", intaglio, pub EG | 45.00 | — |
| ☐ TUTANKHAMUN, ed. 295, s/n, 28" x 40", litho, foil embossed, pub EG | N/A | — |
| ☐ WALL, THE, ed. 50, s/n, 19" x 24", etch, pub EG | 50.00 | — |

# TIM O'KANE

Tim O'Kane paints poetic images with razor-sharp details and disciplined drafts-manship. By the time O'Kane was twenty-three, he had one-man shows, group shows, and regional awards to his credit.

O'Kane has a degree in Painting and Printmaking from Virginia Commonwealth University.

## TIM O'KANE

| | | |
|---|---|---|
| ☐ SAFFRON, rel. 1974. ed. 1,500, s/o, 26" x 18", pub GW | 35.00 | — |
| *ed. 500, s/n | *45.00 | 60.00 |

# JOHN P. O'NEILL

In addition to being one of America's most talented young nature artists, John P. O'Neill is also an internationally recognized ornithologist. O'Neill created an international explosion in the bird world last fall when a UPI news flash revealed that O'Neill had sighted 14 Peruvian White-winged Guans, believed to have been extinct for 100 years. The artist-scientist's other discoveries of six previously unknown species of tropical birds provide him with impressive credentials in the science of bird study. The *New Encyclopedia Britannica* carries more than twenty of his drawings, and he has illustrated numerous articles, scientific reports, and books, the most notable of which is Richard French's *"Guide to the Birds of Trinidad and Tobago"*.

A native Texan, O'Neill studied ornithology under Dr. George M. Sutton at the University of Oklahoma, and earned his master's and doctoral degrees at Louisiana State University. His Doctoral dissertation was based on studies of birds in Peru. O'Neill is presently Curator of Higher Vertebrates at the Louisiana State University Museum of Zoology in Baton Rouge. His annual forays into the still unspoiled mountains and tropical forests of Peru, where he does his research, allow him to carry out field studies as well as make sketches and paintings of the relatively unknown birds in these areas.

O'Neill's dual sensitivity as an artist and a scientist creates national and international excitement for his beautiful gouache and watercolor portraits of American and tropical birds. He feels it is important, scientifically, to paint rare "finds", but his more popular paintings are of the lovely North American species. O'Neill's work has been shown in numerous museums and nature centers around the country.

**SCREECH OWL** *by John P. O'Neill*

### JOHN P. O'NEILL

| | ISSUE PRICE | CURRENT PRICE |
|---|---|---|
| ☐ SCREECH OWL, rel. 1978. ed. 950, s/n, 21½" x 16", pub MPPI . . . . . . . . . . | 45.00 | — |
| ☐ PYGMY OWL, rel. 1978. ed. 950, s/n, 20¼" x 15", pub MPPI . . . . . . . . . . . . | 40.00 | — |

# BILL OWEN

Bill Owen, a Western artist, is a self taught painter.

He works in various media including oil, pencil, pen and ink, and bronze.

Owen is a member of the Cowboy Artists of America. He is a recipient of the Franklin Mint Gold Medal presented by the Franklin Mint Gallery of American Art for Western Art.

### BILL OWEN

| | | |
|---|---|---|
| ☐ SPRING WATER, rel. 1976. ed. 1,000, s/n, 23½" x 33", pub FHG . . . . . . . . . | 100.00 | — |
| ☐ THE LAST ONE, rel. 1976. ed. 250, s/n, 21½" x 39", pub FHG . . . . . . . . . . . | 100.00 | Sold Out |

| | ISSUE PRICE | CURRENT PRICE |
|---|---|---|
| ☐ **SINCE SUNUP,** rel. 1977. ed. 250, s/n, 22″ x 30″, pub FHG............. | 100.00 | — |
| ☐ **CO BAR AT WUPATKI,** rel. 1979. ed. 2,250, s/n, 21½″ x 17″, pub TAP...... | 100.00 | — |
| ☐ **HOLDING UP FOR THE DRAGS,** rel. 1980. ed. 1,000, s/n, 20″ x 30″, pub SCG. | 115.00 | — |
| ☐ **NO PLACE FOR A GUNSEL,** rel. 1980. ed. 1,000, s/n, 22″ x 30″, pub SCG.... | 115.00 | — |
| ☐ **RIMFIRED,** rel. 1980. ed. 1,000, s/n, 21″ x 28″, pub SCG ................ | 115.00 | — |
| ☐ **A LITTLE ENCOURAGEMENT,** rel. 1981. ed. 1,000, s/n, 16″ x 24″, pub SCG.. | 115.00 | — |
| ☐ **MAKING A CUT AT WILD BILL,** rel. 1981. ed. 1,000, s/n, 18″ x 36″, pub SCG. | 115.00 | — |

# FRANK PANABAKER

With a sure hand, the well-known Canadian artist Frank Panabaker paints the powerful rhythms of landscapes in a loose, confident style. For harmonious compositions he scours quiet countrysides from the Atlantic to the Rockies; the British Isles; the great northern forests; Bermuda and Nassau. His landscape paintings are done on location.

He studied with McGillivary Knowles, R.C.A., and then at the Ontario College of Art, Grand Central School of Art, and the Art Students League.

An artist member of the Salmagundi Club, he is a member of the Royal Canadian Academy and former trustee of the National Gallery of Ottawa.

**FRESH SNOW** by Frank Panabaker

## FRANK PANABAKER

| | ISSUE PRICE | CURRENT PRICE |
|---|---|---|
| ☐ **MAPLE SUGARING**, rel. 1980. ed. 950, s/n, 20″ x 24¾″, pub MPPI . . . . . . . . | 75.00 | — |
| ☐ **NORTHWEST WINDS**, rel. 1980. ed. 950, s/n, 20″ x 24¾″, pub MPPI . . . . . . | 75.00 | — |
| ☐ **WINDY ISLAND**, rel. 1980. ed. 950, s/n, 15¾″ x 18¼″, pub MPPI . . . . . . . . . | 60.00 | — |
| ☐ **WINTER IN THE WOODS**, rel. 1980. ed. 950, s/n, 19¾″ x 24″, pub MPPI . . . . | 75.00 | — |
| ☐ **A WINTER FARM**, rel. 1981. ed. 950, s/n, 15¾″ x 18¼″, pub MPPI . . . . . . . . | 60.00 | — |
| ☐ **FRESH SNOW**, rel. 1981. ed. 950, s/n, 19¾″ x 23⅛″, pub MPPI . . . . . . . . . . . | 75.00 | — |
| ☐ **GOLDEN OCTOBER**, rel. 1981. ed. 950, s/n, 20″ x 24½″, pub MPPI . . . . . . . . . | 75.00 | — |

# DINO PARAVANO

Dino Paravano was born in 1935, and has lived in Africa since 1947. Taught by his father, he started painting at an early age, and continued his studies at the Johannesburg School of Art.

Since 1967 Paravano has concentrated on the painting of African wildlife and devotes much of his time to the study of these animals. He travels in the wilds of Botswana, Rhodesia, the Stosha Pan in southwest Africa, observing and sketching, and has had numerous close encounters with them.

Paravano is deeply involved with the preservation of wildlife in its natural environment, and is a member of the African Wildlife Society and a fellow of the Endangered Cheetah Preservation Trust. Since 1969 he has held many highly successful wildlife exhibitions throughout the world.

## DINO PARAVANO

| | | |
|---|---|---|
| ☐ **REGAL DOMAN**, rel. 1979. ed. 950, s/n, 23″ x 35″, pub SEL . . . . . . . . . . . . . | 110.00 | — |
| ☐ **SPRINGBOK**, rel. 1979. ed. 950, s/n, 19¼″ x 29″, pub SEL . . . . . . . . . . . . . . | 90.00 | — |

# RON S. PARKER

Ron Parker, one of the newest and most exciting talents in the field of wildlife art is a native of Vancouver, British Columbia.

Parker showed above normal talent in art as a child, which was not surprising since both parents had artistic abilities. However, as a six-footer in eighth grade, his future seemed to be in basketball. He was the 1966 Canada Decathlon Champion.

After obtaining a degree in education, Parker worked in track and field administration.

But his desire to be an artist overshadowed his education career. Today, Parker is a fine professional artist who paints with watercolors.

## RON S. PARKER

| | | |
|---|---|---|
| ☐ **RACCOON PAIR**, rel. 1982. ed. 950, s/n, 21⅝″ x 17¼″, pub MPPI . . . . . . . . . | 95.00 | 120.00 |
| ☐ **RAIDING THE CACHE**, rel. 1982. ed. 950, s/n, 19⅝″ x 15¾″, pub MPPI . . . . . | 95.00 | — |
| ☐ **SNOW ON THE PINE - CHICKADEES**, rel. 1982. ed. 950, s/n, 21½″ x 17½″, pub MPPI . . . . . . . . . . . . . . . . . . . . . . . . . . . . . . . . . . . . . . . . . . . . . . . . . . | 95.00 | 110.00 |
| ☐ **SPRING MIST — GRAY WOLF**, rel. 1982. ed. 950, s/n, 22⅞″ x 31½″, pub MPPI . . . . . . . . . . . . . . . . . . . . . . . . . . . . . . . . . . . . . . . . . . . . . . . . . . | 155.00 | Sold Out |
| ☐ **WEATHERED WOOD - BLUEBIRDS**, rel. 1982. ed. 950, s/n, 17¾″ x 14¾″, pub MPPI . . . . . . . . . . . . . . . . . . . . . . . . . . . . . . . . . . . . . . . . . . . . . . . . . . | 75.00 | 95.00 |
| ☐ **FAT AND SASSY - ROBIN**, rel. 1983. ed. 950, s/n, 17½″ x 21¼″, pub MPPI . . | 95.00 | — |
| ☐ **MALLARD FAMILY**, rel. 1983. ed. 950, s/n, 17½″ x 21½″, pub MPPI . . . . . . . | 95.00 | — |
| ☐ **MOUNTAIN BLOOMS - GROUND SQUIRREL**, rel. 1983. ed. 950, s/n, 15″ x 12″, pub MPPI . . . . . . . . . . . . . . . . . . . . . . . . . . . . . . . . . . . . . . . . . . . . . . | 50.00 | — |
| ☐ **RED SQUIRREL**, rel. 1983. ed. 950, s/n, 12″ x 14⅝″, pub MPPI . . . . . . . . . . | 65.00 | — |
| ☐ **RIVERSIDE PAUSE - RIVER OTTER**, rel. 1983. ed. 950, s/n, 22¾″ x 17½″, pub MPPI . . . . . . . . . . . . . . . . . . . . . . . . . . . . . . . . . . . . . . . . . . . . . . . . . . | 95.00 | — |

**SNOW ON THE PINE – CHICKADEE** *by Ron Parker*

## PETER PARNALL

Peter Parnall's special fascination is with animal behavior. He has raised and studied dozens of wild creatures including hawks, owls, and raccoons. His drawings portray not only the look of bird or beast, but the animal's essential nature whether shy, bold, predatory or secretive. "I try," he says, "to get the essence of the animal — its temperament and personality."

Parnall's talent for design led him from being a veterinarian, to the life of an editorial and advertising art director in New York City. Living today in Maine on a farm, Parnall says, "In one form or another, animals take up most of my time. If I'm not drawing them, I'm training them."

Parnall has illustrated over 80 books, some of which he has also authored, and has won many awards from the American Institute of Graphic Arts.

| PETER PARNALL | ISSUE PRICE | CURRENT PRICE |
|---|---|---|
| ☐ **FOX,** rel. 1972. ed. 1,500. s/n, 28″ x 21″, pub GW | 60.00 | 150.00 |
| ☐ **HORSEHEAD,** rel. 1972. ed. 1,500, s/n, 28″ x 20″, pub GW | 60.00 | Sold Out |
| ☐ **PIGMY OWL,** rel. 1972. ed. 1,500, s/n, 22″ x 17″, pub GW | 30.00 | 180.00 |
| ☐ **RICHARDSON'S OWL,** rel. 1972. ed. 1,500, s/n, 22″ x 17″, pub GW | 30.00 | 215.00 |
| ☐ **GOSHAWK,** rel. 1973. ed. 1,500, s/n, 17″ x 22″, pub GW | 35.00 | 110.00 |
| ☐ **OSPREY,** rel. 1973. ed. 1,500, s/n, 26″ x 18″, pub GW | 45.00 | 125.00 |
| ☐ **SHORT-EARED OWL,** rel. 1973. ed. 1,500, s/n, 22″ x 17″, pub GW | 30.00 | 175.00 |

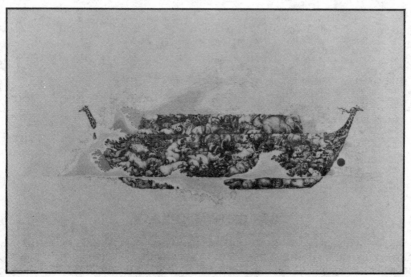

**NOAH'S ARK** *by Peter Parnall*

| | ISSUE PRICE | CURRENT PRICE |
|---|---|---|
| ☐ YOUNG SAW-WHET OWLS, rel. 1973. ed. 1,500, s/n, 22" x 17", pub GW .... | 30.00 | 285.00 |
| ☐ BEE, rel. 1974. ed. 1,000, s/n, 14" x 14", pub GW | 45.00 | 385.00 |
| ☐ BUFFALO SUN, rel. 1974. ed. 1,000, s/n, 31" x 17", pub GW | 45.00 | 375.00 |
| ☐ SANCTUARY, rel. 1974. ed. 1,000, s/n, 17" x 22", pub GW | 45.00 | 125.00 |
| ☐ COYOTE PUPS, rel. 1975. ed. 1,000, s/n, 26" x 19", pub GW | 50.00 | 215.00 |
| ☐ FROG, rel. 1975. ed. 1,000, s/n, 14" x 14", pub GW | 45.00 | 210.00 |
| ☐ GOLDFINCH, rel. 1975. ed. 1,000, s/n, 14" x 14", pub GW | 45.00 | 170.00 |
| ☐ PEREGRINE FALCON, rel. 1975. ed. 500, s/n, 29" x 17", pub GW | 45.00 | 110.00 |
| ed. 1,000, s/n, for Cornell Laboratory of Ornithology | *55.00 | — |
| *Includes one year membership to Laboratory. Proceeds to their ongoing Ornithological Study Programs. | | |
| ☐ ELF OWL, rel. 1976. ed. 1,000, s/n, 22" x 17", pub GW | 35.00 | 155.00 |
| ☐ HONEYCOMB, rel. 1976. ed. 1,000, s/n, 22½" x 14¾", pub GW | 55.00 | — |
| ☐ RACCOON, rel. 1976. ed. 1,000, s/n, 20" x 29¾", pub GW | 50.00 | 140.00 |
| ☐ RIVER OTTER, rel. 1976. ed. 1,000, s/n, 29" x 17", pub GW | 50.00 | 140.00 |
| ☐ SEA OTTERS, rel. 1976. ed. 1,000, s/n, 31" x 17", pub GW | 50.00 | 475.00 |
| ☐ SPERM WHALE, rel. 1976. ed. 1,000, s/n, 31" x 17", pub GW | 50.00 | 525.00 |
| ☐ ADELIE PENGUINS, rel. 1977. ed. 1,000, s/n, 18" x 26", pub GW | 50.00 | 95.00 |
| ☐ BLUE WHALE, rel. 1977. ed. 1,500, s/n, 30½" x 20½", pub GW | 55.00 | 190.00 |
| ☐ BUTTERFLY, rel. 1977. ed. 1,500, s/n, 14" x 14", pub GW | 45.00 | 180.00 |
| ☐ HARBOR SEAL, rel. 1977. ed. 1,000, s/n, 30" x 17", pub GW | 55.00 | 160.00out |
| ☐ ROADRUNNER, rel. 1977. ed. 1,000, s/n, 30" x 17", pub GW | 55.00 | 90.00 |
| ☐ CALIFORNIA QUAIL, rel. 1978. ed. 1,500, s/n, 30" x 15½", pub GW | 60.00 | Sold Out |
| ☐ CHICKADEES, rel. 1978. ed. 1,500, s/n, 18" x 26", pub GW | 55.00 | 115.00 |
| ☐ DEAD-END MOLE, rel. 1978. ed. 1,500, s/n, 14" x 14", pub GW | 45.00 | 100.00 |
| ☐ HUMPBACK WHALE, rel. 1978. ed. 1,500, s/n, 14¼" x 21", pub GW | 55.00 | 170.00 |
| ☐ SNOWY OWL, rel. 1978. ed. 1,500, s/n, 28" x 20", pub GW | 60.00 | 80.00 |
| ☐ BARN OWL, rel. 1979. ed. 1,500, s/n, 17" x 20¼", pub GW | 60.00 | 90.00 |
| ☐ BISON, rel. 1979. ed. 1,500, s/n, 33" x 16¾", pub GW | 65.00 | 90.00 |
| ☐ HARP SEAL, rel. 1979. ed. 1,500, s/n, 30" x 17", pub GW | 55.00 | 105.00 |
| ☐ RIGHT WHALE, rel. 1979. ed. 2,000, s/n, 22" x 14½", pub GW | 60.00 | 90.00 |
| 500 of edition was sold through Center for Environmental Education, Washington, D.C.; net proceeds to the Whale Protection Fund | 60.00 | 90.00 |
| ☐ GREAT HORNED OWL, rel. 1980. ed. 1,500, s/n, 17" x 20½", pub GW | 60.00 | Sold Out |

| | ISSUE PRICE | CURRENT PRICE |
|---|---|---|
| ☐ **LADYBUGS**, rel. 1980. ed. 1,650, s/n, 14" x 14", pub GW . . . . . . . . . . . . . . | 60.00 | 80.00 |
| 150 sold through the Ohio Historical Society, Columbus, Ohio; net proceeds to their ongoing Natural History programs. | | |
| ☐ **ORCA**, rel. 1980. ed. 1,500, s/n, 18¼" x 25", pub GW . . . . . . . . . . . . . . . . . | 85.00 | 120.00 |
| ☐ **PELICAN**, rel. 1980. ed. 1,500, s/n, 17½" x 27", pub GW . . . . . . . . . . . . . . | 70.00 | 95.00 |
| ☐ **THE ALARM**, rel. 1980. ed. 350, signed, titled and numbered, 30½" x 23¼", hand-drawn lithograph, pub GW . . . . . . . . . . . . . . . . . . . . . . . . . . . . . . | 195.00 | — |
| ☐ **AFRICAN SUN**, rel. 1981. ed. 1,000, s/n, 29" x 19½", pub GW . . . . . . . . . . | 125.00 | Sold Out |
| ☐ **BOTTLENOSE PORPOISE**, rel. 1981. ed. 1,000, s/n, 31" x 17", pub GW . . . . . . | 125.00 | — |
| ☐ **MARSH HARBOR COONS**, rel. 1981. ed. 1,500, s/n, 22" x 26½", pub GW . . . | 95.00 | Sold Out |
| ☐ **OWL'S NEST**, rel. 1981. ed. 1,000, s/n, 30" x 19", pub GW . . . . . . . . . . . . . | 95.00 | — |
| ☐ **POLAR BEAR**, rel. 1981. ed. 1,500, s/n, 31" x 18¼", pub GW . . . . . . . . . . . | 95.00 | Sold Out |
| ☐ **ELEPHANTS**, rel. 1982. ed. 1,000, s/n, 19" x 19½", pub GW . . . . . . . . . . . . | 125.00 | — |
| ☐ **HORNED OWL SUN**, rel. 1982. ed. 1,250, s/n, 20⅝" x 21⅛", pub GW . . . . . . . | 95.00 | — |
| ☐ **RECESS**, rel. 1982. ed. 1,000, s/n, 31" x 14", serigraph, pub GW . . . . . . . . . . | 125.00 | — |
| ☐ **MONUMENT VALLEY SUN**, rel. 1983. ed. 1,000, s/n, 23" x 13½", pub GW . . | 95.00 | — |
| ☐ **NOAH'S ARK**, rel. 1983. ed. 2,500, s/n, 30⅜" x 18¼", pub GW . . . . . . . . . . | 60.00 | — |

# GREGORY PERILLO

For more than 20 years, Gregory Perillo has used artistic talents to portray the American West as it was in the 1800s. His paintings, lithographs, and bronzes, showing the nobility of the Indian and the rugged life of the cowboy, have won him recognition as "Artist of the American West".

Although Perillo is often mistaken for an Indian, he is actually a first-generation Italian-American. His love affair with the West and his talent for drawing and painting began early in his life.

His father, a lover of fine art, spent many weekends with his son visiting New York's art galleries and museums.

As Perillo's talent began to grow during the Depression years, his mother would iron brown paper bags for the budding artist to paint on.

Perillo did not actually visit the West until 1949, while in the Navy. One of his shipmates invited him to visit his home in Montana. While hitchhiking to Butte, Perillo was impressed with the incredible beauty of the Western landscape.

"It was my first time ever in such wide open space," he recalls, "and I was simply astounded at the breathtaking beauty of it all."

In the early 1950s, out of the Navy and newly married, Gregory Perillo again visited the West. There he met the man who was to have a profound effect on his career, William Robinson Leigh, one of the 20th century's greatest Western artists.

The master was impressed by what he saw in the young man's sketchbook. Several months later, Perillo began a series of hour-long lessons with Leigh. "They consisted of my working and his criticizing," Perillo recalls.

Guided by Leigh, Perillo learned to draw from life. "Sketch fast," Leigh would say, "to capture the spirit." Horses were especially difficult for the new artist, but he worked hard at them, "because I knew I couldn't very well be a Western painter without being able to do a good horse."

During his period of study under Leigh, Perillo also undertook formal art study at Pratt Institute, the School of Visual Arts, and the Art Students League in New York.

Since those early days, he has made numerous trips to the West to observe the country and the life and action of its inhabitants. He stores all these scenes in memory and vividly recreates them back in his Staten Island studio.

Although recognized as one of the foremost painters of North American wild-life, Perillo has turned his attention to non-western subjects such as the wildlife of Africa. His recent masterpiece, "Peaceable Kingdom," combines both North American and African wildlife in a new translation of the often painted biblical theme.

In recent years, the art of Gregory Perillo has been discovered by a wave of collectors, who have flocked to acquire his limited edition lithographs, bronze plaques, porcelain plates and hand-painted figurines, produced by Vague Shadows Limited.

Perillo is listed in the *Who's Who of Western Art*. His work has been shown in numerous one-man shows at such prestigious galleries as Wally Findlay Galleries in New York, Palm Beach and Beverly Hills and G. Harvey in Austin, Texas.

Perillo oils hang in the permanent collections of the Pettigrew Museum, Sioux Falls, South Dakota; the Denver Museum of Natural History, and the University of New Mexico.

Recently, Gregory Perillo was named "Artist of the Year" by the National Association of Limited Edition Dealers.

**HOOFBEATS** *by Gregory Perillo*

## GREGORY PERILLO

| | ISSUE PRICE | CURRENT PRICE |
|---|---|---|
| ☐ **MADRE**, rel. 1977. ed. 500, s/n, 22" x 28", pub VSL | 125.00 | 300.00 |
| ☐ **MADONNA OF THE PLAINS**, rel. 1978. ed. 500, s/n, 22" x 28", pub VSL | 125.00 | 250.00 |
| ☐ **SIOUX SCOUT and BUFFALO HUNT**, rel. 1978. ed. 500, s/n, 18" x 22", pub VSL | *75.00 Each | — |
| *To be sold as matched number sets | 150.00 Set | 300.00 |
| ☐ **SNOW PALS**, rel. 1978. ed. 500, s/n, 22" x 28", pub VSL | 125.00 | 250.00 |
| ☐ **BABYSITTER**, rel. 1979. ed. 3,000, s/n, 16" x 20", pub VSL | 45.00 | — |
| ☐ **PUPPIES**, rel. 1979. ed. 3,000, s/n, 16" x 20", pub VSL | 45.00 | — |
| ☐ **LONESOME COWBOY**, rel. 1980. ed. 950, s/n, size not available, pub VSL | 75.00 | — |
| ☐ **TENDER LOVE**, rel. 1980. ed. 950, s/n, size not available, pub VSL | 75.00 | — |
| ☐ **CHIEF PONTIAC**, rel. 1981. ed. 950, s/n, size not available, pub VSL | 75.00 | — |
| ☐ **PEACEABLE KINGDOM**, rel. 1981. ed. 950, s/n, 29" x 23", pub VSL | 100.00 | 150.00 |
| ☐ **MARIA**, rel. 1981. ed. 550, s/n, size not available, pub VSL | 150.00 | — |
| ☐ **TINKER**, rel. 1981. ed. 3,000, s/n, 24" x 20", pub VSL | 45.00 | — |

| | ISSUE PRICE | CURRENT PRICE |
|---|---|---|
| ☐ **HOOFBEATS**, rel. 1982. ed. 950, s/n, 29" x 23", pub VSL . . . . . . . . . . . . . . . | 75.00 | — |
| ☐ **INDIAN STYLE**, rel. 1982. ed. 950, s/n, size not available, pub VSL . . . . . . . . . | 75.00 | — |
| ☐ **FLOWERS FOR GRANDMA**, rel. 1983. ed. 475, s/n, size not available, pub VSL | — | — |

# TOM PERKINSON

Tom Perkinson was born in Indianapolis, Indiana in 1940, and spent his early childhood in rural Indiana. He attended the John Herron Art Institute in Indianapolis from 1959-1960. Tom graduated with a B.S. degree in Art from Oklahoma Baptist University in 1964 and received his Master of Arts in Drawing from the University of New Mexico in 1968; his degree was the first ever granted in Drawing by the University.

Tom has spent the last 15 years living and traveling in the Southwest Region of the United States. In 1975 he and his family, wife Louise and daughter Sara, settled in Norman, Oklahoma.

Tom Perkinson's art is unique in that in any one painting he may combine watercolor, colored pencil, ink and transparent watercolor. He will use whatever medium he feels will enhance the painting. Tom has a significant following in the Southwestern and Western regions of the United States. His works are in the most important collections.

## TOM PERKINSON

| | | |
|---|---|---|
| ☐ **CHANGING WEATHER**, ed. 1500, s/n, 10" x 15½", pub PSGI . . . . . . . . . . . . | 35.00 | — |
| ☐ **ORANGE SKY**, ed. 1000, s/n, 17½" x 24½", pub PSGI . . . . . . . . . . . . . . . . . | 80.00 | — |
| ☐ **YELLOW HILLS**, ed. 1000, s/n, 19¼" x 22½", pub PSGI . . . . . . . . . . . . . . . | 80.00 | — |

# ROGER TORY PETERSON

Roger Tory Peterson attended the Art Students League in New York and later the National Academy of Design. He then became an instructor of art and science at the Rivers School in Brookline, Massachusetts.

During this time he developed his unique system for identifying birds in the field. In 1934, after rejection by five publishers, his first *Field Guide to the Birds* was published by Houghton Mifflin. With that publication his life became a whirlwind of activity. He has continued to paint, write, lecture and travel to remote corners of the world to record rare and exotic species of birds. Since then he has written fourteen books.

Peterson has been awarded eleven honorary doctorates and numerous awards and medals including the Presidential Medal of Freedom, the nation's highest civilian honor. Peterson has made a series of motion pictures, lectured, and is a special consultant to the Audubon Society.

## ROGER TORY PETERSON

| | | |
|---|---|---|
| ☐ **BALTIMORE ORIOLE**, rel. 1973. ed. 450, s/n, 18" x 18", pub MPPI . . . . . . . . | 150.00 | 300.00 |
| ☐ **CARDINAL**, rel. 1973. ed. 450, s/n, 18" x 18", pub MPPI . . . . . . . . . . . . . . . | 150.00 | 550.00 |
| ☐ **FLICKER**, rel. 1973. ed. 450, s/n, 18" x 18", pub MPPI . . . . . . . . . . . . . . . | 150.00 | 300.00 |
| ☐ **WOOD THRUSH**, rel. 1973. ed. 450, s/n, 18" x 18", pub MPPI . . . . . . . . . . . | 150.00 | 375.00 |
| ☐ **BALD EAGLE**, rel. 1974. ed. 950, s/n, 31" x 22½", pub MPPI . . . . . . . . . . . | 150.00 | 475.00 |
| ☐ **BARN SWALLOW**, rel. 1974. ed. 750, s/n, 20" x 20", pub MPPI . . . . . . . . . . | 150.00 | 200.00 |
| ☐ **BOB-O-LINK**, rel. 1974. ed. 750, s/n, 20" x 20", pub MPPI . . . . . . . . . . . . . | 150.00 | 200.00 |
| ☐ **GREAT HORNED OWL**, rel. 1974. ed. 950, s/n, 31" x 22½", pub MPPI . . . . . . | 150.00 | 800.00 |
| ☐ **BARN OWL**, rel. 1975. ed. 950, s/n, 38" x 25", pub MPPI . . . . . . . . . . . . . . | 225.00 | — |
| ☐ **BOBWHITE**, rel. 1975. ed. 950, s/n, 31" x 22½", pub MPPI . . . . . . . . . . . . . | 150.00 | 375.00 |

**GREAT HORNED OWL** *by Roger Tory Peterson*

| | ISSUE PRICE | CURRENT PRICE |
|---|---|---|
| ☐ **FUR SEALS**, rel. 1975. ed. 950, s/n, 11″ x 14″, pub MPPI . . . . . . . . . . . . . . . | 25.00 | Sold Out |
| ☐ **JAYS - COLOR PLATE #30**, rel. 1975. ed. 450, s/n, 21½″ x 14″, pub MPPI . . . | 150.00 | — |
| ☐ **OWLS - COLOR PLATE #16**, rel. 1975. ed. 750, s/n, 21½″ x 14″, pub MPPI . . | 150.00 | — |
| ☐ **RUFFED GROUSE**, rel. 1975. ed. 950, s/n, 31″ x 22½″, pub MPPI . . . . . . . . . | 150.00 | 425.00 |
| ☐ **SEA OTTERS**, rel. 1975. ed. 950, s/n, 11″ x 14″, pub MPPI . . . . . . . . . . . . . | 25.00 | 65.00 |
| ☐ **ADELIE PENGUINS**, rel. 1976. ed. 950, s/n, 14″ x 11″, pub MPPI . . . . . . . . . | 35.00 | 70.00 |
| ☐ **BLUE JAY**, rel. 1976. ed. 950, s/n, 22½″ x 29″, pub MPPI . . . . . . . . . . . . . . | 150.00 | 200.00 |
| ☐ **GOLDEN EAGLE**, rel. 1976. ed. 950, s/n, 31″ x 22½″, pub MPPI . . . . . . . . . . | 200.00 | 250.00 |
| ☐ **QUAIL - COLOR PLATE #9**, rel. 1976. ed. 950, s/n, 21½″ x 14″, pub MPPI . . . | 150.00 | — |
| ☐ **ROADRUNNER**, rel. 1976. ed. 950, s/n, 22½″ x 31″, pub MPPI . . . . . . . . . . . | 175.00 | — |
| ☐ **SNOWY OWL**, rel. 1976. ed. 950, s/n, 31″ x 22½″, pub MPPI . . . . . . . . . . . . | 175.00 | 575.00 |
| ☐ **BLUEBIRD**, rel. 1977. ed. 950, s/n, 16¼″ x 14″, pub MPPI . . . . . . . . . . . . . . | 75.00 | 250.00 |
| ☐ **PEREGRINE FALCON**, rel. 1977. ed. 950, s/n, 31″ x 22½″, pub MPPI . . . . . . . | 175.00 | 300.00 |
| ☐ **ROBIN**, rel. 1977. ed. 950, s/n, 19½″ x 16½″, pub MPPI . . . . . . . . . . . . . . . | 125.00 | 325.00 |
| ☐ **SCARLET TANAGER**, rel. 1977. ed. 950, s/n, 19½″ x 16½″, pub MPPI . . . . . . | 125.00 | 200.00 |
| ☐ **SOOTY TERN**, rel. 1977. ed. 450, s/n, 14″ x 11″, pub MPPI . . . . . . . . . . . . . | 50.00 | 85.00 |
| ☐ **WILD ORCHIDS AND TRILLIUMS**, rel. 1977. ed. 450, s/n, 21½″ x 14″, pub MPPI . . . . . . . . . . . . . . . . . . . . . . . . . . . . . . . . . . . . . . . . . | 75.00 | — |
| ☐ **WILLET**, rel. 1977. ed. 450, s/n, 14″ x 11″, pub MPPI . . . . . . . . . . . . . . . . | 50.00 | 85.00 |
| ☐ **MOCKINGBIRD**, rel. 1978. ed. 950, s/n, 19½″ x 16½″, pub MPPI . . . . . . . . . | 125.00 | 275.00 |
| ☐ **RING-NECK PHEASANT**, rel. 1978. ed. 950, s/n, 25″ x 35″, pub MPPI . . . . . . | 200.00 | 250.00 |
| ☐ **ROSE-BREASTED GROSBEAK**, rel. 1978. ed. 950, s/n, 19½″ x 16½″, pub MPPI . . . . . . . . . . . . . . . . . . . . . . . . . . . . . . . . . . . . . . . . . | 125.00 | — |
| ☐ **SHOWY WAYSIDE FLOWERS**, rel. 1978. ed. 450, s/n, 21½″ x 14″, pub MPPI . | 75.00 | — |

| | ISSUE PRICE | CURRENT PRICE |
|---|---|---|
| ☐ **GYRFALCON**, rel. 1979. ed. 950, s/n, 33" x 25", pub MPPI . . . . . . . . . . . . . . | 225.00 | 300.00 |
| ☐ **PUFFIN**, rel. 1979. ed. 950, s/n, 23" x 31½", pub MPPI . . . . . . . . . . . . . . . | 175.00 | — |
| ☐ **WILD TURKEYS**, rel. 1981. ed. 950, s/n, 24½" x 34¼", pub MPPI . . . . . . . . | 195.00 | — |
| ☐ **ARCTIC PAIR — SNOWY OWL**, rel. 1983. ed. 950, s/n, 35¾" x 24½", pub MPPI . . . . . . . . . . . . . . . . . . . . . . . . . . . . . . . . . . . . . . . . . . . . . . . . . . . . | 245.00 | — |

# CARL PHELPS

"Every animal is beautiful in its own way. I want to preserve, through my paintings, what someday might be extinct and gone forever." With this philosophy to guide him, Carl Phelps is rapidly establishing himself as one of the foremost wildlife artists specializing in baby animals and birds.

Already recognized as one of Iowa's most distinguished artists, Mr. Phelps is establishing himself nationally through magazine covers and prints. Currently residing in Marion, Iowa, Phelps' originals are on display in galleries throughout the United States.

## CARL PHELPS

| | | ISSUE PRICE | CURRENT PRICE |
|---|---|---|---|
| ☐ **BABY CHICKADEES**, ed. 500, s/n, 2,500 s/o . . . . . . . . . . . . . . . . . . . . . . . | s/n | 30.00 | — |
| 20" x 14", pub GSP . . . . . . . . . . . . . . . . . . . . . . . . . . . . . . . . . . . . . . . . . . | s/o | 20.00 | — |
| ☐ **BABY RABBIT**, ed. 500, s/n, 2,500 s/o . . . . . . . . . . . . . . . . . . . . . . . . . . | s/n | 30.00 | — |
| 14" x 18", pub GSP . . . . . . . . . . . . . . . . . . . . . . . . . . . . . . . . . . . . . . . . . . | s/o | 20.00 | — |
| ☐ **FOX CUBS**, ed. 500, s/n, 2,500 s/o . . . . . . . . . . . . . . . . . . . . . . . . . . . . | s/n | 30.00 | — |
| 16" x 22", pub GSP . . . . . . . . . . . . . . . . . . . . . . . . . . . . . . . . . . . . . . . . . . | s/o | 20.00 | — |
| ☐ **YOUNG COTTONTAILS**, ed. 500, s/n, 2,500 s/o . . . . . . . . . . . . . . . . . . . | s/n | 30.00 | — |
| 18" x 15", pub GSP . . . . . . . . . . . . . . . . . . . . . . . . . . . . . . . . . . . . . . . . . . | s/o | 20.00 | — |

# WILLIAM S. PHILLIPS

"In my work, I hope to convey to the viewer the beauty and exhilaration of flight." Bill Phillips' words speak of a goal which he renews with each painting. Phillips is a young artist, born in 1945, but is already a member of the Air Force Art Program, and his works hang in numerous public and private collections throughout the world. He's logged hours in F106's, F-25's, RF-4's, to name a few, and spent a tour of duty in the Air Force, which included an assignment at Tan Son Nhut, Vietnam.

Never believing he could make a career of art, however, Phillips chose to major in criminology in college and had been accepted into law school. One afternoon he hung four of his paintings in a restaurant; before the third was up he had sold them all. That was all it took to convince him that his future lay not in legal practice but aviation art.

## WILLIAM S. PHILLIPS

| | ISSUE PRICE | CURRENT PRICE |
|---|---|---|
| ☐ **ADVANTAGE EAGLE**, rel. 1982. ed. 1,000, s/n, 27½" x 22½", pub GW . . . . . . | 135.00 | — |
| ☐ **WELCOME HOME YANK**, rel. 1982. ed. 1,000, s/n, 27½" x 22½", pub GW . . | 135.00 | — |
| ☐ **THE GIANT BEGINS TO STIR**, rel. 1983. ed. 1,250 signed and numbered by the artist, Gen. James H. Doolittle, and 15 Aviators who participated in the Raid Over Tokyo, 29¼" x 23½", pub GW. . . . . . . . . . . . . . . . . . . . . . . . . . . . . . | 185.00 | Sold Out |
| ☐ **THOSE CLOUDS WON'T HELP YOU NOW**, rel. 1983. ed. 625, s/n by artist and countersigned by Marine Corps Ace Marion E. Carl, 27½" x 22½", pub GW . . . | 135.00 | — |
| ☐ **THOSE CLOUDS WON'T HELP YOU NOW**, ed. 25, signed/numbered/countersigned and double remarqued, 27½" x 22½", pub GW . . . . . . . . . . . . . . . . . | 275.00 | Sold Out |

**THE GIANT BEGINS TO STIR** *by Bill Phillips*

# DIANE PIERCE

Diane Pierce has been a free-lance painter, sculptor, lecturer, and illustrator for the past 15 years, specializing in birds.

Being one of the few women to attain prominence as a wildlife artist, she is self-taught except for training in design. Having raised and worked with over a hundred species of birds — from Golden Eagles and owls, ducks and geese, grebes and rails, quail and turkeys, and songbirds, has given given her an extensive background for interpretation and portrayal of avian behavior.

Ms. Pierce is listed in *Who's Who in American Women, The Worlds Who's Who in Women, Dictionary of International Biographies, Who's Who in American Art* . . . Her work has been published in numerous conservation and scientific publications and journals - *Audubon, Ducks Unlimited, The Living Bird of Cornell Laboratory of Ornithology* . . . Pierce belongs to and supports over twenty-five conservation organizations.

Pierce was the first woman to win a state duck stamp contest - Indiana in 1979, and then won the 1980 Long Island Waterfowl Stamp Contest.

In 1979, she was invited to judge the World Championship Wildfowl Carving Competition. Exhibitions and juried shows include; Salisbiry Waterfowl Festival, Easton Waterfowl Festival Society of Animal Artists, International Exhibit of Wildbird Artists, Game Conservation International. . .

Over 500 of her paintings are in private collections internationally. In 1981 she was sent to New Dehli, India to personally present a painting of Siberian Cranes, she was commissioned to do, to Prime Minister Indira Ghandi during the Conference on Internationally Trade of Endangered Species.

Today she resides at the edge of an aquatic preserve near Bonita Springs, Florida, at her studio, Edge of the Wild.

**GOLDEN EAGLES WITH YOUNG** by Diane Pierce

| DIANE PIERCE | ISSUE PRICE | CURRENT PRICE |
|---|---|---|
| **SINGLE COLOR - Brown & White.** | | |
| ☐ SCRATCHBOARD OWLS* - rel. 1973. | | |
| Barn Owl, ed. 500, s/n, 14" x 18", pub EDTW ........................ | 5.00 | 20.00 |
| Great Horned Owl, ed. 500, s/n, 14" x 18", pub EDTW ................. | 5.00 | 20.00 |
| Saw Whet Owl, ed. 500, s/n, 14" x 18", pub EDTW .................... | 5.00 | 25.00 |
| Screech Owl, ed. 500, s/n, 14" x 18", pub EDTW .................... | 5.00 | Sold Out |
| 50 of each donated to Charity. | | |
| ☐ SCRATCHBOARD ANIMALS - rel. 1975. | | |
| Chipmunks, ed. 500, s/n, 11" x 14", pub EDTW ...................... | 5.00 | — |
| Cottontail, ed. 500, s/n, 10" x 12", pub EDTW....................... | 5.00 | — |
| Deermice, ed. 500, s/n, 10" x 12", pub EDTW ....................... | 5.00 | — |
| Flying Squirrels, ed. 500, s/n, 11" x 14", pub EDTW................. | 5.00 | — |
| **MULTI or FULL COLOR** | | |
| ☐ SERIES 1 - WILD INHERITORS. | | |
| Screech Owls, rel. 1973, ed. 200, s/n 16" x 20", pub EDTW............ | 40.00 | Sold Out |
| American Kestrel, rel. 1974, ed. 200, s/n, 16" x 20", pub EDTW ........ | 40.00 | 320.00 |
| Blue Jays with Young, rel. 1975, ed 200, s/n, 16" x 20", pub EDTW....... | 40.00 | 80.00 |
| American Woodcock, rel. 1976, ed. 200, s/n, 16" x 20", pub EDTW ....... | 50.00 | — |
| Cottontail with Young, rel. 1976. ed. 200, s/n, 16" x 20", pub EDTW ...... | 50.00 | — |
| Remarqued prints of the Series ............................. | 80.00 | — |
| ☐ SERIES 2 - WOODLAND LEGACIES. | | |
| Cecropias, rel. 1974, ed. 300, s/n, 11" x 12½", pub EDTW............ | 12.00 | 20.00 |
| Goldfinches, rel. 1974, ed. 300, s/n, 11" x 12½", pub EDTW............ | 12.00 | Sold Out |
| Indigo Bunting, rel. 1974, ed. 300, s/n, 11" x 12½", pub EDTW ......... | 12.00 | 36.00 |
| R-T Hummingbird, rel. 1974, ed. 300, s/n, 11" x 12½", pub EDTW ....... | 12.00 | 36.00 |
| Summer Goldfinches, rel. 1979. ed. 300, s/n, 11½" x 14", pub EDTW..... | 25.00 | — |
| Remarqued prints in this Series - Additional cost .................... | 25.00 | — |

| | ISSUE PRICE | CURRENT PRICE |
|---|---|---|
| ☐ SERIES 3 - WATERFOWL. | | |
| Before the North Wind - Cans, rel. 1977. ed. 750, s/n, 22″ x 28″, pub EDTW | 50.00 | — |
| Circling the Savannah - Snows, rel. 1977. ed. 750, s/n, 22″ x 28″, pub EDTW | 50.00 | — |
| Into the Cypress - Woodies, rel. 1977. ed. 750, s/n, 22″ x 28″, pub EDTW | 50.00 | — |
| Remarqued print in this series | 90.00 | — |
| Up from the Prairie - Sprigs, rel. 1977. ed. 750, s/n, 22″ x 28″, pub EDTW | 50.00 | — |
| Donated to National Wildlife Federation - 150 prints of each in this series | | |
| ☐ SERIES 4 | | |
| Golden Eagles with Young, rel. 1973. ed. 350, s/n, 22″ x 28″, pub EDTW | 60.00 | 75.00 |
| Remarqued | 110.00 | — |
| 25 prints donated to Cornell Laboratory of Ornithology. | | |
| Mute Swan with Young, rel. 1976. ed. 450, s/n, 27½″ x 37½″, pub EDTW | 85.00 | — |
| Remarqued | 160.00 | — |
| 300 prints donated to Kellogg Sanctuary. | | |

# JOHN PITCHER

At nineteen, Michigan-born John C. Pitcher, attracted by wildlife and wilderness, hitchhiked 3500 miles to Alaska for the first time. Now, a decade later, the artist-naturalist is Alaska's leading bird artist.

**AUTUMN BLACKCAPS** *by John Pitcher*

Pitcher was never in doubt about the focus of his life. From childhood his interest in nature, and particularly birds, was enthusiastic and comprehensive. His art reflects very accurately the artist-naturalist title which has been applied to him. The pure fine-artist is evident in the watercolors, oils and mixed media paintings which reflect the spirit and beauty of Alaska through the unusual and intrinsic beauty of its birds and its land.

These works are shown in exhibitions in the United States, Canada, Scotland and England. He is a regular exhibitor at the prestigious Leigh Yawkey Woodson Museum's Annual International Bird Show.

In his scientific illustrations for *World Book Encyclopedia*, *A Guide to the Birds of Alaska* and magazines, the emphasis is based on Pitcher's knowledge of natural history. For the past ten years, he has traveled throughout much of the state sketching, photographing and leading natural history tours over some of the world's most inspiring landscapes.

## JOHN PITCHER

| | ISSUE PRICE | CURRENT PRICE |
|---|---|---|
| ☐ **WHISTLING SWANS - FALL MIGRANTS**, rel. 1978. ed. 950, s/n, 20" x 28", pub MPPI | 85.00 | — |
| ☐ **MORNING FLIGHT - BALD EAGLE**, rel. 1982. ed. 950, s/n, 33¼" x 24½", pub MPPI | 200.00 | — |
| ☐ **AUTUMN BLACKCAPS CHICKADEES**, rel. 1983. ed. 950, s/n, 11¾" x 8½", pub MPPI | 40.00 | — |
| ☐ **COASTAL PEREGRINES**, rel. 1983. ed. 950, s/n, 24" x 17½", pub MPPI | 85.00 | — |
| ☐ **WINDY CARDINAL**, rel. 1983. ed. 950, s/n, 11¾" x 8½", pub MPPI | 40.00 | — |

# JOHN PITRÉ

John Pitré, America's leading surrealist, was born on November 24, 1942 in Huntington, New York. He began seriously painting at 18 years old while he was studying at the Art Students League in New York City. He is indebted to the late Frank Reilly who was America's foremost teacher of fine arts, for his mastery of oils.

At a young age he used to spend time at the Metropolitan Museum of Art. He especially admired the "Hudson River School" and drew inspiration from the paintings of Frederick Edwin Church.

After spending two years in the Army, Pitré returned to New York and became a sidewalk artist. He also traveled the country doing outdoor street shows. In those years (the early 60's) Pitré specialized in marine painting, underwater mood pieces and seascapes. While studying painting, he supplemented his income as a deepwater salvage diver, giving him an insight into the sea as few artists had ever seen it. This culminated with his last marine piece, "Battling Ships", completed in 1967.

Expanding his horizons, John decided to do a series of provocative paintings commenting on society. Accordingly, he produced thirteen pictorial narratives encompassing the entire range of human emotion. These paintings, with such titles as "Domination by Power", "No Greater Love", "Overpopulation", "Retribution", "War", and "Conflict"; have sold over three million copies. These dramatic scenes demonstrated both Pitré's aspiration to reach a universal level of awareness and his meticulous perfection of classical realism.

Two of Pitré's most famous works are "Restrictions" and "Israeli Martyrs", currently hanging in the MGM Grand Gallery in Las Vegas. "Israeli Martyrs" was commissioned in 1972 as a memorial to the eleven members of Israel's Olympic team who were murdered at the Munich games. It has been widely acclaimed by the Jewish communities in Miami and New York. In the painting, the Israeli team watches as the torch bearers descend from the dark and craggy slopes. This has been interpreted by many as symbolizing Masada. Here, surrealism is used to evoke strong emotion, drawing on the memory of a real and terrible event.

Few artists today can match Pitré's technical ability. He has produced fine lithographs and graphics, but today works mostly in oils. Pitré has really never broken with the true classic style of painting as is demonstrated by his incredible attention to detail and brush stroke techniques. He has no peer in the presentation of the human form as readily demonstrated in "Restrictions", "Man and Woman", and his newest pieces "Michelle", "Girl on a Bike", and "Twilight Fantasy". The respect for the "tight" classical painter was shown by Pitré's being chosen as featured artist for the 1974 Spokane World's Fair.

Beyond painting, John's interests include a broad appreciation of outdoor activities, including flying, skin-diving and biking. Having boxed in the Golden Gloves many years ago, John still maintains an avid interest in boxing and the martial arts. At night you may find him at some small club taking in the newest sound of jazz and popular music.

**FOCUS ON LIGHT** *by John Pitré*

### JOHN PITRÉ

| | ISSUE PRICE | CURRENT PRICE |
|---|---|---|
| ☐ **COMMENTARY OF MANKIND,** Portfolio of four original lithographs. . . . . . . . . . | 2300.00 per set | |

    ed. 250, s/n, 1/250 to 250/250
    ed. 250, s/n, I-I/CCL to I-CCL/CCL
    ed. 175 deluxe, s/n, 1/175 to 175/175
    ed. 175 deluxe, s/n, I-I/CLXXV to I-CLXXV/CLXXV
    ed. 75 deluxe, s/n, A.P. 1/75 to A.P. 75/75
    ed. 50 deluxe, s/n, E.A. 1/50 to E.A. 50/50
    *ed. 10 deluxe, s/n, M.E. 1/10 to M.E. 10/10
    *These portfolios have been reserved for donation to museums only.
Publishers Equity Art Fund, Ltd - Greenwich, Connecticut Distributor JTJ Images, Inc.

| | ISSUE PRICE | CURRENT PRICE |
|---|---|---|
| ☐ **DRAGON AND THE KISS,** ed. 750, s/n, 10½" x 14", pub J.T.L.II . . . . . . . . . . | 100.00 | — |
|     ed. 50, artists proofs | | |
| ☐ **DREAM OF FLIGHT,** ed. 750, s/n, 18" x 22", pub J.T.L.II. . . . . . . . . . . . . . . | 225.00 | — |
|     ed. 50, artists proofs | | |
| ☐ **FOCUS ON LIGHT,** ed. 750, s/n, 16" x 20", pub J.T.L.II . . . . . . . . . . . . . . . | 225.00 | — |
|     ed. 50, artists proofs | | |
| ☐ **GIRL ON A BIKE,** ed. 750, s/n, 10" x 14", pub J.T.L.II . . . . . . . . . . . . . . . | 100.00 | — |
|     ed. 50, artists proofs | | |
| ☐ **MICHELLE,** ed. 750, s/n, 9" x 14", pub J.T.L.II . . . . . . . . . . . . . . . . . . . . | 100.00 | — |
|     ed. 50, artists proofs | | |
| ☐ **QUEEN OF SWORDS,** ed. 750, s/n, 16" x 20", pub J.T.L.II . . . . . . . . . . . . | 225.00 | — |
|     ed. 50, artists proofs | | |
| ☐ **THE LAST UNICORN,** ed. 750, s/n, 9" x 14", pub J.T.L.II . . . . . . . . . . . . | 100.00 | — |
|     ed. 50, artists proofs | | |

# RICHARD W. PLASSCHAERT

Born in the picturesque city of New Ulm, Minnesota, Richard W. Plasschaert realized at an early age that he possessed a special ability to capture the beauty of nature on canvas.

Plasschaert has spent over twenty-six years in the fields of commercial art, layout and design, portrait art, landscape and wildlife painting. His work has been displayed in the Twin Cities, Chicago, the National Academy Galleries in New York City and the Leigh Yawkey Woodson Art Museum in Wausau, Wisconsin.

For Richard Plasschaert, success is measured by the amount of enjoyment his paintings bring to others. His selection as the 1980 Federal Duck Stamp Print artist has certainly provided the incentive needed to continue painting for many years to come.

### RICHARD W. PLASSCHAERT

| | | |
|---|---|---|
| ☐ **DRUM SONG,** rel. 1979. ed. 580, s/n, size not available, pub WP . . . . . . . . . . | 55.00 | 275.00 |
| ☐ **AUTUMN RETREAT - WOOD DUCKS,** rel. 1980. ed. 580, s/n, size not available, pub WWI . . . . . . . . . . . . . . . . . . . . . . . . . . . . . . . . . . . . . . . . . . . . . . | 75.00 | 300.00 |
| ☐ **BROKEN COVEY - BOBWHITES,** rel. 1980. ed. 580, s/n, size not available, pub WWI . . . . . . . . . . . . . . . . . . . . . . . . . . . . . . . . . . . . . . . . . . . . . . | 100.00 | — |
| ☐ **MOONAN MARSH - GREENWINGED TEAL,** rel. 1980. ed. 580, s/n, size not available, pub WWI . . . . . . . . . . . . . . . . . . . . . . . . . . . . . . . . . . . . . . . . | 75.00 | 175.00 |
| ☐ **MOONAN MARSH - MALLARDS,** rel. 1980. ed. 580, s/n, size not available, pub WWI . . . . . . . . . . . . . . . . . . . . . . . . . . . . . . . . . . . . . . . . . . . . . . | 55.00 | 300.00 |
| ☐ **SETTLING IN - CANADA GEESE,** rel. 1980. ed. 580, s/n, size not available, pub WWI . . . . . . . . . . . . . . . . . . . . . . . . . . . . . . . . . . . . . . . . . . . . . . | 60.00 | 150.00 |
| ☐ **WINTER FLIGHT - PHEASANTS,** rel. 1980. ed. 580, s/n, size not available, pub WWI . . . . . . . . . . . . . . . . . . . . . . . . . . . . . . . . . . . . . . . . . . . . . . | 60.00 | 350.00 |
| ☐ **GREAT BLUE HERON,** rel. 1981. ed. 750, s/n, size not available, pub WP . . . . . . | 45.00 | Sold Out |
| ☐ **TRANQUIL AUTUMN DAYS - TURKEYS,** rel. 1981. ed. 580, s/n, size not available, pub WWI . . . . . . . . . . . . . . . . . . . . . . . . . . . . . . . . . . . . . . . . | 75.00 | 150.00 |
| ☐ **WOODLOT FEEDING - RINGNECKED PHEASANTS,** rel. 1981. ed. 750, s/n, size not available, pub WWI . . . . . . . . . . . . . . . . . . . . . . . . . . . . . . . . . . | 100.00 | 200.00 |

| | ISSUE PRICE | CURRENT PRICE |
|---|---|---|
| ☐ MOONAN MARSH - WOOD DUCKS, rel. 1982. ed. 580, s/n, size not available, pub WP | 100.00 | 200.00 |
| ☐ OVER THE POINT - BLUEBILLS, rel. 1982. ed. 750, s/n, size not available, pub WP | 100.00 | Sold Out |
| ☐ SECLUDED MARSH - MALLARDS, rel. 1982. ed. 750, s/n, size not available, pub WP | 100.00 | 150.00 |

# OGDEN PLEISSNER

Ogden Pleissner was born in Brooklyn, New York in 1905 and studied at the Art Students League. His work has been very widely exhibited and is in a number of public collections including the Metropolitan Museum of Art, the Brooklyn Museum, the Philadelphia Museum of Art, the Toledo Museum of Art, the Los Angeles County Museum, the Minneapolis Institute of Arts, the Canajoharie Museum, the Worcester Art Museum, the Pennsylvania Academy of Fine Arts, the Amon Carter Museum, the New Britain Museum of American Art, the Shelburne Museum, the Montclair Art Museum, the Cincinnati Art Museum, the Butler Institute of American Art, the Smith College Art Museum, the Columbus Gallery of Fine Arts and the Wilmington Society of the Fine Arts.

Among the many awards Pleissner has won are the National Academy of Design's Samuel F. B. Morse Medal of Honor (1959) and Altman Prize (1961); the Gold Medal of the American Watercolor Society (1956); the Century Club Medal of Honor (for oil painting, 1958, and for watercolor in 1960); the Philadelphia Watercolor Club's Joseph Pennell Medal (1954); and the Audubon Artists' Medal of Honor (1950).

**HEAD OF THE POOL** by Ogden Pleissner

Pleissner is a member and former vice president of the National Academy of Design; a member of the Philadelphia Watercolor Club; the American Watercolor Society; the Century Association; the Louis Comfort Tiffany Foundation, of which he is a former president and director; the Art Commission of the National Collection of Fine Arts; the Royal Society of Art; and a trustee of the Shelburne Museum.

## OGDEN PLEISSNER

| | | ISSUE PRICE | CURRENT PRICE |
|---|---|---|---|
| ☐ | ATLANTIC SALMON FISHING, rel. 1939. ed. 300, pub Frost & Reed . . . . . . . . . | — | 1,200.00 |
| ☐ | CASTING FOR SALMON, rel. 1949. ed. 300, pub Sportsman's Gallery & Bookshelf . . . . . . . . . . . . . . . . . . . . . . . . . . . . . . . . . . . . . . . . . . . . . . . . . . | — | 1,200.00 |
| ☐ | TROUT FISHING IN WYOMING, rel. 1949. ed. 250, pub Sportsman's Gallery & Bookshelf . . . . . . . . . . . . . . . . . . . . . . . . . . . . . . . . . . . . . . . . . . . . . | — | 1,200.00 |
| ☐ | BEAVERKILL BRIDGE, rel. 1953. ed. 221, pub Anglers Club . . . . . . . . . . . . . . | — | 2,000.00 |
| ☐ | DOWNS GULCH, rel. 1957. ed. 300, pub Anglers Club of New York . . . . . . . . . | — | 1,000.00 |
| ☐ | LEAPING SEA TROUT, rel. 1957. ed. 300, pub Frost & Reed . . . . . . . . . . . . . . | — | 1,200.00 |
| ☐ | THE BRIDGE POOL, rel. 1957. ed. 300, pub Frost & Reed . . . . . . . . . . . . . . . . | — | 1,200.00 |
| ☐ | WEST DUNCAN, CLOVE VALLEY, rel. 1957. ed. 104, pub Clove Valley Club . . . | — | 1,500.00 |
| ☐ | BLUE BOAT ON THE SAINT ANNE, rel. 1959. ed. 300, pub Anglers Club of New York . . . . . . . . . . . . . . . . . . . . . . . . . . . . . . . . . . . . . . . . . . . . . . . . . . . | — | 2,000.00 |
| ☐ | DRIVEN GROUSE, GLANCIE BEAT, rel. 1959. ed. 300, pub Frost & Reed . . . . . . | — | 1,750.00 |
| ☐ | GRANDE RIVE, UPPER MALBRAIE, rel. 1959. ed. 300, pub Frost & Reed . . . . . . | — | 1,500.00 |
| ☐ | OCTOBER SNOW, rel. 1959. ed. 350, pub Anglers Club of New York . . . . . . . . | — | 1,750.00 |
| ☐ | RISING SALMON, rel. 1961. ed. 300, pub Sportsman's Gallery & Bookshelf . . . | — | 1,000.00 |
| ☐ | GROUSE SHOOTING, (Unsigned), rel. 1967. ed. 400, pub Vance Hood . . . . . . . | — | 300.00 |
| ☐ | JUNE TROUT FISHING, rel. 1967. ed. 350, pub Theodore Gordon Flyfishers . . . | — | 750.00 |
| ☐ | LYE BROOK POOL, rel. 1971. ed. 400, pub American Museum of Flyfishing . . . | — | 450.00 |
| ☐ | QUAIL HUNTERS, rel. 1973. ed. 425, pub Crossroads of Sport . . . . . . . . . . . . | 225.00 | 500.00 |
| ☐ | HILLSIDE ORCHARD, GROUSE SHOOTING, rel. 1975. ed. 275, pub Crossroads of Sport . . . . . . . . . . . . . . . . . . . . . . . . . . . . . . . . . . . . . . . . . . . . . . . . . | 275.00 | 800.00 |
| ☐ | WOODCOCK COVER, rel. 1976. ed. 275, pub The Crossroads of Sport . . . . . . . | 275.00 | 750.00 |
| ☐ | BATTENKILL AT BENEDICTS CROSSING, rel. 1978. ed. 290, pub Crossroads of Sport & Orvis Co. . . . . . . . . . . . . . . . . . . . . . . . . . . . . . . . . . . . . . . . . . . . | 275.00 | 600.00 |
| ☐ | DAWN ON THE DUCK MARSH, rel. 1978. ed. 275, pub The Crossroads of Sport | 285.00 | 400.00 |
| ☐ | FISHING THE AUSABLE, HENDRICKSON POOL, rel. 1979. ed. 275, pub Trout Unlimited, Mich. . . . . . . . . . . . . . . . . . . . . . . . . . . . . . . . . . . . . . . . . . . . . | — | 280.00 |
| ☐ | HEAD OF THE POOL, rel. 1979. ed. 280, pub Crossroads and Orvis . . . . . . . . . | 285.00 | 500.00 |
| ☐ | HENDRICKSON'S POOL, rel. 1980. ed. 275, pub Crossroads and Orvis . . . . . . . | 300.00 | 300.00 |
| ☐ | CLOVE VALLEY, rel. 1982. ed. 156, s/n, size not available, distr. WWI . . . . . . | 350.00 | — |
| ☐ | DRY FLY FISHING FOR SALMON, rel. 1982. ed. 300, s/n, size not available, pub Theodore Gordon Flyfishers . . . . . . . . . . . . . . . . . . . . . . . . . . . . . . . . | 300.00 | 300.00 |
| ☐ | MARSH GUNNERS, rel. 1982. ed. 300, s/n, size not available, distr. WWI . . . . | 300.00 | 400.00 |

# JO POLSENO

Joe Polseno is no country boy, but rather a product of inner-city New York. Perhaps that is why he was captivated by nature at an early age. Of a visit to rural Kent, Connecticut, when he was 13 years old, Polseno says, "That's when I was really inspired. I decided I wanted to paint birds, to make that my life's work.

He returned to the city, but spent his time in zoos, nature preserves and museums. At New York's Museum of Natural History he spent long hours studying the beautiful bird paintings of Fuertes. After a stint in Europe during World War II, he began to study painting seriously.

Book publishers were among the first to recognize Jo Polseno's talent, and he has now illustrated more than 100 books. He soon moved on to exhibiting in galleries, where his work achieved instant recognition, assuring his success and reputation as a top-flight artist.

**JO POLSENO**

| | ISSUE PRICE | CURRENT PRICE |
|---|---|---|

☐ **CANADA GEESE,** rel. 1973. ed. 1,000, s/n, 24" x 18", pub GW . . . . . . . . . . . .  40.00  —
☐ **GREEN-WINGED TEAL,** rel. 1974. ed. 1,000, s/n, 16" x 12", pub GW . . . . . . .  *40.00  —
  *Portfolio of two prints

# M. C. POULSEN

M. C. Poulsen is a young Wyoming artist who demonstrated his artistic ability at an early age.

Michael studied at the University of Arizona and apprenticed with Larry Roberson of Hawaii before returning to his hometown of Cody, Wyoming to begin his career as a professional artist. He is a qualified guide with over ten years of packing experience. He has illustrated several books and is currently writing and illustrating a book about the guiding and hunting experience.

M. C. Poulsen was featured in Dale Burk's book *"A Brush With The West"*. His work is constantly being sought after and many of his paintings hang in major corporate collections throughout the world.

**. . . AND THE HEARTS OF THE CHILDREN SHALL TURN TO THEIR FATHERS** *by M.C. Poulsen*

| M. C. POULSEN | ISSUE PRICE | CURRENT PRICE |
|---|---|---|
| ☐ **WRANGER IN YELLOW SLICKER,** rel. 1979. ed. 250, s/n, 15½" x 23", pub SP* | 55.00 | 250.00 |
| ☐ **FALES PACK TRAIN,** rel. 1981. ed. 250, s/n, 16½" x 21", pub EP | 100.00 | 225.00 |
| ☐ **. . . AND THE HEARTS OF THE CHILDREN SHALL TURN TO THEIR FATHERS,** rel. 1982. ed. 250, s/n, 17½" x 20¼", by AW. | | |
| Subject of this painting was Ben Nighthorse. Prints were also signed by Ben Nighthorse. | 125.00 | 150.00 |

*M. C. Poulsen prints although published by different companies are available through the artist at 2019 Kerper Blvd., Cody, Wyoming 82414.

# PHIL PRENTICE

Prentice was born in Muncie, Indiana, in 1930. His love of creative art was passed on to him by his late father, a fine artist in his own right. At the age of twelve, Prentice was offered a scholarship to the Dayton Art Institute, which he attended after regular school classes. This dual education was not considered a chore, since he was already caught up in the wonder of creating his own interpretations of flowers, still lifes and life studies. After high school Prentice enrolled at the Pratt Institute in Brooklyn, New York.

A term in the U.S. Air Force followed, the better part of which was spent in Japan. During his off-duty hours, Prentice took in the sights and sounds of Japanese temples and museums, and in this way Prentice's appreciation of the wonderful simplicity of Oriental art began. After his term of enlistment, Prentice settled in Los Angeles to pursue his career in the art world. He attended the Art Center School of Los Angeles.

Prentice started with seascapes, then followed with desert scenes, portraits and animal studies. He sold his first major work, that of a horse set in clouds against a plain background, at his first Laguna Beach Festival of Arts, into which he had been judged. From then on it was one animal commission after another; Prentice had found his milieu. Since the commissions were for varying species, this meant hundreds of hours of research into the animal world and with painstaking efforts, Prentice slowly achieved recognition as a fine wildlife artist. The big cats remain his favorite subjects.

Prentice's works have been reproduced in five countries and he is now recognized by the U.S. Information Agency as one of America's leading international wildlife artists. Lately, Prentice has directed his talents into additional avenues, all closely related to his regular work. Already, three works have been especially designed for one of America's leading pastimes: *"Needlepoint".*

**PHIL PRENTICE**

| | | |
|---|---|---|
| ☐ **THE NAVAJO,** rel. 1975. ed. 500, s/n, 24" x 36", pub DACI | 85.00 | — |
| ☐ **THE LION,** rel. 1975. ed. 300, s/n, 22" x 28", pub DACI | 75.00 | 100.00 |
| ☐ **THE CHEETAH,** rel. 1975. ed. 300, s/n, 22" x 28", pub DACI | 75.00 | 100.00 |
| ☐ **THE LIONESS,** rel. 1976. ed. 300, s/n, 22" x 28", pub DACI | 75.00 | 100.00 |

# ROGER PREUSS

Seldom does a foremost artist in these modern-art times have the esteem of both the public and the recognized art critics and wildlife authorities in quite the same way as Roger Preuss. Of contemporary artists portraying wildlife, none has achieved wider and more enduring recognition. In all the history of the Federal Duck Stamp competition, Preuss is the youngest artist ever to win the award. For many, he is today's ranking wildlife artist.

**SHARP - TAILED GROUSE** *by Roger Preuss*

Notwithstanding the renown of his classic paintings of wildfowl, Preuss has not remained stuck in the marshes. He is an artist of true versatility and unlimited range of wildlife forms throughout the body of his work. World reknown Roger Preuss is one of the few artists in his chosen field, historically, to attain critical success in the fine arts and status as a museum artist. The acknowledged dean of wildfowl painter, Mr. Preuss was unanimously elected a charter member by Wildlife Artists of the World.

Many welcome his brand of outdoor wisdom expressed on the podium about wildlife's problems. A proficient writer about wildlife, he is a recognized authority, a perceptive naturalist in the field, a woodsman whose habitat research is invariably combined with a quest for his favorite mushrooms and other food delicacies found only in the wild. He has been given credit for helping arouse the contemporary concern for nature and the growing movement to safeguard the vital habitat. His broad influence and stature are evidenced by his recognition by more major biographical references books worldwide than any other artist.

The birthplace of Roger Preuss is Waterville, Minnesota. From his Minnesota base he has traveled extensively to observe, sketch and paint nature and to share his experience with others. The artist has been honored 26 times as an award winner in exhibitions judged by art jurors and peers, selected as "International Wildlife Artist of the Year", named "United States Bicentennial Wildlife Artist", and elected a "Knight of Mark Twain" in succession to Thomas Hart Benton, "For outstanding contributions to American Art".

Preuss has for many years purchased wildlife lands that are in danger of development, and set them aside as homes in perpetuity for fish and wildfowl, furbearers and big game, bald eagles and all other creatures native to this sylvan environment.

Preuss has attained a level of worldwide recognition of his accomplishments that is unequaled in the field of contemporary art. He was the first, and for many years the only, painter of wildlife honored by listing in *Who's Who in the World*, *World Biography*, *Who's Who in America*, *Who's Who in American Art*, *International Who's Who in Art*, *International Men of Achievement*, and *Dictionary of International Biography*.

Preuss is the only artist recognized for his premier stature in all thirty of the world's standard bio-reference books. Mr. Preuss is internationally respected as an innovative pioneer among the exceedingly few fine art painters whose wildlife motifs have been exhibited or are represented with the old masters and fashionable moderns in collections of *recognized* fine art museums. Preuss's work signals a breakthrough for animal art in the Real World of Art. His work is also represented in private collections including the Maytag, Michaels and Ridder collections. His painting "Widgeon Along the River" sold for $78,000.00, considered the highest price ever paid for a waterfowl piece.

## ROGER PREUSS

| | ISSUE PRICE | CURRENT PRICE |
|---|---|---|
| ☐ **AMERICAN GOLDENEYE,** rel. 1949. Federal Duck Stamp Print stone lithograph. ed. 250, s/o, 6⅝" x 9⅛", pub WOA | 15.00 | 2600.00 |
| ed. 8, remarqued | 40.00 | 3200.00 |
| ☐ **SHOVELLERS,** rel. 1950. Ducks Unlimited issue. ed. N/A, 9½" x 7⅛", pub WOA | — | 300.00 |
| ☐ **GREENHEADS,** rel. 1951. ed. 300, s/o, 11½" x 15½", pub WOA | 15.00 | 700.00 |
| ☐ **SNOW GEESE WINGING SOUTH,** rel. 1951. ed. 4, s/in plate, 23" x 20", chromolith, pub WOA | 30.00 | 3900.00 |
| ☐ **GOLDENEYES AT LEECH LAKE,** rel. 1952. ed. 400, s/o, 13½" x 18", pub WOA | 20.00 | 650.00 |
| ☐ **TEAL - UP AND AWAY,** rel. 1952. ed. 350, s/o, 13½" x 18", pub WOA | 20.00 | 600.00 |
| ☐ **WOOD DUCKS - ALONG THE CREEK,** rel. 1953. ed. 300, s/in plate, 8⅞" x 6¾", engraving, pub WOA | 25.00 | 400.00 |
| ☐ **WOODIES ON A SPRING MORN,** rel. 1954. ed. 400, s/o, 11½" x 15½", pub WOA | 25.00 | 920.00 |
| ☐ **WILDERNESS YULETIDE,** rel. 1955. ed. 60, s/o, 10" x 7", pub WOA | 20.00 | 140.00 |
| ed. 940, i/o | 10.00 | 90.00 |
| ☐ **FANTASY OF THE GOLDEN VALLEY,** rel. 1956. ed. 940, i/o, 14" x 11", pub WOA | — | 130.00 |
| ed. 60, a/p | — | — |
| ☐ **HERE THEY COME - BLUEBILLS,** rel. 1957. ed. 940, s/in plate, 7" x 9½", pub WOA | 20.00 | 140.00 |
| ed. 60, i/o | — | 175.00 |
| ☐ **AMERICAN WIDGEON,** rel. 1958. ed. 1,140, s/in plate, 38" x 48", pub WOA | 15.00 | 130.00 |
| ed. 60, i/o | — | 150.00 |
| ☐ **FAWNS IN SPRINGTIME,** rel. 1958. ed. 1,000, s/o, 11½" x 15½", pub WOA | 20.00 | 125.00 |
| ☐ **RUFFED GROUSE AT SUNDOWN,** rel. 1959. ed. 200, s/n, 11½" x 15½", pub WOA | 20.00 | 150.00 |
| ed. 500, s/o | 15.00 | 100.00 |
| ed. 300, u/s | — | 75.00 |
| ☐ **WOOD DUCKS ON A SUMMER MARSH,** rel. 1960. ed. 400, s/o, 13½" x 18", pub WOA | 20.00 | 185.00 |
| ed. 600, i/o | 15.00 | 150.00 |
| ☐ **FROM BEYOND THE NORTH WIND,** rel. 1961. ed. 200, s/n, 11½" x 15½", pub WOA | 20.00 | 160.00 |
| ed. 300, s/o | 15.00 | 150.00 |
| ed. 20, artist proofs, remarqued | — | 260.00 |
| ☐ **CANADA GEESE - FEEDING TIME,** rel. 1962. ed. 200, s/n, 11½" x 15½", pub WOA | 20.00 | 140.00 |
| ed. 300, s/o | 15.00 | 100.00 |
| ed. 500, u/s | — | 65.00 |
| ☐ **KING OF THE WEST,** rel. 1962. ed. 200, s/n, 11½" x 15½", pub WOA | 20.00 | 140.00 |
| ed. 300, s/o | 15.00 | 90.00 |
| ed. 500, i/o | — | 75.00 |
| ☐ **MONARCH OF THE WILDERNESS,** rel. 1962. ed. 200, s/n, 11½" x 15½", pub WOA | 20.00 | 125.00 |
| ed. 300, s/o | 15.00 | 75.00 |
| ed. 500, u/s | — | 65.00 |
| ☐ **PHEASANTS IN SPRINGTIME,** rel. 1962. ed. 200, n/o, 11½" x 15½", pub WOA | 20.00 | 120.00 |
| ed. 300, s/o | 15.00 | 80.00 |
| ed. 500, i/o | — | 70.00 |

| | ISSUE PRICE | CURRENT PRICE |
|---|---|---|
| ☐ CANVASBACKS AT DAWN, rel. 1963. ed. 200, s/n, 11½″ x 15½″, pub WOA | 20.00 | 160.00 |
| ed. 300, s/o | 15.00 | 135.00 |
| ed. 500, u/s | — | 70.00 |
| ☐ NIGHT WATCH - RACCOONS, rel. 1964. ed. 200, s/n, 11½″ x 15½″, pub WOA | 20.00 | 130.00 |
| ed. 300, s/o | 15.00 | 85.00 |
| ed. 500, u/s | — | 65.00 |
| ☐ SNOW GEESE, rel. 1964. ed. 100, s/o, 8½″ x 7½″, serigraph, pub WOA | 25.00 | 700.00 |
| ☐ PHEASANTS IN AN AUTUMN MARSH, rel. 1964. ed. 200, s/n, 11½″ x 15½″, pub WOA | 20.00 | 150.00 |
| ed. 300, s/o | 15.00 | 120.00 |
| ed. 500, u/s | — | 60.00 |
| ☐ THE FIRST FLUSH - BOBWHITE, rel. 1965. ed. 740, s/o, 11½″ x 15½″, pub WOA | 30.00 | 60.00 |
| ed. 200, s/n | 50.00 | 70.00 |
| ed. 60, watercolor remarqued artist proofs | — | 400.00 |
| ☐ THE WALLEYE, rel. 1965. ed. 200, s/n, 11½″ x 15½″, pub WOA | 20.00 | 140.00 |
| ed. 300, s/o | 15.00 | 100.00 |
| ed. 500, u/s | — | 65.00 |
| ☐ TAKE A BOY HUNTING, rel. 1967. ed. 250, engraving signed in plate, 10″ x 8″, pub WOA | 30.00 | 500.00 |
| ☐ COUGAR!, rel. 1968. ed. 740, s/o, 13″ x 21″, pub WOA | 50.00 | 60.00 |
| ed. 200, s/n | 60.00 | 70.00 |
| ed. 60, remarqued artist proofs | 175.00 | 500.00 |
| ☐ LARGEMOUTH BASS - FEEDING TIME, rel. 1968. ed. 200, s/n, 11½″ x 15½″, pub WOA | 50.00 | 120.00 |
| ed. 740, s/o | 40.00 | 70.00 |
| ed. 60, artist proofs | — | Sold Out |
| ☐ STARTLED BLUE-WINGED TEAL, rel. 1968. ed. 200, s/n, 11½″ x 15½″, pub WOA | 50.00 | 60.00 |
| ed. 300, s/o | 40.00 | 80.00 |
| ed. 500, i/o | — | — |
| ☐ SHARP-TAILED GROUSE, rel. 1968. ed. 200, s/n, 13″ x 21″, pub WOA | 60.00 | 125.00 |
| ed. 740, s/o | 50.00 | 100.00 |
| ☐ CANADA GEESE AT SUNRISE, rel. 1969. ed. 400, n/o, 16⅛″ x 20¼″, pub WOA | 25.00 | 1,125.00 |
| ed. 20, artist proofs | — | Sold Out |
| ☐ WAITING FOR MOM, rel. 1970. ed. 400, s/n, 16½″ x 21″, pub WOA | 30.00 | 1,050.00 |
| ed. 20, artist proofs | — | Sold Out |
| ☐ THE INTRUDER - COTTONTAILS, rel. 1971. ed. 200, s/n, 11½″ x 15½″, pub WOA | 50.00 | 70.00 |
| ed. 300, s/o | 40.00 | 60.00 |
| ed. 500, i/o | — | Sold Out |
| ☐ BLACK DUCKS AGAINST THE TWILIGHT, rel. 1974. ed. 560, s/n, 18½″ x 23½″, pub WOA | 55.00 | 1,025.00 |
| ed. 25, remarqued | 150.00 | 1,400.00 |
| ☐ FOREST INDIAN - ALASKA, rel. 1975. ed. 100, n/o, 8″ x 6½″, pub WOA | 125.00 | 650.00 |
| ☐ THE SNOW-WHITETAILS, rel. 1975. ed. 500, s/n, 11½″ x 15½″, pub WOA | 40.00 | 65.00 |
| ☐ RUTTING TIME - MISTY MORNING WHITETAILS, rel. 1976. ed. 200, s/n, 11½″ x 15½″, pub WOA | 50.00 | 140.00 |
| ed. 740, s/o | 40.00 | 90.00 |
| ed. 60, artist proofs | — | Sold Out |
| ☐ FLAG UP - WHITETAIL BOUNDS OVER CREEK, rel. 1977. ed. 200, s/n, 11½″ x 15½″, pub WOA | 50.00 | 120.00 |
| ed. 740, s/o | 40.00 | 70.00 |
| ed. 60, artist proofs | — | Sold Out |
| ☐ IN THE MEADOW - WHITETAIL FAMILY, rel. 1977. ed. 200, s/n, 11½″ x 15½″, pub WOA | 50.00 | 60.00 |
| ed. 300, s/o | 40.00 | 60.00 |
| ed. 500, i/o | — | Sold Out |
| ☐ WHITE-TAILED DEER AT TWILIGHT, rel. 1977. ed. 200, s/n, 11½″ x 15½″, pub WOA | 50.00 | 65.00 |
| ed. 300, s/o | 40.00 | 60.00 |
| ed. 500, i/o | — | Sold Out |

| | ISSUE PRICE | CURRENT PRICE |
|---|---|---|
| ☐ **WHITETAILS FEEDING IN THE SNOW,** rel. 1977. ed. 200, s/n, 11½" x 15½", pub WOA | 50.00 | 65.00 |
| ed. 300, s/o | 40.00 | — |
| ed. 500, i/o | — | Sold Out |
| ☐ **OOLINKA - INDIAN GIRL,** rel. 1980. ed. 5, signed in plate, 20" x 16¼", pub WOA | 275.00 | 700.00 |
| ☐ **PHEASANTS IN AUTUMN HABITAT,** rel. 1981. First of Issue, Pheasant Habitat Stamp Print. ed. 1,981, s/n, 6½" x 9½", pub WOA | 125.00 | 175.00 |
| ☐ **WILD TURKEY,** rel. 1981. ed. 5, s/n, 11⅝" x 19½", chromolith, pub WOA | 275.00 | 750.00 |
| ☐ **THE WHITE-TAILED DEER,** rel. 1982. ed. 450, s/n, 18¼" x 25½", pub WOA | 70.00 | 85.00 |
| ed. 25, remarqued | 200.00 | 250.00 |
| ☐ **FORMING THE V,** rel. 1983. ed. 580, s/n, 18⅛" x 23", pub WOA | 85.00 | — |
| ☐ **OUT OF THE NORTH WIND - BLUEBILLS!,** rel. 1983. ed. 580, s/n, 13¾" x 19¾", pub WOA | 75.00 | — |
| ed. 20, remarqued artist proofs | 175.00 | — |

# ROBERT PUMMILL

At 11 years of age, Bob Pummill took his first correspondence course and at 13 signed up for the Famous Artist School, Westport, Connecticut. He served nine years in the U.S. Air Force, and upon discharge worked as a technical illustrator in the Los Angeles area for TRW Systems. During this period he studied at the Art Center, Los Angeles. Later, doing industrial design for an engineering firm, his work took him to many areas of the West. When he became the supervisor of conceptual illustration for LTV, Inc. in Texas, the "ways of the West" took over and he has since devoted himself to painting in that genre. He has had three one-man shows with the Texas Art Gallery, has shown at the Western Heritage show in Houston, and in the OS Ranch show.

Pummill's painting are marked by a strong narrative element and derive their focus from his use of dramatic light. The reality of his story-telling themes is enhanced by his use of brilliant, contrasting values. "Light is one of the strongest tools we have," he says, "to create volume, space and substance."

## ROBERT PUMMILL

| | | |
|---|---|---|
| ☐ **A DRY MATCH,** rel. 1979. ed. 2,250, s/n, 14" x 22", pub TAP | 75.00 | — |
| ☐ **A HOT MEAL AND A WARM FIRE,** rel. 1979. ed. 2,250, s/n, 13½" x 22", pub TAP | 75.00 | — |
| ☐ **A MATTER OF RIGHT-A-WAY,** rel. 1982. ed. 1,000, s/n, 18" x 27", pub TAP | 100.00 | — |
| ☐ **BACK TO TEXAS,** rel. 1980. ed. 2,250, s/n, 12¾" x 22", pub TAP | 85.00 | — |
| ☐ **BRAZOS CROSSING,** rel. 1980. ed. 2,250, s/n, 13¼" x 22", pub TAP | 85.00 | — |
| ☐ **END OF A HARD DAY,** rel. 1980. ed. 2,250, s/n, 17" x 22", pub TAP | 85.00 | — |
| ☐ **MULES AND MODEL T'S,** rel. 1983. ed. 1,000, s/n, 19½" x 27¾", pub TAP | 100.00 | — |
| ☐ **OIL TOWN DEPOT,** rel. 1981. ed. 1,000, s/n, 18" x 27", pub TAP | 100.00 | — |
| ☐ **OVER THE TOP,** rel. 1981. ed. 1,000, s/n, 25¾" x 20½", pub TAP | 100.00 | — |
| ☐ **RAWHIDE AND DUST,** rel. 1979. ed. 2,250, s/n, 14½" x 22", pub TAP | 75.00 | — |
| ☐ **SHADOWS OF THE TETONS,** rel. 1983. ed. 1,000, s/n, 16½" x 27", pub TAP | 100.00 | — |
| ☐ **TAKING THE POINT,** rel. 1980. ed. 2,250, s/n, 13½" x 22", pub TAP | 85.00 | — |
| ☐ **TEAMWORK,** rel. 1982. ed. 1,000, s/n, 20¾" x 27¾", pub TAP | 100.00 | — |
| ☐ **THE PROVIDER,** rel. 1979. ed. 2,250, s/n, 13½" x 22", pub TAP | 75.00 | — |
| ☐ **THREE'S COMPANY,** rel. 1980. ed. 2,250, s/n, 13⅝" x 22", pub TAP | 85.00 | — |
| ☐ **WET WEATHER WANDERERS,** rel. 1980. ed. 2,250, s/n, 14½" x 22", pub TAP | 85.00 | — |

# ROBERT REDBIRD

Robert Redbird, a full-blooded Kiowa Indian, was born in Lawton, Oklahoma, in 1939. Taught as a child about the Peyote religion as well as Kiowa history, his paintings reflect the past. He is well known for his Peyote paintings and sometimes combines the abstract with his traditional art. He always takes care not to let the composition dominate his free flowing style.

A self-taught artist, he works mostly in watercolor and tempera, and has been painting professionally since about 1960. Traveling extensively, Redbird is known nationally and has won awards in all sections of the country.

## ROBERT REDBIRD

| | ISSUE PRICE | CURRENT PRICE |
|---|---|---|
| ☐ PEYOTE CHIEFS, ed. 1,500, s/n, 17½" x 22½", pub AIAC | 30.00 | — |

## ROBERT R. REDDEN

His masterful portrayal of nature has made Robert Redden one of the most popular wildlife painters today.

A noted illustrator, Redden's work has been seen on the covers of many national magazines. Although the term wildlife is applied in an effort to categorize his work, Redden's love is the birds of America. An avid outdoorsman, Redden strives to depict his birds in a setting that portrays the mood he wishes to convey.

## ROBERT R. REDDEN

| | | |
|---|---|---|
| ☐ BLUE BIRD AFTERNOON, ed. 500, s/n, 18½" x 24", litho, pub GSP | 30.00 | 60.00 |
| ☐ HONEY AGARIC/CAESAR'S MUSHROOM, ed. 2,500, s/n, 14" x 18", litho, pub GSP, (sold as a set only) | 20.00 | — |
| ☐ MORNING WATCH (Blue Jay), ed. 500, s/n, 18½" x 24", litho, pub GSP | 30.00 | 60.00 |
| ☐ PASSION FLOWER & CAROLINA WREN, ed. 1,000, s/n, 18" x 22", litho, pub GSP | 30.00 | — |
| ☐ THE FLUSH (Bobwhite), ed. 3,000; 1,000, s/n, 2,000 s/o | 40.00 | — |
| litho, pub GSP | 30.00 | — |

## MARK REECE

Mark Reece was born in Des Moines, Iowa, and has spent most of his life associated with nature. His famous father, Maynard Reece, taught him how the ever-changing elements of nature can be used to the advantage of the wildlife artist. From the time he was a youngster, Reece's family has enjoyed camping trips to a host of different habitats, ranging from marshes and lakes to the tundra regions above the Arctic Circle. These experiences, along with his father's guidance, developed in him a keen appreciation of detail, color, and composition that is so vital to the wildlife artist.

Reece has also been active in academic fields, and has a strong desire to become a physician. His formal education includes a B.S. from Iowa State University, where he majored in zoology, and a M.S. from Drake University in biology. He is a student at Creighton University Medical School.

His academic training has complemented his extensive field studies, and he has incorporated his knowledge of ecology, botany, and anatomy in his paintings.

Reece views his art work as a fascinating adjunct to his interests in medicine. While he was attending college and graduate school, he produced a dozen subjects for calendar reproduction, and won the 1975 Iowa Duck Stamp Design Contest.

In the future, Reese will continue his art work while pursuing his medical career.

**HONKERS** *by Mark Reece*

## MARK REECE

| | ISSUE PRICE | CURRENT PRICE |
|---|---|---|
| ☐ HONKERS - CANADA GEESE, rel. 1977. ed. 950, s/n, 19½" x 22½", pub MPPI | 60.00 | — |
| ☐ QUAIL BREAK - BOBWHITES, rel. 1978. ed. 950, s/n, 19½" x 22½", pub MPPI | 60.00 | — |
| ☐ LOONS, rel. 1979. ed. 950, s/n, 16¾" x 22½", pub MPPI | 60.00 | — |
| ☐ DUCKLINGS - REDHEADS, rel. 1980. ed. 950, s/n, 8" x 10", pub MPPI | 20.00 | — |
| ☐ MALLARDS, rel. 1980. ed. 950, s/n, 13½" x 18¼", pub MPPI | 40.00 | — |
| ☐ RESTING UP - MALLARDS, rel. 1980. ed. 950, s/n, 13½" x 18¼", pub MPPI | 40.00 | — |
| ☐ SNOOZING - MALLARDS, rel. 1980. ed. 950, s/n, 8" x 10", pub MPPI | 20.00 | — |

# MAYNARD REECE

Maynard Reece was born in Iowa, the son of a Quaker minister whose frequent moves gave the boy first-hand knowledge of the beauty of America's heartland. In 1940, Reece was hired as artist for the Iowa Department of History and Archives in the museum at Des Moines. One of his mentors was Ding Darling, a famous political cartoonist and graphic artist.

During W.W. II, Reece served in the Signal Corps as an artist for training aids. Service abroad allowed him to paint in Britain and France and make lasting friendships with leading European wildlife artists and naturalists. After discharge he returned to the museum.

In 1948, he won the Federal Duck Stamp Competition for the first of an unprecedented five times. In 1952 Reece became a full-time free lance artist. Since then he has become one of the leading wildlife artists in America with an international reputation. It is possible that more people possess a print from a Reece painting than from the work of any other wildlife artist.

His work has appeared in prestigious magazines. He has been Artist of the Year for Ducks Unlimited and an Honorary Trustee of that organization. He has received many awards and honors including a commission from the Government of Bermuda to design postage stamps with indigenous wildlife.

**DARK SKY PHEASANT** *by Maynard Reece*

## MAYNARD REECE

| | ISSUE PRICE | CURRENT PRICE |
|---|---|---|
| ☐ **BOBWHITES**, rel. 1964. ed. 950, stone lithograph, 14″ x 18″ . . . . . . . . . . . . . . | 20.00 | 650.00 |
| ☐ **MALLARDS**, rel. 1964. ed. 250, stone lithograph, 14″ x 18″ . . . . . . . . . . . . . . | 20.00 | 650.00 |
| ☐ **MALLARDS - PITCHING IN**, rel. 1969. ed. 500, s/n, 25¾″ x 35½″, pub MPPI . | 40.00 | 600.00 |
| ☐ **EDGE OF THE HEDGEROW - BOBWHITES**, rel. 1970. ed. 1,000, s/n, 25″ x 29½″, pub MPPI . . . . . . . . . . . . . . . . . . . . . . . . . . . . . . . . . . . . . . . . . . . | 60.00 | 700.00 |
| ☐ **AGAINST THE WIND - CANVASBACKS**, rel. 1972. ed. 550, s/n, 23½″ x 29½″, pub MPPI . . . . . . . . . . . . . . . . . . . . . . . . . . . . . . . . . . . . . . . . . . . . . . | 60.00 | 450.00 |
| ☐ **FEEDING TIME - CANADA GEESE**, rel. 1973. ed. 550, s/n, 24½″ x 30″, pub MPPI . . . . . . . . . . . . . . . . . . . . . . . . . . . . . . . . . . . . . . . . . . . . . . . . | 75.00 | 400.00 |
| ☐ **LATER AFTERNOON - MALLARDS**, rel. 1973. ed. 450, s/n, 25″ x 31″, pub MPPI . . . . . . . . . . . . . . . . . . . . . . . . . . . . . . . . . . . . . . . . . . . . . . . . | 150.00 | 150.00 |
| ☐ **MARSHLANDER MALLARDS**, rel. 1973. ed. 600, s/n, 17″ x 26″, pub MPPI . . . | 60.00 | — |
| ☐ **PHEASANT COUNTRY**, rel. 1973. ed. 550, s/n, 22¾″ x 28½″, pub MPPI . . . . | 60.00 | 200.00 |
| ☐ **WOOD DUCKS**, rel. 1973. ed. 550, s/n, 25½″ x 32″, pub MPPI . . . . . . . . . . . | 125.00 | 200.00 |
| ☐ **A BURST OF COLOR - RING-NECKED PHEASANTS**, rel. 1974. ed. 950, s/n, 20″ x 26″, pub MPPI . . . . . . . . . . . . . . . . . . . . . . . . . . . . . . . . . . . . . . . . . . | 75.00 | 175.00 |
| ☐ **COURTSHIP FLIGHT - PINTAILS**, rel. 1974. ed. 950, s/n, 15″ x 21″, pub MPPI | 75.00 | 175.00 |
| ☐ **EARLY ARRIVALS - MALLARDS**, rel. 1974. ed. 950, s/n, 13″ x 18″, pub MPPI | 50.00 | 125.00 |
| ☐ **FLOODED OAKS - MALLARDS**, rel. 1974. ed. 850, s/n, 23″ x 31½″, pub MPPI | 150.00 | 300.00 |
| ☐ **MALLARDS - DROPPING IN**, rel. 1974. ed. 950, s/n, 20″ x 26″, pub MPPI . . . . | 75.00 | 150.00 |
| ☐ **QUAIL COVER**, rel. 1974. ed. 750, s/n, 25″ x 30½″, pub MPPI . . . . . . . . . . . . | 150.00 | 350.00 |
| ☐ **SNOW GEESE - BLUE GEESE**, rel. 1974. ed. 950, s/n, 23″ x 31½″, pub MPPI | 150.00 | 175.00 |
| ☐ **SNOWY CREEK - MALLARDS**, rel. 1974. ed. 950, s/n, 20″ x 26″, pub MPPI . . | 75.00 | 200.00 |
| ☐ **SOLITUDE - WHITETAIL DEER**, rel. 1974. ed. 950, s/n, 20″ x 27½″, pub MPPI | 85.00 | 150.00 |
| ☐ **THE PASSING STORM - CANVASBACKS**, rel. 1974. ed. 950, s/n, 13″ x 18″, pub MPPI . . . . . . . . . . . . . . . . . . . . . . . . . . . . . . . . . . . . . . . . . . . . . . . . | 50.00 | 100.00 |
| ☐ **THE SANDBAR - CANADA GEESE**, rel. 1974. ed. 950, s/n, 13″ x 18″, pub MPPI . . . . . . . . . . . . . . . . . . . . . . . . . . . . . . . . . . . . . . . . . . . . . . . . | 50.00 | 100.00 |

| | ISSUE PRICE | CURRENT PRICE |
|---|---|---|
| ☐ **WINGING SOUTH - CANADA GEESE**, rel. 1974. ed. 750, s/n, 23" x 31¼", pub MPPI. | 150.00 | 275.00 |
| ☐ **WOODED SECLUSION - TURKEY**, rel. 1974. ed. 950, s/n, 20" x 26", pub MPPI | 75.00 | 125.00 |
| ☐ **AFTERNOON SHADOWS - BOBWHITES**, rel. 1975. ed. 950, s/n, 20" x 27½", pub MPPI. | 100.00 | 350.00 |
| ☐ **HAZY DAY - BOBWHITES**, rel. 1975. ed. 950, s/n, 22½" x 31", pub MPPI. | 150.00 | 400.00 |
| ☐ **AUTUMN TRIO - RING-NECK PHEASANTS**, rel. 1976. ed. 950, s/n, 20" x 26", pub MPPI. | 85.00 | 250.00 |
| ☐ **CANADA GEESE - COMING IN**, rel. 1976. ed. 950, s/n, 20" x 25", pub MPPI. | 85.00 | 175.00 |
| ☐ **DARK SKY - MALLARDS**, rel. 1976. ed. 950, s/n, 20" x 26", pub MPPI | 85.00 | 650.00 |
| ☐ **FLIGHT - CANADA GEESE**, rel. 1976. ed. 950, s/n, 14" x 20", pub MPPI | 50.00 | 100.00 |
| ☐ **GENTOO PENGUINS**, rel. 1976. ed. 260, hand-colored stone lithograph, 16" x 20", pub MPPI. | 125.00 | 175.00 |
| ☐ **GOOD FETCH - LABRADOR RETRIEVER**, rel. 1976. ed. 950, s/n, 22½" x 31", pub MPPI. | 150.00 | 200.00 |
| ☐ **SHALLOW POND - MALLARDS**, rel. 1976. ed. 950, s/n, 22" x 29", pub MPPI. | 125.00 | 125.00 |
| ☐ **THE RAIL FENCE - BOBWHITES**, rel. 1976. ed. 950, s/n, 20" x 25", pub MPPI | 85.00 | 175.00 |
| ☐ **THUNDERHEAD - CANADA GEESE**, rel. 1976. ed. 260, stone lithograph, 20½" x 17", pub MPPI. | 125.00 | 300.00 |
| ☐ **WEATHERED WOOD - BOBWHITES**, rel. 1976. ed. 950, s/n, 14" x 20", pub MPPI. | 50.00 | 150.00 |
| ☐ **COVEY RISE - BOBWHITE**, rel. 1977. ed. 950, s/n, 25" x 38", pub MPPI. | 150.00 | 600.00 |
| ☐ **DARK SHADOWS - WHITETAIL DEER**, rel. 1977. ed. 950, s/n, 20" x 26", pub MPPI. | 85.00 | 125.00 |
| ☐ **EASY LANDING - PINTAILS**, rel. 1977. ed. 950, s/n, 21" x 27½", pub MPPI. | 95.00 | 200.00 |
| ☐ **GRACEFUL PAIR - RING-NECKED PHEASANTS**, rel. 1977. ed. 950, s/n, 14" x 20", pub MPPI. | 50.00 | 125.00 |
| ☐ **JUMPING GREENWINGS - GREEN-WINGED TEAL**, rel. 1977. ed. 950, s/n, 24½" x 19½", pub MPPI | 85.00 | 150.00 |
| ☐ **NINE TRAVELERS - CANADA GEESE**, rel. 1977. ed. 950, s/n, 21" x 27½", pub MPPI. | 95.00 | 175.00 |
| ☐ **QUIET POND - MALLARDS**, rel. 1977. ed. 950, s/n, 20½" x 27½", pub MPPI. | 95.00 | 150.00 |
| ☐ **RESTING - WOOD DUCKS**, rel. 1977. ed. 950, s/n, 14" x 20", pub MPPI | 50.00 | 100.00 |
| ☐ **STICK POND - MALLARDS**, rel. 1977. ed. 950, s/n, 22" x 29", pub MPPI | 125.00 | 150.00 |
| ☐ **THE BIRCH - RUFFED GROUSE**, rel. 1977. ed. 950, s/n, 20½" x 27½", pub MPPI. | 85.00 | — |
| ☐ **THE SENTINEL - WHITETAIL DEER**, rel. 1977. ed. 950, s/n, 23" x 31", pub MPPI. | 150.00 | 175.00 |
| ☐ **THROUGH THE TREES - WOOD DUCKS**, rel. 1977. ed. 950, s/n, 21" x 27½", pub MPPI. | 95.00 | 400.00 |
| ☐ **CHINSTRAP PENGUINS**, rel. 1978. ed. 950, s/n, 17½" x 22", pub MPPI. | 50.00 | — |
| ☐ **CRESCENT LAKE - MALLARDS**, rel. 1978. ed. 950, s/n, 22" x 29", pub MPPI. | 125.00 | 175.00 |
| ☐ **DARK SKY - CANADA GEESE**, rel. 1978. ed. 950, s/n, 25" x 35", pub MPPI. | 175.00 | 300.00 |
| ☐ **NEW SNOW - WHITETAIL DEER**, rel. 1978. ed. 950, s/n, 22" x 29", pub MPPI | 95.00 | 110.00 |
| ☐ **OAK FOREST - TURKEY**, rel. 1978. ed. 950, s/n, 22" x 29", pub MPPI. | 125.00 | 215.00 |
| ☐ **OVER THE POINT - LESSER SCAUPS**, rel. 1978. ed. 950, s/n, 21" x 29", pub MPPI. | 125.00 | 135.00 |
| ☐ **RENDEZVOUS - WHITE-FRONTED GEESE**, rel. 1978. ed. 950, s/n, 20" x 27", pub MPPI. | 85.00 | — |
| ☐ **ROUGH WATER - CANVASBACKS**, rel. 1978. ed. 950, s/n, 22" x 30", pub MPPI. | 150.00 | 200.00 |
| ☐ **WINTER COVEY - BOBWHITES**, rel. 1978. ed. 950, s/n, 25" x 38", pub MPPI. | 225.00 | 650.00 |
| ☐ **DARK SKY - BOBWHITES**, rel. 1979. ed. 950, s/n, 25" x 35", pub MPPI. | 225.00 | 400.00 |
| ☐ **PHEASANT COVER - RING-NECKED PHEASANTS**, rel. 1979. ed. 950, s/n, 23½" x 32", pub MPPI. | 175.00 | 275.00 |
| ☐ **QUAIL COUNTRY**, rel. 1979. ed. 950, s/n, 25" x 35", pub MPPI. | 250.00 | 325.00 |
| ☐ **REGAL FLIGHT - WHISTLING SWANS**, rel. 1979. ed. 950, s/n, 29½" x 27½", pub MPPI. | 125.00 | 150.00 |
| ☐ **RENDEZVOUS**, rel. 1979. ed. 950, s/n, 20½" x 27½", pub MPPI. | 85.00 | — |
| ☐ **SUNRISE - GREEN WINGED TEAL**, rel. 1979. ed. 950, s/n, 23" x 31½", pub MPPI. | 150.00 | 200.00 |
| ☐ **THE MARSH**, rel. 1979. ed. 950, s/n, 18" x 23", pub MPPI | 75.00 | 100.00 |
| ☐ **THE QUIET PLACE - CANADA GEESE**, rel. 1979. ed. 950, s/n, 25" x 38", pub MPPI. | 175.00 | 225.00 |

| | ISSUE PRICE | CURRENT PRICE |
|---|---|---|
| ☐ **THE VALLEY - PINTAILS,** rel. 1979. ed. 950, s/n, 23" x 31½", pub MPPI | 150.00 | 200.00 |
| ☐ **WINDY DAY - MALLARDS,** rel. 1979. ed. 950, s/n, 23" x 31½", pub MPPI | 150.00 | 200.00 |
| ☐ **ALONG THE SHORE - REDHEADS,** rel. 1980. ed. 950, s/n, 23" x 31½", pub MPPI | 160.00 | — |
| ☐ **COLD MORNING - MALLARDS,** rel. 1980. ed. 950, s/n, 23⅝" x 33½", pub MPPI | 175.00 | — |
| ☐ **DARK SKY - CANVASBACKS,** rel. 1980. ed. 950, s/n, 24½" x 37¼", pub MPPI | 195.00 | 225.00 |
| ☐ **DIAMOND ISLAND - MALLARDS,** rel. 1980. ed. 950, s/n, 22½" x 38", pub MPPI | 195.00 | 260.00 |
| ☐ **LANDING - CANADA GEESE,** rel. 1980. ed. 950, s/n, 22" x 27½", pub MPPI | 125.00 | 125.00 |
| ☐ **MOUNTAIN SNOW,** rel. 1980. ed. 950, s/n, 22¾" x 29", pub MPPI | 95.00 | 175.00 |
| ☐ **POINTERS AND BOBWHITES,** rel. 1980. ed. 950, s/n, 24⅝" x 35", pub MPPI | 245.00 | 300.00 |
| ☐ **QUAIL COUNTRY,** rel. 1980. ed. 950, s/n, 24⅞" x 35¼", pub MPPI | 250.00 | — |
| ☐ **THE WILLOW - GREEN-WINGED TEAL,** rel. 1980. ed. 950, s/n, 23" x 31½", pub MPPI | 160.00 | 200.00 |
| ☐ **TIMBER - WOOD DUCKS,** rel. 1980. ed. 950, s/n, 23" x 31½", pub MPPI | 160.00 | 200.00 |
| ☐ **TUNDRA - BLACK BRANT,** rel. 1980. ed. 950, s/n, 20½" x 27½", pub MPPI | 85.00 | 100.00 |
| ☐ **TWILIGHT - AMERICAN WIGEON,** rel. 1980. ed. 950, s/n, 18" x 23", pub MPPI | 75.00 | 125.00 |
| ☐ **DARK SKY - RUFFED GROUSE,** rel. 1981. ed. 950, s/n, 24⅝" x 36", pub MPPI | 245.00 | 275.00 |
| ☐ **DARK SKY - SNOW GEESE,** rel. 1981. ed. 950, s/n, 21¾" x 29½", pub MPPI | 175.00 | — |
| ☐ **EARLY SPRING - MALLARDS,** rel. 1981. ed. 950, s/n, 24⅝" x 36", pub MPPI | 220.00 | — |
| ☐ **ESCAPE - RING-NECKED PHEASANTS,** rel. 1981. ed. 950, s/n, 23" x 32¼", pub MPPI | 195.00 | — |
| ☐ **FROSTY MORNING - CANADA GEESE,** rel. 1981. ed. 950, s/n, 28½" x 22¾", pub MPPI | 175.00 | 275.00 |
| ☐ **OUT OF THE PINES - BOBWHITES,** rel. 1981. ed. 950, s/n, 24⅝" x 38", pub MPPI | 245.00 | 300.00 |
| ☐ **SHALLOW RIVER - AMERICAN WIGEON,** rel. 1981. ed. 950, s/n, 24⅝" x 38", pub MPPI | 195.00 | — |
| ☐ **SUNSET - CANADA GEESE,** rel. 1981. ed. 950, s/n, 23" x 32¼", pub MPPI | 195.00 | — |
| ☐ **BASS AND OTHER SUNFISH,** rel. 1982. ed. 950, s/n, 24" x 18", pub MPPI | 10.00 | — |
| ☐ **BREAKING AWAY - PINTAILS,** rel. 1982. ed. 950, s/n, 21¾" x 29½", pub MPPI | 150.00 | — |
| ☐ **FLOODED TIMBER - MALLARDS,** rel. 1982. ed. 450, no other information available | 150.00 | 800.00 |
| ☐ **HEAVY SNOW - RUFFED GROUSE,** rel. 1982. ed. 950, s/n, 20" x 26¼", pub MPPI | 150.00 | — |
| ☐ **MINIATURE SERIES I - MALLARDS,** rel. 1982. ed. 950, s/n, 12" x 15⅞", pub MPPI | 75.00 | — |
| ☐ **MINIATURE SERIES II - WOOD DUCKS,** rel. 1982. ed. 950, s/n, 12" x 15⅞", pub MPPI | 75.00 | — |
| ☐ **QUAIL COVEY - BOBWHITES,** rel. 1982. ed. 950, s/n, 24½" x 35¾", pub MPPI | 245.00 | — |
| ☐ **STONY LAKE - MALLARDS,** rel. 1982. ed. 950, s/n, 17⅞" x 24", pub MPPI | 100.00 | — |
| ☐ **THE SPLASH - SMALLMOUTH BASS,** rel. 1982. ed. 950, s/n, 18¾" x 24", pub MPPI | 95.00 | — |
| ☐ **ALONG THE RIVER - TRUMPETER SWAN,** rel. 1983. ed. 950, s/n, 12" x 16", pub MPPI | 50.00 | — |
| ☐ **COASTING DOWN - CANADA GEESE,** rel. 1983. ed. 950, s/n, 8¼" x 10", pub MPPI | 40.00 | — |
| ☐ **DARK SKY - PHEASANTS,** rel. 1983. ed. 950, s/n, 21¾" x 29½", pub MPPI | 125.00 | — |
| ☐ **PREENING - BLUE WINGED TEAL,** rel. 1983. ed. 950, s/n, 18¾" x 22½", pub MPPI | 115.00 | — |
| ☐ **RUNNING BLUES, SCALED QUAIL,** rel. 1983. ed. 950, s/n, 17⅞" x 24", pub MPPI | 100.00 | — |
| ☐ **TRANQUIL MARSH - MALLARDS,** rel. 1983. ed. 950, s/n, 11" x 15", pub MPPI | 60.00 | — |
| **1948-49 FEDERAL DUCK STAMP PRINT** | | |
| ☐ **BUFFLEHEAD** - Stone Lithograph. 1st edition -200, s/n, 13" x 18" | 15.00 | 1,100.00 |
| 2nd edition - 150, s/n, 13" x 18" | 15.00 | 950.00 |
| 3rd edition - 400, s/n, 13" x 18" | 60.00 | 700.00 |
| Color Edition (reproduced from original watercolor), 350, s/n, 13" x 18" | 250.00 | 400.00 |

| | ISSUE PRICE | CURRENT PRICE |
|---|---|---|
| **1951-52 FEDERAL DUCK STAMP PRINT** | | |
| ☐ **GADWALLS** - Stone Lithograph. 1st edition -250, s/n, 13″ x 18″ | 15.00 | 1,000.00 |
| 2nd edition - 400, s/n, 13″ x 18″ | 60.00 | 700.00 |
| **1959-60 FEDERAL DUCK STAMP PRINT** | | |
| ☐ **LABRADOR RETRIEVER** - Stone Lithograph. 1st edition - 400, s/n, 13″ x 18″ | 60.00 | 1,200.00 |
| 2nd edition - 300, s/n, 13″ x 18″ | 60.00 | 1,000.00 |
| 3rd edition - 400, s/n, 13″ x 18″ | 60.00 | 950.00 |
| **1969-70 FEDERAL DUCK STAMP PRINT** | | |
| ☐ **WHITE-WINGED SCOTERS** -Stone Lithograph. 1st edition -750, s/n, 13″ x 18″ | 60.00 | 850.00 |
| **1971-72 FEDERAL DUCK STAMP PRINT** | | |
| ☐ **CINNAMON TEAL** - Lithograph/Hand-colored. 1st edition - 950, s/n, 13″ x 18″ | 75.00 | 4,500.00 |
| **1972 IOWA DUCK STAMP PRINT** | | |
| ☐ **MALLARDS** - Reproduced from original watercolor. 1st edition - 500, s/n, 13″ x 17″ | 60.00 | 3,500.00 |
| **1977 IOWA DUCK STAMP PRINT** | | |
| ☐ **BLUEBILLS - LESSUR SCAUP** - Reproduced from original watercolor. 1st edition - 950, s/n, 12½″ x 17″ | 80.00 | 700.00 |
| **1973 DUCKS UNLIMITED PRINT** | | |
| ☐ **MARSHLANDER MALLARDS**, ed. 600, s/n, 23½″ x 32″ | Auctioned | 550.00 |
| ☐ **MALLARDS**, rel. 1969. ed. 1,500, s/n, 21¾″ x 26¼″ | *N/A | N/A |
| *Distributed by Winnebago Industries | | |
| ☐ **CANADA GEESE**, rel. 1971. ed. 1,500, s/n, 21¾″ x 26¼″ | *N/A | N/A |
| *Distributed by Winnebago Industries | | |

## JOYCE HAGERBAUMER REED

With a name synonymous with great wildlife art, Joyce has used her inherent talents well. Born in Fullerton, California in 1945, she developed an early interest in animals from weekly visits to the San Diego Zoo and exposure to the taxidermy work of her well known father, David Hagerbaumer.

After majoring in biological illustration at the University of California at Los Angeles, she spent an additional two years studying at UCLA and the University of California at Santa Barbara as a zoology major.

In 1969, Joyce and her husband, Bob, moved to Westham Island in British Columbia near the George C. Teifel Migratory Bird Sanctuary. Through the encouragement of her father and the use of reference material from the Vertebrate Museum at the University of British Columbia, Joyce's work broadened to include not only waterfowl and upland game birds, but most of the non-sporting birds of North America.

Joyce and Bob returned to Oregon to further pursue her interests in wildlife art near her father's 135 acre wildlife farm. Joyce's interests in wildlife art have always included a special appeal to the botanical aspect of her work. Her later works show a great expansion and improvement in the use of plants.

### JOYCE HAGERBAUMER REED

| | | |
|---|---|---|
| ☐ **BACKWATER TEAL**, rel. 1974. ed. 450, s/n, size not available, pub WWI | 85.00 | — |
| ☐ **WINTERING DOVES**, rel. 1975. ed. 450, s/n, size not available, pub WWI | 60.00 | — |
| ☐ **QUIET MORNING - MALLARDS**, rel. 1981. ed. 850, s/n, size not available, pub WWI | 60.00 | — |

# CHUCK REN

After receiving a degree in fine art from the University of Arizona, Chuck Ren worked with Lockheed Aircraft and Computer Sciences Corporation as a commercial artist. He has been commissioned by The North American Hockey League, The North American Soccer League, The National Football League, Paramount Pictures, Universal Pictures, and A&M Records.

He painted the 1980 Super Bowl poster and program cover and also did paintings of several football greats including O. J. Simpson, Joe Namath, Gale Sayers, Frank Gifford, Bobby Lane, Terry Metcalf, and Earl Campbell.

Currently, western themes dominate Ren's paintings.

**HOW THE WEST WAS WON** *by Chuck Ren*

| | ISSUE PRICE | CURRENT PRICE |
|---|---|---|
| ☐ **AFTER THE RIDE,** ed. 600, s/n, 18¾" x 24½", pub GSP | 75.00 | — |
| ☐ **FIRST SNOW,** ed. 600, s/n, 27¾" x 22½", pub GSP | 75.00 | — |
| ☐ **GRAND DAD'S WAGON,** ed. 600, s/n, 21" x 25½", pub GSP | 75.00 | — |
| ☐ **THE CHAMPIONS,** ed. 600, s/n, 29½" x 22½", pub GSP | 75.00 | — |
| ☐ **HOW THE WEST WAS WON,** rel. 1980. ed. 600, s/n, 18¾" x 24½", pub GSP | 75.00 | — |
| ☐ **THE MOUNTAIN MEN,** rel. 1981. ed. 600, s/n, 22" x 24½", pub GSP | 75.00 | 150.00 |
| ed. 100, remarqued artist proofs | 125.00 | — |
| ☐ **DOUBLE TROUBLE,** rel. 1982. ed. 600, s/n, 29" x 21⅛", pub GSP | 75.00 | — |
| ed. 10, remarqued artist proofs | 125.00 | — |
| ☐ **THE STRANGER,** rel. 1982. ed. 600, s/n, 29½" x 22½", pub GSP | 75.00 | — |

# CHET RENESON

Chet Reneson was born and raised in Connecticut on a game farm. He received his training at the University of Hartford Art School and then worked as a book and magazine illustrator.

In recent years Reneson has devoted himself full-time to painting wildlife and fishing scenes which have appeared in Ducks Unlimited Magazine, Gray's Sporting Journal, National Wildlife Magazine and Sports Afield. Reneson travels across this country and into Canada and the island continually inspire new works which have a style that is often compared to Winslow Homer's.

| CHET RENESON | ISSUE PRICE | CURRENT PRICE |
|---|---|---|
| ☐ **SNOW SQUALL,** rel. 1972. ed. 400, s/n, 27″ x 17″, distr. WWI | — | 400.00 |
| ☐ **OPENING DAY,** rel. 1974. ed. 400, s/n, 26″ x 16″, distr. WWI | — | 400.00 |
| ☐ **WINTER GROUSE,** rel. 1974. ed. 400, s/n, 26″ x 16″, distr. WWI | — | 125.00 |
| ☐ **CORN HUNTERS,** rel. 1976. ed. 400, s/n, 27″ x 17″, distr. WWI | — | 150.00 |
| ☐ **ON THE FLATS,** rel. 1976. ed. 200, s/n, 16″ x 26″, pub SEL | 75.00 | 400.00 |
| Remarqued print | 100.00 | 550.00 |
| ☐ **WINTER BROADBILLS,** rel. 1976. ed. 200, s/n, 26″ x 16″, distr. WWI | — | 225.00 |
| ☐ **EARLY VISIT,** rel. 1977. ed. 580, s/n, 26″ x 16″, distr. WWI | — | 350.00 |
| ☐ **AMBUSH,** rel. 1978. ed. 200, s/n, 26″ x 16″, distr. WWI | — | 200.00 |
| ☐ **IN THE KEYS,** rel. 1978. ed. 300, s/n, 16½″ x 25⅛″, pub SEL | 75.00 | 175.00 |
| Remarqued print | 125.00 | 200.00 |
| ☐ **MATCHMAKERS,** rel. 1978. ed. 300, s/n, 26″ x 16″, distr. WWI | — | 200.00 |
| ☐ **WILD FOWLERS,** rel. 1978. ed. 300, s/n, 26″ x 16″, distr. WWI | — | 200.00 |
| ☐ **TEA TIME,** rel. 1979. ed. 400, s/n, 18″ x 27¼″, pub SEL | 100.00 | 125.00 |
| Remarqued print | 150.00 | — |
| ☐ **WINTER MARSH,** rel. 1980. ed. 400, s/n, 26″ x 16″, distr. WWI | — | 75.00 |
| ☐ **FLIGHT BIRDS,** rel. 1981. ed. 400, s/n, size not available, distr. WWI | — | 80.00 |
| ☐ **GOOD LUCK WIND,** rel. 1981. ed. 200, s/n, 16″ x 11″, distr. WWI | — | 125.00 |
| ☐ **OUT OF REACH,** rel. 1981. ed. 500, s/n, size not available, distr. WWI | — | 40.00 |
| ☐ **PARTNERS,** rel. 1981. ed. 500, s/n, size not available, distr. WWI | — | 40.00 |
| ☐ **WALKING THE RIFFLES,** rel. 1981. ed. 500, s/n, 16″ x 11″, distr. WWI | — | 40.00 |
| ☐ **WELL HOOKED,** rel. 1981. ed. 500, s/n, size not available, distr. WWI | — | 40.00 |
| ☐ **BAYGUNNERS,** rel. 1982. ed. 300, s/n, 29″ x 21″, distr. WWI | — | 100.00 |
| ☐ **TROPHY FISH,** rel. 1982. ed. 400, s/n, size not available, distr. WWI | — | 100.00 |

# JAMES REYNOLDS

Among the people who follow contemporary Western art, Jim Reynolds' name will appear at, or near the top of everyone's choices of "the best". This reputation of distinction is widely acknowledged and securely established.

Not only are Reynold's paintings historically authentic, but more importantly, they are aesthetically pleasing and artistically mature.

A Reynold's painting is always, a work of art. The fact that it is also of a Western scene is a secondary consideration. Any painting that attains the distinction of "fine art" must do so primarily on its artistic merit, and not merely because of a fortunate choice of subject matter. The level of artistic merit can be measured by the artist's command of the technical skills of painting, together with the "heart" of the artist, his inspiration, being as much an ingredient of the finished work as the paint itself.

A Westerner with a sensitive eye to the Southwestern surroundings, Reynolds' will continue to produce paintings that are a prime factor in the development of Western art as fine art, instead of just historical illustration.

*Written by Don Hedgpeth, Reprinted with permission.*

**BORN TOO EARLY** *by James Reynolds*

## JAMES REYNOLDS

| | | ISSUE PRICE | CURRENT PRICE |
|---|---|---|---|
| ☐ | **THE GOOD LIFE,** rel. 1975. ed. 950, s/n, 23″ x 31½″, pub MPPI . . . . . . . . . . | 150.00 | 325.00 |
| ☐ | **BORN TOO EARLY,** rel. 1979. ed. 950, s/n, 23″ x 30½″, pub MPPI . . . . . . . . | 150.00 | 175.00 |
| ☐ | **EATIN' DUST,** rel. 1979. ed. 950, s/n, 21″ x 29″, pub MPPI . . . . . . . . . . . . . . | 125.00 | — |
| ☐ | **COFFEE BREAK,** rel. 1981. ed. 950, s/n, 23″ x 31⅛″, pub MPPI . . . . . . . . . . | 175.00 | — |
| ☐ | **SPRING CALVES,** rel. 1981. ed. 950, s/n, 23″ x 32¼″, pub MPPI . . . . . . . . . | 195.00 | — |
| ☐ | **ANOTHER DAY,** rel. 1983. ed. 1,000, s/n, 17″ x 25½″, pub TAP . . . . . . . . . . | 100.00 | — |
| ☐ | **COLORADO COLD,** rel. 1983. ed. 1,000, s/n, 17″ x 25½″, pub TAP . . . . . . . . | 100.00 | — |

# MICHAEL JAMES RIDDET

Michael Riddet was born shortly after the end of World War II in a ship-building town in Lancashire, England called Barrow-in-Furness. This was where his father introduced him to art by teaching him to sketch the many different ships.

While still a very young boy, the family moved to Walney Island, just off the mainland from Barrow. Here, a large bird sanctuary on the southern tip of the island provided the setting and the subject for Michael Riddet to develop his interest in and talent for sketching birds. The tidal flats, dunes and gorse on Walney Island provided a further abundance of material for observation, study and sketching. In 1956, the Riddet family came to America. Riddet was given Audubon's *"Birds of America"* which was to inspire and influence his work from that time on.

"The personality manifests itself in the eyes," he explains. "After spending many hours observing the bird in its natural habitat and researching its range, diet and habits, I begin to sketch. When I have made my final sketch, I begin to paint concentrating first on the eyes. If I can capture the mood in the eyes, then I can build around them much more easily. Each feather I paint separately rather than working in basic color masses in order to produce a more realistic bird painting."

## MICHAEL JAMES RIDDET

| | ISSUE PRICE | CURRENT PRICE |
|---|---|---|
| ☐ **AMERICAN GOLDFINCH,** rel. 1972. ed. 4,700, s/o, 11" x 14", pub CHWA .... | 12.00 | 25.00 |
| ed. 200, s/n ................................. | 30.00 | — |
| ed. 100 Artist proofs | | |
| ☐ **BLUE JAY,** rel. 1972. ed. 4,700, s/o, 11" x 14", pub CHWA............... | 12.00 | 25.00 |
| ed. 200, s/n ................................. | 30.00 | — |
| ed. 100 Artist proofs | | |
| ☐ **CARDINAL,** rel. 1972. ed. 4,700, s/o, 11" x 14", pub CHWA .............. | 12.00 | 25.00 |
| ed. 200, s/n ................................. | 30.00 | — |
| ed. 100 Artist proofs | | |
| ☐ **EASTERN BLUEBIRD,** rel. 1972. ed. 4,700, s/o, 11" x 14", pub CHWA ...... | 12.00 | 25.00 |
| ed. 200, s/n ................................. | 30.00 | — |
| ed. 100 Artist proofs | | |
| ☐ **EASTERN MEADOWLARK,** rel. 1972. ed. 4,700, s/o, 11" x 14", pub CHWA... | 12.00 | 25.00 |
| ed. 200, s/n ................................. | 30.00 | — |
| ed. 100 Artist proofs | | |
| ☐ **ROBIN,** rel. 1972. ed. 4,700, s/o, 11" x 14", pub CHWA ................. | 12.00 | 25.00 |
| ed. 200, s/n ................................. | 30.00 | — |
| ed. 100 Artist proofs | | |
| ☐ **WOOD THRUSH,** rel. 1972. ed. 4,700, s/o, 11" x 14", pub CHWA .......... | 12.00 | 25.00 |
| ed. 200, s/n ................................. | 30.00 | — |
| ed. 100 Artist proofs | | |

# C. FORD RILEY

A young artist with a splendid future, Riley is a watercolorist who paints birds. Each piece of artwork is extensively detailed. He layers colors creating the multitude of shades and illusions in his work.

He has received much acclaim with prints and commissioned works in both private and corporate collections. His work is currently being exhibited in The Leigh Yawkey Woodson Art Museum's 1983 Bird Art Exhibition.

## C. FORD RILEY

| | | |
|---|---|---|
| ☐ **COOPERS HAWK WITH FALL LEAVES,** ed. 350, s/n, 30" x 22", pub CFRC .... | 100.00 | — |
| ☐ **MANDARIN CARDINALS AND MAGNOLIAS,** ed. 350, s/n, 30" x 22", pub CFRC | 100.00 | — |
| ☐ **PARULA WARBLERS ON A FALL MORNING,** ed. 800, s/n, 12" x 16", pub CFRC ................................................. | 30.00 | — |
| ☐ **WOODCOCK AT McGIRTS CREEK,** ed. 500, s/n, 26" x 28", pub CFRC ....... | 100.00 | — |
| ☐ **WOOD DUCKS AT McGIRTS CREEK,** ed. 500, s/n, 26" x 28", pub CFRC ...... | 100.00 | — |

# CHUCK RIPPER

| | | |
|---|---|---|
| ☐ **BRIARPATCH COVEY,** ed. 950, s/n, 16" x 24", pub RAF ................. | 40.00 | — |
| ☐ **CARDINALS,** ed. 950, s/n, 13" x 11", pub RAF ........................ | 25.00 | 50.00 |
| ☐ **EARLY FLIGHT - CANADA GEESE,** ed. 950, s/n, 13" x 18", pub RAF ........ | 30.00 | 60.00 |
| ☐ **MID-WINTER BOBWHITES,** ed. 950, s/n, 16" x 23⅝", pub RAF ........... | 40.00 | — |

# DELLA ROBERTS

Della Roberts studied under Pierre Daura, a student of Emile Bernard and the engraver, Lambert, and was a student at the Boston Museum of Fine Arts. She received a degree in art from Randolph-Macon Woman's College.

In addition to numerous one man shows in North Carolina, Virginia and Georgia, she has had a one man show in New York at Hammer Galleries. One of her paintings was included in their Fiftieth Anniversary Exhibition which toured the south. She has participated in many invitational and juried shows. Her work may also be seen in galleries in Solvang, California and Palm Harbor, Florida. Her paintings have been featured in *Art World, Pace Magazine, G Magazine, Southern World Magazine* and *Southern Accent Magazine.* Her work is in permanent collections of the Arista Corporation, the Danville Museum of Fine Arts and History, McLean Trucking Company, the Northwest Collection, R. J. Reynolds Industries, the Randolph-Macon Collection of American Art, Wachovia Band and Trust, N.A., in private collections in Canada, Panama and throughout this country.

## DELLA ROBERTS

| | ISSUE PRICE | CURRENT PRICE |
|---|---|---|
| ☐ ONE DAY, rel. 1978. ed. 500, s/n, 17¾" x 15½", pub RI | 40.00 | 40.00 |
| ☐ SEA SHELLS, rel. 1978. ed. 500, s/n, 9½" x 19", pub RI | 50.00 | 50.00 |
| ☐ GERANIUM AND SHELLS, rel. 1979. ed. 500, s/n, 17¾" x 15½", pub RI | 50.00 | 50.00 |
| ☐ NARCISSI STUDY, rel. 1981. ed. 750, s/n, 15¾" x 12½", pub RI | 75.00 | 75.00 |

# DOLORES ROBERSON

To be unique among one's peers, is a much sought-after goal for many wildlife artists. For Dolores Roberson it is as natural as the subjects she paints. Intensive research and study assures authentic detail in every painting. But, an academic understanding of her subjects is not enough for her. Only love can endow each work with "individual personality" — the quality which places her paintings in a class by themselves. A case in point is her painting of a Smoky Mountain Black Bear . . . several viewers have exclaimed "That's Kate!" And, so it is. Kate has become well known to many Smoky visitors, and so faithfully does the painting depict her, that she is instantly recognized. All bears may look alike to some folks, but not to Dolores. That same dedication is applied to each painting that flows from her brush.

## DELORES ROBERSON

| | | |
|---|---|---|
| ☐ AUDACITY, ed. 1,000, s/n, 9" x 15", dist. by MMFC | 20.00 | — |
| ☐ BLACK BEAR, ed. 1,000, s/n, 22" x 26", dist. by MMFC | 35.00 | — |
| ☐ TROPHY IN PAINT, ed. 1,000, s/n, 16" x 20", dist. by MMFC | 25.00 | — |
| **FEATHERED FAMILIES SERIES** | | |
| ☐ BOBWHITE QUAIL, ed. 2,056, s/n, 16" x 20", dist. by MMFC | 25.00 | — |
| ☐ CARDINAL, ed. 2,000, s/n, 16" x 20", dist. by MMFC | 25.00 | — |
| ☐ EASTERN BLUEBIRD, ed. 2,000, s/n, 16" x 20", dist. by MMFC | 25.00 | — |
| ☐ SCREECH OWL, ed. 2,100, s/n, 16" x 20", dist. by MMFC | 25.00 | — |
| ☐ SPRING COMES TO THE FOREST FLOOR, ed. 1,000, s/n, 22" x 26", dist. by MMFC | 25.00 | — |
| ☐ THE COLLECTORS, ed. 1,000, s/n, 14" x 18", dist. by MMFC | 35.00 | — |
| ed. 100, s/n, artist's proofs | 70.00 | — |
| ☐ THE SENTINEL, ed. 1,000, s/n, 16" x 20", dist. by MMFC | 25.00 | — |
| **THE FOREST EDGE WILDFLOWER SERIES** | | |
| ☐ BLACK-EYED SUSAN, ed. 1,000, s/n, 5" x 12", dist. by MMFC | 12.50 | — |
| ☐ DOGWOOD, ed. 1,000, s/n, 5" x 12", dist. by MMFC | 12.50 | — |
| ☐ MOUNTAIN LAUREL, ed. 1,000, s/n, 5" x 12", dist. by MMFC | 12.50 | — |
| ☐ OX-EYE DAISY, ed. 1,000, s/n, 5" x 12", dist. by MMFC | 12.50 | — |
| **WORLD OF WONDER WILDLIFE SERIES** | | |
| ☐ EASTERN CHIPMUNK, ed. 1,000, s/n, 16" x 20", dist. by MMFC | 25.00 | — |
| ☐ FAWN AND BUTTERFLY, ed. 1,000, s/n, 16" x 20", dist. by MMFC | 25.00 | — |
| ☐ RACCOON, ed. 1,000, s/n, 16" x 20", dist. by MMFC | 25.00 | — |
| ☐ RED FOX, ed. 1,000, s/n, 16" x 20", dist. by MMFC | 25.00 | — |

# LEE ROBERSON

To paint beautiful feelings . . . capture nostalgic moods . . . these are the goals that challenge and beckon Lee Roberson each time he takes up his brush. His favorite subjects — forests, streams, mountains, ancient structures — lend themselves pleasingly to the accomplishment of his goals.

Roberson spends each day in close communion with the earth. Growing vegetables, tending livestock, chopping firewood, constructing buildings . . . it's all a part of the life he has chosen. The proximity of his remote homestead to the Great Smoky Mountains National Park provides frequent encounters with the flora and fauna that adds so much to his paintings. So, when you view the paintings of this talented artist, don't be surprised if you feel that you have "been there yourself". This kind of authentic mood and detail can come only from experiencing and loving one's subject.

| LEE ROBERSON | ISSUE PRICE | CURRENT PRICE |
|---|---|---|
| ☐ **A TIME TO REMEMBER.** ed. 1,000, s/n, 24″ x 16″, dist. by MMFC . . . . . . . . . This print was produced as a fund raising project for the Maryville, Tennessee Little League Baseball Team. | 25.00 | Sold Out |
| ☐ **COUNTRY STORE.** ed. 1,000, s/n, 20″ x 16″, dist. by MMFC . . . . . . . . . . . . . | 25.00 | — |
| ☐ **EVENING IN THE COVE.** ed. 1,000, s/n, 24″ x 16″, dist. by MMFC . . . . . . . . . | 35.00 | — |
| ☐ **FIRST LIGHT.** ed. 1,000, s/n, 20″ x 16″, dist. by MMFC . . . . . . . . . . . . . . . | 25.00 | — |
| ☐ **PLACE IN THE COUNTRY.** ed. 1,000, s/n, 24″ x 16″, dist. by MMFC . . . . . . . . | | |

# E. JOHN ROBINSON

E. John Robinson was raised along Oregon's rugged coast and began painting the sea at a very early age.

He received his BFA degree at the California College of Arts and Crafts in Oakland and his MFA from the San Francisco State College. He has written two books for artists who are seeking a firm background in marine painting. They are Marine Painting in *Oil and Seascape Painters' Problem Book,* by Watson-Guptill. He also did the cover for *Reader's Digest, October 1976.*

After more than a decade of painting the sea, he remarks, "I have enjoyed and continue to enjoy painting . . . I have never arrived."

| E. JOHN ROBINSON | | |
|---|---|---|
| ☐ **FROLIC,** rel. 1976. ed. 2,000, s/n, 22″ x 28″, pub FHG . . . . . . . . . . . . . . . . | 30.00 | 60.00 |
| ☐ **FULL MOON,** rel. 1976. ed. 2,000, s/n, 22″ x 28″, pub FHG . . . . . . . . . . . . . | 30.00 | 60.00 |
| ☐ **BIG SUR COAST,** rel. 1977. ed. 800, s/n, 28″ x 22″, pub FHG . . . . . . . . . . . . | 40.00 | — |
| ☐ **EVENTIDE,** rel. 1977. ed. 800, s/n, 16″ x 28″, pub FHG . . . . . . . . . . . . . . . | 40.00 | 80.00 |
| ☐ **PACIFIC NORTHWEST,** rel. 1977. ed. 800, s/n, 22″ x 28″, pub FHG . . . . . . . . | 40.00 | 80.00 |
| ☐ **CHANCE OF RAIN,** rel. 1978. ed. 800, s/n, 16″ x 20″, pub FHG . . . . . . . . . . . | 30.00 | — |
| ☐ **KONA SURF,** rel. 1978. ed. 800, s/n, 16″ x 20″, pub FHG . . . . . . . . . . . . . . | 30.00 | — |

# NORMAN ROCKWELL

Norman Rockwell was one of the greatest illustrators of all time. His legendary fame resulted from the decades he worked as primary illustrator for the *Saturday Evening Post.* No one has ever captured the heart and soul of American life quite as well as Rockwell. He painted the everyday scenes we can all identify with in a warm, nostalgic, poignant way that is unmistakably Rockwell. He lived and worked in Stockbridge, Massachusetts for many years prior to his death in 1978; indeed the names Rockwell and Stockbridge are synonymous. The Old Corner House is the museum in Stockbridge which was established to house a collection of original Rockwell oil paintings and is open to the public year round.

## NORMAN ROCKWELL

| | ISSUE PRICE | CURRENT PRICE |
|---|---|---|
| ☐ A DAY IN THE LIFE OF A BOY, rel. 1976. ed. 200, s/n, 19″ x 20″ | 1,000.00 | 5,000.00 |
| ed. 25 on Japon, s/n, 19″ x 20″, litho, pub CFAC | 1,050.00 | 5,150.00 |
| ☐ A STUDY FOR THE DOCTOR'S OFFICE, rel. 1976. ed. 200, s/n, 22″ x 25″, litho, pub CFAC | 600.00 | 4,900.00 |
| ☐ AMERICAN FAMILY FOLIO (consisting of 5 prints). **Teacher's Pet, Fido's House, Two O'Clock Feeding, Debut, Save Me,** rel. 1976. ed. 200, s/n, 20″ x 26″, litho, pub CFAC | 1,500.00 | 9,100.00 |
| ☐ AT THE BARBER, rel. 1976. ed. 200, s/n, 30″ x 22″, litho, pub CFAC | — | 3,300.00 |
| ☐ AVIARY. rel. 1976. ed. 200, s/n, 20″ x 26″, litho, pub CFAC | 200.00 | 3,300.00 |
| ☐ BARBERSHOP QUARTET. rel. 1976. ed. 200, s/n, 24″ x 30″, litho, pub CFAC . | 200.00 | 2,300.00 |
| ☐ BLACKSMITH SHOP. rel. 1976. ed. 200, s/n, 14″ x 30″, litho, pub CFAC | N/A | 5,400.00 |
| ☐ BOOKSELLER, rel. 1976. ed. 200, s/n, 17″ x 23″ | N/A | 1,800.00 |
| ed. 25 on Japon, s/n, 17″ x 23″, litho, pub CFAC | — | 1,850.00 |
| ☐ CHILDREN AT WINDOW. rel. 1976. ed. 200, s/n, 20″ x 26″, litho, pub CFAC .. | 350.00 | 1,700.00 |
| ☐ CIRCUS. rel. 1976. ed. 200, s/n, 20″ x 26″, litho, pub CFAC | N/A | 1,750.00 |
| ☐ COUNTY AGRICULTURAL AGENT. rel. 1976. ed. 200, s/n, 24″ x 35″, collotype, pub CFAC | 250.00 | 2,800.00 |
| ☐ DISCOVERY. rel. 1976. ed. 200, s/n, 28″ x 32″, collotype, pub CFAC | 200.00 | 5,000.00 |
| ☐ DOCTOR AND BOY. rel. 1976. ed. 200, s/n, 20″ x 26″, litho, pub CFAC | N/A | 2,000.00 |
| ☐ DOCTOR AND DOLL. rel. 1976. ed. 200, s/n, 29″ x 35″, collotype, pub CFAC . | N/A | 10,000.00 |
| ☐ DRESSING UP. rel. 1976. ed. 200, s/n, (in pencil), 20″ x 26″ | 300.00 | 2,800.00 |
| ed. 60, s/n (in ink), 20″ x 26″, litho, pub CFAC | 350.00 | 3,500.00 |
| ☐ FAMILY TREE. rel. 1976. ed. 200, s/n, 25″ x 30″, litho, pub CFAC | N/A | 4,500.00 |
| ☐ FOOTBALL MASCOT. rel. 1976. ed. 200, s/n, 20″ x 26″, litho, pub CFAC | N/A | 1,800.00 |
| ☐ FOUR SEASONS FOLIO (consisting of 4 prints). **Winter, Spring, Summer, Autumn,** rel. 1976. ed. 200, s/n, 20″ x 21″ | N/A | 5,700.00 |
| ed. 25 on Japon, s/n, 20″ x 21″, litho, pub CFAC | N/A | 6,200.00 |
| ☐ FREEDOM FROM FEAR. rel. 1976. ed. 200, s/n, 29″ x 35″, collotype, pub CFAC | 200.00 | 5,100.00 |
| ☐ FREEDOM FROM WANT. rel. 1976. ed. 200, s/n, 29″ x 35″, collotype, pub CFAC | 200.00 | 5,100.00 |
| ☐ FREEDOM OF RELIGION. rel. 1976. ed. 200, s/n, 29″ x 35″, collotype, pub CFAC | 200.00 | 5,100.00 |
| ☐ FREEDOM OF SPEECH. rel. 1976. ed. 200, s/n, 29″ x 35″, collotype, pub CFAC | 200.00 | 5,100.00 |
| ☐ GAIETY DANCE TEAM. rel. 1976. ed. 200, s/n, 24″ x 30″, litho, pub CFAC ... | N/A | 3,000.00 |
| ☐ GIRL AT MIRROR. rel. 1976. ed. 200, s/n, 29″ x 35″, collotype, pub CFAC ... | N/A | 7,500.00 |
| ☐ GOLDEN RULE. rel. 1976. ed. 200, s/n, 29″ x 35″, collotype, pub CFAC ..... | N/A | 3,500.00 |
| ☐ GOSSIPS, rel. 1976. ed. 200, s/n, 22″ x 25″ | 700.00 | 3,900.00 |
| ed. 25 on Japon, s/n, 22″ x 25″, litho, pub CFAC | 750.00 | 4,000.00 |
| ☐ HIGH DIVE. rel. 1976. ed. 200, s/n, 24″ x 30″, collotype, pub CFAC | 500.00 | 2,000.00 |
| ☐ HUCK FINN FOLIO (consisting of 8 prints). **Then Miss Watson, Jim Got Down on His Knees, Miss Mary Jane, My Hand Shook, Your Eyes Is Lookin', The For Three Minutes, There Warn't No Harm, When I Lit My Candle,** rel. 1976. ed. 200, s/n, 20″ x 26″, litho, pub CFAC | 1,500.00 | 9,100.00 |
| ☐ ICHABOD CRANE, rel. 1976. ed. 200, s/n, 20″ x 26″, litho, pub CFAC | 700.00 | 5,300.00 |
| ☐ JERRY. rel. 1976. ed. 200, s/n, 20″ x 26″, litho, pub CFAC | N/A | 1,850.00 |
| ☐ LOBSTERMAN, rel. 1976. ed. 200, s/n, 29″ x 22″, litho, pub CFA | — | 4,100.00 |
| ☐ LINCOLN, rel. 1976. ed. 200, s/n, 20″ x 26″, litho, pub CFAC | 600.00 | 10,500.00 |
| ☐ MARRIAGE LICENSE. rel. 1976. ed. 200, s/n, 28″ x 32″, collotype, pub CFAC | 200.00 | 6,000.00 |
| ☐ MOVING DAY. rel. 1976. ed. 200, s/n, 24″ x 30″, collotype, pub CFAC | 200.00 | 2,200.00 |
| ☐ MUSIC HATH CHARM. rel. 1976. ed. 200, s/n, 24″ x 30″, collotype, pub CFAC | 300.00 | 3,000.00 |
| ☐ OUTBOARD BOUND (Looking Out To Sea). rel. 1976. ed. 200, s/n, 29″ x 35″, collotype, pub CFAC | N/A | 7,000.00 |
| ☐ PRESCRIPTION, rel. 1976. ed. 200, s/n, 24″ x 30″ | 800.00 | 3,000.00 |
| ed. 25 on Japon, s/n, 24″ x 30″, litho, pub CFAC | 850.00 | 1,500.00 |

| | ISSUE PRICE | CURRENT PRICE |
|---|---|---|
| ☐ POOR RICHARD'S ALMANAC FOLIO (consisting of 7 prints). **Ben Franklin's Philadelphia, The Drunkard, Ben's Belles, The Village Smithy, Ye Old Print Shoppe, The Golden Age, The Royal Crown**, rel. 1976. ed. 200, s/n, 20″ x 26″, litho, pub CFAC | 2,500.00 | 14,000.00 |
| ☐ PUPPIES. rel. 1976. ed. 200, s/n, 20″ x 26″, litho, pub CFAC | N/A | 1,800.00 |
| ☐ RALEIGH THE DOG. rel. 1976. ed. 200, s/n, 29″ x 35″, collotype, pub CFAC | 200.00 | 2,700.00 |
| ☐ ROCKET SHIP. rel. 1976. ed. 200, s/n, 20″ x 26″, litho, pub CFAC | N/A | 1,750.00 |
| ☐ RUNAWAY. rel. 1976. ed. 200, s/n, 28″ x 32″, collotype, pub CFAC | 200.00 | 4,800.00 |
| ☐ SAFE AND SOUND, rel. 1976. ed. 200, s/n, 17″ x 20″, litho, pub CFAC | N/A | 1,900.00 |
| ☐ SATURDAY PEOPLE. rel. 1976. ed. 200, s/n, 24″ x 30″, collotype, pub CFAC | 200.00 | 2,000.00 |
| ☐ SAYING GRACE. rel. 1976. ed. 200, s/n, 29″ x 35″, collotype, pub CFAC | N/A | 6,500.00 |
| ☐ SCHOOL DAY FOLIO (consisting of 4 prints). **Baseball, Golf, Studying, Cheering**, rel. 1976. ed. 200, s/n, 20″ x 26″, litho, pub CFAC | 1,800.00 | 7,000.00 |
| ☐ SEE AMERICA FIRST, rel. 1976. ed. 200, s/n, 17″ x 24″ | 700.00 | 4,100.00 |
| ed. 25 on Japon, s/n, 17″ x 24″, litho, pub CFAC | 750.00 | 4,250.00 |
| ☐ SETTLING IN. rel. 1976. ed. 200, s/n, 20″ x 26″, litho, pub CFAC | 1,300.00 | 1,500.00 |
| ☐ SHUFFLETON'S BARBERSHOP. rel. 1976. ed. 200, s/n, 28″ x 35″, collotype, pub CFAC | N/A | 6,500.00 |
| ☐ SPELLING BEE. rel. 1976. ed. 200, s/n, 14″ x 30″, litho, pub CFAC | 200.00 | 5,600.00 |
| ☐ SPRING FLOWERS. rel. 1976. ed. 200, s/n, 27″ x 33″, collotype, pub CFAC | 200.00 | 4,300.00 |
| ☐ SUMMER STOCK, rel. 1976. ed. 200, s/n, 21″ x 27″ | 600.00 | 3,600.00 |
| ed. 25 on Japon, 21″ x 27″, litho, pub CFAC | 650.00 | 3,800.00 |
| ☐ THE BRIDGE. rel. 1976. ed. 200, s/n, 20″ x 26″, litho, pub CFAC | N/A | 2,200.00 |
| ☐ THE CRITIC. rel. 1976. ed. 200, s/n, 28″ x 32″, collotype, pub CFAC | 200.00 | 3,750.00 |
| ☐ THE EXPECTED AND UNEXPECTED, rel. 1976. ed. 200, s/n, 17″ x 20″, litho, pub CFAC | 500.00 | 2,500.00 |
| ☐ THE HOMECOMING. rel. 1976. ed. 200, s/n, 25″ x 30″, litho, pub CFAC | N/A | 1,750.00 |
| ☐ THE HOUSE. rel. 1976. ed. 200, s/n, 20″ x 26″, litho, pub CFAC | N/A | 1,850.00 |
| ☐ THE INVENTOR. rel. 1976. ed. 200, s/n, 19″ x 19″, litho, pub CFAC | N/A | 3,000.00 |
| ☐ THE PROBLEM WE ALL LIVE WITH. rel. 1976. ed. 200, s/n, 31″ x 44″, collotype, pub CFAC | 250.00 | 3,000.00 |
| ☐ THE SCHOOLHOUSE, rel. 1976. ed. 200, s/n, 15″ x 18″ | 350.00 | 1.650.00 |
| ed. 25 on Japon, s/n, 15″ x 18″, litho, pub CFAC | 400.00 | 1,750.00 |
| ☐ THE TEACHER, rel. 1976. ed. 200, s/n, 17″ x 23″ | 400.00 | 1,425.00 |
| ed. 25 on Japon, s/n, 17″ x 23″, litho, pub CFAC | 450.00 | 1,525.00 |
| ☐ THE TEXAN. rel. 1976. ed. 200, s/n, 24″ x 30″, collotype, pub CFAC | 300.00 | 2,500.00 |
| ☐ TOM SAWYER FOLIO (consisting of 8 prints). **Church, Smoking, Cat, Out The Window, White Washing, Grotton, Spanking, Medicine**, rel. 1976. ed. 200, s/n, 20″ x 26″, litho, pub CFAC | 3,000.00 | 16,000.00 |
| ☐ TOM SAWYER COLOR SUITE, rel. 1976. ed. 200, s/n, 20″ x 26″, combination of collotypes & lithos, pub CFAC | 5,800.00 | 1,500.00 |
| ☐ TRUMPETER, rel. 1976. ed. 200, s/n, 21″ x 26″ | N/A | 2,900.00 |
| ed. 25 on Japon, s/n, 21″ x 26″, litho, pub CFAC | N/A | 2,900.00 |
| ☐ WELCOME. rel. 1976. ed. 200, s/n, 20″ x 26″, litho, pub CFAC | N/A | 1,600.00 |
| ☐ WET PAINT. rel. 1976. ed. 200, s/n, 24″ x 30″, collotype, pub CFAC | 300.00 | 2,300.00 |
| ☐ WINDOW WASHER. rel. 1976. ed. 200, s/n, 20″ x 26″, litho, pub CFAC | 250.00 | 1,800.00 |
| ☐ THREE FARMERS, rel. 1977. ed. 200, s/n, 20″ x 16″, litho, pub CFAC | 275.00 | 1,500.00 |
| ☐ TICKETSELLER, rel. 1977. ed. 200, s/n, 21″ x 27″ | 800.00 | 2,000.00 |
| ed. 25 on Japon, s/n, 21″ x 27″, litho, pub CFAC | 850.00 | 2,250.00 |
| ☐ TOP OF THE WORLD. rel. 1977. ed. 200, s/n, 29″ x 35″, collotype, pub CFAC | 200.00 | 2,100.00 |
| ☐ AMERICA MARCHES AHEAD, rel. 1976. ed. 260, s/n, 35″ x 20″, litho, pub EEI | 350.00 | 2,200.00 |
| ☐ THREE BOYS FISHING, rel. 1978. ed. 260, s/n, 23″ x 33″, collotype, pub EEI | 350.00 | 2,500.00 |
| ☐ COLONIAL SIGN PAINTER, rel. 1976. ed. 260, s/n, 35″ x 23″, litho, pub EEI | 700.00 | 4,800.00 |
| ☐ THE RIVALS, rel. 1976. ed. 260, s/n, 20″ x 26″, litho, pub EEI | 375.00 | 4,300.00 |
| ☐ APRIL FOOL, rel. 1976. ed. 260, s/n, 24″ x 26″, collotype, pub EEI | 400.00 | 5,800.00 |
| ☐ BUTTERCUP, rel. 1976. ed. 260, s/n, 21″ x 24″, litho, pub EEI | 450.00 | 4,700.00 |
| ed. 25 on Japon, s/n | 500.00 | 4,950.00 |
| ☐ PUPPY LOVE PORTFOLIO, rel. 1978. ed. 260, s/n, litho, pub EEI | 1,500.00 | 10,000.00 |
| ☐ CHARWOMEN, rel. 1976. ed. 260, s/n, 25″ x 31″, collotype, pub EEI | 600.00 | 4,800.00 |
| ☐ GILDING THE EAGLE, rel. 1978. ed. 260, s/n, 20″ x 26″, litho, pub EEI | 600.00 | 3,200.00 |
| ed. 25 on Japon | 650.00 | 3,500.00 |
| ☐ BEN FRANKLIN, rel. 1978. ed. 260, s/n, 20″ x 26″, litho, pub EEI | 1,100.00 | 4,000.00 |
| ed. 25 on Japon | 1,150.00 | 4,250.00 |
| ☐ CONVENTION, rel. 1978. ed. 260, s/n, 25″ x 31″, collotype, pub EEI | 600.00 | 3,000.00 |

| | ISSUE PRICE | CURRENT PRICE |
|---|---|---|
| ☐ THE SWING, rel. 1978. ed. 260, s/n, 20" x 21", litho, pub EEI . . . . . . . . . . . | 600.00 | 4,700.00 |
| ed. 25 on Japon . . . . . . . . . . . . . . . . . . . . . . . . . . . . . . . . . . . . . . . . . . . . . | 650.00 | 4,950.00 |
| ☐ TOP HAT & TAILS, rel. 1978. ed. 260, s/n, 28" x 34", litho, pub EEI . . . . . . . | 1,000.00 | 7,000.00 |
| ☐ RACER, rel. 1978. ed. 260, s/n, 24" x 29", litho, pub EEI . . . . . . . . . . . . . . . | 600.00 | 2,300.00 |
| ed. 25 on Japon . . . . . . . . . . . . . . . . . . . . . . . . . . . . . . . . . . . . . . . . . . . . . | 650.00 | 2,500.00 |
| ☐ FOOTBALL HERO, rel. 1978. ed. 260, s/n, litho, pub EEI . . . . . . . . . . . . . . . . | 600.00 | 2,200.00 |
| ed. 25 on Japon . . . . . . . . . . . . . . . . . . . . . . . . . . . . . . . . . . . . . . . . . . . . . | 650.00 | 2,400.00 |
| ☐ EXTRA GOOD BOYS & GIRLS, rel. 1978. ed. 260, s/n, 24" x 31", litho, pub EEI | 900.00 | 4,000.00 |
| ed. 25 on Japon . . . . . . . . . . . . . . . . . . . . . . . . . . . . . . . . . . . . . . . . . . . . . | 1,000.00 | 4,250.00 |
| ☐ SHE'S MY BABY, rel. 1978. ed. 260, s/n, 23" x 31", litho, pub EEI . . . . . . . . | 600.00 | 2,700.00 |
| ed. 25 on Japon . . . . . . . . . . . . . . . . . . . . . . . . . . . . . . . . . . . . . . . . . . . . . | 650.00 | 2,950.00 |
| ☐ YOUNG LINCOLN, rel. 1978. ed. 260, s/n, 19" x 34", litho, pub EEI . . . . . . . . | 1,200.00 | 9,000.00 |
| ed. 14 on Japon . . . . . . . . . . . . . . . . . . . . . . . . . . . . . . . . . . . . . . . . . . . . . | 1,500.00 | 9,400.00 |
| ☐ REJECTED SUITOR, rel. 1978. ed. 260, s/n, 21" x 26", litho, pub EEI . . . . . . | 700.00 | 2,800.00 |
| ed. 25 on Japon . . . . . . . . . . . . . . . . . . . . . . . . . . . . . . . . . . . . . . . . . . . . . | 750.00 | 3,050.00 |
| ☐ YOUNG SPOONERS, rel. 1978. ed. 260, s/n, 20" x 24", litho, pu4 EEI . . . . . . | 700.00 | 5,600.00 |
| ed. 25 on Japon . . . . . . . . . . . . . . . . . . . . . . . . . . . . . . . . . . . . . . . . . . . . . | 750.00 | 5,850.00 |
| ☐ SPORTS PORTFOLIO (consisting of 4 prints). **Basketball, Baseball, Golf, Football**, rel. 1978. ed. 260, s/n, litho, pub EEI . . . . . . . . . . . . . . . . . . . . . . | 3,000.00 | 10,000.00 |
| ed. 25 on Japon . . . . . . . . . . . . . . . . . . . . . . . . . . . . . . . . . . . . . . . . . . . . . | 3,200.00 | 11,000.00 |
| ☐ HAYSEED CRITIC, rel. 1978. ed. 260, s/n, 20" x 26", litho, pub EEI . . . . . . . . | 700.00 | 3,300.00 |
| ed. 25 on Japon . . . . . . . . . . . . . . . . . . . . . . . . . . . . . . . . . . . . . . . . . . . . . | 750.00 | 3,550.00 |
| ☐ BOY ON STILTS, rel. 1976. ed. 260, s/n, 24" x 31", litho, pub EEI . . . . . . . . | 800.00 | 3,000.00 |
| ed. 25 on Japon, rel. 1978. . . . . . . . . . . . . . . . . . . . . . . . . . . . . . . . . . . . . . | 900.00 | 3,200.00 |
| ☐ BACK FROM CAMP, rel. 1978. ed. 260, s/n, 20" x 26", litho, pub EEI . . . . . . . | 800.00 | 2,800.00 |
| ed. 25 on Japon . . . . . . . . . . . . . . . . . . . . . . . . . . . . . . . . . . . . . . . . . . . . . | 900.00 | 3,050.00 |
| ☐ DREAMS OF LONG AGO, rel. 1978. ed. 260, s/n, 20" x 26", litho, pub EEI . . . | 1,000.00 | 6,500.00 |
| ed. 25 on Japon . . . . . . . . . . . . . . . . . . . . . . . . . . . . . . . . . . . . . . . . . . . . . | 1,100.00 | 6,700.00 |
| ☐- JESTER, rel. 1978. ed. 260, s/n, 20" x 26", litho, pub EEI . . . . . . . . . . . . . . | 800.00 | 2,600.00 |
| ed. 25 on Japon . . . . . . . . . . . . . . . . . . . . . . . . . . . . . . . . . . . . . . . . . . . . . | 900.00 | 2,850.00 |
| ☐ AFTER CHRISTMAS, rel. 1978. ed. 260, s/n, 20" x 26", litho, pub EEI . . . . . . | 800.00 | 4,000.00 |
| ed. 25 on Japon . . . . . . . . . . . . . . . . . . . . . . . . . . . . . . . . . . . . . . . . . . . . . | 900.00 | 4,200.00 |
| ☐ CAN'T WAIT, rel. 1978. ed. 260, s/n, 20" x 26", litho, pub EEI . . . . . . . . . . . | 800.00 | 3,800.00 |
| ed. 25 on Japon . . . . . . . . . . . . . . . . . . . . . . . . . . . . . . . . . . . . . . . . . . . . . | 900.00 | 4,050.00 |
| ☐ CHILD'S SURPRISE, rel. 1978. ed. 260, s/n, 20" x 26", litho, pub EEI . . . . . . | 1,000.00 | 4,200.00 |
| ed. 25 on Japon . . . . . . . . . . . . . . . . . . . . . . . . . . . . . . . . . . . . . . . . . . . . . | 1,100.00 | 4,400.00 |
| ☐ VOYAGER, rel. 1978. ed. 260, s/n, 25" x 32", collotype, pub EEI . . . . . . . . . . | 1,000.00 | 6,800.00 |
| ☐ THE WIND UP, rel. 1978. ed. 260, s/n, 23" x 29", litho, pub EEI . . . . . . . . . . | 1,500.00 | 3,400.00 |
| ed. 25 on Japon . . . . . . . . . . . . . . . . . . . . . . . . . . . . . . . . . . . . . . . . . . . . . | 1,700.00 | 3,650.00 |
| ☐ CATCHING THE BIG ONE, rel. 1978. ed. 260, s/n, 26" x 34", litho, pub EEI . . . | 1,000.00 | 3,300.00 |
| ed. 25 on Japon . . . . . . . . . . . . . . . . . . . . . . . . . . . . . . . . . . . . . . . . . . . . . | 1,200.00 | 3,550.00 |
| ☐ AFTER THE PROM, rel. 1978. ed. 260, s/n, 21" x 27", litho, pub EEI . . . . . . . | 1,500.00 | 4,400.00 |
| ed. 25 on Japon . . . . . . . . . . . . . . . . . . . . . . . . . . . . . . . . . . . . . . . . . . . . . | 1,700.00 | 4,650.00 |
| ☐ HORSESHOE FORGING CONTEST, rel. 1978. ed. 260, s/n, 12" x 25", collotype, pub EEI . . . . . . . . . . . . . . . . . . . . . . . . . . . . . . . . . . . . . . . . . . . . . | 3,500.00 | 9,000.00 |
| ☐ MUGGLETON STAGECOACH, rel. 1978. ed. 260, size not available, s/n, pub EEI . . . . . . . . . . . . . . . . . . . . . . . . . . . . . . . . . . . . . . . . . . . . . . . . . . . | 2,200.00 | 3,000.00 |
| ed. 25 on Japon . . . . . . . . . . . . . . . . . . . . . . . . . . . . . . . . . . . . . . . . . . . . . | 2,400.00 | 3,200.00 |
| ☐ FIRST AIRPLANE RIDE, rel. 1980. ed. 260, s/n, 21" x 26", pub EEI . . . . . . . . | 2,200.00 | 4,200.00 |
| ed. 25 on Japon . . . . . . . . . . . . . . . . . . . . . . . . . . . . . . . . . . . . . . . . . . . . . | 2,400.00 | 4,400.00 |
| ☐ JAZZ IT UP, rel. 1980. ed. 260, s/n, 21" x 28½", pub EEI . . . . . . . . . . . . . . | 2,200.00 | 3,200.00 |
| ed. 25 on Japon . . . . . . . . . . . . . . . . . . . . . . . . . . . . . . . . . . . . . . . . . . . . . | 2,400.00 | 3,400.00 |
| ☐ SCHOOL WALK, rel. 1979. ed. 260, s/n, 25" x 21", pub EEI . . . . . . . . . . . . . . | 2,000.00 | 3,700.00 |
| ed. 25 on Japon . . . . . . . . . . . . . . . . . . . . . . . . . . . . . . . . . . . . . . . . . . . . . | 2,200.00 | 3,900.00 |
| ☐ LAW STUDENT, rel. 1980. ed. 260, s/n, 23¾" x 32½", litho, arches, pub EEI | 3,200.00 | 4,700.00 |
| ed. 25 on Japon . . . . . . . . . . . . . . . . . . . . . . . . . . . . . . . . . . . . . . . . . . . . . | 3,400.00 | 4,900.00 |
| ☐ TRIPLE SELF PORTRAIT, rel. 1979. ed. 260, s/n, 23½" x 31½", litho, arches, pub EEI . . . . . . . . . . . . . . . . . . . . . . . . . . . . . . . . . . . . . . . . . . . . . . . . . | 5,000.00 | 13,000.00 |
| ed. 25 on Japon . . . . . . . . . . . . . . . . . . . . . . . . . . . . . . . . . . . . . . . . . . . . . | 5,500.00 | 13,500.00 |
| ☐ SECRETS, rel. 1979. ed. 260, s/n, 21" x 27", litho, arches, pub EEI . . . . . . . | 2,000.00 | 3,000.00 |
| ed. 25 on Japon . . . . . . . . . . . . . . . . . . . . . . . . . . . . . . . . . . . . . . . . . . . . . | 2,200.00 | 3,200.00 |
| ☐ CONNOISSEUR, rel. 1980. ed. 260, s/n, 24¼" x 30¼", collo, rives, pub EEI . | 6,000.00 | 7,500.00 |
| ☐ DREAMBOATS, rel. 1980. ed. 260, s/n, 24" x 29¾", litho, arches, pub EEI . . | 2,000.00 | 3,300.00 |
| ed. 25 on Japon . . . . . . . . . . . . . . . . . . . . . . . . . . . . . . . . . . . . . . . . . . . . . | 2,200.00 | 3,500.00 |

| | ISSUE PRICE | CURRENT PRICE |
|---|---|---|
| ☐ **STARSTRUCK**, rel. 1980. ed. 260, s/n, 24″ x 29¾″, litho, arches, pub EEI . . . | 2,000.00 | 3,100.00 |
| ed. 25 on Japon . . . . . . . . . . . . . . . . . . . . . . . . . . . . . . . . . . . . . . . . . . . . . . . . . . . . | 2,200.00 | 3,300.00 |
| ☐ **OUR HERITAGE**, rel. 1980. ed. 260, s/n, 25″ x 33¼″, collo, rives, pub EEI . . . | 1,500.00 | 3,500.00 |
| ☐ **UNDER SAIL**, rel. 1981. ed. 260, s/n, 18½″ x 24¾″, litho, arches, pub EEI . . | 2,000.00 | 2,500.00 |
| ed. 25 on Japon . . . . . . . . . . . . . . . . . . . . . . . . . . . . . . . . . . . . . . . . . . . . . . . . . . . . | 2,200.00 | 2,700.00 |
| ☐ **FISHING**, rel. 1981. ed. 260, s/n, 20½″ x 23″, litho, arches, pub EEI . . . . . . . | 1,900.00 | 2,300.00 |
| ed. 25 on Japon . . . . . . . . . . . . . . . . . . . . . . . . . . . . . . . . . . . . . . . . . . . . . . . . . . . . | 2,100.00 | 2,500.00 |
| ☐ **JOHN KENNEDY**, rel. 1982. ed. 260, s/n, 17″ x 23¼″, litho, arches, pub EEI . | 2,000.00 | — |
| ed. 25 on Japon . . . . . . . . . . . . . . . . . . . . . . . . . . . . . . . . . . . . . . . . . . . . . . . . . . . . | 2,200.00 | — |
| ☐ **RUNAWAY**, ed. 200, s/n, 26″ x 20″, litho, pub CFAC . . . . . . . . . . . . . . . . . . | — | 2,500.00 |
| ☐ **THE BIG DAY**, ed. 200, s/n, 29″ x 21″, litho, pub CFAC . . . . . . . . . . . . . . . . | — | 1,750.00 |
| ☐ **THE BIG TOP**, rel. 1982. ed. 200, s/n, 26″ x 20″, litho, pub CFAC . . . . . . . . . . | 875.00 | — |

## GEORGE RODRIGUE

George Rodrigue is a widely acclaimed Louisiana artist and sculptor who has many awards and accomplishments to his credit both nationally and internationally. He studied at the Art Center of Design in California.

His works hang in museums and galleries worldwide. He is listed in *Who's Who in American Art, International Directory of Art,* and *French Artist's Society.*

Rodrigue authored and illustrated a book titled *The Cajuns* which became an official gift to the Carter White House.

### GEORGE RODRIQUE

| | | |
|---|---|---|
| ☐ **AIOLI DINNER**, ed. 300, s/n, 24″ x 32″, pub GRG . . . . . . . . . . . . . . . . . . . . . . | 150.00 | — |
| Artist proof . . . . . . . . . . . . . . . . . . . . . . . . . . . . . . . . . . . . . . . . . . . . . . . . . . . . . | 1,000.00 | — |
| ☐ **BROUSSARD'S BARBER SHOP**, ed. 300, s/n, 24″ x 32″, pub GRG . . . . . . . . . | 150.00 | — |
| Artist proof . . . . . . . . . . . . . . . . . . . . . . . . . . . . . . . . . . . . . . . . . . . . . . . . . . . . . | 1,000.00 | — |
| ☐ **BREAUX BRIDGE BAND**, ed. 300, s/n, 24″ x 32″, pub GRG . . . . . . . . . . . . . . | 150.00 | — |
| Artist proof . . . . . . . . . . . . . . . . . . . . . . . . . . . . . . . . . . . . . . . . . . . . . . . . . . . . . | 1,000.00 | — |
| ☐ **JOLIE BLONDE**, ed. 300, s/n, 16″ x 20″, pub GRG . . . . . . . . . . . . . . . . . . . . . | 150.00 | Sold Out |
| ☐ **MAMOU RIDING ACADEMY**, ed. 300, s/n, 24″ x 32″, pub GRG . . . . . . . . . . . . | 150.00 | — |
| Artist proof . . . . . . . . . . . . . . . . . . . . . . . . . . . . . . . . . . . . . . . . . . . . . . . . . . . . . | 1,000.00 | — |
| ☐ **RAYNE-BO RAMBLERS**, ed. 1,000, s/o, pub GRG . . . . . . . . . . . . . . . . . . . . . | 2,500.00 | — |
| ☐ **THE CLASS**, ed. 1,000, s/o, pub GRG . . . . . . . . . . . . . . . . . . . . . . . . . . . . . . . | 25.00 | — |
| ☐ **THE GOURMET CLUB**, ed. 300, s/n, 23¼″ x 28″, pub GRG . . . . . . . . . . . . . . | 250.00 | — |
| ☐ **WISHING FOR LAFITTE'S GOLD**, ed. 150, s/n, 21½″ x 13½″, pub GRG . . . . . . | 150.00 | — |

## CHARLES D. ROGERS

"You have to find your own niche in art. Mine is watercolor. Moods can change quickly and watercolor is a fast medium. I paint what my emotions tell me," so says Charles D. Rogers, watercolorist and native Coloradoan.

Rogers received his education at the Rocky Mountain School of Art in Denver, Colorado, and studies under nationally known watercolorists such as Robert Wood, John Pellow, Mario Cooper, and Charles Reid. He himself taught classes and workshops at the Rocky Mountain School of Art. Rogers feels communication with other artists and interchange of ideas is very important to the development of art today.

Rogers paintings are in both public and private collections. He has continuous exhibitions at Husberg Gallery, Sedona, Arizona; Carriage Art Galleries, Estes Park, Colorado and Skylight Galleries (Old Town), Albuquerque, New Mexico.

Some of his awards include a "Meritorious Award" at the Colorado State Fair and "Best of Show" and a "Purchase Award" at North Platte Valley Art Show in Scottsbluff, Nebraska.

## CHARLES D. ROGERS

| | ISSUE PRICE | CURRENT PRICE |
|---|---|---|
| ☐ **DEEP SNOW,** ed. 1,200, s/n, 19¾" x 7¼", pub CDR .................. | 25.00 | 40.00 |
| ed. 50 Artist proofs with remarque, s/n ........................... | 55.00 | 65.00 |
| ☐ **GRANDPA'S PLACE,** ed. 1,200, s/n, 19¾" x 10", pub CDR .............. | 25.00 | 40.00 |
| ed. 50 Artist proofs with remarque, s/n ........................... | 55.00 | 65.00 |
| ☐ **MARCH EVENING,** ed. 1,200, s/n, 19¾" x 10", pub CDR................. | 25.00 | 40.00 |
| ed. 50 Artist proofs with remarque, s/n .......................... | 55.00 | 65.00 |
| ☐ **PASSING LEAVES,** ed. 750, s/n, 23½" x 13½", pub CDR .............. | 60.00 | — |
| ed. 50 Artist proofs with remarque, s/n .......................... | 90.00 | 100.00 |
| ☐ **WINTER STORAGE,** ed. 1,200, s/n, 19¾" x 10", pub CDR ............. | 25.00 | 40.00 |
| ed. 50 Artist proofs with remarque, s/n .......................... | 55.00 | 65.00 |
| ☐ **CACTUS WREN,** rel. 1979. ed. 750, s/n, 11" x 14", pub CDR............. | 40.00 | — |
| ed. 50 Artist proofs, remarqued | | |
| ☐ **BLACK CAPPED CHICKADEES,** rel. 1981. ed. 750, s/n, 13" x 19", pub CDR .. | 40.00 | — |
| ed. 50 Artist proofs, remarqued | | |
| ☐ **FANTASY,** rel. 1981. ed. unlimited, s/o, 6½" x 9", pub CRD ............. | 10.00 | — |
| ☐ **MADAME BUTTERFLY,** rel. 1981. ed. unlimited, s/o, 6½" x 9", pub CRD .... | 10.00 | — |
| ☐ **SPRING'S PROMISE,** rel. 1981. ed. unlimited, s/o, 6½" x 9", pub CRD ...... | 10.00 | — |

# ROBERT ROSS

Former student of Robert Bateman, Robert Ross is one of a new breed of artists belonging to a school of art called the "Kodachrome" painters.

**FALL SHORELINE** *by Robert Ross*

The title is misleading, however, for Ross is a great outdoorsman and an explorer with a true feel of the wilderness. He depicts nature in a strong, bold painting technique. He renders enough detail of the scene to give the *impression* of *great* detail.

Robert Ross's work reflects his love of nature. He travels extensively experiencing the beauty and grandeur of the wilderness. He has made himself familiar with all types of foliage, birds and animals. He portrays nature's beauty exactly as it is. Concentrating on landscape, he has achieved a real perfection in his chosen style. Through his paintings, Ross hopes that he will impress upon the public the necessity of retaining a natural balanced environment and encourage respect for ecology.

## ROBERT ROSS

| | ISSUE PRICE | CURRENT PRICE |
|---|---|---|
| ☐ **AUTUMN POPLARS**, rel. 1980. ed. 950, s/n, 17½" x 23¾", pub MPPI . . . . . . | 75.00 | — |
| ☐ **BLUE SHADOWS**, rel. 1981. ed. 550, s/n, 24¾" x 24", pub MPPI . . . . . . . . . | 95.00 | — |
| ☐ **FALL SHORELINE**, rel. 1980. ed. 950, s/n, 24" x 17¼", pub MPPI . . . . . . . . | 75.00 | — |
| ☐ **MORNING FROST**, rel. 1980. ed. 950, s/n, 20" x 27½", pub MPPI . . . . . . . . . | 75.00 | — |
| ☐ **NORTHERN SHORELINE**, rel. 1980. ed. 950, s/n, 18" x 25¼", pub MPPI . . . . | 75.00 | — |
| ☐ **RIVER RAPIDS**, rel. 1981. ed. 550, s/n, 25½" x 20", pub MPPI . . . . . . . . . . . | 95.00 | — |

# TOM ROST

Tom Rost was born in Richmond, Indiana, but, with the exception of five years in New York, has spent most of his life in Wisconsin. As a boy he spent his summers at a lake in Waukesha County where he began his lifelong interest in wildlife. Tom enjoys almost any kind of fishing but fly fishing, especially for trout, is his favorite.

**1981 WISCONSIN TROUT** *by Tom Rost*

His art studies began at Shorewood High School and continued at the University of Wisconsin-Milwaukee School of Fine Art and at the Layton School of Art. He was fortunate enough to get a job with the U.S. Treasury Department to do documentary paintings of life in a Civilian Conservation Corps camp. This was followed by three commissions for Post Office murals in Wisconsin and Indiana which in turn led to a position as illustrator for the *Milwaukee Journal* and, later, for a number of outdoor magazines.

Illustrations by Tom Rost have appeared in *National Wildlife, International Wildlife, Fawcett's Fishing Journal* and in *Field and Stream.*

His award winning artwork is owned by collectors of wildlife art from New England to California. Wisconsin's first Trout Stamp, in 1978, was designed by this artist.

## TOM ROST

| | ISSUE PRICE | CURRENT PRICE |
|---|---|---|
| ☐ **1978 WISCONSIN TROUT STAMP PRINT,** rel. 1978, ed. 600, s/n, 14″ x 17″, pub NC | 60.00 | 300.00 |
| ed. 100 remarqued | 110.00 | 500.00 |
| ☐ **1981 WISCONSIN TROUT STAMP PRINT,** rel. 1981, ed. 500, s/n, 14″ x 12″, pub NC | 100.00 | 250.00 |
| ed. 100 remarqued | 200.00 | 450.00 |

# G. H. ROTHE

Born in Germany, G. H. Rothe studied at the Pforzheim Academy of Design. Working out of her New York studio, Rothe's medium is mezzotint etchings. She grinds her own pigments and underpaints as the Old Masters did. She achieves a warmth in her images. "I believe in the total balance of warm and cold, dark and light, linear expression and all factors which reach into an ethnic of an image," she says.

Rothe's work hangs in museum and corporate collections worldwide. She has had many individual shows and is listed in *Who's Who in American Art* and *Who's Who in America.*

## G. H. ROTHE

| | | |
|---|---|---|
| ☐ **THE HEART,** rel. 1973, ed. 75, s/n, mezzotint, 35″ x 26″, pub HP | — | 600.00 |
| ☐ **ALVIN WITH THE DUTCH,** rel. 1974. ed. 300, s/n, 43″ x 30½″, serigraph, pub HP | — | Sold Out |
| ☐ **PAS DE TROIS,** rel. 1975. ed. 300, s/o, 37½″ x 24¾″ serigraph, pub HP | — | 650.00 |
| ☐ **AMERICA'S PRIDE,** rel. 1976. ed. 150, s/n, 27″ x 26″, mezzotint, pub HP | — | Sold Out |
| ☐ **GLASS ROSE,** rel. 1976. ed. 150, s/n, 23⅝″ x 25¾″, mezzotint, pub HP | — | Sold Out |
| ☐ **MOLLUSK,** rel. 1976. ed. 150, s/n, 24″ x 36″, mezzotint, pub HP | — | Sold Out |
| ☐ **ARISE AROSE,** rel. 1977. ed. 150, s/n, 32⅝″ x 23¾″, mezzotint, pub HP | — | Sold Out |
| ☐ **BUTTERFLY,** rel. 1977. ed. 150, s/n, 23½″ x 23¾″, mezzotint, pub HP | — | Sold Out |
| ☐ **MINDSCAPE,** rel. 1977. ed. 150, s/n, 24″ x 36″, mezzotint, pub HP | — | Sold Out |
| ☐ **PAS DE DEUX,** rel. 1977. ed. 150, s/n, 23½″ x 23½″, mezzotint, pub HP | — | 800.00 |
| ☐ **THOROUGHBRED,** rel. 1977. ed. 150, s/n, 23¾″ x 17¾″, mezzotint, pub HP | — | Sold Out |
| ☐ **THE WINDOW,** rel. 1977. ed. 150, s/n, 25⅝″ x 24″, pub HP | — | 1,300.00 |
| ☐ **AUGUSTA,** rel. 1978. ed. 150, s/n, 21″ x 15″, mezzotint, pub HP | — | 750.00 |
| ☐ **DON QUIXOTE,** rel. 1978. ed. 150, s/n, 27½″ x 22½″, mezzotint, pub HP | — | Sold Out |
| ☐ **HOMECOMING,** rel. 1978. ed. 150, s/n, 15″ x 21″, mezzotint, pub HP | — | Sold Out |
| ☐ **JOY,** rel. 1978. ed. 150, s/n, 21½″ x 9½″, mezzotint, pub HP | — | Sold Out |
| ☐ **MORGANS,** rel. 1978. ed. 150, s/n, 8¾″ x 11½″, mezzotint, pub HP | — | 550.00 |
| ☐ **MORNING,** rel. 1978. ed. 150, s/n, 8½″ x 21½″, mezzotint, pub HP | — | Sold Out |
| ☐ **MYTH,** rel. 1978. ed. 200, s/n, 21″ x 17″, mezzotint, pub HP | — | Sold Out |
| ☐ **NIGHT,** rel. 1978. ed. 150, s/n, 8½″ x 21½″, mezzotint, pub HP | — | Sold Out |
| ☐ **SECRET PLACE,** rel. 1978. ed. 150, s/n, 14¾″ x 20¾″, mezzotint, pub HP | — | 800.00 |
| ☐ **SPANISH ROSE,** rel. 1978. ed. 100, s/n, 7¾″ x 5¾″, pub HP | — | Sold Out |
| ☐ **SUNDAY ROSES,** rel. 1978. ed. 100, s/n, 6″ x 8″, pub HP | — | Sold Out |

**CONQUISTADOR CIELO** *by G.H. Rothe*

| | ISSUE PRICE | CURRENT PRICE |
|---|---|---|
| ☐ **ANCESTORS,** rel. 1979. ed. 150, s/n, 5¾" x 3¾", mezzotint, pub HP | — | 400.00 |
| ☐ **COMPETITORS,** rel. 1979. ed. 150, s/n, 5¾" x 8", mezzotint, pub HP | — | Sold Out |
| ☐ **CORAL CORRAL,** rel. 1979. ed. 150, s/n, 11½" x 35¼", mezzotint, pub HP | — | Sold Out |
| ☐ **DANCE SUITE,** set of five mezzotints, rel. 1979. ed. 200, s/n, pub HP | — | Sold Out |
| ☐ **ENDURANCE,** rel. 1979. ed. 150, s/n, 6" x 7⅞", mezzotint, pub HP | — | Sold Out |
| ☐ **GLASSTOWN,** rel. 1979. ed. 99, s/n, 25½" x 33¾", mezzotint, pub HP | — | Sold Out |
| ☐ **GRACE AND THE STALLION,** rel. 1979. ed. 150, s/n, 5½" x 8", mezzotint, pub HP | — | Sold Out |
| ☐ **HERD,** rel. 1979. ed. 150, s/n, 8" x 6", mezzotint, pub HP | — | 450.00 |
| ☐ **LANDMARK,** rel. 1979. ed. 150, s/o, 27½" x 21¾", mezzotint, pub EWG | — | 750.00 |
| ☐ **MINIATURE SUITE,** set of five mezzotints, rel. 1979. s/n, pub HP | — | Sold Out |
| ☐ **MOONDANCE II,** rel. 1979. ed. 100, s/n, 25⅞" x 15⅞", mezzotint, pub HP | — | Sold Out |
| ☐ **PEACE,** rel. 1979. ed. 150, s/n, 9¾" x 11¾", mezzotint, pub HP | — | 750.00 |
| ☐ **POET,** rel. 1979. ed. 150, s/n, 35¼" x 23½", mezzotint, pub HP | — | Sold Out |
| ☐ **ROSESCAPE,** rel. 1979. ed. 200, s/n, 21¾" x 27½", mezzotint, pub HP | — | 1,000.00 |
| ☐ **SOLITUDE,** rel. 1979. ed. 150, s/n, 20¾" x 14¾", mezzotint, pub HP | — | 800.00 |
| ☐ **SONATA,** rel. 1979. ed. 200, s/n, 5¾" x 4¾", mezzotint, pub HP | — | Sold Out |
| ☐ **STRENGTH,** rel. 1979. ed. 200, s/n, 27⅜" x 16¼", mezzotint, pub HP | — | Sold Out |
| ☐ **BALLET PICTURE I,** rel. 1980. ed. 150, s/n, 35¼" x 23¾", mezzotint, pub HP | — | 1,600.00 |
| ☐ **BALLET PICTURE II,** rel. 1980. ed. 150, s/n, 27½" x 21⅝", mezzotint, pub HP | — | 1,400.00 |
| ☐ **FLOWER LIFE,** rel. 1980. ed. 150, s/n, 7⅞" x 6", mezzotint, pub HP | — | 500.00 |
| ☐ **GROWTH,** rel. 1980. ed. 100, s/n, 15⅝" x 21¾", mezzotint, pub HP | — | 800.00 |
| ☐ **PENSIVE MOTION,** rel. 1980. ed. 100, s/n, 19¾" x 8", mezzotint, pub HP | — | Sold Out |
| ☐ **RED DRESS,** rel. 1980. ed. 200, s/n, 21¾" x 15¾", mezzotint, pub HP | — | Sold Out |
| ☐ **THE FIGHT,** rel. 1980. ed. 150, s/n, 11¾" x 9⅝", mezzotint, pub HP | — | 650.00 |
| ☐ **ALMANAC,** rel. 1981. ed. 150, s/n, 27½" x 22", mezzotint, pub HP | — | 1,350.00 |
| ☐ **BABY BALLERINAS,** rel. 1981. ed. 150, s/n, 27½" x 21½", mezzotint, pub HP | — | Sold Out |
| ☐ **BACHELORS,** rel. 1981. ed. 100, s/n, 13¾" x 10¾", mezzotint, pub HP | — | Sold Out |
| ☐ **BOUGAINVILLEA,** rel. 1981. ed. 150, s/n, 16" x 10¾", mezzotint, pub HP | — | Sold Out |
| ☐ **CHASE,** rel. 1981. ed. 150, s/n, 23¾" x 35¼", mezzotint, pub HP | — | Sold Out |
| ☐ **DANCE FOR PLEASURE,** rel. 1981. ed. 100, s/n, 5¾" x 4", mezzotint, pub HP | — | Sold Out |
| ☐ **DANCE PICTURE I,** rel. 1981. ed. 150, s/n, 27½" x 21½", mezzotint, pub HP | — | 1,300.00 |

| | ISSUE PRICE | CURRENT PRICE |
|---|---|---|
| ☐ **ENDEAVORS,** rel. 1981. ed. 150, s/n, 22½" x 27½", mezzotint, pub HP | — | 1,350.00 |
| ☐ **EXPERIMENT,** rel. 1981. ed. 150, s/n, 15¾" x 21¾", mezzotint, pub HP | — | Sold Out |
| ☐ **HARBOR AT NIGHT,** rel. 1981. ed. 100, s/n, 10¾" x 13¾", mezzotint, pub HP | — | Sold Out |
| ☐ **JULIE,** rel. 1981. ed. 100, s/n, 6¾" x 4", mezzotint, pub HP | — | 325.00 |
| ☐ **JUNCTION,** rel. 1981. ed. 100, s/n, 10¾" x 16¾", mezzotint, pub HP | — | 600.00 |
| ☐ **MOSS LANDING,** rel. 1981. ed. 100, s/n, 11" x 14", mezzotint, pub HP | — | 600.00 |
| ☐ **RHAPSODIC COMMITMENT,** rel. 1981. ed. 150, s/n, 24½" x 17", mezzotint, pub HP | — | Sold Out |
| ☐ **SPRING ROSE,** rel. 1981. ed. 100, s/n, 5⅞" x 7¾", mezzotint, pub HP | — | 350.00 |
| ☐ **TASSAJARA,** rel. 1981. ed. 150, s/n, 13¾" x 10¾", mezzotint, pub HP | — | 550.00 |
| ☐ **WHARF,** rel. 1981. ed. 150, s/n, 16½" x 25", mezzotint, pub HP | — | 1,000.00 |
| ☐ **WHILE THEY WERE RUNNING,** rel. 1981. ed. 150, s/n, 23⅞" x 35¼", mezzotint, pub HP | — | Sold Out |
| ☐ **YOUTH,** rel. 1981. ed. 150, s/n, 27½" x 22", mezzotint, pub HP | — | Sold Out |
| ☐ **BALL DANCE,** rel. 1982. ed. 150, s/n, 27½" x 21½", mezzotint, pub HP | — | 200.00 |
| ☐ **BEECHLANE,** rel. 1982. ed. 75, s/n, 6¾" x 4¾", mezzotint, pub HP | — | 350.00 |
| ☐ **COLTS,** rel. 1982. ed. 150, s/n, 23¾" x 34¾", mezzotint, pub HP | — | 1,800.00 |
| ☐ **CURRENT,** rel. 1982. ed. 150, s/n, 21¾" x 27½", mezzotint, pub HP | — | 1,350.00 |
| ☐ **DEPRIVED CONDITION,** rel. 1982. ed. 96, s/n, 23⅝" x 17⅞", mezzotint, pub HP | — | 1,000.00 |
| ☐ **ELECTRON,** rel. 1982. ed. 96, s/n, 12⅛" x 8¾", mezzotint, pub HP | — | 550.00 |
| ☐ **EMOTIONAL INTENSITY,** rel. 1982. ed. 150, s/n, 27½" x 21¾", mezzotint, pub HP | — | Sold Out |
| ☐ **PATTERN,** rel. 1982. ed. 96, s/n, 7" x 9¾", mezzotint, pub HP | — | 450.00 |
| ☐ **PENUEL,** rel. 1982. ed. 96, s/n, 7" x 9¾", mezzotint, pub HP | — | 475.00 |
| ☐ **PENUEL II,** rel. 1982. ed. 96, s/n, 6⅞" x 10", mezzotint, pub HP | — | 475.00 |
| ☐ **RECITAL,** rel. 1982. ed. 200, s/n, 16⅞" x 24¾", mezzotint, pub HP | — | 1,100.00 |
| ☐ **RECURRENT,** rel. 1982. ed. 96, s/n, 9¾" x 7", mezzotint, pub HP | — | 350.00 |
| ☐ **ROOTS IN LOVE,** rel. 1982. ed. 96, s/n, 24½" x 16¾", mezzotint, pub HP | — | 1,000.00 |
| ☐ **RUNNERS,** rel. 1982. ed. 150, s/n, 9" x 11⅝", mezzotint, pub HP | — | 550.00 |
| ☐ **SALINAS HILL,** rel. 1982. ed. 96, s/n, 11¾" x 8⅞", mezzotint, pub HP | — | 500.00 |
| ☐ **SOLO OF GEMINI,** rel. 1982. ed. 75, s/n, 12" x 9", mezzotint, pub HP | — | 650.00 |
| ☐ **TASSAJARA STAIRS,** rel. 1982. ed. 96, s/n, 11¾" x 17⅞", mezzotint, pub HP | — | 600.00 |
| ☐ **TRADITIONAL STANDARD,** rel. 1982. ed. 150, s/n, 15⅝" x 10¾", mezzotint, pub HP | — | 500.00 |
| ☐ **TRIO,** rel. 1982. ed. 200, s/n, 16⅛" x 11⅛", mezzotint, pub HP | — | 1,000.00 |
| ☐ **BENRABBA,** rel. 1983. ed. 150, s/n, 8½" x 12½", mezzotint, pub HP | — | 600.00 |
| ☐ **CONBRIO,** rel. 1983. ed. 150, s/n, 16" x 11", mezzotint, pub HP | — | 600.00 |
| ☐ **CONQUISTADOR CIELO,** rel. 1983. ed. 150, s/n, 23¾" x 35¾", mezzotint, pub HP | — | Sold Out |
| ☐ **GRAPES,** rel. 1983. ed. 150, s/n, 8½" x 12¼", mezzotint, pub HP | — | — |
| ☐ **SAN BONANCIAO,** rel. 1983. ed. 150, s/n, 24" x 36", mezzotint, pub HP | — | 1,200.00 |

## HAL ROZEMA

Hal Rozema, aviation artist, author, lecturer, pilot, yacht builder/designer, was sketching airplanes by age three. A lifelong love of aircraft, an avocation of reading collecting, studying, and photographing everything about aircraft for nearly fifty years provides him with a unique resource among aviation artists.

Rozema was a graduate of Kendall Art School in 1950, Aquinas College in 1976 and a student at Slade University, London in 1979. As an Engineering Loftsman for F84 and F105 aircrafts and an illustrator of aerospace avionics he has developed hands-on appreciation of the structure and mechanism of flight.

The pilot/artist has logged nearly one thousand hours flying his Mooney, IRF and VFR — an experience that has provided him with a special feel of sky, cloud, and landscape. His paintings exhibit depth, atmosphere and sensation in texture and form that few can achieve.

He has flown missions with the Air Force gathering authentic materials for AWACs, FBIIIA, and KC135A paintings. His cooperation and involvement with the

**T 38 THUNDERBIRDS 1980, Calypso Pass** *by Hal Rozema*

Artists' Guild of Chicago and the Air Force Art Program has expanded his personal resources of reference material to include Air Force files, collections and museums.

Other recent work has included World War I Spad XIII and Fokker Dr 1; Boeing 727 in Pan Am colors, J-3 Piper Cub, Cessna 210 and 310 Q, Piper Cherokee and Heliocopters, Bell 337, Engstrom, Seaknight, and Cobra Gun-ship.

The list of collections is growing: Battle Creek Art Center, Air Force Art Collection, and Smithsonian Air and Space Museum.

| HAL ROZEMA | ISSUE PRICE | CURRENT PRICE |
|---|---|---|
| ☐ ASSAM DAWN FLIGHT, P 40 D Tomahawk Fighters, Flying Tigers, ed. 1,000, s/n, 21″ x 17″, pub RS | 78.00 | — |
| ☐ AWACs REFUELING, ed. 1,000, s/n, 21″ x 17″, pub RS | 78.00 | — |
| ☐ BLUE ANGELS, A4 (MOD) SKYHAWK, ed. 1,000, s/n, 21″ x 17″, pub RS | 78.00 | — |
| ☐ CHRISTIAN EAGLE, ed. 1,000, s/n, 21″ x 17″, pub RS | 78.00 | — |
| ☐ F5E (FM2) WILDCAT, 1939-40 VF41, ed. 1,000, s/n, 21″ x 17″, pub RS | 78.00 | — |
| ☐ F5E TIGER II, ed. 1,000, s/n, 21″ x 17″, pub RS | 78.00 | — |
| ☐ F14 TOMCAT, VF38, ed. 1,000, s/n, 21″ x 17″, pub RS | 78.00 | — |
| ☐ F15 BITBURG EAGLE IN NATO COLORS IN FLIGHT OVER WEST GERMANY, ed. 1,000, s/n, 21″ x 17″, pub RS | 78.00 | — |
| ☐ TALLY HO, ed. 1,000, s/n, 21″ x 17″, pub RS | 78.00 | — |
| ☐ THE PICCARD BALLOON, XJ90 AT SUNSET, ed. 1,000, s/n, 21″ x 17″, pub RS | 78.00 | — |

| | ISSUE PRICE | CURRENT PRICE |
|---|---|---|
| ☐ **THRESHOLD**, Space Shuttle Columbia lifts off, ed. 1,000, s/n, 21″ x 17″, pub RS | 78.00 | – |
| ☐ **T-38 THUNDERBIRDS 1980, CALYPSO PASS**, ed. 1,000, s/n, 21″ x 17″, pub RS | 78.00 | – |

## LOUIS RUSSOMANNO

Born in New York City in 1946, Lou Russomanno has combined a number of life styles into his own personal expression of art. His interest in art was sparked at an early age by a trip to Europe with his family and by acquisition of two books on Degas and Rubins. The impressions were lasting and the result has produced a technique in etching rarely seen in any artist. His prints have the delicate quality of line and mood that portrays his subject in a softer, fuller light, exuding an intimate radiance, similar in feeling to the masters that inspired him but distinctly his own. Russomanno is a member of the Princeton Art Association. He has exhibited his work at the National Academy of Design in New York.

The acclaim for his work has been evident by the widespread success of his exhibitions. Russomanno has won the 1973 N. J. Governors Purchase Award, the 1975 Allied Artist of America Grumbacker Award and the 1971 and 1972 Phillips Mill Annual Art Exhibit 1st Prize. He is represented by some of the finest galleries in the United States, and is enthusiastically sought after by private collectors as well.

### LOUIS RUSSOMANNO

| | ISSUE PRICE | CURRENT PRICE |
|---|---|---|
| ☐ **AT THE SHORE**, ed. 150, s/n, 15″ x 15″, etch, pub EG | 45.00 | 56.50 |
| ☐ **A CLOSE FINISH**, ed. 100, s/n, 14″ x 20″, etch, pub EG | 40.00 | 50.00 |
| ☐ **BALLOONS**, ed. 100, s/n, 20″ x 22″, etch, pub EG | 50.00 | – |
| ☐ **BEFORE CLASS**, ed. 125, s/n, 12″ x 13″, etch, pub EG | 30.00 | 37.50 |
| ☐ **BLUE PERSIAN**, ed. 100, s/n, 16″ x 16″, etch, pub EG | 40.00 | – |
| ☐ **CARNIVAL**, ed. 100, s/n, 16″ x 20″, etch, pub EG | 50.00 | – |
| ☐ **CAPTAIN'S GIG**, ed. 100, s/n, 15″ x 18″, etch, pub EG | 35.00 | – |
| ☐ **DAISY**, ed. 185, s/n, 15″ x 19″, etch, pub EG | 60.00 | – |
| ☐ **DESIREE**, ed. 125, s/n, 14″ x 22″, etch, pub EG | 50.00 | – |
| ☐ **EAGLE ISLAND**, ed. 175, s/n, 19″ x 24″, etch, pub EG | 75.00 | – |
| ☐ **HIDING**, ed. 125, s/n, 17″ x 20″, etch, pub EG | 50.00 | – |
| ☐ **INTERMISSION**, ed. 185, s/n, 13″ x 16″, etch, pub EG | 60.00 | – |
| ☐ **INNOCENCE**, ed. 185, s/n, 14″ x 18″, etch, pub EG | 60.00 | – |
| ☐ **LA BALLERINE**, ed. 185, s/n, 13″ x 16″, etch, pub EG | 60.00 | – |
| ☐ **LA PREMIERE**, ed. 185, s/n, 13″ x 16″, etch, pub EG | 60.00 | – |
| ☐ **LITTLE FRIENDS**, ed. 100, s/n, 20″ x 24″, etch, pub EG | 60.00 | – |
| ☐ **MARIE ANGE**, ed. 100, s/n, 16″ x 20″, etch, pub EG | 50.00 | 65.00 |
| ☐ **MEMORIES**, ed. 175, s/n, 11″ x 14″, etch, pub EG | 20.00 | – |
| ☐ **MIRROR IMAGE**, ed. 100, s/n, 20″ x 24″, etch, pub EG | 50.00 | – |
| ☐ **MISIA**, ed. 175, s/n, 16″ x 19″, etch, pub EG | 60.00 | – |
| ☐ **MORNING LIGHT**, ed. 100, s/n, 16″ x 18″, etch, pub EG | 35.00 | – |
| ☐ **MORNING SHOWER**, ed. 125, s/n, 18″ x 20″, etch, pub EG | 50.00 | 62.50 |
| ☐ **MISTY**, ed. 185, s/n, 16″ x 16″, etch, pub EG | 60.00 | – |
| ☐ **PERSIAN CATS**, ed. 100, s/n, 16″ x 17″, etch, pub EG | 40.00 | 50.00 |
| ☐ **PENSIVE**, ed. 100, s/n, 13″ x 15″, etch, pub EG | 40.00 | – |
| ☐ **RAM**, ed. 75, s/n, 17″ x 18″, etch, pub EG | 35.00 | – |
| ☐ **REVERIE**, ed. 100, s/n, 14″ x 18″, etch, pub EG | 40.00 | – |
| ☐ **REFLECTIONS**, ed. 150, s/n, 18″ x 24″, etch, pub EG | 70.00 | – |
| ☐ **REPOSE**, ed. 185, s/n, 14″ x 20″, etch, pub EG | 60.00 | – |
| ☐ **SOLITUDE**, ed. 185, s/n, 14″ x 16″, etch, pub EG | 60.00 | – |
| ☐ **TABBY**, ed. 185, s/n, 14″ x 14″, etch, pub EG | 40.00 | – |
| ☐ **TIFFANY**, ed. 185, s/n, 13″ x 16″, etch, pub EG | 60.00 | – |
| ☐ **TWILIGHT**, ed. 125, s/n, 15″ x 20″, etch, pub EG | 45.00 | – |
| ☐ **VANITY**, ed. 185, s/n, 14″ x 18″, etch, pub EG | 60.00 | – |
| ☐ **WALK AWAY**, ed. 100, s/n, 16″ x 18″, etch, pub EG | 45.00 | 56.25 |

# JOHN A. RUTHVEN

John A. Ruthven is one of America's foremost wildlife artists. He is a leader in the ever-expanding movement fostering conservation and protection of endangered species and is also widely known as a lecturer and writer. Mr. Ruthven is often called the "20th Century Audubon", and uses the same techniques as his famous predecessor. John Ruthven studies his subject thoroughly — its habitat, its habits — making sure every detail to be used later in the painting is correct. Not satisfied with field research alone, he often obtains a specimen, usually from the bird skin collection at the Cincinnati Museum of Natural History, and proceeds to outline sketch for accurate sizing. When working on a bird painting with opaque watercolors, he painstakingly copies each feather and marking with exact color and infinite detail.

John A. Ruthven grew up in southwestern Ohio near the Ohio River. In early years he developed an interest in woodlands and woodlife. He spent four years of World War II at sea with the Navy and then opened a commercial art studio in Cincinnati. While building his business, he began painting more and more wildlife, combining his two prime interests. In the early 1960's he gave up his flourishing commercial art business turning it over to his employees to concentrate solely on wildlife art.

He and his wife July live in an old Ohio home filled with old furniture and other Americana. The home overlooks the fertile Ohio River Valley. Their home is situated on 165 acres which have been established as a wildlife refuge by Ruthven.

Ruthven's works, found in the nation's leading art galleries are highly prized by collectors. He has had many one-man shows throughout the United States.

| JOHN A. RUTHVEN | ISSUE PRICE | CURRENT PRICE |
|---|---|---|
| **AQUATINT SERIES** | | |
| ☐ CAROLINA PARAQUET, ed. 500, s/n, 25" x 36", pub WII | 300.00 | 1,500.00 |
| ☐ PASSENGER PIGEON, ed. 500, s/n, 25" x 36", pub WII | 350.00 | 1,500.00 |
| ☐ IVORY BILLED WOODPECKER, ed. 500, s/n, 25" x 36", pub WII | 350.00 | 1,000.00 |
| ☐ LABRADOR DUCK, ed. 500, s/n, 25" x 36", pub WII | 350.00 | 500.00 |
| ☐ EASTERN WILD TURKEY, ed. 776, s/n, 30" x 22", pub WII | 350.00 | — |
| **SAFARI SERIES** | | |
| ☐ BENGAL TIGER, ed. 5,000, s/n, 25" x 33", pub WII | 65.00 | 800.00 |
| ☐ AFRICAN ELEPHANTS, ed. 5,000, s/n, 25" x 33", pub WII | 65.00 | 100.00 |
| ☐ GIANT PANDAS, ed. 5,000, s/n, 25" x 33", pub WII | 65.00 | 100.00 |
| ☐ BLACK MANED LION, ed. 5,000, s/n, 27" x 35", pub WII | 65.00 | 100.00 |
| ☐ GRANT'S ZEBRA, ed. 3,500, s/n, 27" x 34", pub WII | 75.00 | 100.00 |
| ☐ LEOPARD, ed. 3,500, s/n, 27" x 35", pub WII | 75.00 | 100.00 |
| **NORTH AMERICAN SERIES** | | |
| ☐ SNOWY OWL, ed. 1,000, s/n, 18" x 24", pub WII | 50.00 | 450.00 |
| ☐ RUDDY DUCKS, ed. 1,000, s/n, 18" x 24", pub WII | 50.00 | 400.00 |
| ☐ CANVASBACKS ON THE OHIO, ed. 1,000, s/n, 18" x 24", pub WII | 50.00 | 400.00 |
| ☐ REDHEADED WOODPECKER, ed. 1,000, s/n, 18" x 24", pub WII | 50.00 | 400.00 |
| ☐ WANDERING BRAVE, ed. 1,000, s/n, 25" x 33", pub WII | 90.00 | 550.00 |
| ☐ N. Y. STATE BLUEBIRD, ed. 1,000, s/n, 18" x 24", pub WII | 50.00 | 300.00 |
| ☐ WOOD DUCKS, ed. 1,000, s/n, 25" x 31", pub WII | 90.00 | 450.00 |
| ☐ RED FOX FAMILY, ed. 1,000, s/n, 25" x 33", pub WII | 90.00 | 1,000.00 |
| ☐ ROBINS, ed. 1,000, s/n, 18" x 24", pub WII | 50.00 | 450.00 |
| ☐ ON THE HUNT, ed. 1,000, s/n, 25" x 33", pub WII | 90.00 | 150.00 |
| **AMERICANA SERIES** | | |
| ☐ ROADRUNNER, ed. 1,000, s/n, 20" x 25", pub WII | 50.00 | 325.00 |
| ☐ HERRING GULLS, ed. 1,000, s/n, 20" x 26½", pub WII | 50.00 | 325.00 |
| ☐ GREAT HORNED OWL, ed. 1,000, s/n, 22½" x 30", pub WII | 90.00 | 375.00 |
| ☐ CANADA GEESE, ed. 1,000, s/n, 24" x 31", pub WII | 95.00 | 225.00 |
| ☐ BOBWHITE QUAIL, ed. 1,000, s/n, 20½" x 24", pub WII | 80.00 | 200.00 |

|  | ISSUE PRICE | CURRENT PRICE |
|---|---|---|
| **GEORGETOWN SERIES** | | |
| ☐ CINNAMON TEAL, ed. 1,000, s/n, 12" x 15", pub WII | 30.00 | 125.00 |
| ☐ ed. 1,000, n/o | 20.00 | — |
| ☐ FOX MASQUE I, ed. 1,000, s/n, 11" x 11", pub WII | 30.00 | 100.00 |
| ☐ FOX MASQUE II, ed. 1,000, s/n, 11" x 11", pub WII | 30.00 | 100.00 |
| ☐ HOODED MERGANSER, rel. 1979, ed. 1,000, s/n, 11" x 10", pub WII | 50.00 | 125.00 |
| ☐ RUDDY DUCK, rel. 1979, ed. 1,000, s/n, 11" x 10", pub WII | 50.00 | — |
| ☐ INDIGO BUNTING, rel. 1980. ed. 950, s/n, 11" x 11", mezzotint, pub WII | 50.00 | — |
| **REGAL SERIES** | | |
| ☐ BENGAL TIGER, ed. 1,000, s/n, 25" x 36", pub WII | 80.00 | 1,800.00 |
| ☐ RED FOX, ed. 1,000, s/n, 25" x 36", pub WII | 90.00 | 1,450.00 |
| **MASTERPIECE SERIES** | | |
| ☐ GRAY FOX, ed. 950, s/n, 25" x 33", pub WII | 125.00 | 1,350.00 |
| ☐ JAGUAR, ed. 950, s/n, 20" x 24", pub WII | 65.00 | 385.00 |
| ☐ FLICKERS, ed. 950, s/n, 20" x 24", pub WII | 65.00 | 150.00 |
| ☐ FLYING SNOW OWL, ed. 950, s/n, 33" x 25", pub WII | 150.00 | — |
| ☐ GRAY FOX FAMILY, ed. 950, s/n, 33" x 25", pub WII | 125.00 | 1,000.00 |
| ☐ WHITE TIGERS, rel. 1981. ed. 1,000, s/n, size not available, pub WII | 150.00 | 300.00 |
| **JOHN A. RUTHVEN SERIES** | | |
| ☐ RUFFED GROUSE, Plate I and Plate II, ed. 99, s/n, 22½" x 29¼", pub WII | *750.00 | 1,850.00 |
| *Sold only as matched pair | | |
| ☐ WOOD DUCK/MALLARD, Plate III & IV, ed. 99, s/n, 22½" x 29¼", pub WII | *750.00 | 1,600.00 |
| *Sold only as matched pair | | |
| ☐ PHEASANTS, Plate V & VI, ed. 99, s/n, 22¼" x 29¼", pub WII | *850.00 | 1,500.00 |
| *Sold only as matched pair | | |
| **INITIAL SERIES** | | |
| ☐ BALD EAGLE, ed. 1,000, s/n, 18" x 24", pub WII | 30.00 | 850.00 |
| ☐ PHEASANT, ed. 1,000, s/n, 18" x 24", pub WII | 30.00 | 550.00 |
| ☐ CARDINALS, ed. 1,000, s/n, 18" x 24", pub WII | 30.00 | 850.00 |
| ☐ QUAIL, ed. 1,000, s/n, 18" x 24", pub WII | 30.00 | 550.00 |
| ☐ WILD TURKEY, ed. 1,000, s/n, 18" x 24", pub WII | 30.00 | 450.00 |
| ☐ BLUEBIRD, ed. 1,000, s/n, 18" x 24", pub WII | 30.00 | 550.00 |
| ☐ SCREECH OWL, ed. 1,000, s/n, 18" x 24", pub WII | 30.00 | 650.00 |
| ☐ WOOD DUCK, ed. 1,000, s/n, 18" x 24", pub WII | 40.00 | 330.00 |
| ☐ RUFFED GROUSE, ed. 1,000, s/n, 18" x 24", pub WII | 40.00 | 450.00 |
| ☐ MALLARD, ed. 1,000, s/n, 18" x 24", pub WII | 50.00 | 350.00 |
| **COMMISSIONS** | | |
| ☐ BARDSTOWN OF CALUMET FARMS, ed. 2,000, s/n, 22" x 17", pub WII | 50.00 | — |
| ☐ BENGAL TIGER, ed. 1,000, s/n, 30" x 40", pub WII | *100.00 | 500.00 |
| *Commissioned by Idaho State University. | | |
| ☐ DECOY (Labrador Retriever), ed. 950, s/n, 21" x 24", pub WII | 125.00 | 850.00 |
| 250 of the edition used as a donation | | |
| 700 released by Wildlife International as a donation | | |
| ☐ EAGLE TO THE MOON, ed. 500, s/n, 30" x 40", pub WII | *150.00 | 2,200.00 |
| *For the Neil A. Armstrong Air & Space Museum and the Ohio Historical Society. | | |
| ☐ EASTERN CHIPMUNK, ed. 750, s/n, 12" x 19", pub WII | 50.00 | 250.00 |
| ☐ FRANCIS OF ASSISI, ed. 2,000, s/n, 20" x 26", pub WII | *60.00 | — |
| *Commissioned by St. Francis College | | |
| ☐ GREAT AUK, ed. 200, s/n, 24" x 33½", pub WII | 250.00 | — |
| ☐ KINGFISHER, ed. 250, size not known, pub WII | 100.00 | — |
| ☐ KIRTLAND'S WARBLER, ed. 1,000, s/n, 18" x 24", pub WII | 100.00 | — |
| ☐ KIT FOX, ed. 500, s/n, 25" x 21", pub WII | 100.00 | 350.00 |
| ☐ OAKGROVE PINTAIL (Small), ed. 3,000, s/n, 16" x 20", pub WII | 50.00 | — |
| ☐ OAKGROVE PINTAIL (Large), ed. 1,000, s/n, 30" x 40", pub WII | 100.00 | — |
| ☐ PASSENGER PIGEON, rel. 1974. ed. 1,000, s/n, 25" x 21", pub WII | 100.00 | — |
| ☐ NATURE CENTER CARDINAL, rel. 1970. ed. 1,000, s/n, 25" x 21", pub WII | 50.00 | 450.00 |
| ☐ REDHEAD DUCKS (Aquatint Process), ed. 450, s/n, 15" x 14" | *350.00 | 450.00 |
| *1960 - 1961 Federal Duck Stamp | | |
| ☐ WHITE TIGERS, ed. 1,000, s/n, size not known, pub WII | 150.00 | 300.00 |

| | ISSUE PRICE | CURRENT PRICE |
|---|---|---|
| **KNOB CREEK SERIES** | | |
| ☐ **WHITE-TAILED DEER**, ed. 750, s/n, 25" x 32", pub WII | 150.00 | 350.00 |
| ☐ **BOBWHITE QUAIL**, ed. 750, s/n, 18" x 24", pub WII | 75.00 | 200.00 |
| ☐ **ALGONQUIN**, ed. 750, s/n, 18" x 24", pub WII | 75.00 | 125.00 |
| ☐ **EASTERN WILD TURKEY**, ed. 750, s/n, 18" x 24", pub WII | 75.00 | 225.00 |
| ☐ **HOODED MERGANSERS**, ed. 750, s/n, 18" x 24", pub WII | 75.00 | 125.00 |
| ☐ **TERNS**, ed. 750, s/n, 30" x 40", pub WII | 150.00 | 325.00 |
| **WILLIAMSBURG SERIES** | | |
| ☐ **THE CARDINALS OF WILLIAMSBURG**, ed. 1,000, s/n, 16" x 20", pub WII | *50.00 | — |
| ☐ **THE MOCKINGBIRDS OF WILLIAMSBURG**, ed. 1,000, s/n, 16" x 20", pub WII | *50.00 | — |
| ☐ **THE BLUE JAYS OF WILLIAMSBURG**, ed. 1,000, s/n, 16" x 20", pub WII | *50.00 | — |
| *Sold only through Craft House, Williamsburg, VA and Williamsburg Shops in Fine Stores throughout the U.S.A. | | |
| **PATRIOT SERIES** | | |
| ☐ **SHAWNEE INDIAN**, ed. 3,000, numbered only, 16" x 20", pub WII | 22.50 | — |
| ☐ **MOURNING DOVE**, ed. 3,000, numbered only, 16" x 20", pub WII | 22.50 | — |
| ☐ **MEADOW LARK**, ed. 3,000, numbered only, 16" x 20", pub WII | 22.50 | — |
| ☐ **BUFFLEHEAD DUCK**, ed. 3,000, numbered only, 16" x 20", pub WII | 22.50 | — |
| **BICENTENNIAL SERIES** | | |
| ☐ **BICENTENNIAL EAGLE**, rel. 1976. ed. 776, s/n, 28" x 42", pub WII | 350.00 | 650.00 |
| ☐ **BICENTENNIAL TURKEYS**, rel. 1977. ed. 776, s/n, 30" x 32", pub WII | 350.00 | — |
| **LIBERTY SERIES** | | |
| ☐ **BLUE WINGED TEAL**, rel. 1977. ed. 500, s/n, 17" x 24", pub WII | 75.00 | 400.00 |
| ☐ **GREEN WINGED TEAL**, rel. 1978. ed. 500, s/n, 17" x 24", pub WII | 75.00 | 350.00 |
| **COASTAL SERIES** | | |
| ☐ **BROWN PELICAN**, rel. 1977. ed. 500, s/n, 29" x 27", pub WII | 125.00 | — |
| ☐ **WILSON'S PLOVER**, rel. 1978. ed. 500, s/n, 16" x 15", pub WII | 75.00 | — |
| **HOMESTEAD SERIES** | | |
| ☐ **SCREECH OWL**, rel. 1977. ed. 950, s/n, 12" x 12", pub WII | 50.00 | 275.00 |
| ☐ **CHICKADEE**, rel. 1978. ed. 950, s/n, 12" x 12", pub WII | 50.00 | 225.00 |
| ☐ **CALIFORNIA VALLEY QUAIL**, rel. 1979. ed. 950, s/n, 11" x 11", pub WII | 50.00 | — |
| **INTERNATIONAL SERIES** | | |
| ☐ **BATELEUR EAGLE**, rel. 1978. ed. 750, s/n, 24" x 34", pub WII | 110.00 | — |
| **AMERICAN INDIAN SERIES** | | |
| ☐ **CHIPPEWA BRAVE**, rel. 1978. ed. 950, s/n, 21" x 18", pub WII | 50.00 | — |
| **ARCTIC SERIES** | | |
| ☐ **ARCTIC FOX**, rel. 1977. ed. 950, s/n, 33" x 25", pub WII | 150.00 | 435.00 |
| ☐ **TIMBER WOLF**, rel. 1978. ed. 950, s/n, 25" x 33", pub WII | 150.00 | — |
| **GAME BIRD SERIES** | | |
| ☐ **AMERICAN WIDGEON**, rel. 1978. ed. 950, s/n, 16" x 19½", pub WII | 65.00 | — |
| ☐ **PHEASANT**, rel. 1980. ed. 950, s/n, 16" x 20", pub WII | 75.00 | — |
| **SONGBIRD SERIES** | | |
| ☐ **CARDINAL**, rel. 1978. ed. 950, s/n, 17" x 21", pub WII | 75.00 | 450.00 |
| ☐ **CAROLINA WREN**, rel. 1979. ed. 950, s/n, 13" x 17", pub WII | 50.00 | — |
| **SPORTING DOG SERIES** | | |
| ☐ **DUSTY (Golden Retriever)**, rel. 1979. ed. 950, s/n, 21" x 24", pub WII | 125.00 | 400.00 |
| ☐ **RUMMY**, rel. 1980. ed. 950, s/n, 21" x 24", pub WII | 150.00 | 400.00 |
| ☐ **DUSTY**, rel. 1981. ed. 950, s/n, 21" x 24", pub WII | 150.00 | 550.00 |
| ☐ **SCARLET**, rel. 1982. ed. 950, s/n, 21" x 24", pub WII | 150.00 | — |
| **WINTER SERIES** | | |
| ☐ **CEDAR WAXWING**, rel. 1978. ed. 950, s/n, 15" x 15", pub WII | 50.00 | — |
| ☐ **SAW-WHET OWL**, rel. 1979. ed. 950, s/n, 11" x 11", pub WII | 50.00 | — |
| **WOODLAND SERIES** | | |
| ☐ **RED FOX (In the snow)**, rel. 1979. ed. 950, s/n, 26" x 33", pub WII | 150.00 | 400.00 |
| ☐ **GRAY FOX**, rel. 1981. ed. 1,500, s/n, 23/" x 30", pub WII | 150.00 | — |
| **HUMMINGBIRDS OF NORTH AMERICA** | | |
| ☐ **RUBY-THROATED**, rel. 1977. ed. 750, s/n, 14" x 17", pub WII | 75.00 | — |
| ☐ **ALLEN'S**, rel. 1977. ed. 750, s/n, 14" x 17", pub WII | 75.00 | — |
| ☐ **RUFOUS**, rel. 1977. ed. 750, s/n, 11" x 14", pub WII | 75.00 | — |
| ☐ **ANNA'S**, rel. 1978. ed. 750, s/n, 14" x 17", pub WII | 75.00 | — |
| ☐ **RIVOLI'S/BLUE THROATED**, rel. 1978. ed. 750, s/n, 14" x 17", pub WII | 75.00 | — |
| ☐ **BROAD-BILLED**, rel. 1978. ed. 750, s/n, 14" x 17", pub WII | 75.00 | — |

| | ISSUE PRICE | CURRENT PRICE |
|---|---|---|
| **OWL FAMILY SERIES** | | |
| ☐ SAW-WHET OWLS, rel. 1982. ed. 1,500, s/n, 14" x 17", pub WII . . . . . . . . . | 75.00 | — |
| ☐ GREAT HORNED OWLS, rel. 1982. ed. 1,500, s/n, 14" x 17", pub WII . . . . . . | 75.00 | — |
| ☐ SNOWY OWLS, rel. 1983. ed. 1,500, s/n, 14" x 17", pub WII . . . . . . . . . . . | 75.00 | — |
| ☐ BARRED OWLS, rel. 1983. ed. 1,500, s/n, 14" x 17", pub WII . . . . . . . . . . . | 75.00 | — |
| **MISCELLANEOUS, not part of a Series** | | |
| ☐ WINGS IN THE WIND (Blue Goose/Snow Goose), rel. 1982. ed. 750, s/n, 25" x 33", pub WII . . . . . . . . . . . . . . . . . . . . . . . . . . . . . . . . . . . . . . . . . . . . . . . . . | 200.00 | — |
| ☐ SAND HILL CRANES, rel. 1982. ed. 950, s/n, 26" x 21", pub WII . . . . . . . . . | 150.00 | — |
| ☐ OSPREY, rel. 1981. ed. 750, s/n, 25" x 34", pub WII . . . . . . . . . . . . . . . . . . . | 175.00 | — |
| ☐ MALLARD, rel. 1981. ed. 500, s/n, 16" x 21½", pub WII . . . . . . . . . . . . . . . . | 75.00 | — |
| ☐ CARDINAL, rel. 1981. ed. 950, s/n, 16" x 20", pub WII . . . . . . . . . . . . . . . . | 75.00 | 150.00 |
| ☐ BALD EAGLE, rel. 1982. ed. 350, s/n, 19½" x 45", pub WWI . . . . . . . . . . . | 350.00 | — |
| ☐ KESTREL & MOUSE, rel. 1982. ed. 950, s/n, 16½" x 40", pub WWI . . . . . . . | 150.00 | — |
| ☐ KINGLETS, rel. 1982. ed. 950, s/n, 16" x 20", pub WWI . . . . . . . . . . . . . . . . | 75.00 | — |
| ☐ NUTHATCH, rel. 1982. ed. 950, s/n, 16" x 20", pub WWI . . . . . . . . . . . . . . . | 75.00 | — |
| ☐ TOWHEES, rel. 1982. ed. 950, s/n, 16" x 20", pub WWI . . . . . . . . . . . . . . . . | 75.00 | — |
| ☐ WINSTON, rel. 1982. ed. 950, s/n, 21" x 25", pub WWI . . . . . . . . . . . . . . . . | 150.00 | — |
| ☐ FRIENDS, rel. 1983. ed. 500, s/n, 16" x 20", pub WWI . . . . . . . . . . . . . . . . | 75.00 | — |
| ☐ GOLDFINCH, rel. 1983. ed. 950, s/n, 16" x 20", pub WWI . . . . . . . . . . . . . . | 75.00 | — |
| ☐ PAPAW BANDIT, rel. 1983. ed. 600, s/n, 16½" x 22½", pub WWI . . . . . . . . | 125.00 | — |
| ☐ PILEATED WOODPECKERS, rel. 1983. ed. 350, s/n, 15" x 39", pub WWI . . . . . | 350.00 | — |

## BILLY SAATHOFF

**BILLY SAATHOFF**

| | | |
|---|---|---|
| ☐ MORNING WATCH, rel. 1981. ed. 1,500, s/n, 23" x 29½", pub ALI . . . . . . . . . | 60.00 | — |

# PHILLIP SAGE

Phillip Sage was born in New Hampshire in 1942 and received his elementary education in Bedford. He attended St. Anselm's College where he obtained a degree in economics and business administration. Subsequently he enrolled in the Cooper Union School of Art and Architecture from which he graduated having completed studies in graphic design, at the same time gaining experience working for New York advertising agencies.

While at the Cooper Union, as a student of Charles Klabunde, Sage developed an interest in expressing himself through the medium of Intaglio Printmaking. His other interest, photography, was pursued under the direction of Michael (Tony) Vaccaro.

Sage works exclusively with copper plates and pulls each print himself on a hand-operated English Intaglio Press. In addition to his black and white prints Sage has become well-known for his color etchings of Mardi Gras characters and New Orleans street scenes. Each color requires a separate plate, all of which must be in perfect register when printed, a difficult and painstaking process.

Sage has enjoyed phenomenal success depicting the southern scene he has come to know and love since his move to New Orleans in the fall of 1971. This success is due mainly to what many patrons have begun to call "the Sage perspective". When viewing people and places common to native New Orleanians, so common in fact, that they are often over-looked, Sage applies this perspective and the result is another part of the city's romantic history.

## PHILLIP SAGE

| | ISSUE PRICE | CURRENT PRICE |
|---|---|---|
| **CARTER COUNTRY, SUITE I** | | |
| ☐ This folio consists of six etchings ed. 350, s/n, approximately 22″ x 19″, pub NG | 600.00 | — |
| ☐ MISS LILLIAN | 125.00 | — |
| ☐ BILLY'S BACK ROOM | 150.00 | — |
| ☐ JOHN HENRY HOLLY AND SPOT | 150.00 | — |
| ☐ PLAINS DEPOT | 100.00 | — |
| ☐ MAIN STREET | 100.00 | — |
| ☐ PLAINS BAPTIST CHURCH | 100.00 | — |
| **CARTER COUNTRY, SUITE II** | | |
| ☐ This folio consists of six etchings. ed. 350, s/n, approximately 22″ x 19″, pub NG | 525.00 | — |
| ☐ RUTH CARTER STAPLETON | 75.00 | — |
| ☐ ALTON CARTER 'UNCLE BUD' | 100.00 | — |
| ☐ HOG FEEDING ON THE CARTER FARM | 150.00 | — |
| ☐ CARTER WAREHOUSE: BAGGING PEANUTS | 125.00 | — |
| ☐ PREPARING FOR SPRING | 75.00 | — |
| ☐ BILLY'S GAS STATION | 100.00 | — |
| ☐ MORNING HITCHUP, ed. 200, s/n, 28″ x 23″, pub NG | 100.00 | — |
| ☐ THE DRILLER, ed. 200, s/n, 17″ x 18″, pub NG | 60.00 | — |
| ☐ SATURDAY AFTERNOON, ed. 200, s/n, 22″ x 19″, pub NG | 75.00 | — |
| ☐ TRUMPET SOLO, ed. 200, s/n, 15″ x 15″, pub NG | 35.00 | — |
| ☐ HEADING OUT, ed. 200, s/n, 18″ x 15″, pub NG | 75.00 | — |
| ☐ CHATRES STREET, ed. 200, s/n, 11″ x 10″, pub NG | 25.00 | — |
| ☐ BEAUREGARD HOUSE, ed. 200, s/n, 11″ x 10″, pub NG | 25.00 | — |
| ☐ DECATUR STREET, ed. 200, s/n, 11″ x 10″, pub NG | 25.00 | — |
| ☐ ROYAL STREET MUSICIANS, ed. 200, s/n, 23″ x 20″, pub NG | 75.00 | — |
| ☐ CORNSTALK HOTEL, ed. 200, s/n, 11″ x 10″, pub NG | 25.00 | — |
| ☐ KING ZULU, ed. 200, s/n, 18″ x 24″, pub NG | 125.00 | — |
| ☐ LETTUCE MAN, ed. 200, s/n, 13″ x 11″, pub NG | 25.00 | — |
| ☐ ROUND THE BEND, ed. 200, s/n, 13″ x 11″, pub NG | 40.00 | — |
| ☐ STRUMMIN, ed. 200, s/n, 15″ x 15″, pub NG | 35.00 | — |
| ☐ LAFITTE'S BLACKSMITH SHOP, ed. 200, s/n, 11″ x 11″, pub NG | 25.00 | — |
| ☐ MADAM JOHN'S LEGACY, ed. 200, s/n, 11″ x 10″, pub NG | 25.00 | — |
| ☐ NORTH CONWAY STATION, ed. 200, s/n, 10″ x 9″, pub NG | 25.00 | — |
| ☐ FIELD HAND, ed. 200, s/n, 14″ x 19″, pub NG | 45.00 | — |
| ☐ MANCHESTER STATION, ed. 200, s/n, 9″ x 9″, pub NG | 25.00 | — |
| ☐ ROAD TO NATCHEZ, ed. 200, s/n, 22″ x 15″, pub NG | 75.00 | — |
| ☐ BEN, ed. 200, s/n, 11″ x 15″, pub NG | 25.00 | — |
| ☐ SADIE, ed. 200, s/n, 11″ x 15″, pub NG | 25.00 | — |
| ☐ ANDERSONVILLE STATION, ed. 200, s/n, 10″ x 9″, pub NG | 25.00 | — |
| ☐ RECLINING NUDE, ed. 200, s/n, 10″ x 10″, pub NG | 25.00 | — |
| ☐ SEATED NUDE, ed. 200, s/n, 11″ x 10″, pub NG | 25.00 | — |
| ☐ BEDFORD CHURCH, ed. 200, s/n, 10″ x 9″, pub NG | 25.00 | — |
| ☐ PASSING TIME, ed. 200, s/n, 20″ x 17″, pub NG | 45.00 | — |
| ☐ SPINNAKER RUN, ed. 200, s/n, 22″ x 20″, pub NG | 75.00 | — |
| ☐ BLACKSMITH SHOP, ed. 200, s/n, 18″ x 15″, pub NG | 40.00 | — |
| ☐ MAKING A TRIP, ed. 200, s/n, 22″ x 19″, pub NG | 65.00 | — |

# MANABU SAITO

Manabu Saito was born in Tokyo, Japan. At an early age he decided to become an artist and, while still in primary school, won an all-Japan award for painting. Saito spent only a year at Rikkyo University and came to America to study at Pratt Institute.

During four years at Pratt, Saito received scholarships from General Motors and the Art School of the Institute. After graduation he returned to Japan as consultant to Japan Design House, but soon returned to New York where he joined Raymond Loewy Associates. On the side he designed exhibits and showrooms for Sony and Nikon. At this time he also illustrated his first book, *The Boy Who Drew Cats*.

He has designed a collection of botanical Christmas cards for American Artists Group and the National Audubon Society, 1976. Among his many published works are *The Golden Guide on Cacti* (183 color illustrations), *What is a Tree?* for Western Publishing Co., *Collier's Encyclopedia Yearbook,* and a children's book, *From One Seed.*

Recently, Saito's work was added to the permanent collection of the prestigious Hunt Botanical Library in Pittsburgh, Pennsylvania.

## MANABU SAITO

| | ISSUE PRICE | CURRENT PRICE |
|---|---|---|
| ☐ **SPRING FLOWERS,** rel. 1972. ed. 750, s/n, 21" x 27", pub FHG | 35.00 | 125.00 |
| ☐ **SUMMER FLOWERS,** rel. 1973. ed. 1,500, s/n, 21" x 27", pub FHG | 45.00 | 75.00 |
| ☐ **AUTUMN FLOWERS,** rel. 1974. ed. 1,500, s/n, 21" x 27", pub FHG | 45.00 | 100.00 |
| ☐ **CACTI,** pair, rel. 1974. ed. 1,500, s/n, 18⅞" x 24¼", pub FHG | 50.00 | 75.00 |
| ☐ **PEONIES,** rel. 1974. ed. 1,500, s/n, 23" x 32", pub FHG | 45.00 | 75.00 |
| ☐ **APPLE,** rel. 1975. ed. 2,250, s/n, 6½" x 9½", pub FHG | 7.00 | 20.00 |
| ☐ **CINNAMON FERN,** rel. 1975. ed. 1,000, s/n, 22" x 29", pub FHG | 50.00 | 125.00 |
| ☐ **ROSE,** rel. 1975. ed. 1,500, s/n, 16" x 20", pub FHG | 25.00 | Sold Out |
| ☐ **SUNFLOWER,** rel. 1975. ed. 1,000, s/n, 28" x 20", pub FHG | 50.00 | Sold Out |
| ☐ **TULIP/DAFFODIL,** pair, rel. 1975. ed. 1,500, s/n, 16" x 20", pub FHG | 40.00 | 95.00 |
| ☐ **SOUTHERN MAGNOLIA,** rel. 1976. ed. 900, s/n, 24" x 28", pub FHG | 50.00 | 75.00 |
| ☐ **BANSHU,** rel. 1977. ed. 750, s/n, 28" x 22", pub FHG | 50.00 | 80.00 |
| ☐ **MAIDENHEAD FERN,** rel. 1977. ed. 750, s/n, 29" x 24", pub FHG | 50.00 | 95.00 |
| ☐ **NIGHT-BLOOMING CACTI,** rel. 1977. ed. 750, s/n, 27" x 22", pub FHG | 50.00 | — |
| ☐ **ORIENTAL POPPY,** rel. 1977. ed. 750, s/n, 30" x 23", pub FHG | 50.00 | 125.00 |
| ☐ **AUTUMN LEAVES,** rel. 1978. ed. 750, s/n, 15½" x 13", pub FHG | 25.00 | — |
| ☐ **FUJI,** rel. 1978. ed. 500, s/n, 33½" x 18¾", pub FHG | 100.00 | — |
| ☐ **NEW MOON,** rel. 1978. ed. 750, s/n, 15½" x 13", pub FHG | 25.00 | Sold Out |
| ☐ **RISQUE,** rel. 1978. ed. 750, s/n, 15½" x 13", pub FHG | 25.00 | — |
| ☐ **SAKURA,** rel. 1978. ed. 500, s/n, 33½" x 18¾", pub FHG | 100.00 | 200.00 |
| ☐ **CHRISTMAS FERN,** rel. 1979. ed. 750, s/n, 23" x 30", pub FHG | 60.00 | — |
| ☐ **BANKA IN STILLWATER,** rel. 1979. ed. 750, s/n, 29½" x 21", pub FHG | 60.00 | — |
| ☐ **MATSU,** rel. 1979. ed. 500, s/n, 33½" x 18¾", pub FHG | 100.00 | — |
| ☐ **MOMIJI,** rel. 1979. ed. 500, s/n, 33½" x 18¼", pub FHG | 100.00 | — |
| ☐ **OYSTER PLANT,** rel. 1979. ed. 5,000, s/o, 15" x 12", pub FHG | 10.00 | — |
| ☐ **TULIP,** rel. 1979. ed. 5,000, s/o, 14" x 14", pub FHG | 20.00 | — |
| ☐ **MAI,** rel. 1980. ed. 375, s/n, 16¾" x 29½", pub FHG | 125.00 | — |
| ☐ **SPRING BOUQUET,** rel. 1980. ed. 600, s/n, 30" x 24", pub FHG | 75.00 | — |
| ☐ **SUMMER BOUQUET,** rel. 1980. ed. 355, s/n, 30" x 24", pub FHG | 75.00 | — |
| ed. 245, s/n, remarqued | 90.00 | — |
| ☐ **RED EMPEROR,** rel. 1981. ed. 1,000, s/n, 20" x 16", pub FHG | 40.00 | — |

## LEE SALBER

| | | |
|---|---|---|
| ☐ **GOSLINGS FOUR,** rel. 1981. ed. 175, s/n, size not available, pub WWI | 40.00 | — |

# JOHN HOWARD SANDEN

John Sanden is a noted portrait painter in New York. His works have included senators and an African king. He was an instructor at Art Students League in New York and is now currently holding studio classes in portrait work for other artists. He founded the Portrait Club of America and is the author of a book on painting the portrait in oil.

## JOHN HOWARD SANDEN

| | | |
|---|---|---|
| ☐ **MORNING ROSE,** ed. 950, s/n, 18¾" x 23", pub CHAL | 131.00 | 150.00 |
| ed. 12, Artist Accented/signed | 375.00 | 420.00 |
| ☐ **DAY'S WORK DONE,** ed. 950, s/n, 18¾" x 23", pub CHAL | 131.00 | 150.00 |
| ed. 12, Artist Accented/signed | 375.00 | 420.00 |

# TOM SANDER

After graduating from the University of Oregon with a degree in architecture, Tom Sander taught art at several levels including adult education, college and high school. For two years, he was the art supervisor for Sheraton public schools, in Sheraton, Wyoming.

As an architect, he has designed several homes, including his present home in Kalispell, Montana.

Sander's work has been exhibited in galleries from New York to the West Coast. He has displayed his paintings at game conservation shows in New York, San Francisco and San Antonio.

**GLACIAL VALLEY** *by Tom Sander*

**TOM SANDER**

| | ISSUE PRICE | CURRENT PRICE |
|---|---|---|
| ☐ **FROM COVER**, rel. 1977. ed. 500, s/n, 24″ x 30″, pub FHG | 40.00 | 115.00 |
| ☐ **BLACK LABRADOR AND MALLARD**, rel. 1977. ed. 500, s/n, 18″ x 26″, pub FHG | 40.00 | 225.00 |
| ☐ **HONORED POINT**, rel. 1977. ed. 750, s/n, 24″ x 30″, pub FHG | 50.00 | 100.00 |
| ☐ **ENGLISH SETTERS AND RUFFED GROUSE**, rel. 1978. ed. 750, s/n, 22″ x 29″, pub FHG | 50.00 | 100.00 |
| ☐ **FINAL APPROACH**, rel. 1978. ed. 750, s/n, 21″ x 30″, pub FHG | 75.00 | 125.00 |
| ☐ **WINTER SUN**, rel. 1978. ed. 750, s/n, 21″ x 30″, pub FHG | 75.00 | 90.00 |
| ☐ **BLACK LAB**, rel. 1979.ed. 850, s/n, 18½″ x 26″, pub FHG | 60.00 | 120.00 |
| ☐ **GOLDEN RETRIEVER**, rel. 1979.ed. 850, s/n, 21″ x 30″, pub FHG | 65.00 | — |
| ☐ **IRISH SETTERS**, rel. 1979.ed. 850, s/n, 20″ x 30″, pub FHG | 65.00 | 125.00 |
| ☐ **OCTOBER'S JOURNEY**, rel. 1979. ed. 750, s/n, 21″ x 30″, pub FHG | 75.00 | 125.00 |
| ☐ **PHEASANT/BOBWHITE**, pair, rel. 1979. ed. 950, s/n, 17½″ x 14½″, pub FHG | 50.00 | 90.00 |
| ☐ **DAWN PATROL**, rel. 1980. ed. 750, s/n, 16½″ x 30″, pub FHG. | 75.00 | 175.00 |
| ☐ **FALL (WHITE-TAIL DEER)**, rel. 1980. ed 750, s/n, 20″ x 11½″, pub FHG | 50.00 | — |
| ☐ **SPRING (RED FOX)**, rel. 1980. ed. 750, s/n, 20″ x 11½″, pub FHG | 50.00 | — |
| ☐ **SUMMER - WOOD DUCKS**, rel. 1980.ed. 750, s/n, 20″ x 11½″, pub FHG | 50.00 | — |
| ☐ **WINTER - CANADA GEESE**, rel. 1980.ed. 750, s/n, 20″ x 11½″, pub FHG | 50.00 | — |
| ☐ **COLD DUCK**, rel. 1981. ed. 850, s/n, 15½″ x 26″, pub SCG. | 85.00 | — |

| | ISSUE PRICE | CURRENT PRICE |
|---|---|---|
| ☐ **RUFFED GROUSE/GAMBEL'S QUAIL,** pair, rel. 1981. ed. 950, s/n, 18½" x 15", pub FHG . . . . . . . . . . . . . . . . . . . . . . . . . . . . . . . . . . . . . . . . . . . pr. | 65.00 | — |
| ☐ **SUMMER PONDERING,** rel. 1981. ed. 750, s/n, 19" x 30", pub FHG . . . . . . . . | 75.00 | — |
| ☐ **SUNNING FOXES,** rel. 1981. ed. 750, s/n, 18" x 24", pub FHG . . . . . . . . . . . | 65.00 | — |
| ☐ **AUTUMN RETREAT,** rel. 1982. ed. 975, s/n, 21" x 28", pub FHG . . . . . . . . . | 75.00 | — |
| ☐ **SPRING SNOW,** rel. 1982. ed. 975, s/n, 21½" x 30", pub FHG . . . . . . . . . . . | 75.00 | — |
| ☐ **THE SENTRIES,** rel. 1982. ed. 975, s/n, 17" x 30", pub FHG. . . . . . . . . . . . | 75.00 | — |
| ☐ **THE APPRENTICE,** rel. 1983. ed. 975, s/n, 21½" x 30", pub FHG . . . . . . . . . | 80.00 | — |

# CAROLYN SANDERS-TURNER

Carolyn Sanders-Turner attended the Chicago Art Institute and Sullins College. Later she participated in Concord College's advance independent study program for two years. She has worked professionally as an artist for the past eleven years.

Sanders-Turner conducts watercolor workshops on all levels as well as short term residencies. She has won over 50 awards and has work exhibited in over 700 corporate and private collections.

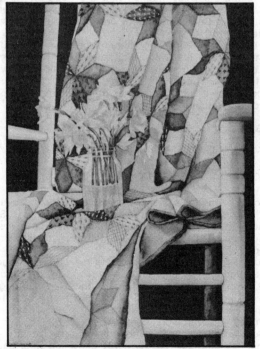

**JONQUILS AND EIGHT PONT STAR**
*by Carolyn Sanders-Turner*

| CAROLYN SANDERS-TURNER | ISSUE PRICE | CURRENT PRICE |
|---|---|---|
| ☐ **FORGOTTEN TREASURES**, rel. 1982. ed. 750, s/n, 18⅛″ x 24½″, pub WP . . . | 45.00 | — |
| ☐ **WEDDING RINGS**, rel. 1982. ed. 750, s/n, 18¼″ x 24½″, pub WP . . . . . . . . . | 50.00 | — |
| ☐ **JONQUILS AND EIGHT POINT STAR**, rel. 1983. ed. 750, s/n, 18⅛″ x 24⅞″, pub WP . . . . . . . . . . . . . . . . . . . . . . . . . . . . . . . . . . . . . . . . . . . . . . . . | 60.00 | — |

# ROBERT SAUBER

A native of Seattle, Washington, Robert Sauber is one of the rising stars among young contemporary artists.

Sauber's latest achievement is having been selected as the cover artist for the Christmas, 1981 number of the *"Saturday Evening Post",* an honor reserved in the past for such immortals as Normal Rockwell and J. L. Lyendecker.

The son of a guided missile technician who moved around the country as his profession required him, Rob spent his childhood in San Diego, Los Angeles, Raleigh, and Washington, D.C.

"I started drawing when I was 14," Rob recalls, "I did it because people liked me better when I showed them my work." At the age of 17 he began his "formal" training — by taking a correspondence school art course. Three years later he was beginning to make his living as a free-lancer and shortly thereafter he enrolled as a student at the Art Center College of Design in Los Angeles, which he calls "the best in the country".

Sauber now lives in New York City, where he feels very much at home. "When I first came to this city I felt like I was inside a painting." Now he is supplementing his collection of paintings of small towns and bucolic country scenes with a series about life in New York.

One of Sauber's recent works is a series of romantic paintings for the limited edition plates of the Signature Collection.

## ROBERT SAUBER

| | | |
|---|---|---|
| ☐ **BUTTERFLY**, rel. 1982. ed. 3,000, s/n, 24″ x 20″, pub VSL. . . . . . . . . . . . . . | 45.00 | — |

# SAM SAVITT

Sam Savitt, one of America's best known horse artists, has been fascinated by horses since his boyhood. He graduated from Pratt Institute Art School and after the war he continued his studies at the Art Students League in New York City. He also pursued his interest in horses and horsemanship with the famous equestrian teacher Gordon Wright.

Savitt and horses have been inseparable. He has written fourteen books and illustrated over a hundred. His illustrations have appeared in *"Sports Illustrated", "True", "Boy's Life"* and other national magazines. His paintings and portraits hang in homes throughout the United States. The famous Savitt horse charts are known throughout the world and his authoritative work has been used in encyclopedias and by The Smithsonian Institute.

Savitt has covered all breeds in every area of horse activity — polo, racing, steeple chasing, fox hunting, rodeos, horse show jumping, and eventing. His knowledge of horses not only as an artist but also as a horseman brings reality and authority for his work and brought about his appointment as official artist for the United States Equestrian Team.

Savitt says: "The horse is beauty, strength, rhythm and achm and action. To really know and understand him, to capture his magnificence with pencil or brush, will to me be forever challenging."

**DROP JUMP** *by Sam Savitt*

| SAM SAVITT | ISSUE PRICE | CURRENT PRICE |
|---|---|---|
| ☐ **SUMMERTIME**, rel. 1978. ed. 950, s/n, 20" x 23", pub MPPI . . . . . . . . . . . . | 65.00 | — |
| ☐ **GOING HOME**, rel. 1978. ed. 950, s/n, 20" x 25", pub MPPI . . . . . . . . . . . . . . | 75.00 | — |
| ☐ **THE DROP JUMP**, rel. 1979. ed. 950, s/n, 20" x 25", pub MPPI . . . . . . . . . . . | 75.00 | — |
| ☐ **THE LAST DAY OF THE RACE**, rel. 1980. ed. 950, s/n, 20" x 25", pub MPPI . . | 65.00 | — |
| ☐ **THE STEEPLE CHASER**, rel. 1980. ed. 950, s/n, 18" x 25", pub MPPI . . . . . . . | 65.00 | — |

# PAUL SAWYIER
## American Impressionist (1865-1917)

Paul Sawyier was born at Table Rock in Madison County, Ohio. When he was barely five years old, his parents, Dr. Nathaniel and Ellen Wingate Sawyier moved with their children to live in Ellen's hometown of Frankfort, Kentucky.

His artistic talent became apparent during his early years. At the age of 19, he studied portraiture under Thomas S. Noble at the Cincinnati Art Academy. Four years later Sawyier went to New York City for further training at the Art Student's League. Studying under William Merritt Chase, he was able to observe the famous portrait painter John Singer Sargent. The next year, 1890, he returned to Cincinnati and worked under Frank Duveneck, who was at the height of his country wide fame as an oil portrait painter.

Sawyier returned to Kentucky after his studying to paint portraits and landscapes of his beloved Frankfort. In 1893, Sawyier went to the Chicago World's Fair Columbian Exhibition where some of his works were in the State of Kentucky display. It was here that Impressionism was formally introduced to the Midwest, and Sawyier was influenced to become an "American Impressionist".

At the age of 22, Sawyier met Mary "Mayme" Thomas Bull of Frankfort, and they became informally engaged. Because of a mutual desire to take care of their ailing parents and his struggle to financially survive as an artist, they never married. In 1908, after the death of his mother, Sawyier decided to fulfill a long restrained desire to travel and paint scenes of the Kentucky River. He spent the next five years on a houseboat, painting in watercolor scenes and an occasional portrait up and down this beautiful river.

Seeking new markets, Sawyier moved to Brooklyn in 1913. While living with his sister, Lillian, he spent two years painting primarily in oils, the beautiful parks in the area. In 1915 he went to the Catskill Mountains, painting in both oils and watercolors. While painting mainly scenes of New York, Sawyier would also work from Photographs and paint Frankfort and Kentucky River scenes, which he often sent back to buyers in Kentucky.

Sawyier died of a heart attack at the age of 52 in Fleischmanns, New York. Five years later, in 1923, his body was reinterred in the Frankfort cemetery.

During his lifetime, it is estimated that he did over 2,000 paintings, mostly watercolor landscapes, but fewer than 100 portraits. Today less than 500 of his works can be accounted for.

**CAMP NELSON PALISADES** *by Paul Sawyier*

**PAUL SAWYIER**

| | ISSUE PRICE | CURRENT PRICE |
|---|---|---|
| ☐ ELKHORN CREEK SCENE, rel. 1965. ed. 1,000, n/o, pub PSGI | 15.00 | 45.00 |
| ☐ KENTUCKY ARSENAL, rel. 1965. ed. 1,000, n/o, pub PSGI | 20.00 | 265.00 |
| ☐ MOONLIGHT ON THE KENTUCKY, rel. 1965. ed. 1,000, n/o, pub PSGI | 20.00 | 165.00 |
| ☐ A RAINY DAY IN FRANKFORT, rel. 1965. ed. 1,000, n/o, pub PSGI | 20.00 | 825.00 |
| ☐ BARGES ON THE KENTUCKY, rel. 1970. ed. 1,000, n/o, pub PSGI | 20.00 | 65.00 |
| ☐ BRIDGE STREET, rel. 1970. ed. 2,000, n/o, pub PSGI | 20.00 | 120.00 |
| ☐ THE FISHERMAN, rel. 1970. ed. 2,000, n/o, pub PSGI | 20.00 | 145.00 |
| ☐ KENTUCKY RIVER, rel. 1970. ed. 1,000, n/o, pub PSGI | 20.00 | 150.00 |
| ☐ NEW YORK HARBOR, rel. 1970. ed. 2,000, n/o, 14⅜" x 20", pub PSGI | 20.00 | — |
| ☐ THE OLD CAPITOL, rel. 1970. ed. 1,000, n/o, pub PSGI | 20.00 | 340.00 |
| ☐ OLD COVERED BRIDGE, rel. 1970. ed. 1,000, n/o, pub PSGI | 5.00 | 25.00 |
| ☐ SOUTH END OF OLD COVERED BRIDGE, rel. 1970. ed. 2,000, n/o, pub PSGI | 20.00 | 40.00 |
| ☐ SOUTH FORK ELKHORN CREEK, rel. 1970. ed. 2,000, n/o, pub PSGI | 10.00 | 25.00 |

| | ISSUE PRICE | CURRENT PRICE |
|---|---|---|
| ☐ WAPPING STREET FOUNTAIN, rel. 1970. ed. 1,000, n/o, pub PSGI | 20.00 | 260.00 |
| ☐ WINTER IN KENTUCKY, rel. 1970. ed. 1,000, n/o, pub PSGI | 20.00 | 370.00 |
| ☐ PEAK'S MILL BEND, rel. 1971. ed. 2,000, n/o, pub PSGI | 5.00 | 15.00 |
| ☐ A RAINY DAY AT THE BRIDGE, rel. 1971. ed. 500, n/o, pub PSGI | 50.00 | 255.00 |
| ☐ SHAKERTOWN ROAD, rel. 1971. ed. 500, n/o, pub PSGI | 50.00 | 455.00 |
| ☐ BIG EDDY, rel. 1972. ed. 2,000, n/o, 13" x 15", pub PSGI | 20.00 | — |
| ☐ DIX RIVER, rel. 1972. ed. 500, n/o, pub PSGI | 50.00 | 235.00 |
| ☐ GOING TO SPRING, rel. 1972. ed. 2,000, n/o, pub PSGI | 20.00 | 55.00 |
| ☐ PALISADES, rel. 1972. ed. 500, n/o, pub PSGI | 50.00 | 175.00 |
| ☐ THE ROCK BREAKER, rel. 1972. ed. 1,000, n/o, pub PSGI | 40.00 | — |
| ☐ SHAKERTOWN FERRY, rel. 1972. ed. 2,000, n/o, 17¾" x 31", pub PSGI | 30.00 | 70.00 |
| ☐ SPRINGTIME, rel. 1972. ed. 2,000, n/o, pub PSGI | 20.00 | 185.00 |
| ☐ THE SUTER HOUSE, rel. 1972. ed. 6,000, n/o, 5½" x 6¼", PSGI | 5.00 | — |
| ☐ THE FOUNTAIN, rel. 1973. ed. 4,000, n/o, pub PSGI | 10.00 | 40.00 |
| ☐ GOOD OLD DAYS, rel. 1973. ed. 2,000, n/o, 14" x 19½", pub PSGI | 20.00 | 45.00 |
| ☐ LANDMARKS, rel. 1973. ed. 2,000, n/o, 16" x 18½", pub PSGI | 20.00 | 30.00 |
| ☐ THE LOWER POOL, rel. 1973. ed. 8,000, n/o, 6¼" x 9½", pub PSGI | 5.00 | — |
| ☐ MISTY EVENING, rel. 1973. ed. 2,000, n/o, 15" x 19", pub PSGI | 20.00 | 30.00 |
| ☐ REFLECTIONS ON ELKHORN CREEK, rel. 1973. ed. 3,000, n/o, pub PSGI | 10.00 | 40.00 |
| ☐ A RIVER VIEW OF FRANKFORT, rel. 1973. ed. 3,000, n/o, pub PSGI | 15.00 | — |
| ☐ A SHADY LANE, rel. 1973. ed. 3,000, n/o, pub PSGI | 20.00 | — |
| ☐ SUNRISE, rel. 1973. ed. 2,000, n/o, pub PSGI | 10.00 | — |
| ☐ BAKING HEMP, rel. 1974. ed. 2,000, n/o, pub PSGI | 30.00 | — |
| ☐ BEND IN THE RIVER, rel. 1974. ed. 2,000, n/o, pub PSGI | 15.00 | — |
| ☐ BOYHOOD MEMORIES, rel. 1974. ed. 3,000, n/o, pub PSGI | 20.00 | 70.00 |
| ☐ THE CHANNEL'S FORD, rel. 1974. ed. 2,000, n/o, pub PSGI | 20.00 | 40.00 |
| ☐ COVERED BRIDGE IN AUTUMN, rel. 1974. ed. 2,000, n/o, pub PSGI | 20.00 | 140.00 |
| ☐ KENTUCKY RIVER SCENE, rel. 1974. ed. 8,000, n/o, pub PSGI | 5.00 | — |
| ☐ LOUISVILLE ROAD, rel. 1974. ed. 2,000, n/o, pub PSGI | 20.00 | — |
| ☐ MACY'S KENTUCKY RIVER, rel. 1974. ed. 2,000, n/o, pub PSGI | 20.00 | — |
| ☐ MORNING MOON, rel. 1974. ed. 2,000, n/o, pub PSGI | 20.00 | — |
| ☐ NORTH FRANKFORT, rel. 1974. ed. 2,000, n/o, pub PSGI | 10.00 | — |
| ☐ RIVER LOGGING, rel. 1974. ed. 2,000, n/o, pub PSGI | 15.00 | — |
| ☐ RIVER VALLEY, rel. 1974. ed. 6,000, n/o, pub PSGI | 5.00 | — |
| ☐ SUMMERTIME, rel. 1974. ed. 2,000, n/o, pub PSGI | 20.00 | — |
| ☐ THE WALLED CITY, rel. 1974. ed. 2,000, n/o, pub PSGI | 20.00 | — |
| ☐ COVERED BRIDGE IN SUMMER, rel. 1975. ed. 3,000, n/o, pub PSGI | 20.00 | 25.00 |
| ☐ THE COVERED POND, rel. 1975. ed. 3,000, n/o, pub PSGI | 20.00 | 70.00 |
| ☐ FISHERMAN'S CATCH, rel. 1975. ed. 3,000, n/o, pub PSGI | 20.00 | — |
| ☐ FORKS OF ELKHORN TURNPIKE, rel. 1975. ed. 6,000, n/o, pub PSGI | 3.00 | — |
| ☐ KENTUCKY RIVER AT CANOE CREEK, rel. 1975. ed. 3,000, n/o, pub PSGI | 20.00 | — |
| ☐ KNOB HILL ROAD, rel. 1975. ed. 6,000, n/o, pub PSGI | 5.00 | — |
| ☐ LOUISVILLE PIKE, rel. 1975. ed. 3,000, n/o, pub PSGI | 20.00 | 85.00 |
| ☐ MILL POND FISHERMAN, rel. 1975. ed. 6,000, n/o, pub PSGI | 3.00 | — |
| ☐ OLD RIVER ROAD, rel. 1975. ed. 6,000, n/o, pub PSGI | 5.00 | — |
| ☐ THE SCENIC KENTUCKY, rel. 1975. ed. 6,000, n/o, pub PSGI | 5.00 | — |
| ☐ SWITZER COVERED BRIDGE, rel. 1975. ed. 3,000, n/o, pub PSGI | 20.00 | — |
| ☐ TURKEY RUN, rel. 1975. ed. 3,000, n/o, pub PSGI | 20.00 | 85.00 |
| ☐ LOVER'S LEAP, rel. 1976. ed. 1,250, n/o, pub PSGI | 50.00 | 260.00 |
| ☐ SHADOWS OF SPRINGTIME, rel. 1976. ed. 2,500, n/o, pub PSGI | 10.00 | 25.00 |
| ☐ SNOWY SENTINEL, rel. 1976. ed. 2,000, n/o, pub PSGI | 20.00 | — |
| ☐ WINTER SOLITUDE, rel. 1976. ed. 3,000, n/o, pub PSGI | 15.00 | 40.00 |
| ☐ BURLEY RIDE, rel. 1977. ed. 2,000, n/o, pub PSGI | 20.00 | — |
| ☐ ELKHORN CREEK DAM, rel. 1977. ed. 2,500, n/o, pub PSGI | 15.00 | — |
| ☐ EVENING REFLECTIONS, rel. 1977. ed. 2,500, n/o, pub PSGI | 20.00 | — |
| ☐ OLD ELK'S CLUB, rel. 1977. ed. 2,500, n/o, pub PSGI | 30.00 | 95.00 |
| ☐ HIGH BRIDGE, rel. 1978. ed. 2,500, n/o, pub PSGI | 25.00 | 85.00 |
| ☐ MAYME ON THE ELKHORN, rel. 1978. ed. 2,500, n/o, pub PSGI | 25.00 | 55.00 |
| ☐ THE ROAD TO TOWN, rel. 1978. ed. 2,000, n/o, pub PSGI | 25.00 | 110.00 |
| ☐ RIVER CLIFFS, rel. 1978. ed. 1,250, n/o, pub PSGI | 65.00 | 215.00 |
| ☐ CAPITOL IN WINTER, rel. 1979. ed. 3,000, n/o, pub PSGI | 30.00 | 165.00 |
| ☐ FISH TRAP, rel. 1979. ed. 1,450, n/o, pub PSGI | 65.00 | 230.00 |
| ☐ RIVER FRIENDS, rel. 1979. ed. 2,500, n/o, pub PSGI | 20.00 | 30.00 |
| ☐ RIVER PATHWAY, rel. 1979. ed. 3,000, n/o, pub PSGI | 25.00 | 35.00 |

|  | ISSUE PRICE | CURRENT PRICE |
|---|---|---|
| ☐ **ROADSIDE SPRING**, rel. 1979. ed. 3,500, n/o, pub PSGI | 5.00 | — |
| ☐ **TOLL GATE**, rel. 1979. ed. 2,500, n/o, pub PSGI | 20.00 | 55.00 |
| ☐ **BRIDGE TO MEMORIES**, rel. 1980. ed. 2,500, n/o, pub PSGI | 15.00 | — |
| ☐ **CAMP NELSON PALISADES**, rel. 1980. ed. 2,500, n/o, pub PSGI | 30.00 | — |
| ☐ **DIX RIVER FISH TRAP**, rel. 1980. ed. 3,000, n/o, pub PSGI | 25.00 | — |
| ☐ **AN OLD KENTUCKY HOME**, rel. 1980. ed. 2,100, n/o, pub PSGI | 65.00 | 110.00 |
| ☐ **LEANING SYCAMORE**, rel. 1980. ed. 2,000, n/o, pub PSGI | 10.00 | — |
| ☐ **VEST—LINDSEY HOUSE**, rel. 1980. ed. 3,500, n/o, pub PSGI | 40.00 | 225.00 |
| ☐ **WAPPING STREET VIEW**, rel. 1980. ed. 3,500, n/o, pub PSGI | 40.00 | 225.00 |
| ☐ **CAPITAL HOTEL GASLIGHT**, rel. 1981. ed. 3,000, n/o, pub PSGI | 20.00 | — |
| ☐ **CLIFFSIDE ROAD**, rel. 1981. ed. 2,500, n/o, pub PSGI | 25.00 | — |
| ☐ **JOURNEY HOME**, rel. 1981. ed. 2,500, n/o, pub PSGI | 45.00 | — |
| ☐ **SECLUDED BYWAY**, rel. 1981. ed. 3,500, n/o, pub PSGI | 10.00 | — |
| ☐ **WINTER STROLL**, rel 1981. ed. 3,800, n/o, pub PSGI | 30.00 | 45.00 |
| ☐ **BEYOND THE HILL**, rel 1982. ed. 2,000, n/o, pub PSGI | 4.00 | — |
| ☐ **FROM THE QUARRY**, rel. 1982. ed. 3,500, n/o, pub PSGI | 35.00 | — |
| ☐ **THE HOLIDAY**, rel. 1982. ed. 2,500, n/o, pub PSGI | 25.00 | — |
| ☐ **INDIAN HEAD ROCK**, rel. 1982. ed. 2,500, n/o, pub PSGI | 45.00 | — |
| ☐ **MAIN STREET 1900**, rel 1982. ed. 3,850, n/o, pub PSGI | 30.00 | 40.00 |
| ☐ **RIVER REFLECTIONS**, rel 1982. ed. 2,000, n/o, pub PSGI | 4.00 | — |
| ☐ **WAPPING STREET REFLECTIONS**, rel 1982. ed. 3,500, n/o, pub PSGI | 35.00 | 55.00 |
| ☐ **KENTUCKY CLIFFS**, rel 1983. ed. 2,000, n/o, pub PSGI | 25.00 | — |
| ☐ **VILLAGE STREAM**, rel 1983. ed. 2,000, n/o, pub PSGI | 25.00 | — |
| ☐ **AUTUMN AT THE BRIDGE**, rel 1983. ed. 2,750, n/o, pub PSGI | 35.00 | Sold Out |
| ☐ **THE UPPER POOL**, rel 1983. ed. 1,000, n/o, pub PSGI | 65.00 | Sold Out |
| ☐ **MORNING RIDE**, rel 1983. ed. 2,000, n/o, pub PSGI | 20.00 | — |
| ☐ **EAST VIEW**, rel 1983. ed. 2,000, n/o, pub PSGI | 5.00 | — |

# MANFRED SCHATZ

Manfred Schatz may well go down in history as the leading painter of animals and hunting scenes of our time. His works give the contemporary observer the sense of tranquility and contentment that is fast becoming extinct.

Schatz was born in 1929 in what is now East Germany. He attended the School of Arts and Crafts in Stetten and the Academy of Pictorial Arts, Berlin-Charlottenburg. He has had exhibitions in over a dozen major cities of the world including Hamburg, Munich, London, New York and Las Vegas. In 1964 he won a Silver Medal for his painting, ELK ON THE MOVE, in Florence, Italy, and a Gold Medal for FLEEING LYNX in Dusseldorf. In 1975 The Royal Ontario Museum in Toronto held an international exhibition, ANIMALS IN ART. Twenty-five nations submitted art from a total of 143 artists (both past and present). Schatz was judged the most significant artist of the exhibition.

The magic of Schatz's paintings lies in his uncanny ability to capture movement. His brush strokes are bold and are set to canvas with a certainty which many artists never acquire. He does not lose himself in the details of the marginal things, but forces the viewer's attention onto the main motif as he proposes to express it.

He portrays wildlife as most of us see it — in quick, often shadowy glimpses rather than sharp, bright portraits. He uses the viewers mind as an extension of his brush to supply needed details, and avoids them where they're not needed and never seen. His work is inevitably real and alive and the viewer cannot help but react. At one of the exhibitions of his paintings a spectator summed it up best when he turned to his companion and said, "It seems as though I can actually hear the painting."

## MANFRED SCHATZ

| | ISSUE PRICE | CURRENT PRICE |
|---|---|---|
| ☐ **BRIEF INTERLUDE,** ed. 500, s/n, 15½" x 21½", pub RAF | 80.00 | 250.00 |
| ☐ **LYNX,** ed. 500, s/n, 18" x 27¼", pub RAF | 100.00 | — |
| ☐ **WINGED MAJESTY,** ed. 500, s/n, 16" x 22", pub RAF | 80.00 | — |
| ☐ **MALLARDS,** ed. 500, s/n, 19" x 25", pub RAF | 100.00 | 400.00 |
| ☐ **OUT OF THE MIST,** ed. 500, s/n, 12" x 16", pub RAF | 60.00 | 125.00 |
| ☐ **WOLF PACK,** ed. 500, s/n, 17½" x 27", pub RAF | 125.00 | 450.00 |
| ☐ **WINTER FOX,** ed. 500, s/n, 12" x 18⅜", pub RAF | 60.00 | — |
| ☐ **OUT OF THE MARSHGRASS,** ed. 750, s/n, 18" x 26¼", pub RAF | 125.00 | — |
| ☐ **SNOW HARE,** ed. 650, s/n, 16" x 19½", pub RAF | 100.00 | — |
| ☐ **SWANS,** ed. 500, s/n, size not available, pub RAF | 150.00 | — |
| ☐ **LATE SEASON - MALLARDS,** rel. 1982. ed. 500, s/n, size not available, pub RAF | 125.00 | — |
| ☐ **FEATHERED MAGIC,** rel. 1983. ed. 750, s/n, 12" x 15", pub RAF | 90.00 | — |
| ☐ **LEADER OF THE PACK,** rel. 1983. ed. 500, s/n, 17" x 23", pub RAF | 150.00 | — |

# A. J. SCHEXNAYDER

A. J. Schexnayder received his art training at the New Orleans Academy of Art, Delgade Museum of Art, and John McCrady Art School.

An accomplished watercolorist, he has a received many awards from juried shows.

## A.J.SCHEXNAYDER

| | | |
|---|---|---|
| ☐ **FOREVER STILL,** rel. 1975. ed. 800, s/n, 19" x 24½" | 35.00 | — |
| ed. 1,200, s/o | 30.00 | — |
| ☐ **GRANDFATHER'S WAGON,** rel. 1975. ed. 800, s/n, 24½" x 19" | 45.00 | — |
| ed. 1,200, s/o | 40.00 | — |
| ☐ **JAN'S RAGGEDY,** rel. 1975. ed. 800, s/n, 24½" x 19" | 45.00 | — |
| ed. 1,200, s/o | 40.00 | — |
| ☐ **QUIET COUNTRY,** rel. 1975. ed. 800, s/n, 19" x 24½" | 35.00 | — |
| ed. 1,200, s/o | 30.00 | — |
| ☐ **FLARING THE EDGE,** rel. 1976. ed. 500, s/n, 33¾" x 25¾" | 60.00 | — |
| ed. 1,000, s/o | 50.00 | — |
| ☐ **FLIGHT OF KINGS,** rel. 1976. ed. 800, s/n, 20" x 16" | 20.00 | — |
| ed. 1,200, s/o | 16.00 | — |
| ☐ **CANADIAN GENERAL,** rel. 1982. ed. 700, s/n, 28" x 23" | 60.00 | — |

# JAY SCHMIDT

**MONEY TO SPEND** *by Jay Schmidt*

| | ISSUE PRICE | CURRENT PRICE |
|---|---|---|
| ☐ **TOMORROW'S DREAM**, rel. 1983. ed. 975, s/n, 18" x 28", pub FHG | 80.00 | — |
| ☐ **MONEY TO SPEND**, rel. 1983. ed. 975, s/o, 17¾" x 21¾", pub FHG | 80.00 | — |

# JOHN SCHOENHERR

John Schoenherr was born in New York City. He has painted animals all his life, starting with those he found in the Bronx and Central Park Zoos. He literally painted his way through the huge Bronx Zoo while studying at the Art Students League and Pratt Institute, and later staged a one-man show there. Inevitably, a painter as taken with animals and as talented as John Schoenherr could not be satisfied with painting animals in zoos. Instead, he traveled widely, capturing animals on his sketchpad and on film. Invited by the National Park Service, Schoenherr roamed the Western parks, painting mountain goats, elk and moose. A cave buff, he has also been commissioned to do paintings for the National Speleological Society. And he has painted for the Air Force and for private collection.

In recent years his book illustrations have won awards and citations. They include illustrations for *Rascal* and *The Wolfing* by Sterling North. Among others are *The Golden Eagle* and *The Fox and the Hound,* as well as numerous children's books. *The Barn* was both written and illustrated by Schoenherr. Today he lives on his farm in New Jersey, where he can study the animals he paints.

## JOHN SCHOENHERR

| | ISSUE PRICE | CURRENT PRICE |
|---|---|---|
| ☐ **SAHIB**, rel. 1975. ed. 850, s/n, 30" x 20", pub GW . . . . . . . . . . . . . . . . . . . . . | 65.00 | 185.00 |
| ☐ **SPOTTED LEOPARD**, rel. 1975. ed. 850, s/n, 18¼" x 18¼", pub GW . . . . . . . | 55.00 | 120.00 |
| ☐ **GRIZZLY**, rel. 1976. ed. 850, s/n, 30½" x 20¾", pub GW . . . . . . . . . . . . . . . | 65.00 | − |
| ☐ **MOUNTAIN LION FAMILY**, rel. 1977. ed. 1,000, s/n, 22" x 29", pub GW . . . . . | 65.00 | − |
| ☐ **CLAM BAR**, rel. 1978. ed. 1,000, s/n, 32" x 22", pub GW . . . . . . . . . . . . . . . | 65.00 | − |
| ☐ **CLOSE ENOUGH**, rel. 1979. ed. 1,000, s/n, 17" x 21", pub GW . . . . . . . . . . . | 60.00 | − |

# THOMAS SCHULTZ

Growing up in Fond du Lac at the southern end of Lake Winnebago, and adjacent to the large natural areas of Horicon Marsh and the Kettle Moraine, Thomas Schultz developed an early interest and appreciation for the wonders of nature.

Graduating from the University of Wisconsin in 1976 with a degree in Wildlife Ecology, Schultz decided to pursue a career in wildlife painting and illustration. That summer he received a university grant to participate in a seminar on bird painting taught by Don Eckelberry. It was conducted on the island of Trinidad where the participants sketched directly from live birds and study skins. Upon his return, Schultz continued gathering experience painting wildlife on a part-time basis, and then in the spring of 1978 decided to make it a full time profession.

Schultz's work is already attractng a large following of supporters. His paintings of a nuthatch was hanging at the Leigh Yawkey Woodson Art Museum Bird Art Exhibition and selected as one to be included on the European tour.

## THOMAS SCHULTZ

| | | |
|---|---|---|
| ☐ **BLUE JAY**, rel. 1980. ed. 400, s/n, 16" x 20", distr. NC . . . . . . . . . . . . . . . . | 35.00 | − |
| ☐ **ROSE-BREASTED GROSBEAKS**, rel. 1980. ed. 400, s/n, 16" x 20", distr. NC . | 35.00 | − |
| ☐ **YOUNG BIRDS-BLUE JAY**, rel. 1980. ed. 400, s/n, 11" x 14", distr. NC . . . . . | 30.00 | − |
| ☐ **YOUNG BIRDS-ROBIN**, rel. 1980. ed. 400, s/n, 11" x 14", distr. NC . . . . . . . | 30.00 | − |

# TIMOTHY C. SCHULTZ

Timothy C. Schultz was born in Fond du Lac, Wisconsin in 1955. Through frequent childhood contacts with the lakes, marshes and woodlands of east central Wisconsin, Schultz developed an early interest and respect for the natural world found around him.

While attending high school and the University of Wisconsin Center-Fond-du-Lac, he continued to intensify his studies in the areas of art and the natural sciences.

Upon the completion of his formal education, Schultz found himself spending an increasing amount of his free time in the production of wildlife paintings. This desire to paint the things that mean so much to him, combined with the increasing demand for his original oil paintings, eventually led Schultz to the decision to paint full time. Schultz's talents were recently formally recognized as his oil painting of a pair of Lesser Scaup was chosen as the winning entry in the prestigious 1981 Wisconsin Waterfowl Stamp Contest.

In addition to painting, Schultz also enjoys hunting, fishing, camping, underwater spearfishing, wildlife photography and participating in all forms of athletics.

**1981 WISCONSIN DUCK** *by Timothy Schultz*

## TIMOTHY C. SCHULTZ

| | ISSUE PRICE | CURRENT PRICE |
|---|---|---|
| ☐ **BLUEBILLS**, rel. 1981. ed. 1,700, s/n, 14″ x 12″, pub NC | 125.00 | 175.00 |
| 1981 Wisconsin Duck Stamp Print. ed. 300 remarqued | 300.00 | — |
| ☐ **PEACEFUL PAIR-WOODIES**, rel 1981. ed. 600, s/n, 28″ x 20½″, pub NC | 75.00 | — |
| ☐ **AT CATTAILS EDGE - HOODED MERGANZERS**, rel 1983. ed. 600, s/n, 14½″ x 25½″, pub NC | 60.00 | — |
| ☐ **1984 WISCONSIN TROUT STAMP PRINT**, rel 1983. ed. 600, s/n, 14″ x 12″, pub NC | 135.00 | — |
| ed. 100, remarqued | 250.00 | — |

## KEN SCHULZ

| | | |
|---|---|---|
| ☐ **CADES COVE**, ed. 350, s/n, 18½″ x 23″, distr. SGL | 75.00 | — |
| ☐ **CHURCH IN THE GLADE**, ed. 500, s/n, 18½″ x 23″, distr. SGL | 60.00 | — |
| ☐ **DOGWOOD**, ed. 500, s/n, 15″ x 19″, distr. SGL | 40.00 | — |
| ☐ **GERANUIM**, ed. 500, s/n, 28″ x 23, distr. SGL | 85.00 | — |
| ☐ **GOVERNOR JOHN SEVIER'S PLACE**, ed. 500, s/n, 22″ x 26″, distr. SGL | 85.00 | — |
| ☐ **GREENBRIER**, ed. 500, s/n, 18½″ x 23″, distr. SGL | 75.00 | — |
| ☐ **JUNGLE BROOK WINTER**, ed. 500, s/n, 15″ x 19″, distr. SGL | 40.00 | — |
| ☐ **PORTRAIT OF AUTUMN**, ed. 500, s/n, 15″ x 19″, distr. SGL | 40.00 | — |
| ☐ **SHADOWS**, ed. 500, s/n, 15″ x 19″, distr. SGL | 50.00 | — |
| ☐ **THE SOWERS**, ed. 500, s/n, 20½″ x 26¾″, distr. SGL | 85.00 | — |
| ☐ **THRU THE BARN**, ed. 350, s/n, 18½″ x 23″, distr. SGL | 85.00 | — |
| ☐ **WINTER WOODLAND**, ed. 500, s/n, 15″ x 19″, distr. SGL | 40.00 | — |

## CARL E. SCHWARTZ

Carl E. Schwartz, well known Chicago artist, painter and teacher, lives with wife, two daughters and impressive turtle collection on the north side of Chicago. A large rock garden occupies most of the back yard of the Schwartz home and in the summer becomes the unlikely urban habitat for his prized turtles.

Schwartz is a charter member of the Chicago Herpetological Society which is dedicated to the study, preservation and protection of reptiles and amphibians. He is also a member of the International Turtle and Tortoise Society.

This avid interest in turtles began for Schwartz when he was a child. His father had an extensive turtle collection which became part of the family. Schwartz has since traveled to many parts of the world - France, Italy, Spain, Mallorca, Mexico and all over the United States - sometimes hunting for turtles, but more often studying art and sketching.

Schwartz has won coveted honors at numerous important art shows around the country and has had many one man exhibitions in the Chicago area as well as elsewhere in the United States. Some of his paintings are among the permanent collections of the Art Institute of Chicago, the American Dental Institute, Borg Warner Corporation, University of Minnesota, Library of Congress and many more. He has been represented in *Who's Who in America* and *Who's Who in American Art*.

Teaching art is one of the most satisfying facets of Schwartz's multidimensional life. Currently he is teaching figure drawing and painting in several Chicago suburban art leagues as well as giving private lessons in his studio.

| CARL E. SCHWARTZ | ISSUE PRICE | CURRENT PRICE |
|---|---|---|
| ☐ AMERICA CROCODILE, rel. 1972. ed. 4,700, s/o, 23" x 17", pub CHWA .... | 20.00 | — |
| ed. 200, s/n ................................................ | 50.00 | — |
| ed. 100 Artist proofs | | |
| ☐ GALAPAGOS TORTOISE, rel. 1972. ed. 4,700, s/o, 23" x 17", pub CHWA .... | 20.00 | — |
| ed. 200, s/n ................................................ | 50.00 | — |
| ed. 100 Artist proofs | | |

## JAMES GODWIN SCOTT

For over 25 years, Jim Scott has painted along the rivers of America. One art critic wrote of his work . . . "Scott's paintings are highly evocative as well as forceful, vigorous and technically immaculate — the introduction of abstraction further emphasizes the importance of feeling rather than a picture pretty copy of nature."

Collectors on both sides of the Atlantic and jurors in Paris, London and New York exhibitions have enthusiastically accepted Scott's highly individual watercolors of river subjects.

In keeping with his philosophy: "To grow, one must give," Scott offers workshops and demonstration lectures to audiences in various parts of the country.

## JAMES GODWIN SCOTT

| | | |
|---|---|---|
| ☐ BECKY THATCHER, rel. 1979. ed. 950, s/n, 20¼" x 25¼", pub MPPI ....... | 75.00 | — |

# JOHN SCOTT

Scott, on graduating from art school, joined the staff of *Yank Magazine* as a combat illustrator early in World War II. He covered the invasion of Normandy traveling with the troops. His sketches are exhibited by the U.S. Army Historical Files in Washington, D.C.

When he returned to the United States after the war, Scott approached the editor of *Sports Afield* with his sketches and an idea. He proposed to do the same thing for sports that he had done for war: sketch the participants in the field. For 33 years, Scott, in a unique arrangement, sketched and painted dozens of covers, hundreds of features and unnumbered illustrations for the magazine. Unlike other outdoor illustrators who free-lanced for different magazines, Scott's magazine work appeared only in *Sports Afield*.

Most outdoorsmen remember the Garcia series. These were paintings of the most famous fishing areas in the world and appeared as foldouts in major outdoor magazines.

His fine art paintings are known throughout the nation. A series of ten which immortalizes the early days in Texas and Oklahoma oil fields hangs in the Oil Museum in Midland, Texas. From a standpoint of size, commissions from the Mormon Church for 12' x 32' murals were the largest.

Since 1978, Scott has turned his professional attention to the old West, its Indians, trappers, explorers and mountain men.

| JOHN SCOTT | ISSUE PRICE | CURRENT PRICE |
|---|---|---|
| ☐ THE WATERFALL, rel. 1981. ed. 950, s/n, 15¼″ x 24½″, pub MPPI . . . . . . . . | 85.00 | — |
| ☐ THE TROUT STREAM, rel. 1982. ed. 950, s/n, 18″ x 24″, pub MPPI . . . . . . . . | 95.00 | — |
| ☐ YELLOWSTONE CROSSING, rel. 1982. ed. 950, s/n, 14¾″ x 24″, pub MPPI . . | 85.00 | — |

# SIR PETER SCOTT

Sir Peter Scott of Gloucester, England, has been a professional painter for more than 40 years. In addition to being a fine artist, he is a great naturalist, author, illustrator, ornithologist, ichthyologist, conservationist, broadcaster, lecturer, and sportsman.

Scott's father, Captain Robert Falcon Scott, became an international hero when he died tragically in the Antarctic in 1912 after reaching the South Pole. Scott grew up amongst distinguished people and memorable events.

At Cambridge, Scott studied zoology. The discovery that he could actually sell his undergraduate paintings led him to the serious study of art. He studied at the Munich State Academy and subsequently at Royal Academy Schools in London. His first art exhibit sold very well and his paintings have been in great demand since.

It is as a painter and as a conservationist that he is best known in the United States. In North America, his paintings have been shown at the Society of Wildlife Artists in New York and at the Royal Ontario Museum International Wildlife Show as well as private galleries.

In 1946, at Slimbridge, England, he established The Wildfowl Trust which has an international reputation in pursuance of its four aims of education, research, conservation, and recreation. There, a unique method of display enables 200,000 people each year to see tame waterfowl from all over the world at close quarters, and wild native species in their natural habitat.

Scott's background is awesome. He has won the coveted Prince of Wales cup three times for sailing dingies. At the 1936 Olympic Games he won a bronze medal for sailing. During World War II, he commanded small ships and was decorated twice for bravery and once for inventing a highly successful method of camouflaging warships.

As an author and co-author he has 14 books to his credit, including his autobiography in 1962, *"The Eye of the Wind"*. He has illustrated another 16 books and many other publications.

He received his M.A. at Cambridge and has received four honorary degrees from leading British universities. For the statutory period of three years he was Rector of Aberdeen University and is now Chancellor of the University of Birmingham.

In 1973, Scott was created a Knight Bachelor for services to conservation and the environment.

Renowned International Chairman of the World Wildlife Fund, he holds numerous prominent positions. His major contributions to wildlife and conservation societies around the world are enormous.

Birds are of primary interest to Scott and his artistic training, talent and study enable him to paint them with a unique, delightful style.

| PETER SCOTT | ISSUE PRICE | CURRENT PRICE |
|---|---|---|
| ☐ CANADA GEESE ARRIVING OUT OF A MIST, rel. 1977. ed. 950, s/n, 22½" x 31", pub MPPI | 125.00 | 250.00 |
| ☐ CANADA GEESE COMING TO THE MARSH, rel. 1981. ed. 950, s/n, 22" x 26. pub MPPI | 125.00 | — |
| ☐ PINTAILS ON A HAZY DAY, rel. 1970. No information available as to edition, size, and etc. | N/A | 350.00 |

# G. CLARK SEALY III

| | ISSUE PRICE | CURRENT PRICE |
|---|---|---|
| ☐ AVOCET, rel. 1976. ed. 100, s/n, etching, pub MMGI | 50.00 | — |
| ☐ CHOUETTE, rel. 1976. ed. 100, s/n, etching, pub MMGI | 50.00 | — |
| ☐ PENGUINS, rel. 1976. ed. 100, s/n, etching, pub MMGI | 50.00 | — |
| ☐ SAILING HOME, rel. 1976. ed. 100, s/n, etching, pub MMGI | 50.00 | — |
| ☐ SWAN LAKE, rel. 1976. ed. 100, s/n, etching, pub MMGI | 50.00 | — |
| ☐ ANGELFISH, rel. 1977. ed. 100, s/n, etching, pub MMGI | 50.00 | — |
| ☐ BIRD IN NEST, rel. 1977. ed. 100, s/n, etching, pub MMGI | 50.00 | — |
| ☐ BLUEBIRDS, rel. 1977. ed. 100, s/n, etching, pub MMGI | 50.00 | — |
| ☐ FINCHES, rel. 1977. ed. 100, s/n, etching, pub MMGI | 50.00 | — |
| ☐ GREY MORNING, rel. 1977. ed. 100, s/n, etching, pub MMGI | 60.00 | — |
| ☐ LOON, rel. 1977. ed. 100, s/n, etching, pub MMGI | 60.00 | — |
| ☐ PORTRAIT OF WINTER, rel. 1977. ed. 100, s/n, etching, pub MMGI | 50.00 | — |
| ☐ REDWING, rel. 1977. ed. 100, s/n, etching, pub MMGI | 60.00 | — |
| ☐ WILL IT FLY?, rel. 1977. ed. 100, s/n, etching, pub MMGI | 60.00 | — |
| ☐ CASARES, rel. 1978. ed. 100, s/n, etching, pub MMGI | 60.00 | — |
| ☐ COCKATOO, rel. 1978. ed. 100, s/n, etching, pub MMGI | 60.00 | — |

# ADOLF SEHRING

Adolf Sehring's individual approach to art started at the prodigal age of six, in his birthplace of Russia. Seriously ill in the hospital, he occupied his time by drawing pictures of his roommate. The sketches were so authenic, both his doctor and his family encouraged him to continue drawing; by age eight, he had already won a number of local awards for his work. Later, while only in his teens, he began an apprenticeship under his father, a theatrical set designer in the German movie industry. Faced with the task of creating elaborate illusions that would translate realistically onto film, he learned how to convey the precise sense of distance that marks his work today, through study of careful craftsmanship and use of color.

Eventually, at 23, Sehring made his new home in the United States, and began work as a free lance designer and illustrator. Soon, he realized his real love was painting and Sehring began the successful career as an artist he enjoys today. Living and working on a 125-year-old, sprawling farm in the Southern United States, rich with trees, meadows, ponds and vistas, he finds life in artistic stimulus. "People are always surprised," he says, "that a painter should be interested in anything but painting. But the realistic painter must know his subject thoroughly: from the difference between a pheasant's and duck's tracks, to why an old cedar fence ages the way it does."

Adolf Sehring's works are in the permanent art collections of Temple University, the Hamilton Insurance Company, the Bailey Museum, and the U.S. State Department's "Art for Embassies" program. In 1975, his paintings were selected to represent American Realism at the prestigious Grand Palais Paris; in 1977, *Adolf Sehring and Realism,* a book on his life and work was published by *Kembel press.*

## ADOLPF SEHRING

| | ISSUE PRICE | CURRENT PRICE |
|---|---|---|
| ☐ **END OF DAY**, rel. 1980. ed. 300, s/n, litho, arches, 24½" x 29", pub EEI . . . . | 450.00 | — |
| ☐ **GATHERING FLOWERS**, rel. 1980. ed. 300, s/n, litho, arches, 25" x 28", pub EEI. . . . . . . . . . . . . . . . . . . . . . . . . . . . . . . . . . . . . . . . . . . . . . . . . . | 275.00 | 325.00 |
| ☐ **GOLDEN HARVEST**, rel. 1980. ed. 300, s/n, litho, arches, 29" x 24¼", pub EEI. . . . . . . . . . . . . . . . . . . . . . . . . . . . . . . . . . . . . . . . . . . . . . . . . . | 350.00 | 375.00 |
| ☐ **PRUNING**, rel. 1980. ed. 300, s/n, litho, arches, 33¼" x 24", pub EEI . . . . . . | 275.00 | 325.00 |
| ☐ **SNOWDRIFT**, rel. 1980. ed. 300, s/n, litho, arches, 34" x 22½", pub EEI . . . . | 350.00 | — |
| ☐ **SUMMER WOODS**, rel. 1980. ed. 300, s/n, litho, arches, 24" x 29", pub EEI . . | 275.00 | 325.00 |
| ☐ **VIOLETS**, rel. 1980. ed. 300, s/n, litho, arches, 25" x 29", pub EEI . . . . . . . . | 275.00 | 400.00 |

# JOE SEME

Joe Seme was born and raised near the once waterfowl-rich Barnegat Bay, and now resides with his family high on a mountaintop deep in the Blue Ridge Mountains. He graduated from Florida State University with a B.A. in American Literature.

While his early paintings were successful, Seme felt that to really improve he must narrow down his scope and zero in on those things which are intensely personal and with which he had a deep emotional involvement. Seme says "To maintain the intensity necessary to bring a three or four month painting to a conclusion you have to be just about in love with the subject, or at the very least, deeply interested." He is an avid collector of decoys and waterfowling artifacts which frequently become subjects for paintings.

In the last few years, Seme has become recognized as one of the foremost tromp l'oeil painters in the Southeast. His still-life paintings have been featured in leading magazines. His work can be found in ii..portant corporate and private collections in the U.S. and several foreign countries. Museum shows include the North Carolina Museum of Art, the Asheville Art Museum, the Mint Museum of Art, the prestigious Southeastern Center for Contemporary Art, and several others.

## JOE SEME

| | | |
|---|---|---|
| ☐ **BACK BAY GUNNER**, rel. 1981. ed. 450, s/n, 25¼" x 20", pub MPPI. . . . . . . . | 85.00 | — |

# KEITH SHACKLETON

Keith Shackleton, artist, naturalist, and author, was born in Weybridge, England. After intensive schooling in Australia and England, he spent five years in the R.A.F. in Europe and in the Far East. He was a war artist with the Army and Naval Coastal forces of Great Britain. From 1947 to 1963, he divided his time between painting, writing, and working with an aircraft brokerage firm as a licensed civil pilot.

Shackleton has traveled extensively visiting the Far East, Himalayas, Americas, Europe, and the North and South Polar Regions.

One of his major hobbies, small-boat sailing, has led to his being a three-time member of the British International 14' team, and a four-time winning crew member of the Prince of Wales' Cup competition.

He is an author of five books including *"Tidelines"*, *"Wake"*, *"A Sailor's Guide to Ocean Birds"*, *"Birds of the Atlantic Ocean"*, and *"Wild Animals of Britain"*.

Shackleton has had art exhibitions at the Royal Academy, the Royal Society of British Artists, and the Royal Society of Marine Artists. Commerical galleries representing him are located in London, New York, Johannesburg, Nairobi, and Bermuda.

**IN THE ISLAND BALD EAGLE** *by Keith Shackleton*

## KEITH SHACKLETON

| | ISSUE PRICE | CURRENT PRICE |
|---|---|---|
| ☐ **ADELIE PENGUINS,** rel. 1977. ed. 950, s/n, 13" x 9", pub MPPI | 25.00 | — |
| ☐ **IN THE ISLANDS - BALD EAGLE,** ed. 950, s/n, 17¾" x 24½", pub MPPI | 95.00 | — |
| ☐ **GENTOO PENGUINS,** rel. 1977. ed. 450, s/n, 19½" x 24", pub MPPI | 75.00 | — |
| ☐ **M.S. LINDBALD EXPLORER,** rel. 1977. ed. 950, s/n, 9" x 12", pub MPPI | 25.00 | — |
| ☐ **SKI SCENE,** ed. 950, s/n, 9½" x 16⅜", pub MPPI | N/A | — |
| ☐ **TIGER IN BAMBOO GRASS,** ed. 950, s/n, 27" x 18", pub MPPI | 85.00 | — |

# LEO SHANIKA

Born in St. Louis, Missouri in 1930, Leo Shanika (Sha' ni ka) demonstrated a strong interest in drawing and painting at an early age.

Today, Shanika is recognized as one of the Midwest's finest artists. He began his professional career nearly 25 years ago touring within the Famous-Barr Department Stores of St. Louis and engaging in private shows at the city's most highly regarded hotels. During an exhibition at the Chase Park Plaza many of Shanika's works were purchased by prominent St. Louisans as well as out-of-towners, one of the most noted being "Doc" Severinsen of the "Tonight Show". This was a key exhibition for Shanika creating for him a significant public following.

Shanika is most widely known for his rural landscapes depicting scenes from the Ozark Mountains of Missouri, and rural Illinois, to the serene Cumberland Valley in Pennsylvania, and the beautiful Blue Ridge Mountain areas of Virginia. Several of his works are on permanent display at the Harry S. Truman Center in Kansas City and several others have been displayed in Better Homes and Gardens magazines.

For the past ten years, Shanka has exhibited his work in many local, state, and regional compeitions and one man shows, and has won many awards — first prize awards and purchase awards. However, consistent with his philosophy of painting for other people, Shanika's favorite award came from the Jefferson College Art Fair in 1978. He won the "People's Choice Award" for best artist where everyone attending the fair was asked to vote.

| LEO SHANIKA | ISSUE PRICE | CURRENT PRICE |
|---|---|---|
| ☐ **MAX CREEK ROAD**, rel. 1979. ed. 1000, s/n, 19" x 12⅞", pub PSGI ........ | 20.00 | — |
| ☐ **HERSHEY'S MILL**, rel. 1979. ed. 1000, s/n, 19" x 16⅞", pub PSGI ......... | 20.00 | |

# MORI SHIZUME

| | | |
|---|---|---|
| ☐ **BALLOON FLIGHT**, ed. 150, s/n, 29" x 21½", original color lithograph, pub FI | 200.00 | — |
| ☐ **CONSTITUTION**, ed. 300, s/n, 42½" x 31", original color silkscreen, pub FI .. | 125.00 | — |
| ☐ **NEW YORK**, ed. 150, s/n, 41" x 25", original color lithograph, pub FI. ....... | 50.00 | — |
| ☐ **PARIS**, ed. 150, s/n, 41" x 25", original color lithograph, pub FI ........... | 50.00 | — |
| ☐ **ST. PATRICK'S**, ed. 225, s/n, 40½" x 26½", original color lithograph, pub FI . | 125.00 | — |

# DAN SHORT

Dan Short, the son of a coal miner, was born and raised in the back woods of Kentucky.

Despite an impoverished childhood, Short worked his way through high school and college, graduating from Berea College, Berea, Kentucky, in December 1975. Short feels fortunate to have grown up in an area which enjoyed clean air, thousands of acres of fresh virgin timber land, and an abundance of wildlife to observe and enjoy.

## DAN SHORT

**THE DECORATOR SERIES**

| | | |
|---|---|---|
| ☐ **THE BLUE JAYS**, rel. 1976. ed. 1,500, s/n, 20" x 16", pub NWAEI ......... | 30.00 | — |
| ☐ **INQUISITIVE RACCOONS**, rel. 1976. ed. number unknown, s/n, 20" x 16", pub NWAEI ...................................................... | 30.00 | 40.00 |

# GEORGE SHUMATE

George Shumate is a self taught artist. Before becoming a professional fine art painter, he was an architect designer. Shumate paints wildlife and "old things with strong textures." Many of his ideas come from an old plow, unusual barn board, a dented oil can and then "I change them, add to them — a bit more rust here, another knot there until I can touch them and until they touch me. They are treasures; I try to put life into them."

| GEORGE SHUMATE | ISSUE PRICE | CURRENT PRICE |
|---|---|---|
| ☐ LOOKOUT POINT, rel. 1981. ed. 3,000, s/o, 23¾" x 18", pub FHG. | 25.00 | — |
| ☐ NORRIS' DECOYS, rel. 1981. ed. 975, s/n, 21¼" x 30", pub FHG. | 65.00 | — |
| ☐ AUTUMN FROLIC, rel. 1982. ed. 975, s/n, 20" x 28", pub FHG. | 60.00 | — |
| ☐ ROCKY HAVEN, rel. 1982. ed. 975, s/n, 21" x 38", pub FHG. | 65.00 | — |

# HUBERT SHUPTRINE

Hubert Shuptrine is a native Tennessean who made his early mark as an abstract painter, winning every award the South had to offer. Then in 1970, Shuptrine became the artist he is: a Watercolorist in the new American realist tradition.

It was a trip to a fishing village on the coast of Maine that focused and concentrated his vision into honest statements of realism. He discovered that there is a timeless beauty in the plainest face and in the most barren landscape. It was also at that time he began working in transparent watercolors.

In 1974, Shuptrine received national recognition for his award winning book, "Jericho: The South Beheld". Text for Jericho was written by the noted Southern poetry and prose writer, James Dickey, a two time winner of the National Book Award. Jericho broke all records for art book sales with an initial first edition of 150,000 copies and Hubert Shuptrine was firmly established as one of the South's leading artists.

| HUBERT SHUPTRINE | | |
|---|---|---|
| ☐ PLANTATION TUB, rel. 1977. ed. 300, s/n, 30" x 21", pub HP | 500.00 | 625.00 |
| ☐ SUMMER AGAIN, rel. 1977. ed. 300, s/n, 28" x 40", pub HP | 500.00 | 625.00 |
| ed. 750, s/o | 20.00 | — |

# MICHAEL SIEVE

Born in Wilmont, Minnesota in 1951, Michael Sieve was raised in what was once known as the pheasant hunting capital of Minnesota. He spent much time as a youth hunting and fishing with his father and brothers around south-western Minnesota, Iowa and northwestern Colorado. These experiences spurred a lifetime interest in the outdoors, and he began drawing wildlife long before starting school.

Sieve went on to study art at Southern Minnesota State College in Marshall. After his graduation in 1975, he spent the next few years at various jobs, working toward his goal of becoming a full-time wildlife artist. In March of 1979, he was able to make the decision to devote all of his time to painting. Although accomplished in several mediums, he specializes in big game oils.

Sieve's works have been featured in such periodicals as the Minnesota *Volunteer* magazine and *Gray's Sporting Journal,* and he has exhibited at the Leigh Yawkey Woodson Museum in Wausau, Wisconsin and the Minnesota Wildlife Heritage Show for the past two years.

### MICHAEL SIEVE

| | ISSUE PRICE | CURRENT PRICE |
|---|---|---|
| ☐ OCTOBER SNOWFALL - WHITETAIL DEER, rel. 1980. ed. 850, s/n, size not available, pub WWI. | 65.00 | 300.00 |
| ☐ ALPINE MEADOW - ELK, rel. 1981. ed. 850, s/n, size not available, pub WWI. | 75.00 | — |
| ☐ EDGE OF THE FOREST - BALD EAGLE, rel. 1981. ed. 850, s/n, size not available, pub WWI. | 75.00 | 150.00 |
| ☐ FAST BREAK - WHITETAIL DEER, rel. 1981. ed. 850, s/n, size not available, pub WWI. | 75.00 | 250.00 |
| ☐ ALASKAN CLASSIC - DALL SHEEP, rel. 1982. ed. 850, s/n, size not available, pub WWI. | 75.00 | — |
| ☐ DECEMBER SNOWFALL - RED FOX, rel. 1982. ed. 850, s/n, size not available, pub WWI. | 75.00 | — |
| ☐ RIVER BOTTOM BUCK - WHITETAIL DEER, rel. 1982. ed. 950, s/n, size not available, pub WWI. | 85.00 | — |

# ARTHUR SINGER

The sidewalks of New York would seem an unlikely place for a wildlife painter and interpreter of nature to spend his early days, but such was the case with Arthur Singer. His love of nature and the out-of-doors seemed instinctive, his happiest moments being spent looking at animals in the Bronx Zoo or wandering up mountain trails on short vacations.

Singer graduated from art school at Cooper Union (and later taught there) but no one rushed forward to commission paintings of wildlife. So for a time he worked at a printing firm and, later, as art director for an advertising agency. Just when things seemed to be picking up a little — The New York Zoological Society gave him a one-man show — along came World War II.

Gradually his unmistakable talent began to bring him assignments. He did several projects for *Sports Illustrated* including an article by Dr. Robert Cushman Murphy of the American Museum of Natural History. Then he provided drawings for Murphy on the seabirds of North America.

Another turning point was a series of eight color plates of the state birds and flowers for *American Home* magazine. Also issued as a separate portfolio, it sold several million sets. Following this, he did illustrations for the *World Book Encyclopedia*.

Even at this time, though, perhaps not many serious bird watchers or naturalists were aware of his work, but when he teamed up with the well-known ornithologist Oliver L. Austin, Jr. to produce a sumptuous, lavishly illustrated volume, *Birds of the World,* his recognition was complete.

One of the most widely circulated works he did was *Birds of North America.* Singer is one of the few wildlife artists honored by membership in the American Ornithologists Union.

An expert photographer, he does his field research with a camera, traveling all over the world.

### ARTHUR SINGER

| | | |
|---|---|---|
| ☐ BALTIMORE ORIOLE, rel. 1973. ed. 4,000, s/o, 20" x 26", pub FHG | 45.00 | — |
| ☐ PHEASANT, rel. 1973. ed. 1,000, s/n, 32½" x 24", pub FHG | 75.00 | Sold Out |
| ed. 2,500, s/o | 60.00 | — |
| ☐ BROWN PELICAN, rel. 1974. ed. 1,000, s/n, 33½" x 24", released FHG | 40.00 | Sold Out |
| ☐ CLOUDED LEOPARD, rel. 1974. ed. 4,000, s/o, 22" x 28", pub FHG | 45.00 | 70.00 |
| ☐ ROADRUNNER, rel. 1974. ed. 3,500, s/o, 16" x 22½", pub FHG | 30.00 | Sold Out |
| ☐ ROBIN, rel. 1974. ed. 4,000, s/o, 16" x 22½", pub FHG | 30.00 | Sold Out |
| ☐ BELTED KINGFISHER, rel. 1975. ed. 3,000, s/o, 17" x 22", pub FHG | 30.00 | — |
| ☐ BURROWING OWL, rel. 1975. ed. 3,000, s/o, 16" x 20", pub FHG | 30.00 | — |
| ☐ ON THE ALERT, rel. 1975. ed. 1,000, s/n, 30½" x 23½", pub FHG | 65.00 | Sold Out |
| ed. 1,500, s/o | 50.00 | Sold Out |

| | ISSUE PRICE | CURRENT PRICE |
|---|---|---|
| ☐ **RACCOON,** rel. 1975. ed. 2,000, s/n, 20″ x 24″, pub FHG . . . . . . . . . . . . . . . | **50.00 | — |
| **This limited edition print was released in the AMERICA's WILDLIFE HERITAGE PORTFOLIO, which consists of six prints in all, each by a different Frame House Gallery artist. | | |
| ☐ **GOLDEN EAGLE,** rel. 1976. ed. 1,200, s/n, 30″ x 27″, pub FHG . . . . . . . . . . . | 50.00 | Sold Out |
| ☐ **RED-HEADED WOODPECKER,** rel. 1976. ed. 1,000, s/o, 22½″ x 16″, pub FHG | 30.00 | — |
| ☐ **RED-TAILED HAWK,** rel. 1976. ed. 1,500, s/o, 18″ x 24″, pub FHG . . . . . . . . . | *30.00 | 75.00 |
| *A portion of the edition reserved for The Museum of Arts and Sciences of Macon, Georgia. | | |
| ☐ **CARDINAL,** rel. 1977. ed. 1,000, s/o, 20″ x 16″, pub FHG . . . . . . . . . . . . . . . | 45.00 | 110.00 |
| ☐ **EASTERN BLUEBIRD,** rel. 1977. ed. 1,000, s/o, 20″ x 16″, pub FHG . . . . . . . . | 45.00 | — |
| ☐ **HERON AND EGRET,** rel. 1977. ed. 500, s/n, 24″ x 30″, pub FHG . . . . . . . . . . | *75.00 | 125.00 |
| *Of the edition, 100 prints were reserved for the Florida Audubon Society. | | |
| ☐ **SONGBIRD TRIO,** rel. 1977. ed. 1,500, s/o, 15″ x 12″, pub FHG. . . . . . . . .set | 45.00 | — |
| ☐ **JAPANESE CRANES,** rel. 1978. ed. 800, s/n, 14″ x 42″, pub FHG . . . . . . . . . | 60.00 | — |
| ☐ **PEREGRINE FALCON,** rel. 1978. ed. 800, s/n, 37⅞″ x 18″, pub FHG . . . . . . . . | 60.00 | 115.00 |

# ANTON SIPOS

Anton Sipos was born in Yugoslavia in 1938. His excellent draftsmanship earned him his first professional experience as assistant to an art director of Yugoslavian films. During this time he won a prize for his poster design for the film "Phaedra".

Asked to teach at the Academy of Fine Arts in Belgrade, Sipos decided instead to go to Paris, where for the next two years he studied the techniques of the old masters at the Louvre and those of the Impressionists at the Jeu de Paume. He had his first European showings in Paris, at the Yugoslavian Embassy and at the Galerie Lucas. In 1968 he had one man shows in Cannes and Beirut.

Attracted by the vitality of American art, Sipos moved to Los Angeles. He had several exhibitions in California, Oklahoma and Texas. Today he lives and works in New York. He is represented in private collections in France, England, Italy and Japan.

## ANTON SIPOS

| | | |
|---|---|---|
| ☐ **HANSOM CAB,** rel. 1977. ed. 250, s/n, size not available, litho, arches, pub WWI. . . . . . . . . . . . . . . . . . . . . . . . . . . . . . . . . . . . . . . . . . . . | 100.00 | — |
| ☐ **PEOPLE,** rel. 1977. ed. 250, s/n, 21½″ x 43″, litho, arches, pub EEI. . . . . . . . | 100.00 | — |

# ROBERT OLIVER SKEMP

Robert Oliver Skemp cannot recall a time when the sea has not held a fascination for him. From his first sight of salt water, at the age of four, Skemp has been enchanted by the sea and the ships that sail upon it.

Impressed by the illustrations of N. C. Wyeth and Meade Schaffer, Skemp enrolled at the Art Students League of New York under the tutelage of Thomas Hart Benton, George Bridgeman, and Frank V. DuMond.

He wanted to paint the sea and ships. To do this, he reasoned, the best way would be to go to sea to get first-hand experience as a foremast hand. The following years were spent doing just that. The ports of Japan, China, Sumatra and the French coast became familiar to him.

As an illustrator, Skemp worked for Studebaker, Schlitz, Coca Cola, *Liberty Magazine, Collier's, The Saturday Evening Post,* and *Sports Afield.* This work brought him three Gold Medals and numerous other awards from the Art Director's Clubs of New York and Chicago.

Skemp's works are the result of the artist's fine talent, knowledge of the sea, meticulous drawing, measuring, and the projection of the original lines and sail-plans, composing and re-composing before undertaking the final rendering.

For those who love the sea, Skemp has captured the never-to-be-forgotten romance of the great clipper ships.

| ROBERT OLIVER SKEMP | ISSUE PRICE | CURRENT PRICE |
|---|---|---|
| FLYING CLOUD, rel. 1978. ed. 950, s/n, 21" x 29", pub MPPI . . . . . . . . . . . . . | 125.00 | 150.00 |
| HONG KONG HARBOR/NIGHTINGALE GETTING UNDER WAY, rel. 1978. ed. 950, s/n, 23" x 29", pub MPPI . . . . . . . . . . . . . . . . . . . . . . . . . . . . . . . . . . . . | 125.00 | — |

# PETER SKIRKA

During his youth, wildlife artist Peter Skirka had dreams of becoming a veternarian. His love for animals seemed to steer him toward a vocation where he could study and work with animals.

Serious painting began in high school. After serving in the Armed Forces, Pete continued his art education for several years.

**FOREST WATCH** *by Peter Skirka*

"After leaving art school, I found a job in construction; I had a family to support, and in those days, even the most established wildlife artists had a very hard time. I never had any desire to paint anything 'manufactured'. So I painted a bit in my spare time and finally became so discouraged that I threw my paint set away. I gave up painting for five years."

This was only the first of many times that Peter Skirka gave up painting. But there has always been that drive which must be present in all great artists — that need to paint, to express something to others, to give them a beautiful moment — and so Skirka now paints full time.

## PETER SKIRKA

| | ISSUE PRICE | CURRENT PRICE |
|---|---|---|
| ☐ **STORM WATCH**, rel. 1981. ed. 1,500, s/n, 22½" x 38", pub FHG. | 80.00 | Sold Out |
| ☐ **BAMBOO BEARS**, rel. 1982. ed. 4,000, s/o, 15" x 12", pub FHG. | 25.00 | — |
| ☐ **THE HUNTER'S RETURN**, rel. 1982. ed. 1,500, s/n, 20" x 29½", pub FHG. | 80.00 | — |
| ☐ **FOREST WATCH**, rel. 1982. ed. 1,500, s/n, 28" x 22", pub FHG. | — | — |
| ☐ **BOBCAT**, rel. 1983. ed. 300, s/o, 17¼" x 14¼", pub FHG. | — | — |
| ☐ **PURSUIT**, rel. 1983. ed. 1,500, s/n, 23" x 30", pub FHG. | — | — |
| ☐ **WAIT**, rel. 1983. ed. 1,500, s/n, 23¼" x 18¾", pub FHG. | — | — |

# DORLA DEAN SLIDER

Dorla Dean Slider began her formal artistic education under a scholarship with Dr. Walter Emerson Baum at the young age of ten. She received her next honor, a silver medal for outstanding art activities, during ninth grade in junior high school.

Later, marriage, interrupted her studies, but in 1960 she started painting seriously again, taking the Commercial Art and Illustration Course from the Famous Artists Schools of Westport, Connecticut. At that time, her concentration was drawing.

Since 1964, Dorla has worked professionally, exhibiting in numerous regional, national and area shows. And museums including the Philadelphia Museum of Art, the Pennsylvania Academy of Fine Arts, the American Watercolor Society of New York, and the Allentown and Reading Art Museums. Additionally, she is the recipient of more than 100 awards, such as C. L. Wolfe Art Club Gold Medal, the Award of Excellence and Purchase Awards in the Mainstreams International Competition, Marietta, Ohio; and others.

But, possibly her proudest achievement, awarded in 1972, is membership in the prestigious American Watercolor Society: its initials now appear after her signature.

In speaking about her art and the challenge to stay fresh, Dorla reports that she varies her approach — either impressionistic or realistic, according to her mood. But regardless of mood, Dorla Dean Slider repeatedly achieves artistic excellence in watercolors, producing works which take new looks at our surroundings.

## DORLA DEAN SLIDER

| | | |
|---|---|---|
| ☐ **SNOW VALLEY**, rel. 1975. ed. 1,000, s/n, 19¼" x 26½", pub DDS | 30.00 | — |
| ☐ **COUNTRY VIEW**, rel. 1976. ed. 500, s/n, 20" x 28½", pub DDS | 50.00 | — |

# MICHAEL SLOAN

The ability to capture the feeling of nostalgia through his painting has led Michael Sloan to become one of the nation's most collected landscape artists. A graduate of the Memphis Art Academy, Sloan has seen his illustrations used on magazine covers worldwide. In constant demand, his commissions have taken him as far away as Mexico where he did a series of illustrations for Cook Industries.

| MICHAEL SLOAN | ISSUE PRICE | CURRENT PRICE |
|---|---|---|
| FOGGY MOUNTAIN MORNING. ed. 2,500; 500 s/n; 2,000 s/o . . . . . . . . . s/n | 40.00 | 150.00 |
| 29¼" x 23¼", litho, pub GSP . . . . . . . . . . . . . . . . . . . . . . . . . . . . . . . s/o | 25.00 | — |
| OTHER AUTUMNS. ed. 2,000; 500 s/n; 1,500 s/o . . . . . . . . . . . . . . . s/n | 40.00 | 80.00 |
| 29¼" x 23¼", litho, pub GSP . . . . . . . . . . . . . . . . . . . . . . . . . . . . . . . s/o | 20.00 | — |
| SPRING HOUSE. ed. 1,000, s/n, 25½" x 21¾", litho, pub GSP . . . . . . . . . . . . | 25.00 | Sold Out |
| s/o 1,500 . . . . . . . . . . . . . . . . . . . . . . . . . . . . . . . . . . . . . . . . . . . . . . . | 20.00 | Sold Out |
| SUMMERSET. ed. 3,100; 1,000 s/n; 2,000 s/o; 100 R/AP . . . . . . . . . . . . . s/n | 40.00 | 80.00 |
| 25¾" x 18", litho, pub GSP . . . . . . . . . . . . . . . . . . . . . . . . . . . . . . . . . s/o | 30.00 | — |
| . . . . . . . . . . . . . . . . . . . . . . . . . . . . . . . . . . . . . . . . . . . . . . . . . . . . . . . R/AP | 100.00 | — |
| TENNESSEE WINTER. ed. 2,500, s/n, 29½" x 23½", litho, pub GSP . . . . . . . . | 20.00 | 225.00 |

# RICHARD SLOAN

"What I want to convey is the full feeling of the subject and the setting, and while accuracy is certainly an important element, there is also the matter of mood and tone and some asthetics that can't really be defined. Absolutely flawless detail is commendable, of course, but it can be cold, too. If I couldn't breathe life and warmth into a painting, my purpose would be lost, regardless of the skill the work might depict otherwise!"

Richard Sloan's point is well taken, and as one of the top bird painters in the world, he has proved it through the tremendous acceptance of his work, some of which hangs in the Smithsonian Institution, state museums and prestigious private collections, not to mention the thousands of individuals who own prints from his limited edition series.

A native of Chicago, Sloan received his art education at the American Academy of Art. After graduation he spent several years as a staff artist for the Lincoln Park Zoo in that city. Later he traveled widely over the United States, Canada and Central and South America while in the process of doing research for his paintings of birds of prey, North American game birds and birds of the tropics. As a falconer, he has been a long-time advocate of protection for birds of prey.

A member of the International Society of Artists and the Society of Animal Artists, Sloan's works have appeared in and on the covers of many state and national magazines.

## RICHARD SLOAN

| | | |
|---|---|---|
| EASTERN BLUEBIRD, rel. 1968. ed. 5,000, s/o, 22"x 28", pub NHI . . . . . . . . | 30.00 | 400.00 |
| PURPLE MARTIN, rel. 1968. ed. 5,000, s/o, 22"x 28", pub NHI . . . . . . . . . . . | **30.00 | 125.00 |
| RING-NECKED PHEASANT, rel. 1969. ed. 5,000, s/o, 22"x 28", pub NHI . . . . | 30.00 | 300.00 |
| CARDINAL, rel. 1970. ed. 5,000, s/o, 22"x 28", pub NHI . . . . . . . . . . . . . . . | 30.00 | 150.00 |
| CHICKADEE, rel. 1970. ed. 5,000, s/o, 22"x 28", pub NHI . . . . . . . . . . . . . . | 30.00 | 100.00 |
| GREAT HORNED OWL, rel. 1970. ed. 5,000, s/o, 22"x 28", pub NHI . . . . . . . . | 30.00 | 150.00 |
| MALLARDS, rel. 1970. ed. 5,000, s/o, 22"x 28", pub NHI . . . . . . . . . . . . . . | 30.00 | 225.00 |
| MOUNTAIN BLUEBIRD, rel. 1970. ed. 5,000, s/o, 22"x 28", pub NHI . . . . . . . | 30.00 | 150.00 |
| ROBIN, rel. 1970. ed. 5,000, s/o, 22"x 28", pub NHI . . . . . . . . . . . . . . . . . . | 30.00 | 125.00 |
| WOOD DUCK, rel. 1970. ed. 5,000, s/o, 22"x 28", pub NHI . . . . . . . . . . . . . | 30.00 | 200.00 |

**HUMMINGBIRDS** *by Richard Sloan*

| | ISSUE PRICE | CURRENT PRICE |
|---|---|---|
| ☐ AMERICAN GOLDFINCH/WILLOW GOLDFINCH, rel. 1971. ed. 5,000, s/o, 22"x 28", pub NHI | 30.00 | 125.00 |
| ☐ CANADA GOOSE, rel. 1971. ed. 5,000, s/o, 22"x 28", pub NHI | 30.00 | 200.00 |
| ☐ MOCKINGBIRD, rel. 1971. ed. 5,000, s/o, 22"x 28", pub NHI | 30.00 | 150.00 |
| ☐ PEREGRINE FALCON, rel. 1971. ed. 5,000, s/o, 22"x 28", pub NHI | 30.00 | 125.00 |
| ☐ PRAIRIE CHICKEN, rel. 1971. ed. 5,000, s/o, 22"x 28", pub NHI | 30.00 | 75.00 |
| ☐ RUFFED GROUSE, rel. 1971. ed. 5,000, s/o, 22"x 28", pub NHI | 30.00 | 250.00 |
| ☐ BALTIMORE ORIOLE, rel. 1972. ed. 5,000, s/o, 22"x 28", pub NHI | 30.00 | 100.00 |
| ☐ BOBWHITE, rel. 1972. ed. 5,000, s/o, 22"x 28", pub NHI | 30.00 | 100.00 |
| ☐ BROWN PELICAN, rel. 1972. ed. 5,000, s/o, 22"x 28", pub NHI | 30.00 | 125.00 |
| ☐ ROADRUNNER, rel. 1972. ed. 5,000, s/o, 22"x 28", pub NHI | 30.00 | 100.00 |
| ☐ YELLOW-SHAFTED FLICKER, rel. 1972. ed. 5,000, s/o, 22"x 28", pub NHI | 30.00 | 100.00 |
| ☐ BROWN THRASHER, rel. 1973. ed. 5,000, s/o, 22"x 28", pub NHI | 30.00 | 75.00 |
| ☐ CACTUS WREN, rel. 1973. ed. 5,000, s/o, 22"x 28", pub NHI | 30.00 | 50.00 |
| ☐ CALIFORNIA QUAIL, rel. 1973. ed. 5,000, s/o, 22"x 28", pub NHI | 30.00 | 75.00 |
| ☐ EASTERN MEADOWLARK/WESTERN MEADOWLARK, rel. 1973. ed. 5,000, s/o, 22"x 28", pub NHI | 30.00 | 75.00 |
| ☐ GREEN-WINGED TEAL, rel. 1973. ed. 5,000, s/o, 22"x 28", pub NHI | 30.00 | 100.00 |
| ☐ RED-TAILED HAWK, rel. 1973. ed. 5,000, s/o, 22"x 28", pub NHI | 30.00 | 125.00 |
| ☐ CALIFORNIA GULL, rel. 1974. ed. 5,000, s/o, 22"x 28", pub NHI | 30.00 | 50.00 |
| ☐ COMMON LOON, rel. 1974. ed. 5,000, s/o, 22"x 28", pub NHI | 30.00 | 50.00 |
| ☐ PINTAIL, rel. 1974. ed. 5,000, s/o, 22"x 28", pub NHI | 30.00 | 75.00 |
| ☐ SCISSOR-TAILED FLYCATCHER, rel. 1974. ed. 5,000, s/o, 22" x 28", pub NHI | 30.00 | 50.00 |
| ☐ SNOWY OWL, rel. 1974. ed. 5,000, s/o, 22"x 28", pub NHI | 30.00 | 50.00 |

| | ISSUE PRICE | CURRENT PRICE |
|---|---|---|
| ☐ **CANVASBACK**, rel. 1975. ed. 5,000, s/o, 22″x 28″, pub NHI . . . . . . . . . . . . . | 30.00 | 50.00 |
| ☐ **CAROLINA WREN**, rel. 1975. ed. 5,000, s/o, 22″x 28″, pub NHI . . . . . . . . . . . | 30.00 | 50.00 |
| ☐ **GREAT EGRET**, rel. 1975. ed. 5,000, s/o, 22″x 28″, pub NHI . . . . . . . . . . . . . | 30.00 | 50.00 |
| ☐ **HERMIT THRUSH**, rel. 1975. ed. 5,000, s/o, 22″x 28″, pub NHI . . . . . . . . . . . | 30.00 | 50.00 |
| ☐ **PRAIRIE FALCON**, rel. 1975. ed. 5,000, s/o, 22″x 28″, pub NHI . . . . . . . . . . . | 30.00 | 50.00 |
| ☐ **WILLOW PTARMIGAN**, rel. 1975. ed. 5,000, s/o, 22″x 28″, pub NHI . . . . . . . . | 30.00 | 50.00 |
| ☐ **BALD EAGLE**, rel. 1976. ed. 650, 36″ x 46″ . . . . . . . . . . . . . . . . . . . . . . . | * | |
| *150 of these will be used for educational programs, *500 will be sold at - . . . | *500.00 | — |
| ed. 4,350, s/o, 22″x 28″, pub NHI . . . . . . . . . . . . . . . . . . . . . . . . . . . . | 30.00 | 125.00 |
| ☐ **NENE**, rel. 1976. ed. 5,000, s/o, 22″x 28″, pub NHI . . . . . . . . . . . . . . . . . | 30.00 | 50.00 |
| ☐ **SPRUCE GROUSE**, rel. 1976. ed. 5,000, s/o, 22″x 28″, pub NHI . . . . . . . . . . | 30.00 | 50.00 |
| ☐ **BLUE HEN**, rel. 1977. ed. 5,000, s/o, 22″x 28″, pub NHI . . . . . . . . . . . . . | 30.00 | 50.00 |
| ☐ **BLUE JAY**, rel. 1977. ed. 5,000, s/o, 22″x 28″, pub NHI . . . . . . . . . . . . . . | 30.00 | 50.00 |
| ☐ **HUMMINGBIRD**, rel. 1977. ed. 5,000, s/o, 22″x 28″, pub NHI . . . . . . . . . . . | 30.00 | 50.00 |
| ☐ **LARK BUNTING**, rel. 1977. ed. 5,000, s/o, 22″x 28″, pub NHI . . . . . . . . . . . | 30.00 | 50.00 |
| ☐ **LIGHTNING THROUGH THE CYPRESS**, rel. 1977. ed. 400, s/n, 18¾″ x 24″, pub RS . . . . . . . . . . . . . . . . . . . . . . . . . . . . . . . . . . . . . . . . . | 100.00 | — |
| ☐ **PURPLE FINCH**, rel. 1977. ed. 5,000, s/o, 22″x 28″, pub NHI . . . . . . . . . . . | 30.00 | 50.00 |
| ☐ **WHERE THE WILD AZALEAS GROW**, rel. 1977. ed. 400, s/n, 20″ x 24″, pub RS . . . . . . . . . . . . . . . . . . . . . . . . . . . . . . . . . . . . . . . . . . | 100.00 | 145.00 |
| ☐ **AMBUSH**, rel. 1978. ed. 600, s/n, 18″ x 24″, pub RS . . . . . . . . . . . . . . . . | 100.00 | — |
| ☐ **ICY STILLNESS**, rel. 1978. ed. 600, s/n, 23½″ x 19″, pub RS . . . . . . . . . . . | *100.00 | — |
| *In lieu of remarques, the artist will produce 25 original pencil drawings. . . . | 100.00 | |
| ☐ **LESSER SCAUP**, rel. 1978. ed. 5,000, s/o, 22″x 28″, pub NHI . . . . . . . . . . . | 30.00 | 50.00 |
| ☐ **PILEATED WOODPECKER**, rel. 1978. ed. 5,000, s/o, 22″x 28″, pub NHI . . . . . | 30.00 | 50.00 |
| ☐ **GREAT DAY IN THE MORNIN'**, rel. 1979. ed. 950, s/n, 23″ x 18″, pub RS . . . . | 75.00 | — |
| ☐ **ON THE BEACH**, rel. 1979. ed. 600, s/n, 18¾″ x 22″, pub RS . . . . . . . . . . . | 100.00 | — |
| ☐ **RHODE ISLAND RED HEN**, rel. 1979. ed. 5,000, s/o, 22″ x 28″ . . . . . . . . . | 30.00 | 50.00 |

**Prints were sold as collection at issue price shown, providing the collector purchased each print when published. Individual purchases were $50.00 issue.

| | | |
|---|---|---|
| ☐ **CANADA GEESE PAIR**, ed. 1,000, s/n, 16″ x 12″, distr. MM. . . . . . . . . . . . | 50.00 | — |
| ☐ **CANVASBACK PAIR**, ed. 1,000, s/n, 16″ x 12″, distr. MM. . . . . . . . . . . . . | 50.00 | — |
| ☐ **MALLARD PAIR**, ed. 1,000, s/n, 16″ x 12″, distr. MM. . . . . . . . . . . . . . | 50.00 | — |
| ☐ **PINTAIL PAIR**, ed. 1,000, s/n, 16″ x 12″, distr. MM. . . . . . . . . . . . . . . | 50.00 | — |
| ☐ **THE ORCHARD**, ed. 600, s/n, 18″ x 27″, distr. MM. . . . . . . . . . . . . . . . | 100.00 | — |
| ☐ **RAPTOR FUND PEREGRINE FALCON, Print and Stamp**, rel. 1981. ed. 1,500, s/n, 6½″ x 9″ image, overall size 12″ x 14″, pub The Raptor Fund. . . . . . . | 125.00 | — |
| ☐ **LOUISIANA WILD TURKEY STAMP AND PRINT**, rel. 1982. ed. 1,500, s/n, 6½″ x 9″ image, overall size 12″ x 14″, pub The Louisiana Wild Turkey Federation. . | 125.00 | — |
| ☐ **FIRST NEBRASKA CONSERVATION STAMP PRINT, MOURNING DOVE**, rel. 1983. ed. 650, s/n, 6½″ x 9″ image, overall size 12″ x 14″, pub Widgeon Enterprises, Inc. . . . . . . . . . . . . . . . . . . . . . . . . . . . . . . . . . . . . . . | 100.00 | — |

# KEN SMALLWOOD

Ken Smallwood developed a deep love and understanding of nature and its beauty early in life, growing up in a rural New Jersey town. His feelings are conveyed in the oil paintings he produces.

Ken's work has appeared on the covers of books and national magazines including, *Outdoor Life* and *Fish and Tackle Digest*.

His unmistakable style in depicting wildlife has made Ken's work justly popular and in demand by both the private collector and discerning sportsman.

## KEN SMALLWOOD

| | | |
|---|---|---|
| ☐ **AUTUMN MEADOW**, ed. 800, s/n, 24″ x 18″, pub PP. . . . . . . . . . . . . . . . | 75.00 | — |
| Remarqued, signed and numbered . . . . . . . . . . . . . . . . . . . . . . . . . . . | 165.00 | — |
| ☐ **DRIFTING IN**, ed. 800, s/n, 24″ x 18″, pub PP. . . . . . . . . . . . . . . . . . . | 75.00 | — |
| Remarqued, signed and numbered . . . . . . . . . . . . . . . . . . . . . . . . . . . | 165.00 | — |

# JOE SMITH

Joe Smith has worked and experimented to develop his technique of still life painting. It has evolved into a complex blend of "Pointillism", used extensively in the mid-1800's by the French Post-impressionists. The flexibility is provided by contemporary acrylic materials.

Pointillism involves the use of thousands of tiny dots to form the areas and textures of work. The density of dots determines the texture of the subject being painted. For example, smooth objects are composed of dots so small they can not be detected in normal lighting. However, rough textured objects, such as a rusty can, are composed of larger more visible dots. Pointillism also enables Joe to utilize a wide range of colors. These dots, under close scrutiny, form a subtle mosaic of hues and tones. Yet, when the same object is viewed from a slight distance, the mosaic merges to form a single tone.

Smith received his art degree from Ohio State University in 1971 and in addition to his painting, he works in the family lumber business.

| JOE SMITH | ISSUE PRICE | CURRENT PRICE |
|---|---|---|
| ☐ BITTERSWEET, ed. 750, s/n, 18¼" x 23", distr. WII | 75.00 | — |
| ☐ COFFEE BIN, ed. 750, s/n, 23" x 18½", distr. WII | 75.00 | — |

# TUCKER SMITH

Tucker Smith lives and works on a small ranch in the Rocky Mountains near Helena, Montana, He roams the back country, camera in hand, photographing wilderness scenes that will later become the subjects of his paintings. For recreation he, his wife and two sons canoe, backpack and cross-country ski.

Smith is receiving a great deal of attention as a Western artist. He is showing his work — and selling everything he shows — at galleries in Helena, Denver, Minneapolis, Columbus and New York. In 1978, he won best-in-show at Montana's Electrum Festival of Arts.

Smith made the decision to pursue art full time in 1971. He was born in St. Paul, Minnesota, and at the age of 12 moved with his parents to Wyoming. He graduated from the University of Wyoming in 1963 with a major in math and a minor in art. He immediately went to work for the State of Montana as a computer programmer and systems analyst. But Tucker Smith had painted since he was a boy, and the urge to make it his life's work finally prevailed.

Smith paints in oil primarily, but also in watercolor and dry-brush sepia. He is not a prolific painter; he may spend a month on a large oil. But he enjoys his work and his subject matter, and he is steadily winning recognition.

TUCKER SMITH

| | | |
|---|---|---|
| ☐ FOAL, rel. 1977. ed. 1,000, s/n, 24" x 20", pub GW | 55.00 | 250.00 |
| ☐ HAY SLED, rel. 1977. ed. 1,000, s/n, 24" x 20", pub GW | 55.00 | 430.00 |
| ☐ SILL, rel. 1978. ed. 1,000, s/n, 20" x 23", pub GW | 55.00 | 180.00 |
| ☐ SODA SPRINGS, rel. 1978. ed. 1,000, 27" x 17", pub GW | 60.00 | — |
| ☐ A BREAK, rel. 1979. ed. 1,000, s/n, 28½" x 19⅝", pub GW | 75.00 | 135.00 |
| ☐ MALAMUTE, rel. 1979. ed. 1,000, s/n, 17" x 20½", pub GW | 65.00 | 215.00 |
| ☐ BARN CAT, rel. 1980. ed. 1,000, s/n, 21" x 15½", pub GW | 80.00 | — |
| ☐ FIRST LIGHT, rel. 1980. ed. 1,000, s/n, 29" x 18½", pub GW | 75.00 | 125.00 |
| ☐ SKIDDING LOGS, rel. 1980. ed. 1,000, s/n, 28" x 20", pub GW | 80.00 | — |
| ☐ CHAUNCEY'S CORRALS, rel. 1981. ed. 1,000, s/n, 28" x 17", pub GW | 95.00 | — |
| ☐ SHALLOW WATER, rel. 1981. ed. 1,000, s/n, 27½" x 22", pub GW | 95.00 | — |
| ☐ FEEDING ON THE MILLER PLACE, rel. 1982. ed. 1,000, s/n, 31" x 19", pub GW | 125.00 | — |
| ☐ McCLELLAN CREEK, rel. 1983. ed. 850, s/n, 20⅛" x 24", pub GW | 125.00 | — |

# GORDON SNIDOW

"I paint real cowboys doin' real things," says Gordon Snidow.

Snidow graduated from the Art Center School in Los Angeles. For many years Snidow was a commercial artist. Today he is a full time fine art painter. He was among the early artists invited to join the Cowboy Artists of America, and over the years has collected nearly 20 major awards at the annual CA show.

While Snidow paints the contemporary cowboy, he illuminates his work with a light from the past. It is Snidow's dramatic lighting that most often fascinates people about his work. He says he has been greatly influenced by the Old Masters and their use of light.

**BUCKAROOS** *by Gordon Snidow*

| GORDON SNIDOW | ISSUE PRICE | CURRENT PRICE |
|---|---|---|
| ☐ AMERICAN PAINT, rel. 1976. ed. 250, s/n, 19½" x 29½", pub FHG | 100.00 | — |
| ☐ 10 A.M. AND DONE A DAY'S WORK, rel. 1976. ed. 1,000, s/n, 31" x 25½", pub FHG | 100.00 | — |
| ☐ BUILDING A SMOKE, rel. 1977. ed. 250, s/n, 24" x 28", pub FHG | 100.00 | — |
| ☐ THE HAPPY HOUR, rel. 1980. ed. 1,500, s/n, 21¾" x 22", pub SCG | 100.00 | — |
| ☐ THE LITTLEST STRAGGLER, rel. 1980. ed. 2,250, s/n, 15" x 22", pub TAP | 100.00 | — |
| ☐ A REMNANT OF ANOTHER TIME, rel. 1980. ed. 1,500, s/n, 26½" x 20", pub SCG | 110.00 | — |
| ☐ SUNUP, rel. 1980. ed. 1,000, s/n, 21½" x 28", pub SCG | 115.00 | — |
| ☐ BUCKAROOS, rel. 1981. ed. 2,250, s/n, 28" x 22", pub TAP | 100.00 | — |
| ☐ LOOKING FOR THE OLD PIEBALD MARE, rel. 1981. ed. 2,250, s/n, 28" x 18", pub TAP | 100.00 | — |
| ☐ SHIPPING THE O-6, rel. 1981. ed. 2,250, s/n, 24" x 20", pub TAP | 100.00 | — |
| ☐ WHEN THE TRUCKS ARE LOADED, rel. 1981. ed. 1,000, s/n, 19" x 28", pub SCG | 115.00 | — |
| ☐ SWEET TALKIN MAN, rel. 1982. ed. 1,000, s/n, 29" x 20⅛", pub GW | 150.00 | — |

# EDWARD SOKOL

Edward Sokol is a native New Yorker whose training in art started at the High School of Music and Art, and continued with a Bachelor of Fine Arts in Painting from Hunter College with additional training at the School of Visual Arts. After completing his education, he lived in Hawaii. While there, he painted many jungle scenes and seascapes which have become part of his unique trademark. His work has the charm of the primitive along with the sophistication of urbanized modern man. Sokol now makes his home in Mt. Kisco, New York.

Sokol has exhibited in galleries across the country. Among these are: The Lillian Heidenberg Gallery, New York City; Kretschmer Gallery, New York City; Haller Gallery, New York City; Robley Gallery, Roslyn, New York; The Smithsonian Institute, Washington, D.C.; Hunicutt Gallery, Hawaii; Steckler-Haller Gallery, Scottsdale, Arizona; Evans Gallery, Toronto.

| EDWARD SOKOL | ISSUE PRICE | CURRENT PRICE |
|---|---|---|
| A VIEW OF THE METROPOLITAN MUSEUM, ed. 300, s/n, 36″ x 37″, original color silkscreen, pub Fl | 250.00 | 350.00 |
| AMSTERDAM, ed. 250, s/n, 19½″ x 27¾″, original color silkscreen, pub Fl | 250.00 | — |
| APPLE ORCHARD, ed. 300, s/n, 28″ x 28″, original color silkscreen, pub Fl | 150.00 | 175.00 |
| BACKYARDS, ed. 250, s/n, 25½″ x 25½″, original color silkscreen, pub Fl | 250.00 | — |
| BLUE HOUSE, ed. 300, s/n, 24″ x 15″, original color silkscreen, pub Fl | 75.00 | — |
| BLUE ROOM, ed. 375, s/n, 26⅛″ x 26⅛″, original color silkscreen, pub Fl | 350.00 | — |
| CABIN IN PUNALUU, ed. 375, s/n, 20¼″ x 24″, original color silkscreen, pub Fl | 250.00 | — |
| CHANGING SEASONS, ed. 250, s/n, 22″ x 26¼″, original color silkscreen, pub Fl | 250.00 | — |
| THE CRESCENT, ed. 250, s/n, 21½″ x 26½″, original color silkscreen, pub Fl | 350.00 | — |
| FIRST SNOW, ed. 300, s/n, 22″ x 26″, original color silkscreen, pub Fl | 175.00 | 200.00 |
| FISHING PIER, ed. 300, s/n, lithograph, 30″ x 42″ | 200.00 | — |
| FULL SAILS, rel. in future, ed. 300, s/n, unknown as of this date, original color silkscreen, pub Fl | 300.00 | — |
| GOLD JUNGLE, ed. 250, s/n, 22¼″ x 28¼″, original color silkscreen, pub Fl | 200.00 | — |
| THE ICE SKATES, rel. 1980, ed. 300, s/n, 38¾″ x 27⅛″, original color silkscreen, pub Fl | 300.00 | — |
| INSIDE THE CITY AND OUT, ed. 300, s/n, 36″ x 36″, original color silkscreen, pub Fl | 250.00 | 400.00 |
| JUNGLE HIDEAWAY, ed. 250, s/n, 26″ x 26″, original color silkscreen, pub Fl | 400.00 | — |
| JUNGLE SUNRISE, ed. 250, s/n, 28″ x 28″, original color silkscreen, pub Fl | 350.00 | — |
| JUNGLE SUNSET, ed. 250, s/n, 20¼″ x 28″, original color silkscreen, pub Fl | 250.00 | — |
| LONDON AT DUSK, ed. 300, s/n, 32″ x 32″, original color silkscreen, pub Fl | 200.00 | 250.00 |
| LOOKING ACROSS AT THE CITY, ed. 250, s/n, 17″ x 33¼″, original color silkscreen, pub Fl | 250.00 | — |
| MORNING HAZE, ed. 300, s/n, 26½″ x 35½″, original color lithograph, pub Fl | 200.00 | — |
| MY STUDIO, ed. 300, s/n, 28¾″ x 20¾″, original color lithograph, pub Fl | 150.00 | — |
| NASHUA, ed. 250, s/n, 20″ x 28″, original color silkscreen, pub Fl | 250.00 | — |
| NIGHT JUNGLE, ed. 250, s/n, 22″ x 27¾″, original color silkscreen, pub Fl | 250.00 | — |
| ON THE MANTEL, ed. 300, s/n, 28″ x 22″, original color silkscreen, pub Fl | 150.00 | — |
| POPPIES, ed. 300, s/n, 21″ x 25¾″, original color lithograph, pub Fl | 150.00 | 200.00 |
| RED ROOM, ed. 200, s/n, 27½″ x 22″, original color silkscreen, pub Fl | 350.00 | — |
| SPANISH ROOFTOPS, ed. 250, s/n, 21¼″ x 25¾″, original color silkscreen, pub Fl | 150.00 | — |
| SUMMER JUNGLE, ed. 300, s/n, 30″ x 30″, original color silkscreen, pub Fl | 200.00 | — |
| SUMMER STILL LIFE, ed. 300, s/n, 24¾″ x 25½″, original color lithograph, pub Fl | 150.00 | 175.00 |
| TUG BOATS, ed. 300, s/n, 27½″ x 20″, original color silkscreen, pub Fl | 150.00 | 175.00 |
| WEST STREET, ed. 300, s/n, 28″ x 22″, original color silkscreen, pub Fl | 150.00 | 175.00 |
| YELLOW HOUSE, ed. 300, s/n, 24″ x 14″, original color silkscreen, pub Fl | 75.00 | — |
| YELLOW TULIPS, ed. 250, s/n, 28¼″ x 22″, original color silkscreen, pub Fl | 250.00 | — |

# MORTEN E. SOLBERG

Mort Solberg enjoys an enviable life style, living high in the San Bernardino mountains of Southern California.

Although Solberg was involved in art as a teenager and pursued art commercially after graduating from high school in Cleveland, Ohio, he did not really begin to paint seriously until he moved to California where, in the early 70's, he decided to commit himself full time to fine art.

His unique style has earned him considerable national recognition, including listing in *Who's Who in America, Who's Who in America Art* and *Who's Who in the West*. His work has been purchased by the National Academy of Design. He is a member of the American Watercolor Society, where he has won three major awards. Also a member and past vice president of the National Watercolor Society, he has taken the top award in the Society.

"National competitions are very important," says Morten Solberg, "as they tend to keep me honest with myself. I need to know that I am continually growing as a fine artist and that people not only respond to my work but enjoy and respect what they see in it."

**WINTER'S CHILL** *by Morton Solberg*

| MORTON SOLBERG | ISSUE PRICE | CURRENT PRICE |
|---|---|---|
| ☐ **CHIPPEWA LAKE,** rel. 1978. ed. 1,000, s/n, 29" x 22", pub GW . . . . . . . . . . . . | 65.00 | — |
| ☐ **KODIAK BEARS,** rel. 1978. ed. 1,000, s/n, 29" x 22", pub GW . . . . . . . . . . . . . | 65.00 | 375.00 |
| ☐ **POLAR BEAR,** rel. 1978. ed. 1,000. s/n, 23⅛" x 11⅛", pub GW . . . . . . . . . . . | 55.00 | 450.00 |
| ☐ **WATCHING,** rel. 1978. ed. 1,000, s/n, 29" x 22", pub GW . . . . . . . . . . . . . . . | 65.00 | 220.00 |
| ☐ **BENGAL TIGER,** rel. 1979. ed. 1,500, s/n, 14½" x 20", pub GW . . . . . . . . . . | 65.00 | 100.00 |
| ☐ **ON WINTER WINDS,** rel. 1979. ed. 1,000, s/n, 19" x 14½", pub GW . . . . . . . . | 55.00 | 475.00 |
| ☐ **TAWNY,** rel. 1979. ed. 1,500, s/n, 18¼" x 13¾", pub GW . . . . . . . . . . . . . . | 55.00 | 125.00 |

| | ISSUE PRICE | CURRENT PRICE |
|---|---|---|
| ☐ **ARTIC MONARCH,** rel. 1980. ed. 1,500, s/n, 29″ x 22½″, pub GW. | 90.00 | 135.00 |
| ☐ **AT WATER'S EDGE,** rel. 1980. ed. 1,500, s/n, 20¼″ x 17″, pub GW. | 75.00 | 125.00 |
| ☐ **AUTUMN REPOSE,** rel. 1980. ed. 1,500, s/n, 28⅜″ x 21½″, pub GW. | 75.00 | 95.00 |
| ☐ **BROWN BEAR,** rel. 1980. ed. 1,500, s/n, 26″ x 16⅛″, pub GW | 75.00 | 150.00 |
| ☐ **EDGE OF YESTERDAY,** rel. 1980. ed. 1,500, s/n, 29″ x 22½″, pub GW. | 75.00 | 90.00 |
| ☐ **FIRST WINTER,** rel. 1980. ed. 1,500, s/n, 28½″ x 21½″, pub GW. | 75.00 | 115.00 |
| ☐ **TO THE VICTOR,** rel. 1980. ed. 1,500, s/n, 32″ x 24″, pub GW. | 85.00 | 110.00 |
| ☐ **BIRDS OF FRESH WATER MARSHES,** rel. 1981. (Suite of 4). ed. 1,500, s/n, 17″ x 11″, pub GW. | 75.00 | 115.00 |
| ☐ **EARLY SNOW,** rel. 1981. ed. 1,500, s/n, 35½″ x 23″, pub GW. | 110.00 | 140.00 |
| ☐ **FIRST REFLECTION,** rel. 1981. ed. 1,500, s/n, 34½″ x 19¾″, pub GW. | 125.00 | 145.00 |
| ☐ **FRESH TRACKS,** rel. 1981. ed. 1,500, s/n, 28¼″ x 22¼″, pub GW. | 110.00 | — |
| ☐ **INNOCENT,** rel. 1981. ed. 1,500, s/n, 24¼″ x 13¾″, pub GW. | 85.00 | 100.00 |
| ☐ **ACCEPT MY FATHER'S SPIRIT,** rel. 1982. ed. 950, s/n, 30½″ x 24″, pub GW. | 95.00 | — |
| ☐ **BEGIN THE HUNT,** rel. 1982. ed. 950, s/n, 27 3/16″ x 15⅞″, pub GW. | 125.00 | — |
| ☐ **ONE WITH EARTH AND SKY,** rel. 1982. ed. 950, s/n, 30½″ x 24″, pub GW. | 95.00 | — |
| ☐ **SEA OTTERS,** rel. 1982. ed. 1,250, s/n, 25″ x 18⅜″, pub GW. | 145.00 | — |
| ☐ **YEAR OF THE EAGLE,** rel. 1982. ed. 950, s/n, 32″ x 24½″, pub GW. | 150.00 | 160.00 |
| ☐ **DARK WATERS,** rel. 1983. ed. 1,000, s/n, 16½″ x 11½″, pub GW. | 70.00 | — |
| ☐ **THE BANDITS,** rel. 1983. ed. 950, s/n, 26⅜″ x 13¼″, pub GW. | 125.00 | — |
| ☐ **WINTER'S CHILL,** rel. 1983. ed. 675, s/n, 19½″ x 13⅛″, pub GW. | 95.00 | Sold Out |

## FRANK SOLTESZ

Frank Soltesz travels to observe and photograph the farms, landscapes, and villages which are the initial inspiration for his artwork.

His art work focuses on New England, the Rocky Mountain regions of the West, the Spanish-American villages of the Southwest, and the Canadian provinces. The numerous photographs Soltesz accumulates on these trips are stored in files for future use as inspiration. These reference slides, together with his on-location pencil sketches and notes regarding colors and values, later become finished paintings in his studio.

The traditional realism of his painting style always seems appropriate to the subject whether old farms, fishing villages, mills, locomotives, weathered buildings, or boats.

Soltesz's art training included studies at the Art Students League. The instruction which has always had the greatest affect on his career was watercolor technique under Charles Kinghan at the Huguenot School at New Rochelle, New York. Soltezs also has taught watercolor painting. His artwork has been used by magazines. Soltesz is an active member of the American Watercolor Society.

### FRANK SOLTESZ

| | | |
|---|---|---|
| ☐ **SKIING ALONE,** rel. 1981. ed. 950, s/n, 18″ x 24″, pub MPPI. | 75.00 | — |
| ☐ **BACKYARD AT THE HARBOR,** rel. 1981. ed. 475, s/n, 22¾″ x 29½″, pub MPPI. | 85.00 | — |

## GARY SORRELS

Gary Sorrels was born in Baudette, Minnesota and is the second oldest of eleven children. He always enjoyed drawing and his artistic ability began to show in the early elementary grades. Sorrels credits much of his talent to a correspondence course he took from an art instruction school in Minneapolis where he was encouraged tremendously to pursue an art related career.

Sorrels strives for realism in his paintings using exciting colors and outstanding brush treatment. Concentrating on big game animals of North America, he has done extensive study and research work on many of his subjects, particularly the Whitetail Deer. "You have to have an intimate knowledge of animals in their own world to make them life-like when you paint," he says. "The real beauty of wildlife is in its natural surroundings. If you can't paint them as they are, why paint?"

| GARY SORRELS | ISSUE PRICE | CURRENT PRICE |
|---|---|---|
| ☐ WINTER RENDEZVOUS - WHITETAIL DEER, rel. 1974. ed. 580, s/n, 16½" x 25", pub WWI | 50.00 | 250.00 |
| ed. 75 remarque artist proof | 100.00 | 275.00 |
| ☐ EARLY WINTER - WHITETAIL DEER, rel. 1975. ed. 600, s/n, 14" x 21", pub WWI | 40.00 | 550.00 |
| ed. 75 remarque artist proof | 75.00 | 600.00 |
| ☐ PRONGHORN RANGE, rel. 1978. ed. 600, s/n, 16½" x 25", pub WWI | 60.00 | |
| ed. 75 remarque artist proof | 130.00 | 75.00 |
| ☐ INTO THE CLEARING - ELK, rel. 1981. ed. 850, s/n, 16½" x 25", pub WWI. | 65.00 | — |
| Remarqued | 150.00 | — |

# DON SPAULDING

In the tradition of Remington and Schreyvogel, Don Spaulding is an eastern painter with a lifelong obsession with the legend of the Old West.

Spaulding brings to his paintings a sound background of academic training in art. Four years of study at the Art Students League of New York with Frank DuMond, William McNulty, and Robert Beverly Hale were climaxed by the unique opportunity to study with Norman Rockwell at his studio in West Arlington, Virginia.

In 1979, impressed by his cavalry paintings and by his careful attention to the accuracy of uniforms, accouterments and weapons, West Point Museum honored Spaulding with a three month exhibition of his paintings entitled "The American Cavalry in the West," a rare experience for a living artist.

A founding member of The Society of American Historical Artist, Spaulding also belongs to The Company of Military Historians, and The Order of the Indian Wars. His illustrations have appeared in many books and magazines, and he is well known among plate collectors for his "Americana Holidays" series for the Edwin M. Knowles China Co. His work is in many private collections, as well as the permanent collection of West Point Museum and The Bradford Museum.

| DON SPAULDING | | |
|---|---|---|
| ☐ THREE MILES TO THE FORT, rel. 1981. ed. 750, s/n, 23½" x 16¾", pub SGL. | 75.00 | — |
| ☐ FIGHTING TO SAVE THEIR HIDES, rel. 1982. ed. 750, s/n, 26" x 17", pub SGL. | 75.00 | — |

# IRENE SPENCER

When Irene Spencer was born in Chicago it must have been with a paint brush in her hand. At an early age, she was studying at the Academy of Art and the Chicago Art Institute. After completing her formal education, she did something that most people only dream of doing; she "ran away and joined the circus," where she portrayed life under the big top, both as painter and performer, leaving after two years for marriage and the field of commercial art.

During the next twenty years Spencer exhibited her award-winning talent and versatility as a writer and illustrator of children's books, staff cartoonist on a Michigan newspaper, and advertising artist. But as she had once been lured by the smell of grease-paint, so was she lured by the smell of oil paint, and she abandoned commercial art for fine art.

Her sensitive paintings and etchings speak as if alive. There is a softness, a tenderness in these works, but still there is a quality of strength. The moods which she invokes, her subtle tones, and her excellent draftsmanship are reminiscent of the Old Masters, and combine to produce paintings and etchings which are timeless.

Numerous works of the artist have been reproduced and are currently being shown and distributed worldwide. Perhaps her best known work to date is the annual *Franklin Mint Mother's Day Plate.*

**A TAIL OF TWO KITTIES** *by Irene Spencer*

| IRENE SPENCER | ISSUE PRICE | CURRENT PRICE |
|---|---|---|
| ☐ **BEYOND THE SUN**, ed. 400, s/n, litho, pub IS, dist. Armstrong's . . . . . . . . . . | 185.00 | 400.00 |
| ☐ **BITTERSWEET**, ed. 300, s/n, litho, pub IS, dist. Armstrong's . . . . . . . . . . . . . . | 150.00 | 500.00 |
| ☐ **CAREFREE**, ed. 100, s/n, 10″ x 12″, etching, pub IS, dist. Armstrong's . . . . . | 110.00 | 300.00 |
| ☐ **CHRISTMAS MOURNING**, ed. 31,50, s/n, litho, pub IS, distr. GBS. . . . . . . . . | 75.00 | 165.00 |
| ☐ **CONTENTMENT**, ed. 350, s/n, litho, pub IS, distr. GBS. . . . . . . . . . . . . . . . . | 125.00 | 175.00 |
| ☐ **DANNY'S TUNE**, ed. 50, s/n, 14″ x 18″, etching, pub IS, dist. Armstrong's . . | 110.00 | 200.00 |
| ☐ **DEAR CHILD**, ed. 100, s/n, 10″ x 12″, etching, pub IS, dist. Armstrong's . . . . | 110.00 | 300.00 |

| | ISSUE PRICE | CURRENT PRICE |
|---|---|---|
| ☐ **EMPTY SADDLES**, ed. 500, s/n, litho, pub IS, dist. Armstrong's . . . . . . . . . . | 125.00 | 150.00 |
| ☐ **FIRST EDITION**, ed. 550, s/n, litho, pub IS, dist. Armstrong's . . . . . . . . . . . . | 135.00 | 550.00 |
|    ed. 25 Artist proof . . . . . . . . . . . . . . . . . . . . . . . . . . . . . . . . . . . . . . . . . . . . | | |
| ☐ **FIRST KISS**, ed. 275, s/n, litho, pub IS . . . . . . . . . . . . . . . . . . . . . . . . . . . | 15.00 | 450.00 |
| ☐ **FLOWER PRINCESS**, ed. 550, s/n, litho, pub IS, dist. Armstrong's . . . . . . . . . | 185.00 | — |
|    ed. 25 Artist proof . . . . . . . . . . . . . . . . . . . . . . . . . . . . . . . . . . . . . . . . . . . . | | |
| ☐ **HILLS OF HOME**, ed. 100, s/n, 11″ x 15″, etching, pub IS, dist. Armstrong's . | 110.00 | 400.00 |
| ☐ **HUG ME**, ed. 350, s/n, litho, pub IS, dist. Armstrong's . . . . . . . . . . . . . . . . . | 80.00 | 800.00 |
| ☐ **I LOVE LITTLE KITTY**, ed. 500, s/n, 22″ x 28″, litho, pub IS, dist. Armstrong's | 95.00 | 150.00 |
| ☐ **I LOVE YOU**, ed. 550, s/n, litho, pub IS, dist. Armstrong's . . . . . . . . . . . . . . . | 285.00 | — |
|    ed. 25 Artist proof . . . . . . . . . . . . . . . . . . . . . . . . . . . . . . . . . . . . . . . . . . . . | | |
| ☐ **LARMETTE**, ed. 100, s/n, 9″ x 11″, etching, pub IS, dist. Armstrong's . . . . . . | 110.00 | 700.00 |
| ☐ **L'ENVOI**, ed. 500, s/n, 20″ x 30″, litho, pub IS, dist. Armstrong's . . . . . . . . . . | 95.00 | — |
| ☐ **LONESOME MELODY**, ed. 50, s/n, etching, pub IS, dist. Armstrong's . . . . . . . | 220.00 | 500.00 |
| ☐ **LONG, LONG DAYS**, ed. 100, s/n, 13″ x 16″, etching, pub IS, dist. Armstrong's | 110.00 | 450.00 |
| ☐ **MARK ANTHONY**, ed. 350, s/n, litho, pub Plate n Pace, distr. GBS. . . . . . . . . | 225.00 | — |
| ☐ **MIRACLE**, ed. 500, s/n, litho, pub IS, dist. Armstrong's . . . . . . . . . . . . . . . . . | 125.00 | 600.00 |
| ☐ **MOON GODDESS**, ed. 500, s/n, litho, pub IS, dist. Armstrong's . . . . . . . . . . | 185.00 | 190.00 |
| ☐ **MOTHER'S HERE**, ed. 500, s/n, 20¾″ x 26″, litho, pub IS, dist. Armstrong's . | 95.00 | 150.00 |
| ☐ **MY DEVOTION**, ed. 175, s/n, litho, pub IS, dist. Ira Roberts . . . . . . . . . . . . . | 60.00 | 1,000.00 |
| ☐ **NO MORE TEARS**, ed. 350, s/n, litho, pub IS, dist. GBS. . . . . . . . . . . . . . . . . | 125.00 | 210.00 |
| ☐ **OH, MOM!**, ed. 550, s/n, litho, pub IS, distr. GBS. . . . . . . . . . . . . . . . . . . . . | 135.00 | — |
| ☐ **PACHAMAMA**, ed. 500, s/n, litho, pub IS, dist. Armstrong's . . . . . . . . . . . . . | 95.00 | — |
| ☐ **PRECIOUS MOMENT**, ed. 550, s/n, litho, pub IS, dist. Armstrong's . . . . . . . . | 135.00 | 250.00 |
|    ed. 25 Artist proof . . . . . . . . . . . . . . . . . . . . . . . . . . . . . . . . . . . . . . . . . . . . | | |
| ☐ **QUEEN GUINEVERE**, ed. 350, s/n, litho, pub IS, distr. GBS. . . . . . . . . . . . . . | 185.00 | — |
| ☐ **SANDY CLAWS**, ed. 1,500, s/n, litho, pub IS, distr. GBS. . . . . . . . . . . . . . . . . | 85.00 | — |
| ☐ **SECRETS**, ed. 275, s/n, litho, pub IS, dist. Ira Roberts . . . . . . . . . . . . . . . . . | 60.00 | 1,000.00 |
| ☐ **SIR LANCELOT**, ed. 350, s/n, litho, pub IS, distr. GBS. . . . . . . . . . . . . . . . . . | 185.00 | 200.00 |
| ☐ **SLEEP LITTLE BABY**, ed. 500, s/n, litho, pub IS, dist. Armstrong's . . . . . . . . | 95.00 | 400.00 |
| ☐ **SLEEP LITTLE BABY**, ed. 100, s/n, 9″ x 12″, etching, pub IS, dist. Armstrong's | 110.00 | 700.00 |
| ☐ **SMOKE DREAMS**, ed. 50, s/n, etching, pub IS, dist. Ira Roberts . . . . . . . . . . | 55.00 | 2,000.00 |
| ☐ **STORYTIME**, ed. 500, s/n, 20″ x 30″, litho, pub IS, dist. Armstrong's . . . . . . . | 95.00 | 600.00 |
| ☐ **SUMMER AFTERNOON**, ed. 100, s/n, 9″ x 12″, etching, pub IS, dist. Armstrong's | 110.00 | 300.00 |
| ☐ **THE GREATEST GIFT**, ed. 550, s/n, litho, pub IS, distr. GBS. . . . . . . . . . . . . . | 135.00 | — |
| ☐ **THE PAW THAT REFRESHES**, ed. 1,500, s/n, litho, pub IS, distr. GBS. . . . . . . | 75.00 | 115.00 |
| ☐ **THIS IS WHAT IT'S ALL ABOUT**, ed. 50, s/n, 12″ x 18″, etching, pub IS, dist. Armstrong's . . . . . . . . . . . . . . . . . . . . . . . . . . . . . . . . . . . . . . . . . . . . . | 110.00 | 400.00 |
| ☐ **YESTERDAY, TODAY & TOMORROW**, ed. 100, s/n, 10″ x 12″, etching, pub IS, dist. Armstrong's . . . . . . . . . . . . . . . . . . . . . . . . . . . . . . . . . . . . . . . . . . . . . | 110.00 | 700.00 |
| ☐ **CLEOPATRA**, rel. 1982. ed. 350, s/n, 16″ x 20″, offset litho, pub IS. . . . . . . . . | 225.00 | — |
| ☐ **A TAIL OF TWO KITTIES**, rel. 1982. ed. 1,500, s/n, 14″ x 13″, original litho, pub IS. . . . . . . . . . . . . . . . . . . . . . . . . . . . . . . . . . . . . . . . . . . . . . . . . . . . . | 85.00 | — |
| ☐ **THE CAPISTRANO MADONNA**, rel. 1982. ed. 350, s/n, 16″ x 21″, offset litho, pub IS. . . . . . . . . . . . . . . . . . . . . . . . . . . . . . . . . . . . . . . . . . . . . . . . . . . . | 225.00 | — |

# WAYNE SPRADLEY

A native of Pell City, Alabama, Wayne Spradley began painting seriously when he was in high school. He left the cotton mill village for a tour with the U.S. Navy and began doing commission paintings only. After returning to Alabama, Spradley decided to concentrate on watercolor. He began a three-year extensive study to complement his self-taught style.

Spradley is a member of the Southern Watercolor Society.

## WAYNE SPRADLEY

| | ISSUE PRICE | CURRENT PRICE |
|---|---|---|
| ☐ **BILLY RAY'S PLANTER**, rel. 1977. ed. 2,000, s/n, 14" x 19¼", pub CSI..... | 25.00 | Sold Out |
| ☐ **EARLY MORNING MIST**, rel. 1977. ed. 2,000, s/n, 18" x 25", pub CSI ..... | 35.00 | Sold Out |
| ☐ **KYLMULIGA GRIST MILL**, rel. 1977. ed. 2,000, s/n, 13" x 19", pub CSI ..... | 25.00 | Sold Out |
| ☐ **SWEET WILLIAMS**, rel. 1977. ed. 2,000, s/n, 16" x 20", pub CSI .......... | 25.00 | Sold Out |
| ☐ **HUCKLEBERRY POND**, rel. 1978. ed. 1,000, s/n, 19" x 22½", pub CSI ...... | 35.00 | — |
| ☐ **EASTON HONKERS**, rel. 1979. ed. 500, s/n, 19" x 26¼", pub CSI.......... | 50.00 | — |

## HENRY STALLWORTH

| | | |
|---|---|---|
| ☐ **TEN FLEW - TWO FELL**, rel. 1981. ed. 600, s/n, size not available, pub WWI. . | 95.00 | — |

# STANLEY STEARNS

After a series of commerical art jobs which included work as an IBM technical illustrator, Stanley Stearns became art director of a national magazine.

Stearns has mastered the techniques of airbrushing, etching, stone lithography, sculpturing, woodcutting, oils, watercoloring and silkscreen printing.

Although known for his versatility, Stearns is considered a waterfowl artist having won the Federal duck stamp.

Currently, Stearns is working on limited edition serigraphs of a variety of subjects.

**PUFFINS** *by Stanley Stearns*

## STANLEY STEARNS

| | ISSUE PRICE | CURRENT PRICE |
|---|---|---|
| ☐ COW MOOSE, rel. 1955. ed. 6, s/n, 5″ x 8″, two color etching, pub SS | 10.00 | Unknown |
| ☐ HALF-GROWN WHITETAIL, rel. 1957. ed. 24, s/n, 10½″ x 13″, etching, 6 states, pub SS | 10.00 | 400.00 |
| ☐ ALONE AT SEA, rel. 1965. ed. 53, s/n, 14″ x 15½″, ten color woodcut, pub SS | 20.00 | Unknown |
| ☐ MARGOT'S BATH, rel. 1965. ed. 13, s/n, 15″ x 19½″, three color woodcut, pub SS | 15.00 | Unknown |
| ☐ OPEN WATER, rel. 1971. ed. 190, s/n, b/w, 14″ x 17″, pub SS | 12.00 | 80.00 |
| ☐ SPRIG, rel. 1971. ed. 190, s/n, b/w, 14″ x 17″, pub SS | 12.00 | 80.00 |
| ☐ TAKING OFF, rel. 1971. ed. 190, s/n, b/w, 14″ x 17″, pub SS | 12.00 | 80.00 |
| ☐ WINTER WHEAT, rel. 1971. ed. 190, s/n, b/w, 14″ x 17″, pub SS | 12.00 | 100.00 |
| ☐ TOLLING IN, rel. 1976. ed. 110, s/n, 19″ x 22½″, four color stone lithograph, pub Geo. C. Miller & Son, Inc. | 75.00 | 300.00 |
| ☐ FISHING CREEK, rel. 1977. ed. 950, s/n, color, 21″ x 26″, pub SS | 40.00 | 400.00 |
| ☐ CHIAROSCURO PORTRAIT, rel. 1980. ed. 100, s/n, 10″ x 14″, fourteen color serigraph, pub SS | 80.00 | 300.00 |
| ☐ PUFFINS, rel. 1982. ed. 100, s/n, 10″ x 14″, nineteen color serigraph, pub SS | 380.00 | 300.00 |
| ☐ EARLY SNOW, rel. 1983. ed. 100, s/n, 14″ x 8½″, nine colors in seven runs, pub SS | 250.00 | — |

# RANDY STEFFEN

Of Sioux and Cheyenne descent, Randy Steffen has studied old-time Indian dress and customs by spending countless hours with the old men who hunted buffalo in their youth and even some who fought General Custer's men at the Battle of the Little Big Horn.

A prolific writer, more than 1,500 of his illustrated articles have appeared in leading magazines. His extensive reference library reflects his insistence that every detail of his paintings be correct.

## RANDY STEFFEN

| | ISSUE PRICE | CURRENT PRICE |
|---|---|---|
| ☐ INDIANS OF THE PLAINS, pair, rel. 1971. ed. 1,000, s/n, 17″ x 28″, pub FHG | 50.00 | 150.00 |
| ☐ INDIANS OF THE PLAINS - PORTFOLIO OF FOUR, rel. 1971. ed. 1,500, s/n, 11″ x 14″, pub FHG | 60.00 | 125.00 |
| ☐ TWELVE MILES TO FORT WORTH, ed. 1,000, s/n | 25.00 | — |

# WILLIAM JAMES STEPHENSON

| | | |
|---|---|---|
| ☐ RING-NECKED PHEASANT, Plate I, ed. 500, s/n, 23″ x 35″, pub KNC | 75.00 | — |
| ☐ WOOD DUCK, Plate II, ed. 500, s/n, 23″ x 35″, pub KNC | 75.00 | — |
| ☐ SNOWY OWL, Plate III, ed. 500, s/n, 23″ x 35″, pub KNC | 75.00 | — |
| ☐ MALLARD, Plate IV, ed. 500, s/n, 23″ x 35″, pub KNC | 75.00 | — |
| ☐ BOBWHITE, Plate V, ed. 500, s/n, 23″ x 35″, pub KNC | 75.00 | — |
| ☐ RAINBOW TROUT, Plate XI, ed. 500, s/n, 23″ x 35″, pub KNC | 75.00 | — |
| ☐ RING-NECKED PHEASANT/CORNFIELD, Plate XII, ed. 500, s/n, 23″ x 35″, pub KNC | 75.00 | — |

# PEGGY STEWART

Peggy Stewart is an unusual artist who captures an unusual subject in a surprising manner. To many outsiders, the Amish are simple folk who seem to lead rather drab, colorless lives devoted to their religion, family and farm.

Stewart has come to know and love the fine people that comprise the Amish community in a way that we can share through her paintings and prints. Her keen eye and exceptional color sense bring out all the joy and life to be found . . . all with the tiniest touch of humor.

"All of my research had not prepared me for the joy of my first experience in Amish country. On a remote gravel road, with a picture perfect farm in the distance, the silence was overwhelming. Suddenly emerging over the hill was a black buggy and the soft clop-clop of horses hooves. Inside was a young family dressed in their wonderful blues, purples and teals . . . and of course, their traditional black hats and bonnets. We waved and shyly, they waved back. The charm and beauty of that moment was most certainly influential in my decision to paint the Amish and their lifestyle," recalls Stewart.

The colors found in these serigraph prints are based on fabric samples purchased at various community dry good stores. Each color is painstakingly applied in a thin layer upon thin layer, so the finished work appears virtually devoid of brush strokes.

Following a fine arts education, Stewart began her career as Advertising Manager for a high fashion, specialty shop in Cincinnati and later in New York. She eventually returned to the Cincinnati area as a highly successful illustrator of design fashions.

### PEGGY STEWART

| | ISSUE PRICE | CURRENT PRICE |
|---|---|---|
| ☐ **AMANDA AND MAMA**, ed. 500, s/n, 18″ x 21½″, distr. WII. | 75.00 | — |
| ☐ **BLUE BALLOONS**, ed. 350, s/n, 16″ x 20″, distr. WII. | 55.00 | — |
| ☐ **PINK KITES**, ed. 350, s/n, 16″ x 20″, distr. WII. | 45.00 | — |
| ☐ **PUMPKIN HARVEST**, ed. 500, s/n, 18″ x 21½″, distr. WII. | 75.00 | — |

## MIKE STIDHAM

| | | |
|---|---|---|
| ☐ **CANADA GEESE**, rel. 1981. ed. 150, 15″ x 18½″, original hand colored, etching, pub WWI. | 75.00 | — |
| ☐ **MALLARDS**, rel. 1981. ed. 150, 15″ x 18½″, original hand colored, etching, pub WWI. | 75.00 | — |
| ☐ **PINTAILS**, rel. 1981. ed. 150, 15″ x 18½″, original hand colored, etching, pub WWI. | 75.00 | — |
| ☐ **WOODDUCKS**, rel. 1981. ed. 150, 15″ x 18½″, original hand colored, etching, pub WWI. | 75.00 | — |

## DON STIVERS

Like a latter-day Frederic Remington, Don Stivers rides the West with the people who become the subjects of his paintings. Like the famed artist of a century ago, Stivers is virtually indefatigable. When he's not out gathering material, he's back at his studio in Connecticut painting from dawn to dusk seven days a week: "I don't have to wait for a phase of the moon to paint. I'm a pro. I'd rather be painting than anything else."

A native of upper Wisconsin, Stivers migrated with his parents to California when he was in high school. After serving in the Navy, he attended the California College of Arts and Crafts, and was graduated in 1951. His first job came that same year with a San Francisco commercial art firm. It was there that he learned his trade, Stivers says, and for 15 years he followed a successful career in the West. But gradually he came to feel that his career was in the East. In 1966, Stivers moved to Connecticut and there built an even larger following as an il-

**HURRY AND WAIT** by Don Stivers

lustrator and portrait painter. Slowly he was able to wean himself from commercial work, and today is painting the things he loves — the people, the horses, the life of the Old West. And every now and then he mounts up and makes that West come alive again.

## DON STIVERS

| | ISSUE PRICE | CURRENT PRICE |
|---|---|---|
| ☐ **ALL WORK, NO PLAY,** rel. 1980. ed. 1,000, s/n, 32″ x 20¼″, pub GW. . . . . . . | 85.00 | — |
| ☐ **BIVOUAC,** rel. 1981. ed. 1,000, s/n, 33½″ x 20¾″, pub GW. . . . . . . . . . . . . | 125.00 | — |
| ☐ **THE STAFF RIDE,** rel. 1981. ed. 500, s/n, 28″ x 25″, pub GW. . . . . . . . . . . . . | 75.00 | 120.00 |
| ed. 1,000, s/n, bearing logo of the Centennial Class, U.S. Army Command and General Staff College; proceeds to the Fort Leavenworth Museum Association. . . . . . . . . . . . . . . . . . . . . . . . . . . . . . . . . . . . . . . . . . . . . | 75.00 | Sold Out |
| ☐ **BREAKING CAMP,** rel. 1982. ed. 1,000, s/n, 26¾″ x 22½″, pub GW. . . . . . . | 125.00 | — |
| ☐ **HURRY AND WAIT,** rel. 1982. ed. 1,000, s/n, 32″ x 19¾″, pub GW. . . . . . . . | 125.00 | — |
| ☐ **PORTRAIT OF A POSSE,** rel. 1982. ed. 1,000, s/n, 21″ x 17⅞″, pub GW. . . . . . | 85.00 | — |

# FRED STONE

After many years as a commercial illustrator, scenic painter, and muralist, Fred Stone has embarked on the most exciting phase of his career. Since becoming involved in racing art, he has painted many of the world's most famous race horses, and his paintings hang in the homes of such notable racing personalities as Nelson Bunker Hunt, Charlie Whittingham, Connie Ring, and Kentucky governor, John Y. Brown.

Stone's paintings are not at all like those of other successful artists who have painted the racing scene over the past two hundred years. His interest lies not in the traditional posed conformation study or the full racing scene where the horse is but a small part of the total painting, but in the stop action close ups of that which is not obvious to the human eye.

His mares and foals are unique because of their extreme close up angles. The horses' eyes can really be studied, and it is in the horses' eyes that, according to Stone, the complete story of the horse is truly told.

## FRED STONE

| | ISSUE PRICE | CURRENT PRICE |
|---|---|---|
| ☐ AFFIRMED, STEVE CAUTHEN UP, rel. 1979. ed. 750, s/n, 21" x 23", offset/litho, distr. GBSL | 100.00 | 300.00 |
| ☐ MARE AND FOAL, rel. 1979. ed. 500, s/n, 17" x 21", offset/litho, distr. GBSL. | 90.00 | 300.00 |
| ☐ ONE, TWO, THREE, rel. 1979. ed. 500, s/n, 17" x 23", offset/litho, distr. GBSL. | 100.00 | 500.00 |
| ☐ PATIENCE, rel. 1979. ed. 1,000, s/n, 24" x 18", offset/litho, distr. GBSL. | 90.00 | 400.00 |
| ☐ THE MOMENT AFTER - LAFFIT PINCAY, rel. 1979. ed. 500, s/n, 17" x 16", offset/litho, distr. GBSL. | 90.00 | — |
| ☐ THE RIVALS - AFFIRMED AND ALYDAR, rel. 1979. ed. 500, s/n, 18" x 20", offset/litho, distr. GBSL. | 90.00 | 255.00 |
| ☐ EXCELLER - BILL SHOEMAKER UP, rel. 1980. ed. 500, s/n, 18" x 20", offset/litho, distr. GBSL. | 90.00 | 500.00 |
| ☐ GENUINE RISK, rel. 1980. ed. 500, s/n, 17" x 19", offset/litho, distr. GBSL. | 100.00 | 300.00 |
| ☐ PASTURE PEST, rel. 1980. ed. 500, s/n, 18" x 21", offset/litho, distr. GBSL. | 100.00 | 300.00 |
| ☐ THE BELMONT - BOLD FORBES, rel. 1980. ed. 500, s/n, 17" x 26", offset/litho, distr. GBSL. | 100.00 | — |
| ☐ THE KENTUCKY DERBY - SEATTLE SLEW, rel. 1980. ed. 500, s/n, 24" x 20", offset/litho, distr. GBSL. | 100.00 | 400.00 |
| ed. 1,000, s/o, for Special Kentucky Derby Governor Series, State of Kentucky | 100.00 | 400.00 |
| ☐ CONTENTMENT, rel. 1981. ed. N/A, s/n, size not available, offset/litho, distr. GBSL. | 115.00 | — |
| ☐ JOHN HENRY, rel. 1981. ed. N/A, s/n, size not available, offset/litho, distr. GBSL. | 160.00 | 500.00 |
| ☐ OFF AND RUNNING, rel. 1982. ed. N/A, s/n, size not available, offset/litho, distr. GBSL. | 125.00 | — |
| ☐ THE ARABIANS, rel. 1981. ed. N/A, s/n, size not available, offset/litho, distr. GBSL. | 115.00 | 230.00 |
| ☐ THE KIDNAPPED MARE - Fanfreluche and Secretariat Colt, Sain et Sauf, rel. 1981. ed. 750, s/n, 20" x 21", offset/litho, distr. GBSL. | 115.00 | 200.00 |
| ☐ T..c SHOE - 8000 WINS, rel. 1981. ed. N/A, s/n, size not available, offset/litho, distr. GBSL. | 200.00 | 600.00 |
| ☐ THE THOROUGHBREDS, rel. 1981. ed. N/A, 16" x 22", offset/litho, distr. GBSL. | 115.00 | 150.00 |
| ☐ THE WATER TROUGH, rel. 1982. ed. N/A, s/n, size not available, offset/litho, distr. GBSL. | 125.00 | — |

# WILLIAM F. STONE, JR.

William F. Stone, Jr. has the remarkable ability to transfer himself to his surroundings and identify with them no matter where he is. A painter as versatile as Stone could practice no one style; and perhaps that is why his style has evolved into what he calls a "watercolor montage". "I brought it about, myself — without any external influences," Stone says. "Every artist looks for his own individual style, and some never find it. I'm glad I did."

While Stone taught his unique style to himself, he also received a degree from the University of California at Berkeley. He studied at San Jose State, and then began teaching art in his home town of Pacific Grove on California's colorful Monterey Peninsula. Stone is also a certified medical and scientific illustrator ("I learned precision that way"). His work is included in the permanent collection of the Monterey Peninsula Museum of Art, and he is president of the Carmel Art Association.

## WILLIAM F. STONE

| | | |
|---|---|---|
| ☐ NEW ENGLAND BARN, rel. 1976. ed. 1,000, s/n, 21½" x 17¾", pub GW | 35.00 | — |
| ☐ QUIET COVE, rel. 1976. ed. 1,000, s/n, 22½" x 16", pub GW | 35.00 | — |
| ☐ WHARFSIDE, rel. 1976. ed. 1,000, s/n, 13¾" x 15½", pub GW | 50.00 | — |

# QUEENA STOVALL
## (1887-1980)

| | ISSUE PRICE | CURRENT PRICE |
|---|---|---|
| ☐ **CABIN ON TRIPLE OAKS FARM,** rel. 1976. ed. 600, s/o, 15″ x 20″, pub VA. . . | 30.00 | 185.00 |
| ☐ **END OF THE LINE,** rel. 1976. ed. 950, s/o, 16″ x 22″, pub VA. . . . . . . . . . . . . | 40.00 | 225.00 |
| ☐ **MARCH FURY,** rel. 1976. ed. 950, s/o, 16″ x 20″, pub VA. . . . . . . . . . . . . . . | 30.00 | 185.00 |
| ☐ **COMP'NY COMIN',** rel. 1977. ed. 275, s/o, 20″ x 24″, pub VA. . . . . . . . . . . . | 60.00 | 275.00 |
| ☐ **HFREFORDS IN THE SNOW,** rel. 1977. ed. 275, s/o, 19″ x 24″, pub VA. . . . . . | 60.00 | 275.00 |
| ☐ **FAMILY PRAYERS,** rel. 1978. ed. 300, s/o, 18″ x 24″, pub VA. . . . . . . . . . . . . | 60.00 | 250.00 |
| ☐ **FIRESIDE IN VIRGINIA,** rel. 1978. ed. 300, s/o, 18″ x 24″, pub VA. . . . . . . . . | 60.00 | 250.00 |
| ☐ **MAKING APPLE CIDER,** rel. 1978. ed. 200, s/o, 16″ x 20″, pub VA. . . . . . . . . | 60.00 | 200.00 |
| ☐ **MAKING SORGHUM MOLASSES,** rel. 1978. ed. 200, s/o, 17″ x 22″, pub VA. . | 60.00 | 250.00 |

# VIRGINIA STROUD

At a time when many Native American artists are working in styles and media foreign to their heritage, Virginia Stroud is dedicated to making an individual artistic statement in the most traditional of Indian styles. She uses the ancient pictographic and "x-ray" techniques, and has devoted her life to a careful study of the customs, history and legends of her people, the Cherokee.

Stroud started painting seriously when she was 13 and established herself in the Indian art world by winning a First Award in the prestigious Philbrook Annual American Indian Artists Exhibition — the youngest artist to receive such an honor. Stroud's first original stone lithograph, ENEMY TREASURES, won the First Award at both the Heard Museum and the Philbrook Museum 1978-79 exhibits — no other artist has ever taken the top award in both of these important competitions in the same season. She has also won the Heritage Award from the Five Tribes Museum, and awards at the American Indian Exhibition and the Gilcrease Institute.

## VIRGINIA STROUD

| | | |
|---|---|---|
| ☐ **ENEMY TREASURER,** edition and size of print not available, stone lithograph, pub NWDHG . . . . . . . . . . . . . . . . . . . . . . . . . . . . . . . . . . . . . . . . . . . . . . . . . . | 300.00 | 1,200.00 |
| ☐ **WE ARE COMING BACK,** ed. 80, s/n, 20″, x 28″, stone lithograph, pub NWDHG . . . . . . . . . . . . . . . . . . . . . . . . . . . . . . . . . . . . . . . . . . . . . . . . . | 300.00 | — |
| ☐ **THE CHASE,** ed. 650, s/n, 8″ x 10″, pub NWDHG . . . . . . . . . . . . . . . . . . . . . | 60.00 | — |
| Portfolio of three | | |
| **THE ROBES** | | |
| ☐ **STATE ONE,** ed. 80, s/n, 15″ x 22½″, 5 stones . . . . . . . . . . . . . . . . . . . . . | 300.00 | — |
| ☐ **STATE TWO,** ed. 80, s/n, 15″ x 22½″, 4 stones . . . . . . . . . . . . . . . . . . . . . | 300.00 | — |
| lithograph, pub NWDHG | | |

# ROBERT SUMMERS

HOUSTON, Texas—"I think people like my kind of painting because they're reminded of a simpler time, a simpler way of life. A time when people had more control over their lives." So Robert Summers philosophizes about his earthy, dramatic-yet-subtle paintings of the American West. Born in Glen Rose, Texas in 1940, Bob and his wife Boo, continue to make their home there with sons, Temple, Trent and Tyler. He took his first art lesson at age nine and since that time has become a renowned painter and sculptor largely through self-instruction. The artist uses oils because they allow him to create the soft, loose appearance that is instrumental in evoking the relaxing, peaceful mood of his art. "Mine is a realistic, but not a photographic style," he comments. "I like for my paintings to radiate an inner glow, and oils help to create the feel."

Robert Summers is a founding member of the Texas Association of Professional Artists. In 1975, he was named Bicentennial Artist of Texas by the Governor and State Legislature. He has also been awarded the gold medal by the Franklin Mint, as well as numerous other national and regional honors.

## ROBERT SUMMERS

| | ISSUE PRICE | CURRENT PRICE |
|---|---|---|
| ☐ BOSQUE TERRITORY, rel. 1978. ed. 1,500, s/n, 18" x 27", pub AMF........ | 35.00 | 110.00 |
| ☐ FORBIDDING WILDERNESS, rel. 1978. ed. 1,500, s/n, 18" x 27", pub AMF... | 35.00 | 80.00 |
| ☐ THE MIGHTY OAK ENDURETH, rel. 1978. ed. 1,500, s/n, 14" x 21", pub AMF. | 25.00 | 65.00 |
| ☐ WHITE BUFFALO, rel. 1978. ed. 1,500, s/n, 16" x 26½", pub AMF......... | 35.00 | 225.00 |
| ☐ COLTERS QUEST, rel. 1979. ed. 1,500, s/n, 19" x 32", pub AMF.......... | 50.00 | 210.00 |
| ☐ FOOTPRINTS IN THE SNOW, rel. 1979. ed. 1,500, s/n, 18" x 27", pub AMF. . | 40.00 | 510.00 |
| ☐ ANOTHER DAY, rel. 1980. ed. 1,500, s/n, 17" x 26", pub AMF........... | 52.00 | 150.00 |
| ☐ RECEDING STORM, rel. 1980. ed. 1,500, s/n, 18" x 27", pub AMF......... | 50.00 | 225.00 |
| ☐ SLICKER TIME, rel. 1980. ed. 1,500, s/n, 18" x 27", pub AMF........... | 52.00 | 550.00 |
| ☐ CAMP COFFEE, rel. 1981. ed. 1,500, s/n, 19" x 31", pub AMF........... | 75.00 | 145.00 |
| ☐ COMMUNE WITH GOD, rel. 1981. ed. 1,500, s/n, 18" x 24", pub AMF....... | 75.00 | 125.00 |
| ☐ FIRST VISIT, rel. 1981. ed. 1,500, s/n, 18" x 27", pub AMF............ | 62.00 | 125.00 |
| ☐ LEADIN LOOSE, rel. 1981. ed. 1,500, s/n, 16" x 24", pub AMF. .......... | 60.00 | 65.00 |
| ☐ COMMANCHE MOON, rel. 1982. ed. 1,500, s/n, 16" x 23", pub AMF........ | 36.00 | 75.00 |
| ☐ COOLING OFF, rel. 1982. ed. 500, s/n, 17" x 27", pub AMF............. | 80.00 | 135.00 |
| ☐ RENDEVOUS, rel. 1982. ed. 1,500, s/n, 18" x 27", pub AMF............. | 55.00 | 90.00 |
| ☐ BOOM TOWN, rel. 1982. ed. 1,950, s/n, 17" x 26", pub AMF............. | 75.00 | 375.00 |
| ☐ FAMILY TREE, rel. 1982. ed. 1,500, s/n, 16" x 24", pub AMF............ | 85.00 | — |
| ☐ I'D LIKE TO BE THERE, rel. 1982. ed. 1,500, s/n, 17" x 26", pub AMF..... | 80.00 | 155.00 |
| ☐ PEACEFUL VALLEY, rel. 1982. ed. 1,500, s/n, 16" x 26", pub AMF........ | 80.00 | 110.00 |
| ☐ TEXAS GOLD, rel. 1982. ed. 1,950, s/n, 18" x 27", pub AMF............. | 90.00 | 150.00 |
| ☐ ALL IS CALM, rel. 1983. ed. 1,500, s/n, 18" x 27", pub AMF............ | 90.00 | — |

# GEORGE SUTTON

George Sutton — writer, artist, teacher, internationally acclaimed ornithologist — is currently Professor Emeritus of Zoology at the University of Oklahoma and Curator of Birds at its Stovall Museum.

He has misgivings when referred to as "dean of American bird artists". He says, "I am a student of birds, I like to draw birds, and I like to write. That's enough."

Dr. Sutton has written many scientific articles for journals and several books, including *High Arctic* (1971), *Oklahoma Birds* (1967) and *Iceland Summer* (1961). In 1972 he was awarded Knight Cross of the Falcon.

## GEORGE SUTTON

| | | |
|---|---|---|
| ☐ SCISSOR-TAILED FLYCATCHER, rel. 1972. ed. 1,500, s/n, 18½" x 25", pub FHG ........................................................ | 20.00 | — |

# RAY SWANSON

Ray Swanson is recognized as a leading painter of Southwest Indian tribes of our day. Yet he did not start his life or career in the Southwest. He started drawing while growing up on a farm in South Dakota. Although he attended college and received a degree in another field, Swanson is basically a self-taught artist.

During the past 22 years of his art career, he has painted various subject matter and worked in oil, watercolor and pencil. During this time, Swanson has received many awards including a Gold Medal for watercolor from the National Academy of Western Art and two Gold Medals for western art from the Franklin Mint. Swanson's paintings are best known for a strong sense of sunlight, composition and values.

**A DAY AT THE FAIR**
*by Ray Swanson*

He found the real focus of his career 15 years ago when he began painting the Navajo and Hopi Indians of Arizona. The Navajo people have a very special place in his heart, and this is reflected in his paintings. Swanson can capture the innocence of a young child as well as the strength and tenacity in the facial lines of an old Indian. His paintings are all done with sensitivity and an understanding of his subjects and their land.

## RAY SWANSON

| | ISSUE PRICE | CURRENT PRICE |
|---|---|---|
| ☐ **AUTUMN IN CANYON DE CHELLY**, rel. 1979. ed. 950, s/n, 21″ x 29″, pub MPPI. | 95.00 | — |
| ☐ **PLAYING WITH THE KIDS**, rel. 1979. ed. 950, s/n, 21″ x 28½″, pub MPPI ... | 125.00 | — |
| ☐ **TAKING NO SHORTCUTS**, rel. 1979. ed. 950, s/n, 20″ x 23¾″, pub MPPI.... | 75.00 | — |
| ☐ **PIKI BREAD MAKER**, rel. 1980. ed. 950, s/n, 32″ x 24¾″, pub MPPI. | 135.00 | — |
| ☐ **WELL, IT MUST BE LUNCHTIME**, rel. 1980. ed. 950, s/n, 20″ x 23¾″, pub MPPI. | 75.00 | — |
| ☐ **LITTLE SIOUX**, rel. 1981. ed. 650, s/n, 20″ x 17½″, pub MPPI. | 135.00 | 185.00 |
| ☐ **MEDICINE MAN**, rel. 1981. ed. 950, s/n, 19⅛″ x 32¼″, pub MPPI. | 150.00 | — |
| ☐ **THE NAVAJO DAILY WORD**, rel. 1981. ed. 750, s/n, 32½″ x 24½″, pub MPPI. | 195.00 | — |
| ☐ **THE OLD MAN AND HIS LAND**, rel. 1981. ed. 450, s/n, 29″ x 24″, pub MPPI. . | 135.00 | 200.00 |
| ☐ **THE OLD MAN AND THE CANYON**, rel. 1981. ed. 750, s/n, 32½″ x 24½″, pub MPPI. | 195.00 | — |
| ☐ **LITTLE APACHE**, rel. 1982. ed. 750, s/n, 29¾″ x 17½″, pub MPPI. | 135.00 | — |
| ☐ **NAVAJO LITTLE ONE**, ed. 950, s/n, 17½″ x 23½″, pub MPPI. | — | — |
| ☐ **A DAY AT THE FAIR**, rel. 1983, ed. 950, s/n, 17½″ x 10⅞″, pub MPPI ...... | 65.00 | — |

# HAZEL SWEENEY

A native of Arkansas, Hazel Sweeney paints from a childhood full of memories. "The simple down home life-style of the late 30's and early 40's has all but vanished from the South. It is interesting to see how this nostalgic atmosphere is being rediscovered in the art world today. This simple haunting quality has always been a part of my life and my art," said Sweeney.

Sweeney began her career by taking a home study course in commercial art. Since then, she has done work for several ad agencies and publishing houses. Her illustrations have appeared in the United States and ten foreign countries.

**TOP OF THE SUMMER** *by Hazel Sweeney*

| HAZEL SWEENEY | ISSUE PRICE | CURRENT PRICE |
|---|---|---|
| ☐ **MORTON'S SALT**, ed. 500, s/n, 23¾" x 18¾", pub GSP | 30.00 | — |
| ed. 2,000, s/o | 20.00 | — |
| ☐ **ROCK ISLAND LINE**, ed. 500, s/n, 18¾" x 22", pub GSP | 30.00 | — |
| ed. 2,000, s/o | 20.00 | — |
| ☐ **TRUE SUNSHINE**, ed. 500, s/n, 21¼" x 18½", pub GSP | 40.00 | — |
| ed. 1,000, s/o | 30.00 | — |
| ☐ **BREAD OF LIFE**, rel. 1981. ed. 1,000, s/n, 25" x 20", pub GSP | 40.00 | — |

# FRED SWENEY

A Pennsylvania native, Fred Sweney has been a professional artist since 1933. Over the years, he has led a diversified career as a wildlife illustrator for several major outdoor magazines, children's books and calendars. He has written and illustrated three published books on art and his wildlife paintings can be found in private collections all across the country.

He recently retired as instructor and head of the Graphics Department of the Ringling School of Art in Sarasota, Florida, where he had taught since 1949.

A talented and widely respected man well known for his writing abilities as well as his artistic achievements, Sweney is listed in *Contemporary Authors, Who's Who in American Art* as well as *Who's Who in the South and Southwest*.

| FRED SWENEY | ISSUE PRICE | CURRENT PRICE |
|---|---|---|
| ☐ **THE HEDGEHOPPERS - BOBWHITE QUAIL**, rel. 1980. ed. 850, s/n, size not available, pub WWI. | 65.00 | — |
| ☐ **THE OUTSIDER - COUGARS**, rel. 1982. ed. 600, s/n, size not available, pub WWI. | 75.00 | — |

## ZOLTAN SZABO

Born in Hungary, Zoltan Szabo studied at the National Academy of Industrial Art in Budapest. Internationally respected as a water color artist, Szabo's career has included five years as resident artist and faculty member at Sault College in Canada.

Szabo has authored a book, *Landscape Painting in Watercolor*. His paintings hang in public and private collections worldwide.

### ZOLTAN SZABO

| | | |
|---|---|---|
| ☐ **RED ROSES**, ed. 2,500, s/n, 9" x 16¼", pub GSP. | 15.00 | — |
| ☐ **WHITE ROSES**, ed. 2,500, s/n, 9" x 16¼", pub GSP. | 15.00 | — |
| ☐ **ZOLTAN SZABO COMMEMORATIVE PRINT - WHITE ROSE**, ed. 500, s/n, 16" x 22¾", pub GSP. | 30.00 | Sold Out |
| ed. 1,500, s/o. | 25.00 | — |
| This limited edition was issued to commemorate the opening of the Zoltan Szabo Gallery. | | |
| ☐ **COOL DATE**, rel. 1981. ed. 1,000, s/n, 18½" x 26½", pub GSP. | 60.00 | — |
| ☐ **FOREST RENEGADE**, rel. 1981. ed. 2,000, s/n, 13¾" x 20", pub GSP. | 25.00 | — |
| ☐ **LOGAN SPRING**, rel. 1981. ed. 1,000, s/n, 18½" x 26½", pub GSP. | 60.00 | — |
| ☐ **NEW APPLES**, rel. 1981. ed. 2,000, s/n, 13¾" x 20", pub GSP. | 25.00 | — |
| ☐ **NIGHT SENTRY**, rel. 1982. ed. 500, s/n, 29½" x 21½", pub GSP. | 100.00 | — |
| ☐ **VANITY FAIR**, rel. 1982. ed. 1,000, s/n, 28½" x 22½", pub GSP. | 60.00 | — |

## JOHATHAN TALBOT

| | | |
|---|---|---|
| ☐ **SHIP IN A BOTTLE**, rel. 1977. ed. 100, s/n, etching, pub MMGI | 40.00 | — |
| ☐ **TERRARIUM**, rel. 1977. ed. 100, s/n, etching, pub MMGI | 30.00 | — |
| ☐ **THE BRIDGE**, rel. 1977. ed. 125, s/n, etching, pub MMGI | 60.00 | — |
| ☐ **CHICKADEES**, rel. 1978. ed. 100, s/n, etching, pub MMGI | 50.00 | — |
| ☐ **MARKET STREET**, rel. 1978. ed. 100, s/n, etching, pub MMGI | 70.00 | — |

## DAVID TAMERIN

David Tamerin was born in Israel in 1946. After graduating from the Bezalel Academy of Arts, he exhibited his works at the Bait Haomanim in Jerusalem, and was awarded a grant by the American-Israeli Cultural Foundation.

In 1972, after studying in France, Tamerin came to the United States, where he studied at the School of Visual Art, the Art Student's league, and the Pratt Graphic Center. The artist currently lives and works in New York.

One can see the high degree of technical ability in Tamerin's work, and feel at the same time the artist's sensitive attitude towards his subjects.

### DAVID TAMERIN

| | | |
|---|---|---|
| ☐ **DANCERS**, rel. 1977. ed. 250, s/n, 19" x 24", litho, arches, pub EEI. | 90.00 | 100.00 |
| ed. 25, japon | 110.00 | 120.00 |

## WILLIAM R. TAYLOR

|  | ISSUE PRICE | CURRENT PRICE |
|---|---|---|
| ☐ CAUTIOUS DESCENT - BLACK DUCKS, ed. 580, s/n, 17" x 23", pub WWI .... | 60.00 | — |
| ed. 30 remarque artist proof .................................... | 125.00 | — |
| ☐ SAFETY OF THE BAR - CANADA GEESE, rel. 1977. ed. 600, s/n, 24" x 17", pub WWI .................................................. | 75.00 | — |
| Remarqued ................................................. | 125.00 | — |
| ☐ PUTTIN' OUT, rel. 1980. ed. 500, s/n, 18" x 14", pub WWI .............. | 60.00 | — |
| Remarqued ................................................. | 110.00 | — |
| ☐ BACK WATER - WOODIES, rel. 1981. ed. 750, s/n, size not available, pub WWI | 65.00 | — |

## BRUCE TEALE

|  | | |
|---|---|---|
| ☐ TEN O'CLOCK COVEY, rel. 1981. ed. 600, s/n. size not available, pub WWI ... | 65.00 | — |
| ☐ SUN AND SHADE, rel 1982. ed. 600, s/n, size not available, pub WWI ....... | 75.00 | — |

## HOWARD TERPNING

Born in Oak Park, Illinois, and educated at the Chicago Academy of Fine Art and the American Academy of Art, Howard Terpning went the apprentice route to work his way to New York and big-time commercial illustraton. Movie assignments included, *The Guns of Navarone, Dr. Zhivago, A Man for All Seasons, The Sound of Music* and *Cleopatra.* He did covers for *Time, Newsweek, The Reader's Digest* and other magazines. But those who knew his work best, told him it deserved to be in museums, not magazines.

So he headed West for Tucson, and like those a century before him, he blazed a new trial to success. Just three years after that move, in 1979, he was elected to the National Academy of Western Art, and the same year, by unanimous vote, to the prestigious Cowboy Artists of America.

In 1980, he was awarded the National Academy's Gold Medal for his outstanding exhibition in oil, and the same year at the Cowboy Artists of America's 15th Annual Exhibition, he took four major prizes ... the Men's Arts Council award; the Colt Award, and two silver awards, one for oil and one for a drawing.

Terpning sums it up best; "It never occurred to me to make a living doing fine art paintings ... I started as an illustrator and it took a lot of time to realize that I really could earn a living painting the kind of pictures I want to paint most."

### HOWARD TERPNING

|  | | |
|---|---|---|
| ☐ SIOUX FLAG CARRIER, rel. 1981. ed. 1,000, s/n, 19" x 21½", pub GW...... | 125.00 | Sold Out |
| ☐ SMALL COMFORT, rel. 1981. ed. 1,000, s/n, 30" x 24½", pub GW......... | 135.00 | 220.00 |
| ☐ STONES THAT SPEAK, rel. 1981. ed. 1,000, s/n, 32" x 25½", pub GW ...... | 150.00 | 250.00 |
| ☐ THE SPECTATORS, rel. 1981. ed. 1,000, s/n, 32" x 19¾", pub GW........ | 135.00 | 160.00 |
| ☐ THE VICTORS, rel. 1981. ed. 1,000, s/n, 30" x 25", pub GW ............ | 150.00 | 200.00 |
| ☐ CHIEF JOESPH RIDES TO SURRENDER, rel. 1982. ed. 1,000, s/n, 31½" x 25½", pub GW .............................................. | 150.00 | 185.00 |
| ☐ DUST OF MANY PONY SOLDIERS, rel. 1982. ed. 1,000, s/n, 33" x 24½", pub GW.................................................. | — | — |
| ☐ SEARCH FOR THE RENEGADES, rel. 1982. ed. 1,000, s/n, 35½" x 20¾", pub GW.................................................. | 150.00 | Sold Out |
| ☐ SHIELD OF HER HUSBAND, rel. 1982. ed. 1,000, s/n, 20½" x 16¼", pub GW. | 150.00 | Sold Out |
| ☐ THE WARRIOR, rel. 1982. ed. 1,000, s/n, 14⅞" x 24½", pub GW ......... | 200.00 | Sold Out |
| ☐ CROSSING MEDICINE LODGE CREEK, rel. 1983. ed. 1,000, s/n, 22½" x 26½", pub GW .............................................. | 150.00 | — |
| ☐ PAINTS, rel. 1983. ed. 1,000, s/n, 23" x 18¼", pub GW ............... | 140.00 | — |
| ☐ SHOSHONIS, rel. 1983. ed. 1,000, s/n, 16½" x 13½", pub GW .......... | 85.00 | Sold Out |
| ☐ THE STAFF CARRIER, rel. 1983. ed. 1,250, s/n, 13⁹⁄₁₆" x 16¹⁵⁄₁₆", pub GW.... | 90.00 | — |

# J. SHARKEY THOMAS

The sensitive interpretations of wildlife by Canadian artist J. Sharkey Thomas are familiar to animal lovers throughout North America.

Born in the Hudson Valley in 1930, the artist enjoyed early exposure to the arts under the guidance and encouragement of her father, the late pen and ink portrait artist Bert Sharkey. She received her formal training in New York City, and followed a professional art career there until 1963, at which time she immigrated to Canada and became a naturalized Canadian.

Sharkey spends her summers teaching wildlife drawing at the Okanagan Summer school of the Arts in Penticton, B.C., where the Okanagan Game Farm offers a natural setting for a wide variety of breeding animals. She exhibits annually with the Society of Animal Artists in New York; at the Lock Gallery in Winnipeg, Manitoba, and participates in numerous international group exhibitions. The artist supports the major conservation appeals which are not hunter-oriented. She is an honorary President of the *World Wildlife Fund (Canada) Panda Club* and is on the Board of Directors at the *Owl Rehabilitation Research Foundation,* Vineland, Ont.

| J. SHARKEY THOMAS | ISSUE PRICE | CURRENT PRICE |
|---|---|---|
| ☐ **ELEPHANT,** rel. 1972. ed. 150, s/n, 33″ x 25″, litho, pub PHFA . . . . . . . . . . . . | 75.00 | Sold Out |
| ☐ **GRIZZLY & CUBS,** rel. 1972. ed. 150, s/n, 30″ x 36″, litho, pub PHFA . . . . . . . | 75.00 | Sold Out |
| ☐ **LION CUB,** rel. 1972. ed. 150, s/n, 17″ x 20″, litho, pub PHFA. . . . . . . . . . . | 35.00 | Sold Out |
| ☐ **LION FAMILY,** rel. 1972. ed. 150, s/n, 22″ x 38″, litho, pub PHFA . . . . . . . . . | 75.00 | Sold Out |
| ☐ **RACCOON HEAD,** rel. 1972. ed. 150, s/n, 17″ x 20″, litho, pub PHFA . . . . . . . | 35.00 | Sold Out |
| ☐ **STALKING TIGER,** rel. 1972. ed. 150, s/n, 20″ x 32″, litho, pub PHFA . . . . . . . | 75.00 | Sold Out |
| ☐ **BEAVER FAMILY,** rel. 1975. ed. 150, s/n, 26″ x 34″, litho, pub PHFA . . . . . . . | 70.00 | Sold Out |
| ☐ **POLAR & CUBS,** rel. 1975. ed. 150, s/n, 28″ x 25″, litho, pub PHFA . . . . . . . | 75.00 | Sold Out |
| ☐ **COUGAR & CUBS,** rel. 1976. ed. 150, s/n, 25″ x 32″, litho, pub PHFA . . . . . . . | 100.00 | — |
| ☐ **LONG-EARED OWL,** rel. 1976. ed. 150, s/n, 25″ x 40″, litho, pub PHFA . . . . . . | 75.00 | — |
| ☐ **NURSING LYNX,** rel. 1976. ed. 150, s/n, 25″ x 32″, litho, pub PHFA . . . . . . . . | 190.00 | — |
| ☐ **SHORT-EARED OWL,** rel. 1976. ed. 150, s/n, 25″ x 40″, litho, pub PHFA. . . . . | 75.00 | — |
| ☐ **GREVY'S ZEBRA,** rel. 1977. ed. 150, s/n, 21″ x 29″, litho, pub PHFA . . . . . . . | 175.00 | — |
| ☐ **SLEEPING TIGER,** rel. 1977. ed. 150, s/n, 30″ x 18″, litho, pub PHFA . . . . . . . | 125.00 | — |
| ☐ **STALKING JAGUAR,** rel. 1978. ed. 150, s/n, 25″ x 32″, litho, pub PHFA . . . . . | 175.00 | — |

# RICHARD E. THOMPSON

Richard Thompson sums up his painting simply, "I hope I have sincerity. I have tried to interpret things as I feel inside."

Entering the Chicago Academy of Fine Art at the age of 15, he was taken under the wing of Frederick Grant, who was a student of William Merritt Chase, one of America's great painters. From there he continued studying at the American Academy of Art and the Chicago Art Institute. Due to the depression and the insurgency of the Modern Art Era Thompson pursued a career as a commercial artist. During World War II he was commission by the U.S. Government to do War Bond Posters. His commercial art career was very successful, however, his ambition to have a fine art career was still with him. In 1959 when commercial art was being replaced substantially by photography he embarked upon a full time "fine arts" career.

Thompson appears in several publications including *Who's Who in American Art, Personalities of the West and Midwest, American Artists of Renown,* and *Contemporary Western Artists.* A book about the artist was released in 1982. It is titled *Richard Earl Thompson, American Impressionist, A Prophetic Odyssey in Paint.*

**BEACH STROLL** *by Richard Earl Thompson*

| RICHARD E. THOMPSON | ISSUE PRICE | CURRENT PRICE |
|---|---|---|
| ☐ **DOWNWIND**, rel. 1978. ed. 800, s/n, 24″ x 29″, pub RTG | 100.00 | 150.00 |
| ☐ **AUTUMN DAY**, rel. 1979. ed. 350, s/n, 29″ x 23″, pub RTG | 100.00 | — |
| ☐ **BRUCE'S BARN**, rel. 1979. ed. 1,000, s/n, 22″ x 28″, pub RTG | 60.00 | 100.00 |
| ☐ **BY THE ARBOR**, rel. 1979. ed. 350, s/n, 23″ x 28″, pub RTG | 100.00 | — |
| ☐ **MOODY DAY**, rel. 1979. ed. 350, s/n, 23″ x 29″, pub RTG | 100.00 | — |
| ☐ **IMPRESSION IN SPRINGTIME**, rel. 1979. ed. 350, s/n, 29″ x 23″, pub RTG | 100.00 | — |
| ☐ **IN THE SUMACS**, rel. 1979. ed. 350, s/n, 29″ x 23″, pub RTG | 100.00 | — |
| ☐ **SPRING SUNSET**, rel. 1979. ed. 1,500, s/n, 16″ x 20″, pub RTG | 40.00 | 75.00 |
| ☐ **SUGAR MAPLE**, rel. 1979. ed. 1,500, s/n, 20″ x 16″, pub RTG | 40.00 | — |
| ☐ **BEAVER'S HAUNT**, rel. 1980. ed. 1,000, s/n, 22″ x 28″, pub RTG | 60.00 | Sold Out |
| ☐ **CLOUD REFLECTION**, rel. 1980. ed. 1,000, s/n, 22″ x 28″, pub RTG | 60.00 | 100.00 |
| ☐ **HERON HOME**, rel. 1980. ed. 1,000, s/n, 22″ x 28″, pub RTG | 60.00 | 100.00 |
| ☐ **LAZY RIVER**, rel. 1980. ed. 1,000, s/n, 22″ x 28″, pub RTG | 60.00 | 100.00 |
| ☐ **NEW FALLEN SNOW**, rel. 1980. ed. 1,000, s/n, 22″ x 28″, pub RTG | 60.00 | 100.00 |
| ☐ **A SIGN OF WINTER**, rel. 1981. ed. 1,000, s/n, 22″ x 28″, pub RTG | 60.00 | 100.00 |
| ☐ **AUTUMN BIRCHES**, rel. 1981. ed. 1,000, s/n, 22″ x 28″, pub RTG | 80.00 | 100.00 |
| ☐ **BEN'S ACRES**, rel. 1981. ed. 1,000, s/n, 22″ x 28″, pub RTG | 80.00 | 100.00 |
| ☐ **CECILEY**, rel. 1981. ed. 1,500, s/n, 16″ x 20″, pub RTG | 50.00 | 75.00 |
| ☐ **FROSTY MORN**, rel. 1981. ed. 1,000, s/n, 22″ x 28″, pub RTG | 80.00 | 100.00 |
| ☐ **HEADING HOME**, rel. 1981. ed. 1,500, s/n, 20″ x 16″, pub RTG | 50.00 | 75.00 |
| ☐ **LES CANADIANS**, rel. 1981. ed. 1,000, s/n, 22″ x 28″, pub RTG | 80.00 | Sold Out |
| ☐ **ONLY IN AUTUMN**, rel. 1981. ed. 1,000, s/n, 22″ x 28″, pub RTG | 80.00 | 100.00 |
| ☐ **SKIM ICE**, rel. 1981. ed. 1,000, s/n, 22″ x 28″, pub RTG | 60.00 | 100.00 |
| ☐ **OCTOBER SERMON**, rel. 1982. ed. 1,000, s/n, 22″ x 28″, pub RTG | 100.00 | — |
| ☐ **SIDE YARD**, rel. 1982. ed. 1,000, s/n, 22″ x 28″, pub RTG | 100.00 | — |
| ☐ **WINDY**, rel. 1982. ed. 1,000, s/n, 22″ x 29″, pub RTG | 100.00 | — |
| ☐ **AUTUMN MOOD**, rel. 1983. ed. 1,000, s/n, 28″ x 22″, pub RTG | 150.00 | — |
| ☐ **BEACH STROLL**, rel. 1983. ed. 1,000, s/n, 24″ x 29″, pub RTG | 150.00 | — |
| ☐ **WOODLAND GLEN**, rel. 1983. ed. 1,000, s/n, 29″ x 29″, pub RTG | 150.00 | — |

| | ISSUE PRICE | CURRENT PRICE |
|---|---|---|
| ☐ **WOODLAND POND**, rel. 1983. ed. 1,000, s/n, 23" x 28", pub RTG . . . . . . . . . | 150.00 | – |
| ☐ **BROOKIE'S LAIR**, rel. 1984. ed. 1,000, s/n, 22" x 28", pub RTG . . . . . . . . . . | 150.00 | – |
| ☐ **NOT A SOUND**, rel. 1984. ed. 1,000, s/n, 24" x 18", pub RTG . . . . . . . . . . . . | 100.00 | – |
| ☐ **SLIGHT RIPPLE**, rel. 1984. ed. 1,000, s/n, 18" x 24", pub RTG . . . . . . . . . . . | 100.00 | – |

# SHELLEY M. THORSTENSEN

Shelley Thorstensen graduated from Syracuse University with a BFA in printmaking and has continued to be fully involved in the print medium. She uses printmaking as a primary means of expression as a major art form, utilizing its traditional and more experimental forms.

Thorstensen has won many awards for her color etchings, lithographs and exhibits on a national scale. She currently resides in New Jersey.

**YOU OUGHT TO SEE THE GERANIUMS** *by Shelley Thorstensen*

## SHELLEY M. THORSTENSEN

| | ISSUE PRICE | CURRENT PRICE |
|---|---|---|
| ☐ **BEHIND THE SHOP**, rel. 1983. ed. 50, 6" x 8", etching, pub JGE . . . . . . . . . . | 90.00 | – |
| ☐ **CEDAR STREET**, rel. 1982. ed. 50, 9" x 12", etching, pub JGE . . . . . . . . . . . . | 70.00 | 70.00 |
| ☐ **LATE AFTERNOONS**, rel. 1981. ed. 150, 8" x 12", etching, pub JGE . . . . . . . . | 60.00 | Sold Out |
| ☐ **MAKING RAINBOWS**, rel. 1983. ed. 50, 12" x 14", hand colored litho, pub JGE | 90.00 | – |
| ☐ **MOSS ISLAND**, rel. 1982. ed. 50, 6" x 9", hand colored litho, pub JGE . . . . . . | 65.00 | 65.00 |

|  | ISSUE PRICE | CURRENT PRICE |
|---|---|---|
| ☐ **OUT THE FRONT PORCH,** rel. 1982. ed. 75, 16″ x 20″, hand colored litho, pub JGE | 50.00 | 80.00 |
| ☐ **POINSETTA,** rel. 1981. ed. 50, 2″ x 4″, etching, pub JGE | 30.00 | 70.00 |
| ☐ **STREAM BANK,** ed. 50, 6″ x 9″, hand colored litho, pub JGE | 65.00 | 65.00 |
| ☐ **THE BACK PORCH,** rel. 1983. ed. 50, 7″ x 9″, etching, pub JGE | 85.00 | — |
| ☐ **WINTERED GERANIUM,** rel. 1983. ed. 50, 8″ x 10″, etching, pub JGE | 95.00 | — |
| ☐ **YOU OUGHT TO SEE THE GERANIUMS,** rel. 1983. 12″ x 14″, hand colored litho, pub JGE | 90.00 | — |

# JEROME TIGER
## (1941-1967)

Jerome Tiger was born July 8, 1941, in Tahlequah, Oklahoma, capitol of the Cherokee Indian Nation. He spent most of his childhood in the predominently Creek Indian town of Eufaula.

In both subject matter and the abiding spiritual quality of Tiger's paintings are seen poignant proof of his obedience to the charge of his Older One — "put into paper what the Creek has in his heart". Tiger recorded the life and legends of his people.

In 1966, he won the four major competitions for traditional Indian art held in the United States. These include first place honors in the First Annual National Exhibition of American Indian Artists, Oakland, California; Twenty-first Annual American Indian Artists Exhibition, Philbrook Art Center, Tulsa, Oklahoma; Inter-Tribal Indian Ceremonial Exhibit, Gallup, New Mexico; All-American Indian Days Art Show, Sheridan, Wyoming.

The finest collection of Tiger's work available for public viewing is housed in the Gallery of the Five Civilized Tribes Museum, Muskogee, Oklahoma.

## JEROME TIGER

| | | |
|---|---|---|
| ☐ **THE COMING WEATHER,** rel. 1970. ed. 300, n/o, 12″ x 14½″, pub JTAC | 100.00 | 1,000.00 |
| ☐ **OBSERVING THE ENEMY,** rel. 1973. ed. 1,500, n/o, 18″ x 20″, pub JTAC | 20.00 | 750.00 |
| ☐ **THE GUIDING SPIRIT,** rel. 1973. ed. 1,500, n/o, 16″ x 22″, pub JTAC | 30.00 | 750.00 |
| ☐ **YESTERDAY, TODAY, and TOMORROW,** rel. 1973. ed. 1,500, n/o, 11″ x 15″, pub JTAC | 20.00 | 450.00 |
| ☐ **INTERMISSION,** rel. 1974. ed. 1,500, n/o, 13″ x 22½″, pub JTAC | 30.00 | 250.00 |
| ☐ **SEMINOLE FISHERMAN,** rel. 1974. ed. 1,500, n/o, 18″ x 22″, pub JTAC | 30.00 | 550.00 |
| ☐ **THE MIGHTY STICKBALLER,** rel. 1974. ed. 300, n/o, 18″ x 27″, pub JTAC | 100.00 | 1,500.00 |
| ☐ **WALK THROUGH THE GREAT MYSTERIES,** rel. 1974. ed. 1,500, n/o, 16″ x 22″, pub JTAC | 30.00 | 250.00 |
| ☐ **TRAIL OF TEARS,** rel. 1975. ed. 750, n/o, 21″ x 28″, pub JTAC | 100.00 | 750.00 |
| ☐ **INDIAN BURIAL,** rel. 1976. ed. 350, n/o, 17½″ x 36″, pub JTAC | 100.00 | 750.00 |
| ☐ **NEVER GET AWAY,** rel. 1977. ed. 1,500, n/o, 13⅞″ x 18⅝″, pub JTAC | 50.00 | 60.00 |
| ☐ **PROTECTIVE ONES,** rel. 1977. ed. 1,500, n/o, 14⅜″ x 19⅝″, pub JTAC | 50.00 | 250.00 |
| ☐ **STICKBALLER,** rel. 1977. ed. 650, n/o, 18″ x 27″, pub JTAC | 150.00 | 700.00 |
| ☐ **THROUGH THE EVERGLADES,** rel. 1977. ed. 1,500, n/o, 15″ x 24¾″, pub JTAC | 50.00 | 300.00 |
| ☐ **BUFFALO HUNT,** rel. 1978. ed. 1,500, n/o, 7⁹⁄₁₆″ x 6″, pub JTAC | 60.00 | — |
| Portfolio of three miniatures. Each print same size. | | |
| ☐ **DEPARTURE,** rel. 1978. ed. 650, n/o, 23¼″ x 33¼″, pub JTAC | 150.00 | 600.00 |
| ☐ **BEGINNING,** rel. 1979. ed. 1,500, n/o, 16″ x 19″, pub JTAC | 50.00 | 120.00 |
| ☐ **HIS SPIRIT CALLS,** rel. 1979. ed. 650, n/o, 21″ x 26″, pub JTAC | 150.00 | 300.00 |
| ☐ **LITTLE ARROW FIXER/INNOCENT,** rel. 1979. ed. 1,500, n/o, 5″ x 7″, pub JTAC | 60.00 | 60.00 |
| *Sold as a set only | | |
| ☐ **ROUGHING IT UP,** rel. 1979. ed. 1,500, n/o, 14″ x 19″, pub JTAC | 60.00 | — |
| ☐ **THE INTRUDERS,** rel. 1979. ed. 1,500, n/o, 22″ x 27″, pub JTAC | 50.00 | 60.00 |
| ☐ **PEACE OFFERING,** rel. 1980. ed. 750, n/o, size not available, pub JTAC | 150.00 | 300.00 |
| ☐ **AGONY,** rel. 1981. ed. 1,500, n/o, 12″ x 16″, pub JTAC | 60.00 | — |

| | ISSUE PRICE | CURRENT PRICE |
|---|---|---|
| ☐ GETTING READY, rel. 1981. ed. 1,500, n/o, 12½" x 17", pub JTAC......... | 60.00 | — |
| ☐ OSCEOLA DEFIANT ONE, rel. 1981. ed. 1,500, n/o, 15" x 20", pub JTAC .... | 60.00 | — |
| ☐ SEMINOLE 1803, SEMINOLE 1903 MINIATURE SERIES, rel. 1981. ed. 1,500, n/o, 4½" x 6½", pub JTAC ........................................ | 60.00 | — |
| ☐ YESTERDAY THEY RODE, rel. 1981. ed. 750, n/o, 15" x 20", pub JTAC ...... | 150.00 | — |
| ☐ TANGLE AT STICKBALL, rel. 1982. ed. 750, n/o, size not available, pub JTAC . | 150.00 | — |

## JOHNNY TIGER

Johnny Tiger was born in Tahlequah, Oklahoma, once the capital of the Cherokee nation. He was raised according to Indian traditions by his grandparents. "Many of the ideas that I use in my paintings are derived from old stories and customs that my parents and grandmother taught me. They learned them as children from the elder tribesmen." He also attended Bacone College for a time where he studied under a prominent Cheyenne artist, Dick West.

Although he had been painting and drawing all of his life, Tiger did not begin his career as a professional artist until 1967. In the years since, he has developed a fine reputation and following. He has participated in many exhibitions all over the country, including shows at the *Philbrook Art Center* and the *Heard Gallery,* as well as shows at other galleries in Red Cloud, Gallup, Pawnee, Scottsdale, Tahlequah, Muskogee and Okmulgee. He has won a number of awards, and has twice received the Most Popular Painting of Show Award from the Five Civilized Tribes Museum of Muskogee.

### JOHNNY TIGER

| | | |
|---|---|---|
| ☐ DANCER'S DESIRE, rel. 1973. ed. 1,500, s/n, 8¾" x 11¼", pub NWDHG.... | 15.00 | 60.00 |
| remarqued ...................................................... | 50.00 | — |
| ☐ PORTFOLIO OF INDIAN LIFE (Six prints), rel. 1975: FIREWOOD NEEDED, 9½" x 5½"; BUFFALO SCOUT, 4¼" x 5½"; FAREWELL, 2½" x 5⅛"; WARRIOR SEARCHES, 6" x 6"; NIGHT SCOUT, 4" x 5"; CAMP SCENE, 11" x 7¼"; ed. 3,000 sets, numbered and initialed, pub NWDHG ...................... | 30.00 | 90.00 |

## BOB TIMBERLAKE

In the many articles written about Bob Timberlake in recent years — including major pieces in *Reader's Digest, American Way, Southern Living, Today's Art, Southwest Art* and *Audubon* — much is made of his meeting with Andrew Wyeth in 1969. At that time the old master thought enough of Timberlake's talent to advise him to drop everything and, ". . . go home and paint". In fact, for a few years it was fashionable to call Timberlake, "the Andrew Wyeth of the South".

However, for those who have followed this artist's development, it is quite obvious that Timberlake's art is unique. It has a universal quality which has attracted collectors worldwide.

Technically, the work is masterful. Timberlake's attention to light and detail seems to improve with each painting. His use of watercolor, tempera and gouache is perplexing, but effective. Mostly, his ability to accurately render the texture and depth of the most banal object, brings poetry and life to his work.

Born in Lexington, North Carolina in 1937, Timberlake spent his youth in the rural South. Upon graduation from college, he entered the family business where he remained until 1970 when he decided to turn his full attention to painting in 1970.

In 1973, Timberlake had his first one man exhibition in New York at the Hammer Galleries. By that time, he already had a large following of loyal collectors. The

**WELL AT THE STUDIO** *by Bob Timberlake*

show sold out days before the opening night preview. Succeeding shows in 1975 and 1977 were also sold out before the opening night. Today, Timberlake originals sell for as much as $25,000.00.

Other important exhibitions include major showings at the R. W. Norton Gallery in Shreveport, Louisiana in October, 1974, The North Carolina Museum of Art in Raleigh, North Carolina in September of 1979; and the Corcoran Gallery of Art in Washington, D.C. in August of 1981.

In May of 1978, Timberlake was summoned to the White House to be named by President Carter the official artist for the "Keep America Beautiful" campaign. For this, Timberlake created a painting entitled "Daisies" which is recognized as the national symbol for this campaign.

Timberlake has also been a guest of Prince Charles in Buckingham Palace and was recognized by President Reagan in the Oval Office in 1981.

Two major books of the artist's work have been published. The first, entitled *The Bob Timberlake Collection,* was authored by "On the Road" journalist Charles Kuralt. Limited to only 2,125 copies, this collection was printed on 100% rag paper and sold for $600.00 per copy. The second book, entitled *The World of Bob Timberlake,* was published by Oxmoor House at $45.00 per copy. Sales figures point to this book as being the most successful trade edition art book in America in 1979.

### TOM TIMBERLAKE

| | ISSUE PRICE | CURRENT PRICE |
|---|---|---|
| ☐ ELLA'S CUPBOARD, rel. 1971. ed. 250, s/n, pub BT | 35.00 | 500.00 |
| ☐ MR. GARRISON'S SLAB PILE, rel. 1971. ed. 100, s/n, pub BT | 35.00 | 1,500.00 |
| ☐ MY YANKEE DRUM, rel. 1972. ed. 1,500, s/n, 17″ x 25½″, pub FHG | 30.00 | 150.00 |
| ☐ ROWBOAT, rel. 1973. ed. 750, s/n, pub THC | 60.00 | 450.00 |
| ☐ AFTERNOON AT THE PETREA'S, rel. 1974. ed. 1,000, s/n, pub THC | 75.00 | 300.00 |
| ☐ BALDHEAD ISLAND RESCUE STATION, rel. 1974. ed. 1,000, s/n, pub THC... | **75.00 | 200.00 |
| ed. 24, A/P | 75.00 | 250.00 |
| **A special edition of 250 with an embossed seal was prepared for BaldHead Island Property owners and fewer than 50 of these prints are available. | — | 500.00 |
| ☐ BALDHEAD LIGHTHOUSE, rel. 1974. ed. 300, s/n, released by FKH Editions | 175.00 | 450.00 |
| ☐ MRS. LEONARD'S MARIGOLD, rel. 1974. ed. 1,000, s/n, pub THC | 60.00 | 350.00 |
| ☐ THE ALEXANDER LONG HOUSE, rel. 1974. ed. 300, s/n, released by FKH Editions | 175.00 | 650.00 |
| ☐ FRONT PORCH, rel. 1975. ed. 1,000, s/n, pub THC | 75.00 | 275.00 |
| ☐ LATE SNOW AT RIVERWOOD, rel. 1975. ed. 1,000, s/n, pub THC | 150.00 | 650.00 |
| ☐ MAY, rel. 1975. ed. 1,000, s/n, pub THC | 75.00 | 375.00 |
| ☐ ANOTHER WORLD, rel. 1976. ed. 300, s/n, etching, 18″ x 24″, released by Hammer Publishing | 500.00 | 750.00 |
| ☐ DAILY SUNNING, rel. 1976. ed. 1,000, s/n, 32¾″ x 24½″, pub THC | 150.00 | 350.00 |
| ☐ MY CIDER BARREL, rel. 1976. ed. 1,000, s/n, 18″ x 24″, pub THC | 150.00 | 400.00 |
| ☐ SOUR PIE CHERRIES, rel. 1976. ed. 1,000, s/n, pub THC | 100.00 | 175.00 |
| ☐ BEAN POT, rel. 1977. ed. 300, s/n, 29½″ x 22½″, etching, pub HP | 600.00 | — |
| ed. 50, Artists Proofs | | |
| ☐ KNOTTS ISLAND DECOYS, rel. 1977. ed. 1,000, s/n, pub THC | 150.00 | 250.00 |
| ☐ MORNING SUN, rel. 1977. ed. 1,000, s/n, 24″ x 33″, pub THC | 150.00 | 350.00 |
| ☐ DAISIES, rel. 1978. ed. 1,000, s/n, 20½″ x 26½″, pub THC | *350.00 | — |
| *All proceeds from sales will be donated to achieving the goals of Keep America Beautiful, Inc., a non-profit public service organization. | | |
| ☐ GILLEYS' HOUSE, rel. 1978. ed. 1,000, s/n, 30″ x 22¼″, pub THC | 150.00 | 450.00 |
| ☐ JULY, rel. 1978. ed. 1,000, s/n, 19¾″ x 15¼″, pub THC | 125.00 | 350.00 |
| ed. 30, Artists Proofs | | |
| ☐ POTTED, rel. 1978. ed. 300, s/n, 10″ x 7″, etching, pub HP | 450.00 | — |
| ☐ STUDY OF HIS COAT, rel. 1978. ed. 100, s/n, 20″ x 16, etching, pub HP | 1,250.00 | — |
| ☐ IRON EYES, rel. 1979. ed. 1,000, s/n, 22½″ x 16½″, pub THC | 200.00 | — |
| *all proceeds from sales donated to Keep America Beautiful, Inc., a non-profit public service organization. | | |
| ☐ MR. ZIMMERMAN'S CORN, rel. 1979. ed. 1,000, s/n, 21″ x 27½″, pub THC | 150.00 | — |
| ☐ SNOW WORLD, rel. 1979. ed. 300, s/n, 22″ x 15″, etching, pub HP | 500.00 | — |
| ed. 50 artist proofs | | |
| ☐ SUMMER DAY, rel. 1979. ed. 1,000, s/n, 29″ x 20¾″, pub THC | 150.00 | 225.00 |
| ☐ THE FAKES, rel. 1979. ed. 300, s/n, 9″ x 26″, etching, pub HP | 400.00 | 550.00 |
| ed. 50 artist proofs | | |
| ☐ PUMPKINS IN THE SNOW, rel. 1980. ed. 1,000, s/n, pub THC | 150.00 | — |
| ☐ STRAWBERRIES, rel. 1980. ed. 1,000, s/n, 22½″ x 17″, pub THC | 125.00 | — |
| ☐ WATERED, rel. 1980. ed. 1,000, s/n, 29″ x 22″, pub THC | 150.00 | 250.00 |
| ☐ FEBRUARY AT RIVERWOOD, rel. 1981. ed. 1,000, s/n, 29″ x 22″, pub THC | 150.00 | 500.00 |
| ☐ ISLAND CRAB, rel. 1981. ed. 1,000, s/n, 12″ x 13½″, pub THC | 85.00 | — |
| ☐ QUILTS, rel. 1981. ed. 1,000, s/n, 12½″ x 14¾″, pub THC | 150.00 | — |
| two prints - sold as a pair | | |
| ☐ CAPT. CHARLIE'S VIEW, rel. 1982. ed. 1,000, s/n, 18¼″ x 25¼″, pub THC | 150.00 | — |
| ☐ GILLEY'S WELL, rel. 1982. ed. 1,000, s/n, 20″ x 26¾″, pub THC | 150.00 | 350.00 |
| ☐ SNOW AT THE STUDIO, rel. 1982. ed. 1,000, s/n, 21¾″ x 26¾″, pub THC | 185.00 | 350.00 |
| ☐ SPRING SNOW, ed. 1,000, s/n, 28¼″ x 22¾″, pub THC | 185.00 | 300.00 |
| ☐ SOMEWHERE IN TIME, ed. 1,000, s/n, 23½″ x 29″, pub THC | 185.00 | 250.00 |

# RICHARD TIMM

**PRAIRIE DOG** *by Richard Timm*

| | ISSUE PRICE | CURRENT PRICE |
|---|---|---|
| ☐ **RACCOON**, rel. 1972. ed. 5,000, s/o, 22″ x 28″, pub NHI | 30.00 | 125.00 |
| ☐ **RED FOX**, rel. 1972. ed. 5,000, s/o, 22″ x 28″, pub NHI | 30.00** | 175.00 |
| ☐ **EASTERN CHIPMUNK**, rel. 1973. ed. 5,000, s/o, 22″ x 28″, pub NHI | 30.00 | 75.00 |
| ☐ **ELK**, rel. 1973. ed. 5,000, s/o, 22″ x 28″, pub NHI | 30.00 | 125.00 |
| ☐ **RIVER OTTER**, rel. 1973. ed. 5,000, s/o, 22″ x 28″, pub NHI | 30.00 | 75.00 |
| ☐ **STRIPED SKUNK**, rel. 1973. ed. 5,000, s/o, 22″ x 28″, pub NHI | 30.00 | 75.00 |
| ☐ **WHITE-TAILED DEER**, rel. 1973. ed. 5,000, s/o, 22″ x 28″, pub NHI | 30.00 | 100.00 |
| ☐ **BADGER**, rel. 1974. ed. 5,000, s/o, 22″ x 28″, pub NHI | 30.00 | 75.00 |
| ☐ **BEAVER**, rel. 1974. ed. 5,000, s/o, 22″ x 28″, pub NHI | 30.00 | 50.00 |
| ☐ **BOBCAT**, rel. 1974. ed. 5,000, s/o, 22″ x 28″, pub NHI | 30.00 | 125.00 |
| ☐ **EASTERN COTTONTAIL**, rel. 1974. ed. 5,000, s/o, 22″ x 28″, pub NHI | 30.00 | 75.00 |
| ☐ **MOUNTAIN LION**, rel. 1974. ed. 5,000, s/o, 22″ x 28″, pub NHI | 30.00 | 75.00 |
| ☐ **PRONGHORN**, rel. 1974. ed. 5,000, s/o, 22″ x 28″, pub NHI | 30.00 | 75.00 |
| ☐ **ALASKA MOOSE**, rel. 1975. ed. 5,000, s/o, 22″ x 28″, pub NHI | 30.00 | 50.00 |
| ☐ **FOX SQUIRREL**, rel. 1975. ed. 5,000, s/o, 22″ x 28″, pub NHI | 30.00 | 50.00 |
| ☐ **GRAY FOX**, rel. 1975. ed. 5,000, s/o, 22″ x 28″, pub NHI | 30.00 | 50.00 |
| ☐ **KEY DEER**, rel. 1975. ed. 5,000, s/o, 22″ x 28″, pub NHI | 30.00 | 50.00 |
| ☐ **MUSKRAT**, rel. 1975. ed. 5,000, s/o, 22″ x 28″, pub NHI | 30.00 | 50.00 |
| ☐ **WOLVERINE**, rel. 1975. ed. 5,000, s/o, 22″ x 28″, pub NHI | 30.00 | 50.00 |
| ☐ **ARMADILLO**, rel. 1976. ed. 5,000, s/o, 22″ x 28″, pub NHI | 30.00 | 50.00 |
| ☐ **BISON**, rel. 1976. ed. 5,000, s/o, 22″ x 28″, pub NHI | 30.00 | 50.00 |
| ☐ **BLACK BEAR**, rel. 1976. ed. 5,000, s/o, 22″ x 28″, pub NHI | 30.00 | 50.00 |
| ☐ **COYOTE**, rel. 1976. ed. 5,000, s/o, 22″ x 28″, pub NHI | 30.00 | 50.00 |
| ☐ **MINK**, rel. 1976. ed. 5,000, s/o, 22″ x 28″, pub NHI | 30.00 | 50.00 |

**Prints were sold as collections at issue price as shown, providing the collector purchased each print when published. Individual purchases were $50.00 issue.

| | ISSUE PRICE | CURRENT PRICE |
|---|---|---|
| ☐ SNOWSHOE HARE, rel. 1976. ed. 5,000, s/o, 22" x 28", pub NHI .......... | 30.00 | 50.00 |
| ☐ COLUMBIAN GROUND SQUIRREL, rel. 1977. ed. 5,000, s/o, 22" x 28", pub NHI ................. | 30.00 | 50.00 |
| ☐ LYNX, rel. 1977. ed. 5,000, s/o, 22" x 28", pub NHI .................... | 30.00 | 50.00 |
| ☐ POLAR BEAR, rel. 1977. ed. 5,000, s/o, 22" x 28", pub NHI ............. | 30.00 | 50.00 |
| ☐ PRAIRIE DOG, rel. 1977. ed. 5,000, s/o, 22" x 28", pub NHI .............. | 30.00 | 50.00 |
| ☐ MOUNTAIN GOAT, rel. 1977. ed. 5,000, s/o, 22" x 28", pub NHI .......... | 30.00 | 50.00 |
| ☐ WOODCHUCK, rel. 1977. ed. 5,000, s/o, 22" x 28", pub NHI ............. | 30.00 | 50.00 |
| ☐ HOARY MARMOT, rel. 1978. ed. 5,000, s/o, 22" x 28", pub NHI ........... | 30.00 | 50.00 |
| ☐ MULE DEER, rel. 1978. ed. 5,000, s/o, 22" x 28", pub NHI ............. | 30.00 | 50.00 |
| ☐ CALIFORNIA SEA LION, rel. 1979. ed. 5,000, s/o, 22" x 28", pub NHI....... | 30.00 | 50.00 |
| ☐ CARIBOU, rel. 1979. ed. 5,000, s/o, 22" x 28", pub NHI ............... | 30.00 | 50.00 |
| ☐ LONG TAILED WEASEL, rel. 1979. ed. 5,000, s/o, 22" x 28", pub NHI....... | 30.00 | 50.00 |
| ☐ PORCUPINE, rel. 1979. ed. 5,000, s/o, 22" x 28", pub NHI .............. | 30.00 | 50.00 |
| ☐ TIMBER WOLF, rel. 1979. ed. 5,000, s/o, 22" x 28", pub NHI ............. | 30.00 | 50.00 |
| ☐ MUSK OX, rel. 1981. ed. 5,000, s/o, 22" x 28", pub NHI ................. | 50.00 | — |
| ☐ PINE MARTEN, rel. 1981. ed. 5,000, s/o, 22" x 28", pub NHI ............. | 50.00 | — |

## HARRY TOLLAS

| | | |
|---|---|---|
| ☐ BLACK LAB W/GREEN WING TEAL, ed. 500, s/n, 17" x 21", litho, dist MM ... | — | 30.00 |
| ☐ BRITTANY W/QUAIL, ed. 450, s/n, 17" x 21", litho, dist MM............. | — | 30.00 |
| ☐ YELLOW LAB W/MALLARD, ed. 500, s/n, 17" x 21", litho, dist MM ........ | — | 30.00 |

## LOREN PAHSE TOPAH

| | | |
|---|---|---|
| ☐ BUFFALO CALLING, ed. 1,500, s/n, pub NWDHG ..................... | 50.00 | 200.00 |

## PAUL PAHSE TOPAH

| | | |
|---|---|---|
| ☐ BUFFALO HUNT, ed. 1,500, s/n, 20½" x 21¾", pub NWDHG ............. | 30.00 | 150.00 |
| remarqued ................... | 60.00 | — |
| ☐ OSAGE CHIEF, ed. 1,500, s/n, 28" x 22", pub NWDHG.................. | 30.00 | 60.00 |
| remarqued ................... | 100.00 | — |
| ☐ OSAGE WEDDING DAY, ed. 1,500, s/n, 18½" x 17", pub NWDHG .......... | 20.00 | 75.00 |
| remarqued ................... | 60.00 | — |

## LARRY TOSCHIK

| | | |
|---|---|---|
| ☐ AHEAD OF THE STORM (Mallards). ed. 800, s/n, 19" x 25¼", litho, pub PP .. | 60.00 | 140.00 |
| ☐ BATTLE CRY OF WINTER (Canada Geese). ed. 1,500, s/n, 20" x 28", litho, pub AMF ................... | 40.00 | — |
| ☐ BURNISHED BRONZE (Wild Turkey). ed. 1,500, s/n, 19" x 32", litho, pub AMF | 40.00 | — |
| ☐ CALLED IN - CANADA GEESE. ed. 800, s/n, 25" x 17", litho, pub PP ....... | 60.00 | Sold Out |
| ☐ CALLED IN - MALLARDS. ed. 800, s/n, 16¼" x 25", litho, pub PP .......... | 60.00 | — |
| ☐ CUMBERLAND SPRING. ed. 800, s/n, 16" x 24", litho, pub PP .......... | 60.00 | — |
| ☐ FIRST DRUMMER OF SPRING (Ruffed Grouse). ed. 1,500, s/n, 22" x 28", litho, pub AMF................... | 40.00 | — |
| ☐ PATTERN FOR THE DAY (Bobwhite Quail). ed. 1,500, s/n, 20" x 29", litho, pub AMF ................... | 40.00 | — |
| ☐ PLACE WHERE THEY NOW GATHER (Bald Eagles). ed. 1,500, s/n, 19" x 28", litho, pub AMF................... | 40.00 | — |
| ☐ PRESENT TENANTS (Wild Turkey). ed. 1,500, s/n, 21" x 29", litho, pub AMF . | 40.00 | — |
| ☐ SALMON CAMP ON THE LINIK TIDAL BASIN (Gulls and Old Squaws). ed. 1,500, s/n, 19" x 28", litho, pub AMF ..................... | 40.00 | — |
| ☐ SANTEE PASS—WOOD DUCKS, ed. 800, s/n, 16" x 24", pub PP .......... | 75.00 | — |
| remarqued, signed and numbered ....................... | 165.00 | — |
| ☐ SCOUTING FOR A HAVEN (Pintail Ducks). ed. 800, s/n, 19" x 25¾", litho, pub PP ................... | 60.00 | — |

| | ISSUE PRICE | CURRENT PRICE |
|---|---|---|
| ☐ **SNOWS UPON THE AUTUMN GOLD (Snow Geese).** ed. 1,500, s/n, 22″ x 28″, litho, pub AMF | 40.00 | — |
| ☐ **SUNDOWN BALLET - MALLARDS,** rel. 1976. ed. 580, s/n, 16″ x 25½″ pub WWI | 75.00 | — |
| ☐ **TEAL MORNING (Green Wing Teals).** ed. 800, s/n, 18″ x 25″, litho, pub PP | 60.00 | — |
| ☐ **THE BEET FIELD (Mallards Landing on Pond).** ed. 750, s/n, 21½″ x 12½″, litho, pub PP | 60.00 | — |
| ☐ **THE MALLARD HOLE.** ed. 750, s/n, 21½″ x 12½″, litho, pub PP | 60.00 | — |
| ☐ **UP & AWAY - GEESE.** ed. 750, s/n, 27½″ x 21″, litho, pub PP | 65.00 | — |
| ☐ **WHISTLING IN - MALLARDS,** rel. 1976. ed. 580, s/n, 22″ x 17¾″ pub WWI | 70.00 | — |

## CATHERINE TOUSSAINT

| | ISSUE PRICE | CURRENT PRICE |
|---|---|---|
| ☐ **CARAVAN,** ed. 225, s/n, 35½″ x 25″, original color lithograph, pub FI | 75.00 | — |
| ☐ **CHEVAUCHEE MYSTERIEUSE,** ed. 225, s/n, 25½″ x 25″, original color lithograph, pub FI | 75.00 | — |
| ☐ **L'ENVOLEE,** ed. 150, s/n, 27¾″ x 18¾″, original color lithograph, pub FI | 75.00 | — |

## JEAN-PIERRE TREVOR

Born in London in 1948 and educated in England, France and Switzerland, Jean-Pierre Trevor's art training began at age of 14 at the Centre d'Art Mediterance in Vallauris, the French village made famous by Picasso's studio. By age 20, his work was attracting critical acclaim.

To Trevor, his painting of "Summer Mountains" was a study in textures and a challenge to his artistry. "Every cloud and every blade of grass is different, ever changing with morning light to dusk. I loved to sit on a grassy knoll watching this beautiful creation unravel before my eyes and analyzing the ways I would eventually translate the ballot of color, shape and form onto the empty white surface of my canvas."

**WHITEMANTLE** *by Jean Pierre Trevor*

## JEAN-PIERRE TREVOR

| | ISSUE PRICE | CURRENT PRICE |
|---|---|---|
| ☐ **GRAND TETONS,** ed. 1,500, s/n, 24″ x 20″, pub FFFAI | 40.00 | — |
| ☐ **SUMMER MOUNTAINS & WHITEMANTLE,** ed. 1,500, s/n, 15″ x 12″, pub FFFAI | 45.00 | — |

## PETER URBANSKI

| | ISSUE PRICE | CURRENT PRICE |
|---|---|---|
| ☐ **BLUE BIRD,** rel. 1981. ed. 950, s/n, size not available, pub WWI | 30.00 | — |
| ☐ **WHITE-BREASTED NUTHATCH,** rel. 1981. ed. 950, s/n, size not available, pub WWI | 30.00 | — |

## MARLOWE URDAHL

| | ISSUE PRICE | CURRENT PRICE |
|---|---|---|
| ☐ **PUPPY LOVE - YELLOW LAB,** rel. 1981. ed. 750, s/n, size not available, pub WWI | 50.00 | 60.00 |

# THORNTON UTZ

Utz's studies at the American Academy of Arts in Chicago and teaching at the Art Institute of Chicago were followed by several years of commercial art and illustrations for American and European magazines. His credits include fifty commissions for *Saturday Evening Post* covers.

Since 1960 Utz has attacked the problems of portraiture, sculpture, architecture and reintroduced the classic nude to a culture which knew only the pin-up and the centerfold.

**INTERLUDE** *by Thornton Utz*

"Drawing and painting the nude is a classic, endless challenge," Utz explains. "For subject matter I prefer a model to perform an action or chore she would normally and naturally do alone, such as bathing, fixing her nails, and so forth. In my paintings I want to express a respect for the particular young woman portrayed and for women in general."

Utz is a trustee of the Ringling School of Art and a member of the Official Artists, United States Air Force.

## THORNTON UTZ

| | ISSUE PRICE | CURRENT PRICE |
|---|---|---|
| ☐ **LAVENDER LACE,** rel. 1981. ed. 950, s/n, 12⅝″ x 24″, pub MPPI .......... | 75.00 | — |
| ☐ **MELANIE,** rel. 1981. ed. 450, s/n, 27½″ x 19¾″, pub MPPI .............. | 85.00 | 100.00 |
| ☐ **PICNIC,** rel. 1981. ed. 550, s/n, 20″ x 27½″, pub MPPI ................. | 110.00 | — |
| ☐ **PINK LADY,** rel. 1981. ed. 450, s/n, 26″ x 20¼″, pub MPPI .............. | 85.00 | 110.00 |
| ☐ **THE GREENHOUSE NUDE,** rel. 1981. ed. 550, s/n, 35″ x 19⅞″, pub MPPI .... | 95.00 | — |
| ☐ **THE SOFT WIND,** rel. 1982. ed. 950, s/n, 23¾″ x 11¼″, pub MPPI ........ | 75.00 | — |
| ☐ **INTERLUDE,** rel. 1983. ed. 950, s/n, 8¾″ x 10⅝″, pub MPPI ............. | 40.00 | — |

# GEORGE CAMERON VAIL

George Cameron Vail is a historian, teacher, and artist. He is a man firmly rooted in the graphic and creative arts.

Vail is a keen observer of life and a respected portrait artist. He is a self-taught artist whose peripatetic interests have lead him to use all of life as his subject matter and to work in all media.

**SHOALS CLEAR** *by George Cameron Vail*

His work has been shown in many shows in the Mid-Atlantic states and is included in numerous prominent private collections.

Today, he brings the experiences of the past 40 years to his students and his work. A well known teacher for the past 20 years, he has held positions ranging from private school and studio teaching to that of instructor at Leesburg State Prison and Gloucester County Prison. He has served as an adjunct faculty member at Rutgers State University.

In 1972, he founded the Vail School of Design and Illustration which emphasizes the need for sound drawing practices.

Vail has served as the Executive Director of the Camden County Historic Society and in 1967 became a governor-appointed member of the Batsto Citizens Committee, a group significant in the restoration of the historic village in the famous Pine Barrens of South Jersey. Vail is also a member of the prestigious International Society of Marine Painters.

## GEORGE CAMERON VAIL

| | ISSUE PRICE | CURRENT PRICE |
|---|---|---|
| ☐ AUTUMN WARM, ed. 285, s/n, litho, pub JGE | 60.00 | 75.00 |
| ☐ BLUES, ed. 175, s/n, 15" x 17", etch, pub JGE | 25.00 | 35.00 |
| ☐ CHERI, ed. 175, s/n, 12" x 17", etch, pub JGE | 25.00 | 35.00 |
| ☐ CHESAPEAKE SCHOONER, ed. 285, s/n, 25" x 30", litho, pub JGE | 70.00 | 90.00 |
| ☐ THE FAN, ed. 175, s/n, 12" x 15", etch, pub JGE | 25.00 | 30.00 |
| ☐ FLIGHT, ed. 175, s/n, 15" x 17", etch, pub JGE | 25.00 | 35.00 |
| ☐ GULLS, ed. 175, s/n, 11" x 15", etch, pub JGE | 20.00 | 25.00 |
| ☐ THE HIGH SEAS, ed. 185, s/n, 17" x 20", etch, pub JGE | 50.00 | 70.00 |
| ☐ MORNING SUN, ed. 175, s/n, size N/A, etch, pub JGE | 35.00 | 45.00 |
| ☐ O'ER THE WAVES, ed. 175, s/n, size N/A, etch, pub JGE | 35.00 | 50.00 |
| ☐ PALAVER, ed. 285, s/n, 26" x 30", litho, pub JGE | 50.00 | 75.00 |
| ☐ PLEASANT MILLS, ed. 250, s/n, 25" x 30", litho, pub JGE | 50.00 | 65.00 |
| ☐ RED SAILS, ed. 225, s/n, 25" x 30", etch, pub JGE | 60.00 | 75.00 |
| ☐ SAILING, ed. 185, s/n, 17" x 18", etch, pub JGE | 40.00 | 50.00 |
| ☐ SHOALS CLEAR, ed. 285, s/n, 25" x 30", litho, pub JGE | 70.00 | 100.00 |
| ☐ SUNDOWN, ed. 175, s/n, 14" x 18", etch, pub JGE | 35.00 | 50.00 |
| ☐ SHOSHONE, ed. 175, s/n, 14" x 17", etch, pub JGE | 35.00 | 45.00 |
| ☐ SHOWDOWN, ed. 285, s/n, 26" x 31", litho, pub JGE | 75.00 | 100.00 |
| ☐ SHOOTOUT, ed. 225, s/n, 25" x 30", etch, pub JGE | 80.00 | 100.00 |

# DOUGLAS VAN HOWD

Douglas Van Howd's personal philosophy and his professional attitude blend in his belief ". . . I cannot paint wildlife unless I come as close to living with it as I can."

Van Howd's travels have taken him literally everywhere there is the promise of wilderness. And it's quite obvious that his career is very heavily influenced by the great amount of time he has spent in Africa; some of which is on work as the official artist for the Safari Club International. No doubt much of Van Howd's impressive artistic ability comes from his generous talents and academic achievements — but throughout everything this man's deep and understanding love for his subjects is both obvious and gratifying to the viewer.

## DOUGLAS VAN HOWD

| | | |
|---|---|---|
| ☐ BOB WHITE FLUSHED, ed. 800, s/n, size not available, litho, pub PP | 65.00 | 150.00 |
| ☐ COVEY BREAK, ed. 800, s/n, 16½" x 25", litho, pub PP | 60.00 | 120.00 |
| ☐ FIRST OUTING, ed. 800, s/n, 16" x 24", litho, pub PP | 60.00 | 120.00 |
| ☐ HIS MAJESTY - LION, ed. 800, s/n, 17" x 25½", litho, pub PP | 60.00 | — |
| ☐ INDIAN SUMMER (Pintails), ed. 800, s/n, size not available, litho, pub PP | 60.00 | 125.00 |
| ☐ PASSING PARADE, ed. 750, s/n, size not available | 60.00 | 125.00 |
| ☐ SERENGETI EVENING, ed. 800, s/n, 18" x 24", pub PP | 75.00 | — |
| remarqued, signed and numbered | 165.00 | — |

| | ISSUE PRICE | CURRENT PRICE |
|---|---|---|
| ☐ THE AFRICAN BIG FIVE, ed. 3,000, s/o, set consists of Leopard, Lion, Elephant, Buffalo and Rhino, lithos, pub PP | 100.00 | — |
| ☐ THE RESTING PLACE, ed. 750, s/n, 21″ x 28″, litho, pub PP | 65.00 | 125.00 |
| ☐ TSAVO MONARCH, ed. 800, s/n, 16¾″ x 25¼″, pub PP | 75.00 | — |
| remarqued, signed and numbered | 165.00 | — |
| ☐ TSAVO MONARCH (Elephant), ed. 800, s/n, 16¾″ x 25¼″, litho, pub PP | 60.00 | — |

# RICHARD VAN ORDER

Richard Van Order grew up in the north woods of Wisconsin where he grew to love and respect the natural beauty around him. His love of the forest is reflected in his artwork, as he combines woods and wildlife to create a very natural scene.

Van Order's fine touch with charcoal allows him to create superb detail. He is completely self-taught and attributes his success to many years of practice. He emphasizes that art is not something you learn overnight.

Besides charcoal, Van Order works in oils and he has developed an unusual technique using watercolor and pastels to achieve a very soft, yet realistic effect.

Because Van Order's new colored prints are low in number, and his admirers are increasing, the prints are reaching a high secondary market volume. His prints and originals can be seen in some of the finest collections throughout the country.

## RICHARD VAN ORDER

| | ISSUE PRICE | CURRENT PRICE |
|---|---|---|
| ☐ DISTURBING THE PEACE, rel. 1981. ed. 1,000, s/n, 12″ x 16″, pub VOS | 11.50 | — |
| ed. 2,200, s/n, 18″ x 24″ | 30.00 | — |
| ed. 135, remarqued | 30.00 | — |
| ☐ HARRISON HILLS, rel. 1981. ed. 1,000, s/n, 12″ x 16″, pub VOS | 11.50 | — |
| ed. 2,200, s/n, 18½″ x 16″ | 30.00 | 200.00 |
| ed. 304, remarqued | 30.00 | 300.00 |
| ☐ PAPOOSE LAKE, rel. 1981. ed. 1,000, s/n, 12″ x 16″, pub VOS | 11.50 | — |
| ed. 1,000, s/n, 14″ x 18″ | 15.00 | 60.00 |
| ☐ WINGS, rel. 1981. ed. 1,000, s/n, 12″ x 16″, pub VOS | 11.50 | — |
| ed. 2,200, s/n, 18″ x 24″ | 25.00 | 150.00 |
| ed. 100, remarqued | 25.00 | 250.00 |
| ☐ THE MEETING PLACE, rel. 1982. ed. 1,000, s/n, 12″ x 16″, pub VOS | 11.50 | — |
| ed. 1,000, s/n, 18″ x 24½″ | 37.50 | 50.00 |
| ed. 138, remarqued | 37.50 | 50.00 |
| ☐ THE MILE LINE, rel. 1982. ed. 1,000, s/n, 12″ x 16″, pub VOS | 11.50 | 50.00 |
| ed. 500, s/n, 18″ x 24½″ | 50.00 | 400.00 |
| ed. 55, remarqued | 50.00 | 600.00 |
| ☐ A NORTHWOODS LEGEND, PORTER DEAN, rel. 1983. ed. 300, s/n, 19″ x 25″, pub VOS | 100.00 | — |
| ☐ HIGH COUNTRY, rel. 1983. ed. 500, s/n, 11″ x 15″, pub VOS | 12.50 | — |
| ☐ ISLAND LAKE WOODY'S, rel. 1983. ed. 350, s/n, pub VOS | 30.00 | — |
| ed. 150, s/n, 23″ x 29″ | 100.00 | — |
| remarqued | 200.00 | — |
| ☐ MANITOWISH STOPOVER, rel. 1983. ed. 250, s/n, 12″ x 16″, pub VOS | 25.00 | 75.00 |
| ed. 250, s/n, 19″ x 25″ | 65.00 | 300.00 |
| ☐ NORTH WOOD'S PRIDE, rel. 1983. ed. 500, s/n, 11″ x 15″, pub VOS | 12.50 | — |
| ☐ SPRING THAW, rel. 1983. ed. 150, s/n, 23″ x 29″, pub VOS | 50.00 | 150.00 |
| ed. 22, remarqued | 50.00 | 250.00 |
| ☐ STANDING GUARD, rel. 1983. ed. 250, s/n, 11″ x 15″, pub VOS | 25.00 | 40.00 |
| ed. 250, s/n, 19″ x 25″ | 65.00 | — |
| ☐ TENDING TO BUSINESS, rel. 1983. ed. 300, Artists Proofs, s/n, 23″ x 29″, pub VOS | 100.00 | 250.00 |
| ed. 36 Artists proof, remarques | 200.00 | 300.00 |
| 3,000 signed and numbered prints were donated to Ducks Unlimited. | | |
| ☐ THE AMERICAN TRADITION, BALD EAGLE, rel. 1983. ed. 25, s/n, 23″ x 29″, remarqued, pub VOS | 500.00 | 1,000.00 |

# DONALD VANN

The chronicles of the Indian people are known to many, but few have ever been able to capture the unspoken emotions like Donald Vann. The subtle colors and graceful lines of Vann's style give his works a remarkable — some would say mystical — quality that allows us to share some of the inner facets of the Indian soul. In the words of the artist: "In our world there is an unspoken quality, a feeling, that touches and flows through everything, all of us as well as all things of the earth. If one listens to these forces he will find himself painting instinctively with the feelings of his heart, about his ancestral beliefs and the way he lives his life today."

| DONALD VANN | ISSUE PRICE | CURRENT PRICE |
|---|---|---|
| ☐ BUFFALO DREAM, edition and print size not available, pub NWDHG . . . . . . . . . | 40.00 | 75.00 |
| ☐ ENDLESS JOURNEY, ed. 1,500, s/n, 23" x 30", pub NWDHG . . . . . . . . . . . . . . | 75.00 | 150.00 |
| ☐ GIFT OF PEACE, ed. 950, s/n, 16" x 24", pub NWDHG . . . . . . . . . . . . . . . . . . | 60.00 | — |
| ☐ THE LAST FAREWELL, edition and print size not available, pub NWDHG . . . . . . | 50.00 | 450.00 |

# LLOYD VAN-PITTERSON

| | ISSUE PRICE | CURRENT PRICE |
|---|---|---|
| ☐ BLUE DOOR, ed. 275, s/n, 26" x 32", serigraph, pub EG . . . . . . . . . . . . . . . . | 90.00 | — |
| ☐ BLUE LAGOON, ed. 255, s/n, 24" x 29", serigraph, pub EG . . . . . . . . . . . . . . | 70.00 | — |
| ☐ PALISADES, ed. 275, 27" x 33", serigraph, pub EG . . . . . . . . . . . . . . . . . . . . | 90.00 | — |
| ☐ ST TROPIZ, ed. 270, s/n, 25" x 28", serigraph, pub EG . . . . . . . . . . . . . . . . | 70.00 | — |

# MARY VICKERS

Mary Vickers—who is widely regarded as one of the greatest Romantic artists in the world today, was born and raised in the small English village of Dagenham, just outside of London. Her formal training was completed at the St. Martine School of Art in London and the England Art Students League.

Admiring the development of American art, Vickers arrived in the United States in 1960, and promptly secured a position in a well-known New York publishing firm. That same year Vickers married a man she had known in England and, in the ensuing years, she balanced her endeavors between the lively problems of raising three children and painting.

In recent years, Vickers had developed a substantial following in both Europe and the Americans, and since 1969 she has numeous one-woman shows in the United States and on the Continent. The Duke and Duchess of Marlborough, Sarah Churchill, and Mario Puzo are among those who include her oils, lithographs and etchings in their private collections, and her work is on permanent exhibit in a number of major galleries. She has also earned singular renown as one of the most sought-after of all limited-edition collector's plate artists.

Vickers considers her work to be most influenced by the French Impressionists. And surely there is much of Corot and particularly Renoir in her palette. However, hers is a uniquely personal style which ultimately allows her, in her words, "to give people warmth and happiness . . . to create love in my life".

| MARY VICKERS | ISSUE PRICE | CURRENT PRICE |
|---|---|---|
| ☐ AGE OF INNOCENCE, rel. 1970. ed. 200, s/n, litho, pub MMGI . . . . . . . . . . . . | 40.00 | 325.00 |
| ☐ ALICE, rel. 1975. ed. 150, s/n, etching, pub MMGI . . . . . . . . . . . . . . . . . . . . | 50.00 | 150.00 |
| ☐ ALL MINE, rel. 1977. ed. 175, s/n, etching, pub MMGI . . . . . . . . . . . . . . . . . | 40.00 | 100.00 |
| ☐ APRIL, rel. 1973. ed. 100, s/n, etching, pub MMGI . . . . . . . . . . . . . . . . . . . . | 30.00 | 125.00 |
| ☐ ATTIC TREASURES, rel. 1978. ed. 275, s/n, litho, pub MMGI . . . . . . . . . . . . . | 200.00 | 300.00 |

| | ISSUE PRICE | CURRENT PRICE |
|---|---|---|
| ☐ AUTUMN, rel. 1973. ed. 200, s/n, hand colored litho, pub MMGI | 60.00 | 225.00 |
| ☐ AUTUMN BOUQUET, rel. 1973. ed. 150, s/n, etching, pub MMGI | 60.00 | 225.00 |
| ☐ BROTHER & SISTER, rel. 1970. ed. 200, s/n, litho, pub MMGI | 40.00 | 350.00 |
| ☐ BLUE MOON, rel. 1974. ed. 150, s/n, etching, pub MMGI | 80.00 | 150.00 |
| ☐ BREATH OF SPRING, rel. 1973. ed. 100, s/n, etching, pub MMGI | 50.00 | 250.00 |
| ☐ CAMEO, rel. 1975. ed. 150, s/n, etching, pub MMGI | 30.00 | 150.00 |
| ☐ CAROLINE, rel. 1975. ed. 150, s/n, etching, pub MMGI | 35.00 | 150.00 |
| ☐ CARRIE, rel. 1977. ed. 250, s/n, litho, pub NG | 70.00 | — |
| ☐ CLIMBING, rel. 1974. ed. 200, s/n, litho, pub MMGI | 50.00 | 150.00 |
| ☐ DAWN, rel. 1975. ed. 175, s/n, etching, pub MMGI | 35.00 | 100.00 |
| ☐ DRYING OFF, rel. 1977. ed. 250, s/n, litho, pub MMGI | 70.00 | 150.00 |
| ☐ EMBRACE, rel. 1975. ed. 200, s/n, litho, pub MMGI | 60.00 | 200.00 |
| ☐ ENGAGEMENT, rel. 1975. ed. 150, s/n, etching, pub MMGI | 90.00 | 250.00 |
| ☐ FACE IN THE WINDOW, rel. 1971. ed. 200, s/n, litho, pub MMGI | 35.00 | 200.00 |
| ☐ FACE TO THE WIND, rel. 1971. ed. 200, s/n, litho, pub MMGI | 40.00 | 250.00 |
| ☐ FANTASY, rel. 1976. ed. 175, s/n, etching, pub MMGI | 100.00 | — |
| ☐ FAY, rel. 1978. ed. 175, s/n, hand colored etching, pub MMGI | 50.00 | 75.00 |
| ☐ FIRST DAY, rel. 1974. ed. 150, s/n, etching, pub MMGI | 20.00 | 75.00 |
| ☐ FIRST GRADE, rel. 1974. ed. 150, s/n, etching, pub MMGI | 20.00 | 75.00 |
| ☐ FLAPPERS, rel. 1977. ed. 250, s/n, litho, pub MMGI | 70.00 | — |
| ☐ FLIGHT OF FANCY, rel. 1973. ed. 200, s/n, litho, pub MMGI | 50.00 | 200.00 |
| ☐ FORTY-THREE MINUTES FROM BOARDWAY, rel. 1975. ed. 150, s/n, etching, pub MMGI | 100.00 | 150.00 |
| ☐ GAY, rel. 1977. ed. 175, s/n, etching, pub MMGI | 38.00 | 125.00 |
| ☐ GOOD TIMES, rel. 1976. ed. 175, s/n, hand colored etching, pub MMGI | 90.00 | 225.00 |
| ☐ GRACE, rel. 1975. ed. 150, s/n, etching, pub MMGI | 30.00 | 125.00 |
| ☐ GROWING TOGETHER, rel. 1975. ed. 200, s/n, litho, pub MMGI | 60.00 | 190.00 |
| ☐ GUITAR SOLO, rel. 1971. ed. 200, s/n, litho, pub MMGI | 40.00 | 250.00 |
| ☐ HAPPY BIRTHDAY, rel. 1977. ed. 175, s/n, hand colored etching, pub MMGI | 50.00 | — |
| ☐ HIDE 'N SEEK, rel. 1975. ed. 175, s/n, etching, pub MMGI | 75.00 | 175.00 |
| ☐ HIGHER, rel. 1974. ed. 150, s/n, hand colored etching, pub MMGI | 30.00 | 150.00 |
| ☐ IS LUNCH READY MOM, rel. 1972. ed. 75, s/n, hand colored etching, pub MMGI | 60.00 | 200.00 |
| ☐ JANINE, rel. 1973. ed. 150, s/n, hand colored etching, pub MMGI | 70.00 | 200.00 |
| ☐ JEANNA, rel. 1976. ed. 250, s/n, hand colored litho, pub MMGI | 100.00 | 235.00 |
| ☐ JOY, rel. 1974. ed. 150, s/n, etching, pub MMGI | 40.00 | 100.00 |
| ☐ JUNE, rel. 1973. ed. 100, s/n, etching, pub MMGI | 30.00 | 125.00 |
| ☐ KATHERINE, rel. 1978. ed. 175, s/n, etching, pub MMGI | 45.00 | 100.00 |
| ☐ KEEPING COOL, rel. 1972. ed. 200, s/n, litho, pub MMGI | 35.00 | 125.00 |
| ☐ LADY MARLENE, rel. 1976. ed. 175, s/n, etching, pub MMGI | 35.00 | 100.00 |
| ☐ LETTER FROM DADDY, rel. 1977. ed. 175, s/n, etching, pub MMGI | 70.00 | 125.00 |
| ☐ LITTLE GIRLS ARE MADE OF, rel. 1977. ed. 175, s/n, hand colored etching, pub MMGI | 65.00 | 125.00 |
| ☐ LOVE IN BLOOM, rel. 1974. ed. 200, s/n, litho, pub MMGI | 50.00 | 250.00 |
| ☐ LOVE STORY, rel. 1975. ed. 150, s/n, etching, pub MMGI | 125.00 | Sold Out |
| ☐ LOVERS, rel. 1972. ed. 100, s/n, etching, pub MMGI | 50.00 | 150.00 |
| ☐ MAY, rel. 1973. ed. 100, s/n, etching, pub MMGI | 30.00 | 125.00 |
| ☐ MOTHER & CHILD, rel. 1970. ed. 150, s/n, litho, pub MMGI | 40.00 | 300.00 |
| ☐ MY GARDEN, rel. 1974. ed. 150, s/n, etching, pub MMGI | 50.00 | 125.00 |
| ☐ OCTOBER, rel. 1974. ed. 150, s/n, etching, pub MMGI | 80.00 | 225.00 |
| ☐ ONE MORE GAME, rel. 1975. ed. 150, s/n, etching, pub MMGI | 100.00 | 225.00 |
| ☐ OUR HOUSE, rel. 1976. ed. 175, s/n, etching, pub MMGI | 100.00 | 235.00 |
| ☐ PATIENCE, rel. 1972. ed. 25, s/n, etching, pub MMGI | 25.00 | 125.00 |
| ☐ PATIENCE, rel. 1977. ed. 250, s/n, litho, pub MMGI | 70.00 | 150.00 |
| ☐ PIGGY BACK, rel. 1973. ed. 250, s/n, etching, pub MMGI | 60.00 | 250.00 |
| ☐ RAG DOLL, rel. 1977. ed. 250, s/n, hand colored litho, pub MMGI | 100.00 | 225.00 |
| ☐ RAINY DAY, rel. 1973. ed. 150, s/n, etching, pub MMGI | 50.00 | 175.00 |
| ☐ REFLECTIONS, rel. 1974. ed. 200, s/n, litho, pub MMGI | 50.00 | 200.00 |
| ☐ REPOSE, rel. 1975. ed. 175, s/n, etching, pub MMGI | 50.00 | 100.00 |
| ☐ ROCKING CHAIR, rel. 1974. ed. 200, s/n, litho, pub MMGI | 50.00 | 150.00 |
| ☐ SEATED CHILD, rel. 1970. ed. 150, s/n, litho, pub MMGI | 35.00 | 175.00 |
| ☐ SECRET PATH, rel. 1974. ed. 150, s/n, etching, pub MMGI | 50.00 | 100.00 |
| ☐ SECRETS, rel. 1976. ed. 175, s/n, etching, pub MMGI | 65.00 | 160.00 |
| ☐ SEPTEMBER, rel. 1974. ed. 150, s/n, hand colored etching, pub MMGI | 90.00 | 175.00 |

| | ISSUE PRICE | CURRENT PRICE |
|---|---|---|
| ☐ SHARING, rel. 1971. ed. 200, s/n, litho, pub MMGI | 40.00 | 250.00 |
| ☐ SHE LOVES ME, rel. 1975. ed. 200, s/n, litho, pub MMGI | 60.00 | 175.00 |
| ☐ SMALL MIRACLES, rel. 1976. ed. 175, s/n, etching, pub MMGI | 90.00 | — |
| ☐ SOMEDAY, rel. 1974. ed. 150, s/n, etching, pub MMGI | 60.00 | 125.00 |
| ☐ SOUND OF MUSIC, rel. 1974. ed. 150, s/n, etching, pub MMGI | 50.00 | 150.00 |
| ☐ SPRING, rel. 1975. ed. 175, s/n, etching, pub MMGI | 50.00 | 125.00 |
| ☐ SPRING BONNETS, rel. 1976. ed. 250, s/n, litho, pub MMGI | 50.00 | 150.00 |
| ☐ SPRINGTIME, rel. 1971. ed. 200, s/n, litho, pub MMGI | 40.00 | 175.00 |
| ☐ STRING OF PEARLS, rel. 1975. ed. 200, s/n, litho, pub MMGI | 60.00 | 200.00 |
| ☐ SUNSHINE 'N SAND, rel. 1976. ed. 250, s/n, litho, pub MMGI | 60.00 | 200.00 |
| ☐ SUZIE, rel. 1972. ed. 150, s/n, etching, pub MMGI | 60.00 | 150.00 |
| ☐ SWEET NOTHINGS, rel. 1976. ed. 250, s/n, litho, pub MMGI | 60.00 | 200.00 |
| ☐ SWEET SIXTEEN, rel. 1973. ed. 100, s/n, etching, pub MMGI | 30.00 | 100.00 |
| ☐ TATTERED HERO, rel. 1973. ed. 100, s/n, etching, pub MMGI | 60.00 | 235.00 |
| ☐ TENDER MOMENT, rel. 1971. ed. 200, s/n, litho, pub MMGI | 40.00 | 225.00 |
| ☐ TENDER MOMENT II, rel. 1977. ed. 250, s/n, litho, pub MMGI | 70.00 | 125.00 |
| ☐ THREE'S A CROWD, rel. 1973. ed. 100, s/n, etching, pub MMGI | 50.00 | 200.00 |
| ☐ THREE OF A KIND, rel. 1972. ed. 200, s/n, litho, pub MMGI | 40.00 | 120.00 |
| ☐ TODAY'S FORECAST - SUNNY, rel. 1978. ed. 175, s/n, hand colored etching, pub MMGI | 100.00 | — |
| ☐ TOGETHER, rel. 1972. ed. 200, s/n, litho, pub MMGI | 40.00 | 120.00 |
| ☐ TOGETHER WE'RE STRONGER, rel. 1973. ed. 100, s/n, etching, pub MMGI | 40.00 | 150.00 |
| ☐ THE LOCKET, rel. 1977. ed. 175, s/n, etching, pub MMGI | 60.00 | 100.00 |
| ☐ TULIPS, rel. 1976. ed. 250, s/n, litho, pub MMGI | 100.00 | 325.00 |
| ☐ TWILIGHT, rel. 1975. ed. 175, s/n, etching, pub MMGI | 65.00 | 160.00 |
| ☐ TWINS, rel. 1974. ed. 200, s/n, hand colored litho, pub MMGI | 60.00 | 90.00 |
| ☐ TWO CHILDREN IN FIELD, rel. 1970. ed. 150, s/n, litho, pub MMGI | 40.00 | 150.00 |
| ☐ WADING, rel. 1972. ed. 200, s/n, litho, pub MMGI | 40.00 | 215.00 |
| ☐ WAITING FOR DADDY, rel. 1974. ed. 150, s/n, etching, pub MMGI | 50.00 | 235.00 |
| ☐ WATER BABIES, rel. 1972. ed. 200, s/n, litho, pub MMGI | 70.00 | 350.00 |
| ☐ WELCOME HOME, rel. 1976. ed. 250, s/n, litho, pub MMGI | 50.00 | 100.00 |
| ☐ WICKER CHAIR, rel. 1977. ed. 250, s/n, litho, pub MMGI | 70.00 | — |
| ☐ YESTERDAY'S TOMORROW, rel. 1974. ed. 150, s/n, hand colored etching, pub MMGI | 80.00 | 250.00 |
| ☐ YOUNG GARDENER, rel. 1972. ed. 200, s/n, litho, pub MMGI | 35.00 | 150.00 |
| ☐ JANUARY, rel. 1977. ed. 175, s/n, hand colored etching, pub MMGI | 120.00 | 175.00 |
| ☐ CLASS OF '92, rel. 1978. ed. 175, s/n, hand colored etching, pub MMGI | 150.00 | — |
| ☐ A GIRL'S BEST FRIEND, rel. 1979. ed. 275, s/n, litho, pub MMGI | 150.00 | — |
| ☐ CONNOISSEUR, rel. 1979. ed. 175, s/n, etching, pub MMGI | 50.00 | — |
| ☐ GOLDEN TRESSES, rel. 1978. ed. 275, s/n, hand colored etching, pub MMGI | 150.00 | 250.00 |
| ☐ WHO ME?, rel. 1979. ed. 275, s/n, litho, pub MMGI | 100.00 | — |
| ☐ EASTERN FLOWER, rel. 1980. ed. 275, s/n, mixed media, pub MMGI | 200.00 | 250 |
| ☐ MARY ROSE, rel. 1980. ed. 350, litho/etch, 10″ x 13½″, distr. GBSL | 90.00 | 425.00 |
| ☐ SPRING FLOWERS, rel. 1981. ed. 350, litho/etch, 10″ x 13½″, distr. GBSL | 125.00 | 155.00 |
| ☐ SUMMER REFLECTIONS, rel. 1981. ed. 350, litho/etch, 10″ x 13½″, distr. GBSL | 155.00 | — |
| ☐ LONG AGO, rel. 1981. ed. 350, litho/etch, 10″ x 13½″, distr. GBSL | 125.00 | — |
| ☐ FAR AWAY, rel. 1981. ed. 350, litho/etch, 10″ x 13½″, distr. GBSL | 125.00 | — |
| ☐ MARY ELLEN, rel. 1981. ed. 350, litho/etch, 10″ x 13½″, distr. GBSL | 105.00 | — |
| ☐ AUTUMN LEAVES, rel. 1981. ed. 350, litho/etch, 10″ x 13½″, distr. GBSL | 125.00 | — |
| ☐ NANCY, rel. 1981. ed. 350, litho/etch, 10″ x 13½″, distr. GBSL | 75.00 | — |

# RUSS VICKERS

Russ Vickers, the son of a horse trader, has a thorough knowledge of horses, a subject he often paints. While in the Marine Corps, he acquired a reputation as an artist, took a mail order course in art and when he retired went to work for North American Rockwell.

After 17 years of schematics and projections, Vickers became a full-time painter of the historical West. His miniatures, which started the current craze, and his larger paintings reveal impeccable research and painting technique.

**THEY LIVED WITH THE LAND** by *Russ Vickers*

## RUSS VICKERS

| | ISSUE PRICE | CURRENT PRICE |
|---|---|---|
| ☐ **THE BEEF RATION,** rel. 1979. ed. 950, s/n, 6¾″ x 14¾″, pub MPPI ........ | 35.00 | – |
| ☐ **THE COMMISSIONER,** rel. 1979. ed. 950, s/n, 6¾″ x 14¾″, pub MPPI ...... | 35.00 | – |
| ☐ **THE SETTLEMENT,** rel. 1979. ed. 950, s/n, 6¾″ x 14¾″, pub MPPI ........ | 35.00 | – |
| ☐ **THE UNTAMED LAND,** rel. 1979. ed. 950, s/n, 6¾″ x 14¾″, pub MPPI ...... | 35.00 | – |
| ☐ **APACHE ARROW,** rel. 1980. ed. 950, s/n, 19″ x 25½″, pub MPPI ......... | 65.00 | – |
| ☐ **ATTACK,** rel. 1980. ed. 950, s/n, 15¾″ x 19″, pub MPPI ................ | 45.00 | – |
| ☐ **RETURN TO HER PEOPLE,** rel. 1980. ed. 950, s/n, 16½″ x 20″, pub MPPI .... | 45.00 | – |
| ☐ **THE STORY OF THE RIFLES,** rel. 1980. ed. 950, s/n, 16½″ x 19⅝″, pub MPPI | 45.00 | – |
| ☐ **WHEN GAME IS SCARCE,** rel. 1980. ed. 950, s/n, 16¼″ x 19½″, pub MPPI .. | 45.00 | – |
| ☐ **RUN FOR THE RIVER,** rel. 1981. ed. 950, s/n, 18¾″ x 32½″, pub MPPI ..... | 95.00 | – |
| ☐ **RUNNING WATER LEAVES NO TRAIL,** rel. 1982. ed. 950, s/n, 18¼″ x 24″, pub MPPI.................................................... | 85.00 | – |
| ☐ **THEY LIVED WITH THE LAND,** rel. 1982. ed. 950, s/n, 15″ x 24″, pub MPPI .. | 75.00 | – |

## HAHN VIDAL

Hahn Vidal has a deep and abiding love of flowers, plus the ability to characterize them on canvas with technical proficiency.

Born in Hamburg, Germany, Vidal's potential was recognized in her early teens. She studied under a distinguished Argentinian portrait artist, Eduardo Couce Vidal, whom she later married. It was he who taught her the technique of classical painting, and gave her the advice she has followed to this day: "Paint what you know and love best." That was an easy choice of subject, since Vidal had loved flowers all her life.

Vidal has developed her technique and the results have been enchanting: romantic flowers exploding with color.

Now an American citizen, Vidal was the first Western floral artist to exhibit officially in Taipei. Her work is represented in museums in South America, the Orient, and the United States.

### HAHN VIDAL

| | ISSUE PRICE | CURRENT PRICE |
|---|---|---|
| ☐ **COUNTRY BOUQUET,** rel. 1977. ed. 950, s/n, 19½″ x 23½″, pub MPPI ..... | 75.00 | 100.00 |

# JEAN VIETOR

Wildlife artist Jean Vietor says she became a watercolorist by accident. When she first began doing art demonstrations, her media were pastel, ink and gouache. While developing a chickadee and weeds (her first bird painting), she decided to switch to watercolor because she wanted to enter Watercolor USA in 1971. The work was accepted and sold. She relates, "I did another one, and another. Now I am almost exclusively a watercolorist."

Since she began showing her work in 1969, she has won over fifty awards including the Jury Designated Purchase Award in the Watercolor USA National Watercolor Competition in 1971 and 1974; the Museum Purchase Award in 1975, and in 1976 first place in the "500" Exhibition in 1976.

Vietor attended Lindenwood College for Women in St. Charles, Missouri, and Indiana University.

Jean now does watercolor and gouache demonstrations for art interest groups and teaches watercolor.

**WELCOME SPRING** by Jean Vietor

| JEAN VIETOR | ISSUE PRICE | CURRENT PRICE |
|---|---|---|
| ☐ CARDINAL, rel. 1979. ed. 700, s/n, 23½" x 18½", pub FHG | 40.00 | Sold Out |
| ☐ TUFTED TITMOUSE, rel. 1979. ed. 700, s/n, 19½" x 14½", pub FHG | 35.00 | — |
| ☐ WOOD THRUSH, rel. 1979. ed. 700, s/n, 19" x 24", pub FHG | 40.00 | — |
| ☐ I WISH LIFE WERE A BUTTERFLY, rel. 1980. ed. 800, s/n, 18¾" x 25½", pub FHG | 50.00 | 100.00 |
| ed. 100, s/n and remarqued | 75.00 | 110.00 |
| ☐ RACCOONS, rel. 1980. ed. 750, s/n, 18" x 24", pub FHG | 45.00 | 125.00 |
| ☐ RED SQUIRREL, rel. 1980. ed. 750, s/n, 18½" x 23½", pub FHG | 45.00 | — |
| ☐ RIGHT SIDE UP . . . DOWN?, rel. 1980. ed. 750, s/n, 27" x 21", pub FHG | 45.00 | 125.00 |
| ☐ SOM'BRELLA, rel. 1980. ed. 800, s/n, 27" x 21", pub FHG | 50.00 | 100.00 |
| ☐ A RELUCTANT FAREWELL, rel. 1981. ed. 1,000, s/n, 21½" x 27½", pub FHG | 50.00 | 100.00 |
| ☐ COTTONWORLD, rel. 1981. ed. 1,000, s/n, 21½" x 27½", pub FHG | 50.00 | 90.00 |

| | ISSUE PRICE | CURRENT PRICE |
|---|---|---|
| ☐ **IN MY SPIFFY RED BANDANA,** rel. 1981. ed. 1,000, s/n, 24″ x 19″, pub FHG. | 50.00 | 85.00 |
| ☐ **KNOCK-KNOCK . . . WHO WHO WHO'S THERE?,** rel. 1981. ed. 1,000, s/n, 19″ x 24″, pub FHG. | 50.00 | 85.00 |
| ☐ **WORLD OF WONDER,** rel. 1981. ed. 1,000, s/n, 19″ x 26″, pub FHG. | 50.00 | Sold Out |
| ☐ **A TOUCH OF BLUSH,** rel. 1982. ed. 1,000, s/n, 18¾″ x 23¾″, pub FHG. | 60.00 | — |
| ☐ **DEERWATCHER,** rel. 1982. ed. 1,000, s/n, 27½″ x 21½″, pub FHG. | 60.00 | Sold Out |
| ☐ **FLUFF AND STUFF,** rel. 1982. ed. 4,000, s/o, 13½″ x 17″, pub FHG. | 25.00 | Sold Out |
| ☐ **OH, RED BIRD, OH, RED BIRD,** rel. 1982. ed. 1,000, s/n, 19″ x 24″, pub FHG. | 60.00 | Sold Out |
| ed. 300, exlusive, available at the World's Fair | 65.00 | — |
| ☐ **PARASOLS AND TABLETOPS,** rel. 1982. ed. 1,000, s/n, 13½″ x 18½″, pub FHG. (Sold as a set) | 50.00 | Sold Out |
| ☐ **THE GOLDEN DAYS,** rel. 1982. ed. 1,000, s/n, 27½″ x 21½″, pub FHG. | 60.00 | — |
| ☐ **RACCOON . . . SEQUEL,** rel. 1983. ed. 1,000, s/n, 19″ x 24″, pub FHG | — | — |
| ☐ **RENDEVOUS,** rel. 1983. ed. 1,000, s/n, 19″ x 30″, pub FHG | — | — |
| ☐ **VINES AND FINDS,** rel. 1983. ed. 1,000, s/n, 32″ x 19″, pub FHG | — | — |
| ☐ **WELCOME SPRING,** rel. 1983. ed. 1,000, s/n, 19″ x 24″, pub FHG | — | — |

# HAROLD VON SCHMIDT

During his younger years, Harold Von Schmidt made it a practice to seek out part-time jobs. Through these experiences he gained insight into the rugged lives of turn-of-the-century loggers and miners and the dreary toil of the cowboy. He used these experiences for his paintings.

Over the years, Von Schmidt has achieved a place in American painting beside Frederic Remington and Charles M. Russell.

The similarities between the three are many; not the least being that their work was first known and cherished through reproductions in such things as major periodicals and calendars. It wasn't until later that these same works graced the walls of galleries and museums. Their impressions of the West capture the essence of a time that existed only briefly. Through their paintings that time will live forever.

Many of Schmidt's canvases now hang in museums and galleries throughout the country. He has received many awards over his long career including the first Gold Medal ever awarded by the National Cowboy Hall of Fame.

### HAROLD VON SCHMIDT

| | | |
|---|---|---|
| ☐ **BUFFALO BILL CODY,** rel. 1982. *ed. 950, embossed and numbered, 24½″ x 30½″ | 245.00 | — |
| **ed. 56, artist's proofs, pub MPPI | 294.00 | — |
| **ed. 20, publisher's proofs | 294.00 | — |
| **Fewer than half of the artist's proofs and publisher's proofs are available for sale, as the others are donated to museums and other institutions. | | |
| *Embossed with signature seal | | |

# BRUCE VON STETINA

"I find the sailing ship as the finest and most artistically beautiful creation that man has ever made," says Bruce Von Stetina.

A painter of ships, Von Stetina spends as much time researching his subjects as he spends painting them. The result is a realistic, beautiful piece of artwork.

### BRUCE VON STETINA

| | | |
|---|---|---|
| ☐ **ANOTHER VICTORY FOR OLD IRONSIDES,** ed. 500, s/n, 21″ x 32″, pub CII | 95.00 | — |
| ☐ **SECOND DAY OF THE FOUR DAY BATTLE OF 1666,** ed. 500, s/n, 21″ x 32″, pub CII | 95.00 | — |

| | ISSUE PRICE | CURRENT PRICE |
|---|---|---|
| ☐ **SOUTH STREET SEAPORT 1865**, rel. 1983. ed. 500, s/n, 20" x 30", pub CII .. | 95.00 | — |
| ☐ **THE LIGHTNING**, ed. 500, s/n, 18" x 24", pub CII | 85.00 | — |
| ☐ **THE RAINBOW**, ed. 500, s/n, 18" x 24", pub CII | 85.00 | — |

# WAYNE WALDRON

Since 1976, Wayne Waldron has won over 60 awards for his nostalgic water-colors, including 12 "First's" and six "Best of Show's". Wayne describes his art as "interpretive realism". When he sees a subject that evokes a memory of another time, he seeks to bring that subject back to life through his painting.

That focal point of his first FoxFire print, "Grandma's Quilt" is an antique "double wedding ring" quilt, resting on an old rocker in the "Traveler's Room" of a farmhouse built in 1896. "Stirring the viewer's emotions is my primary goal," says the artist, "as well as communicating my own pride in our heritage."

**GRANDMA'S QUILT** *by Wayne Waldron*

## WAYNE WALDRON

| | | |
|---|---|---|
| ☐ **COUNTRY KITCHEN**, ed. 1,500, s/n, 20" x 26", pub FFFAI | 40.00 | 100.00 |
| ☐ **GRANDMA'S QUILT**, ed. 1,500, s/n, 20" x 26", pub FFFAI | 40.00 | — |

# RALPH WALL

| | | |
|---|---|---|
| ☐ **PAINTED MORNING**, ed. 500, s/n, 13½" x 21", distr. GI | 55.00 | — |
| ☐ **PEACE**, ed. 500, s/n, 13½" x 21", distr. GI | 55.00 | — |
| ☐ **THE BULLBOATS**, ed. 650, s/n, 16½" x 33", distr. GI | 65.00 | Sold Out |
| ☐ **WHEN MEAT WAS SCARCE**, ed. 500, s/n, 16½" x 25", distr. GI | 60.00 | — |
| ☐ **WHERE THE HEART IS**, ed. 650, s/n, 22" x 33", distr. GI | 60.00 | — |

# MARY ROSE WAMPLER

"I have become intrigued with the places flowers grow and enjoy capturing their whole personality by using the things we normally don't notice — such as dry leaves, mosses and twigs," says Mary Rose Wampler one of the finest painters of flowers in contemporary American artistry.

Winner of the 1974 national flower contest, she was selected from a competition including over five hundred of the country's best nature artists.

In her search for floral specimens, Wampler is very exacting about the smallest of details, often spending months researching and painting.

**GOLDENROD** *by Maryrose Wampler*

| MARY ROSE WAMPLER | ISSUE PRICE | CURRENT PRICE |
|---|---|---|
| ☐ BLACK-EYED SUSAN, rel. 1974. ed. 5,000, s/o, 22" x 28", pub NHI. | **30.00 | 350.00 |
| ☐ DAISY MUMS, rel. 1974. ed. 5,000, s/o, 22" x 28", pub NHI. | 30.00 | 75.00 |
| ☐ DOGWOOD AND VIOLETS, rel. 1974. ed. 5,000, s/o, 22" x 28", pub NHI. | 30.00 | 75.00 |
| ☐ IRIS AND OLD ROSES, rel. 1974. ed. 5,000, s/o, 22" x 28", pub NHI. | 30.00 | 75.00 |
| ☐ TRAILING ARBUTUS, rel. 1974. ed. 5,000, s/o, 22" x 28", pub NHI. | 30.00 | 75.00 |
| ☐ CARDINAL FLOWER AND TICKSEED, rel. 1975. ed. 5,000, s/o, 22" x 28", pub NHI. | 30.00 | 50.00 |

**Prints were sold as collections at issue price as shown, providing the collector purchased each print when published. Individual purchases were $50.00 issue.

|  | ISSUE PRICE | CURRENT PRICE |
|---|---|---|
| ☐ HIBISCUS AND ORANGE BLOSSOM, rel. 1975. ed. 5,000, s/o, 22″ x 28″, pub NHI. | 30.00 | 50.00 |
| ☐ LILAC AND APPLE BLOSSOM, rel. 1975. ed. 5,000, s/o, 22″ x 28″, pub NHI. . | 30.00 | 50.00 |
| ☐ PIEDMONT AZALEA, rel. 1975. ed. 5,000, s/o, 22″ x 28″, pub NHI. | 30.00 | 50.00 |
| ☐ RED CLOVER AND ROADSIDE FLOWERS, rel. 1975. ed. 5,000, s/o, 22″ x 28″, pub NHI. | 30.00 | 50.00 |
| ☐ SINGLE YELLOW ROSE, rel. 1975. ed. 5,000, s/o, 22″ x 28″, pub NHI. | 30.00 | 50.00 |
| ☐ GOLDENROD, rel. 1976. ed. 5,000, s/o, 22″ x 28″, pub NHI. | 30.00 | 50.00 |
| ☐ HEPATICA, rel. 1976. ed. 5,000, s/o, 22″ x 28″, pub NHI. | 30.00 | 50.00 |
| ☐ PEACE ROSE AND PEONY, rel. 1976. ed. 5,000, s/o, 22″ x 28″, pub NHI. | 30.00 | 50.00 |
| ☐ PEACH BLOSSOM, rel. 1976. ed. 5,000, s/o, 22″ x 28″, pub NHI. | 30.00 | 50.00 |
| ☐ SOUTHERN MAGNOLIA, rel. 1976. ed. 5,000, s/o, 22″ x 28″, pub NHI. | 30.00 | 50.00 |
| ☐ YELLOW JESSAMINE, rel. 1976. ed. 5,000, s/o, 22″ x 28″, pub NHI. | 30.00 | 50.00 |
| ☐ CAMELLIA, rel. 1977. ed. 5,000, s/o, 22″ x 28″, pub NHI. | 30.00 | 50.00 |
| ☐ DUNE FLOWERS, rel. 1977. ed. 5,000, s/o, 22″ x 28″, pub NHI. | 30.00 | 50.00 |
| ☐ LILLIES AND TR. VINE, rel. 1977. ed. 5,000, s/o, 22″ x 28″, pub NHI. | 30.00 | 50.00 |
| ☐ PASSION VINE, rel. 1977. ed. 5,000, s/o, 22″ x 28″, pub NHI. | 30.00 | 50.00 |
| ☐ TRILLIM, rel. 1977. ed. 5,000, s/o, 22″ x 28″, pub NHI. | 30.00 | 50.00 |
| ☐ WILD ROSE, rel. 1977. ed. 5,000, s/o, 22″ x 28″, pub NHI. | 30.00 | 50.00 |
| ☐ BUTTERFLIES (SET OF THREE), rel. 1978. ed. 2,500, i/o, 5″ x 7″, pub NHI. . . | 25.00 | — |
| ☐ COMMON SUNFLOWER, rel. 1978. ed. 5,000, s/o, 22″ x 28″, pub NHI. | 30.00 | 50.00 |
| ☐ BLUE BELLS, rel. 1979. ed. 5,000, s/o, 22″ x 28″, pub NHI. | 30.00 | 50.00 |
| ☐ INDIAN PAINTBUSH, rel. 1979. ed. 5,000, s/o, 22″ x 28″, pub NHI. | 30.00 | 50.00 |
| ☐ SPING BULBS, rel. 1979. ed. 5,000, s/o, 22″ x 28″, pub NHI. | 30.00 | 50.00 |
| ☐ THISTLE, rel. 1979. ed. 5,000, s/o, 22″ x 28″, pub NHI. | 30.00 | 50.00 |
| ☐ MOUNTAIN FLOWERS, rel. 1981. ed. 5,000, s/o, 22″ x 28″, pub NHI. | 50.00 | — |
| ☐ OLD FASHIONED ROSES, rel. 1981. ed. 1,000, s/o, 16″ x 20″, pub NHI. | 50.00 | — |
| ☐ RHODODENDRON, rel. 1981. ed. 5,000, s/o, 22″ x 28″, pub NHI. | 50.00 | — |

# EDWARD WARD

Edward Ward is a master printmaker. He began his career in art as an apprentice in a large graphic workshop. He advanced his technical skills until he became the supervisor of the workshop. Ward studied art at Trenton State College, receiving his Bachelor of Art degree in 1972. During the time he was a journeyman printmaker, Ward developed a deep affection and respect for traditional printmaking as a unique art form. As a result, he prefers to execute all of his work himself. He specializes in handprinted collographs, engraving, and intaglio relief prints.

Ward's distinctive style, combined with the small number of prints in each of his limited editions, has brought him enthusiastic recognition among print collectors. His work is included in hundreds of private and corporate collections around the United States. His work has also been featured in many juried shows, receiving in the process, over one hundred awards. Ward is a member of many art organizations, including the Philadelphia Print Club and the Printmaking Council of New Jersey. His work appeared on the cover of *Arts New Jersey Magazine*, spring issue, 1982.

## ED WARD

| | | |
|---|---|---|
| ☐ "A" CONVERTIBLE, rel. 1982. ed. 100, s/n, 1″ x 2″, etching, pub EW. | 18.00 | — |
| ☐ AMERICANA, rel. 1979. ed. 100, s/n, 21″ x 27″, collograph engraving, pub EW. | 60.00 | 75.00 |
| ☐ APOLLO XIII, rel. 1979. ed. 75, s/n, 22″ x 22″, collograph linocut, pub EW. . . | 50.00 | 95.00 |
| ☐ ARMADILLO, rel. 1982. ed. 100, s/n, 1″ x 2″, etching, pub EW. | 18.00 | — |
| ☐ AT & SF, rel. 1980. ed. 100, s/n, 16″ x 16″, collograph engraving, pub EW. . . | 30.00 | 35.00 |
| ☐ "B" CONVERTIBLE, rel. 1982. ed. 100, s/n, 2″ x 2″, etching, pub EW. | 18.00 | — |
| ☐ BIOSYNTHESIS, rel. 1976. ed. 75, s/n, 24″ x 20″, collograph, pub EW. | 60.00 | Sold Out |
| ☐ BONDED HOMAGE, rel. 1976. ed. 75, s/n, 20″ x 25″, woodcut, pub EW. | 30.00 | 45.00 |
| ☐ BUZZARD'S BAY, rel. 1974. ed. 75, s/n, 22″ x 28″, woodcut, pub EW. | 45.00 | Sold Out |

**SIC TRANSIT** *by Ed Ward*

| | ISSUE PRICE | CURRENT PRICE |
|---|---|---|
| ☐ **CARIBE**, rel. 1981. ed. 175, s/n, 11" x 13", linocut engraving, pub EW. . . . . | 18.00 | 24.00 |
| ☐ **CUZCO I**, rel. 1978. ed. 100, s/n, 26" x 31", intaglio relief, pub EW. . . . . . . . | 60.00 | 75.00 |
| ☐ **CUZCO II**, rel. 1978. ed. 100, s/n, 23" x 30", intaglio relief, pub EW. | 60.00 | 95.00 |
| ☐ **CUZCO III**, rel. 1978. ed. 100, s/n, 25" x 30", collograph engraving, pub EW. . | 60.00 | 75.00 |
| ☐ **DANFORTHE, COOKE**, rel. 1981. ed. 100, s/n, 16" x 18", collograph engraving, pub EW. . . . . . . . . . . . . . . . . . . . . . . . . . . . . . . . . . . . . . . . . . | 30.00 | 35.00 |
| ☐ **DANDYLION**, rel. 1976. ed. 75, s/n, 12" x 17", linocut, pub EW. . . . . . . . . . . | 18.00 | 24.00 |
| ☐ **DAYBREAKERS**, rel. 1976. ed. 75, s/n, 17" x 27", collograph engraving, pub EW. . . . . . . . . . . . . . . . . . . . . . . . . . . . . . . . . . . . . . . . . . . . . | 24.00 | Sold Out |
| ☐ **DUSK**, rel. 1978. ed. 150, s/n, 18" x 24", collograph engraving, pub EW. . . . . | 30.00 | 45.00 |
| ☐ **EDIFICATION OF MAN**, rel. 1981. ed. 75, s/n, 24" x 24", collograph engraving, pub EW. . . . . . . . . . . . . . . . . . . . . . . . . . . . . . . . . . . . . | 90.00 | 95.00 |
| ☐ **EGRET**, rel. 1978. ed. 150, s/n, 14" x 27", engraving, pub EW. . . . . . . . . . . . | 30.00 | 60.00 |
| ☐ **EHLYSUN**, rel. 1980. ed. 175, s/n, 11" x 12", collograph engraving, pub EW. | 18.00 | 24.00 |
| ☐ **ELEMENTAL LANDSCAPE**, rel. 1978. ed. 150, s/n, 19" x 26", collograph engraving, pub EW. . . . . . . . . . . . . . . . . . . . . . . . . . . . . . . . . . . . . . . | 45.00 | 60.00 |
| ☐ **EVENTIDE**, rel. 1978. ed. 175, s/n, 24" x 30", collograph engraving, pub EW. | 50.00 | 75.00 |
| ☐ **FAST BREAK**, rel. 1978. ed. 150, s/n, 14" x 17", collograph engraving, pub EW. . . . . . . . . . . . . . . . . . . . . . . . . . . . . . . . . . . . . . . . . . . . . . | 18.00 | 24.00 |
| ☐ **GANYMEDE**, rel. 1975. ed. 50, s/n, 22" x 28", collograph, pub EW. . . . . . . . | 45.00 | Sold Out |
| ☐ **GOLD FISH**, rel. 1982. ed. 100, s/n, 2" x 2", etching, pub EW. . . . . . . . . . . | 18.00 | — |
| ☐ **HARVEST MOON**, rel. 1977. ed. 125, s/n, 22" x 28", collograph engraving, pub EW. . . . . . . . . . . . . . . . . . . . . . . . . . . . . . . . . . . . . . . . . . . . . | 30.00 | Sold Out |
| ☐ **HUNTSMEN**, rel. 1978. ed. 175, s/n, 16" x 20", collograph engraving, pub EW. . . . . . . . . . . . . . . . . . . . . . . . . . . . . . . . . . . . . . . . . . . . . . . | 30.00 | 40.00 |

|  | ISSUE PRICE | CURRENT PRICE |
|---|---|---|
| ☐ **INDIANA**, rel. 1975. ed. 100, s/n, 16″ x 16″, etching, pub EW. | 18.00 | 35.00 |
| ☐ **INDIAN LAKE**, rel. 1981. ed. 100, s/n, 14″ x 18″, collograph engraving, pub EW. | 45.00 | — |
| ☐ **KANSAS LIMITED**, rel. 1981. ed. 150, s/n, 11″ x 12″, collograph engraving, pub EW. | 18.00 | — |
| ☐ **KINDRED**, rel. 1978. ed. 100, s/n, 24″ x 32″, intaglio relief, pub EW. | 60.00 | 95.00 |
| ☐ **LEO**, rel. 1977-78. ed. 125, s/n, 24″ x 27″, intaglio relief, pub EW. | 45.00 | 55.00 |
| ☐ **LES FLEURS**, rel. 1976. ed. 75, s/n, 20″ x 24″, intaglio relief, pub EW. | 24.00 | Sold Out |
| ☐ **LO!**, rel. 1977. ed. 100, s/n, 18″ x 18″, collograph, pub EW. | 30.00 | Sold Out |
| ☐ **LUNA**, rel. 1980. ed. 150, s/n, 26″ x 29″, collograph engraving, pub EW. | 50.00 | Sold Out |
| ☐ **LORELLI**, rel. 1976. ed. 50, s/n, 21″ x 27″, collograph, pub EW. | 18.00 | Sold Out |
| ☐ **MAGONIAN MOON**, rel. 1978. ed. 100, s/n, 24″ x 30″, intaglio relief, pub EW. | 45.00 | Sold Out |
| ☐ **MEDIEVAL**, rel. 1977. ed. 100, s/n, 28″ x 28″, intaglio relief, pub EW. | 50.00 | 95.00 |
| ☐ **MIDDAY**, rel. 1979. ed. 175, s/n, 24″ x 28″, collograph engraving, pub EW. | 60.00 | 95.00 |
| ☐ **MIRAGE**, rel. 1978. ed. 150, s/n, 24″ x 32″, intaglio relief, pub EW. | 40.00 | 95.00 |
| ☐ **MONTEGO DUSK**, rel. 1976. ed. 75, s/n, 20″ x 24″, collograph engraving, pub EW. | 24.00 | 45.00 |
| ☐ **MOONLIT WATERS**, rel. 1981. ed. 100, s/n, 14″ x 14″, engraving, pub EW. | 30.00 | Sold Out |
| ☐ **MOON'S RISE**, rel. 1978. ed. 150, s/n, 11″ x 12″, collograph engraving, pub EW. | 14.00 | Sold Out |
| ☐ **MORNING MISTS**, rel. 1979. ed. 175, s/n, 22″ x 24″, engraving, pub EW. | 45.00 | 60.00 |
| ☐ **N de M**, rel. 1980. ed. 100, s/n, 11″ x 14″, engraving, pub EW. | 18.00 | — |
| ☐ **NATCHEZ**, rel. 1977. ed. 100, s/n, 24″ x 30″, collograph engraving, pub EW. | 45.00 | Sold Out |
| ☐ **NIGHTFLIGHT**, rel. 1983. ed. 100, s/n, 8″ x 10″, woodcut, pub EW. | 28.00 | — |
| ☐ **NOD**, rel. 1980. ed. 100, s/n, 13″ x 14″, collograph engraving, pub EW. | 18.00 | 24.00 |
| ☐ **OCCULARITY**, rel. 1976. ed. 100, s/n, 24″ x 30″, intaglio relief, pub EW. | 30.00 | Sold Out |
| ☐ **ORBIS**, rel. 1977. ed. 100, s/n, 20″ x 24″, collograph, pub EW. | 24.00 | 35.00 |
| ☐ **OWL**, rel. 1982. ed. 100, s/n, 1″ x 1″, etching, pub EW. | 18.00 | Sold Out |
| ☐ **PEACE ROSE**, rel. 1977. ed. 100, s/n, 11″ x 13″, collograph, pub EW. | 18.00 | 35.00 |
| ☐ **POINT OF VIEW**, rel. 1978-82. ed. 100, s/n, 31″ x 38″, collograph engraving, pub EW. | 150.00 | 275.00 |
| ☐ **QZYCAUTL**, rel. 1976. ed. 100, s/n, 24″ x 26″, intaglio relief, pub EW. | 35.00 | 75.00 |
| ☐ **ROSE**, rel. 1976. ed. 100, s/n, 13″ x 14″, collograph, pub EW. | 18.00 | Sold Out |
| ☐ **RUDEBECKIAS**, rel. 1976. ed. 100, s/n, 20″ x 22″, collograph, pub EW. | 18.00 | Sold Out |
| ☐ **SAIL AWAY**, rel. 1981. ed. 100, s/n, 31″ x 38″, collograph engraving, stencil, pub EW. | 90.00 | 125.00 |
| ☐ **SEAFARER**, rel. 1979-81. ed. 100, s/n, 31″ x 36″, collograph engraving, pub EW. | 90.00 | 125.00 |
| ☐ **SEASON'S FLOW**, rel. 1979. ed. 100, s/n, 21″ x 32″, collograph engraving, pub EW. | 75.00 | Sold Out |
| ☐ **SIC TRANSIT**, rel. 1978. ed. 100, s/n, 24″ x 32″, collograph engraving, pub EW. | 45.00 | Sold Out |
| ☐ **SILENT REFLECTIONS**, rel. 1977. ed. 100, s/n, 16″ x 20″, collograph, pub EW. | 24.00 | 75.00 |
| ☐ **SNOWDRIFTING**, rel. 1979. ed. 100, s/n, 16″ x 22″, engraving, pub EW. | 30.00 | 35.00 |
| ☐ **SNOWFLAKES**, rel. 1980. ed. 100, s/n, 13″ x 24″, engraving, pub EW. | 24.00 | 30.00 |
| ☐ **SOUTHWESTERN**, rel. 1980. ed. 100, s/n, 12″ x 13″, collograph engraving, pub EW. | 18.00 | — |
| ☐ **SPRING MOON**, rel. 1978. ed. 100, s/n, 18″ x 22″, collograph engraving, pub EW. | 40.00 | 45.00 |
| ☐ **SUMMER SOLSTACE**, rel. 1976. ed. 100, s/n, 18″ x 24″, collograph engraving, pub EW. | 24.00 | Sold Out |
| ☐ **SUNFLOWERS**, rel. 1976. ed. 100, s/n, 16″ x 20″, intaglio relief, pub EW. | 24.00 | Sold Out |
| ☐ **SUNSET**, rel. 1978. ed. 100, s/n, 18″ x 22″, collograph engraving, pub EW. | 30.00 | 45.00 |
| ☐ **SUNSET FIRES**, rel. 1977. ed. 100, s/n, 24″ x 30″, collograph engraving, pub EW. | 45.00 | 75.00 |
| ☐ **TIP-IN**, rel. 1980-81. ed. 100, s/n, 23″ x 26″, collograph engraving, pub EW. | 50.00 | 75.00 |
| ☐ **TITAN**, rel. 1978. ed. 100, s/n, 25″ x 32″, intaglio relief, pub EW. | 60.00 | Sold Out |
| ☐ **TWILIGHT**, rel. 1978. ed. 100, s/n, 11″ x 12″, collograph engraving, pub EW. | 18.00 | 24.00 |

| | ISSUE PRICE | CURRENT PRICE |
|---|---|---|
| ☐ UNION PACIFIC, rel. 1977. ed. 100, s/n, 24" x 30", collograph engraving, pub EW. | 45.00 | Sold Out |
| ☐ WANING AFTERNOON, rel. 1979. ed. 100, s/n, 24" x 28", collograph engraving, pub EW. | 60.00 | 95.00 |
| ☐ WINTER FIELDS, rel. 1979. ed. 100, s/n, 17" x 26", collograph engraving, pub EW. | 30.00 | 45.00 |
| ☐ WINTER SOLSTICE, rel. 1979. ed. 100, s/n, 17" x 19", collograph engraving, pub EW. | 30.00 | 45.00 |

## WELLINGTON WARD, JR.

Wellington Ward Jr. chose to be an artist at the age of five after he made his first drawing of a grasshopper. While majoring in commercial art at Richmond Professional Institute (now Virginia Commonwealth University) he did everything from washing dishes and house painting to working on an automotive assembly line.

His favorite subject matter is nautical, usually old and weathered. "The minute details of whatever I paint are most important to me and the challenge to pass along the beauty that I see to my fellow man is my goal. I try to go beyond what a camera could record, always trying to capture the full sensitivity of my subject." His home is Ft. Myers, Florida.

## WELLINGTON WARD

| | ISSUE PRICE | CURRENT PRICE |
|---|---|---|
| ☐ PORT AND STARBOARD WATCH, rel. 1973. ed. 1,500, s/n, 34½" x 17½", pub FHG. | 40.00 | 100.00 |
| ☐ CHESAPEAKE BAY SKIPJACK, rel. 1973. ed. 2,000, s/n, 32½" x 18¼", pub FHG. | 40.00 | 75.00 |
| ☐ THE DORYMAN, rel. 1973. ed. 1,500, s/n, 33" x 18½", pub FHG. | 40.00 | 75.00 |
| ☐ SPONGE BOAT, rel. 1973. ed. 1,500, s/n, 32½" x 18", pub FHG. | 40.00 | 85.00 |
| ☐ BAHAMIAN SLOOP, rel. 1974. ed. 2,000, s/n, 32¾" x 18¼", pub FHG. | 40.00 | 100.00 |
| ☐ CATBOAT, rel. 1974. ed. 2,000, s/n, 17" x 21½", pub FHG. | 35.00 | 85.00 |
| ☐ FRIENDSHIP SLOOP, rel. 1974. ed. 2,000, s/n, 17" x 21½", pub FHG. | 35.00 | 110.00 |
| ☐ CHAMPION OF THE RIVER, rel. 1975. ed. 1,500, s/n, 20½" x 24", pub FHG. | 30.00 | Sold Out |
| ☐ LONELY SENTINEL, rel. 1976. ed. 1,000, s/n, 20" x 24", pub FHG. | 40.00 | 55.00 |
| ☐ PEBBLES OF TIME, rel. 1976. ed. 1,000, s/n, 24" x 20", pub FHG. | 40.00 | 75.00 |
| ☐ STILL WATERS, rel. 1976. ed. 1,000, s/n, 33" x 18½", pub FHG. | 40.00 | 100.00 |
| ☐ AT WATER'S EDGE, rel. 1977. ed. 700, s/n, 14" x 24", pub FHG. | 40.00 | 100.00 |
| ☐ HAPPY DAYS, rel. 1977. ed. 600, s/n, 12" x 19", pub FHG. | 40.00 | Sold Out |
| ☐ SALTY SUNSHINE, rel. 1977. ed. 600, s/n, 14¾" x 18¾", pub FHG. | 40.00 | Sold Out |
| ☐ SUMMER REFLECTIONS, rel. 1977. ed. 600, s/n, 20" x 16", pub FHG. | 40.00 | 75.00 |
| ☐ COUNTRY ROAD, rel. 1978. ed. 750, s/n, 20" x 28", pub FHG. | 50.00 | 65.00 |
| ☐ CRESCENT MOON, rel. 1978. ed. 750, s/n, 21" x 30", pub FHG. | 50.00 | Sold Out |
| ☐ QUEENS LACE, rel. 1978. ed. 750, s/n, 18½" x 27", pub FHG. | 50.00 | 125.00 |
| ☐ RETURN OF THE MONARCH, rel. 1978. ed. 600, s/n/remarqued, 24" x 20", pub FHG. | 75.00 | Sold Out |
| ☐ ABANDONED, rel. 1979. ed. 950, s/n, 16¾" x 30", pub FHG. | 55.00 | — |
| ☐ ANTIQUES, rel. 1979. ed. 950, s/n, 18" x 30", pub FHG. | 55.00 | — |
| ☐ DOWN AT THE DOCKS, rel. 1979. ed. 950, s/n, 14½" x 24½", pub FHG. | 50.00 | — |
| ☐ FEATHERED FRIENDS, rel. 1979. ed. 950, s/n, 19¼" x 27½", pub FHG. | 50.00 | 80.00 |
| ☐ FEATHERED QUARTET, rel. 1979. ed. 950, s/n, 23½" x 29½", pub FHG. | 50.00 | Sold Out |
| ☐ LAZY RIVER, rel. 1979. ed. 950, s/n, 15½" x 27", pub FHG. | 50.00 | — |
| ☐ MAIN STREET, rel. 1980. ed. 750, s/n, 17" x 30", pub FHG. | 65.00 | — |
| ☐ MEMORY LANE, rel. 1980. ed. 950, s/n, 18½" x 28", pub FHG. | 60.00 | — |

| | ISSUE PRICE | CURRENT PRICE |
|---|---|---|
| ☐ **ROCKPORT**, rel. 1980. ed. 950, s/n, 14¾" x 27¼", pub FHG. | 60.00 | — |
| ☐ **SOUTHPORT**, rel. 1980. ed. 950, s/n, 14½" x 30", pub FHG. | 60.00 | — |
| ☐ **THE MILL**, rel. 1980. ed. 950, s/n, 23¾" x 20", pub FHG. | 60.00 | — |
| ☐ **WINDBLOWN**, rel. 1980. ed. 950, s/n, 18¾" x 27½", pub FHG. | 60.00 | — |
| ☐ **BACKWATERS**, ed. 950, s/n, 16" x 28", pub MMFC. | 65.00 | — |
| ☐ **FEATHERED SKIPPER**, ed. 950, s/n, 18" x 25", pub MMFC. | 65.00 | — |
| ☐ **GENERAL STORE**, ed. 950, s/n, 19½" x 24", pub MMFC. | 65.00 | — |
| ☐ **PORK AND BEANS**, ed. 950, s/n, 18" x 25", pub MMFC. | 65.00 | — |
| ☐ **THE ROAD HOME**, ed. 950, s/n, 16" x 28", pub MMFC. | 65.00 | — |

# EDWARD V. WARNER

"My hope has been to capture in oils some small but eloquent scenes from our world, and by putting it on canvas and framing it to attract the attention of my fellow nature-lovers who may have missed what I saw and felt," said Edward Warner.

Born and raised in congested urban areas of Chicago and New York City, Warner's love affair with the wilderness began during his wartime duty with the army engineers in the rugged, mountainous Aleutian Islands from 1942-45.

An insatiable traveler, Warner has circled the earth many times studying the ancient as well as present culture and visiting art museums in most of the major cities of Europe including Moscow, Leningrad and Warsaw.

## EDWARD V. WARNER

| | ISSUE PRICE | CURRENT PRICE |
|---|---|---|
| ☐ **BITTERSWEET**, rel. 1974. ed. 500, s/o, 16" x 20", pub CHWA. <br> ed. 2,000 unsigned | 20.00 | — |
| ☐ **BLUE VASE**, rel. 1974. ed. 500, s/o, 16" x 20", pub CHWA. <br> ed. 2,000 unsigned | 20.00 | — |
| ☐ **EASTER MORNING DUNES**, rel. 1974. ed. 500, s/o, 31" x 22", <br> pub CHWA. <br> ed. 2,000 unsigned | 30.00 | — |
| ☐ **HUNTING OAK**, rel. 1974. ed. 500, s/o, 28" x 24⅛", pub CHWA. <br> ed. 2,000 unsigned | 30.00 | — |
| ☐ **IRIS BEAUTIES**, rel. 1974. ed. 500, s/o, 21¾" x 26¼", pub CHWA. <br> ed. 2,000 unsigned | 30.00 | — |
| ☐ **LILACS**, rel. 1974. ed. 500, s/o, 20" x 24", pub CHWA. <br> ed. 2,000 unsigned | 20.00 | — |
| ☐ **SUNNY AFTERNOON**, rel. 1974. ed. 500, s/o, 24" x 20", pub CHWA. <br> ed. 2,000 unsigned | 20.00 | — |
| ☐ **THE BRASS THING**, rel. 1974. ed. 500, s/o, 20" x 16", pub CHWA. <br> ed. 2,000 unsigned | 20.00 | — |
| ☐ **TIGERLILIES**, rel. 1974. ed. 500, s/o, 16" x 20", pub CHWA. <br> ed. 2,000 unsigned | 20.00 | — |
| ☐ **WINTER WOODLAND**, rel. 1974. ed. 500, s/o, 24" x 20", pub CHWA. <br> ed. 2,000 unsigned | 20.00 | — |

# MELVIN C. WARREN

Melvin Warren's love of the Southwest is deep and his knowledge of the cowboy personal. His father, a ranch hand, moved the family frequently which allowed him to store visual images to be used decades later in brilliant paintings.

After high school, Warren served in the Army Air Corps during World War II. He attended Texas Christian University as an art major. Commercial art was his only choice when he left the University for, as he ways, "Paintings just weren't selling."

However, he continued to paint during every available moment, and after several one-man shows, left the commercial field for full-time fine art.

**WHEN COWBOYS GET EDGY** *by Melvin Warren*

Warren is represented in collections throughout the United States. Late President Lyndon B. Johnson commissioned twenty paintings. One of Warren's sculptures is in the Cowboy Hall of Fame, and he has twice received the Franklin Mint Award as one of the ten best western artists.

## MELVIN WARREN

| | ISSUE PRICE | CURRENT PRICE |
|---|---|---|
| ☐ **TOP HAND OF THE CONCHO,** rel. 1974. ed. 700, s/n, 23″ x 31½″, pub MPPI. . | 150.00 | 400.00 |
| ☐ **A COLD DAY,** rel. 1981. ed. 550, s/n, 24⅝″ x 38″, pub MPPI. . . . . . . . . . . . . | 245.00 | 375.00 |
| ☐ **APPROACHING STORM,** rel. 1981. ed. 750, s/n, 22″ x 32½″, pub MPPI. . . . . | 195.00 | — |
| ☐ **THEN COWBOYS GET EDGY,** rel. 1981. ed. 750, s/n, 24½″ x 38″, pub MPPI. . | 245.00 | — |
| ☐ **NIGHT IN CHIMAYO,** rel. 1982. ed. 950, s/n, 18¼″ x 23⅞″, pub MPPI. . . . . . . | 125.00 | — |

## ANTOWINE WARRIOR

| | ISSUE PRICE | CURRENT PRICE |
|---|---|---|
| ☐ **FRY BREAD - MY GRANDMOTHERS WAY,** ed. 80, s/n, 22″ x 28″, stone lithograph, pub NWDHG. . . . . . . . . . . . . . . . . . . . . . . . . . . . . . . . . . . . . . | 250.00 | 500.00 |
| ☐ **THE HISTORIAN,** ed. 950, s/n, 16″ x 20″, stone lithograph, pub NWDHG. . . . . | 50.00 | — |
| ☐ **SCOUT - THE WATCHFUL ONE,** ed. 80, s/n, 22″ x 15″, stone lithograph, pub NWDHG. . . . . . . . . . . . . . . . . . . . . . . . . . . . . . . . . . . . . . . . . . . . | 175.00 | 450.00 |
| ☐ **WINTER CROSSING,** ed. 650, s/n, 24″ x 32″, stone lithograph, pub NWDHG. . | 75.00 | 150.00 |
| ☐ **VICTORY GALLOP,** ed. 1,500, s/n, 18″ x 20″, stone lithograph, pub NWDHG. . | 40.00 | 105.00 |
| ☐ **SURPRISE ATTACK,** ed. 950, s/n, 24″ x 27″, stone lithograph, pub NWDHG. . . | 50.00 | — |
| ☐ **MONARCH OF THE PLAINS,** ed. 1,500, s/n, 22″ x 33″, stone lithograph, pub NWDHG. . . . . . . . . . . . . . . . . . . . . . . . . . . . . . . . . . . . . . . . . . . . . | 80.00 | — |

## BURL WASHINGTON

His grandmother gave Burl Washington his first set of watercolors when he was only five years old, and he hasn't put them down since.

"I was told by people when I was coming up that it was hard, if not impossible, to do portraits or human figures in watercolor." But credit him now with having proved that the so-called "experts" were wrong. His portraits and figure studies project a lifelike, dimensional quality while his extraordinary command of the translucence of watercolor enables him to render landscapes, weatherbeaten buildings and the like that seem to shimmer in the sunlight.

The thrust of Washington's work is black history, and recently he has been inspired to undertake a new project — a series of 18 watercolors commemorating the Buffalo Soldier. These were black cavalry units, formed in the early 1870's and comprised chiefly of freed slaves. Their exploits on America's western frontier have been almost complete overlooked or ignored by historians and artists alike.

Washington's originals are in the private collections of notable figures such as former President Jimmy Carter, Congressman Jim Wright, and the Texas Boys' Choir.

| BURL WASHINGTON | ISSUE PRICE | CURRENT PRICE |
|---|---|---|
| ☐ **BREAK TIME**, ed. 500, s/n, 27" x 19", distr. GI | 50.00 | — |
| ☐ **LONE SOLDIER**, ed. 650, s/n, 16" x 24", distr. GI | 55.00 | — |
| ☐ **SOLDIER OF SOLITUDE**, ed. 650, s/n, 16" x 21", distr. GI | 55.00 | — |

## WALTER WEBER

| | | |
|---|---|---|
| ☐ **SNOW GEESE**, ed. 550, s/n, 17" x 22", pub RAF | 60.00 | — |

## MILTON C. WEILER

| | | |
|---|---|---|
| ☐ **VIRGIN WATER**, rel. 1980. ed. 500 s/n, size not available, pub WWI | — | 150.00 |

## JOHN WEISS

"I enjoy painting things that people can relate to," John Weiss says, "perhaps because I can relate to them myself. They're familiar things, really, but they are a part of everyday life we can understand and enjoy."

Weiss was born and reared in Akron, Ohio, the son of a draftsman with whom he credits his discipline approach to art. As a child, Weiss always had the ability to draw. He developed his innate skill through high school art classes. On a trip to Maine, he encountered an exhibition of work by Andrew Wyeth, an experience that further stimulated his own desire to be an artist. He studied art at Kent State University, but left after two years to go into the landscape business.

The attractions of art had become much a part of him by this time, however, and he returned to drawing and painting — on a casual basis at first, but with more time and intensity as four years passed. "My painting is basically self-taught," Weiss says. "I would study the work of artists I admired and learn from their methods and techniques. I studied color theory with a color wheel and by mixing paints. Then I started in drawing and painting, as experience is the best teacher."

Hand-in-glove with experience goes perseverance. His dedication paid off, and in 1977 Weiss began painting full-time, primarily in oil. Today a resident of Sharon Center, Ohio, Weiss uses his art to support worthy causes in the area, and shows his work in a number of regional galleries.

**GOLDEN RETRIEVER PUPPIES** *by John Weiss*

## JOHN WEISS

| | ISSUE PRICE | CURRENT PRICE |
|---|---|---|
| ☐ **LAB PUPPIES,** rel. 1982. ed. 1,000, s/n, 19″ x 15″, pub GW . . . . . . . . . . . . | 65.00 | — |
| ☐ **REBEL & SODA,** (matching pair), rel. 1982. ed. 1,000, s/n, 15″ x 11½″, pub GW . . . . . . . . . . . . . . . . . . . . . . . . . . . . . . . . . . . . . . . . . . . . | 45.00 | — |
| ☐ **GOLDEN RETRIEVER PUPPIES,** rel. 1983. ed. 1,000, s/n, 19½″ x 13⅛″, pub GW . . . . . . . . . . . . . . . . . . . . . . . . . . . . . . . . . . . . . . . . . . | 65.00 | — |

## DON WELLER

| | ISSUE PRICE | CURRENT PRICE |
|---|---|---|
| ☐ **OREGON,** ed. 750, s/n, 24″ x 30″, litho, pub SGC. . . . . . . . . . . . . . . . . . | 64.00 | — |
| ☐ **WASHINGTON,** ed. 750, s/n, 24″ x 30″, litho, pub SGC. . . . . . . . . . . . . . . | 64.00 | — |
| ☐ **CALIFORNIA,** ed. 750, s/n, 30″ x 25″, litho, pub SGC. . . . . . . . . . . . . . . | 64.00 | — |
| ☐ **NEW ENGLAND,** ed. 450, s/n, 20″ x 24″, litho, pub SGC. . . . . . . . . . . . . | 60.00 | — |
| ☐ **WONDER,** ed. 450, s/n, 14″ x 18″, litho, pub SGC. . . . . . . . . . . . . . . . . | 50.00 | — |
| ☐ **WANAYAMA,** ed. 450, s/n, 18″ x 11″, litho, pub SGC. . . . . . . . . . . . . . . | 50.00 | — |
| ☐ **SAN FRANCISCO,** ed. 250, s/n, 26″ x 24″, litho, pub SGC. . . . . . . . . . . . | 68.00 | 100.00 |
| ☐ **BEE,** ed. 250, s/n, 14″ x 16″, litho, pub SGC. . . . . . . . . . . . . . . . . . . . | 68.00 | — |
| ☐ **BULL RIDER,** rel. 1980. ed. 400, s/n, 16″ x 20″, litho, pub SGC. . . . . . . . . . . | 80.00 | — |
| ☐ **BARE BACK,** rel. 1980. ed. 250, s/n, 16″ x 18″, litho, pub SGC. . . . . . . . . . | 80.00 | — |
| ☐ **GRASSHOPPER,** rel. 1980. ed. 250, s/n, 14″ x 16″, litho, pub SGC. . . . . . . . . | 80.00 | — |
| ☐ **MOTH,** rel. 1980. ed. 250, s/n, 14″ x 16″, litho, pub SGC. . . . . . . . . . . . . | 80.00 | — |
| ☐ **BUTTERFLY,** rel. 1980. ed. 250, s/n, 14″ x 16″, litho, pub SGC. . . . . . . . . . | 80.00 | — |

## RONNIE WELLS

| | ISSUE PRICE | CURRENT PRICE |
|---|---|---|
| ☐ **A MOMENT IN MARCH,** ed. 1,000, s/n, 29½″ x 20½″ . . . . . . . . . . . . . . . . . | 50.00 | — |
| ☐ **COOLING SHED,** rel. 1976. ed. 850, s/n, 33″ x 25″, pub ALI . . . . . . . . . . . . | 50.00 | — |
| ☐ **RURAL SETTING,** rel. 1976. ed. 850, s/n, 33″ x 25″, pub ALI . . . . . . . . . . . | 40.00 | — |

# JAMES D. WERLINE

James D. Werline, watercolorist, is a native of Southern Ohio and spends much of his time haunting the hills and quiet hamlets of Brown County. Because Interstate highways have yet to invade the area, much of the natural beauty of a quieter time still remain.

He enrolled in college and studied fine art, receiving a Bachelor of Arts degree and then went on to post graduate art studies. He received his Masters Degree in Art with emphasis in Watercolor Painting and Ceramics from Morehead State University. In addition to his dedication to painting, he teaches art at Southern State College in Fincastle, Ohio.

| JAMES D. WERLINE | ISSUE PRICE | CURRENT PRICE |
|---|---|---|
| ☐ **COUNTRY WINTER**, ed. 750, s/n, 18½" x 24", distr. WII. | 30.00 | — |
| ☐ **COUNTRY MEMORIES**, ed. 750, s/n, 24" x 18", distr. WII. | 45.00 | — |
| ☐ **COUNTRY SUMMER**, ed. 750, s/n, 24" x 18", distr. WII. | 45.00 | — |
| ☐ **GEORGETOWN COMMERCIAL ROW**, ed. 500, s/b, 15" x 18", distr. WII. | 50.00 | — |
| ☐ **STONY HOLLOW**, ed. 500, s/n, 20" x 26", distr. WII. | 75.00 | — |

# BILL WESLING

Hundreds of research hours enter into each of Bill Wesling's designs of nature, beginning with observation and photography in the field, then to the studio where sketch after sketch is made. Only in this manner can each exquisite detail of our wild animals and birds be documented for future generations.

**RED TAIL HAWK** *by Bill Wesling*

A native of Pennsylvania, Wesling received his Art and Advertising training at the Art Institute of Pittsburg. He has studied under notable artists such as Pulitzer prize winner Vincent Nesbert and John Jellico, director of the Art Institute of Colorado.

For several years the artist served as Art Director for the State of Florida managing the production of all the printing for Industrial and Tourist development. Wesling's work has appeared in publications throughout the United States and in foreign markets. Wesling originals hang in hundreds of public and private collections worldwide.

Wesling is listed in *Personalities of the South* and *Who's Who In American Art* and is an active member of Florida Audubon Society, National Wildlife Federation, National Wild Turkey Federation, Ducks Unlimited, Bass Anglers Sportsman Society, Nature Conservancy, International Society of American Artists and many other conservation and civic associations. Thousands of dollars of prints and originals have been donated to these various organizations for fund raising.

| BILL WESLING | ISSUE PRICE | CURRENT PRICE |
|---|---|---|
| ☐ **A PAIR OF WOODIES, Plate I,** ed. 500, s/n, sealed, 16″ x 20″, pub SSWASI. . . | 50.00 | — |
| ☐ **AMERICAN BALD EAGLE,** ed. 500, s/n, sealed, 22″ x 28″, pub WAS. . . . . . . . | 40.00 | 75.00 |
| ☐ **AUTUMN IN ALL ITS GLORY - Pheasant,** ed. 500, s/n, sealed, 22″ x 24″, pub SSWASI. . . . . . . . . . . . . . . . . . . . . . . . . . . . . . . . . . . . . . | 75.00 | — |
| ☐ **BASS PRINTS** (3 prints) - Set, ed. 2,500, s/n, sealed, pub SSWASI, set. . . . . . | 20.00 | 30.00 |
| ☐ **BARRED OWL,** ed. 500, s/n, sealed, 22″ x 28″, pub SSWASI. . . . . . . . . . . . . | 50.00 | 75.00 |
| ☐ **BLUE SENTINELS, Plate IV,** ed. 500, s/n, sealed, 22″ x 28″, pub SSWASI. . . . | 100.00 | 450.00 |
| ☐ **BOB WHITE QUAIL,** ed. 500, s/n, sealed, pub SSWASI. . . . . . . . . . . . . . . . . | 40.00 | 2,500.00 |
| ☐ **CHEETAHS,** ed. 750, s/n, sealed, pub SSWASI. . . . . . . . . . . . . . . . . . . . . . | *50.00 | — |
| *Fund raising program for Jacksonville Zoological Society. | | |
| ☐ **CHIMPANZEES,** ed. 750, s/n, sealed, pub SSWASI. . . . . . . . . . . . . . . . . . . . | *50.00 | — |
| *Fund raising program for Jacksonville Zoological Society. | | |
| ☐ **DRUMMER GOES A COURTIN',** ed. 500, s/n, sealed, 21″ x 26½″, pub WAS. . | 100.00 | 125.00 |
| ☐ **EIGHT IS ENOUGH,** ed. 500, s/n, sealed, 16″ x 20″, pub SSWASI. . . . . . . . . . | 75.00 | — |
| ☐ **FOREST NURSERY,** ed. 500, s/n, sealed, 16″ x 20″, pub SSWASI. . . . . . . . . | 75.00 | — |
| ☐ **GRAY SQUIRRELS,** ed. 500, s/n, sealed, 16″ x 20″, pub WAS. . . . . . . . . . . . | 75.00 | — |
| ☐ **GREAT BLUE HERON,** ed. 500, s/n, sealed, pub SSWASI. . . . . . . . . . . . . . . | 75.00 | 350.00 |
| ☐ **GREAT HORNED OWL,** ed. 500, s/n, sealed, pub SSWASI. . . . . . . . . . . . . . . | 40.00 | 450.00 |
| ☐ **IN THE EYES OF THE BEHOLDER, Plate V,** ed. 500, s/n, sealed, 22″ x 28″, pub SSWASI. . . . . . . . . . . . . . . . . . . . . . . . . . . . . . . . . . . . . . | 75.00 | — |
| ☐ **INTERRUPTED INTERLUDE - Bob White Quail,** ed. 500, s/n, sealed, 22″ x 24″, pub SSWASI. . . . . . . . . . . . . . . . . . . . . . . . . . . . . . . . . . . . . | 75.00 | — |
| ☐ **IT'S RUDE TO POINT,** ed. 500, s/n, sealed, 20″ x 24″, pub WAS. . . . . . . . . | 100.00 | 125.00 |
| ☐ **JUST A PAIR OF HOODS,** ed. 500, s/n, sealed, 16″ x 20″, pub WAS. . . . . . . . | 50.00 | — |
| ☐ **LIKE FATHER-LIKE SON - Canada Geese,** ed. 500, s/n, sealed, 22″ x 28″, pub SSWASI. . . . . . . . . . . . . . . . . . . . . . . . . . . . . . . . . . . . . . | 100.00 | 500.00 |
| ☐ **OSPREY,** ed. 500, s/n, sealed, 22″ x 28″, pub SSWASI. . . . . . . . . . . . . . . . | 50.00 | 75.00 |
| ☐ **PAIR OF GREAT HORNED OWLS,** ed. 500, s/n, sealed, 20″ x 24″, pub SSWASI. . . . . . . . . . . . . . . . . . . . . . . . . . . . . . . . . . . . . . . . . . | 75.00 | 450.00 |
| ☐ **PARTNERS FOR LIFE, Plate IV,** ed. 500, s/n, sealed, 16″ x 20″, pub SSWASI. | 50.00 | — |
| ☐ **PINTAIL DUCKS,** ed. 500, s/n, sealed, pub SSWASI. . . . . . . . . . . . . . . . . . . | 75.00 | — |
| ☐ **RACCOON FAMILY,** ed. 500, s/n, sealed, 23″ x 29″, pub SSWASI. . . . . . . . . | 50.00 | 75.00 |
| ☐ **RED SHOULDER HAWK,** ed. 975, s/n, sealed, 22″ x 28″, pub SSWASI. . . . . . | 50.00 | 75.00 |
| ☐ **RED TAIL HAWK,** ed. 975, s/n, sealed, 22″ x 28″, pub SSWASI. . . . . . . . . . . | 50.00 | 75.00 |
| ☐ **RING NECK PHEASANTS,** ed. 500, s/n, sealed, 22″ x 28″, pub SSWASI. . . . . | 40.00 | 650.00 |
| ☐ **SIBERIAN TIGER,** ed. 750, s/n, sealed, pub SSWASI. . . . . . . . . . . . . . . . . . | *50.00 | — |
| *Fund raising program for Jacksonville Zoological Society. | | |
| ☐ **SONGBIRD SERIES,** (3 prints) - Set, ed. 2,500, s/n, sealed, pub SSWASI, set. | 30.00 | 50.00 |
| ☐ **THE LITTLEST PUDDLE JUMPER,** ed. 500, s/n, sealed, 16″ x 20″, pub WAS. . | 50.00 | — |
| ☐ **THE TRANQUIL PAIR, Plate II,** ed. 500, s/n, sealed, 16″ x 20″, pub SSWASI. . | 50.00 | — |
| ☐ **WHITE TAIL DEER AND JAYS,** ed. 500, s/n, sealed, 23″ x 29″, pub SSWASI. . | 40.00 | 300.00 |
| ☐ **WILD TURKEY,** ed. 750, s/n, sealed, pub SSWASI. . . . . . . . . . . . . . . . . . . . | *50.00 | 75.00 |
| *Additional 500 edition for National Wild Turkey Federation Fund Raising. | | |
| ☐ **WINNER AND STILL CHAMPION, Plate III,** ed. 500, s/n, sealed, 16″ x 20″, pub SSWASI. . . . . . . . . . . . . . . . . . . . . . . . . . . . . . . . . . . . . . . . | 50.00 | — |
| ☐ **WOOD DUCK DRAKE,** ed. 500, s/n, sealed, pub SSWASI. . . . . . . . . . . . . . . | 40.00 | 1,400.00 |

# E. GORDON WEST

| | ISSUE PRICE | CURRENT PRICE |
|---|---|---|
| ☐ **BARRED OWL**, ed. 1,000, s/n, 16″ x 20″, pub ALI. | 30.00 | — |
| ☐ **BUSHY TAIL**, rel. 1973. ed. 1,500, s/n, 20″ x 16″, pub ALI. | 20.00 | — |
| ☐ **CHATTER BOX**, rel. 1973. ed. 1,500, s/n, 16″ x 20″, pub ALI. | 20.00 | — |
| ☐ **CORKY**, rel. 1974. ed. 1,500, s/n, 16″ x 20″, pub ALI. | 20.00 | — |
| ☐ **CORN PATCH RASCAL**, rel. 1973. ed. 1,500, s/n, 20″ x 26″, pub ALI. | 20.00 | 30.00 |
| ☐ **PORCUPINE**, ed. 1,000, s/n, 16″ x 20″, pub ALI. | 30.00 | — |
| ☐ **SCREECH OWLS**, ed. 1,000, s/n, 20″ x 16″, pub ALI. | 30.00 | — |

# OLAF WIEGHORST

When Olaf Wieghorst landed in New York from Denmark in 1918 at the age of nineteen, he has $1.25 in his pocket and spoke no English. From this modest beginning, which saw his paintings traded for almost anything, he vaulted to prominence in the 1960's as the foremost painter of the Great American West.

Wieghorst has had a varied career as a child acrobat, member of the 5th Cavalry on the Mexican border, working cowboy, member of "New York's Finest" mounted police, and above all a brilliant creator on canvas of the life of the West. An uncompromising realist with no formal art training he has lived and worked with horses all his life.

**ARIZONA RANGE** by Olaf Wieghorst

Wieghorst paintings hang in the private collections of J. P. Morgan, Acton Griscomb, K. C. Li, Clint Murchison, Leonard Firestone, Barry Goldwater, Sam Campbell, Jack Goodman, Read Mullan, C. P. Smith, Bruce Gelker, Fred Utter and countless others.

November 15, 1974, Oklahoma City, the National Cowboy Hall of Fame joined the Eisenhower Library, the Whitney Gallery, Cody, Wyoming, The Kabilbakker American Historical Museum in Jutland in honoring the epic work of Olaf Wieghorst. He was awarded the Trustees Gold Medal.

The Wieghorst gallery of Western paintings represents a lifetime of scrupulous translation in paint-on-canvas of the very sights, sounds, and smells of the Old West. Wieghorst has said that he makes a point of leaving his paintings "unfinished" in the sense that he encourages viewers to complete them in their imaginations.

"I only hope that my canvases will in some small measure add to the historical recording of an era."

## OLAF WIEGHORST

| | ISSUE PRICE | CURRENT PRICE |
|---|---|---|
| ☐ **NAVAJO MADONNA,** rel. 1972. ed. 1,500, s/n, 20⅛" x 22", pub FGH....... | 40.00 | 6,000.00 |
| ☐ **BOYS IN THE BUNKHOUSE,** ed. 1,000, s/n, 26" x 32", distr. Armstrong's.... | 150.00 | — |
| ☐ **BUFFALO SCOUT,** ed. 1,000, s/n, 26" x 32", distr. Armstrong's........... | 100.00 | 500.00 |
| ☐ **CALIFORNIA WRANGLER,** ed. 1,000, s/n, 26" x 32", distr. Armstrong's. ... | 100.00 | 150.00 |
| ☐ **CORRALLING THE CAVVY,** ed. 1,000, s/n, 26" x 32", distr. Armstrong's..... | 100.00 | 150.00 |
| ☐ **MISSING IN THE ROUNDUP,** ed. 1,000, s/n, 26" x 32", distr. Armstrong's. .. | 100.00 | 150.00 |
| ☐ **NAVAJO PORTRAIT,** ed. 1,000, s/n, 26" x 32", distr. Armstrong's. ......... | 75.00 | 150.00 |
| ☐ **PACKING IN,** ed. 1,000, s/n, 26" x 32", distr. Armstrong's.............. | 100.00 | 150.00 |
| ☐ **APACHE RENEGADE,** rel. 1978. ed. 500, s/n, 24" x 22", pub ALL.......... | 125.00 | 250.00 |
|     ed. 50, artist proofs .......... | 125.00 | — |
| ☐ **DRIFTING,** rel. 1978. ed. 500, s/n, 24½" x 22½", pub ALL. .......... | 125.00 | 250.00 |
|     ed. 50, artist proofs .......... | 125.00 | 900.00 |
| ☐ **HORSE WRANGLERS,** rel. 1978. ed. 500, s/n, 24½" x 22", pub ALL. ....... | 4125.00 | — |
|     ed. 50, artist proofs .......... | 125.00 | — |
| ☐ **MOGOLLON TRAIL,** rel. 1978. ed. 500, s/n, sealed, 22" x 26½", pub ALL. ... | 125.00 | — |
|     ed. 50, artist proofs .......... | 125.00 | — |
| ☐ **TALKING SIGN,** rel. 1978. ed. 500, s/n, sealed, 24" x 22", pub ALL......... | 125.00 | — |
|     ed. 50, artist proofs .......... | 125.00 | — |
| ☐ **THE LOST TRAIL,** rel. 1978. ed. 500, s/n, 24" x 22", pub ALL. ........... | 125.00 | — |
|     ed. 50, artist proofs .......... | 125.00 | — |
| ☐ **ARIZONA RANGE,** rel. 1979. ed. 500, s/n, 22½" x 25½", pub ALL. ....... | 125.00 | 250.00 |
|     ed. 50, artist proofs .......... | 125.00 | — |
| ☐ **COW COUNTRY,** rel. 1979. ed. 500, s/n, 15" x 20¼", pub ALL. ......... | 125.00 | — |
|     ed. 50, artist proofs .......... | 125.00 | — |
| ☐ **INDIAN SCOUT,** rel. 1979. ed. 500, s/n, 26½" x 22", pub ALL............ | 125.00 | 1,000.00 |
|     ed. 50, artist proofs .......... | 125.00 | — |
| ☐ **INDIAN TRAIL,** rel. 1979. ed. 500, s/n, 22" x 25", pub ALL. ............. | 125.00 | — |
|     ed. 50, artist proofs .......... | 125.00 | — |
| ☐ **PLEASANT CREEK,** rel. 1979. ed. 500, s/n, 15" x 20", pub ALL.......... | 125.00 | 250.00 |
|     ed. 50, artist proofs .......... | 125.00 | 300.00 |
| ☐ **RANGE CHUCK,** rel. 1979. ed. 500, s/n, 15" x 20½", pub ALL............ | 125.00 | 250.00 |
|     ed. 50, artist proofs .......... | 125.00 | — |
| ☐ **RANGE PONIES,** rel. 1979. ed. 500, s/n, 15" x 20¼", pub ALL............ | 125.00 | 250.00 |
|     ed. 50, artist proofs .......... | 125.00 | — |
| ☐ **WATER AHEAD,** rel. 1979. ed. 500, s/n, 22" x 25", pub ALL............ | 125.00 | 500.00 |
|     ed. 50, artist proofs .......... | 125.00 | — |
| ☐ **CHIEF SIOUX HUMP,** rel. 1980. ed. 900, s/n, litho, 26½" x 22", pub ALL. ... | 150.00 | — |
| ☐ **DEAD COTTONWOOD,** rel. 1980. ed. 900, s/n, litho, 25" x 30", pub ALL...... | 150.00 | — |
| ☐ **LOS CHARROS,** rel. 1980. ed. 999, s/n, litho, 25" x 30", pub ALL. ......... | 150.00 | — |
| ☐ **NIGHTHAWK,** rel. 1980. ed. 999, s/n, litho, 25" x 29", pub ALL............ | 150.00 | — |
| ☐ **TIRED,** rel. 1980. ed. 900, s/n, litho, 24" x 31", pub ALL............... | 150.00 | — |
| ☐ **WAGON AND REMUDA,** rel. 1980. ed. 1,000, s/n, litho, 25½" x 33½", pub ALL. ........ | 150.00 | — |
| ☐ **CANYON TRAIL,** rel. 1982. ed. 900, s/n, 21" x 27¾", pub Wooden Bird...... | 150.00 | — |
|     ed. 90, artist proofs ........... | 150.00 | — |

| | ISSUE PRICE | CURRENT PRICE |
|---|---|---|
| ☐ **MOONLIGHT AND SHADOWS,** rel. 1982. ed. 900, s/n, 21" x 27¼", pub Wooden Bird. | 150.00 | — |
| ed. 90, artist proofs. | 150.00 | — |
| ☐ **NAVAHO AT CASTLE CREEK,** rel. 1982. ed. 900, s/n, 21" x 28½", pub Wooden Bird. | 150.00 | — |
| ed. 90, artist proofs. | 150.00 | — |
| ☐ **ROCKY MOUNTAIN TRAIL,** rel. 1982. ed. 900, s/n, 21" x 25½", pub Wooden Bird. | 150.00 | — |
| ed. 90, artist proofs. | 150.00 | — |
| ☐ **SALT RIVER CANYON,** rel. 1982. ed. 900, s/n, 21" x 35", pub Wooden Bird. . | 150.00 | — |
| ed. 90, artist proofs. | 150.00 | — |
| ☐ **WATERING THE REMUDA,** rel. 1982. ed. 900, s/n, 21" x 28¼", pub Wooden Bird. | 150.00 | — |
| ed. 90, artist proofs. | 150.00 | — |
| ☐ **APPALOOSA,** rel. 1983. ed. 950, s/n, 18½" x 22", pub WB. | 200.00 | — |
| ☐ **INDIAN COUNTRY,** rel. 1983. ed. 950, s/n, 19½" x 24¾", pub WB. | 200.00 | — |
| ☐ **NEZ PERCE ON APPALOOSA,** rel. 1983. ed. 950, s/n, 19½" x 23¾", pub WB. | 200.00 | — |
| ☐ **RANGE BOSS,** rel. 1983. ed. 950, s/n, 18½" x 28", pub WB. | 200.00 | — |
| ☐ **RANGE HORSES,** rel. 1983. ed. 950, s/n, 18½" x 22½", pub WB. | 200.00 | — |
| ☐ **THE NAVAJO,** rel. 1983. ed. 950, s/n, size N/A, pub WB. | 500.00 | 800.00 |
| ☐ **TRACKING THE STRAYS,** rel. 1983. ed. 950, s/n, 18½" x 22", pub WB. | 200.00 | — |

# GARY WHITE DEER

The deep rich colors and the bold sweeping motions that are typical of Gary White Deer's work seem to freeze the surge of life found in a particular moment. He is an artist who has a special gift, the ability to capture a feeling or thought, the spirit of Indian life, and share it with us.

He is particularly interested in the history of his Choctaw people. Inspired by his work with tribal history and folklore, he portrays many subjects that have previously gone unrecorded.

After attending the Institute of American Indian Arts in Santa Fe, White Deer graduated from Haskell Indian College with a degree in Fine Arts. His work has won awards at the Philbrook Annual as well as shows at the Five Civilized Tribes Museum. His paintings have an unusual depth that creates striking effects of mood and movement; an almost mystical quality. He says: "My personal feeling about traditional Indian art is that it is a pictorial expression of the Indian soul. Through my work, I hope to preserve the beauty of the Indian culture and share its spirit with the minds and ears of others."

### GARY WHITE DEER

| | ISSUE PRICE | CURRENT PRICE |
|---|---|---|
| ☐ **SEARCH FOR THE EAGLE'S WAY,** ed. 1,500, s/n, 14" x 21", pub NWDHG.... | 30.00 | 75.00 |
| ☐ **PEYOTE EAGLE SONG,** ed. 20, original lithographs, pub NWDHG | 250.00 | 1,000.00 |

# LESLIE A. WILCOX

Leslie Arthur Wilcox, English artist and author, is well known for his interest in the sea and ships, particularly the magnificent clipper style and his technical knowledge is evident in his works.

Wilcox was born in London in 1904. As a youth he delighted in making things in his workshop, especially ship's models. It is generally agreed that much of his accuracy is due to the fact that he uses models in painting the great ships. The use of models also enables him to paint ships of different periods.

For more than 30 years Wilcox has been a member of the Royal Society of Marine Artists. He has received many honors and has fulfilled many commissions. Paintings by the artist hang in prestigious collections in the United States as well as Great Britain. He has written and illustrated numerous books about ships.

By sheer merit along, Wilcox has won his place among the great artists of all time, not just of this age along; and his work will be cherished for as long as men love ships and the sea.

| **LESLIE A. WILCOX** | ISSUE PRICE | CURRENT PRICE |
|---|---|---|
| ☐ **SOVEREIGN OF THE SEAS**, rel. 1978. ed. 950, s/n, 21″ x 28″, pub MPPI . . . . . | **95.00** | **110.00** |

# JASON WILLIAMSON

Educated at Emory and Henry College and Vesper George School of Art in Boston, Jason Williamson is a nationally known watercolorist.

Working out of his studio, The Golden Fleece Gallery in Arizona, Williamson captures scenes of the southwest.

Williamson is a member of the American Watercolor Society, the National Watercolor Society, and is co-founder of the Tennessee Watercolor Society, the Southern Watercolor Society and the 22 x 30 Painters of Arizona.

He has receive many awards in prestigious competitions, some of which include the AWS, the NWS and the Rocky Mountain National.

**WATER SPRITE** *by Jason Williamson*

| JASON WILLIAMSON | ISSUE PRICE | CURRENT PRICE |
|---|---|---|
| ☐ **BURNT WATER,** ed. 500, s/n, 27″ x 22½″, pub GSP. | 100.00 | — |
| ☐ **GRIST,** ed. 1,500, s/n, 27″ x 21″, pub GSP. | 30.00 | — |
| ☐ **PATCHWORK,** ed. 1,500, s/n, 27″ x 21″, pub GSP. | 20.00 | — |
| ☐ **PEGGY'S PATCH,** ed. 1,500, s/n, 27″ x 21″, pub GSP. | 20.00 | — |
| ☐ **THE DREAMER,** ed. 500, s/n, 29½″ x 19½″, pub GSP. | 100.00 | — |
| ☐ **THE PROVIDER,** ed. 500, s/n, 22″ x 29½″, pub GSP. | 100.00 | — |
| ☐ **THUNDER GOD,** ed. 500, s/n, 29½″ x 20″, pub GSP. | 100.00 | — |
| ☐ **TUMBLEWEED,** ed. 500, s/n, 29½″ x 22½″, pub GSP. | 100.00 | — |
| ☐ **WATER SPRITE,** ed. 500, s/n, 21½″ x 29¾″, pub GSP. | 100.00 | — |
| ☐ **WATER BRIDGE,** rel. 1981. ed. 500, s/n, 29½″ x 21½″, pub GSP. | 100.00 | Sold Out |
| ☐ **MISSION VISIT,** rel. 1981. ed. 500, s/n, 22½″ x 24¾″, pub GSP. | 100.00 | — |
| ☐ **ACT II,** rel. 1982. ed. 500, s/n, 29″ x 24¾″, pub GSP. | 100.00 | — |

## JAN WILLS

| | ISSUE PRICE | CURRENT PRICE |
|---|---|---|
| ☐ **A PAIL OF CLAMS,** ed. 950, s/n, 24½″ x 16½″, pub CGAL. | 131.00 | 150.00 |
| ed. 12, Artist Accented/signed | 375.00 | 420.00 |
| ☐ **AN EIGHTY ACRE PLACE,** ed. 950, s/n, 24½″ x 16″, pub CGAL. | 131.00 | 150.00 |
| ed. 12, Artist Accented/signed | 375.00 | 420.00 |
| ☐ **BAILEY'S TRAWLER,** ed. 950, s/n, 15½″ x 23″, pub CGAL. | 131.00 | 150.00 |
| ed. 12, Artist Accented/signed | 375.00 | 420.00 |
| ☐ **CORNERS POSTS,** ed. 950, s/n, 16″ x 24½″, pub CGAL. | 131.00 | 150.00 |
| ed. 12, Artist Accented/signed | 375.00 | 420.00 |
| ☐ **END OF THE LANE,** ed. 300, s/n, 24½″ x 16½″, pub CGAL. | 300.00 | 330.00 |
| ed. 38, s/o, Artist proofs | 300.00 | 330.00 |
| ed. 12, Artist Accented/signed | 375.00 | 420.00 |
| ed. 600, General print | 75.00 | 90.00 |
| ☐ **HUNTING THE HEDGEROWS,** ed. 950, s/n, 25½″ x 17″, pub CGAL. | 131.00 | 150.00 |
| ed. 12, Artist Accented/signed | 375.00 | 420.00 |
| ☐ **LIGHT IN THE KITCHEN,** ed. 950, s/n, 25½″ x 17″, pub CGAL. | 131.00 | 150.00 |
| ed. 12, Artist Accented/signed | 375.00 | 420.00 |
| ☐ **MENDING CHORES,** ed. 950, s/n, 24½″ x 16″, pub CGAL. | 131.00 | 150.00 |
| ed. 12, Artist Accented/signed | 375.00 | 420.00 |
| ☐ **MOVING ON,** ed. 950, s/n, 17″ x 25″, pub CGAL. | 131.00 | 150.00 |
| ed. 12, Artist Accented/signed | 375.00 | 420.00 |
| ☐ **OFF THE HARD ROAD,** ed. 950, s/n, 24″ x 17½″, pub CGAL. | 150.00 | — |
| ed. 12, Artist Accented/signed | 420.00 | — |
| ☐ **ON THE GRADE,** ed. 950, s/n, 16½″ x 24″, pub CGAL. | 131.00 | 150.00 |
| ed. 12, Artist Accented/signed | 375.00 | 420.00 |
| ☐ **OUT OF NANTUCKET,** ed. 950, s/n, 17″ x 24½″, pub CGAL. | 131.00 | 150.00 |
| ed. 12, Artist Accented/signed | 375.00 | 420.00 |
| ☐ **OVERSHOT WHEEL,** ed. 950, s/n, 16″ x 24½″, pub CGAL. | 131.00 | 150.00 |
| ed. 12, Artist Accented/signed | 375.00 | 420.00 |
| ☐ **PRAIRIE FARM,** ed. 950, s/n, 15″ x 24½″, pub CGAL. | 131.00 | 150.00 |
| ed. 12, Artist Accented/signed | 375.00 | 420.00 |
| ☐ **SEPARATOR,** ed. 950, s/n, 24½″ x 16″, pub CGAL. | 131.00 | 150.00 |
| ed. 12, Artist Accented/signed | 375.00 | 420.00 |
| ☐ **SETTING IN,** ed. 300, s/n, 17″ x 25½″, pub CGAL. | 300.00 | 330.00 |
| ed. 38, s/o, Artist proof | 300.00 | 330.00 |
| ed. 12, Artist Accented/signed | 375.00 | 420.00 |
| ed. 600, General print | 75.00 | 90.00 |
| ☐ **SOUTHWEST HACIENDA,** ed. 950, s/n, 24½″ x 16½″, pub CGAL. | 131.00 | 150.00 |
| ed. 12, Artist Accented/signed | 375.00 | 420.00 |

# CHARLES BANKS WILSON

Few artists have become so identified with their state as Oklahoma's Charles Banks Wilson. Painter, printmaker, magazine and book illustrator, teacher, lecturer and historian, his work has been shown in over 200 exhibitions worldwide. The permanent collections of major museums and galleries contain his paintings and prints of Oklahoma life. These include New York's Metropolitan and Washington's Library of Congress, Corcoran Gallery and the Smithsonian.

Author and editor of a standard work on the Indian Tribes of Eastern Oklahoma, he is also the illustrator of 22 books. The Oklahoma painter is best known for his pictures of contemporary Indian life, a project which has engaged him since the early 1930's.

Honored by the U.S. State Department as well as the International Institute of Arts and Letters in Geneva, Wilson received the first Governor's Art Award and the D.S.C. from the University of Oklahoma. His career that spans five decades is chronicled in *Who's Who* and *Who's Who in American Art.* He has appeared on several national television shows such as the Today Show. He is a member of the Oklahoma Hall of Fame and is also a recipient of the Western Heritage Trustee's Award from the National Cowboy Hall of Fame.

**THE YOUNG CHIEF** *by Charles Banks Wilson*

## CHARLES BANKS WILSON

| | ISSUE PRICE | CURRENT PRICE |
|---|---|---|
| ☐ **CHEROKEE FARMER,** rel. 1938. ed. 10, 10¾" x 13¾", original lithograph, pub CBW. | 3.50 | — |
| ☐ **TRIBAL HONOR,** rel. 1939. ed. 10, 15¼" x 9¾", original lithograph, pub CBW. | 5.00 | — |
| ☐ **NEW RICH,** rel. 1939. ed. 20, 13" x 10⅝", original lithograph, pub CBW. | 5.00 | 250.00 |
| ☐ **TRIBAL BAND,** rel. 1939. ed. 10, 13¾" x 9¾", original lithograph, pub CBW. | N/A | — |
| ☐ **DANCE DRUM,** rel. 1939. ed. 10, 12¾" x 8⅛", original lithograph, pub CBW. | N/A | — |
| ☐ **OKLAHOMA,** rel. 1939. ed. 15, 15⅝" x 13½", original lithograph, pub CBW. | 5.00 | — |
| ☐ **WHITETREE,** rel. 1939. ed. 10, 12¼" x 5⅛", original lithograph, pub CBW. | N/A | — |
| ☐ **PETE BUCK,** rel. 1939. ed. 22, 12¾" x 8¾", original lithograph, pub CBW. | 10.00 | 350.00 |
| ☐ **MAN WITH A PLOW,** rel. 1939. ed. 26, 12" x 7½", original lithograph, pub CBW. | 10.00 | 500.00 |
| ☐ **AFTERNOON DANCE,** rel. 1939. ed. 16, 13⅜" x 10¼", original lithograph, pub CBW. | 10.00 | 500.00 |
| ☐ **SAVAGE,** rel. 1939. ed. 12, 9⅞" x 4⅜", original lithograph, pub CBW. | 7.50 | 750.00 |
| ☐ **STORY TELLER,** rel. 1939. ed. 23, 12⅞" x 10", original lithograph, pub CBW. | 10.00 | 500.00 |
| ☐ **KIOWA DANCER,** rel. 1940. ed. 19, 12" x 7¾", original lithograph, pub CBW. | 12.00 | 750.00 |
| ☐ **INDIAN SMOKE,** rel. 1940. ed. 10, 9⅜" x 5⅜", original lithograph, pub CBW. | 7.50 | — |
| ☐ **MEAL TIME AT A QUAPAW POW WOW,** rel. 1940. ed. 19, 13⅜" x 9⅝", original lithograph, pub CBW. | 25.00 | — |
| ☐ **PAINTING HER SON,** rel. 1940. ed. 21, 13¼" x 9½", original lithograph, pub CBW. | 5.00 | 500.00 |
| ☐ **OTOE EAGLE DANCE,** rel. 1940. ed. 14, 12⅞" x 9½", original lithograph, pub CBW. | 12.50 | 750.00 |
| ☐ **HENRY TURKEYFOOT,** rel. 1940. ed. 25, 13⅛" x 10", original lithograph, pub CBW. | 15.00 | 750.00 |
| ☐ **NAVAJO HORSES,** rel. 1941. ed. 20, 11⅝" x 9½", original lithograph, pub CBW. | 10.00 | 350.00 |
| ☐ **SENECA GREENCORN,** rel. 1941. ed. 24, 12⅞" x 10⅜", original lithograph, pub CBW. | 7.50 | 350.00 |
| ☐ **HANDGAME FEAST,** rel. 1941. ed. 30, 15¼" x 9", original lithograph, pub CBW. | 12.50 | 750.00 |
| ☐ **VISITING INDIANS,** rel. 1941. ed. 20, 13" x 9⅝", original lithograph, pub CBW. | 7.50 | 500.00 |
| ☐ **WAR DANCE FOR LITTLE INDIANS,** rel. 1941. ed. 16, 13" x 14", original lithograph, pub CBW. | 5.00 | 350.00 |
| ☐ **INDIAN PEYOTE MUSIC,** rel. 1941. ed. 35, 13" x 9⅞", original lithograph, pub CBW. | 15.00 | 1,500.00 |
| ☐ **OLD MEDICINE SINGER,** rel. 1941. ed. 34, 13¼" x 8⅞", original lithograph, pub CBW. | 15.00 | 1,500.00 |
| ☐ **QUAPAW POW WOW,** rel. 1941. ed. 26, 14" x 10", original lithograph, pub CBW. | 12.00 | 750.00 |
| ☐ **DANCERS DRESSING,** rel. 1941. ed. 23, 14" x 8⅞", original lithograph, pub CBW. | 12.00 | 500.00 |
| ☐ **THE CHIEF,** rel. 1941. ed. 20, 10¾" x 7⅜", original lithograph, pub CBW. | 12.00 | 500.00 |
| ☐ **COMANCHE PORTRAIT,** rel. 1941. ed. 200, 14½" x 10¼", original lithograph, pub CBW. | 5.00 | 150.00 |
| ☐ **OZARK SUMMER SWIMMIN' HOLE,** rel. 1942. ed. 200, 13½" x 10", original lithograph, pub CBW. | 5.00 | 2,500.00 |
| ☐ **OZARK SNOW,** rel. 1942. ed. 25, 13¾" x 9¾", original lithograph, pub CBW. | 15.00 | 2,500.00 |
| ☐ **JUDGE ROY BEAN,** rel. 1942. ed. 25, 12⅝" x 10¼", original lithograph, pub CBW. | 25.00 | 2,500.00 |
| ☐ **HANDGAME,** rel. 1942. ed. 25, 9⅞" x 7⅞", original lithograph, pub CBW. | 25.00 | — |
| ☐ **FREEDOM'S WARRIOR,** rel. 1943. ed. 50, 13¾" x 10", original lithograph, pub CBW. | 5.00 | — |
| ☐ **END MEN,** rel. 1943. ed. 25, 14⅛" x 9⅞", original lithograph, pub CBW. | 15.00 | — |
| ☐ **SHAWNEE RIBBON BETS,** rel. 1947. ed. 25, 13½" x 9⅜", original lithograph, pub CBW. | 20.00 | — |
| ☐ **HARD ROCK,** rel. 1943. ed. 25, 13¾" x 9¾", original lithograph, pub CBW. | 10.00 | — |
| ☐ **OLD INJUN,** rel. 1950. ed. 200, 11⅞" x 8⅜", original lithograph, pub CBW. | 5.00 | 100.00 |

| | ISSUE PRICE | CURRENT PRICE |
|---|---|---|
| ☐ **SMALL OPERATOR,** rel. 1952. 10¼" x 14", original lithograph, pub CBW. | 12.50 | 250.00 |
| ☐ **INDIAN COOKS,** rel. 1953. ed. 24, 9" x 5½", original lithograph, pub CBW. | 15.00 | 750.00 |
| ☐ **THE CHALLENGE,** rel. 1961. ed. 100, 13¾" x 9⅛", original lithograph, pub CBW. | 25.00 | 250.00 |
| ☐ **PRINCE ESQUIRE ROYAL BREED,** rel. 1954. ed. 200, 14⅞" x 10⅝", original lithograph, pub CBW. | 15.00 | 100.00 |
| ☐ **BOX HOLDER,** rel. 1954. ed. 43, 13" x 8¾", original lithograph, pub CBW. | 20.00 | 95.00 |
| ☐ **PIGEONS,** rel. 1954. ed. 50, 12" x 6¼", original lithograph, pub CBW. | 20.00 | 75.00 |
| ☐ **EDGE OF TOWN,** rel. 1956. ed. 50, 15" x 7¾", original lithograph, pub CBW. | 25.00 | — |
| ☐ **THE OKLAHOMAN,** rel. 1956. ed. 25, 13¾" x 9⅝", original lithograph, pub CBW. | 25.00 | — |
| ☐ **ROADSIDE WILLOWS,** rel. 1956. ed. 14, 14½" x 11⅛", original lithograph, pub CBW. | 45.00 | — |
| ☐ **INDIOS ARAPAHO MAN,** rel. 1958. ed. 20, 9⅝" x 6⅜", original lithograph, pub CBW. | 20.00 | 75.00 |
| ☐ **SMILING COWBOY,** rel. 1961. ed. 20, 12¾" x 9½", original lithograph, pub CBW. | 30.00 | 150.00 |
| ☐ **ADVENTURE,** rel. 1961. ed. 25, 12⅛" x 9¾", original lithograph, pub CBW. | 30.00 | 300.00 |
| ☐ **WILD AND FREE,** rel. 1962. ed. 50, 14⅝" x 11¼", original lithograph, pub CBW. | 35.00 | 300.00 |
| ☐ **RHYTHM OF THE WAR DANCE,** rel. 1963. ed. 55, 16⅞" x 8", original lithograph, pub CBW. | 20.00 | 100.00 |
| ☐ **TOM BENTON,** rel. 1963. ed. 45, 9⅝" x 7", original lithograph, pub CBW. | 45.00 | 350.00 |
| ☐ **MORNING ON THE CREEK,** rel. 1967. ed. 50, 14⅛" x 9⅝", original lithograph, pub CBW. | 25.00 | 250.00 |
| ☐ **ANY SUMMER AFTERNOON,** rel. 1967. ed. 45, 12¾" x 10¼", original lithograph, pub CBW. | 25.00 | 350.00 |
| ☐ **TEN LITTLE INDIANS,** (set), rel. 1957. ed. 50, 5" x 9", original lithograph, pub CBW. | 50.00 | 500.00 |
| ☐ **WHITE HATS,** rel. 1967. ed. 10, 7⅝" x 7⅝", original lithograph, pub CBW. | 12.00 | 100.00 |
| ☐ **BLACKOWL,** rel. 1967. ed. 30, 7¾" x 6", original lithograph, pub CBW. | 10.00 | 50.00 |
| ☐ **BOY FISHING,** rel. 1968. ed. 50, 15¾" x 10¼", original lithograph, pub CBW. | 30.00 | 100.00 |
| ☐ **FISHING JOE'S CREEK,** rel. 1969. ed. 45, 14½" x 10⅞", original lithograph, pub CBW. | 45.00 | 350.00 |
| ☐ **SUGAR IN THE GOURD,** rel. 1968. ed. 45, 17¼" x 12¾", original lithograph, pub CBW. | 45.00 | 500.00 |
| ☐ **BOYS IN SUMMER,** rel. 1968. ed. 45, 15⅞" x 12½", original lithograph, pub CBW. | 45.00 | 350.00 |
| ☐ **POW WOW DANCERS,** rel. 1969. ed. 45, 12" x 10", original lithograph, pub CBW. | 25.00 | 150.00 |
| ☐ **POW WOW SINGERS,** rel. 1969. ed. 45, 12" x 10", original lithograph, pub CBW. | 25.00 | 150.00 |
| ☐ **INDIAN PROFILE,** rel. 1969. ed. 75, 15⅝" x 10", original lithograph, pub CBW. | 45.00 | 500.00 |
| ☐ **NEW CHAMPION,** rel. 1972. ed. 75, 12½" x 10¾", original lithograph, pub CBW. | 45.00 | 250.00 |
| ☐ **TRAILS END,** rel. 1973. ed. 150, 10⅞" x 9¼", original lithograph, pub CBW. | 25.00 | 65.00 |
| ☐ **INDIAN SKETCHES,** rel. 1975. ed. 25, 16¼" x 10¼", original lithograph, pub CBW. | 30.00 | 100.00 |
| ☐ **WET WEATHER SPRING,** rel. 1974. ed. 50, 15¼" x 10¼", original lithograph, pub CBW. | 45.00 | 150.00 |
| ☐ **SUSANNA,** rel. 1970. ed. 10, 16" x 8", original lithograph, pub CBW. | 65.00 | 250.00 |
| ☐ **SUPERSTAR,** rel. 1975. ed. 60, 10½" x 6¾", original lithograph, pub CBW. | 35.00 | 125.00 |
| ☐ **SORGHUM TIME,** rel. 1975. ed. 75, 17" x 11", original lithograph, pub CBW. | 45.00 | 150.00 |
| ☐ **BULL RIDER,** rel. 1972. ed. 200, 15" x 10¼", original lithograph, pub CBW. | 45.00 | 65.00 |
| ☐ **YOUNG FISHERMAN,** rel. 1976. ed. 45, 8⅝" x 6¼", original lithograph, pub CBW. | 25.00 | 75.00 |
| ☐ **BOY ON THE CREEK,** rel. 1976. ed. 120, 8¾" x 6⅛", original lithograph, pub CBW. | 45.00 | 50.00 |
| ☐ **ENTER CORONADO,** rel. 1976. ed. 100, 17½" x 11", original lithograph, pub CBW. | 65.00 | 150.00 |
| ☐ **OSAGE TRADE,** rel. 1977. ed. 250, 16¼" x 13", original lithograph, pub CBW. | 65.00 | 300.00 |
| ☐ **THE RACE,** rel. 1976. ed. 200, 14½" x 10⅝", original lithograph, pub CBW. | 65.00 | 300.00 |
| ☐ **PLAINS MADONNA,** rel. 1977. ed. 300, 17" x 11½", original lithograph, pub SRS. | 50.00 | 800.00 |

| | | ISSUE PRICE | CURRENT PRICE |
|---|---|---|---|
| ☐ | **PLAINS MADONNA**, rel. 1982. ed. 1,500, s/n, 18″ x 23½″, original lithograph, pub CBW. | — | — |
| ☐ | **THE YOUNG CHIEF**, rel. 1983. ed. 1,500, 17¾″ x 23⅛″, original lithograph, pub SRS. | 150.00 | — |

## JOHN WILSON

| | | | |
|---|---|---|---|
| ☐ | **EARLY AUTUMN — WHITETAIL DEER**, rel. 1981. ed. 850, s/n, size N/A, pub WWI. | 65.00 | — |
| ☐ | **FIRST SNOW — PHEASANTS**, rel. 1981. ed. 850, s/n, size N/A, pub WWI. | 75.00 | — |
| ☐ | **CANADAS IN SPRING**, rel. 1982. ed. 850, s/n, size N/A, pub WWI. | 75.00 | — |

## NICK WILSON

Known for his artistic abilities even as a youngster, Nick Wilson began drawing seriously after high school.

In the summer of 1696, he was commissioned by the Nevada State Fish and Game Commission to do eleven pen and ink illustrations on the Chukar partridge. Soon after the release of the *Chukar Partridge Bulletin,* local advertising and commercial art studios sought his talents.

**OCELOT** *by Nick Wilson*

Currently, Wilson is an associate artist with the Arizona-Sonara Desert Museum. His works concentrate on North American mammals.

His work has been reproduced in such publications as *Arizona Highways, Southwest Art, Desert Silhouettes,* and *Persimmon Hill.*

Painting by the artist hang in personal, public, and art museum collections across the country.

### NICK WILSON

| | ISSUE PRICE | CURRENT PRICE |
|---|---|---|
| ☐ **BIGHORN SHEEP,** rel. 1977. ed. 950, s/n, 18½" x 18½", pub MPPI. | 60.00 | — |
| ☐ **ELEPHANTS AND BAOBOB TREE,** rel. 1977. ed. 260, s/n, 23" x 18", stone litho, pub MPPI. | 100.00 | — |
| ☐ **JAGUAR,** rel. 1977. ed. 950, s/n, 17" x 24", pub MPPI. | 75.00 | 125.00 |
| ☐ **KIT FOX,** rel. 1977. ed. 950, s/n, 18½" x 18½", pub MPPI. | 60.00 | — |
| ☐ **MOUNTAIN LION,** rel. 1977. ed. 950, s/n, 17" x 24", pub MPPI. | 75.00 | — |
| ☐ **OCELOT,** rel. 1977. ed. 950, s/n, 26" x 18½", pub MPPI. | 75.00 | — |
| ☐ **PRONGHORN ANTELOPE,** rel. 1977. ed. 950, s/n, 24" x 17", pub MPPI. | 60.00 | — |
| ☐ **TIMBER WOLF,** rel. 1977. ed. 950, s/n, 18½" x 18½", pub MPPI. | 60.00 | 80.00 |
| ☐ **TWILIGHT - GREAT HORNED OWL,** rel. 1978. ed. 260, s/n, 20" x 16½", pub MPPI. | 100.00 | — |
| ☐ **BEAR CUB,** rel. 1979. ed. 260, s/n, 14¾" x 13¾", pub MPPI. | 50.00 | — |
| ☐ **BOBCAT,** rel. 1979. ed. 950, s/n, 20" x 16", pub MPPI. | 60.00 | — |
| ☐ **BURROWING OWL,** rel. 1979. ed. 260, s/n, 14¾" x 13¾", stone litho, pub MPPI. | 50.00 | — |
| ☐ **COTTONTAIL RABBITS,** rel. 1979. ed. 260, s/n, 13¾" x 14¾", stone litho, pub MPPI. | 50.00 | — |
| ☐ **RACCOON,** rel. 1979. ed. 260, s/n, 13¾" x 14¾", stone litho, pub MPPI. | 50.00 | 70.00 |
| ☐ **REMNANTS,** rel. 1980. ed. 200, s/n, 21¾" x 35", pub MPPI. | 200.00 | Sold Out |
| ☐ **HOT AFTERNOON — MOUNTAIN LION,** rel. 1981. ed. 950, s/n, 18" x 24¼", pub MPPI. | 75.00 | — |
| ☐ **SNOW BUNNY — COTTONTAIL RABBIT,** rel. 1981. ed. 950, s/n, 21⅞" x 18¼", pub MPPI. | 75.00 | — |

## DALHART WINDBERG

As a young man, Dalhart Windberg toured the museums of Europe, studying the development of European art through the centuries. Thus began the evolution of Windberg's own distinctive art — contemporary American rendered in traditional European style.

The smooth brush technique made popular by Windberg in this country is his own variation of the masters' styles. Unlike familiar oil paintings, his have no trace of brush strokes.

Windberg often borrows elements from different countryside scenes and skillfully reconstructs them on canvas in a new refreshing setting. With artful use of light and shadow, his landscapes capture an isolated peaceful moment.

Windberg was awarded the 1979-80 Texas Artist of the Year Award. His book "Dalhart Windberg . . . In the Path of the Masters" has also won the "Mead Award of Excellence" symbolic of highest honors in the Mead paper national competition for the Graphic Arts.

### DALHART WINDBERG

| | | |
|---|---|---|
| ☐ **AUTUMN'S GOLD,** rel. 1973. ed. 1,567-TIME-LIMITED, s/dated, 18" x 24", pub AMFI. | 30.00 | 220.00 |
| ☐ **AUTUMN MEMORIES,** rel. 1973. ed. 1,000, s/n, 18" x 24", pub AMFI. | 40.00 | 850.00 |
| ed. 2,000, s/o | 30.00 | 650.00 |
| ☐ **BLUE SPRINGTIME,** rel. 1974. ed. 1,000, s/n, 18" x 24", pub AMFI. | 50.00 | 295.00 |
| ed. 2,000, s/o | 30.00 | 190.00 |
| ☐ **OLD HOME PLACE,** rel. 1974. ed. 750, s/n, 12" x 24", pub AMFI. | 50.00 | 275.00 |
| ed. 2,250, s/o | 30.00 | 170.00 |

**OLD FRIENDS** by Dalhart Windberg

| | ISSUE PRICE | CURRENT PRICE |
|---|---|---|
| ☐ **SECLUSION**, rel. 1974. ed. 1,000-TIME-LIMITED, s/n, 18″ x 24″, pub AMFI. . | 50.00 | 650.00 |
| ☐ **SUNDAY OUTING**, rel. 1974. ed. 1,428-TIME-LIMITED, s/dated, 12″ x 16″, pub AMFI. . | 30.00 | 225.00 |
| ☐ **AUTUMN'S WAY**, rel. 1975. ed. 1,000-TIME-LIMITED, s/n, 16″ x 16″, pub AMFI. . | 40.00 | 350.00 |
| ☐ **GOIN' COURTIN'**, rel. 1975. ed. 1,000, s/n, 12″ x 16″, pub AMFI. . | 35.00 | 200.00 |
| ed. 1,000, s/o . | 25.00 | 175.00 |
| ☐ **HILL COUNTRY**, rel. 1975. ed. 1,000, s/n, 18″ x 27″, pub AMFI. . | 50.00 | 275.00 |
| ed. 1,000, s/o . | 30.00 | 190.00 |
| ☐ **LOVE'S REFLECTIONS/GLOW OF LOVE**, rel. 1975. ed. 1,000, s/o, 12″ x 24″, pub AMFI. . | *60.00 | 1,050.00 |
| *Sold as a set | | |
| ☐ **MORNING MIST**, rel. 1975. ed. 1,000, s/n, 12″ x 16″, pub AMFI. . | 35.00 | 550.00 |
| ed. 1,000, s/o . | 25.00 | 400.00 |
| ☐ **SAFE PASSAGE**, rel. 1975. ed. 1,000, s/n, 16″ x 20″, pub AMFI. . | 50.00 | 220.00 |
| ed. 2,000, s/o . | 30.00 | 140.00 |
| ☐ **SECLUDED FALLS**, rel. 1975. ed. 1,000, s/n, 12″ x 24″, pub AMFI. . | 60.00 | 400.00 |
| ☐ **SPRING'S WAY**, rel. 1975. ed. 1,000-TIME-LIMITED, s/n, 16″ x 16″, pub AMFI. . | 50.00 | 350.00 |
| ☐ **SUMMER'S WAY**, rel. 1975. ed. 1,000-TIME-LIMITED, s/n, 16″ x 16″, pub AMFI. . | 50.00 | 135.00 |
| ed. 1,000-TIME-LIMITED, s/o . | 35.00 | 85.00 |
| ☐ **UNDISTURBED**, rel. 1975. ed. 1,000, s/n, 18″ x 27″, pub AMFI. . | 50.00 | 500.00 |
| ☐ **WINTRY PASTORAL**, rel. 1975. ed. 1,000, s/n, 18″ x 24″, pub AMFI. . | 40.00 | 225.00 |
| ed. 2,000, s/o . | 30.00 | 160.00 |
| ☐ **WINTER'S WAY**, rel. 1975. ed. 1,000-TIME-LIMITED, s/n, 16″ x 16″, pub AMFI. . | 50.00 | 100.00 |
| ed. 1,000-TIME-LIMITED, s/o . | 35.00 | 70.00 |
| ☐ **CONTENTMENT**, rel. 1976. ed. 1,000, s/n, 12″ x 38″, pub AMFI. . | 80.00 | 725.00 |
| ☐ **FLEETING SPLENDOR**, rel. 1976. ed. 1,000, s/n, 18″ x 24″, pub AMFI. . | 60.00 | 210.00 |
| ed. 1,250, s/o . | 36.00 | 175.00 |

| | ISSUE PRICE | CURRENT PRICE |
|---|---|---|
| ☐ **FOUR FACES OF AMERICA,** rel. 1976. ed. 1,000, s/n, 16″ x 16″, pub AMFI... | *200.00 | 600.00 |
| ed. 1,000, s/o | *150.00 | 425.00 |
| *This folio consists of four prints. | | |
| ☐ **LOVE'S REFLECTIONS/GLOW OF LOVE,** rel. 1976. ed. 1,000, s/n, 12″ x 24″, pub AMFI. | *100.00 | 1,500.00 |
| *Sold as a set | | |
| ☐ **NATURE'S INNER GLOW,** rel. 1976. ed. 1,000, s/n, 12″ x 24″, pub AMFI. ... | 50.00 | 300.00 |
| ed. 1,250, s/o | 35.00 | 195.00 |
| ☐ **PELICAN'S WHARF,** rel. 1976. ed. 1,000, s/n, 12″ x 16″, pub AMFI. | 40.00 | 450.00 |
| ed. 1,000, s/o | 30.00 | 225.00 |
| ☐ **TRANQUIL TIMES,** rel. 1976. ed. 1,000, s/n, 12″ x 24″, pub AMFI. | 80.00 | 650.00 |
| ☐ **EVENING RADIANCE,** rel. 1977. ed. 1,000-TIME-LIMITED, s/n, pub AMFI. ... | 65.00 | 325.00 |
| ed. 3,000-TIME-LIMITED, s/o | 45.00 | 130.00 |
| ☐ **GLADSTONE SOLITUDE,** rel. 1977. ed. 1,000, s/n, 14″ x 28″, pub AMFI. .... | 60.00 | 150.00 |
| ed. 2,000, s/o | 50.00 | 90.00 |
| ☐ **HARMONY IN THE HIGHLAND,** rel. 1977. ed. 1,000, s/n, 12″ x 24″, pub AMFI. | 55.00 | 140.00 |
| ed. 3,000, s/o | 45.00 | 75.00 |
| ☐ **LAST STAND,** rel. 1977. ed. 1,000, s/n, 20″ x 30″, pub AMFI. | 70.00 | 1,350.00 |
| ☐ **NIGHTLONG SENTINELS,** rel. 1977. ed. 1,000, s/n, 18″ x 24″, pub AMFI. ... | 60.00 | 300.00 |
| ed. 2,500, s/o | 45.00 | 170.00 |
| ☐ **REFLECTIVE ELEGANCE,** rel. 1977. ed. 1,000-TIME-LIMITED, s/n, pub AMFI. | 80.00 | 300.00 |
| ed. 3,000-TIME-LIMITED, s/o | 50.00 | 175.00 |
| ☐ **SNOW CLAD RELICS,** rel. 1977. ed. 1,000, s/n, 18″ x 24″, pub AMFI. | 60.00 | 800.00 |
| ed. 1,250, s/o | 45.00 | 700.00 |
| ☐ **IN SEASONAL ATTIRE,** rel. 1978. ed. 1,000, s/n, 18″ x 24″, pub AMFI. | 65.00 | 170.00 |
| ed. 3,100, s/o | 50.00 | 100.00 |
| ☐ **ROSEATE-SHORELINE,** rel. 1978. ed. 1,000, s/n, 12″ x 24″, pub AMFI. | 65.00 | 120.00 |
| ed. 3,100, s/o | 45.00 | 75.00 |
| ☐ **PERPETUAL HAVEN,** rel. 1978. ed. 1,000, s/n, 18″ x 24″, pub AMFI. | 90.00 | 275.00 |
| ed. 3,100, s/o | 60.00 | 170.00 |
| ☐ **SPANNING THE STREAM OF TIME,** rel. 1978. ed. 9,109-TIME-LIMITED, 18″ x 24″, pub AMFI. | 30.00 | — |
| ☐ **NOCTURNAL HARMONY,** rel. 1979. ed. 1,000, s/n, 18″ x 24″, pub WEI. | 80.00 | 275.00 |
| ed. 3,500, s/o | 60.00 | 190.00 |
| ☐ **SEASON OF RENEWAL,** rel. 1979. ed. 1,000, s/n, 18″ x 24″, pub WEI. | 80.00 | 250.00 |
| ed. 3,500, s/o | 60.00 | 150.00 |
| ☐ **SNOW CROWNED SILENCE,** rel. 1979. ed. 1,000, s/n, 18″ x 24″, pub WEI. ... | 90.00 | 450.00 |
| ed. 3,500, s/o | 70.00 | 225.00 |
| ☐ **GIFT OF LOVE,** rel. 1980. ed. 1,000, s/n, 29″ x 11½″, pub WEI. | 120.00 | 250.00 |
| ed. 3,500, s/o | 80.00 | 100.00 |
| ☐ **MOTHER EARTH, FATHER SKY,** rel. 1980. ed. 1,000, s/n, 18″ x 24″, pub WEI. | 90.00 | 200.00 |
| ed. 3,500, s/o | 70.00 | 70.00 |
| ☐ **TIME WORN SHELTER,** rel. 1980. ed. 1,000, s/n, 18″ x 24″, pub WEI. | 90.00 | 260.00 |
| ed. 3,500, s/o | 70.00 | 100.00 |
| ☐ **DELIGHTFUL RETREAT,** rel. 1981. ed. 1,000, s/n, 30″ x 20″, pub WEI. | 120.00 | 200.00 |
| ed. 3,500, s/o | 80.00 | |
| ☐ **ENDURING REFUGE,** rel. 1981. ed. 1,000, s/n, 18″ x 24″, pub WEI. | 120.00 | Sold Out |
| ed. 3,500, s/o | 80.00 | Sold Out |
| ☐ **SLUMBROUS INTERLUDE,** rel. 1981. ed. 1,000, s/n, 18″ x 24″, pub WEI. ... | 120.00 | 250.00 |
| ed. 3,500, s/o | 80.00 | 100.00 |
| ☐ **TRANQUIL CROSSING,** rel. 1982. ed. 1,000, s/n, 18″ x 24″, pub WEI. | 120.00 | Sold Out |
| ed. 3,500, s/o | 80.00 | Sold Out |
| ☐ **A REFRESHING PAUSE,** rel. 1982. ed. 1,000, s/n, 18″ x 24″, pub WEI. | 120.00 | — |
| ed. 3,500, s/o | 80.00 | — |
| ☐ **WINTER'S VELVET MANTLE,** rel. 1982. ed. 1,000, s/n, 12″ x 36″, pub WEI. .. | 150.00 | — |
| ed. 2,500, s/o | 90.00 | — |
| ☐ **OLD FRIENDS,** rel. 1983. ed. 1,000, s/n, 12″ x 16″, pub WEI. | 150.00 | — |
| ed. 2,250, s/o | 90.00 | Sold Out |
| ☐ **SPRING VELVET,** rel. 1983. ed. 1,000, s/n, 12″ x 16″, pub WEI. | 150.00 | Sold Out |
| ed. 2,000, s/o | 90.00 | — |

# JONATHAN WINTERS

Known to most people as a comedian, Jonathan Winters is expanding his talents into limited edition lithographs.

Winters studied art in college, but was sidelined by his career as a professional entertainer. After more than 30 years in the entertainment business, Winters has resumed his painting.

**THE UMBRELLA DANCERS** *by Jonathan Winters*

| JONATHAN WINTERS | ISSUE PRICE | CURRENT PRICE |
|---|---|---|
| ☐ A LIGHT IN THE ATTIC, ed. 475, s/n, 25" x 19", litho, pub DPC. . . . . . . . . . . | 150.00 | — |
| ☐ THE THOUGHTS OF A MATADOR, ed. 475, s/n, 25" x 19", litho, pub DPC. . . . . | 150.00 | — |
| ☐ THE UMBRELLA DANCERS, ed. 475, s/n, 25" x 19", litho, pub DPC. . . . . . . . . | 150.00 | — |
| ☐ THOUGHTS OF A HOLLYWOOD ACTOR WHILE DROWNING IN HIS POOL, ed. 475, s/n, 25" x 19", litho, pub DPC. . . . . . . . . . . . . . . . . . . . . . . . . . . . . . . . | 150.00 | — |

## SUE WISE

| | | |
|---|---|---|
| ☐ COURTSHIP, rel. 1978. ed. 950, s/n, 26" x 34", pub FHG. . . . . . . . . . . . . . . | 50.00 | — |
| ☐ EYRIE, rel. 1979. ed. 950, s/n, 23" x 38", pub FHG. . . . . . . . . . . . . . . . . . | 50.00 | — |

## WALTER WOLFE

| | | |
|---|---|---|
| ☐ A LITTLE SPICE — CINNAMON TEAL, rel. 1981. ed. 600, s/n, size N/A, pub WWI. . . . . . . . . . . . . . . . . . . . . . . . . . . . . . . . . . . . . . . . . . . . . . . . . . . . . | 65.00 | — |

## SCOTT WOOLEVER

|  | ISSUE PRICE | CURRENT PRICE |
|---|---|---|
| ☐ WATER'S EDGE — GEESE, ed. 750, s/n, 18⅛″ x 27¼″, pub SEL. | 120.00 | — |

# FRANK WOOTTON

No discussion of aviation art can be complete without the name of Frank Wootton entering in, for it is he who is credited in large measure with taking it into an entirely new era. A very English painter, Wootton portrays land and sky with the hand of a fine landscapist, which, in fact, he is. It just so happened that he was maturing as a painter at the same time World War II was breaking out; he volunteered for the Royal Air Force, and, as events developed, spent the years between 1939 and 1945 painting the conflict from vantage points that ranged from the front lines of France to remote airstrips carved from the jungles of Southeast Asia. His contribution comes from the fact that his aircraft fit their surroundings naturally. When airborne, they look as though they are flying. When on the ground, their surroundings are the work of a fine landscapist.

**THE BATTLE OF BRITAIN** *by Frank Wooton*

## FRANK WOOTTON

| | | |
|---|---|---|
| ☐ KNIGHTS OF THE SKY, rel. 1982. ed. 850, s/n, 34½″ x 23″, pub GW. | 165.00 | — |
| ☐ THE BATTLE OF BRITAIN, rel. 1983. ed. 850, s/n, 29½″ x 23¾″, pub GW. | 150.00 | — |

# REAGAN WORD

Characterized by an attention to detail that separates his work from that of other wildlife artists, Reagan Word has been painting and drawing since he was very young. Always a perfectionist, Word strived to make each painting better than his last. "I may not always achieve this goal, but it is my nature to never stop trying."

The ability to convey a three-dimensional look to his paintings has prompted massive public acceptance of his work.

A resident of Dallas, Texas, Word is considered one of America's favorite wildlife artists. His main desire is "to express the perfection I see in nature." Always striving for this goal, he continues to capture the authentic character of the wildlife he paints.

**WILD OATES** *by Regan Word*

| REAGAN WORD | ISSUE PRICE | CURRENT PRICE |
|---|---|---|
| ☐ **AFRICAN LION**, ed. 2,500, s/n, 26½" x 20½", litho, pub GSP. . . . . . . . . . . . . | 30.00 | — |
| ☐ **BORN FREE**, ed. 1,000, s/n, 28" x 21½", litho, pub GSP. . . . . . . . . . . . . . . . | 75.00 | — |
|     ed. 100, a/p, remarqued, pub GSP . . . . . . . . . . . . . . . . . . . . . . . . . . . . . . . | 125.00 | — |
| ☐ **DANDELION**, ed. 850, s/n, 20" x 16", litho, pub GSP. . . . . . . . . . . . . . . . . . . | 30.00 | — |
| ☐ **POLAR BEARS**, rel. 1982. ed. 1,000, s/n, 28½" x 21¼", pub GSP. . . . . . . . . | 75.00 | — |
| ☐ **RACCOON**, rel. 1982. ed. 1,000, s/n, 27" x 22", pub GSP. . . . . . . . . . . . . . . | 75.00 | — |
| ☐ **SIBERIAN TIGER**, ed. 2,500, s/n, 26¾" x 20½", litho, pub GSP. . . . . . . . . . . | 30.00 | — |
| ☐ **SNOWY OWL**, ed. 2,500, s/n, 18" x 22", litho, pub GSP. . . . . . . . . . . . . . . . . | 30.00 | — |
| ☐ **THE CHIPMUNK & THE ANT**, ed. 1,000, s/n, 23½" x 17⅞", future release, | | |
|     pub GSP. . . . . . . . . . . . . . . . . . . . . . . . . . . . . . . . . . . . . . . . . . . . . . . . . . . . . | 50.00 | — |
| ☐ **THE HIGH COUNTRY**, ed. 1,000, s/n, 27" x 22½", pub GSP. . . . . . . . . . . . . . | 75.00 | — |
| ☐ **THE WATER HOLE**, rel. 1981. ed. 1,000, s/n, 24¼" x 18¾", pub GSP. . . . . . | 55.00 | — |
| ☐ **WINTER'S SONG**, ed. 1,000, s/n, 18¾" x 23½", pub GSP. . . . . . . . . . . . . . . | 45.00 | — |
|     ed. 1,000, s/o, pub GSP . . . . . . . . . . . . . . . . . . . . . . . . . . . . . . . . . . . . . . . . | 35.00 | — |

# DAVID WRIGHT

Characterized by a warmth and flavor of our past, the paintings of David Wright have the unique ability to recreate that segment of our heritage in a permanent form.

Faithfully researched, each work tells the story of the people that shaped our lives. Preferring to work in watercolor, tempera and pencil, Wright accurately records the moments that formed the everyday life for our ancestors.

Selected for inclusion in *Who's Who in American Art,* Wright's works have appeared on various magazine covers. His background includes formal art study and a travel study program in Italy. The winner of numerous awards, his illustrations are in much demand.

His limited editions have increased in value rapidly, establishing him as one of America's leading collector print artists.

**FRIEND OR FOE** *by David Wright*

| DAVID WRIGHT | ISSUE PRICE | CURRENT PRICE |
|---|---|---|
| ☐ **A WAY OF LIFE,** ed. 1,500, s/n, 18¾″ x 25″, litho, pub GSP. | 40.00 | 80.00 |
| ☐ **BRIAR SCYTHE,** ed. 700, s/n, 24¾″ x 19″, litho, pub GSP. | 30.00 | 50.00 |
| ☐ **COLORADO CROSSING,** rel. 1981. ed. 1,000, s/n, 22½″ x 29″, pub GSP. | 75.00 | 200.00 |
| ed. 100 remarqued artist proof | 125.00 | 300.00 |
| ☐ **FRIEND OR FOE,** edition number and size not available, s/n, pub GSP. | 75.00 | 100.00 |
| ☐ **GOLDEN-MOUNTAIN MAN,** rel. 1983. s/n, edition number and size not available, pub GSP. | 75.00 | 250.00 |
| Artist proof | 125.00 | 500.00 |
| ☐ **GREEN RIVER TRAPPER,** rel. 1980. ed. 1,000, s/n, size N/A, pub GSP. | 60.00 | 200.00 |
| ed. 100 remarqued artist proofs | 100.00 | 175.00 |
| ☐ **STARTLED FLIGHT,** ed. 500, s/n, 29½″ x 19″, litho, pub GSP. | 40.00 | 125.00 |
| ed. 1,500, s/o, pub GSP | 25.00 | — |
| ☐ **SYCAMORES AT DUSK,** ed. 1,000, s/n, 23¾″ x 18½″, litho, pub GSP. | 25.00 | 450.00 |
| ed. 1,500, s/o, pub GSP | 20.00 | 175.00 |
| ☐ **THE BUCKSKINNER,** ed. 1,000, s/n, 18¼″ x 24″, pub GSP. | 75.00 | 150.00 |
| Artist proof, remarqued | 125.00 | 200.00 |

| | ISSUE PRICE | CURRENT PRICE |
|---|---|---|
| ☐ **THE CONTINENTAL SOLDIER***, ed. 1,000, s/n and dated 1976, 12″ x 15″, pub GSP. | 10.00 | — |
| ☐ **THE FRONTIERSMAN**, rel. 1979. ed. 1,500, s/n, size N/A, pub GSP. | 40.00 | — |
| ☐ **THE HUNTER**, rel. 1981. ed. 1,000, s/n, 22½″ x 29″, pub GSP. | 75.00 | 200.00 |
| ed. 100 remarqued artist proof | 125.00 | 200.00 |
| ☐ **THE MINUTEMAN***, ed. 1,000, s/n and dated 1976, 12″ x 15″, pub GSP. | 10.00 | — |
| ☐ **WAGON AT CADES COVE**, ed. 2,500, s/n, 29½″ x 23½″, litho, pub GSP. | 20.00 | — |
| ☐ **WIND RIVER MAN**, ed. 1,000, s/n, 21″ x 29″ | 50.00 | 300.00 |
| ed. 100, a/p, remarqued, pub GSP | 100.00 | 250.00 |
| ☐ **WINTER MEMORIES**, ed. 500, s/n, 23″ x 29¼″, litho, pub GSP. | 40.00 | 125.00 |

*These prints were commissioned by American Advertisers for special promotional distribution by them. In order to make this edition available to collectors 1,000 sets were signed and dated by the artist.

# BOB WYGANT

| | | |
|---|---|---|
| ☐ **FRIENDS**, ed. 750, s/n, 18½″ x 25½″, distr. Gl. | 50.00 | Sold Out |
| ☐ **SUMMERTIME**, ed. 750, s/n, 20¼″ x 26½″, distr. Gl. | 50.00 | Sold Out |

# CHARLES WYSOCKI

"My love is for patterns. My interest is in fitting them together." Thus does Charles Wysocki explain his colorful patchwork paintings of Early American life in New England, Pennsylvania and the Old South.

Born in Detroit in 1928, Wysocki enjoyed an active and happy boyhood, which seems reflected in the spirit of his work. After studying at the Art Center School of Design in Los Angeles, he began a career as a commercial artist in Detroit. He soon abandoned it, however, for the more independent life of free-lancing. Returning to California, he married and established his home there.

Chuck and Elizabeth Wysocki have a great deal in common. They share an art background and the ethic of hard work. They have succeeded in capturing that rare sense of serenity that results from being content with the simple things of life, for which Wysocki gives his wife much of the credit. Vacations spent in New England have enhanced this feeling. Browsing through the historic countryside, collecting old brass and pewter, chests and crocks, they envision an earlier, slower paced life-style in tune with their own thinking and philosophy.

"I consider myself a painter of Early American life," he says. "The people in my pictures are country folk, simple in manner and happy in their activities. If some naivete appears in my work, it is because it was planned that way and is undoubtedly a desire to live that way, myself."

## CHARLES WYSOCKI

| | ISSUE PRICE | CURRENT PRICE |
|---|---|---|
| ☐ **BUTTERNUT FARMS**, rel. 1979. ed. 1,000, s/n, 30″ x 26″, pub GW. | 75.00 | 315.00 |
| ☐ **FAIRHAVEN BY THE SEA**, rel. 1979. ed. 1,000, s/n, 31″ x 17″, pub GW. | 75.00 | 190.00 |
| ☐ **FOX RUN**, rel. 1979. ed. 1,000, s/n, 30″ x 26″, pub GW. | 75.00 | 450.00 |
| ☐ **SHALL WE?**, rel. 1979. ed. 1,000, s/n, 22″ x 26¾″, pub GW. | 75.00 | Sold Out |
| ☐ **CALEB'S BUGGY BARN**, rel. 1980. ed. 1,000, s/n, 25″ x 20″, pub GW. | 80.00 | Sold Out |
| ☐ **DERBY SQUARE**, rel. 1980. ed. 1,000, s/n, 36″ x 28¼″, pub GW. | 90.00 | 225.00 |
| ☐ **JOLLY HILL ARMS**, rel. 1980. ed. 1,000, s/n, 22½″ x 25½″, pub GW. | 75.00 | 180.00 |
| ☐ **YANKEE WINK HOLLOW**, rel. 1980. ed. 1,000, s/n, 30½″ x 24″, pub GW. | 95.00 | 165.00 |
| ☐ **CARVER COGGINGS**, rel. 1981. ed. 1,000, s/n, 30″ x 21½″, pub GW. | 145.00 | — |
| ☐ **OLDE AMERICA**, rel. 1981. ed. 1,500, s/n, 30″ x 23½″, pub GW. | 125.00 | 165.00 |
| ☐ **PAGE'S BAKE SHOPPE**, rel. 1981. ed. 1,000, s/n, 25″ x 20″, pub GW. | 115.00 | 175.00 |
| ☐ **PRAIRIE WIND FLOWERS**, rel. 1981. ed. 1,000, s/n, 25″ x 20″, pub GW. | 125.00 | 160.00 |
| ☐ **NANTUCKET**, rel. 1982. ed. 1,000, s/n, 24⅜″ x 22″, pub GW. | 145.00 | — |
| ☐ **SLEEPY TOWN WEST**, rel. 1982. ed. 1,500, s/n, 26½″ x 23¾″, pub GW. | 150.00 | — |

**APPLE BUTTER MAKERS** *by Charles Wysocki*

| | ISSUE PRICE | CURRENT PRICE |
|---|---|---|
| ☐ **SUNSET HILLS TEXAS, WILDCATTERS**, rel. 1982. ed. 1,000, s/n, 23¾″ x 24¼″, pub GW. | 125.00 | — |
| ☐ **The 1982 GREENWICH WORKSHOP, CHRISTMAS PRINT**, rel. 1982. ed. 2,000, s/n, 18″ x 18½″, pub GW. | 80.00 | 200.00 |
| ☐ **AMISH NEIGHBORS**, rel. 1983. ed. 1,000, s/n, 22½″ x 23″, pub GW. | 150.00 | — |
| ☐ **APPLE BUTTER MAKERS**, rel. 1983. ed. 1,000, s/n, 21½″ x 22″, pub GW. | 135.00 | Sold Out |
| ☐ **COUNTRY RACE**, rel. 1983. ed. 1,000, s/n, 31″ x 22⅛″, pub GW. | 150.00 | — |
| ☐ **PLUM ISLAND SOUND (Poster)**, rel. 1983. ed. 1,000, s/n, 32″ x 21″, pub GW. | 55.00 | Sold Out |
| ☐ **TEA BY THE SEA**, rel. 1983. ed. 1,000, s/n, 30″ x 17″, pub GW. | 145.00 | Sold Out |
| ☐ **1983 COMMEMORATIVE PRINT**, rel. 1983. ed. 2,000, s/n, 13¾″ x 14¼″, pub GW. | 55.00 | — |

# RICHARD EVANS YOUNGER

Richard Evans Younger started drawing at the age of ten. Having only colored chalk and brown paper from his father's butcher store for supplies, he would draw his surrounding Mid-West environment. These simple renderings of landscapes, still lifes and animals revealed the natural talent that was well beyond his years.

While a Navy diver stationed in the Pacific during World War II, he would paint portraits of his shipmates and scenes of the Orient. Younger returned from the war and attended formal art school at the Kansas City Art Institute and was later

**TOUCANS** *by Richard Younger*

chosen to receive special training under the late Remington Schuyler at Missouri Valley College. Younger returned to Missouri Valley twenty years later to receive an Honorary Doctorate of Fine Arts.

Younger's love of the outdoors and wildlife led to a decision to move his family to Florida from Missouri after being exposed, while on vacation there, to the lush Everglades and its abundance of wildlife. Younger's paintings were sought out for publication in nature magazines and private collections. He was commissioned by the late Julius Fleischmann to research and paint his collection of waterfowl. His paintings of the endangered species brought about international attention.

Richard Evans Younger's paintings of fish for "McLeans International Angling Guide" earned his the title "Audubon of Fish". His paintings were used in the recently released books "Field Guide to Fresh Water Fish of North America" and "Field Guide to Salt Water Fish of North America", published by Holt, Rinehart, Winston, Inc. Dick also collaborated with botanist, Julia Morton, on the Golden Book publication "Exotic Plants" in which he did watercolor paintings of the plants and flowers.

Younger's paintings are now displayed around the world in private, business and government collections. Younger now makes his home in Washington State but maintains a studio in his summer home in North Carolina.

## RICHARD EVANS YOUNGER

| | ISSUE PRICE | CURRENT PRICE |
|---|---|---|
| ☐ **BALD EAGLE**, rel. 1978. ed. 1,500, s/n, 22″ x 30″, pub FHG. . . . . . . . . . . . | 50.00 | Sold Out |
| ☐ **BEACH PEEPS**, rel. 1974. ed. 3,000, s/n, 30½″ x 22″, pub WHI, distr. FHG. . | 35.00 | 50.00 |
| ☐ **BENGAL TIGER**, rel. 1975. ed. 3,000, s/o, 20″ x 16″, pub FHG. . . . . . . . . . . . | 30.00 | Sold Out |

| | ISSUE PRICE | CURRENT PRICE |
|---|---|---|
| ☐ **BLUE AND GOLD MACAW**, rel. 1972. ed. 2,896, x/o, 17″ x 30″, pub WHI, distr. FHG. | 35.00 | 115.00 |
| ed. 104, s/n | 35.00 | Sold Out |
| ☐ **BOBCAT (ON GROUND)**, rel. 1972. ed. 2,000, s/o, 25¾″ x 17″, pub FHG. | 20.00 | 150.00 |
| ☐ **BOBCAT (ON ROCK)**, rel. 1976. ed. 1,200, x/n, 18″ x 24″, pub FHG. | 60.00 | — |
| ☐ **BOBWHITE**, rel. 1974. ed. 4,000, s/o, 37½″ x 17″, pub FHG. | 40.00 | Sold Out |
| ☐ **BROWN PELICAN**, rel. 1977. ed. 3,000, s/n, 15½″ x 17½″, pub WHI, released FHG. | 25.00 | 75.00 |
| ☐ **CANADA GOOSE (IN FLIGHT)**, rel. 1976. ed. 1,500, s/n, 18″ x 25″, pub FHG. | 40.00 | 75.00 |
| ☐ **CANADA GOOSE (IN WATER)**, rel. 1976. ed. 1,500, x/o, 14″ x 18″, pub FHG. | 35.00 | — |
| ☐ **CHEETAH**, rel. 1973. ed. 1,000, s/n, 40″ x 20″, pub FHG. | 75.00 | 150.00 |
| ed. 4,000, s/o | 60.00 | 100.00 |
| ☐ **CHIMPANZEE**, rel. 1975. ed. 2,000, s/o, 20″ x 16″, pub FHG. | 25.00 | 60.00 |
| ☐ **EASTERN COUGAR FAMILY**, rel. 1978. ed. 1,400, s/n, 20″ x 40″, pub FHG. | 75.00 | — |
| ed. 100, s/n were sold in conjunction with a membership in North Carolina Zoological Society embossed with the North Carolina state seal and signed by the Governor. | 1,000.00 | Sold Out |
| ☐ **EASTERN TIMBER WOLF**, rel. 1974. ed. 1,000, s/n, 33″ x 20″, pub FHG. | 65.00 | Sold Out |
| ed. 3,000, s/o | 50.00 | Sold Out |
| ☐ **ELK**, rel. 1977. ed. 1,500, s/n, 22″ x 28″, pub FHG. | 50.00 | Sold Out |
| ☐ **GOING TO ROOST (Wild Turkeys)**, rel. 1979. ed. 950, s/n, 21″ x 27″, pub TCG. | 125.00 | — |
| ☐ **GREAT HORNED OWL**, rel. 1975. ed. 2,500, s/o, 19″ x 24″, pub FHG. | 40.00 | Sold Out |
| ☐ **JAGUAR**, rel. 1974. ed. 5,000, s/o, 16″ x 20″, pub FHG. | 30.00 | Sold Out |
| ☐ **MALLARD**, rel. 1976. ed. 1,500, s/n, 18″ x 25″, pub FHG. | 40.00 | — |
| ☐ **MOCKINGBIRD**, rel. 1974. ed. 5,000, s/o, 20″ x 24″, pub FHG. | *50.00 | Sold Out |
| *A portion of the edition donated to Florida Audubon Society for 1974 membership campaign. | | |
| ☐ **MOURNING DOVE**, rel. 1975. ed. 1,500, s/o, 16″ x 20″, pub FHG. | 25.00 | 45.00 |
| ☐ **OCELOT**, rel. 1975. ed. 3,000, s/o, 16″ x 20″, pub FHG. | 30.00 | — |
| ☐ **OCTOBER MORNING**, rel. 1979. ed. 950, s/n, 20″ x 24″, pub TCG. | 150.00 | — |
| ☐ **RACCOON**, rel. 1977. ed. 1,500, s/n, 20″ x 24″, pub FHG. | 50.00 | — |
| ☐ **RING-NECKED PHEASANT**, rel. 1978. ed. 1,000, s/n, 20″ x 26″, pub FHG. | 50.00 | — |
| ☐ **RUDDY DUCK**, rel. 1977. ed. 1,500, s/n, 15½″ x 21½″, pub FHG. | 50.00 | — |
| ☐ **RUFOUS-THIGHED FALCONETS**, rel. 1973. ed. 3,500, s/o, 16″ x 20″, pub FHG. | 20.00 | 50.00 |
| ☐ **SCARLET MACAW**, rel. 1979. ed. 950, s/n, 17″ x 30″, pub TCG. | 95.00 | — |
| ☐ **SCRUB JAY**, rel. 1973. ed. 5,000, s/o, 16″ x 20″, pub FHG. | 30.00 | Sold Out |
| ☐ **SERVAL**, rel. 1974. ed. 5,000, s/o, 22″ x 22½″, pub FHG. | 35.00 | 50.00 |
| ☐ **SMALL ANIMAL FOLIO**, rel. 1974. ed. 1,000, s/n, pub WHI, released FHG. Folio consists of - Four prints - **COTTONTAIL RABBIT**, 29″ x 12¼″, **EASTERN GRAY SQUIRREL**, 13¼″ x 30″, **RACCOON**, 13¼″ x 30″, **STRIPED SKUNK**, 29″ x 12¼″. | 100.00 | Sold Out |
| ☐ **SNOW GOOSE AND BLUE GOOSE**, rel. 1976. ed. 1,500, s/n, 18″ x 25″, pub FHG. | 50.00 | — |
| ☐ **SNOWY OWL**, rel. 1977. ed. 1,500, s/n, 20″ x 30″, pub FHG. | 50.00 | — |
| ☐ **SQUEAKY (Baby Cougar)**, rel. 1979. ed. 950, s/n, 15½″ x 30″, pub FHG. | 55.00 | — |
| ☐ **THE VANISHING SPECIES SERIES**, rel. 1973. The Vanishing Species was published by Caribbean Gardens, Naples, Florida (1969) in an edition of 1,000, 21½″ x 35¼″, reproductions of each subject, of which 300 were signed and numbered. The prints remaining unsold by Caribbean Gardens were acquired by Frame House Gallery in 1972 and released in February, 1973. Complete portfolio of eight prints, signed and numbered. | 400.00 | Sold Out |
| Portfolio consists of the following: | | |
| ☐ **AMERICAN EAGLE**, s/n | 50.00 | 150.00 |
| s/o | 35.00 | 125.00 |
| ☐ **CANADA GOOSE**, s/n | 50.00 | Sold Out |
| s/o | 35.00 | Sold Out |
| ☐ **EVERGLADE KITE**, s/n | 50.00 | Sold Out |
| s/o | 35.00 | — |
| ☐ **LAYSAN DUCK**, s/n | 50.00 | Sold Out |
| s/o | 35.00 | — |
| ☐ **NENE GOOSE**, s/n | 50.00 | Sold Out |
| s/o | 35.00 | Sold Out |

|  | ISSUE PRICE | CURRENT PRICE |
|---|---|---|
| ☐ SANDHILL CRANE, s/n | 50.00 | Sold Out |
| s/o | 35.00 | — |
| ☐ TULE GOOSE, s/n | 50.00 | Sold Out |
| s/o | 35.00 | Sold Out |
| ☐ WHOOPING CRANE, s/n | 50.00 | Sold Out |
| s/o | 35.00 | Sold Out |
| ☐ WHITE-TAILED DEER, rel. 1975. ed. 2,000, s/n, 20″ x 24″, pub FHG. | 50.00 | — |

This limited edition print was released in the AMERICA'S WILDLIFE HERITAGE PORTFOLIO, which consists of six print in all, each by a different Frame House Gallery Artist.

|  | ISSUE PRICE | CURRENT PRICE |
|---|---|---|
| ☐ WILD TURKEYS, rel. 1973. ed. 500, s/n, 40″ x 30″, pub FHG. | 225.00 | — |
| ☐ WOOD DUCK, rel. 1973. ed. 1,000, s/n, 30″ x 23½″, pub FHG. | 45.00 | Sold Out |
| ed. 4,000, s/o | 45.00 | Sold Out |
| ☐ WOOD DUCK (ON FENCE), rel. 1976. ed. 1,500, s/n, 17″ x 23½″, pub FHG. | 50.00 | — |

# BILL ZANER

Bill Zaner is a naturalist with brush, paper and canvas, painting with zeal the natural landscape. He paints nature "as he sees it", but he is able to capture the essence of the landscape, demanding of himself an "experience" rather than a mere observation.

Although he painted portraits for many years, Zaner returned to landscape, which as he says, fulfills every need of the artist from variety of subject, and mood to color transitions and compositional arrangements.

His work hangs in public and private collections including the Texas Artists at Texas A & M University, and the Frost Bank collection in San Antonio.

**BILL ZANER**

|  | ISSUE PRICE | CURRENT PRICE |
|---|---|---|
| ☐ 6 A.M. GULF BEACH, rel. 1981. ed. 1,500, s/n, 30″ x 25″, pub ALI. | 60.00 | — |
| ☐ SURFWIND, rel. 1981. ed. 1,500, s/n, 27″ x 19¼″, pub ALI. | 60.00 | — |

# JESSICA ZEMSKY

Although advertising and book illustration occupied many of her early years as a professional, serious painting also became a constant factor in Jessica Zemsky's life with many of her works finding their ways into important collections in the United States and abroad. She is the author of an extensive series of slide and sound lectures on Great Art of the World and Great Cities of the World.

Zemsky also served as official artist for the New York City Opera Company.

**JESSICA ZEMSKY**

|  | ISSUE PRICE | CURRENT PRICE |
|---|---|---|
| ☐ WHEN THE THEN AND NOW HOLD HANDS, rel. 1979. ed. 950, s/n, 18″ x 24½″, pub MPPI. | 65.00 | 125.00 |
| ☐ JORDAN'S DOLLY, rel. 1979. ed. 950, s/n, 24½″ x 19½″, pub MPPI. | 65.00 | — |
| ☐ LOVE AT FIRST SIGHT, rel. 1979. ed. 950, s/n, 18″ x 27½″, pub MPPI. | 75.00 | — |
| ☐ COME SEE THE NEW COLT, rel. 1979. ed. 950, s/n, 18″ x 23½″, pub MPPI. | 65.00 | — |
| ☐ JORDAN AT THE WEDDING, rel. 1979. ed. 950, s/n, 24¾″ x 20″, pub MPPI. | 65.00 | — |
| ☐ JORDAN'S SPRING, rel. 1979. ed. 950, s/n, 25¼″ x 19¾″, pub MPPI. | 65.00 | — |

**JORDAN'S SPRING** *by Jessica Zemsky*

# WILLIAM ZIMMERMAN

| | ISSUE PRICE | CURRENT PRICE |
|---|---|---|
| ☐ **EASTERN BLUEBIRD**, rel. 1973. ed. 3,500, s/o, 16" x 20", pub FHG . . . . . . . | 20.00 | 50.00 |
| ☐ **SWALLOW-TAILED KITE**, rel. 1973. ed. 1,000, s/n, 30" x 25¼", pub FHG . . . | 50.00 | Sold Out |
|      ed. 1,500, s/o . . . . . . . . . . . . . . . . . . . . . . . . . . . . . . . . . . . . . . . . . . . . . . . . . . . | 35.00 | Sold Out |
|      ed. 1,500 signed and bearing embossed seal, benefit Columbia, S.C. Zoological Park . . . . . . . . . . . . . . . . . . . . . . . . . . . . . . . . . . . . . . . . . . . . . . . . | 50.00 | — |
| ☐ **BOBWHITE**, rel. 1977. ed. 1,750, s/n, 16" x 20", pub SG . . . . . . . . . . . . . . . | 35.00 | — |
| ☐ **MOURNING DOVE**, rel. 1977. ed. 1,000, s/n, 16" x 20", pub SG . . . . . . . . . . | 40.00 | — |
| ☐ **MALLARD**, rel. 1978. ed. 950, s/n, 20" x 24", pub SG . . . . . . . . . . . . . . . . . . | 75.00 | 125.00 |
| ☐ **WOOD DUCK**, rel. 1978. ed. 950, s/n, 20" x 24", pub SG . . . . . . . . . . . . . . . | 75.00 | 125.00 |
| ☐ **NESTING GROUND**, rel. 1979. ed. 600, s/n, 22" x 28", pub FHG . . . . . . . . . . | 55.00 | — |
|      300 Exclusive for Ducks Unlimited | | |
| ☐ **OPEN WATER**, rel. 1979. ed. 400, s/n, 24" x 30" . . . . . . . . . . . . . . . . . . . . . . | 75.00 | 175.00 |
|      ed. 100, s/n, remarqued, pub FHG . . . . . . . . . . . . . . . . . . . . . . . . . . . . . . . | 125.00 | 200.00 |
| ☐ **OUTFOXED**, rel. 1979. ed. 600, s/n, 23" x 30", pub FHG . . . . . . . . . . . . . . . | 80.00 | — |
|      ed. 100, s/n, remarqued . . . . . . . . . . . . . . . . . . . . . . . . . . . . . . . . . . . . . . . . . | 130.00 | Sold Out |
| ☐ **SOARING AMERICAN EAGLE**, rel. 1979. ed. 5,000, s/o, 24" x 20", pub FHG . . | 25.00 | — |
| ☐ **THE EAGLES**, rel. 1979. ed. 5,000, s/o, 14" x 11", pub FHG . . . . . . . . . . . . . | 20.00 | |

| | ISSUE PRICE | CURRENT PRICE |
|---|---|---|
| ☐ **WATERFOWL OF NORTH AMERICA**, rel. 1979. ed. 1,000, s/n, . . . . . . . . . . . . . single deluxe volume, 42 elephant folio size color plates, 27¾" x 22", pub FHG. Included w/book were two color plates of identical size, not bound into book, signed & numbered by the artist. | 1,000.00 | Sold Out |
| ☐ **HARVEST MOON**, rel. 1980. ed. 750, s/n, 22" x 28", pub FHG . . . . . . . . . . . . . | 50.00 | — |
| ed. 100, s/n, remarqued . . . . . . . . . . . . . . . . . . . . . . . . . . . . . . . . . . . . . . | 130.00 | Sold Out |
| ☐ **SILENT WINGS**, rel. 1980. ed. 600, s/n, 30" x 21", pub FHG . . . . . . . . . . . . . | 75.00 | — |

## SCOTT ZOELLICK

Scott Zoellick, born and raised in Wisconsin, has been painting, drawing and studying wildlife since he was a youngster. He spends many hours in the field observing, sketching and shooting photos. This kind of study has taken him to many remote wilderness areas, from Resolute Bay, 90 miles from the North Pole, where he fished for Arctic char and sketched Eskimos bringing in polar bear, seals, and musk ox, to the far corners of Maine.

Zoellick graduated from the Milwaukee Institute of Art and Design, where he studied illustration, painting and print making. Also, he spent three years studying art at the University of Wisconsin in Stevens Point, Wisconsin. This is the home of the college of Natural Resources where Zoellick was the official staff artist. Here, he worked with the taxidermists creating and painting dioramas and other wildlife exhibits. While there, he was commissioned by the Isaac Walton League to do a sixty-five foot mural on Wisconsin wildlife in the rotunda of the new multi-million dollar college of Natural Resouces central building.

In addition, Zoellick has had many one-man gallery shows. His paintings, drawings, and prints hang in the homes and offices of private and corporate collectors throughout the country. Ducks Unlimited, Safari Club International, and Trout Unlimited have requested his shows at many of their fund raising banquets, where he has donated many paintings and prints for auction. Among his many art awards and honors are the winning of the 1981 Trilene Outdoor Illustration Award in national competition and winning the 1983 Wisconsin Inland Trout Stamp Design competition.

Zoellick's editorial magazine illustrations are well known to the sportsmen of the midwest. They can be found in magazines such as *"Wisconsin Sportsman,"* *"The In-Fisherman,"* *"Field and Stream,"* *"Outdoor Life,"* *"Fins and Feathers,"* *"Fishing Fact,"* *"Ontario Out-Of-Doors,"* and *"Wisconsin Natural Resources,"* a publication of the Wisconsin D.N.R. Also hardcover books for Raintree Publishing Company and Willow Creek Press.

He is an avid hunter and fisherman, and maintains a studio and show room in downtown Milwaukee.

## SCOTT ZOELLICK

| | | |
|---|---|---|
| ☐ **WISCONSIN TROUT STAMP PRINT**, rel. 1982. ed. 500, s/n, 14" x 12", pub NC. . . . . . . . . . . . . . . . . . . . . . . . . . . . . . . . . . . . . . . . . . . . . . . . . | 125.00 | — |
| ed. 100, remarqued . . . . . . . . . . . . . . . . . . . . . . . . . . . . . . . . . . . . . . . | 125.00 | — |
| ☐ **STEELHEAD**, rel. 1982. ed. 400, s/n, 14" x 12", pub NC. . . . . . . . . . . . . . . . . | 45.00 | — |
| ☐ **TIP-UP**, rel. 1982. ed. 450, s/n, 24" x 17½", pub NC. . . . . . . . . . . . . . . . . . | 50.00 | — |
| ☐ **AUTUMN MIST-RUFFED GROUSE**, rel. 1983. ed. 600, s/n, 28¼" x 20¼", pub NC. . . . . . . . . . . . . . . . . . . . . . . . . . . . . . . . . . . . . . . . . . . . . . . . . . . . | 95.00 | — |
| ☐ **LAST RUN MUSKIE**, rel. 1983. ed. 500, s/n, 21½" x 29", pub NC. . . . . . . . . . | 60.00 | — |
| ☐ **1983 WISCONSIN TROUT STAMP PRINT**, rel. 1983. ed. 600, s/n, 14" x 12", pub NC. . . . . . . . . . . . . . . . . . . . . . . . . . . . . . . . . . . . . . . . . . . . . . . . . | 125.00 | — |
| ed. 100, remarqued . . . . . . . . . . . . . . . . . . . . . . . . . . . . . . . . . . . . . . . | 250.00 | 400.00 |

# DONALD JAMES ZOLAN

Donald James Zolan did his first oil at nine. At ten he won a scholarship to the Chicago Art Institute. He developed his lifelong admiration of Rembrandt in his teens and at fifteen did an exceptional reproduction of *"Rembrandt's Father by Rembrandt"*. At eighteen he won a scholarship to the American Academy of Art. After his schooling he worked with other artists for several years before going out on his own as a fine artist.

In the years since then, he has had exhibits and one-man shows here and overseas and earned his fame as a painter of people. He still mixes his own paints and glazes, stretches his own canvasses and works eighty-hour weeks, always seeking to immortalize in paint the people who fascinate him.

| DONALD JAMES ZOLAN | ISSUE PRICE | CURRENT PRICE |
|---|---|---|
| ☐ A GARDEN OF POEMS, ed. 950, s/n, 12" x 16", pub CGAL. | 131.00 | 150.00 |
| ed. 12, Artist accented/signed | 375.00 | 420.00 |
| ☐ CHIEFTAN ONE SPOT, ed. 950, s/n, 23½" x 18½", pub CGAL. | 131.00 | 150.00 |
| ed. 12, Artist accented/signed | 375.00 | 420.00 |
| ☐ DRUMMER BOY, ed. 950, s/n, 28" x 22", pub CGAL. | 131.00 | 150.00 |
| ed. 12, Artist accented/signed | 375.00 | 420.00 |
| ☐ FANTASY AND FAIRYTALES, ed. 950, s/n, 24½" x 18½", pub CGAL. | 131.00 | 150.00 |
| ed. 12, Artist accented/signed | 375.00 | 420.00 |
| ☐ FLOWERS FOR GRANDMA, rel. 1982. ed. 475, s/n, 16" x 20", distr. by GBSL. | 135.00 | — |
| ☐ FOG IN THE MORNING, ed. 950, s/n, 19" x 24", pub CGAL. | 131.00 | 150.00 |
| ed. 12, Artist accented/signed | 375.00 | 420.00 |
| ☐ GERONIMO, ed. 950, s/n, 11½" x 16", pub CGAL. | 131.00 | 150.00 |
| ed. 12, Artist accented/signed | 375.00 | 420.00 |
| ☐ GOING TO GRANDMA'S HOUSE, ed. 950, s/n, 23" x 19", pub CGAL. | 131.00 | 150.00 |
| ed. 12, Artist accented/signed | 375.00 | 420.00 |
| ☐ INDIAN BASKETWEAVER, ed. 950, s/n, 22½" x 18", pub CGAL. | 131.00 | 150.00 |
| ed. 12, Artist accented/signed | 375.00 | 420.00 |
| ☐ INTERMEZZO, ed. 950, s/n, 16" x 19", pub CGAL. | 131.00 | 150.00 |
| ed. 12, Artist accented/signed | 375.00 | 420.00 |
| ☐ NAVAJO MOTHER & CHILD, ed. 950, s/n, 22" x 28", pub CGAL. | 131.00 | 150.00 |
| ed. 12, Artist accented/signed | 375.00 | 420.00 |
| ☐ NEW ORLEANS FLOWERMARKET, ed. 950, s/n, 24" x 16", pub CGAL. | 150.00 | — |
| ed. 12, Artist accented, s/n | 420.00 | |
| ☐ OLD RENAISSANCE PHILOSOPHER, ed. 950, s/n, 23½" x 18", pub CGAL. | 150.00 | — |
| ed. 12, Artist accented, s/n | 420.00 | |
| ☐ PETIT FLEUR, rel. 1982. ed. 950, s/n, 16" x 20", distr. GBSL. | 95.00 | — |
| ☐ RED SHIRT SIOUX, ed. 950, s/n, 19½" x 24", pub CGAL. | 150.00 | — |
| ed. 12, Artist accented, s/n | 420.00 | |
| ☐ ROSES OF MONTMARTE, ed. 950, s/n, 16" x 20", pub CGAL. | 131.00 | 150.00 |
| ed. 12, Artist accented/signed | 375.00 | 420.00 |
| ☐ SABINES DELIGHT, rel. 1980. ed. 485, s/n, 18" x 21½", distr. GBSL. | 135.00 | 140.00 |
| ☐ SPECIAL MOMENTS, rel. 1980. ed. 485, s/n, 21" x 16", distr. GBSL. | 135.00 | — |
| ☐ SPRINGTIME, ed. 950, s/n, 16" x 20", pub CGAL. | 131.00 | 150.00 |
| ed. 12, Artist accented/signed | 375.00 | 420.00 |
| ☐ SUNDAY RECITAL, ed. 950, s/n, 18½" x 23", pub CGAL. | 131.00 | 150.00 |
| ed. 12, Artist accented/signed | 375.00 | 420.00 |
| ☐ THE MARVELOUS MAGICAL CLOWN, ed. 950, s/n, 18½" x 24", pub CGAL. | 150.00 | — |
| ed. 12, Artist accented/signed | 420.00 | |
| ☐ THE MASTERS TOUCH, ed. 950, s/n, 24" x 16", pub CGAL. | 150.00 | — |
| ed. 12, Artist accented/signed | 420.00 | |
| ☐ THE YOUNG VIRTUOSO, ed. 950, s/n, 22" x 28", pub CGAL. | 139.00 | 160.00 |
| ed. 12, Artist accented/signed | 450.00 | 500.00 |
| ☐ UMBRELLA VENDOR OF FOUNTAIN SQUARE, ed. 950, s/n, 19" x 24", pub CGAL. | 150.00 | — |
| ed. 12, Artist accented/signed | 420.00 | |
| ☐ VIOLIN CONCERTO, ed. 950, s/n, 18½" x 23½", pub CGAL. | 131.00 | 150.00 |
| ed. 12, Artist accented/signed | 375.00 | 420.00 |

| | ISSUE PRICE | CURRENT PRICE |
|---|---|---|
| ☐ **VIOLIN CRAFTSMAN**, ed. 950, s/n, 17″ x 22″, pub CGAL. | 131.00 | 150.00 |
| ed. 12, Artist accented/signed | 375.00 | 420.00 |
| ☐ **WHITE BUFFALO ARAPAHO**, ed. 950, s/n, 16″ x 20″, pub CGAL. | 131.00 | 150.00 |
| ed. 12, Artist accented/signed | 375.00 | 420.00 |

## RICHARD JUDSON ZOLAN

Richard Judson Zolan was born in Chicago, Illinois in 1931. A scholarship was granted to him while a young boy to attend Art Institute of Chicago.

The artist is said to be one of America's most dedicated artists of impressionistic realism. Those who are fortunate enough to possess a work of this artist are indeed taking an important part in America's history of art.

### RICHARD JUDSON ZOLAN

| | ISSUE PRICE | CURRENT PRICE |
|---|---|---|
| ☐ **FLOWER PETALS**, ed. 300, s/n, 16½″ x 20″, pub CGAL | 300.00 | 330.00 |
| ed. 38, s/o Artist proofs | 300.00 | 330.00 |
| ed. 12, Artist accented/signed | 375.00 | 420.00 |
| ed. 600 General print | 75.00 | 90.00 |
| ☐ **FOREVER YOUNG**, ed. 300, s/n, 16″ x 20″, pub CGAL | 300.00 | 330.00 |
| ed. 38, s/o Artist proofs | 300.00 | 330.00 |
| ed. 12, Artist accented/signed | 375.00 | 420.00 |
| ed. 600 General print | 75.00 | 90.00 |
| ☐ **THE ANTIQUE SHOP**, ed. 950, s/n, 18″ x 23″, pub CGAL | 131.00 | 150.00 |
| ed. 12, Artist accented/signed | 375.00 | 420.00 |
| ☐ **MEADOW FLOWERS**, ed. 950, s/n, 16″ x 20″, pub CGAL | 131.00 | 150.00 |
| ed. 12, Artist accented/signed | 375.00 | 420.00 |
| ☐ **CHILD READING**, ed. 950, s/n, 15½″ x 19½″, pub CGAL | 131.00 | 150.00 |
| ed. 12, Artist accented/signed | 375.00 | 420.00 |
| ☐ **LONDON BALLERINA**, ed. 950, s/n, 16″ x 20″, pub CGAL | 131.00 | 150.00 |
| ed. 12, Artist accented/signed | 375.00 | 420.00 |
| ☐ **GRANDMOTHER'S PORCH**, ed. 950, s/n, 19½″ x 16″, pub CGAL | 131.00 | 150.00 |
| ed. 12, Artist accented/signed | 375.00 | 420.00 |
| ☐ **SOUTHERN BELLE**, ed. 950, s/n, 18½″ x 23½″, pub CGAL | 131.00 | 150.00 |
| ed. 12, Artist accented/signed | 375.00 | 420.00 |
| ☐ **GARDEN PARTY**, ed. 950, s/n, 17½″ x 23½″, pub CGAL | 131.00 | 150.00 |
| ed. 12, Artist accented/signed | 375.00 | 420.00 |
| ☐ **SUMMER FAIR - HYDE PARK**, ed. 950, s/n, 18½″ x 24½″, pub CGAL | 131.00 | 150.00 |
| ed. 12, Artist accented/signed | 375.00 | 420.00 |
| ☐ **LITTLE MISS**, ed. 950, s/n, 16″ x 20″, pub CGAL | 131.00 | 150.00 |
| ed. 12, Artist accented/signed | 375.00 | 420.00 |
| ☐ **PARISIAN ARTIST**, ed. 950, s/n, 19″ x 23″, pub CGAL | 131.00 | 150.00 |
| ed. 12, Artist accented/signed | 375.00 | 420.00 |
| ☐ **THE CRITIQUE**, ed. 950, s/n, 24″ x 16″, pub CGAL | 160.00 | — |
| ed. 12, Artist accented, s/n | 500.00 | — |
| ☐ **BROWNIE**, ed. 950, s/n, 19½″ x 23½″, pub CGAL | 150.00 | — |
| ed. 12, Artist accented, s/n | 420.00 | — |
| ☐ **PIONEER MOTHER**, ed. 950, s/n, 15½″ x 19½″ | 150.00 | — |
| ed. 12, Artist accented, s/n | 420.00 | — |
| ☐ **QUEST FOR KNOWLEDGE**, General Run, 19½″ x 23½″, pub CGAL | 19.00 | — |
| ed. 12, Artist accented, s/n | 420.00 | — |
| ☐ **OPENING NIGHT**, General Run, 18½″ x 24″, pub CGAL | 19.00 | — |
| ed. 12, Artist accented, s/n | 420.00 | — |
| ☐ **JACK OF HEARTS**, General Run, 18½″ x 24″, pub CGAL | 19.00 | — |
| ed. 12, Artist accented, s/n, pub CGAL | 420.00 | — |
| ☐ **IN THE PARK**, General Run, 23″ x 17¾″, pub CGAL | 19.00 | — |
| ed. 12, Artist accented, s/n | 420.00 | — |
| ☐ **THE REHEARSAL**, ed. 495, s/n, 16″ x 20″, pub GBS. | 105.00 | — |
| ☐ **CORA'S RECITAL**, rel. 1982. ed. 450, s/n, 16″ x 20″, pub GBS. | 125.00 | — |

# THE FEDERAL DUCK STAMP

For sometime in the early years of this century there was a great concern for some type of program which would help the United States preserve their wetlands and their waterfowl. Early in the 1930's an idea was presented to the government by J. N. "Ding" Darling who at that time was Chief of the U.S. Bureau of Biological Survey, for a Federal Duck Stamp program and the proceeds to be used for this purpose. In 1934 President Roosevelt signed the Migratory Bird Hunting Stamp Act. At the time few sportsmen, conservationists and others realized how significant its passing was.

This law was probably the single most important step toward the conservation of waterfowl in United States history. A little known fact is that 90 cents of every dollar collected on the sale of Duck stamps goes toward the purchase and maintenance of waterfowl refuges throughout the United States.

The designer of the first stamp in 1934 was J. H. "Ding" Darling. Then the U.S. Bureau of Biological Survey and the U.S. Bureau of Sport Fisheries and Wildlife, Department of Interior, began a program of stamp design selection through a national contest. The artist is allowed to market prints (original or reproductive) in limited or unlimited editions in order to obtain renumerative benefit from the signal honor of his painting having been selected for the design.

The prints have been issued every year since Mr. Darling's first one in various media and varying editions. Because the second winning design was issued in an edition of only 100 it follows that there can be only 100 complete collections in existence; however, there are many other collections partially complete and naturally many who may own just one print. The companion duck stamp print, signed by the artist and framed along with the duck stamp, has become a very desirable collectible. This makes the print much more meaningful and enjoyable.

The original Duck Stamp sold for $1.00 and the print for $15.00. Over the years the price for the print remained much lower than comparable prints on the market until 1966 when that year's winner, Stanley Stearns, raised the price to $40 to equal the market. The Duck Stamp now costs $7.50.

All of the prints have risen in value since original issuance, many substantially. A few have been printed in second editions. They are available from several dealers throughout the country. A few of these are Russell A. Fink, Wild Wings, Inc., Sportsman Edge, Ltd. and Midwest Marketing. Please refer to the pages listing Publishers and Distributors for the addresses of these companies.

There are several good sources of additional information about Duck Stamps and prints. Available from the U.S. Government Printing Office, Bureau of Sport Fisheries and Wildlife, Washington, D.C. 20402 are DUCK STAMP DATA, price $10.00 Domestic, $12.50 Foreign; BUY A DUCK STAMP: THE MONEY FROM DUCK STAMP SALES BUYS MORE WETLANDS, price $5.00 Domestic, $6.25 Foreign; DUCK STAMP STORY, which is a small folder, price $1.75 Domestic, $2.20 Foreign; DUCK STAMP PRINTS, third edition, compiled by Jean Pride Stearns and revised by Russell A. Fink, available through Mr. Fink at P.O. Box 250, Lorton, Virginia 22079. It contains much information very useful and valuable to anyone interested in collecting these prints and is updated annually with an inexpensive addition.

## FEDERAL DUCK STAMP PRINTS

| YEAR | PRINT DESIGN | ARTIST | MEDIUM | EDITION | CURRENT RETAIL PRICE |
|------|--------------|--------|--------|---------|----------------------|
| ☐1934 | MALLARDS | Ding Darling | Etching | 300* | 4,400.00 |
| ☐1935 | CANVASBACKS | Frank W. Benson | Etching | 100 | 6,800.00 |
| ☐1936 | CANADA GEESE | Richard E. Bishop | Etching | unlimited | 1,000.00 |
| ☐1937 | GREATER SCAUP | J. D. Knap | Gravure | 260 | 3,000.00 |

| YEAR | PRINT DESIGN | ARTIST | MEDIUM | EDITION | CURRENT RETAIL PRICE |
|---|---|---|---|---|---|
| ☐1938 | PINTAILS | Roland Clark | Etching | 300 | 3,700.00 |
| ☐1939 | GREEN WING TEAL | Lynn Bogue Hunt | Stone Litho | 1st ed. 100* | 6,200.00 |
| | | | | 2nd ed. 100* | 5,700.00 |
| ☐1940 | BLACK DUCKS | Francis L. Jacques | Stone litho | 1st ed. 30 | 7,000.00 |
| | | | | 2nd ed. 30 | 6,000.00 |
| | | | | 3rd ed. 200 | 3,500.00 |
| ☐1941 | RUDDY DUCKS | E. R. Kalmback | Gravure (rev.) | 100-110 | 3,600.00 |
| | | | (reg.) | unknown | 1,300.00 |
| ☐1942 | WIGEON | A. Lassell Ripley | Etching | unlimited | 1,200.00 |
| | | (signed by Mrs. Ripley) | | | 600.00 |
| ☐1943 | WOOD DUCKS | Walter E. Bohl | Etching | unlimited | 1,000.00 |
| | | | | 2nd ed. | 500.00 |
| ☐1944 | WHITE FRONT GEESE | Walter A. Weber | Stone litho (rev.) | 100 | 4,500.00 |
| | | | | 2nd ed. 200 | 2,500.00 |
| | | | | 3rd ed. 90 | 850.00 |
| ☐1945 | SHOVELERS | Owen J. Gromme | Gravure | 250 | 6,200.00 |
| ☐1946 | REDHEADS | Robert W. Hines | Stone litho | 1st ed. 300* | 2,000.00 |
| | | | | 2nd ed. 380 | 150.00 |
| ☐1947 | SNOW GEESE | Jack Murray | Gravure | 300 | 2,400.00 |
| ☐1948 | BUFFLEHEADS | Maynard Reece | Stone litho | 200 | 1,200.00 |
| | | | | 150 | 1,000.00 |
| | | | | 400 | 600.00 |
| ☐1949 | GOLDEN EYES | Roger E. Preuss | Stone litho | 250 | 3,200.00 |
| ☐1950 | TRUMPETERS | Walter A. Weber | Gravure | 1st ed. 250* | 1,500.00 |
| | | | | 2nd ed. 300 | 400.00 |
| ☐1951 | GADWALL | Maynard Reece | Stone litho | 1st ed. 250 | 1,100.00 |
| | | | | 2nd ed. 400 | 750.00 |
| ☐1952 | HARLEQUINS | John H. Dick | Stone litho | 250* | 1,100.00 |
| ☐1953 | BLUE WING TEAL | Clayton B. Seagears | Stone litho | 250* | 1,100.00 |
| ☐1954 | RING NECKS | Harvey D. Sandstrom | Stone litho | 275 | 1,100.00 |
| ☐1955 | BLUE GEESE | Stanley Stears | Etching | 1st ed. 1st pr. 250 | 1,100.00 |
| | | | | 1st ed. 2nd pr. 53 | 1,100.00 |
| | | | | 2nd ed. 100 | 600.00 |
| ☐1956 | MERGANSERS | Edward J. Bierly | Etching | 1st ed. 325 | 1,000.00 |
| | | | | 2nd pr. 125 | 800.00 |
| ☐1957 | EIDERS | Jackson Miles Abbott | Stone litho | 1st ed. 253 | 1,100.00 |
| | | | | 500 | 300.00 |
| ☐1958 | CANADA GEESE | Leslie C. Kouba | Stone litho | 1st ed. 250 | 1,100.00 |
| | | | | 2nd ed. 250 | 1,000.00 |
| ☐1959 | LABRADOR DOG | Maynard Reece | Stone litho | 1st ed. 400 | 2,700.00 |
| | | | | 2nd ed. 300 | 1,600.00 |
| | | | | 3rd ed. 400 | 900.00 |
| ☐1960 | REDHEADS | John A. Ruthven | Litho | 1st ed. 400 | 1,000.00 |
| | | | | 2nd ed. 400 | 600.00 |
| ☐1961 | MALLARDS | Edward A. Morris | Etching | 275 | 1,100.00 |
| ☐1962 | PINTAILS | Edward A. Morris | Etching | 275 | 1,100.00 |
| ☐1963 | BRANT | Edward J. Bierly | Etching | 1st ed. 550 | 1,000.00 |
| | | | | 2nd pr. 125 | 800.00 |
| ☐1964 | NENE GEESE | Stanley Stearns | Stone litho | 1st ed. 300 | 1,100.00 |
| | | | | 2nd ed. 300 | 700.00 |
| ☐1965 | CANVASBACKS | Ron Jenkins | Stone litho | 1st ed. 700 | 850.00 |
| | | | | 2nd ed. 100 | 600.00 |
| | | | | 3rd ed. 250 | 200.00 |
| ☐1966 | WHISTLING SWANS | Stanley Stearns | Stone litho | 1st ed. 300 | 1,100.00 |
| | | | | 2nd ed. 300 | 500.00 |
| ☐1967 | OLD SQUAWS | Leslie C. Kouba | Etching | 275 | 900.00 |
| ☐1968 | MERGANSERS | Claremont G. Pritchard | Stone litho | 750 | 1,100.00 |
| ☐1969 | SCOTERS | Maynard Reece | Stone litho | 750 | 1,000.00 |
| ☐1970 | ROSS GEESE | Edward J. Bierly | Photo litho-rem. | 1,000 | 3,200.00 |
| | | | -reg. | total | 2,500.00 |
| | | | | 2nd ed. 2,150 | 150.00 |
| ☐1971 | CINNAMON TEAL | Maynard Reece | Stone litho | 950 | 5,000.00 |

| YEAR | PRINT DESIGN | ARTIST | MEDIUM | EDITION | CURRENT RETAIL PRICE |
|------|--------------|--------|--------|---------|----------------------|
| ☐1972 | EMPEROR GEESE | Arthur M. Cook | Photo litho-rem. | 950 | 4,000.00 |
| | | | -reg. | total | 2,800.00 |
| ☐1973 | STELLER'S EIDERS | Lee LeBlanc | Photo litho-rem. | 1,000 | 2,300.00 |
| | | | -reg. | total | 2,000.00 |
| ☐1974 | WOOD DUCKS | David A. Maass | Photo litho | unknown | 1,300.00 |
| ☐1975 | CANVASBACK DECOY | James Fisher | Photo litho-rem. | 3,150 | 1,300.00 |
| | | | -reg. | total | 1,100.00 |
| ☐1976 | CANADA GEESE | Alderson Magee | Photo litho with companion pc. | 1,000 | 2,100.00 |
| | | | without companion pc. | 3,600 | 900.00 |
| ☐1977 | ROSS' GEESE | Martin Murk | Photo litho-rem. | 5,800 | 750.00 |
| | | | -reg. | total | 600.00 |
| ☐1978 | HOODED MERGANSER | Albert Earl Gilbert | Photo litho-rem. | 5,800 | 1,100.00 |
| | | | -reg. | total | 550.00 |
| ☐1979 | GREEN WING TEAL | Ken Michaelson | Photo litho with companion pc. | | 600.00 |
| | | | -reg. | | 450.00 |
| ☐1980 | MALLARDS | Richard Plasschaert | Photo litho | N/A | 500.00 |
| ☐1981 | RUDDY DUCKS | John Wilson | Photo litho | N/A | 250.00 |
| ☐1982 | CANVAS BACK | David Maass | Photo litho | N/A | 200.00 |
| ☐1983 | PINTAILS | Phil Scholer | Photo w/medallion- -rem. | | 250.00 |
| | | | -reg. | | 135.00 |

# STATE DUCK STAMPS

Within the last few years a number of states have been issuing Duck Stamp prints also, and below you will find listed the information we have been able to assemble for this edition.

**ALABAMA**

| | | | |
|--|--|--|--|
| ☐1979 | Barbara Keel | | 250.00 |
| ☐1980 | Wayne Spradley | | 100.00 |
| ☐1981 | Jack Deloney | | |

**ARKANSAS**

| | | | |
|--|--|--|--|
| ☐1981 | Lee LeBlanc | | 125.00 |
| ☐1982 | Maynard Reece | -rem. | 250.00 |

**CALIFORNIA**

| | | | |
|--|--|--|--|
| ☐1971-1977 | Paul Johnson was artist on this entire series | | 1,500.00 |
| ☐1978 | | | 600.00 |
| ☐1979 | | | 400.00 |
| ☐1980 | | | 150.00 |

**DELAWARE**

| | | | |
|--|--|--|--|
| ☐1980 | | | 300.00 |

**FLORIDA**

| | | | |
|--|--|--|--|
| ☐1979 | Bob Binks | -reg. | 500.00 |
| | | -rem. | 650.00 |
| ☐1980 | Ernest C. Simmons | -reg. | 100.00 |
| | | -rem. | 175.00 |
| ☐1981 | Clark Sullivan | -reg. | |
| | | -rem. | |
| ☐1982 | Lee Cable | | 125.00 |

**ILLINOIS**

| | | | |
|--|--|--|--|
| ☐1975 | Robert F. Eschenfeldt | 500 | 850.00 |
| ☐1976 | R. G. Larson | 500 | 400.00 |
| ☐1977 | Richard Lynch | 500 | 300.00 |
| ☐1978 | Unknown | 500 | 200.00 |
| ☐1979 | Unknown | | 150.00 |
| ☐1980 | Unknown | | 150.00 |

| YEAR | PRINT DESIGN | ARTIST | MEDIUM | EDITION | CURRENT RETAIL PRICE |
|------|--------------|--------|--------|---------|----------------------|
| **INDIANA** | | | | | |
| ☐1976 | | Sonny Bashore | | 500 | 300.00 |
| **IOWA** | | | | | |
| ☐1972 | | Maynard Reece | -reg. | | 2,700.00 |
| | | | -rem | | 3,700.00 |
| ☐1973 | | Tom Murphy | | | 400.00 |
| ☐1974 | | Jim Landenburger | | | 750.00 |
| ☐1975 | | Mark Reece | | | 150.00 |
| ☐1976 | | Nick Klepinger | | 560 | 150.00 |
| ☐1977 | | Maynard Reece | | 900 | 500.00 |
| ☐1978 | | Nick Klepinger | | 600 | 150.00 |
| ☐1979 | | Unknown | | | 150.00 |
| ☐1980 | | Unknown | | | 150.00 |
| **MARYLAND** | | | | | |
| ☐1974 | | John W. Taylor | | 500 | 1,500.00 |
| ☐1975 | | Stanley Stearns | | 650 | 1,200.00 |
| | | | | 2nd ed. 300 | 400.00 |
| ☐1976 | | Louis Frisino | reg. | 500 | 450.00 |
| | | | rem. | 200 | — |
| ☐1977 | | Jack Schroeder | | 850 | 350.00 |
| ☐1978 | | Stanley Stearns | reg. | 1,200 | 300.00 |
| | | | rem. | 10 | 1,800.00 |
| ☐1979 | | John W. Taylor | reg. | 950 | 100.00 |
| | | | rem. | 200 | — |
| ☐1980 | | Jack Schroeder | reg. | 1,175 | 200.00 |
| | | | spec. | 480 | — |
| ☐1981 | | Arthur R. Eakin | reg. | 1,250 | — |
| | | | rem. | 125 | — |
| ☐1982 | | Roger Bucklin | | 1,575 | |
| ☐1983 | | Roger Lent | | | |
| **MASSACHUSETTS** | | | | | |
| ☐1975 | | Tom Hennessey | | | 350.00 |
| ☐1976 | | Wm. P. Tyner | | | 85.00 |
| ☐1977 | | Wm. P. Tyner | | | 850.00 |
| ☐1978 | | Wm. P. Tyner | | | 400.00 |
| ☐1979 | | | | | 350.00 |
| ☐1980 | | | | | 125.00 |
| **MICHIGAN** | | | | | |
| ☐1976 | | Oscar Warbach | | | 400.00 |
| ☐1977 | | Larry Hayden | | | 600.00 |
| ☐1978 | | | | | 125.00 |
| ☐1979 | | | | | 100.00 |
| ☐1980 | | | | | 450.00 |
| ☐1983 | | Rod Lawrence | | 950 | 125.00 |
| **MINNESOTA** | | | | | |
| ☐1977 | | David Maass | | | 700.00 |
| ☐1978 | | Les Kouba | | | 400.00 |
| ☐1979 | | Davis Maass | | | 300.00 |
| ☐1980 | | Jim Meger | | | 400.00 |
| ☐1981 | | Terry Redlin | | | 125.00 |
| ☐1982 | | Phil Scholer | | | 125.00 |
| **MISSISSIPPI** | | | | | |
| ☐1976 | | | | | 650.00 |
| ☐1977 | | | | | 450.00 |
| ☐1978 | | | | | 300.00 |
| ☐1979 | | | | | 250.00 |
| ☐1980 | | | | | 200.00 |
| **MISSOURI** | | | | | |
| ☐1979 | | Charles W. Schwartz | | | 250.00 |
| ☐1980 | | David Plank | | | 100.00 |
| ☐1981 | | Tom Crain | | | 125.00 |
| ☐1982 | | Gary Lucy | | | 120.00 |

| YEAR | PRINT DESIGN | ARTIST | MEDIUM | EDITION | CURRENT RETAIL PRICE |
|---|---|---|---|---|---|
| **MONTANA** | | | | | |
| ☐1978 | | Marlowe Urdahl | | | 150.00 |
| ☐1979 | | | | | 100.00 |
| ☐1980 | | | | | 100.00 |
| **NEVADA** | | | | | |
| ☐1979 | | Larry Hayden | | | 550.00 |
| ☐1980 | | Dick McRill | | | 100.00 |
| ☐1981 | | Phil Scholer | | | 100.00 |
| **OKLAHOMA** | | | | | |
| ☐1974 | | Pat Sawyer | | | 300.00 |
| ☐1974 | | Hoyt Smith | | | 100.00 |
| ☐1974 | | Jeffrey Frey | | | 125.00 |
| **OHIO** | | | | | |
| ☐1982 | | John Ruthven | | | 125.00 |
| **SOUTH DAKOTA** | | | | | |
| ☐1976 | | Bob Kusserow | | | 750.00 |
| ☐1977 | | | | 1st ed. 150 | |
| | | | | 2nd ed. 150 | |
| | | | | | 400.00 |
| | | | | | 250.00 |
| ☐1978 | | John G. Moisan | | 300 | 250.00 |
| ☐1979 | | | | | 350.00 |
| ☐1980 | | | | | 150.00 |
| **TENNESSEE** | | | | | |
| ☐1979 | | Dick Elliott | | | 250.00 |
| ☐1980 | | Philip Crowe | | | 150.00 |
| ☐1981 | | Bob Gillespie | | | 125.00 |
| ☐1982 | | Ken Schulz | | | 125.00 |
| **TEXAS** | | | | | |
| ☐1974 | | Jim Landenburger | | | 750.00 |
| **WISCONSIN** | | | | | |
| ☐1978 | | Owen Gromme | | | 175.00 |
| ☐1979 | | Rockne Knuth | | | 100.00 |
| ☐1980 | | Martin Murk | | | 400.00 |
| ☐1981 | | Timothy Schultz | | | 125.00 |

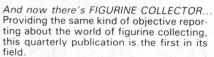

# TRADE PRICE GUIDE SERIES

■ **Collectible Cameras** — Today **astonishing prices** are being paid for many **fine antique, classic,** and even **secondhand cameras.** • *More than* **5,000 selling prices** *for all types of popular collector cameras.* • *Information on manufacturer, model name, model number, specifications, and date.* • *Advice on buying and building a collection.* • *A step-by-step guide through the hobby.* • *ILLUSTRATED.*
**1st Edition, 320 pgs., 5⅜" x 8", Paperback, ISBN: 383-X, $9.95.**

■ **Collectibles of the Third Reich** — **Phenomenal** is the only word to describe the **rising interest** in **Nazi militaria.** *Perhaps our desire never to forget the horror of Hitler is the root cause of this astonishing collectible field.* • *Included in this extensive guide are firearms, badges, insignia, flags, standards, banners, uniforms, bayonets, daggers, swords, and much more.* • *ILLUSTRATED.*
**1st Edition, 320 pgs., 5⅜" x 8", Paperback, ISBN: 422-4, $9.95.**

■ **Military Collectibles** — The **definitive guide** to war memorabilia containing military objects from all over the world, 15th century to date: armor, weapons, uniforms, bayonets, rare, and unusual objects. • *Over* **12,000 totally revised prices** *assembled from actual nationwide sales results!* • *Advice on buying and selling from auction houses, mail order, and retail dealers.* • *Museums.* • *Glossary.* • *ILLUSTRATED.*
**3rd Edition, 608 pgs., 5⅜" x 8", Paperback, ISBN: 398-8, $9.95.**

■ **Music Collectibles** — This revised and expanded edition is the **best selling reference guide** in the music memorabilia field. • *Over* **11,000 current market values.** • *Detailed descriptions, historical backgrounds, and values for all types of American and foreign made music machines from the 15th century to the present.* • *Expert advice on grading condition, restoration, and buying and selling.* • *ILLUSTRATED.*
**3rd Edition, 576 pgs., 5⅜" x 8", Paperback, ISBN: 406-2, $9.95.**

■ **Old Books & Autographs** — Fully revised and updated, this is the **most comprehensive** guide to vintage books and autographs **in print today.** • *Over* **11,000 current market values** *for children's books, the old West, novels, detective fiction, book sets, Bibles, and collectible autographs.* • *Glossary of collector terminology.* • *Biographies of the great printers and bibliophiles.* • *Care and repair of old books.* • *ILLUSTRATED.*
**5th Edition, 576 pgs., 5⅜" x 8", Paperback, ISBN: 410-0, $9.95.**

■ **Oriental Collectibles** — **Unravel the mystique** of the Orient with this fascinating guide **documented in detail.** • *Over* **10,000 current market values** *compiled from actual sales records from auctions and private sales throughout the U.S.* • *Detailed listings for Chinese, Japanese, and Asian collectors' items including pottery, Japanese weapons, jade carvings, ivories, netsuke, rugs and more.* • *ILLUSTRATED.*
**1st Edition, 512 pgs., 5⅜" x 8", Paperback, ISBN: 375-9, $9.95.**

■ **Paper Collectibles** — Tour the **fabulous** world of paper collectibles. • *Over* **27,000 prices** *for paper items of every description dating from medieval times to the present including books, posters, checks, documents, photographs, newspapers, celebrity autographs, and much more!* • *Sections on buying, selling, and caring for paper collectibles.* • *Find the bargains and enjoy the hobby like never before!* • *ILLUSTRATED.*
**3rd Edition, 608 pgs., 5⅜" x 8", Paperback, ISBN: 394-5, $9.95.**

■ **Pottery & Porcelain** — This comprehensive guide has *over* **12,000 current market values** for American pottery and porcelain of **all types** and **all periods** from the 18th to the 20th century! • *Art pottery, tableware, functional pieces, and novelties.* • *Backgrounds for all the major manufacturers including Rookwood, Roseville, Weller, Hull, and more.* • *Trademark reference guide.* • *Tips on building a collection.* • *ILLUSTRATED.*
**3rd Edition, 576 pgs., 5⅜" x 8", Paperback, ISBN: 403-8, $9.95.**

*For your convenience use the handy order form.*

# TRADE PRICE GUIDE SERIES

■ **Radio, TV, and Movie Memorabilia** — For the first time ever, *a comprehensive value guide is devoted* **exclusively** *to these collectibles.* • *Includes thousands of actual selling prices gathered from across the country on animated cels, autographs and autographed articles, books, buttons, pins, rings, costumes, design sketches, fanzines, figurines, games, magazines, posters, press kits, and much more.* • *ILLUSTRATED.*
**1st Edition, 576 pgs., 5⅜" x 8", Paperback, ISBN: 416-X, $9.95.**

■ **Records** — Find out if your **'golden oldies'** are worth a small fortune. • *More than* **32,000 current collector prices** *for all categories of old, rare, and modern records from 1953 to date!* • *Exclusive photos and biographies of nearly 200 recording stars.* • *Collecting advice on condition, care, and storage.* • *Complete discographies for Motown and Philles records* • *Inventory checklist.* • *ILLUSTRATED.*
**5th Edition, 576 pgs., 5⅜" x 8", Paperback, ISBN: 409-7, $9.95.**

■ **Royal Doulton** — Acclaimed by critics as the **definitive value guide** to the delightful world of **Royal Doulton figurines.** • *Over 5,500 current collector market values.* • *Features market trends, areas of collector interest, and the investment potential.* • *A handy "quick" reference numerical index for all HN and M model numbers.* • *Includes the Kate Greenaway series, Gilbert and Sullivan, and more.* • *ILLUSTRATED.*
**3rd Edition, 576 pgs., 5⅜" x 8", Paperback, ISBN: 407-0, $9.95.**

■ **Science Fiction and Fantasy Collectibles** — The interest has never been **greater** for a guide devoted exclusively to this fascinating field. • *Thousands of values given for "sci-fi" autographs, original art, posters, paperbacks, novels, Big Little books, games, fanzines, lobby cards, comics, toys, and much more.* • *Advice on buying and selling, care, display, and condition.* • *ILLUSTRATED.*
**1st Edition, 576 pgs., 5⅜" x 8", Paperback, ISBN: 418-6, $9.95.**

■ **Wicker** — The most detailed guide to the fabulous world of vintage wicker on the market today! • *All types of American made wicker furniture and accessories from the Victorian, Turn of the Century, and Art Deco eras.* • *Over* **600 photos** • **Detailed descriptions** *for positive identification.* • **Current collector values.** • *A guide to restoring wicker with professional repair methods.* • *ILLUSTRATED.*
**2nd Edition, 480 pgs., 5⅜" x 8", Paperback, ISBN: 380-5, $9.95.**

■ **Collectible Toys** — This is the **book** no toy collector can afford to be **without!** • *Over* **25,000 current values** *for trains, windups, autos, soldiers, boats, banks, guns, musical toys, Disneyana, comic characters, Star Trek, Star Wars, and more.* • *Major manufacturers from the Civil War to the present.* • *Valuable collecting tips.* • *Toy manufacturing in America.* • *The Evolution of toy collecting.* • *ILLUSTRATED.*
**1st Edition, 576 pgs., 5⅜" x 8", Paperback, ISBN: 384-8, $9.95.**

■ **Collector Cars** — The worldwide love affair with the automobile has **resulted in unprecedented profits.** • *Over 37,000 actual current prices for 4,100 models of U.S. and Foreign antique and classic automobiles.* • *United States production figures — 1897 to date.* • *A list of reference publications, museums, and collector clubs.* • *Advice on how to buy and sell successfully at auctions, to dealers, and individuals.* • *ILLUSTRATED.*
**5th Edition, 576 pgs., 5⅜" x 8", Paperback, ISBN: 408-9, $9.95.**

■ **Collector Handguns** — No other book on the subject **comes close** to supplying the **concise** and **comprehensive** information found here. • *More than* **5,000 current retail prices** *for handguns of all styles and all calibers.* • *Every gun identified by manufacturer, model name, action, caliber, length, date, type of stock, weight, serial number, and markings.* • *Extensive ammo section.* • *Advice on buying and selling.* • *ILLUSTRATED.*
**1st Edition, 544 pgs., 5⅜" x 8", Paperback, ISBN: 367-8, $9.95.**

*For your convenience use the handy order form.*

# TRADE PRICE GUIDE SERIES

■ **Collector Knives** — Endorsed by the American Blade Collectors. • *Over 14,000 current collector values.* • *1,250 worldwide knife manufacturers.* • *Special section for Case, Ka-Bar, and limited edition knives.* • *Valuable collector information.* • *Exclusive identification guide for pocket knife shields, knife nomenclature, and blade and knife patterns.* • *Up-to-date list of knife organizations and trade publications.* • *ILLUSTRATED.* **6th Edition, 736 pgs., 5⅜" x 8", Paperback, ISBN: 389-9, $9.95.**

■ **Collector Plates** — The plate collector's bible! Contains the **most complete listing** of all U.S. and foreign plate manufacturers and distributors **in print!** • *Over 18,000 current collectors values.* • *Includes thousands of collector plates from 1895 to date.* • *Tips on cleaning, shipping, storing, and displaying.* • *A glossary and complete list of plate publications and clubs.* • *How to buy and an investment review.* • *ILLUSTRATED.* **2nd Edition, 672 pgs., 5⅜" x 8", Paperback, ISBN: 393-7, $9.95.**

■ **Collector Prints** — The **most accurate** and **authoritative work** on limited edition prints in publication today. • *Over 14,750 listings of collector prints for more than 400 of the world's leading artists.* • *A list of galleries, agents and publishers.* • *Information on buying, selling, storing, and caring for prints.* • *A glossary of printmaking and print collecting terminology.* • *Artists' biographies.* • *ILLUSTRATED.* **5th Edition, 576 pgs., 5⅜" x 8", Paperback, ISBN: 395-3, $9.95.**

■ **Comic Books and Collectibles** — America's **indispensable guide** to comic books and related collectibles. • *Over 50,000 current values compiled from marketplace transactions.* • *Exclusive sections on Big Little Books, Comic Character Memorabilia, Original Art, and Newspaper Comic Art.* • *Advice on buying, selling, investing, and swapping.* • *An in-depth glossary.* • *ILLUSTRATED.* **7th Edition, 672 pgs., 5⅜" x 8", Paperback, ISBN: 411-9, $9.95.**

■ **Depression Glass** — The **largest price guide** devoted exclusively to depression glass in print today! *Thousands of items listed, every known pattern and manufacturer included.* • *Clear and concise line drawings illustrate each pattern.* • *Valuable collector tips on buying and selling, care and display, fakes, reproductions, and much more.* • *Complete list of collector publications, museums, and clubs.* • *ILLUSTRATED.* **1st Edition, 576 pgs., 5⅜" x 8", Paperback, ISBN: 433-X, $9.95.**

■ **Glassware** — For the first time in print, the **most comprehensive** price guide to collectible glassware **ever produced!** • *Over 60,000 current market values for all of the major types of collectible glass including Art, Carnival, Cut, Depression, and Pattern.* • *Collecting advice and informative background histories.* • *Includes museums, clubs, and manufacturers' marks.* • *ILLUSTRATED.* **1st Edition, 672 pgs., 5⅜" x 8", Paperback, ISBN: 125-X, $9.95.**

■ **Hummel Figurines & Plates** — Hummel collectors are **unanimous** in their **praise** of this **comprehensive** guide! • *Over 18,000 current market values for every known Hummel.* • *Complete guide to trademarks and variations.* • *A detailed history of Berta Hummel and the Goebel factory.* • *Tips on collecting, care, and repair.* • *Information on clubs, exhibits, publications, and contests.* • *ILLUSTRATED.* **4th Edition, 480 pgs., 5⅜" x 8", Paperback, ISBN: 390-2, $9.95.**

■ **Kitchen Collectibles** — This is the only value guide in print today devoted **exclusively** to collectible kitchenware. • *More than 28,000 current selling prices.* • *China, glassware, silver, copper, iron, and wood.* • *Historical backgrounds.* • *Comprehensive descriptions of every item, including use, manufacturer, material, style, date, and size.* • *Hints on buying, selling, care, and storage.* • *ILLUSTRATED.* **1st Edition, 544 pgs., 5⅜" x 8", Paperback, ISBN: 371-6, $9.95.**

*For your convenience use the handy order form.*

# MINI PRICE GUIDE SERIES

■ **Military Collectibles** — The **indispensable carry along guide** to the fascinating and historical world of **war souvenirs.** • *Over* **4,000 current prices** *for a wide assortment of military objects from all over the world* — *19th century to World War II.* • **Positive identification** *with dates, markings, country of origin, army, and thorough descriptions.* • **Valuable collecting tips** — *How to build a collection, grading condition, displaying your collection, and glossary of collectors' terms.* • *ILLUSTRATED.*
**1st Edition, 240 pgs., 4" x 5½", Paperback, ISBN: 378-3, $2.95.**

■ **Paperbacks & Magazines** — Your **old paperbacks and magazines** could be worth a **fortune** today! • *Over* **10,000 values** *are given on paperbacks and magazines dating from the 1800's through the 1980's compiled from actual sales between dealers and collectors.* • *Learn what makes them valuable and why!* • *ILLUSTRATED.*
**2nd Edition, 288 pgs., 4" x 5½", Paperback, ISBN: 405-4, $3.95.**

■ **Pocket Knives** — A **complete price listing** of all **Case** and **Kabar pocket knives** plus **thousands of current values** *for all popular collector knives.* • **Complete identification** *of every knife by manufacturer, pattern, stamping, year of manufacture, length, and handle type.* • **Helpful advice** *on buying, selling, and caring for your knife collection.* • *Pocket knife terminology, grading condition, blade patterns, knife collector organizations, counterfeit specimens, and much more.* • *ILLUSTRATED.*
**2nd Edition, 288 pgs., 4" x 5½", Paperback, ISBN: 443-7, $3.95.**

■ **Scouting Collectibles** — **Attention, Scouts!** Here's your **"field guide"** to the profitable hobby of scouting memorabilia. • **Price listings for thousands of scouting items** *in all categories.* • *You'll learn about the fascinating history of scouting and the accessories that were in use over the past years including tools, gadgets, badges, and medals.* • *ILLUSTRATED.*
**2nd Edition, 288 pgs., 4" x 5½", Paperback, ISBN: 397-X, $3.95.**

■ **Sports Collectibles** — **Whatever** your sport, you will **find it here! All the popular collectibles** of baseball, football, basketball, hockey, boxing, hunting, fishing, horse racing, and other top sports. • *Over* **12,000 current prices** *that collectors are actually paying for a host of sports memorabilia.* • **Old and modern sports collectibles** *from the 17th to the 20th century.* • **The inside facts** *on buying from dealers and selling your sports collectibles for maximum prices!* • *ILLUSTRATED.*
**1st Edition, 240 pgs., 4" x 5½", Paperback, ISBN: 379-1, $2.95.**

■ **Star Trek / Star Wars Collectibles** — The **phenomenal popularity** of these space age collectibles continues to skyrocket! • *Over* **6,000 current values** *for every category of Star Trek and Star Wars collector's items.* • **Fascinating information** *on the history of the television show and the making of the movies. Tips on building and caring for a collection to buying and selling.* • **Special sections** *on the conventions with a complete calendar of events.*
**2nd Edition, 288 pgs., 4" x 5½", Paperback, ISBN: 437-2, $3.95.**

■ **Toys** — Whether eight to eighty, you are **never too old** to seriously enjoy toy collections. • *Over* **8,000 current values** *for every category of toys* **from animal-drawn vehicles to rocketships.** • **A toy encyclopedia** — *histories of the manufacturers, valuable collector information on buying, selling, and grading condition.* • *ILLUSTRATED.*
**2nd Edition, 288 pgs., 4" x 5½", Paperback, ISBN: 436-4, $3.95.**

*For your convenience use the handy order form.*

# MINI PRICE GUIDE SERIES

■ **Collectible Records** — One of the **most enjoyable and profitable hobbies** today. • *Over* **11,000 current market prices** for *Rock and Country recordings. A chronological listing of discs from 1953 to date.* • *Listed by their original label and issue number.* • **Collecting tips** — *How to begin a collection, buying, selling, and grading the condition of records and jackets.* • *A handy guide to "Golden Oldie" shops, conventions, flea markets, and garage sales.* • *ILLUSTRATED.*
**1st Edition, 240 pgs., 4" x 5½", Paperback, ISBN: 400-3, $2.95.**

■ **Collector Guns** — This **handy pocket guide** contains **over 9,000 dealer prices** *compiled from nationwide sales records for handguns, rifles, and shotguns. Covers American and foreign manufacturers.* • **Complete data** *on model names, barrel lengths, calibers, and sight types.* • *Information on the history of firearms, biographies of famous gunmakers, and collecting techniques!* • *ILLUSTRATED.*
**1st Edition, 240 pgs., 4" x 5½", Paperback, ISBN: 396-1, $2.95.**

■ **Comic Books** — Join the **thousands** who have discovered the fascinating world of comic collecting, one of the nation's fastest-growing hobbies. • **Current market values for over 5,000 old and new comics.** • **Learn how** to start a comic collection and watch it grow into a **profitable investment.** • Tips on buying, selling, and swapping your comics. *Start a comic collection with purchases from the newsstand.* • *ILLUSTRATED.*
**2nd Edition, 288 pgs., 4" x 5½", Paperback, ISBN: 382-1, $3.95.**

■ **Dolls** — Reap pleasure and profit! • **Over 3,000 current market prices** *for dolls of all types and all manufacturers.* • **Positive identification** *by maker, name of doll, markings, hair color, eye color, type of eye, date of manufacture, and size.* • **Valuable collector information** *on buying and selling, fakes, repairs, and how to care for your dolls.* • **Extensive glossary** *of doll making and collecting terms.* • *ILLUSTRATED.*
**2nd Edition, 288 pgs., 4" x 5½", Paperback, ISBN: 434-8, $3.95.**

■ **Football Cards** — Call the right signals every time with the most **authoritative** guide to football cards **in print today!** This revised edition features all the latest cards and price changes. • *Over* **50,000 current market values** *for collectible football cards.* • **Valuable collector information** — *tips on trading, buying and selling, and how to grade condition to determine the value of your collection.* • **Exclusive checklist system.** • *ILLUSTRATED.*
**3rd Edition, 288 pgs., 4" x 5½", Paperback, ISBN: 388-0, $2.95.**

■ **Glassware** — The handiest guide to collectible glassware on the market today! *Contains thousands of values for the five major types of collectible glass — art, carnival, cut, depression, and pattern.* • *Includes history of each period, manufacturer's marks, pattern and motif identification guide, extensive glossary, and much more.* • *Plus valuable collector advice on buying, selling, care, display, collector publications, clubs, organizations, and museums.* • *ILLUSTRATED.*
**1st Edition, 288 pgs., 4" x 5½", Paperback, ISBN: 432-1, $3.95.**

■ **Hummels** — **Handy pocket guide** with *over* **2,000 current collector prices** *for the most common and most popular Hummels. All the latest releases are included.* • *A Hummel encyclopedia — from Berta Hummel's beginnings to the growth of the Goebel firm, plus a collector's glossary.* • **Valuable collector information** *on buying, selling, storage, and display.* • *Pictures for each listing from 1923 to date.* • *ILLUSTRATED.*
**2nd Edition, 288 pgs., 4" x 5½", Paperback, ISBN: 435-6, $3.95.**

*For your convenience use the handy order form.*

# NUMISMATIC SERIES

■ **1984 Blackbook Price Guide of United States Coins** — A coin collector's guide to current market values for all U.S. coins from 1616 to date — over **16,500 prices.** THE OFFICIAL BLACKBOOK OF COINS has gained the reputation as the most reliable, up-to-date guide to U.S. Coin values. This new edition features, an exclusive gold and silver identification guide. Learn how to test, weigh and calculate the value of any item made of gold or silver. Proven professional techniques revealed for the first time. Detecting altered coins section. Take advantage of the current "BUYERS' MARKET" in gold and silver. *ILLUSTRATED.*
**$2.95-22nd Edition, 288 pgs., 4" x 5½", Paperback, Order #: 385-6**

■ **1984 Blackbook Price Guide of United States Paper Money** — Over **9,000 buying and selling prices** covering U.S. currency from 1861 to date. Every note issued by the U.S. government is listed and priced including many Confederate States notes. Error Notes are described and priced, and there are detailed articles on many phases of the hobby for beginner and advanced collector alike. Comprehensive grading section. *ILLUSTRATED.*
**$2.95-16th Edition, 240 pgs., 4" x 5½", Paperback, Order #: 387-2**

■ **1984 Blackbook Price Guide of United States Postage Stamps** — *Featuring all U.S. stamps from 1847 to date pictured in full color.* Over **19,000** current selling prices. General issues, airmails and special delivery. United Nations, first day covers, and more. New listings for the most current commemorative and regular issue stamps, a feature not offered in any other price guide, at any price! Numerous important developments in the fast moving stamp market during the past year are all included in this *NEW REVISED EDITION. ILLUSTRATED.*
**$2.95-6th Edition, 240 pgs., 4" x 5½", Paperback, Order #: 386-4**

# INVESTORS SERIES

■ **Investors Guide to Gold, Silver, Diamonds** — *All you need to know* about making money trading in the precious metals and diamonds markets. This practical, easy-to-read investment guide is for everyone in all income brackets. How to determine authenticity and value of gold, silver, and diamonds. *ILLUSTRATED.*
**$6.95-1st Edition, 208 pgs., 5⅜" x 8½", Paperback, Order #: 171-3**

■ **Investors Guide to Gold Coins** — *The first complete book* on investing in gold coins. Eclusive price performance charts trace all U.S. gold coins values from *1955 to date.* Forecast price trends and best bets. *ILLUSTRATED.*
**$6.95-1st Edition, 288 pgs., 5⅜" x 8½", Paperback, Order #: 300-7**

■ **Investors Guide to Silver Coins** — *The most extensive listing* of all U.S. Silver coins. Detailed price performance charts trace actual sales figures from *1955 to date.* Learn how to figure investment profit. *ILLUSTRATED.*
**$6.95-1st Edition, 288 pgs., 5⅜" x 8½", Paperback, Order #: 301-5**

■ **Investors Guide to Silver Dollars** — Regardless of your income, you can *become a successful silver dollar investor.* Actual sales figures for every U.S. silver dollar *1955 to date.* Comprehensive grading section. *ILLUSTRATED.*
**$6.95-1st Edition, 192 pgs., 5⅜" x 8½", Paperback, Order #: 302-3**

*— For your convenience use the handy order form. —*